G000254434

COMPLETE ANGLICAN
HYMNS OLD & NEW

MELODY EDITION

Kevin Mayhew

Acknowledgements

The publishers wish to express their gratitude to the copyright holders who have granted permission to include their material in this book.

Every effort has been made to trace the copyright holders of all the songs in this collection and we hope that no copyright has been infringed. Apology is made and pardon sought if the contrary be the case, and a correction will be made in any reprint of this book.

Important Copyright Information

We would like to remind users of this hymnal that the reproduction of any song texts or music without the permission of the copyright holder is illegal. Details of all copyright holders are clearly indicated under each song.

Many of the song *texts* may be covered either by a Christian Copyright Licensing (CCL) licence or a Calamus licence. If you possess a CCL or Calamus licence, it is essential that you check your instruction manual to ensure that the song you wish to use is covered.

If you are *not* a member of CCL or Calamus, or the song you wish to reproduce is not covered by your licence, you must contact the copyright holder direct for their permission.

Christian Copyright Licensing (Europe) Ltd., have also now introduced a *Music Reproduction Licence.* Again, if you hold such a licence it is essential that you check your instruction manual to ensure that the song you wish to reproduce is covered. The reproduction of any music not covered by your licence is both illegal and immoral.

If you are interested in joining CCL or Calamus they can be contacted at the following addresses:

Christian Copyright Licensing (Europe) Ltd. P.O. Box 1339, Eastbourne,
East Sussex. BN 21 1AD.
Tel: 01323 417711, Fax: 01323 417722

Calamus, 30 North Terrace, Mildenhall, Suffolk, IP28 7AB.
Tel: 01638 716579, Fax: 01638 510390.

Published in Great Britain in 2002 by
KEVIN MAYHEW LIMITED
Buxhall, Stowmarket
Suffolk IP14 3BW

Compilation © Kevin Mayhew Ltd 2000

The right of Geoffrey Moore, Susan Sayers, Michael Forster and Kevin Mayhew to be idetified as the compilers and editors of this work has been asserted by them in accordance with the Copyght, Designs and Patents Act 1988.

All rights reserved. No part of this publication may be reproduced, stored in a retrial system, or transmitted, in any form or by any means, electronic, mechanical, photocopying, recordin or otherwise, without the prior written permission of the publisher.

The following editions are available.

Words edition	Catalogue No.1413131 ISBN No. 1 84003 566 8	ISMN No. M 57004 700
Organ/choir	Catalogue No. 1413134 ISBN No. 1 84003 565 X	ISMN No. M 57004 697
Melody edition	Catalogue No. 1413133 ISBN No. 1 84003 898 5	ISMN No. M 57024 0[illegible]2

Printed and bound in Great Britain by William Clowes Ltd, Beccles, Suffolk

Contents

COMPLETE ANGLICAN
HYMNS OLD & NEW

Foreword

Hymns Old & New was first published in 1986, to be followed a decade later by *Hymns Old & New, New Anglican Edition. New Anglican* has amply justified its claim to be 'the most exhaustive and all-embracing collection of hymns available' and has proved to be one of the country's most popular and widely used hymn books, reprinting on numerous occasions.

The continuing rich outpouring of new Christian hymns and worship songs since their publication is a sign of the vitality of the Church. This flow of contemporary material springs naturally from the earlier tradition in which it is firmly rooted, addressing contemporary issues in the unequivocal context of the underlying truth of our faith.

It became evident to us that this was an appropriate time to enlarge *New Anglican* to embrace the best of the new material, whilst taking the opportunity to include further treasures from an earlier age. *Complete Anglican Hymns Old & New* is the result.

There is much here to accommodate all preferences, with something suitable for every occasion and season; but, of course, it would be surprising (and disappointing), in an eclectic collection of this kind, if everything in it had an immediate and universal appeal. Most importantly, within the covers of this book, many new and exciting discoveries await the user.

Complete Anglican Hymns Old & New is at once traditional and radical. The radical aspects will be self-evident in what follows and in the texts of some of the new hymns we have included. It is traditional partly because a large number of the texts have stood the test of time; and it is 'traditional' in another sense, for the process of critical scrutiny and rewriting of established texts has itself a long and honourable history. Throughout the time hymns have been in use they have been reviewed, adapted and rewritten; many of the hymns now regarded as classics are in reality very different from the original texts.

This is the tradition in which we, as an editorial panel, felt ourselves to be placed, and we sought to discharge our responsibilities as faithfully as we were able. We were a diverse group of people both denominationally and doctrinally: a diversity which was vital to the breadth and richness of the hymnody we were considering. Yet there were some basic principles upon which we were absolutely of common mind.

We wanted the overall tone of the book to be positive: to bear witness to the abundant grace and unconditional love of God; to enable the Church to sing of the *Good News* of salvation; to celebrate humanity as God's creation, fallen though we are, and affirm the essential goodness of the world which he has made and to which he has shown himself to be committed even unto death. Of course, we recognise the reality of sin and evil, and we would not for a moment deny that the world can be a dark and fearful place, but as Christians we believe we are called to point to the light that is never overcome; the darkness of the *background* to that is then self-evident.

We were also concerned that the book should use positive and appropriate images, and decided that militarism and triumphalism were, therefore, not appropriate. We recognise that military imagery is used in the Bible, but history, including current events, shows only too clearly the misuse to which those images are open. All too often in the Christian and other religions, texts advocating *spiritual* warfare are used to justify the self-serving ambitions behind *temporal* conflicts. Christian 'triumph' is the triumph of love which 'is not envious or boastful or arrogant' (1 Corinthians 13:4): the triumph of the cross.

Another fundamental principle was the use of inclusive language in referring to the human race. Rare exceptions were only made for very clear reasons and after much deliberation. Non-copyright texts were amended by members of the editorial panel while those by living authors were referred back. We are grateful to the authors concerned for their willingness to co-operate.

Some traditional hymns have been difficult for congregations to sing effectively because of variations in metre from verse to verse. Most of those, except for those few which are so well known that it would be counterproductive, have now been adapted so that the words fit easily and consistently to the tune. A classic example, of course, is *God is working his purpose out:* a deservedly well-loved hymn which is now much easier to sing well and therefore more enjoyable for all concerned.

We were also aware that a number of hymns which have served well down the ages are now being seriously questioned. Some hymns are clearly manipulative, often written by adults for children and trying to impose values which were in reality more social and cultural than religious. In other cases we felt that God was being pushed out of this world at times when we should be looking to find him within it. In cases such as these, we attempted to redress the emphasis by rewriting, rather than by deleting well-loved hymns from the book. Whether that has been worthily done will be for the churches to decide as they use the texts.

In applying our criteria, we inevitably encountered a problem: there are a number of hymns which, however doubtful the text, are rightly loved for their music; and music is an essential part of our glorifying God in worship. We then had to establish another final criterion: ultimately, what we say to and about God and each other matters, and no dubious text would be included solely because of its tune. The solution we found was, in certain cases, to commission new texts to be sung to those tunes, hence such new hymns as *Stand up, stand up for Jesus, God is our strength from days of old* and *Onward, Christian pilgrims.*

While thus occupied with the classic texts we were also aware of the enormous number of new hymns and worship songs of recent years. Jesus said that being involved in the kingdom of heaven means treasuring things both old and new, and so we turned our attention to the new. Here we found an almost bewildering diversity. As well as the offerings of communities such as Taizé and Iona, we took into account a wide range of new hymns and songs, from texts using traditional metres to the freely expressive styles with which the Church has been blessed through the renewal movement. Through these modern texts we restate the ancient traditions of the faith, explore new insights, proclaim hope, protest, express solidarity with the poor, call ourselves and others to penitence and faith; and in all that we celebrate the eternal Mystery who surrounds, embraces and permeates creation. In other words, we do what hymns have always done.

The tunes in *Hymns Old & New* are no less eclectic than the texts. We hope that our attempt to be generous and broad in our selection will be self-evident, with much-loved traditional tunes rubbing shoulders with equally revered modern compositions and worship songs.

Another feature of *Hymns Old & New* is the large number of hymn tunes that are given in two keys: the first for everyday use and the second, usually lower, where special circumstances prevail, such as when the organist is called upon to accompany older people, adolescent boys, men's services, or simply for those early morning services where higher notes might not be comfortable. As a general rule we have tried to avoid taking the melody line above D so that congregations feel comfortable with the pitch of the hymn. While we hope this will make the book even more useful, we should add a word of warning: some of the lower settings may not be suitable for singing in harmony because the bass part, especially, goes lower than will normally be comfortable. In such cases, if a choir is present, the singers should be advised to sing in unison.

As the number of hymns has increased to over nine hundred, we felt it would be useful to divide the book into various sections. This has been done purely as an aid to the user of the book as we certainly do not wish to 'compartmentalise' any hymns or songs. We have added a Children's Section, a Chant Section and a section containing Music for the Eucharist. These headings have also been used in the Index of Uses and the Index for the Common Worship Lectionary.

It is impossible to undertake a project of this magnitude without the help of many people. We wish to express our immense gratitude to all those whose opinions and help we sought during the compilation of *Hymns Old & New.*

The singing of hymns and psalms in worship pre-dates Christianity. It is something that Jesus himself would have been familiar with in the temple, and he certainly sang at the Last Supper – 'After psalms had been sung they left for the Mount of Olives', writes Matthew. What a wonderful tradition we share!

We hope that in this diverse and approachable collection of hymns we have sown some seeds; that is all we can do. It is in the worship of the churches that those seeds must be brought to glorious flower.

GEOFFREY MOORE
Compiler

SUSAN SAYERS
Liturgical Adviser

MICHAEL FORSTER
Theological Editor

KEVIN MAYHEW
Publisher

Hymns and Songs

1 Abba, Father, let me be

Words and music: Dave Bilbrough

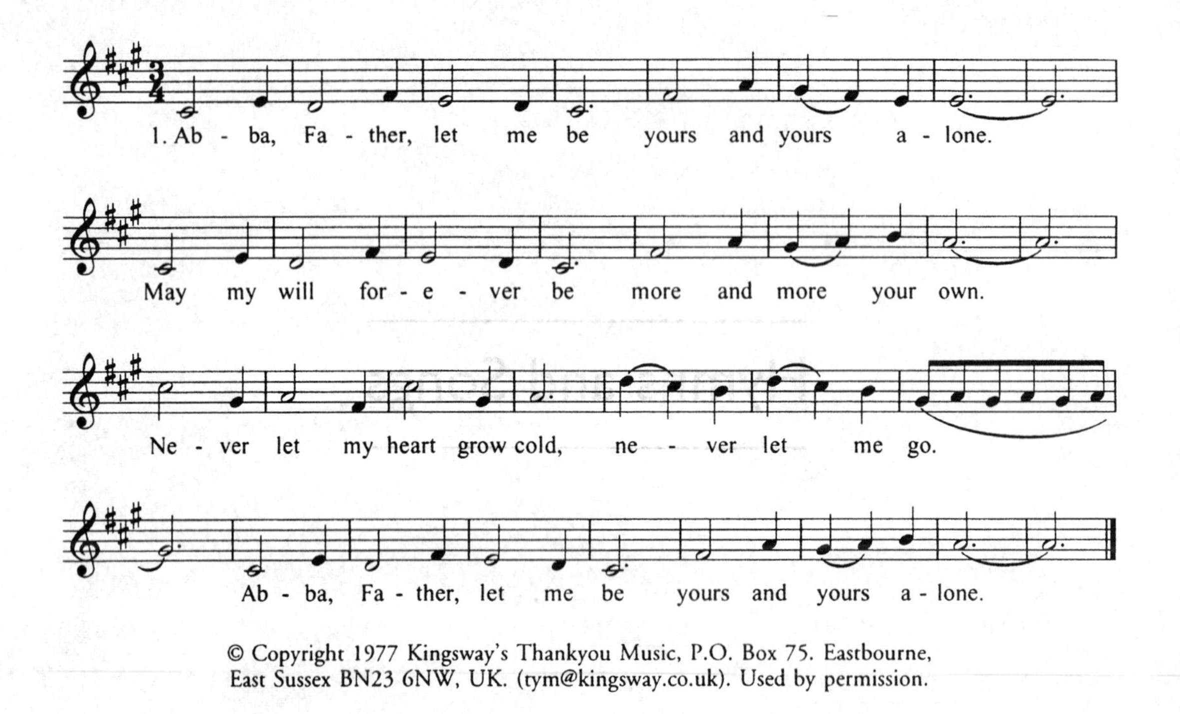

© Copyright 1977 Kingsway's Thankyou Music, P.O. Box 75. Eastbourne, East Sussex BN23 6NW, UK. (tym@kingsway.co.uk). Used by permission.

2 Abide with me

Henry Francis Lyte (1793-1847) William Henry Monk (1823-1889)

EVENTIDE 10 10 10 10

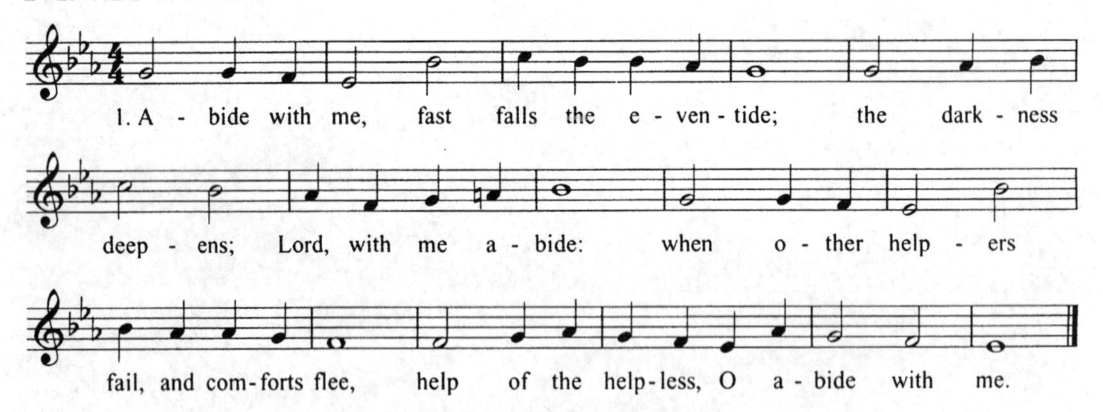

2. Swift to its close ebbs out life's little day;
earth's joys grow dim, its glories pass away;
change and decay in all around I see;
O thou who changest not, abide with me.

3. I need thy presence ev'ry passing hour;
what but thy grace can foil the tempter's pow'r?
Who like thyself my guide and stay can be?
Through cloud and sunshine, Lord, abide with me.

4. I fear no foe with thee at hand to bless
   ills have no weight, and tears no bitterness.
   Where is death's sting? Where, grave, thy victory?
   I triumph still, if thou abide with me.

5. Hold thou thy cross before my closing eyes;
   shine through the gloom, and point me to the skies;
   heav'n's morning breaks, and earth's vain shadows flee;
   in life, in death, O Lord, abide with me.

3 A brighter dawn is breaking

Percy Dearmer (1867-1936)

Later form of a melody in Selnecker's *Christliche Psalmen*, Leipzig (1587)

NUN LASST UNS GOTT 77 77

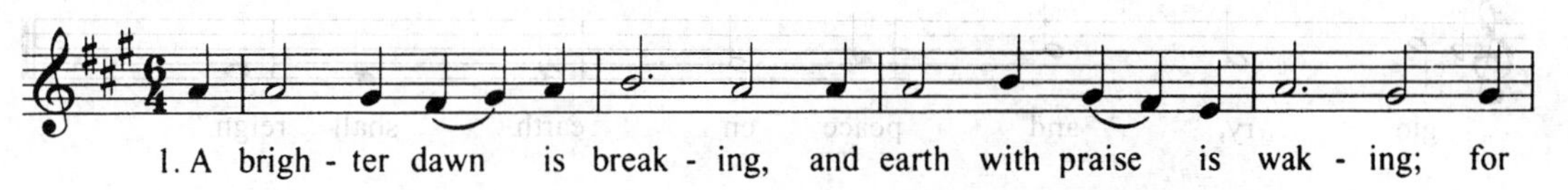

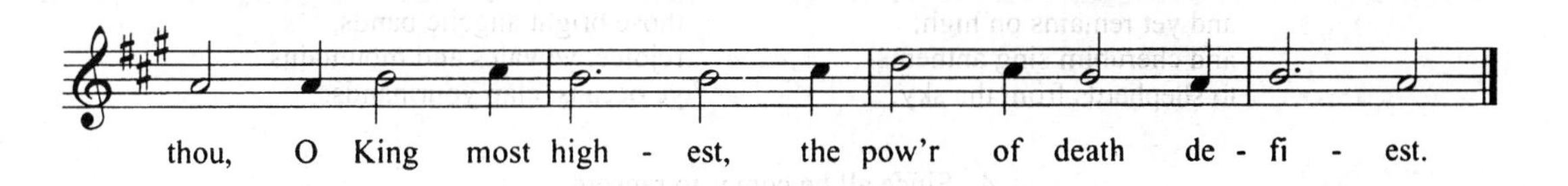

2. And thou hast come victorious,
   with risen body glorious,
   who now for ever livest,
   and life abundant givest.

3. O free the world from blindness,
   and fill the earth with kindness,
   give sinners resurrection,
   bring striving to perfection.

4. In sickness give us healing,
   in doubt thy clear revealing,
   that praise to thee be given
   in earth as in thy heaven.

Text © Copyright 1996 Oxford University Press,
Great Clarendon Street, Oxford OX2 6DP. Used by permission.

4 A great and mighty wonder

St Germanus (c.634-734) trans.
John Mason Neale (1818-1866)

German carol melody

ES IST EIN' ROS' ENTSPRUNGEN 76 76 676

2. The Word becomes incarnate,
and yet remains on high;
and cherubim sing anthems
to shepherds from the sky:

3. While thus they sing your monarch,
those bright angelic bands,
rejoice, ye vales and mountains,
ye oceans, clap your hands:

4. Since all he comes to ransom
by all be he adored,
the infant born in Bethl'em,
the Saviour and the Lord:

5 Ah, holy Jesu, how hast thou offended

Robert Bridges (1844-1930) from J. Heerman (1585-1647) alt.
based on an 11th century Latin meditation

Johann Crüger (1598-1662)

HERZLIEBSTER JESU 11 11 11 5

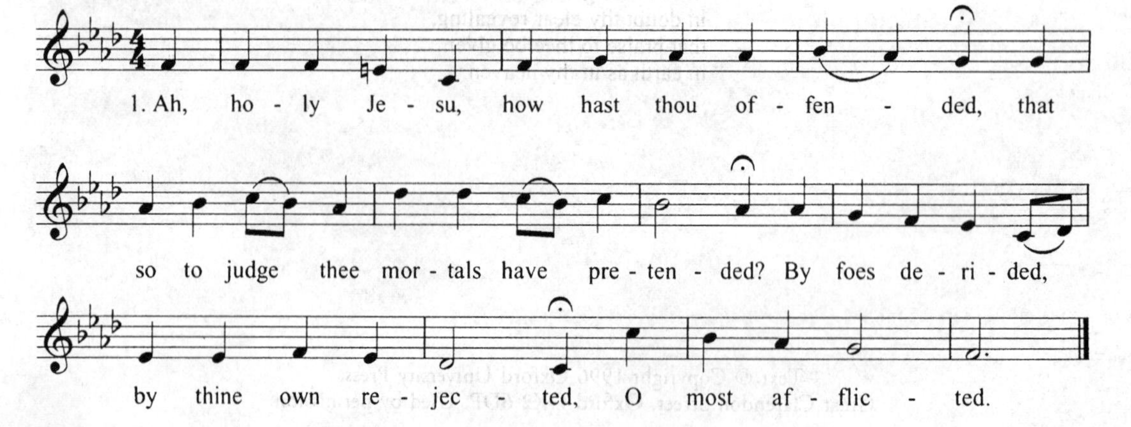

2. Who was the guilty? Who brought this upon thee?
Alas, O Lord, my treason hath undone thee.
'Twas I, Lord Jesu, I it was denied thee:
I crucified thee.

3. Lo, the good shepherd for the sheep is offered;
the slave hath sinnèd, and the Son hath suffered;
for our atonement Christ himself is pleading,
still interceding.

4. For me, kind Jesu, was thy incarnation,
thy mortal sorrow, and thy life's oblation;
thy death of anguish and thy bitter passion,
for my salvation.

5. Therefore, kind Jesu, since I cannot pay thee,
I do adore thee, and will ever pray thee,
think on thy pity and thy love unswerving,
not my deserving.

6 All creatures of our God and King

William Henry Draper (1855-1933) alt.
based on the *Cantico di Frate Sole* of
St Francis of Assisi (1182-1226)

Geistliche Kirchengesang, Cologne (1623)

LASST UNS ERFREUEN 88 44 88 and Alleluias

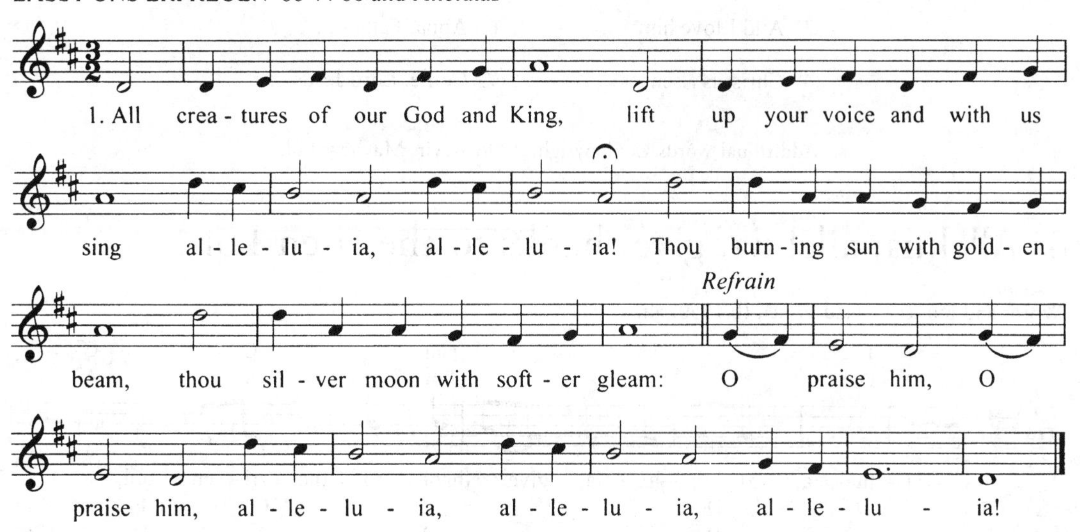

2. Thou rushing wind that art so strong,
ye clouds that sail in heav'n along,
O praise him, alleluia!
Thou rising morn, in praise rejoice,
ye lights of evening, find a voice:

3. Thou flowing water, pure and clear,
make music for thy Lord to hear,
alleluia, alleluia!
Thou fire so masterful and bright,
that givest us both warmth and light:

4. Dear mother earth, who day by day
unfoldest blessings on our way,
O praise him, alleluia!
The flow'rs and fruits that in thee grow,
let them his glory also show.

5. All you with mercy in your heart,
forgiving others, take your part,
O sing ye, alleluia!
Ye who long pain and sorrow bear,
praise God and on him cast your care:

6. And thou, most kind and gentle death,
waiting to hush our latest breath,
O praise him, alleluia!
Thou leadest home the child of God,
and Christ our Lord the way hath trod:

7. Let all things their Creator bless,
and worship him in humbleness,
O praise him, alleluia!
Praise, praise the Father, praise the Son,
and praise the Spirit, Three in One.

Text © Copyright J. Curwen & Sons Ltd., 8/9 Frith Street, London W1D 3JB.
All rights reserved. International copyright secured. Used by permission.

7 Alleluia (x8)

vs. 1-4 unknown;
vs. 5-7 Damian Lundy (1944-1997)

Unknown

Additional verses may be composed to suit the occasion. For example:

2. Jesus is Lord . . .
3. And I love him . . .
4. Christ is risen . . .
5. Send your Spirit . . .
6. Abba, Father . . .
7. Come, Lord Jesus . . .

Additional words © Copyright 1996 Kevin Mayhew Ltd.

8 Alleluia, alleluia, give thanks to the risen Lord

Words and music: Donald Fishel, (b.1950) alt.

2. Spread the good news o'er all the earth.
Jesus has died and is risen.

3. We have been crucified with Christ.
Now we shall live for ever.

4. God has proclaimed the just reward:
'Life for us all, alleluia!'

5. Come, let us praise the living God,
joyfully sing to our Saviour.

© Copyright 1973 Word of God Music. Administered by CopyCare, P.O. Box 77, Hailsham, East Sussex BN27 3EF, UK. (music@copycare.com). Used by permission.

9 Alleluia, alleluia, hearts to heaven and voices raise

Christopher Wadsworth (1807-1885)

Arthur Seymour Sullivan (1842-1900)

LUX EOI 87 87 D

2. Christ is risen, Christ the first-fruits
of the holy harvest field,
which will all its full abundance
at his second coming yield;
then the golden ears of harvest
will their heads before him wave,
ripened by his glorious sunshine,
from the furrows of the grave.

3. Christ is risen, we are risen;
shed upon us heav'nly grace,
rain, and dew, and gleams of glory
from the brightness of thy face;
that we, with our hearts in heaven,
here on earth may fruitful be,
and by angel-hands be gathered,
and be ever, Lord, with thee.

4. Alleluia, alleluia,
glory be to God on high;
alleluia to the Saviour,
who has gained the victory;
alleluia to the Spirit,
fount of love and sanctity;
alleluia, alleluia,
to the Triune Majesty.

10 Alleluia: All the earth

Hubert J. Richards (b.1921) based on Psalm 100

Andrew Moore (b.1954)

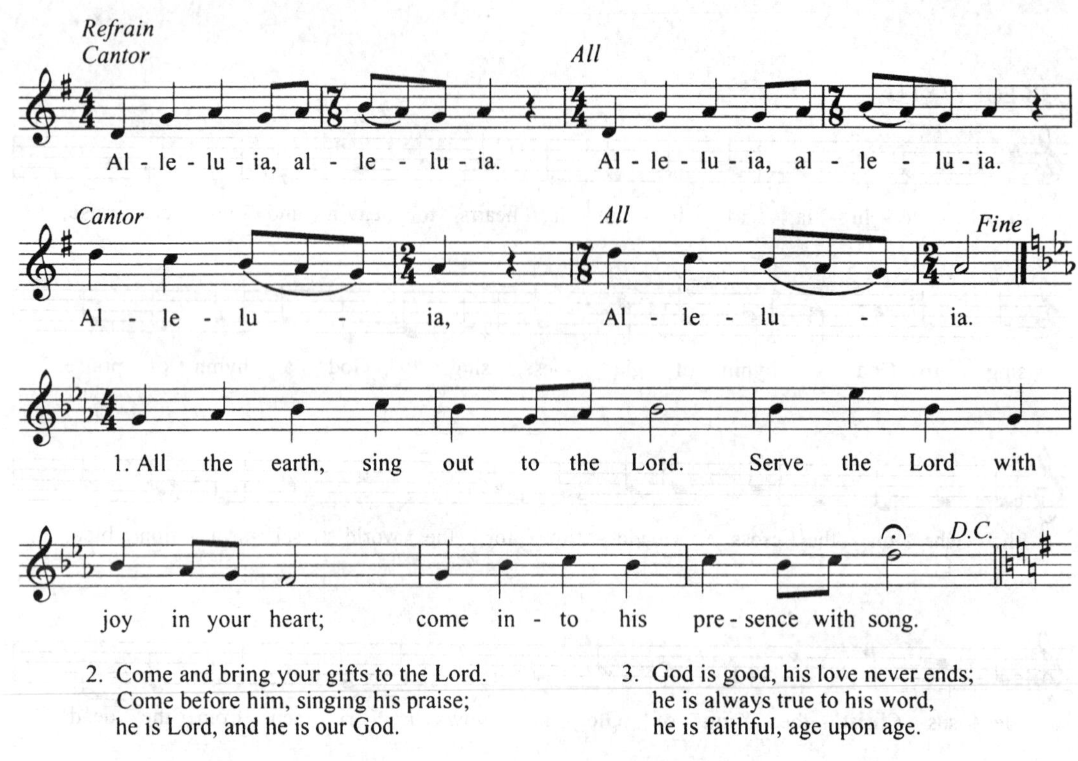

2. Come and bring your gifts to the Lord.
Come before him, singing his praise;
he is Lord, and he is our God.

3. God is good, his love never ends;
he is always true to his word,
he is faithful, age upon age.

© Copyright 1996 Kevin Mayhew Ltd.

11 Alleluia: Praise God

Hubert J. Richards (b.1921)
based on Psalms 103 and 105

Richard Lloyd (b.1933)

© Copyright 1995 Kevin Mayhew Ltd.

2. Our God is all kindness and love,
so patient and rich in compassion;
not treating us as we deserve:
not paying us back for our sins.

3. As heaven is high over earth,
so strong is his love for his people.
As far as the east from the west,
so far he removes all our sins.

4. As fathers take pity on sons,
we know God will show us compassion;
for he knows of what we are made:
no more than the dust of the earth.

12 Alleluia, sing to Jesus

William Chatterton Dix (1837-1898), alt. the editors

Rowland Huw Pritchard (1811-1887)

HYFRYDOL 87 87 D

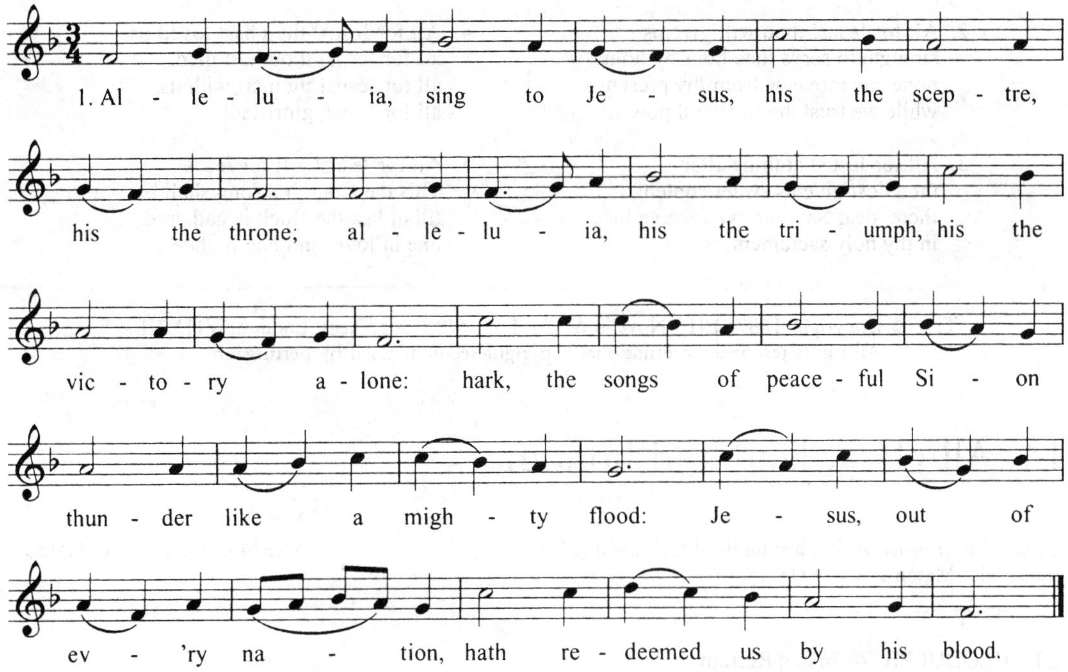

1. Al - le - lu - ia, sing to Je - sus, his the scep - tre,
his the throne; al - le - lu - ia, his the tri - umph, his the
vic - to - ry a - lone: hark, the songs of peace - ful Si - on
thun - der like a migh - ty flood: Je - sus, out of
ev - 'ry na - tion, hath re - deemed us by his blood.

2. Alleluia, not as orphans
are we left in sorrow now;
alleluia, he is near us,
faith believes, nor questions how;
though the cloud from sight received him
when the forty days were o'er,
shall our hearts forget his promise,
'I am with you evermore'?

3. Alleluia, bread of angels,
here on earth our food, our stay;
alleluia, here the sinful
come to you from day to day.
Intercessor, friend of sinners,
earth's redeemer, plead for me,
where the songs of all the sinless
sweep across the crystal sea.

4. Alleluia, King eternal,
he the Lord of lords we own;
alleluia, born of Mary,
earth his footstool, heav'n his throne;
he within the veil has entered
robed in flesh, our great High Priest;
he on earth both priest and victim
in the Eucharistic Feast.

This version of text © Copyright 1999 Kevin Mayhew Ltd.

13 All for Jesus!

William John Sparrow-Simpson (1859-1952) alt. John Stainer (1840-1901)

ALL FOR JESUS 87 87

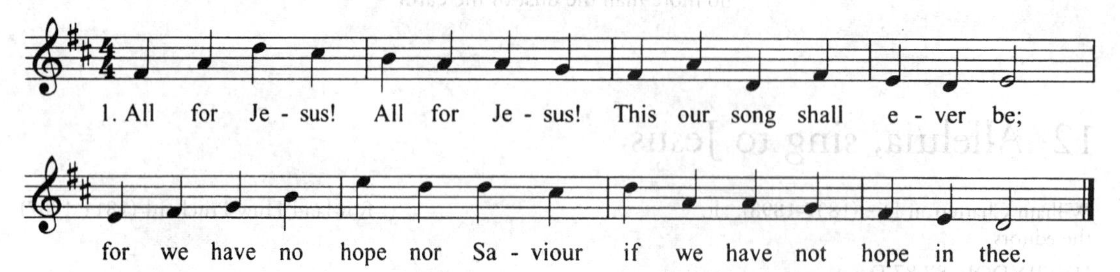

2. All for Jesus! thou wilt give us
strength to serve thee hour by hour;
none can move us from thy presence
while we trust thy love and pow'r.

3. All for Jesus! at thine altar
thou dost give us sweet content;
there, dear Saviour, we receive thee
in thy holy sacrament.

4. All for Jesus! thou hast loved us,
all for Jesus! thou hast died,
all for Jesus! thou art with us,
all for Jesus, glorified!

5. All for Jesus! All for Jesus!
This the Church's song shall be,
till at last the flock is gathered
one in love, and one in thee.

Text © Copyright 1887, 1915 Novello & Co. Ltd., 8/9 Frith Street, London W1D 3JB.
All rights reserved. International copyright secured. Used by permission.

14 All glory, laud and honour

Gloria, laus et honor by St Theodulph of Orleans (d.821)
trans. John Mason Neale (1818-1866)
Melchior Teschner (1584-1635)

ST THEODULPH 76 76 and Refrain

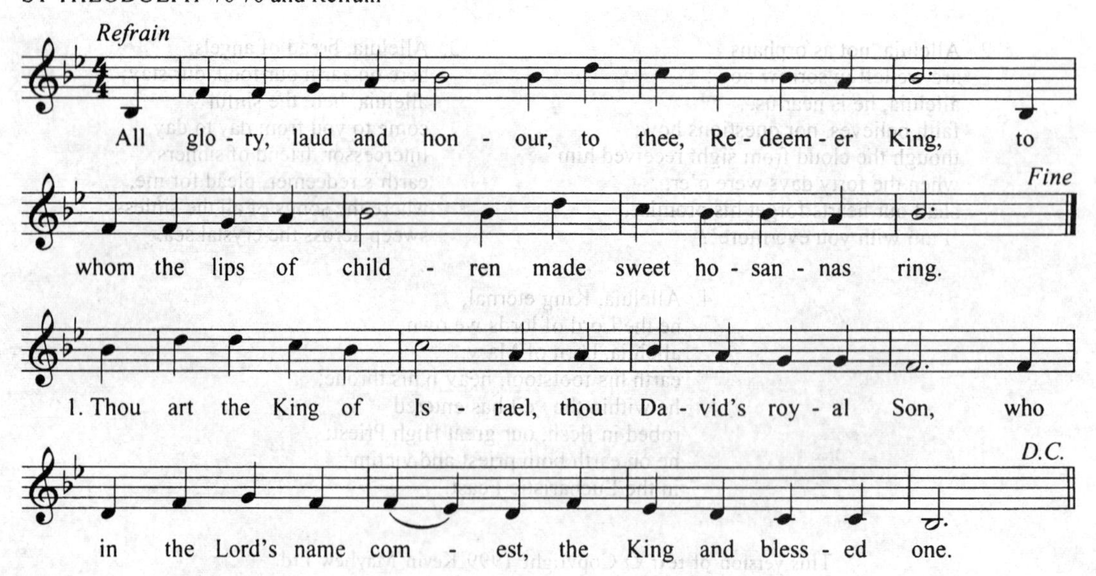

2. The company of angels
are praising thee on high,
and mortals, joined with all things
created, make reply.

3. The people of the Hebrews
with palms before thee went:
our praise and prayer and anthems
before thee we present.

4. To thee before thy passion
they sang their hymns of praise:
to thee now high exalted
our melody we raise.

5. Thou didst accept their praises,
accept the prayers we bring,
who in all good delightest,
thou good and gracious king.

15 All hail and welcome, holy child

Aodh MacCathmhaoil (1571-1626)
trans. George Otto Simms (1910-1991)

Traditional Irish melody

LUINNEACH 87 87

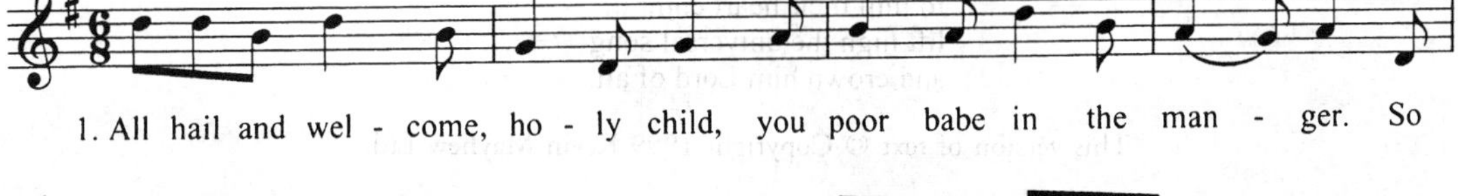

2. God bless you, Jesus, once again!
Your life in its young body,
your face more lovely than the sun –
a thousand welcomes, baby!

3. Tonight we greet you in the flesh;
my heart adores my young king.
You came to us in human form –
I bring you a kiss and a greeting.

Text © Copyright Oxford University Press, Great Clarendon Street, Oxford OX2 6DP.
Used by permission from *Irish Church Praise*.

16 All hail the power of Jesus' name

Edward Perronet (1726-1792)
adapted by Michael Foster (b.1946)

William Shrubsole (1760-1806)

TUNE 1: MILES LANE CM

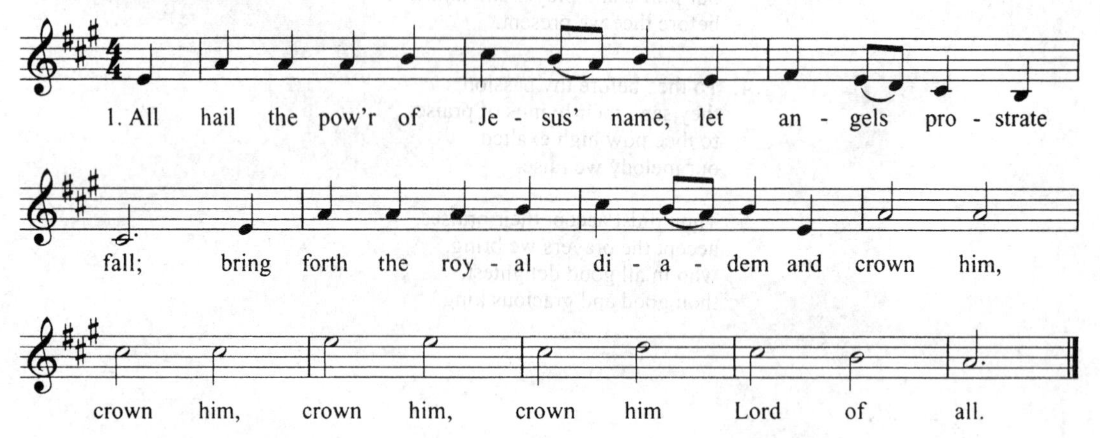

2. Crown him, all martyrs of your God,
who from his altar call;
praise him whose way of pain you trod,
and crown him Lord of all.

3. O prophets faithful to his word,
in matters great and small,
who made his voice of justice heard,
now crown him Lord of all.

4. All sinners, now redeemed by grace,
who heard your Saviour's call,
now robed in light before his face,
O crown him Lord of all.

5. Let every tribe and every race
who heard the freedom call,
in liberation, see Christ's face,
and crown him Lord of all.

6. Let every people, every tongue
to him their heart enthral:
lift high the universal song
and crown him Lord of all.

This version of text © Copyright 1999 Kevin Mayhew Ltd.

Edward Perronet (1726-1792)
adapted by Michael Foster (b.1946)

James Ellor (1819-1899)

TUNE 2: DIADEM 86 86 extended

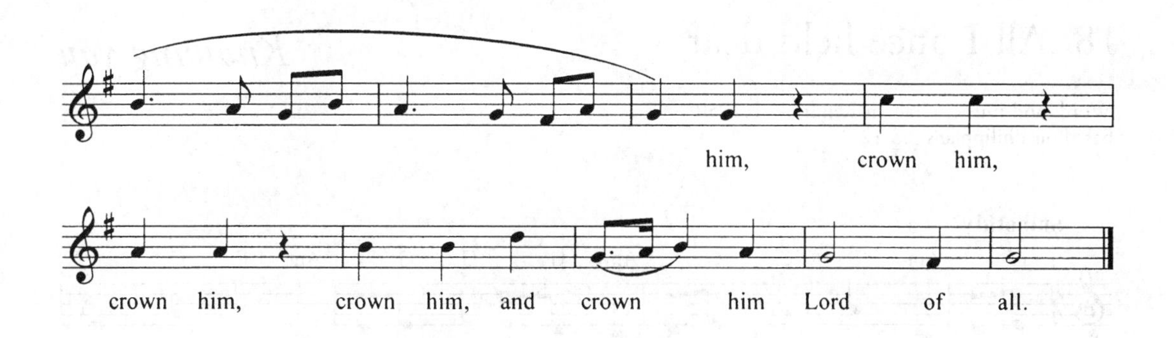

17 All heaven declares

Tricia Richards

Noel Richards

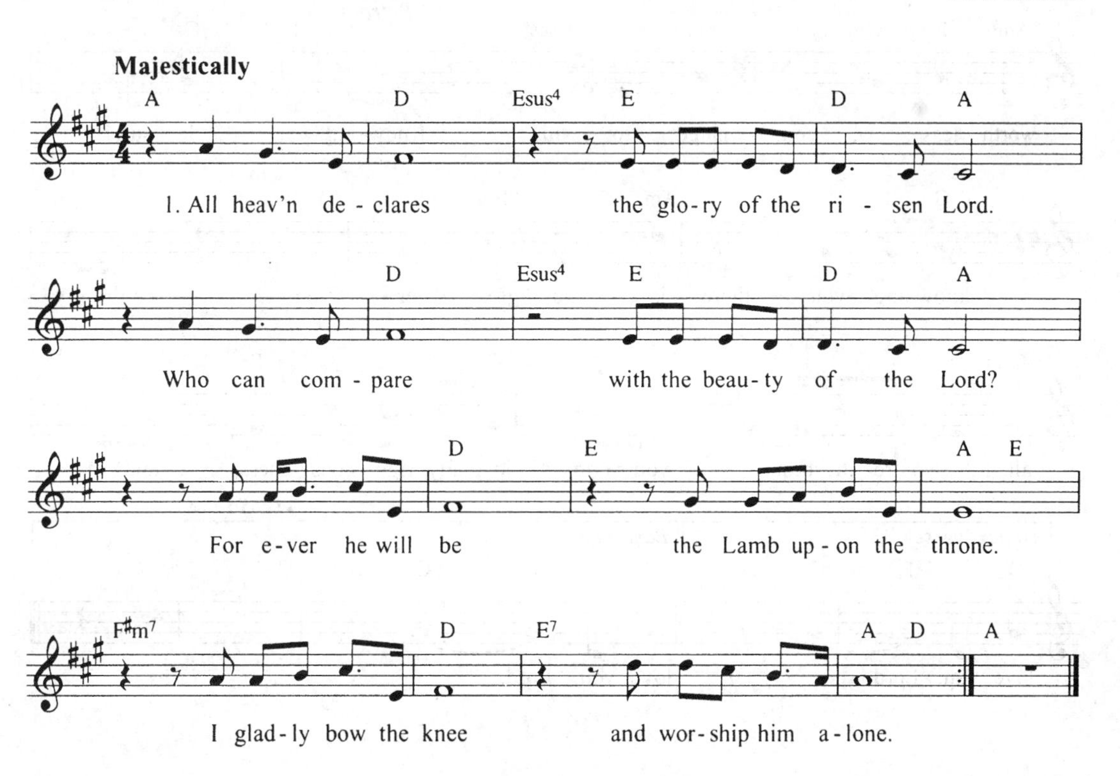

2. I will proclaim
the glory of the risen Lord.
Who once was slain
to reconcile us all to God.
For ever you will be
the Lamb upon the throne.
I gladly bow the knee
and worship you alone.

© Copyright 1987 Kingsway's Thankyou Music, P.O. Box 75,
Eastbourne, East Sussex BN23 6NW, UK. (tym@kingsway.co.uk). Used by permission.

18 All I once held dear

Knowing you

Words and music: Graham Kendrick (b.1950)
based on Philippians 3:8-12

2. Now my heart's desire is to know you more,
to be found in you and known as yours.
To possess by faith what I could not earn,
all-surpassing gift of righteousness.

3. Oh, to know the pow'r of your risen life,
and to know you in your sufferings.
To become like you in your death, my Lord,
so with you to live and never die.

© Copyright 1993 Make Way Music, P.O. Box 263, Croydon, Surrey CR9 5AP, UK.
International copyright secured. All rights reserved. Used by permission.

19 All my hope on God is founded

Paraphrased by Robert Bridges (1844-1930) alt.
based on *Meine Hoffnung stehet feste*
by Joachim Neander (1650-1680)

Herbert Howells (1892-1983)

MICHAEL 87 87 33 7

2. Human pride and earthly glory,
sword and crown betray his trust;
what with care and toil he buildeth,
tow'r and temple, fall to dust.
But God's pow'r, hour by hour,
is my temple and my tow'r.

3. God's great goodness aye endureth,
deep his wisdom, passing thought:
splendour, light and life attend him,
beauty springeth out of naught.
Evermore, from his store,
new-born worlds rise and adore.

4. Still from earth to God eternal
sacrifice of praise be done,
high above all praises praising
for the gift of Christ his Son.
Christ doth call one and all:
ye who follow shall not fall.

Music © Copyright 1968 Novello & Co. Ltd., 8/9 Frith Street, London W1D 3JB.
All rights reserved. International copyright secured. Used by permission.

20 All over the world

Words and music: Roy Turner (b.1940)

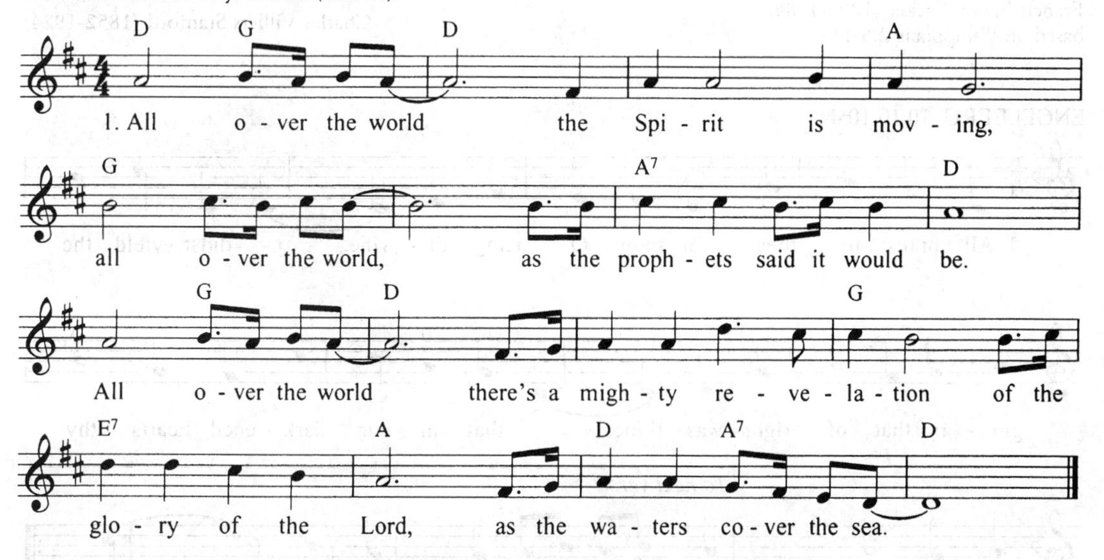

2. All over this land the Spirit is moving . . .

3. All over the Church the Spirit is moving . . .

4. All over us all the Spirit is moving . . .

5. Deep down in my heart the Spirit is moving . . .

© Copyright 1984 Kingsway's Thankyou Music, P.O. Box 75, Eastbourne,
East Sussex BN23 6NW, UK. (tym@kingsway.co.uk). Used by permission.

21 All people that on earth do dwell

William Kethe (d.1594) from
Day's Psalter (1560) alt.

Genevan Psalter (1551), attributed to
Louis Bourgeois (c.1510-c.1561)

OLD HUNDREDTH LM

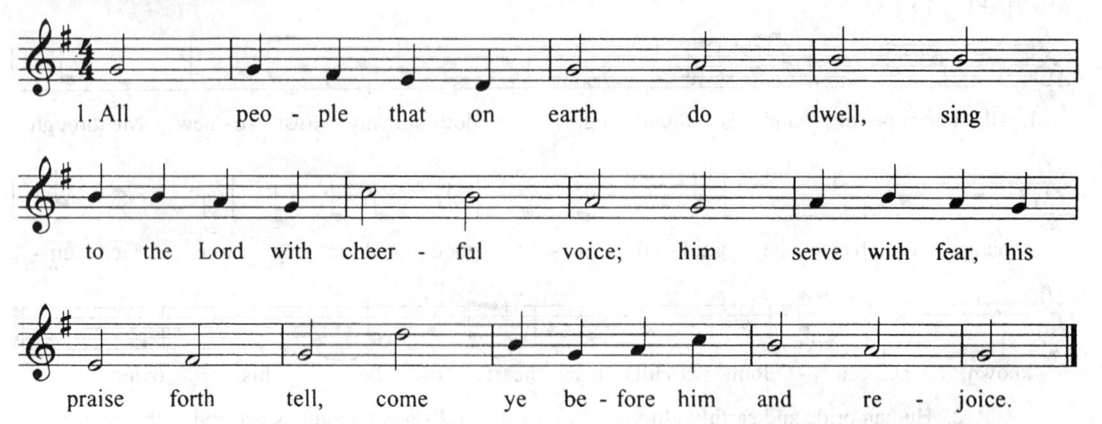

2. The Lord, ye know, is God indeed,
without our aid he did us make;
we are his folk, he doth us feed
and for his sheep he doth us take.

3. O enter then his gates with praise,
approach with joy his courts unto;
praise, laud and bless his name always,
for it is seemly so to do.

4. For why? the Lord our God is good:
his mercy is for ever sure;
his truth at all times firmly stood,
and shall from age to age endure.

5. To Father, Son and Holy Ghost,
the God whom heav'n and earth adore,
from us and from the angel-host
be praise and glory evermore.

22 All praise to thee, for thou, O King divine

Francis Bland Tucker (1895-1984)
based on Philippians 2:5-11

Charles Villiers Stanford (1852-1924)

ENGELBERG 10 10 10 4

Text © Copyright 1982 Church Pension Fund, 445 Fifth Avenue, New York 10016-0109, USA.
Reproduced by permission from *The Hymnal*

2. Thou cam'st to us in lowliness of thought;
by thee the outcast and the poor were sought,
and by thy death was God's salvation wrought:
Alleluia.

3. Let this mind be in us which was in thee,
who wast a servant that we might be free,
humbling thyself to death on Calvary:
Alleluia.

4. Wherefore, by God's eternal purpose,
thou art high exalted o'er all creatures now,
and giv'n the name to which all knees shall bow:
Alleluia.

5. Let ev'ry tongue confess with one accord
in heav'n and earth that Jesus Christ is Lord;
and God the Father be by all adored:
Alleluia.

23 All that I am

Words and music: Sebastian Temple (1928-1997)

2. All that I dream, all that I pray,
all that I'll ever make, I give to you today.
Take and sanctify these gifts for your honour, Lord.
Knowing that I love and serve you is enough reward.
All that I am, all that I do,
all that I'll ever have I offer now to you.

© Copyright 1967 OCP Publications, 5536 NE Hassalo, Portland OR 97213, USA.
All rights reserved. Used by permission.

24 All the ends of the earth

Susan Sayers (b.1946)
based on Psalm 98

Andrew Moore (b.1954)

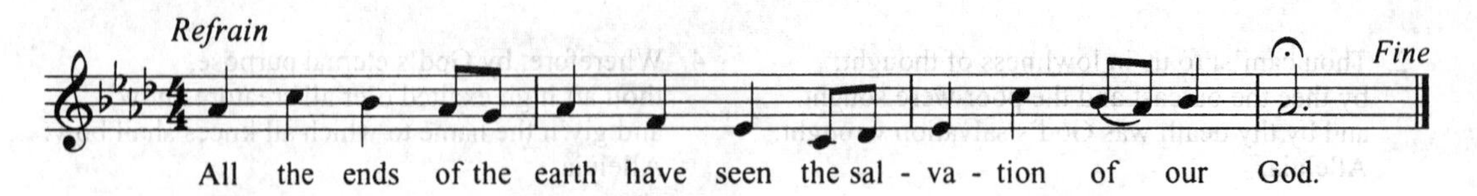

2. His salvation is known on the earth,
all the nations can see he is just;
he will never neglect to be true
to the people he knows as his own.

3. Ev'ry part of creation has seen
the salvation our God has bestowed.
Let the earth shout aloud to our God,
and the universe ring with delight.

4. O sing songs to our God with the harp,
and with music sing praise to the Lord;
let the horn and the trumpet give voice,
we acknowledge the Lord who is King.

© Copyright 1995 Kevin Mayhew Ltd.

25 All things bright and beautiful

Cecil Frances Alexander (1818-1895)

William Henry Monk (1823-1889)

TUNE 1: ALL THINGS BRIGHT AND BEAUTIFUL 76 76 and Refrain

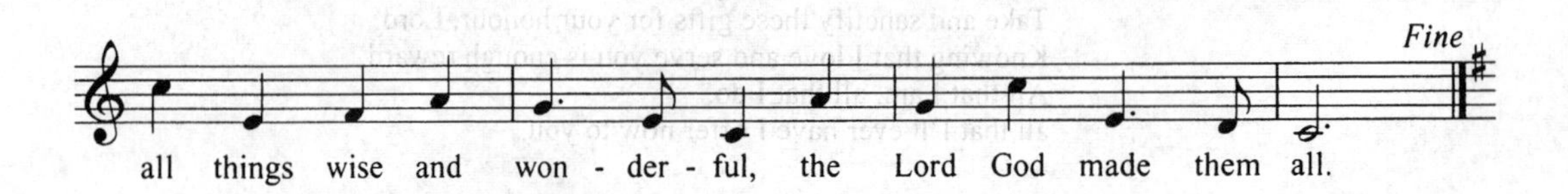

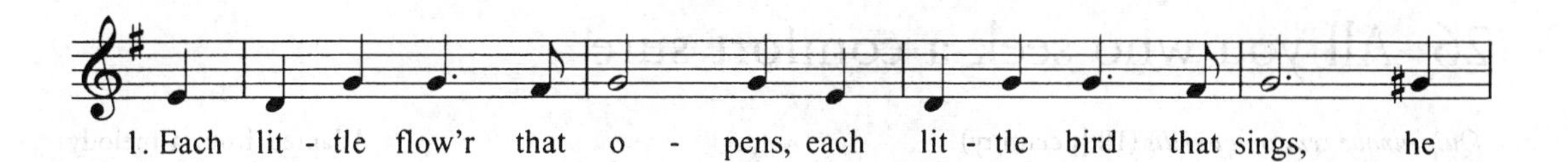

2. The purple-headed mountain,
the river running by,
the sunset and the morning
that brightens up the sky.

3. The cold wind in the winter,
the pleasant summer sun,
the ripe fruits in the garden,
he made them every one.

4. The tall trees in the greenwood,
the meadows for our play,
the rushes by the water,
to gather ev'ry day.

5. He gave us eyes to see them,
and lips that we might tell
how great is God Almighty,
who has made all things well.

Cecil Frances Alexander (1818-1895) Traditional English melody

TUNE 2: ROYAL OAK 76 76 and Refrain

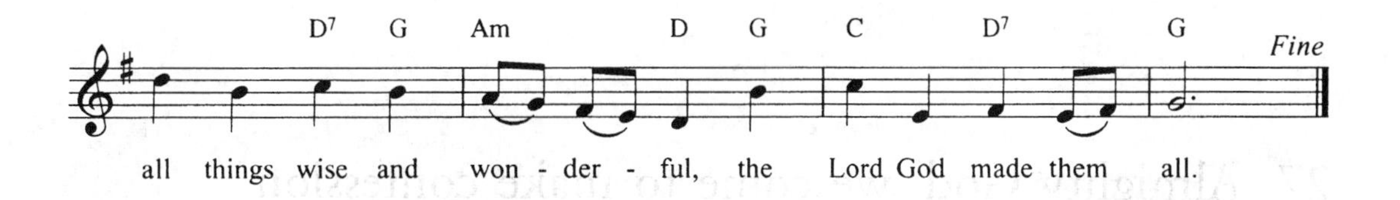

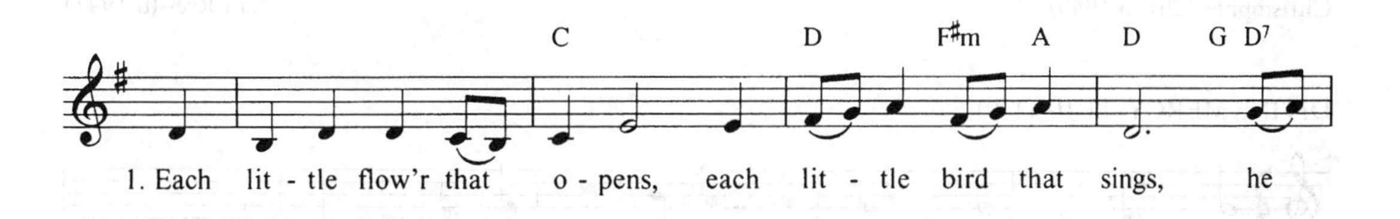

26 All you who seek a comfort sure

Quincunque centum quæritis (18th century)
trans. Edward Caswall (1814-1878) alt. the editors

Adapted from a melody
in *Tochter Sion* (1741)

ST BERNARD CM

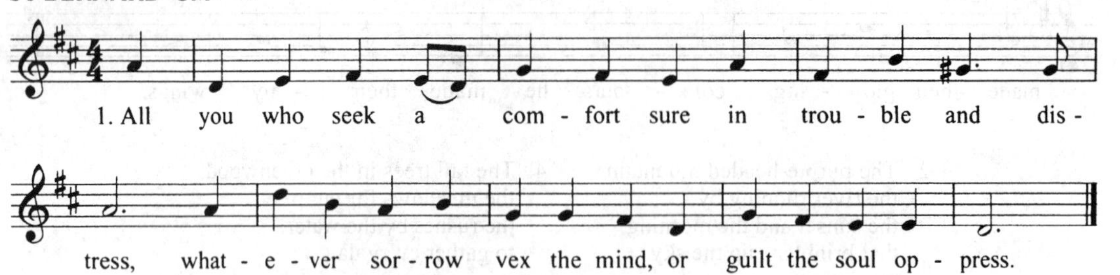

2. Jesus, who gave himself for you
upon the cross to die,
opens to you his sacred heart;
O, to that heart draw nigh.

3. You hear how kindly he invites;
you hear his words so blest:
'All you that labour, come to me,
and I will give you rest.'

4. What meeker than the Saviour's heart?
As on the cross he lay,
it did his murderers forgive,
and for their pardon pray.

5. Jesus, the joy of saints on high,
the hope of sinners here,
attracted by those loving words
to you I lift my prayer.

6. Wash then my wounds in that dear blood
which forth from you does flow;
by grace a better hope inspire,
and risen life bestow.

This version of text © Copyright 1999 Kevin Mayhew Ltd.

27 Almighty God, we come to make confession

Christopher Ellis (b.1949)

Alan Rees (b.1941)

DIVINE MERCY 11 10 11 10

© Copyright 1999 Kevin Mayhew Ltd.

2. Forgiving God, I come to make confession
of all the harm and hurt that I have done;
of bitter words and many selfish actions,
forgive me, Lord, and make me like your Son.

3. Forgiving God, I come to make confession
of all that I have failed to do this day;
of help withheld, concern and love restricted,
forgive me, Lord, and lead me in your way.

4. Redeeming God, we come to seek forgiveness,
for Jesus Christ has died to set us free.
Forgive the past and fill us with your Spirit
that we may live to serve you joyfully.

28 A man there lived in Galilee

Somerset Corry Lowry (1855-1932)

Tyrolean melody

TYROL DCM

2. A man there died on Calvary
above all others brave;
the human race he saved and blessed,
himself he scorned to save.
No thought can gauge the weight of woe
on him, the sinless, laid;
we only know that with his blood
our ransom price was paid.

3. A man there reigns in glory now,
divine, yet human still;
that human which is all divine
death sought in vain to kill.
All pow'r is his; supreme he rules
the realms of time and space;
yet still our human cares and needs
find in his heart a place.

Text © Copyright Oxford University Press, Great Clarendon Street, Oxford OX2 6DP.

29 Amazing grace

vs. 1-4: John Newton (1725-1807) alt.
v. 5: John Rees (1828-1900)

American folk melody

2. 'Twas grace that taught my heart to fear,
and grace my fears relieved.
How precious did that grace appear
the hour I first believed.

3. Through many dangers, toils and snares
I have already come.
'Tis grace that brought me safe thus far,
and grace will lead me home.

4. The Lord has promised good to me,
his word my hope secures;
he will my shield and portion be
as long as life endures.

5. When we've been there a thousand years,
bright shining as the sun,
we've no less days to sing God's praise
than when we first begun.

30 Among us and before us

Words and music: John L. Bell (b.1949) and Graham Maules (b.1958)

2. Who dare say No, when such is your resolve
our worst to witness, suffer and absolve,
our best to raise in lives by God forgiv'n,
our souls to fill on earth with food from heav'n?

3. Who dare say No, when such is your intent
to love the selves we famish and resent,
to cradle our uncertainties and fear,
to kindle hope as you in faith draw near?

4. Who dare say No, when such is your request
that each around your table should be guest,
that here the ancient word should live as new
'Take, eat and drink – all this is meant for you.'?

5. No more we hesitate and wonder why;
no more we stand indiff'rent, scared or shy.
Your invitation leads us to say 'Yes',
to meet you where you nourish, heal and bless.

© Copyright 1989 WGRG, Iona Community, Glasgow G2 3DH, Scotland,
from the *Love From Below* collection (Wild Goose Publications 1989). Used by permission.

31 An army of ordinary people

Words and music: Dave Bilbrough

© Copyright 1983 Kingsway's Thankyou Music, P.O. Box 75, Eastbourne, East Sussex BN23 6NW, UK. (tym@kingsway.co.uk). Used by permission.

32 And can it be

Charles Wesley (1707-1788)

Thomas Campbell (1824-1876)

2. 'Tis myst'ry all! th'Immortal dies:
who can explore his strange design?
In vain the first-born seraph tries
to sound the depths of love divine!
'Tis mercy all! Let earth adore,
let angel minds inquire no more.

3. He left his Father's throne above
so free, so infinite his grace;
emptied himself of all but love,
and bled for Adam's helpless race;
'tis mercy all, immense and free;
for, O my God, it found out me.

4. Long my imprisoned spirit lay
fast bound in sin and nature's night;
thine eye diffused a quick'ning ray,
I woke, the dungeon flamed with light;
my chains fell off, my heart was free;
I rose, went forth, and followed thee.

5. No condemnation now I dread;
Jesus, and all in him, is mine!
Alive in him, my living Head,
and clothed in righteousness divine,
bold I approach the eternal throne,
and claim the crown, through Christ my own.

33 And did those feet in ancient time *Jerusalem*

William Blake (1757-1827)

Charles Hubert Hastings Parry (1848-1918)

34 And now, O Father, mindful of the love

William Bright (1824-1901) William Henry Monk (1823-1889)

TUNE 1: UNDE ET MEMORES 10 10 10 10 10 10

2. Look, Father, look on his anointed face,
and only look on us as found in him;
look not on our misusings of thy grace,
our prayer so languid, and our faith so dim:
for lo, between our sins and their reward
we set the Passion of thy Son our Lord.

3. And then for those, our dearest and our best,
by this prevailing presence we appeal:
O fold them closer to thy mercy's breast,
O do thine utmost for their souls' true weal;
from tainting mischief keep them pure and clear,
and crown thy gifts with strength to persevere.

4. And so we come: O draw us to thy feet,
most patient Saviour, who canst love us still;
and by this food, so aweful and so sweet,
deliver us from ev'ry touch of ill:
in thine own service make us glad and free,
and grant us never more to part with thee.

William Bright (1824-1901) Orlando Gibbons (1583-1625)

TUNE 2: SONG 1 10 10 10 10 10 10

1. And now, O Fa-ther, mind-ful of the love that bought us, once for all, on
Cal-v'ry's tree, and hav-ing with us him that pleads a - bove, we
here pre-sent, we here spread forth to thee that on-ly of-f'ring per-fect
in thine eyes, the one true, pure, im-mor-tal sac - ri - fice.

35 A new commandment

v.1 unknown based on John 13:34-35;
vs.2-4 Aniceto Nazareth
based onJohn 15 and 1 Corinthians 13

Unknown

2. You are my friends if you do what I command you.
Without my help you can do nothing. *(Repeat)*

3. I am the true vine, my Father is the gard'ner.
Abide in me: I will be with you. *(Repeat)*

4. True love is patient, not arrogant nor boastful;
love bears all things, love is eternal. *(Repeat)*

Text © Copyright 1984 Kevin Mayhew Ltd.

36 Angels from the realms of glory

James Montgomery (1771-1854)

French or Flemish melody

IRIS 87 87 and Refrain

2. Shepherds, in the field abiding,
watching o'er your flocks by night,
God with us is now residing,
yonder shines the infant Light:

3. Sages, leave your contemplations;
brighter visions beam afar:
seek the great Desire of Nations;
ye have seen his natal star:

4. Saints before the altar bending,
watching long in hope and fear,
suddenly the Lord, descending,
in his temple shall appear:

5. Though an infant now we view him,
he shall fill his Father's throne,
gather all the nations to him;
ev'ry knee shall then bow down:

37 Angel-voices ever singing

Francis Pott (1832-1909) alt.

Edwin George Monk (1819-1900)

ANGEL VOICES 85 85 843

2. Thou who art beyond the farthest
mortal eye can see,
can it be that thou regardest
our poor hymnody?
Yes, we know that thou art near us
and wilt hear us constantly.

3. Yea, we know that thou rejoicest
o'er each work of thine;
thou didst ears and hands and voices
for thy praise design;
craftsman's art and music's measure
for thy pleasure all combine.

4. In thy house, great God, we offer
of thine own to thee;
and for thine acceptance proffer
all unworthily,
hearts and minds and hands and voices
in our choicest psalmody.

5. Honour, glory, might and merit,
thine shall ever be,
Father, Son and Holy Spirit,
blessèd Trinity.
Of the best that thou hast given
earth and heaven render thee.

38 An upper room did our Lord prepare

Fred Pratt Green (1903-2000)

Somerset folk song collected by
Cecil Sharp (1859-1924)

O WALY WALY LM

2. A lasting gift Jesus gave his own:
to share his bread, his loving cup.
Whatever burdens may bow us down,
he by his cross shall lift us up.

3. And after supper he washed their feet
for service, too, is sacrament.
In him our joy shall be made complete –
sent out to serve, as he was sent.

4. No end there is! We depart in peace,
he loves beyond our uttermost:
in ev'ry room in our Father's house
he will be there, as Lord and host.

Text © Copyright 1974 Stainer & Bell Ltd., P.O. Box 110, Victoria House,
23 Gruneison Road, Finchley, London N3 1DZ. Used by permission

39 A purple robe

Timothy Dudley-Smith (b.1926)

David Wilson (b.1940)

A PURPLE ROBE 86 86 Triple

Text © Copyright Timothy Dudley-Smith, 9 Ahslands, Ford, Salisbury, Wiltshire SP4 6DY.
Music © Copyright David Wilson/Jubilate Hymns. 4 Thorne Park Road,
Chelston, Torquay TQ2 6RX. Used by permission.

40 Arise to greet the Lord of light

Michael Foster (b.1946)
based on Isaiah 60:1-6

Charles Hubert Hastings Parry (1848-1918)

REPTON 86 88 6

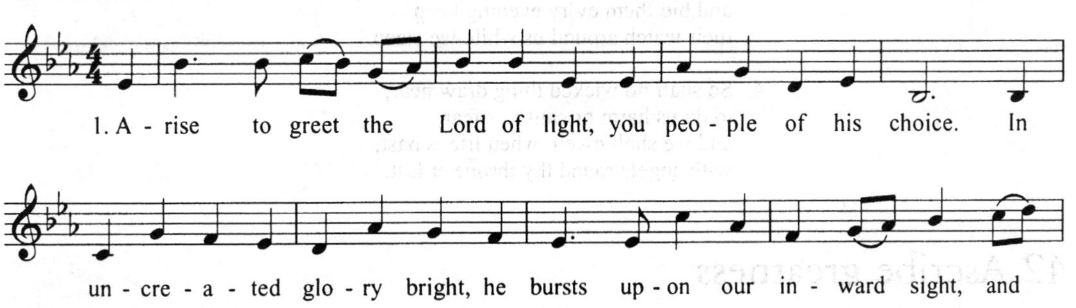

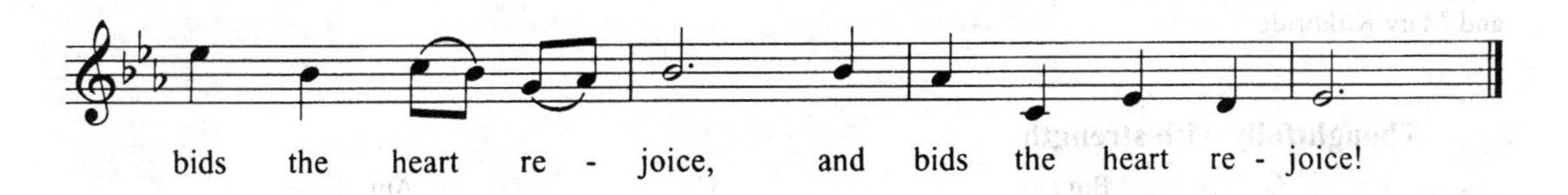

2. Towards his light shall kings be drawn
this majesty to see;
and in the brightness of the dawn
shall see the world in hope reborn,
in justice full and free,
in justice full and free.

3. The holy light in Judah's skies
calls sages from afar.
The hope of kings they recognise
which, in the virgin mother's eyes,
outshines the guiding star,
outshines the guiding star.

4. This majesty for long concealed
from longing human sight,
in Jesus Christ is now revealed,
and God's eternal promise sealed
in love's unending light,
in love's unending light.

Text © Copyright 1993 Kevin Mayhew Ltd.

41 Around the throne of God

John Mason Neale (1818-1866)

Traditional Swiss melody

SOLOTHURN LM

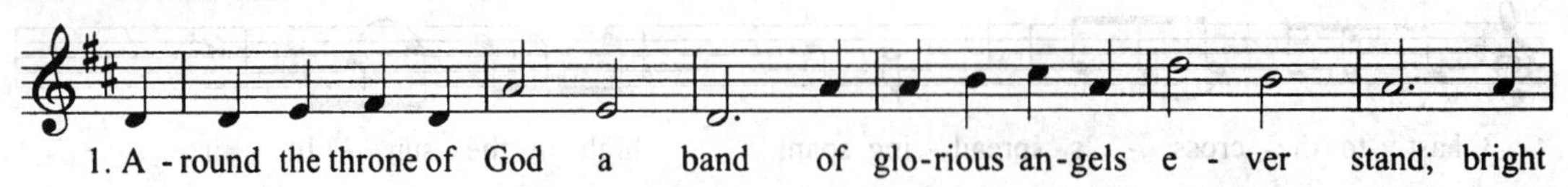

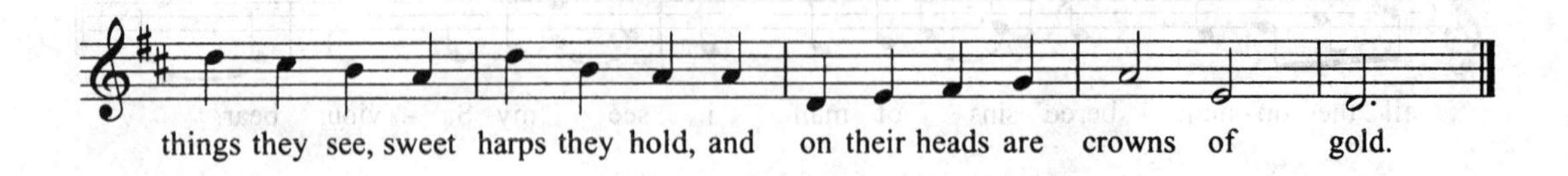

2. Some wait around him, ready still
   to sing his praise and do his will;
   and some, when he commands them, go
   to guard his servants here below.

3. Lord, give thy angels ev'ry day
   command to guide us on our way,
   and bid them ev'ry evening keep
   their watch around us while we sleep.

4. So shall no wicked thing draw near,
   to do us harm or cause us fear;
   and we shall dwell, when life is past,
   with angels round thy throne at last.

42 Ascribe greatness

Words and music: Peter West, Mary Lou Locke
and Mary Kirkbride

© Copyright 1979 Peter West, Mary Lou Locke & Mary Kirkbride.
© Copyright Control.

43 As now the sun's declining rays

Charles Coffin (1676-1749)
trans. John Chandler (1806-1876)

Alexander Robert Reinagle (1799-1877)

ST PETER CM

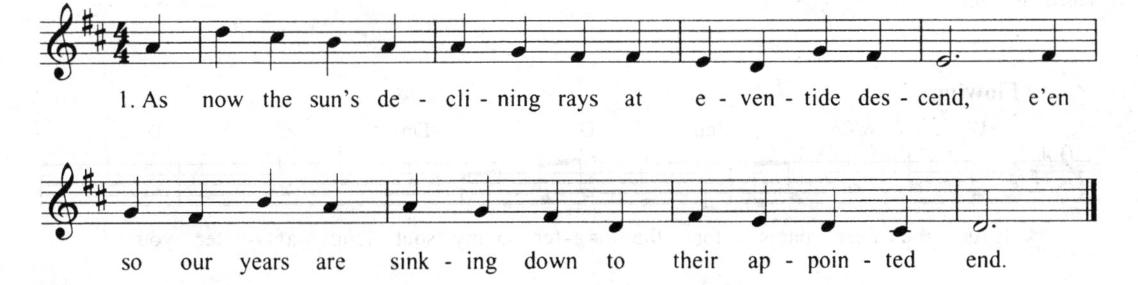

2. Lord, on the cross thine arms were stretched
to draw the nations nigh;
O grant us then that cross to love,
and in those arms to die.

3. To God the Father, God the Son,
and God the Holy Ghost,
all glory be from saints on earth
and from the angel host.

44 As pants the hart for cooling streams

Psalm 42 in *New Version*
(Tate and Brady, 1696)

Hugh Wilson (1766-1824)

MARTYRDOM CM

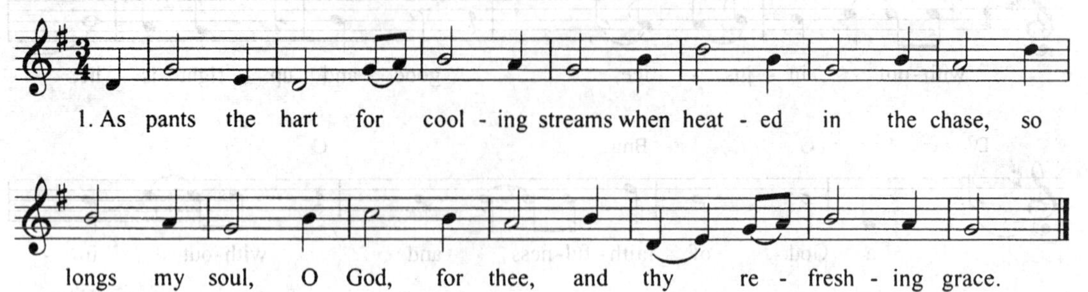

2. For thee, my God, the living God,
my thirsty soul doth pine:
O when shall I behold thy face,
thou majesty divine?

3. Why restless, why cast down, my soul?
hope still, and thou shalt sing
the praise of him who is thy God,
thy health's eternal spring.

4. To Father, Son and Holy Ghost,
the God whom we adore,
be glory, as it was, is now,
and shall be evermore.

45 As the deer pants for the water

Words and music: Martin Nystrom
based on Psalm 42:1-2

© Copyright 1983 Restoration Music Ltd., Sovereign Music UK.
P.O. Box 356, Leighton Buzzard, Beds. LU7 3WP, UK. Used by permission.

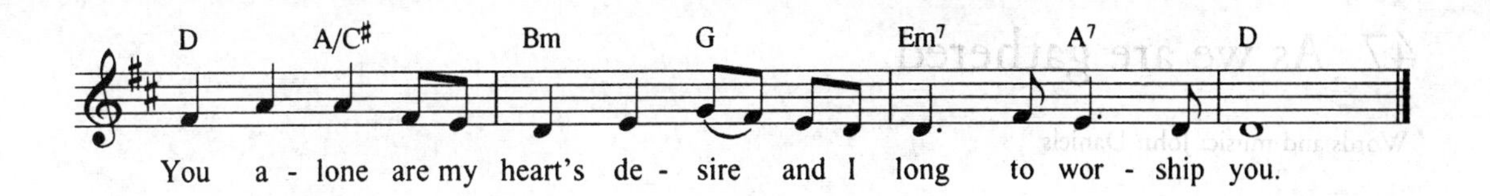

2. I want you more than gold or silver,
only you can satisfy.
You alone are the real joy-giver
and the apple of my eye.

3. You're my friend and you are my brother,
even though you are a king.
I love you more than any other,
so much more than anything.

46 A still small voice

Words and music: Jancis Harvey

2. The voice of God in a place that is troubled,
the voice of God in the dawning,
through the noise of the shouting,
through the stillness of the sleeping,
it can only be heard if you listen.

3. Give time to hear, give us love that will listen,
give wisdom for understanding,
there's a voice of stillness
that to each of us is speaking,
it can only be heard if you listen.

© Copyright Jancis Harvey. Used by permission.

47 As we are gathered

Words and music: John Daniels

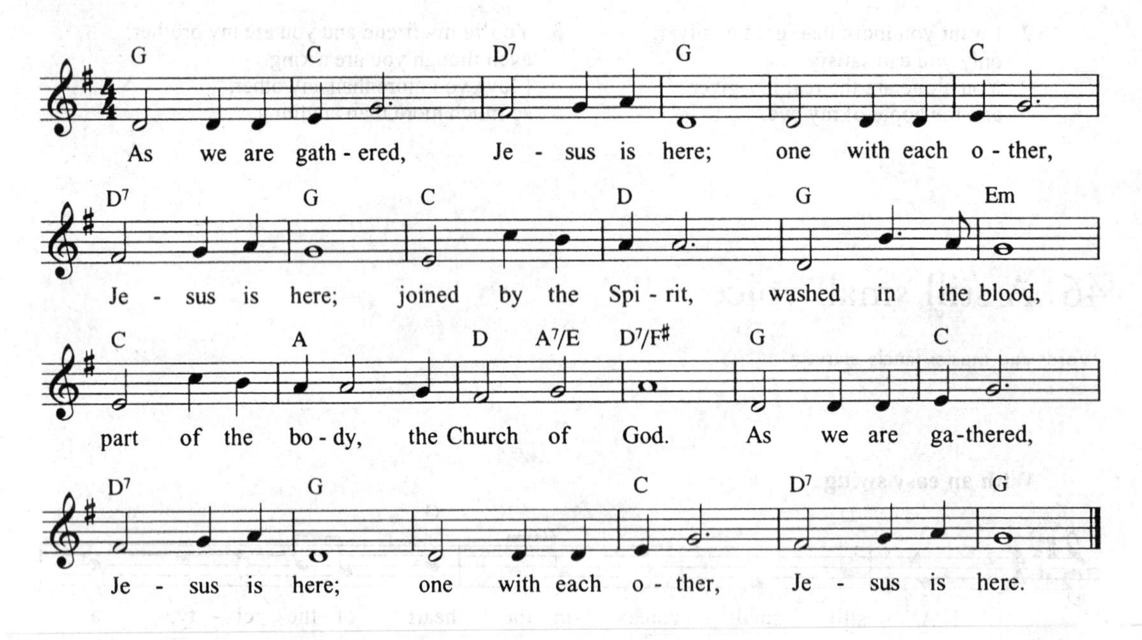

© Copyright 1979 Word's Spirit of Praise Music. Administered by CopyCare, P.O. Box 77, Hailsham, East Sussex BN27 3EF, UK. (music@copycare.com). Used by permission.

48 As we break the bread

Fred Kaan (b.1929) — Evelyn Sharpe (1884-1969) alt.

PLATT'S LANE 56 64

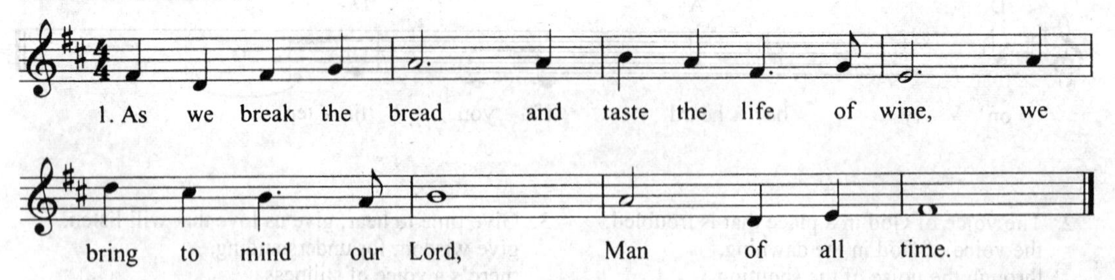

2. Grain is sown to die;
it rises from the dead,
becomes through human toil
our daily bread.

Text © Copyright 1968 Stainer & Bell Ltd., P.O. Box 110, Victoria House, 23 Gruneison Road, Finchley, London N3 1DZ.
Music © Copyright Oxford University Press, Great Clarendon Street, Oxford OX2 6DP. Used by permission.

3. Pass from hand to hand
the living love of Christ!
Machines and people raise
bread for this feast.

4. Jesus binds in one
our daily life and work;
he is of humankind
symbol and mark.

5. Having shared the bread
that died to rise again,
we rise to serve the world
scattered as grain.

49 As with gladness men of old

William Chatterton Dix (1837-1898) alt.

Adapted from Conrad Kocher (1786-1872)
by William Henry Monk (1823-1889)

DIX 77 77 77

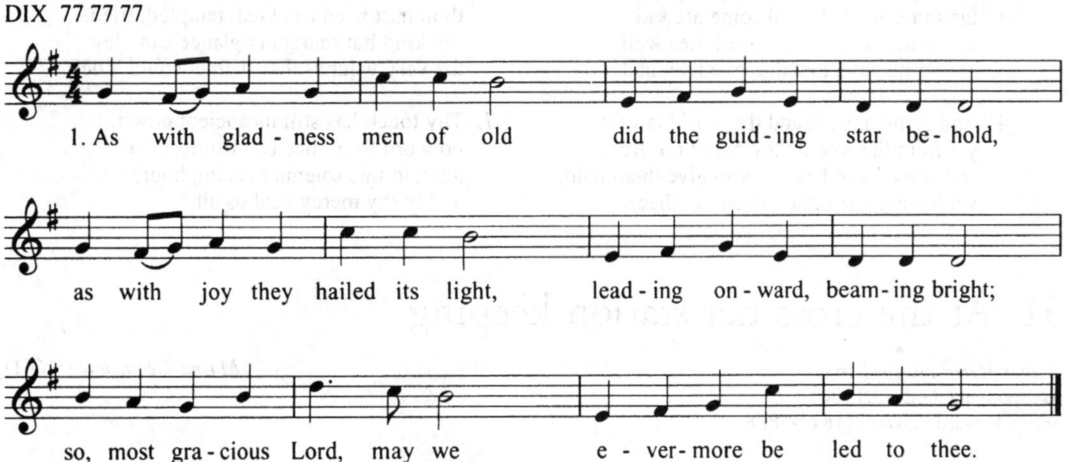

2. As with joyful steps they sped,
to that lowly manger-bed,
there to bend the knee before
him whom heav'n and earth adore,
so may we with willing feet
ever seek thy mercy-seat.

3. As their precious gifts they laid,
at thy manger roughly made,
so may we with holy joy,
pure, and free from sin's alloy,
all our costliest treasures bring,
Christ, to thee our heav'nly King.

4. Holy Jesu, ev'ry day
keep us in the narrow way;
and, when earthly things are past,
bring our ransomed souls at last
where they need no star to guide,
where no clouds thy glory hide.

5. In the heav'nly country bright
need they no created light,
thou its light, its joy, its crown,
thou its sun which goes not down;
there for ever may we sing
alleluias to our King.

50 At even, ere the sun was set

Henry Twells (1823-1900) alt.

Adapted from a melody by Georg Joseph in Scheffler's *Heilige Seelenlust*, Breslau (1657)

ANGELUS LM

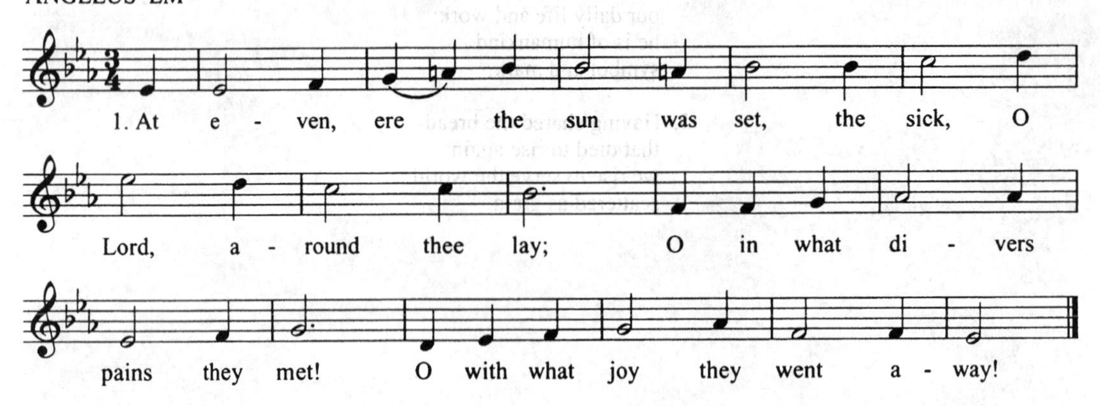

2. Once more 'tis eventide, and we
oppressed with various ills draw near;
what if thy form we cannot see?
We know and feel that thou art here.

3. O Saviour Christ, our woes dispel;
for some are sick, and some are sad,
and some have never loved thee well,
and some have lost the love they had.

4. And some have found the world is vain,
yet from the world they break not free;
and some have friends who give them pain,
yet have not sought a friend in thee.

5. And none, O Lord, has perfect rest,
for none is wholly free from sin;
and they who fain would serve thee best
are conscious most of wrong within.

6. O Christ, thou hast been human too,
thou hast been troubled, tempted, tried;
thy kind but searching glance can view
the very wounds that shame would hide.

7. Thy touch has still its ancient pow'r;
no word from thee can fruitless fall:
hear, in this solemn evening hour,
and in thy mercy heal us all.

51 At the cross her station keeping

Stabat Mater, ascribed to
Jacopone da Todi (d.1306)
trans. Edward Caswall (1814-1878)

Mainz Gesangbuch (1661)

STABAT MATER 887

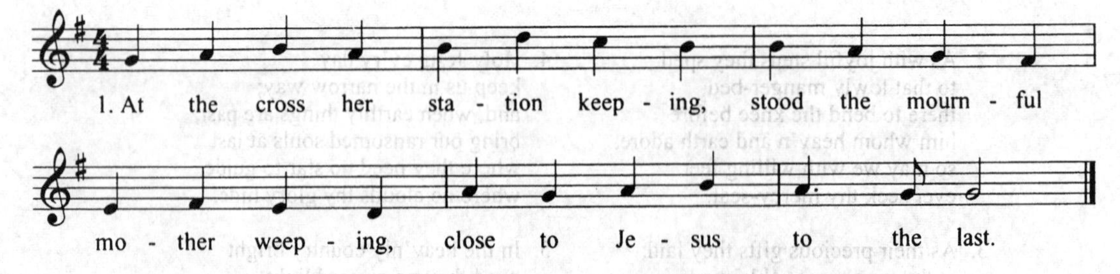

2. Through her heart, his sorrow sharing,
all his bitter anguish bearing,
now at length the sword has passed.

3. O, how sad and sore distressed
was that mother highly blest,
of the sole-begotten One.

4. Christ above in torment hangs;
she beneath beholds the pangs
of her dying glorious Son.

5. Is there one who would not weep,
whelmed in miseries so deep,
Christ's dear mother to behold?

6. Can the human heart refrain
   from partaking in her pain,
   in that mother's pain untold?

7. Bruised, derided, cursed, defiled,
   she beheld her tender child,
   all with bloody scourges rent.

8. For the sins of his own nation,
   saw him hang in desolation,
   till his spirit forth he sent.

9. O thou mother! Fount of Love!
   Touch my spirit from above,
   make my heart with thine accord.

10. Make me feel as thou hast felt;
    make my soul to glow and melt
    with the love of Christ my Lord.

11. Holy Mother, pierce me through,
    in my heart each wound renew
    of my Saviour crucified.

12. Let me share with thee his pain
    who for all my sins was slain,
    who for me in torments died.

13. Let me mingle tears with thee,
    mourning him who mourned for me,
    all the days that I may live.

14. By the cross with thee to stay,
    there with thee to weep and pray,
    this I ask of thee to give.

52 At the dawning of creation

David Fox (b.1956) — John Stainer (1840-1901)

CROSS OF JESUS 87 87

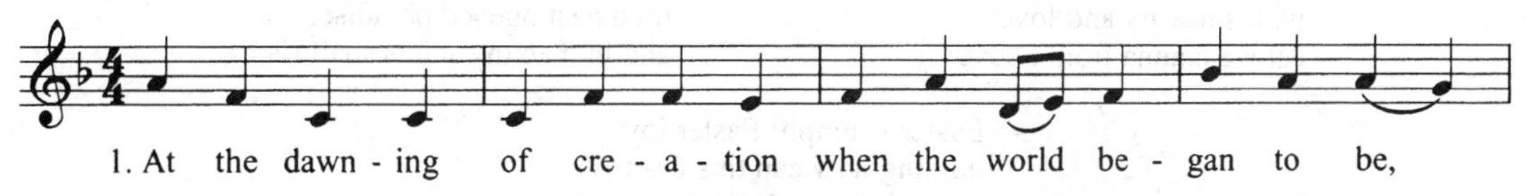

2. When the Lord delivered Israel
   out of Egypt's bitter yoke,
   then the parting of the waters
   of the living water spoke.

3. Water from the rock of Moses,
   water from the temple's side,
   water from the heart of Jesus,
   flow in this baptismal tide.

4. Thus united in this water
   each to all, and each to Christ;
   to his life of love he calls us
   by his total sacrifice.

53 At the Lamb's high feast we sing

Ad regias Agni dapes (7th century)
trans. Robert Campbell (1814-1868)

Jacob Hintze (1622-1702)

SALZBURG 77 77 D

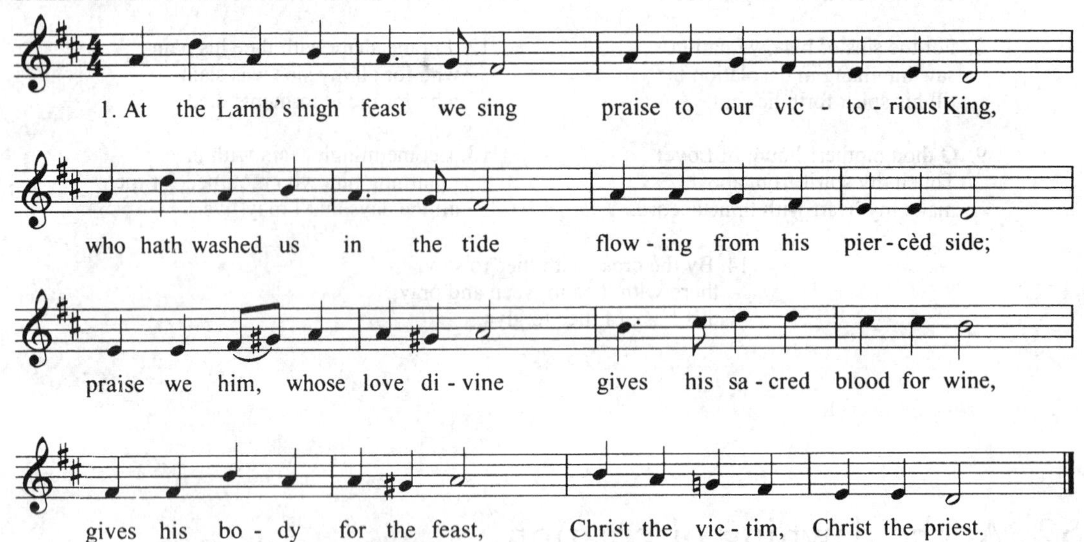

2. Where the paschal blood is poured,
death's dark angel sheathes his sword;
faithful hosts triumphant go
through the wave that drowns the foe.
Praise we Christ, whose blood was shed,
paschal victim, paschal bread;
with sincerity and love
eat we manna from above.

3. Mighty victim from above,
conqu'ring by the pow'r of love;
thou hast triumphed in the fight,
thou hast brought us life and light.
Now no more can death appal,
now no more the grave enthral:
thou hast opened paradise,
and in thee thy saints shall rise.

4. Easter triumph, Easter joy,
nothing now can this destroy;
from sin's pow'r do thou set free
souls new-born, O Lord, in thee.
Hymns of glory and of praise,
risen Lord, to thee we raise;
holy Father, praise to thee,
with the Spirit, ever be.

54 At the name of Jesus

Caroline Maria Noel (1817-1877) alt.

William Henry Monk (1823-1889)

TUNE 1: EVELYNS 65 65 D

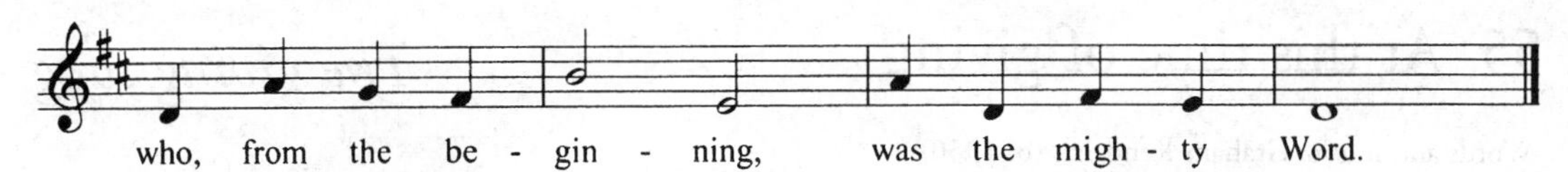

2. At his voice creation
sprang at once to sight,
all the angels' faces,
all the hosts of light,
thrones and dominations,
stars upon their way,
all the heav'nly orders
in their great array.

3. Humbled for a season,
to receive a name
from the lips of sinners
unto whom he came,
faithfully he bore it,
spotless to the last,
brought it back victorious
when from death he passed.

4. Bore it up triumphant
with its human light,
through all ranks of creatures
to the central height,
to the throne of Godhead,
to the Father's breast,
filled it with the glory
of that perfect rest.

5. In your hearts enthrone him;
there let him subdue
all that is not holy,
all that is not true;
crown him as your captain
in temptation's hour;
let his will enfold you
in its light and pow'r.

6. Truly, this Lord Jesus
shall return again,
with his Father's glory,
with his angel train;
for all wreaths of empire
meet upon his brow,
and our hearts confess him
King of glory now.

Caroline Maria Noel (1817-1877) alt. Michael Brierley (b.1932)

TUNE 2: CAMBERWELL 65 65 D

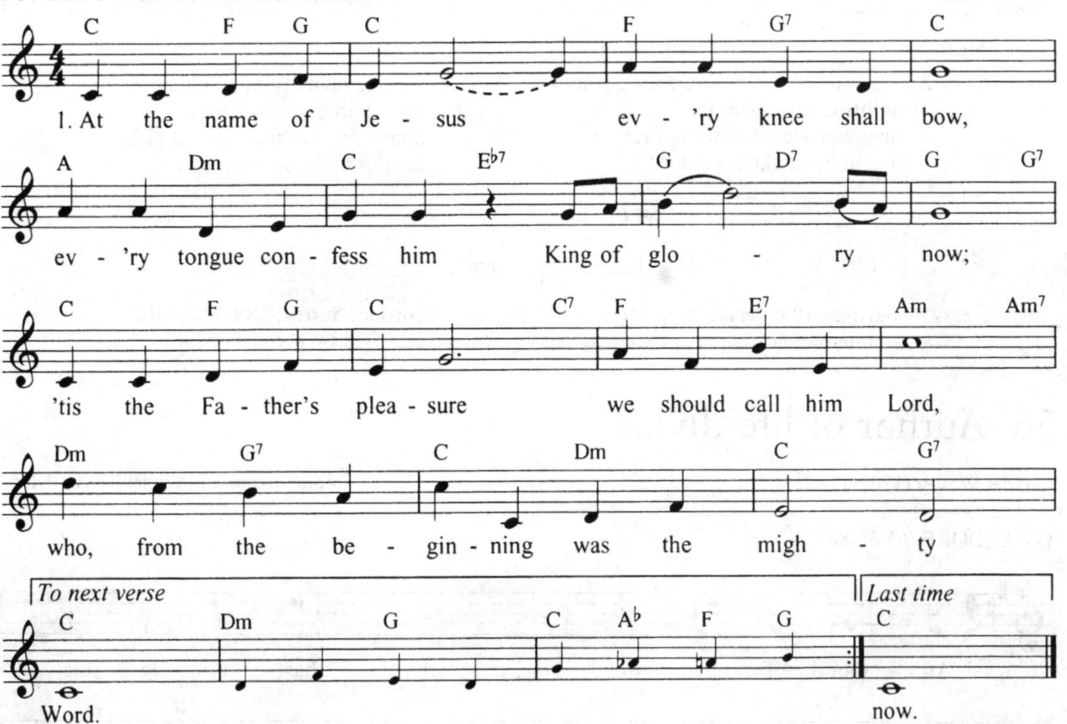

Music © Copyright 1960 Josef Weinberger Ltd., 12-14 Mortimer Street, London W1N 7RD.
Used by permission.

55 At this time of giving

The giving song

Words and music: Graham Kendrick (b. 1950)

2. May his tender love surround you
at this Christmastime;
may you see his smiling face
that in the darkness shines.

3. But the many gifts he gives
are all poured out from one;
come, receive the greatest gift,
the gift of God's own Son.

Last two choruses and verses:

Lai, lai, lai . . . etc

© Copyright 1988 Make Way Music, P.O. Box 263, Croydon, Surrey CR9 5AP, UK.
International copyright secured. All rights reserved. Used by permission.

56 Author of life divine

Charles Wesley (1707-1788)

Samuel Sebastian Wesley (1810-1876)

GWEEDORE 66 66 88

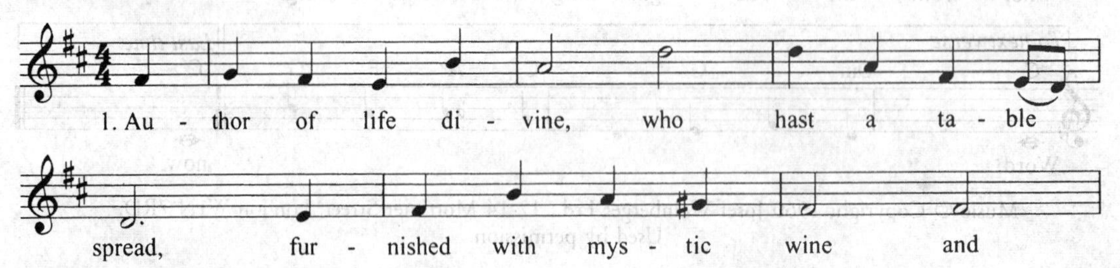

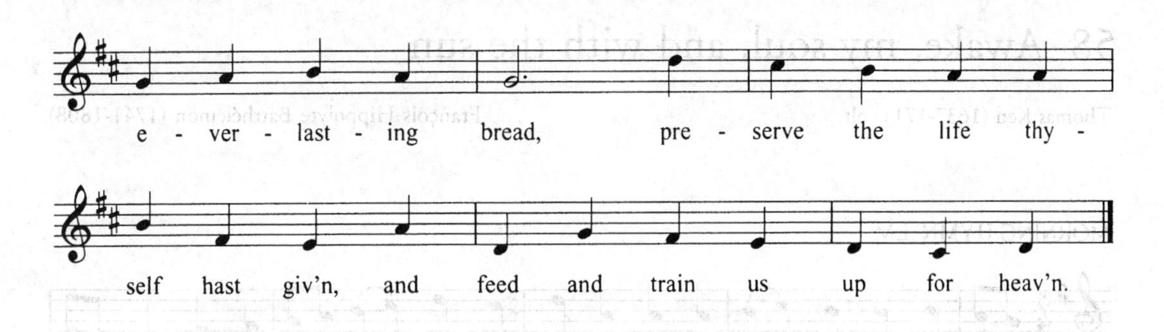

2. Our needy souls sustain
with fresh supplies of love,
till all thy life we gain,
and all thy fulness prove,
and, strengthened by thy perfect grace,
behold without a veil thy face.

57 Awake, awake: fling off the night

John Raphael Peacey (1896-1971)
based on Ephesians 5:6-20 alt.

Grenoble Antiphoner (1753)

DEUS TUORUM MILITUM LM

2. Awake and rise, in Christ renewed,
and with the Spirit's pow'r endued.
The light of life in us must glow,
and fruits of truth and goodness show.

3. Let in the light; all sin expose
to Christ, whose life no darkness knows.
Before his cross for guidance kneel;
his light will judge and, judging, heal.

4. Awake, and rise up from the dead,
and Christ his light on you will shed.
Its pow'r will wrong desires destroy,
and your whole nature fill with joy.

5. Then sing for joy, and use each day;
give thanks for everything alway.
Lift up your hearts; with one accord
praise God through Jesus Christ our Lord.

Text © Copyright the Revd. Mary J. Hancock.
Used by kind permission.

58 Awake, my soul, and with the sun

Thomas Ken (1637-1711) alt.

François Hippolyte Barthélémon (1741-1808)

MORNING HYMN LM

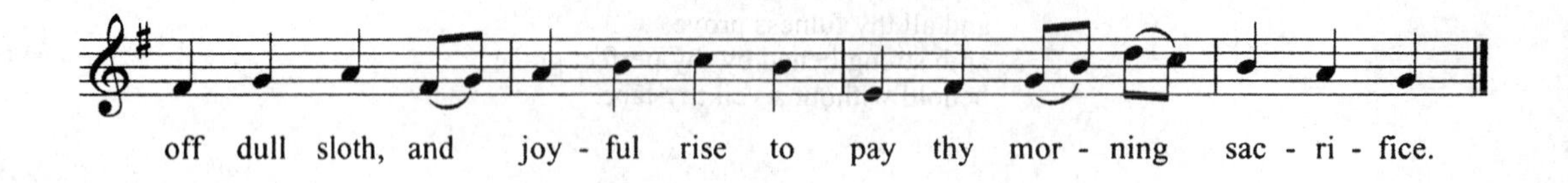

2. Redeem thy mis-spent time that's past,
and live this day as if thy last;
improve thy talent with due care;
for the great day thyself prepare.

3. Let all thy converse be sincere,
thy conscience as the noon-day clear;
think how all-seeing God thy ways
and all thy secret thoughts surveys.

4. Wake, and lift up thyself, my heart,
and with the angels bear thy part,
who all night long unwearied sing
high praise to the eternal King.

PART 2

5. Glory to thee, who safe hast kept
and hast refreshed me whilst I slept;
grant, Lord, when I from death shall wake,
I may of endless light partake.

6. Lord, I my vows to thee renew;
disperse my sins as morning dew;
guard my first springs of thought and will,
and with thyself my spirit fill.

7. Direct, control, suggest, this day,
all I design or do or say;
that all my pow'rs, with all their might,
in thy sole glory may unite.

This Doxology is sung after either part:

8. Praise God, from whom all blessings flow,
praise him, all creatures here below,
praise him above, angelic host,
praise Father, Son and Holy Ghost.

59 Awake, our souls

Isaac Watts (1674-1748)
based on Isaiah 40:28-31

D.S. Bortniansky (1752-1825)

ST PETERSBURG LM

2. True, 'tis a strait and thorny road,
and mortal spirits tire and faint;
but they forget the mighty God
that feeds the strength of ev'ry saint.

3. The mighty God, whose matchless pow'r
is ever new and ever young,
and firm endures, while endless years
their everlasting circles run.

4. From thee, the overflowing spring,
our souls shall drink a fresh supply,
while such as trust their native strength
shall melt away, and drop, and die.

5. Swift as an eagle cuts the air,
we'll mount aloft to thine abode;
on wings of love our souls shall fly,
nor tire amidst the heav'nly road.

60 Beauty for brokenness

God of the poor

Words and music: Graham Kendrick (b.1950)

2. Shelter for fragile lives,
cures for their ills,
work for the craftsmen,
trade for their skills.
Land for the dispossessed,
rights for the weak,
voices to plead the cause
of those who can't speak.

3. Refuge from cruel wars,
havens from fear,
cities for sanctu'ry,
freedoms to share.
Peace to the killing fields,
scorched earth to green,
Christ for the bitterness,
his cross for the pain.

4. Rest for the ravaged earth,
oceans and streams,
plundered and poisoned,
our future, our dreams.
Lord, end our madness,
carelessness, greed;
make us content with
the things that we need.

5. Lighten our darkness,
breathe on this flame,
until your justice
burns brightly again;
until the nations
learn of your ways,
seek your salvation
and bring you their praise.

© Copyright 1993 Make Way Music, P.O. Box 263, Croydon, Surrey CR9 5AP, UK.
International copyright secured. All rights reserved. Used by permission.

61 Before the ending of the day

Te lucis ante terminum (pre 8th century)
trans. John Mason Neale (1818-1866)

Proper Sarum Melody Mode VIII

TE LUCIS ANTE TERMINUM LM

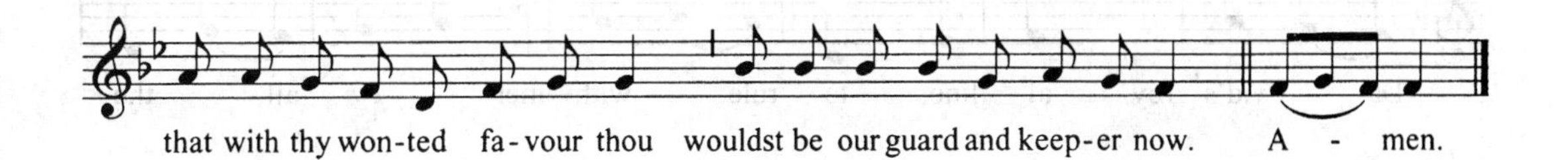

2. From all ill dreams defend our eyes,
from nightly fears and fantasies;
tread under foot our ghostly foe,
that no pollution we may know.

3. O Father, that we ask be done,
through Jesus Christ thine only Son,
who, with the Holy Ghost and thee,
doth live and reign eternally. Amen.

62 Behold, the great Creator

Thomas Pestel (1585-1659) alt.

Neil Dougall (1776-1862)

KILMARNOCK CM

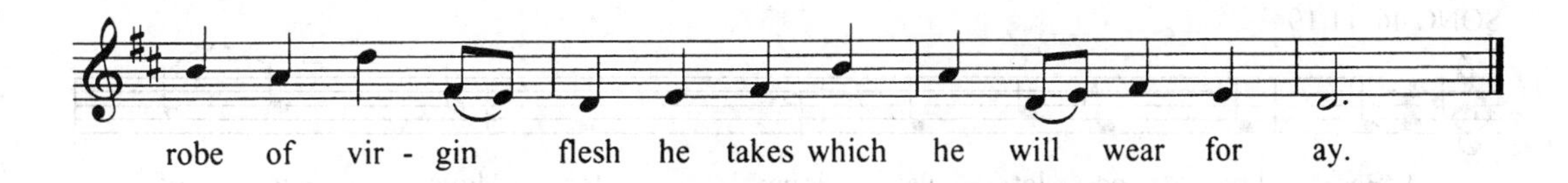

2. Hark, hark! the wise eternal Word
like a weak infant cries;
in form of servant is the Lord,
and God in cradle lies.

3. This wonder struck the world amazed,
it shook the starry frame;
squadrons of angels stood and gazed,
then down in troops they came.

4. Glad shepherds run to view this sight;
a choir of angels sings,
and eastern sages with delight
adore this King of kings.

5. Join then, all hearts that are not stone,
and all our voices prove;
to celebrate this Holy One,
the God of peace and love.

63 Behold, the Saviour of the nations

Michael Foster (b.1946)
based on Isaiah 11:1-10

Clement Cotterill Scholefield (1839-1904)

ST CLEMENT 98 98

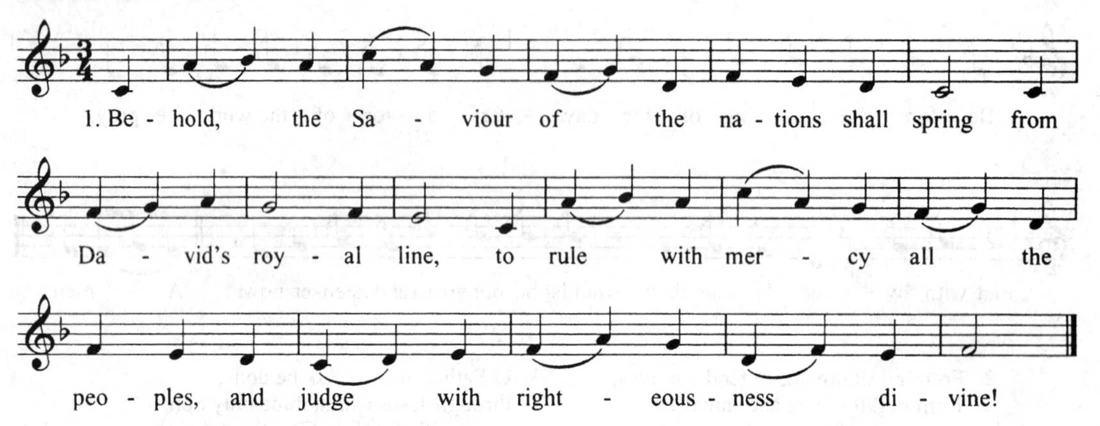

2. He shall delight in truth and wisdom,
with justice for the meek and poor,
and reconcile his whole creation,
where beasts of prey shall hunt no more.

3. Here may his word, with hope abounding,
unite us all in peace and love,
to live as one with all creation,
redeemed by mercy from above.

4. Prepare the way with awe and wonder;
salvation comes on judgement's wing,
for God will purify his people,
and 'Glory!' all the earth shall sing.

Text © Copyright 1993 Kevin Mayhew Ltd.

64 Beloved, let us love

Horatius Bonar (1808-1889)
based on 1 John 4:7

Orlando Gibbons (1583-1625)

SONG 46 11 10

2. Beloved, let us love:
for those who love,
they only, are his children from above.

3. Beloved, let us love:
for love is rest,
and those who do not love cannot be blessed.

4. Beloved, let us love:
for love is light,
and those who do not love still live in night.

5. Beloved, let us love:
for only thus
shall we see God, the Lord who first loved us.

65 Beneath the cross of Jesus

Elizabeth C. Clephane (1830-1869) alt. Frederick C. Maker (1844-1927)

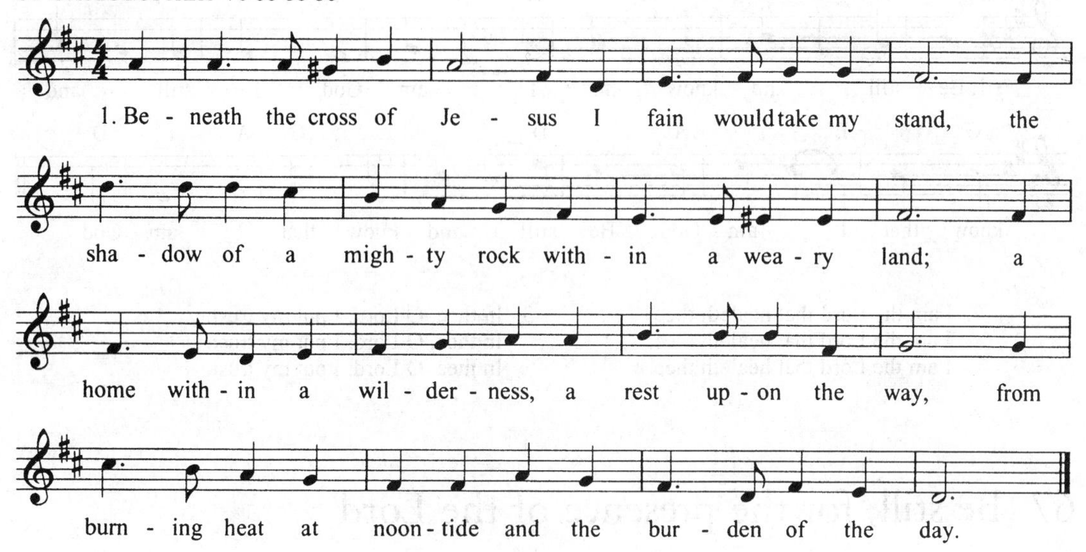

2. O safe and happy shelter!
O refuge tried and sweet!
O trysting place where heaven's love
and heaven's justice meet!
As to the holy patriarch
that wondrous dream was giv'n,
so seems my Saviour's cross to me
a ladder up to heav'n.

3. There lies, beneath its shadow,
but on the farther side,
the darkness of an awful grave
that gapes both deep and wide;
and there between us stands the cross,
two arms outstretched to save;
a watchman set to guard the way
from that eternal grave.

4. Upon that cross of Jesus
mine eye at times can see
the very dying form of One
who suffered there for me;
and from my stricken heart, with tears,
two wonders I confess –
the wonders of redeeming love,
and my unworthiness.

5. I take, O cross, thy shadow
for my abiding place!
I ask no other sunshine than
the sunshine of his face;
content to let the world go by,
to reckon gain as loss –
my sinful self, my only shame,
my glory all – the cross.

66 Be still and know that I am God

Unknown, based on Psalm 46 — Unknown

BE STILL AND KNOW 888

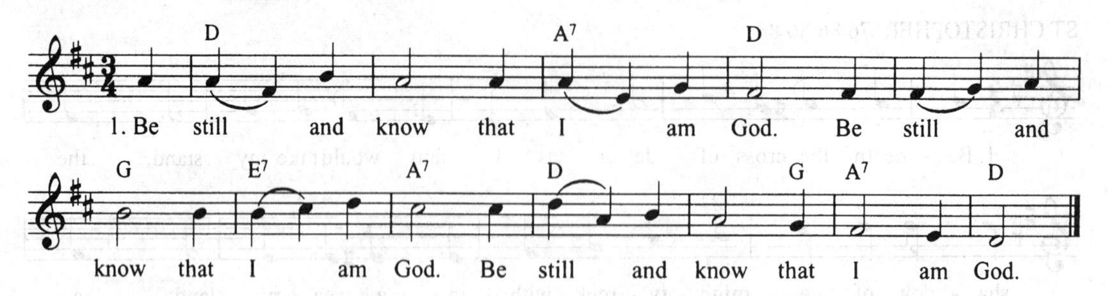

2. I am the Lord that healeth thee.
I am the Lord that healeth thee.
I am the Lord that healeth thee.

3. In thee, O Lord, I put my trust.
In thee, O Lord, I put my trust.
In thee, O Lord, I put my trust.

67 Be still, for the presence of the Lord

Words and music: David J. Evans (b.1957)

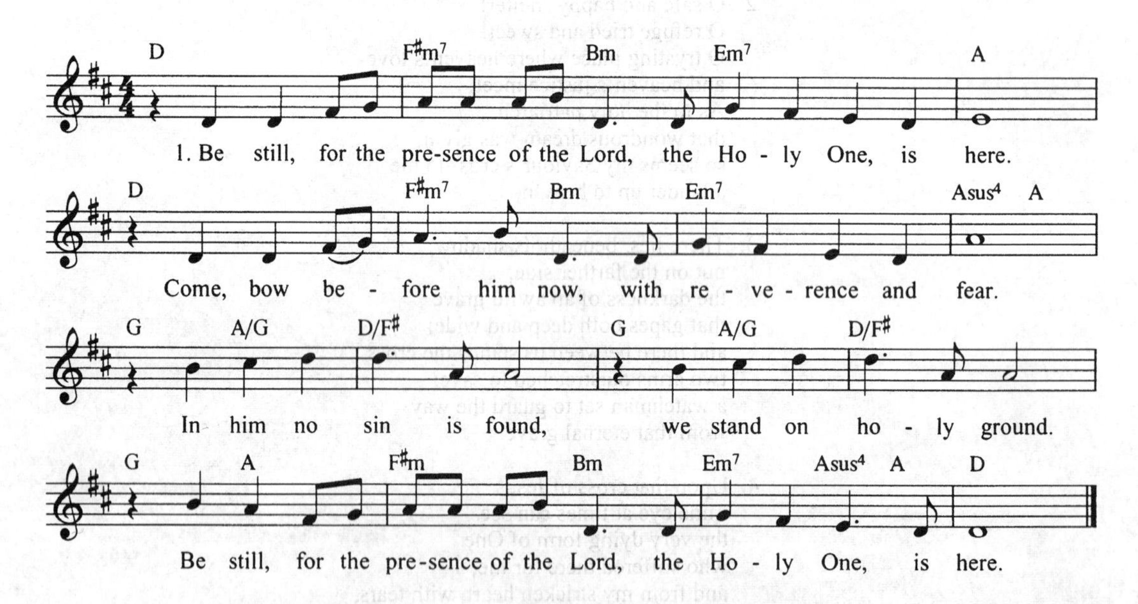

2. Be still, for the glory of the Lord is shining all around;
he burns with holy fire, with splendour he is crowned.
How awesome is the sight, our radiant King of light!
Be still, for the glory of the Lord is shining all around.

3. Be still, for the power of the Lord is moving in this place;
he comes to cleanse and heal, to minister his grace.
No work too hard for him, in faith receive from him.
Be still, for the power of the Lord is moving in this place.

© Copyright 1986 Kingsway's Thankyou Music. P.O. Box 75, Eastbourne, East Sussex BN23 6NW, UK. (tym@kingsway.co.uk). Used by permission.

68 Be still, my soul

Katherina von Schlegel (b.1697)
trans. Jane L. Borthwick alt.

Jean Sibelius (1865-1957)

FINLANDIA 10 10 10 10 10 10

2. Be still, my soul: your God will undertake
to guide the future as he has the past.
Your hope, your confidence let nothing shake,
all now mysterious shall be clear at last.
Be still, my soul: the tempests still obey
his voice, who ruled them once on Galilee.

3. Be still, my soul: the hour is hastening on
when we shall be for ever with the Lord,
when disappointment, grief and fear are gone,
sorrow forgotten, love's pure joy restored.
Be still, my soul: when change and tears are past,
all safe and blessèd we shall meet at last.

Music © Copyright Breitkopf and Härtel, Walkmühlstrasse 52, D-65195 Wiesbaden, Germany .
Used by permission.

69 Be thou my guardian and my guide

Isaac Williams (1802-1865)

Isaac Smith (1734-1805)

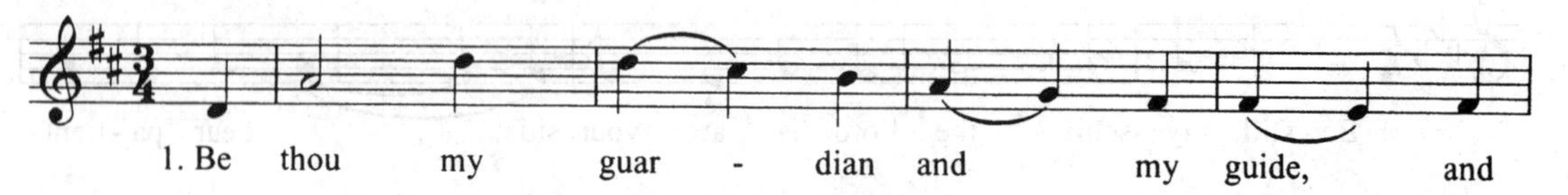

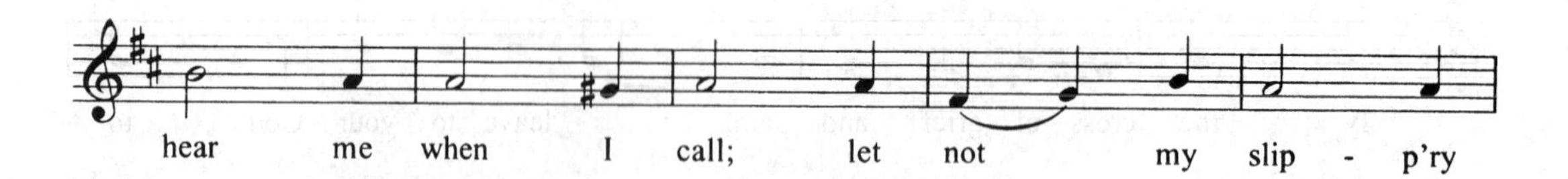

2. The world, the flesh, and Satan dwell
around the path I tread;
O save me from the snares of hell,
thou quick'ner of the dead.

3. And if I tempted am to sin,
and outward things are strong,
do thou, O Lord, keep watch within,
and save my soul from wrong.

4. Still let me ever watch and pray,
and feel that I am frail;
that if the tempter cross my way,
yet he may not prevail.

70 Be thou my vision

Irish (c.18th century)
trans. Mary Byrne (1880-1931)
and Eleanor Hull (1860-1935)

Traditional Irish melody

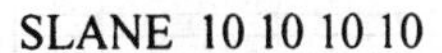

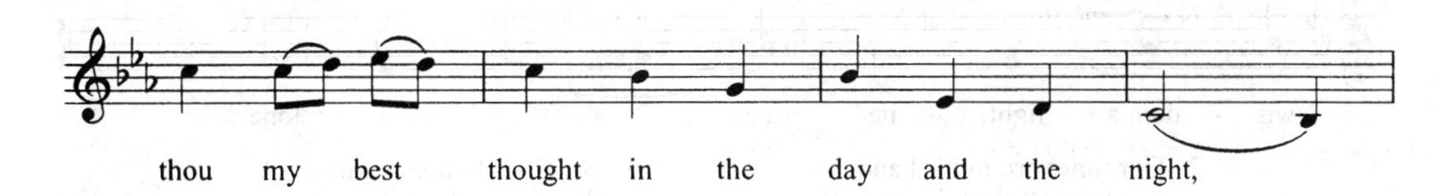

2. Be thou my wisdom, be thou my true word,
   I ever with thee and thou with me, Lord;
   thou my great Father, and I thy true heir;
   thou in me dwelling, and I in thy care.

3. Be thou my breastplate, my sword for the fight,
   be thou my armour, and be thou my might,
   thou my soul's shelter, and thou my high tow'r,
   raise thou me heav'nward, O Pow'r of my pow'r.

4. Riches I need not, nor all the world's praise,
   thou mine inheritance through all my days;
   thou, and thou only, the first in my heart,
   high King of heaven, my treasure thou art!

5. High King of heaven, when battle is done,
   grant heaven's joy to me, O bright heav'n's sun;
   Christ of my own heart, whatever befall,
   still be my vision, O Ruler of all.

Text © Copyright Control.

71 Beyond all mortal praise

Timothy Dudley-Smith (b.1926)
from Daniel 2

Arthur Hutchings (1906-1989)

DOLPHIN STREET 66 66 88

2. Our times are in his hand
to whom all flesh is grass,
while as their Maker planned
the changing seasons pass.
He orders all:
before his eyes
earth's empires rise,
her kingdoms fall.

3. He gives to humankind,
dividing as he will,
all pow'rs of heart and mind,
of spirit, strength and skill:
nor dark nor night
but must lay bare
its secrets, where
he dwells in light.

4. To God the only Lord,
our fathers' God, be praise;
his holy name adored
through everlasting days.
His mercies trace
in answered prayer,
in love and care,
and gifts of grace.

Text © Copyright Timothy Dudley-Smith, 9 Ashlands, Ford, Salisbury, Wiltshire SP4 6DY.
Music © Copyright Hymns Ancient & Modern, St Mary's Works,
St. Mary's Plain, Norwich NR3 3BH. Used by permission.

72 Bind us together, Lord

Words and music: Bob Gilman

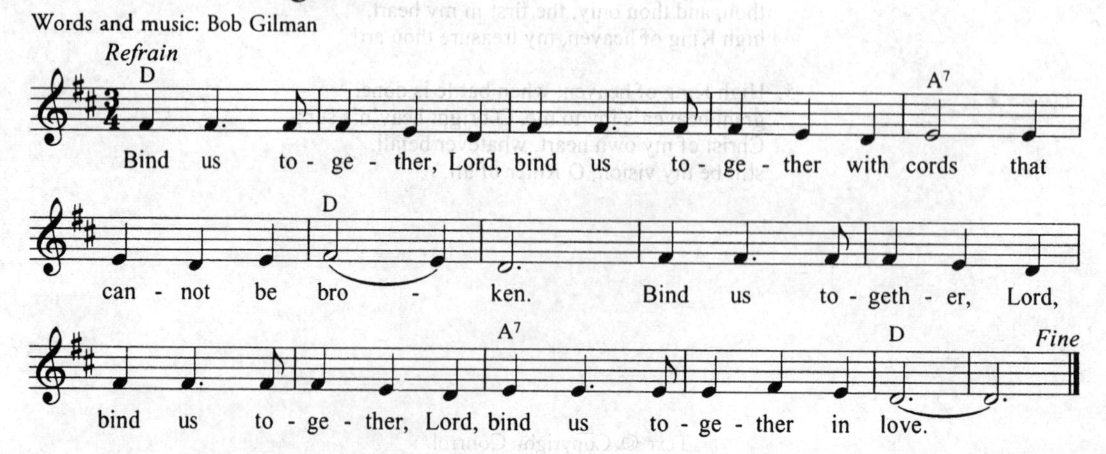

2. Fit for the glory of God,
purchased by his precious Blood,
born with the right to be free:
Jesus the vict'ry has won.

3. We are the fam'ly of God,
we are his promise divine,
we are his chosen desire,
we are the glorious new wine.

© Copyright 1977 Kingsway's Thankyou Music. P.O. Box 75, Eastbourne, East Sussex BN23 6NW, UK. (tym@kingsway.co.uk). Used by permission.

73 Bless, and keep us, God

Dieter Trautwein (b.1928)
trans. Fred Kaan (b.1929)

Dieter Trautwein

KOMM, HERR, SEGNE UNS 11 11 5 66 5

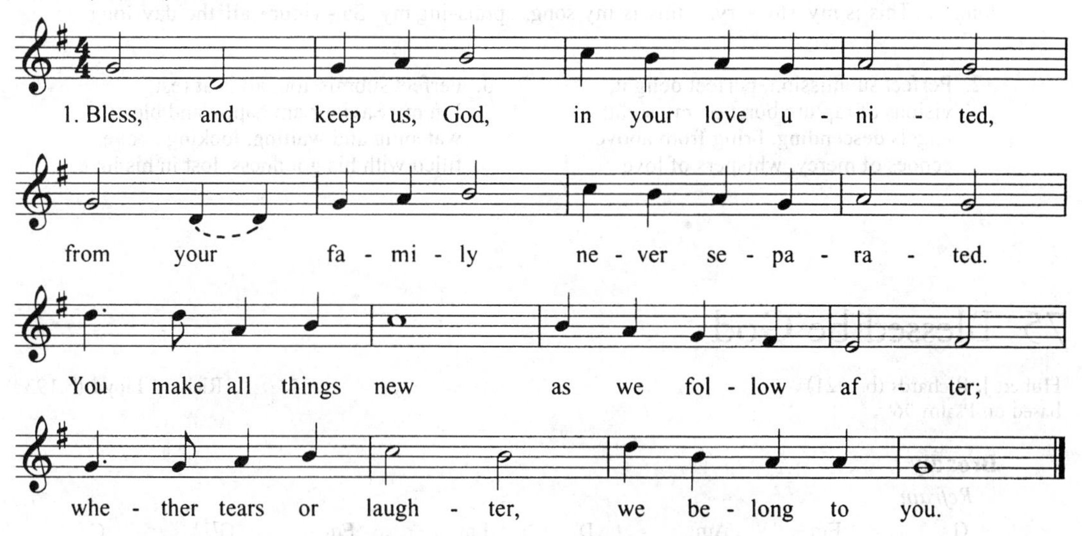

2. Blessing shrivels up when your children hoard it;
move us then to share, for we can afford it.
Blessing only grows in the act of sharing,
in a life of caring; love that heals and grows.

3. Fill your world with peace, such as you intended.
Teach us to prize the earth, love, replenish, tend it.
God, uplift, fulfil all who sow in sadness:
let them reap with gladness, by your kingdom thrilled.

4. You renew our life, changing tears to laughter;
we belong to you, so we follow after.
Bless and keep us, God, in your love united,
never separated from your living Word.

Text © Copyright 1985 Stainer & Bell Ltd., P.O. Box 110, Victoria House, 23 Gruneison Road, Finchley, London N3 1DZ.
Music © Copyright Strube Verlag, Pettenkoferstrasse 24, 80336 München, Germany. Used by permission.

74 Blessed assurance

Frances Jane van Alstyne
(Fanny J. Crosby) (1820-1915)

Phoebe Palmer Knapp (1839-1908)

2. Perfect submission, perfect delight,
visions of rapture burst on my sight;
angels descending, bring from above
echoes of mercy, whispers of love.

3. Perfect submission, all is at rest,
I in my Saviour am happy and blest;
watching and waiting, looking above,
filled with his goodness, lost in his love.

75 Blessed be God

Hubert J. Richards (b.1921)
based on Psalm 96

Richard Lloyd (b.1933)

© Copyright 1996 Kevin Mayhew Ltd.

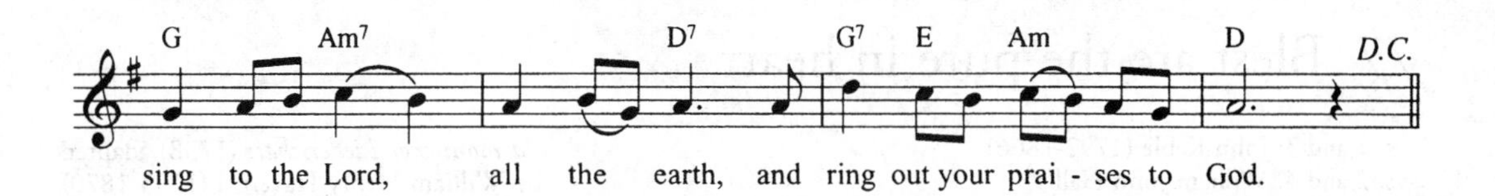

2. Come, tell of all his wondrous deeds,
   come, thank him for all he has done,
   and offer your gifts to the Lord.

3. Let all creation shout for joy;
   come worship the Lord in his house,
   the Lord who made heaven and earth.

76 Bless the Lord, my soul

Words and music: Mike Anderson (b.1956)

2. Praise the Lord on trumpet,
   praise the Lord in song,
   praise him all who stand before his throne.

3. Praise him for his mercy,
   praise him for his pow'r,
   praise him for his love which conquers all.

© Copyright 1999 Kevin Mayhew Ltd.

77 Blest are the pure in heart

vs. 1 and 3: John Keble (1792-1866)
vs. 2 and 4: William John Hall's
Psalms and Hymns (1836) alt.

Harmonischer Liederschatz (1738) adapted
by William Henry Havergal (1793-1870)

FRANCONIA SM

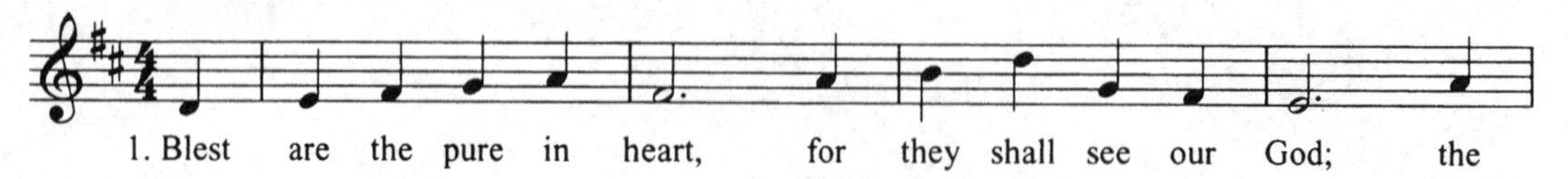

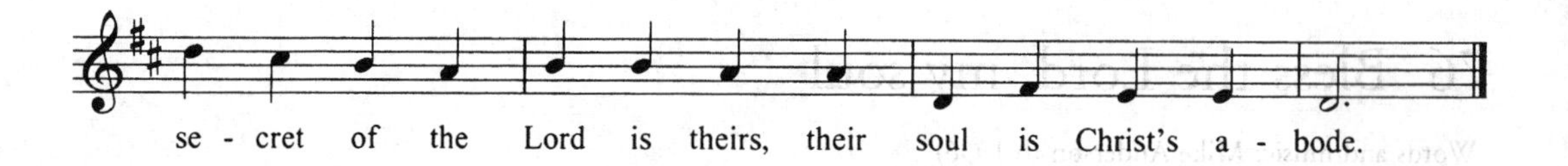

2. The Lord who left the heav'ns
our life and peace to bring,
to dwell in lowliness with us,
our pattern and our King.

3. Still to the lowly soul
he doth himself impart,
and for his dwelling and his throne
chooseth the pure in heart.

4. Lord, we thy presence seek;
may ours this blessing be:
give us a pure and lowly heart,
a temple meet for thee.

78 Blest are you, Lord of creation

Hubert J. Richards (b.1921)
based on the prayers at the preparation of the gifts

Richard Shephard (b.1949)

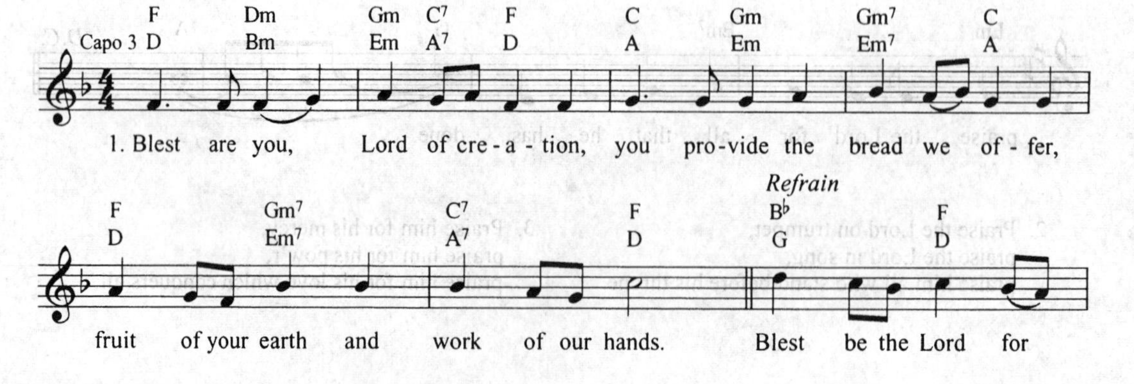

© Copyright 1996 Kevin Mayhew Ltd.

2. Blest are you, Lord of creation,
   you provide the wine we offer,
   fruit of your earth and work of our hands.

3. Blest are you, Lord of creation,
   look with favour on our off'rings,
   pour out your Spirit over these gifts.

79 Blest Creator of the light

Lucis Creator Optime trans. unknown

Justin Heinrich Knecht (1752-1817)

VIENNA 77 77

2. Thou didst mark the night from day
   with the dawn's first piercing ray;
   darkness now is drawing nigh;
   listen to our humble cry.

3. May we ne'er by guilt depressed
   lose the way to endless rest;
   nor with idle thoughts and vain
   bind our souls to earth again.

4. Rather may we heav'nward rise
   where eternal treasure lies;
   purified by grace within,
   hating ev'ry deed of sin.

5. Holy Father, hear our cry
   through thy Son our Lord most high,
   whom our thankful hearts adore
   with the Spirit evermore.

80 Born in the night, Mary's child

Words and music: Geoffrey Ainger (b.1925)

MARY'S CHILD 76 76

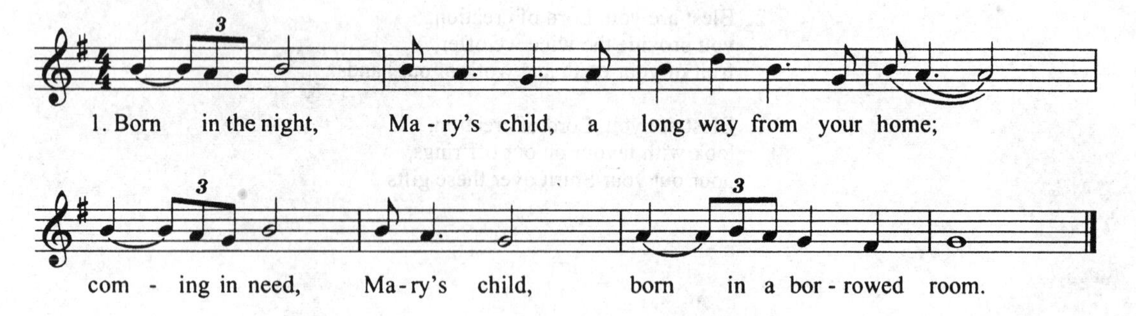

2. Clear shining light, Mary's child,
your face lights up our way;
light of the world, Mary's child,
dawn on our darkened day.

3. Truth of our life, Mary's child,
you tell us God is good;
prove it is true, Mary's child,
go to your cross of wood.

4. Hope of the world, Mary's child,
you're coming soon to reign;
King of the earth, Mary's child,
walk in our streets again.

© Copyright 1964 Stainer & Bell Ltd., P.O. Box 110, Victoria House,
23 Gruneison Road, Finchley, London N3 1DZ. Used by permission.

81 Bread is blessed and broken

Words and music: John L. Bell (b.1949)
and Graham Maule (b.1958)

GRACE IN ESSENCE 65 63

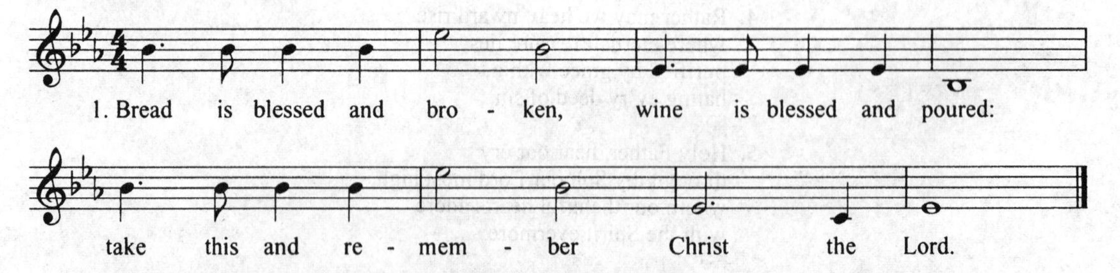

© Copyright 1989 WGRG, Iona Community, Glasgow G2 3DH, Scotland,
from the *Love From Below* collection (Wild Goose Publications 1989). Used by permission.

2. Share the food of heaven
earth cannot afford.
Here is grace in essence –
Christ the Lord.

3. Know yourself forgiven,
find yourself restored,
meet a friend for ever –
Christ the Lord.

4. God has kept his promise
sealed by sign and word:
here, for those who want him –
Christ the Lord.

82 Bread of heaven, on thee we feed

Josiah Conder (1789-1855) William Dalrymple Maclagan (1826-1910)

BREAD OF HEAVEN 77 77 77

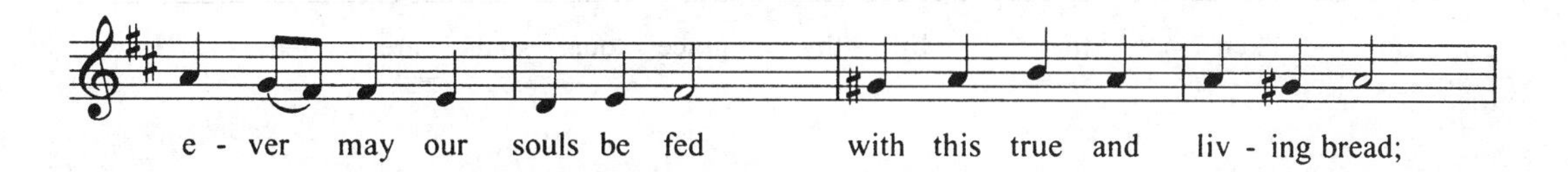

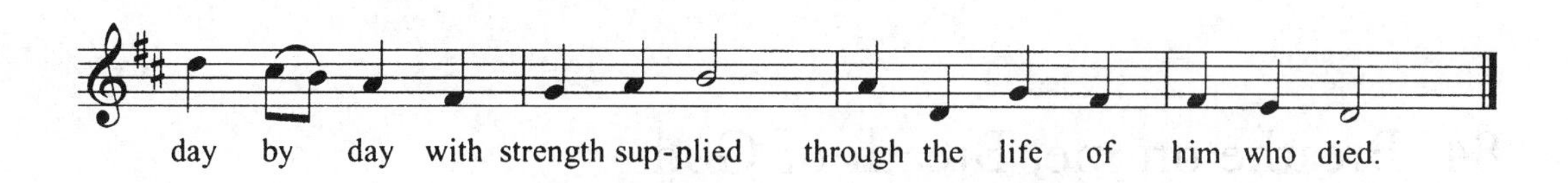

2. Vine of heav'n, thy blood supplies
this blest cup of sacrifice;
Lord, thy wounds our healing give,
to thy cross we look and live:
Jesus, may we ever be
grafted, rooted, built in thee.

83 Bread of the world in mercy broken

Reginald Heber (1783-1826)

Louis Bourgeois (c.1510-1561)
from the *Genevan Psalter* (1551)

RENDEZ A DIEU 98 98 D

84 Breathe on me, Breath of God

Edwin Hatch (1835-1889)
alt. the editors

Charles Lockhart (1745-1815)

TUNE 1: CARLISLE SM

This version of text © Copyright 1999 Kevin Mayhew Ltd.

2. Breathe on me, Breath of God,
until my heart is pure:
until my will is one with yours
to do and to endure.

3. Breathe on me, Breath of God,
fulfil my heart's desire,
until this earthly part of me
glows with your heav'nly fire.

4. Breathe on me, Breath of God,
so shall I never die,
but live with you the perfect life
of your eternity.

Edwin Hatch (1835-1889)
alt. the editors

Robert Jackson (1840-1914)

TUNE 2: TRENTHAM SM

85 Brightest and best

Reginald Heber (1783-1826) | Joseph Francis Thrupp (1827-1867)

TUNE 1: EPIPHANY 11 10 11 10

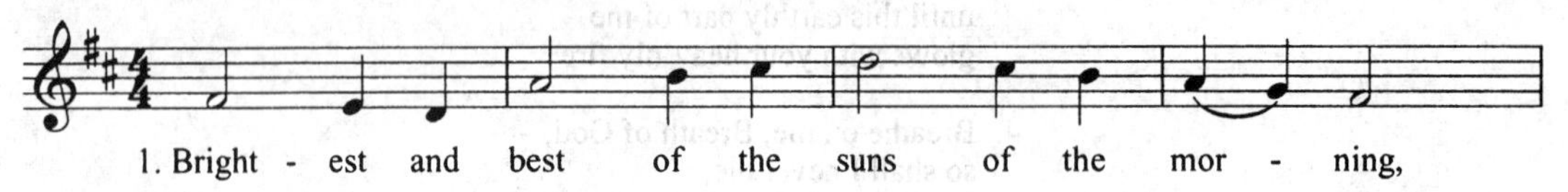

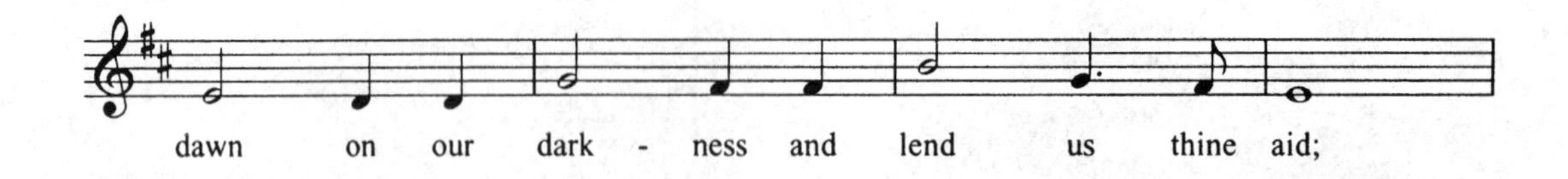

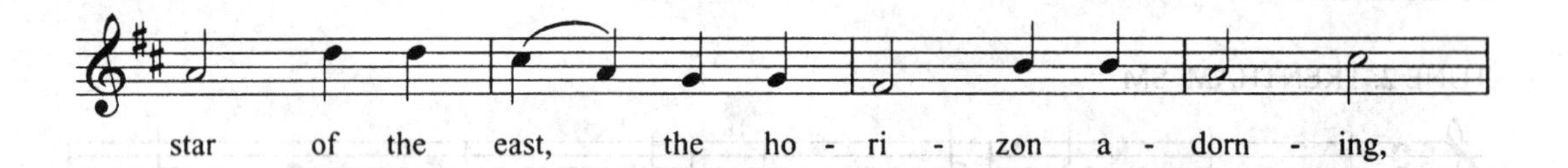

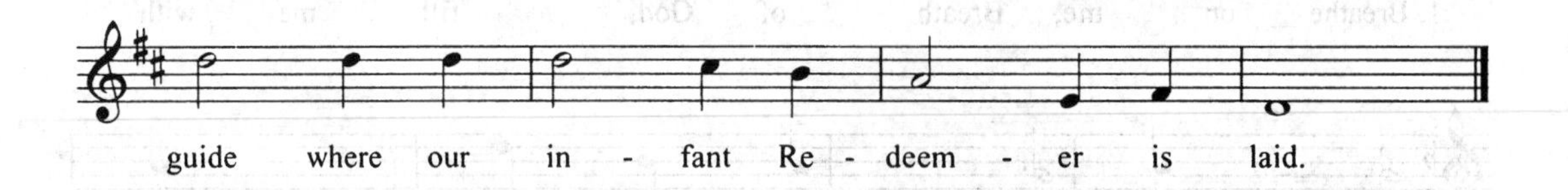

2. Cold on his cradle the dew-drops are shining;
low lies his head with the beasts of the stall;
angels adore him in slumber reclining,
Maker and Monarch and Saviour of all.

3. Say, shall we yield him, in costly devotion,
odours of Edom, and off'rings divine,
gems of the mountain, and pearls of the ocean,
myrrh from the forest, or gold from the mine?

4. Vainly we offer each humble oblation,
vainly with gifts would his favour secure:
richer by far is the heart's adoration,
dearer to God are the prayers of the poor.

Reginald Heber (1783-1826) | Adapted from *Himmels-Lust*, Jena (1679)

TUNE 2: LIEBSTER IMMANUEL 11 10 11 10

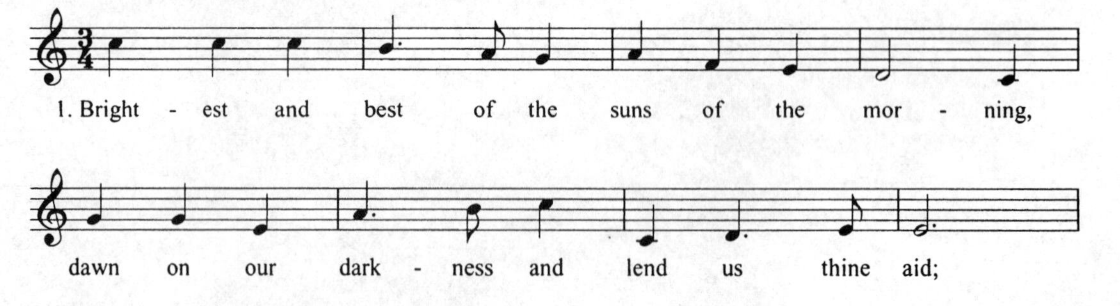

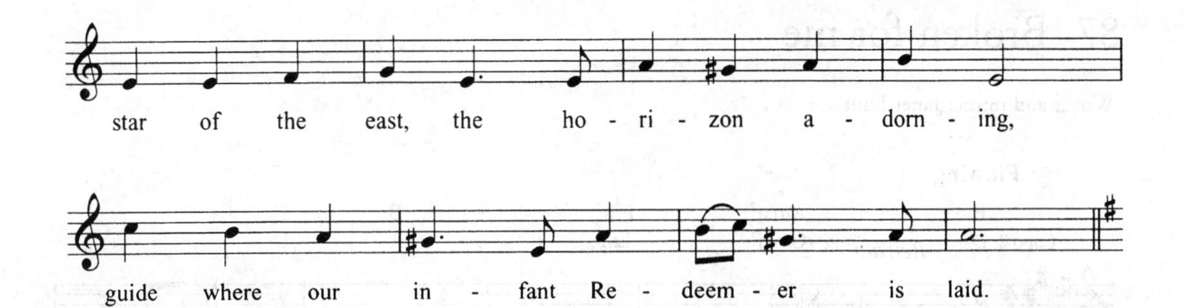

86 Bright the vision that delighted

Richard Mant (1776-1848)

Richard Redhead (1820-1901)

LAUS DEO (REDHEAD NO. 46) 87 87

2. Round the Lord in glory seated
   cherubim and seraphim
   filled his temple, and repeated
   each to each the alternate hymn:

3. 'Lord, thy glory fills the heaven;
   earth is with its fulness stored;
   unto thee be glory given,
   holy, holy, holy, Lord.'

4. Heav'n is still with glory ringing,
   earth takes up the angels' cry,
   'Holy, holy, holy,' singing,
   'Lord of hosts, the Lord most high.'

5. With his seraph train before him,
   with his holy Church below,
   thus unite we to adore him,
   bid we thus our anthem flow:

6. 'Lord, thy glory fills the heaven;
   earth is with its fulness stored;
   unto thee be glory given,
   holy, holy, holy, Lord.'

87 Broken for me

Words and music: Janet Lunt

2. Come to my table and with me dine;
eat of my bread and drink of my wine.

3. This is my body given for you;
eat it remembering I died for you.

4. This is my blood I shed for you,
for your forgiveness, making you new.

© Copyright 1978 Sovereign Music UK, P.O. Box 356,
Leighton Buzzard, LU7 3WP, UK. Used by permission.

88 Brother, sister, let me serve you *The servant song*

Words and music: Richard Gillard

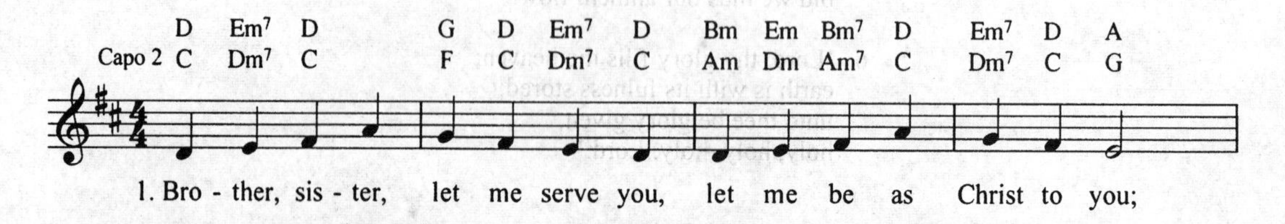

© Copyright 1977 Scripture Song (a division of Integrity Music Inc.)/Sovereign Music UK.,
P.O. Box 356, Leighton Buzzard LU7 3WP, UK. Used by permission.

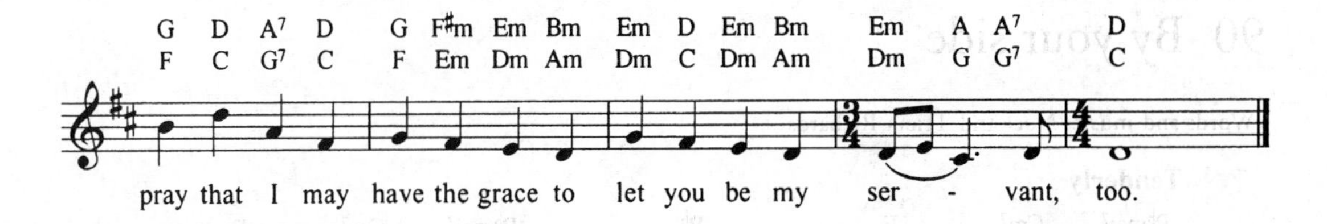

2. We are pilgrims on a journey,
fellow trav'llers on the road;
we are here to help each other
walk the mile and bear the load.

3. I will hold the Christlight for you
in the night-time of your fear;
I will hold my hand out to you,
speak the peace you long to hear.

4. I will weep when you are weeping;
when you laugh, I'll laugh with you.
I will share your joy and sorrow
till we've seen this journey through.

5. When we sing to God in heaven,
we shall find such harmony,
born of all we've known together
of Christ's love and agony.

6. Brother, sister, let me serve you,
let me be as Christ to you;
pray that I may have the grace to
let you be my servant, too.

89 By his grace

Words and music: Steven Fry

© Copyright 1994 Deep Fryed Music/Word Music Inc./Maranatha! Music. Administered by CopyCare, P.O. Box 77, Hailsham, East Sussex BN27 3EF, UK. (music@copycare.com) Used by permission.

90 By your side

Words and music: Noel and Tricia Richards

© Copyright 1989 Kingsway's Thankyou Music, P.O. Box 75, Eastbourne, East Sussex BN23 6NW, UK. (tym@kingsway.co.uk). Used by permission.

91 Captains of the saintly band

J.B. de Santeuil (1630-1697)
trans. Henry William Baker (1821-1877)

Benjamin Milgrove (1731-1810)

HARTS 77 77

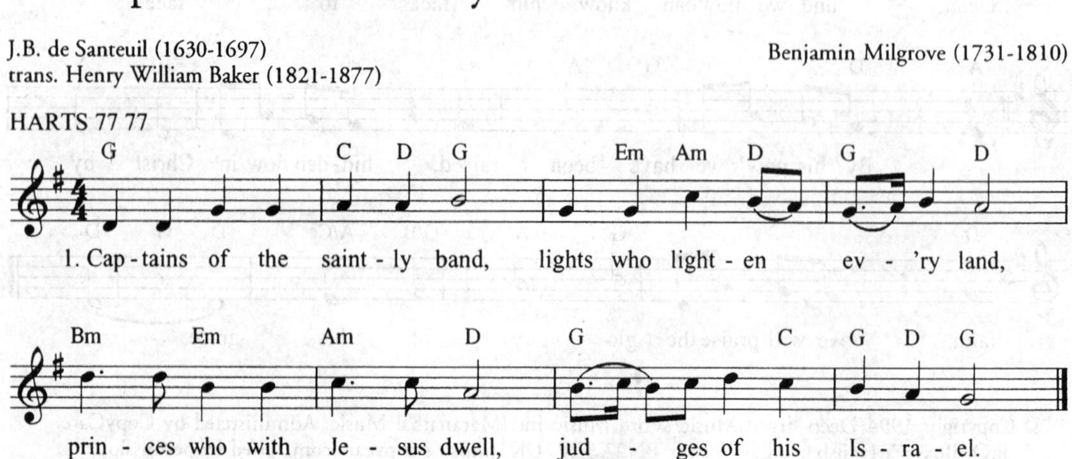

2. On the nations sunk in night
ye have shed the Gospel light;
sin and error flee away;
truth reveals the promised day.

3. Not by warrior's spear and sword,
not by art of human word,
preaching but the Cross of shame,
rebel hearts for Christ ye tame.

4. Earth, that long in sin and pain
groaned in Satan's deadly chain,
now to serve its God is free
in the law of liberty.

5. Distant lands with one acclaim
tell the honour of your name,
who, wherever man has trod,
teach the mysteries of God.

6. Glory to the Three in One
while eternal ages run,
who from deepest shades of night
called us to his glorious light.

92 Change my heart, O God

Words and music: Eddie Espinosa
based on Isaiah 64:8

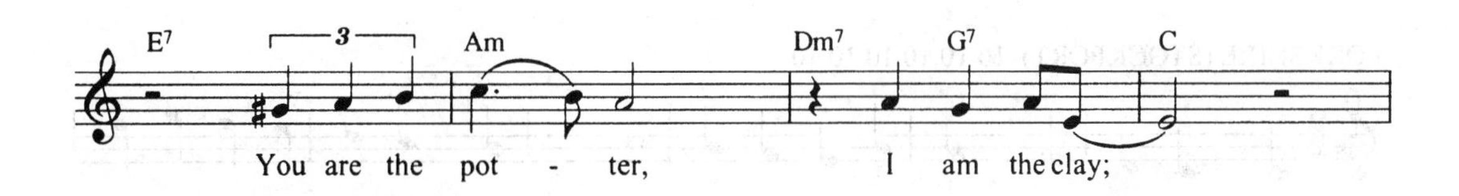

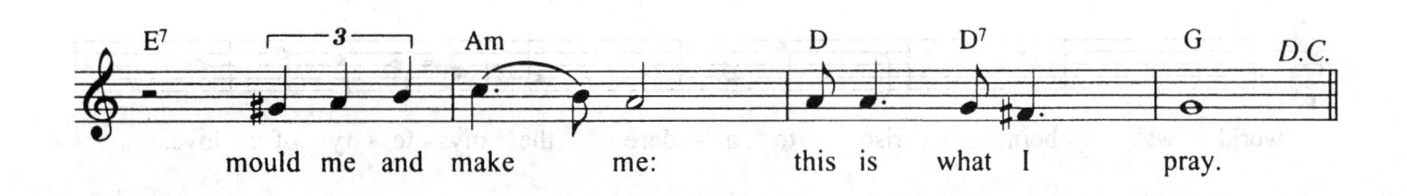

© Copyright 1982 Mercy/Vineyard Publishing. Administered by CopyCare,
P.O. Box 77, Hailsham, East Sussex BN27 3EF, UK. (music@copycare.com). Used by permission.

93 Child in the manger

Mary MacDonald (1817-1890)
trans. Lachlan MacBean (1853-1931)

Traditional Gaelic melody

BUNESSAN 55 53 D

2. Once the most holy child of salvation
gently and lowly lived below;
now as our glorious mighty Redeemer,
see him victorious o'er each foe.

3. Prophets foretold him, infant of wonder;
angels behold him on his throne;
worthy our Saviour of all their praises;
happy for ever are his own.

94 Christians, awake!

John Byrom (1692-1763) alt.

John Wainwright (1723-1768)

YORKSHIRE (STOCKPORT) 10 10 10 10 10 10

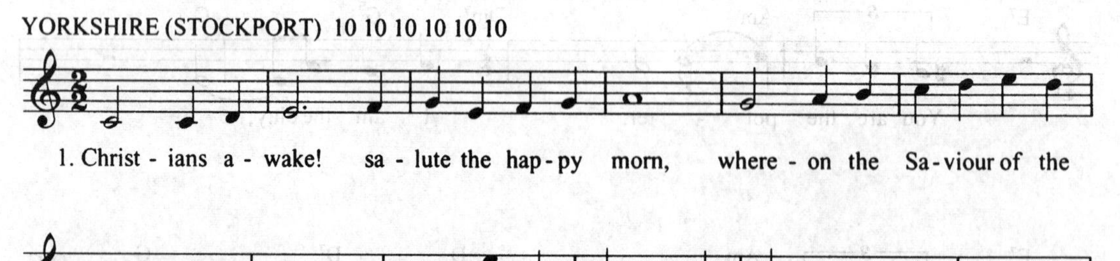

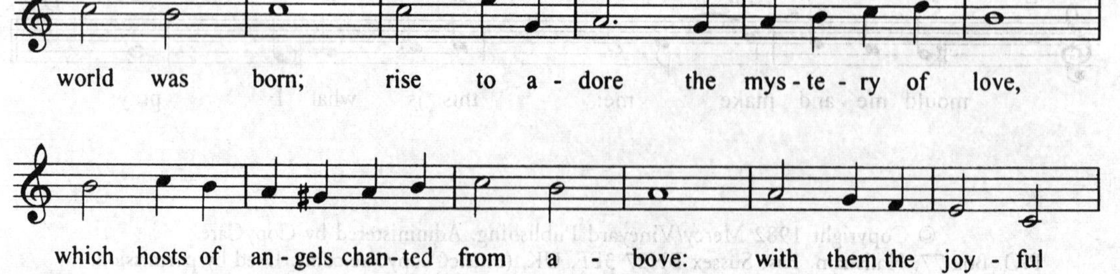

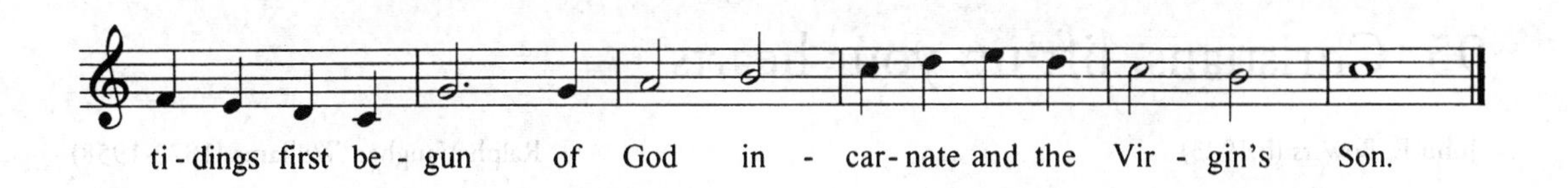

2. Then to the watchful shepherds it was told,
   who heard th' angelic herald's voice, 'Behold,
   I bring good tidings of a Saviour's birth
   to you and all the nations on the earth:
   this day hath God fulfilled his promised word,
   this day is born a Saviour, Christ the Lord.'

3. He spake; and straightway the celestial choir
   in hymns of joy, unknown before, conspire;
   the praises of redeeming love they sang,
   and heav'n's whole orb with alleluias rang:
   God's highest glory was their anthem still,
   peace on the earth, in ev'ry heart good will.

4. To Bethl'em straight th'enlightened shepherds ran,
   to see, unfolding, God's eternal plan,
   and found, with Joseph and the blessèd maid,
   her Son, the Saviour, in a manger laid:
   then to their flocks, still praising God, return,
   and their glad hearts with holy rapture burn.

5. O may we keep and ponder in our mind
   God's wondrous love in saving lost mankind;
   trace we the babe, who hath retrieved our loss,
   from his poor manger to his bitter cross;
   tread in his steps assisted by his grace,
   till our first heav'nly state again takes place.

6. Then may we hope, th'angelic hosts among,
   to sing, redeemed, a glad triumphal song:
   he that was born upon this joyful day
   around us all his glory shall display;
   saved by his love, incessant we shall sing
   eternal praise to heav'n's almighty King.

95 Christians, lift up your hearts

John E. Bowers (b.1923) Ralph Vaughan Williams (1872-1958)

Text © Copyright John E. Bowers
Music © Copyright Oxford University Press, Great Clarendon Street, Oxford OX2 6DP. Used by permission.

96 Christ is alive!

Brian Wren (b.1936)

From Thomas Williams'
Psalmodia Evangelica (1789)

TRURO LM

2. Christ is alive! No longer bound
to distant years in Palestine,
but saving, healing, here and now,
and touching ev'ry place and time.

3. In ev'ry insult, rift and war,
where colour, scorn or wealth divide,
Christ suffers still, yet loves the more,
and lives, where even hope has died.

4. Women and men, in age and youth,
can feel the Spirit, hear the call,
and find the way, the life, the truth,
revealed in Jesus, freed for all.

5. Christ is alive, and comes to bring
good news to this and ev'ry age,
till earth and sky and ocean ring
with joy, with justice, love and praise.

Text © Copyright 1969, 1995 Stainer & Bell Ltd., P.O. Box 110, Victoria House,
23 Gruneison Road, Finchley, London N3 1DZ. Used by permission.

97 Christ is made the sure foundation

Urbs beata Jerusalem (c.7th century)
trans. John Mason Neale (1818-1866) alt.

Henry Purcell (1659-1695)

TUNE 1: WESTMINSTER ABBEY 87 87 87

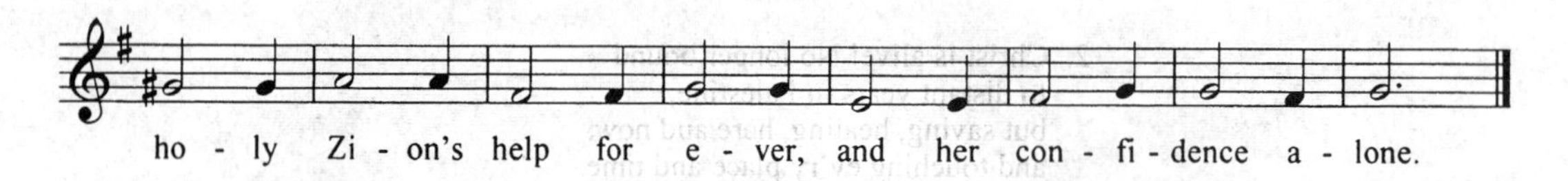

2. To this temple, where we call you,
come, O Lord of hosts, today;
you have promised loving kindness,
hear your servants as we pray,
bless your people now before you,
turn our darkness into day.

3. Hear the cry of all your people,
what they ask and hope to gain;
what they gain from you, for ever
with your chosen to retain,
and hereafter in your glory
evermore with you to reign.

4. Praise and honour to the Father,
praise and honour to the Son,
praise and honour to the Spirit,
ever Three and ever One,
One in might and One in glory,
while unending ages run.

Urbs beata Jerusalem (c.7th century)
trans. John Mason Neale (1818-1866) alt.

Henry Smart (1813-1879)

TUNE 2: REGENT SQUARE 87 87 87

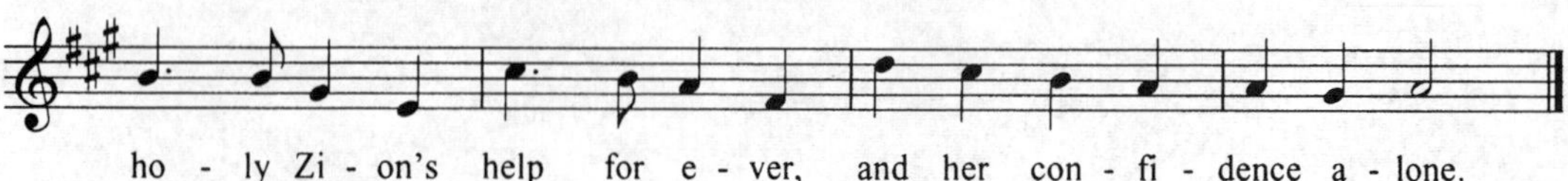

98 Christ is our cornerstone

Latin (pre 9th century)
trans. John Chandler (1806-1876)

Samuel Sebastian Wesley (1810-1876)

HAREWOOD 66 66 44 44

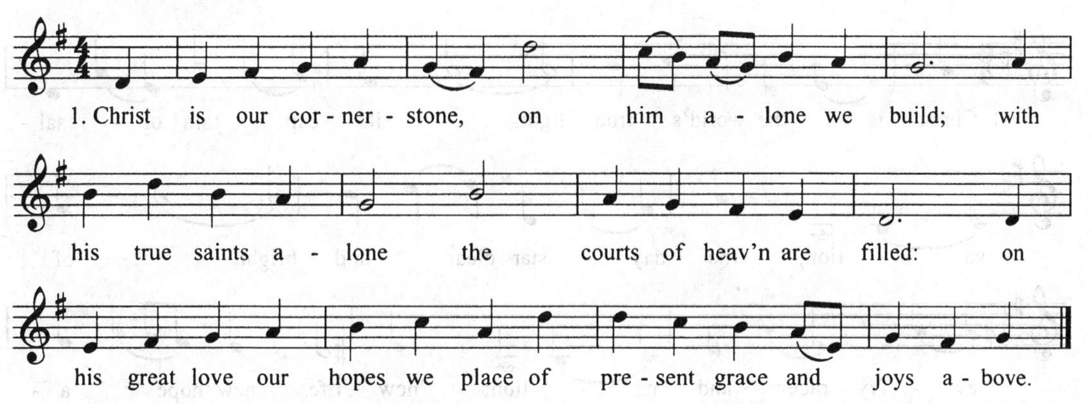

2. O then with hymns of praise
these hallowed courts shall ring;
our voices we will raise
the Three in One to sing;
and thus proclaim in joyful song,
both loud and long, that glorious name.

3. Here, gracious God, do thou
for evermore draw nigh;
accept each faithful vow,
and mark each suppliant sigh;
in copious show'r on all who pray
each holy day thy blessings pour.

4. Here may we gain from heav'n
the grace which we implore;
and may that grace, once giv'n,
be with us evermore,
until that day when all the blest
to endless rest are called away.

99 Christ is the world's Light

Fred Pratt Green (b.1903-2000)

From *Paris Antiphoner* (1681)

CHRISTE SANCTORUM 10 11 11 6

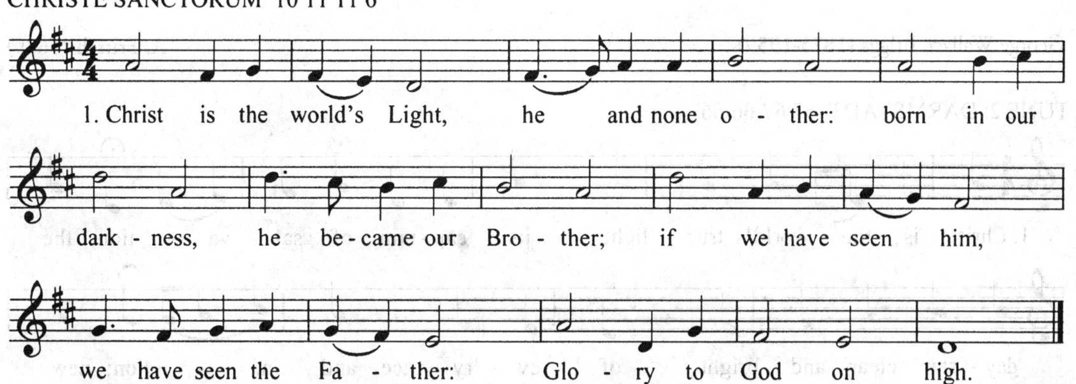

2. Christ is the world's Peace, he and none other;
no-one can serve him and despise another;
who else unites us, one in God the Father?
Glory to God on high.

3. Christ is the world's Life, he and none other;
sold once for silver, murdered here, our Brother -
he who redeems us, reigns with God the Father:
Glory to God on high.

4. Give God the glory, God and none other;
give God the glory, Spirit, Son and Father;
give God the glory, God in Man my Brother:
Glory to God on high.

Text © Copyright 1969 Stainer & Bell Ltd., P.O. Box 110, Victoria House,
23 Gruneison Road, Finchley, London N3 1DZ. Used by permission.

100 Christ is the world's true light

George Wallace Briggs (1875-1959) — Johann Sebastian Bach (1685-1750)

TUNE 1: RINKART (KOMMT SEELEN) 67 67 66 66

2. In Christ all races meet,
their ancient feuds forgetting,
the whole round world complete,
from sunrise to its setting:
when Christ is throned as Lord,
all shall forsake their fear,
to ploughshare beat the sword,
to pruning-hook the spear.

3. One Lord, in one great name
unite us all who own thee;
cast out our pride and shame
that hinder to enthrone thee;
the world has waited long,
has travailed long in pain;
to heal its ancient wrong,
come, Prince of Peace, and reign!

George Wallace Briggs (1875-1959) — A. Fritsch (1679)

TUNE 2: DARMSTADT 67 67 66 66

Text © Copyright Oxford University Press, Great Clarendon Street, Oxford OX2 6DP.
Used by permission.

101 Christ's is the world

A touching place

John L. Bell (b.1949)
Graham Maule (b.1958)

Traditional Scottish melody

DREAM ANGUS Irregular

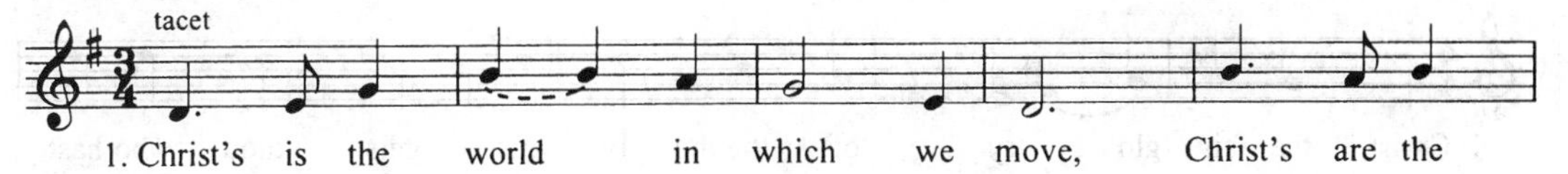

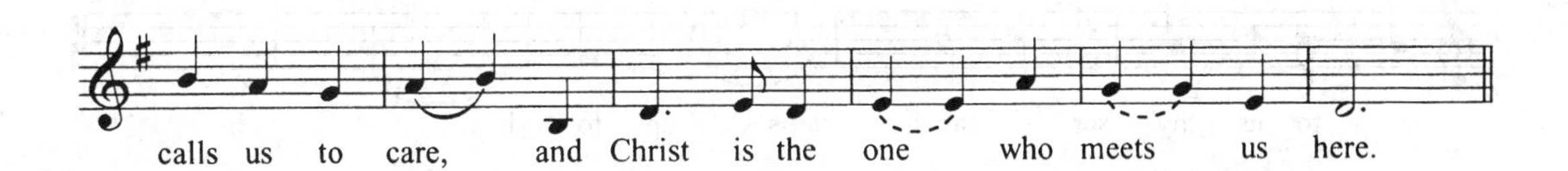

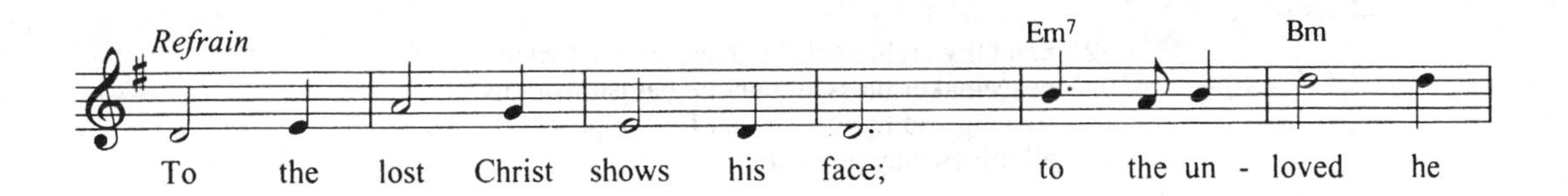

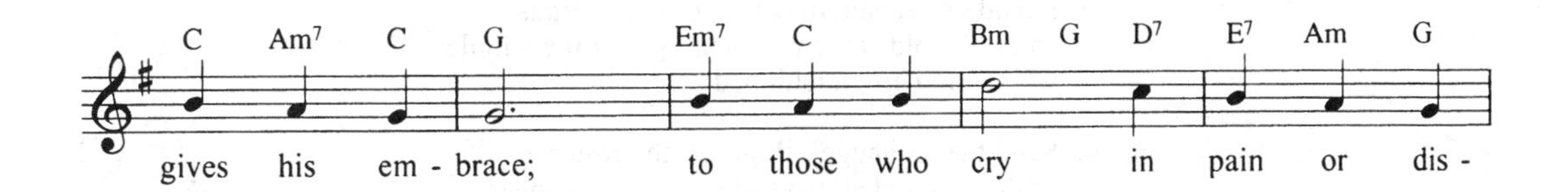

2. Feel for the people we most avoid,
strange or bereaved or never employed;
feel for the women, and feel for the men
who fear that their living is all in vain.

3. Feel for the parents who've lost their child,
feel for the women whom men have defiled,
feel for the baby for whom there's no breast,
and feel for the weary who find no rest.

4. Feel for the lives by life confused,
riddled with doubt, in loving abused;
feel for the lonely heart, conscious of sin,
which longs to be pure but fears to begin.

Text © Copyright 1989 WGRG, Iona Community, Glasgow G2 3DH, Scotland.
Used by permission from the *Love from Below* collection. (Wild Goose Publications 1989)

102 Christ, the fair glory of the holy angels

Latin, ascribed to Rabanus Maurus (776-856)
trans. Athelstan Riley (1858-1945)

From *Rouen Antiphoner* (1728)

COELITES PLAUDANT 11 11 11 5

2. Send thy archangel, Michael, to our succour;
peacemaker blessèd, may he banish from us
striving and hatred, so that for the peaceful
all things may prosper.

3. Send thy archangel, Gabriel, the mighty;
herald of heaven, may he from us mortals
spurn the old serpent, watching o'er the temples
where thou art worshipped.

4. Send the archangel, Raphael, the restorer
of the misguided ways of those who wander,
who at thy bidding strengthens soul and body
with thine anointing.

5. May the blest Mother of our God and Saviour,
may the assembly of the saints in glory,
may the celestial companies of angels
ever assist us.

6. Father Almighty, Son and Holy Spirit,
God ever blessèd, be thou our preserver;
thine is the glory which the angels worship,
veiling their faces.

Text © Copyright Hymns Ancien & Modern, St. Mary's Works, St. Mary's Plain, Norwich NR3 3BH, UK.
Used by permission from the *English Hymnal.*

103 Christ the Lord is risen again

Michael Weisse (c.1480-1534)
trans. Catherine Winkworth (1827-1878) alt.

From *Hundert Arien* Dresden (1694)

WÜRTTEMBERG 77 77 with Alleluia

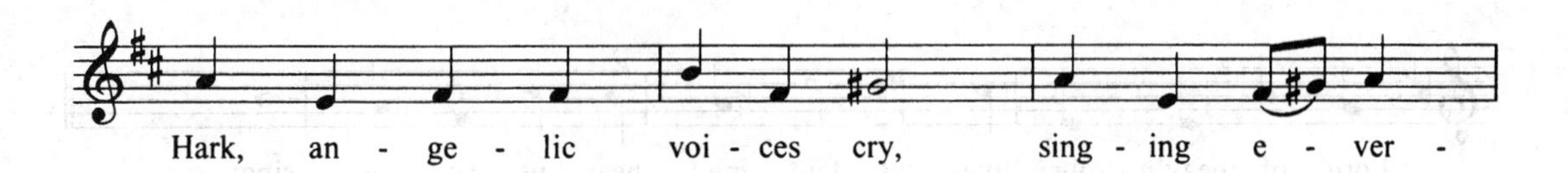

2. He who gave for us his life,
   who for us endured the strife,
   is our paschal Lamb today;
   we too sing for joy, and say:
   Alleluia.

3. He who bore all pain and loss
   comfortless upon the cross,
   lives in glory now on high,
   pleads for us, and hears our cry:
   Alleluia.

4. He whose path no records tell,
   who descended into hell,
   who the strongest arm hath bound,
   now in highest heav'n is crowned.
   Alleluia.

5. He who slumbered in the grave
   is exalted now to save;
   now through Christendom it rings
   that the Lamb is King of kings.
   Alleluia.

6. Now he bids us tell abroad
   how the lost may be restored,
   how the penitent forgiv'n,
   how we too may enter heav'n.
   Alleluia.

7. Thou, our paschal Lamb indeed,
   Christ, thy ransomed people feed;
   take our sins and guilt away;
   let us sing by night and day:
   Alleluia.

104 Christ triumphant

Michael Saward (b.1932)

John Barnard (b.1948)

GUITING POWER 85 85 and Refrain

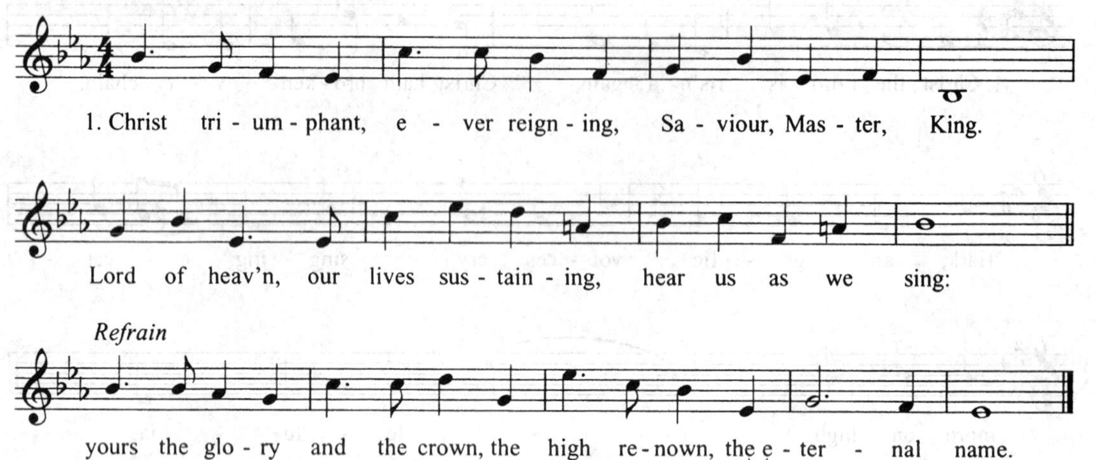

2. Word incarnate, truth revealing,
Son of Man on earth!
Pow'r and majesty concealing
by your humble birth:

3. Suff'ring servant, scorned, ill-treated,
victim crucified!
Death is through the cross defeated,
sinners justified:

4. Priestly King, enthroned for ever
high in heav'n above!
Sin and death and hell shall never
stifle hymns of love:

5. So, our hearts and voices raising
through the ages long,
ceaselessly upon you gazing,
this shall be our song:

Text © Copyright Michael Saward/Jubilate Hymns.
Music © Copyright John Barnard/Jubilate Hymns, 4 Thorne Park Road, Chelston, Torquay TQ2 6RX, UK.
Used by permission.

105 Christ, whose glory fills the skies

Charles Wesley (1707-1788)

Johann Gottlob Werner's *Choralbuch*, Leipzig (1815)

RATISBON 77 77 77

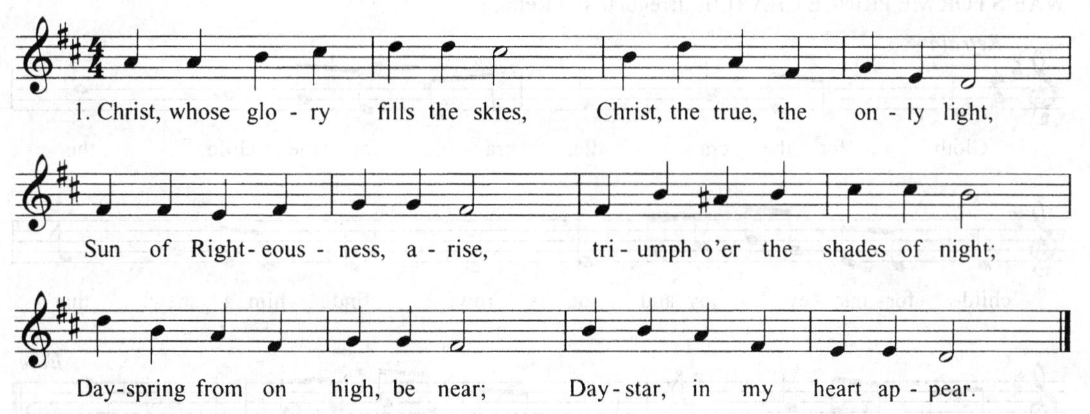

2. Dark and cheerless is the morn
unaccompanied by thee;
joyless is the day's return,
till thy mercy's beams I see,
till they inward light impart,
glad my eyes, and warm my heart.

3. Visit then this soul of mine,
pierce the gloom of sin and grief;
fill me, radiancy divine,
scatter all my unbelief;
more and more thyself display,
shining to the perfect day.

106 City of God, how broad and far

Samuel Johnson (1822-1882) alt.

Adapted from Thomas Haweis (1734-1820)

RICHMOND CM

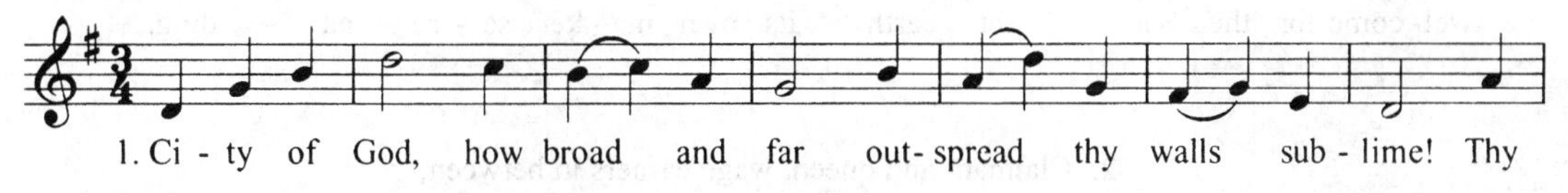

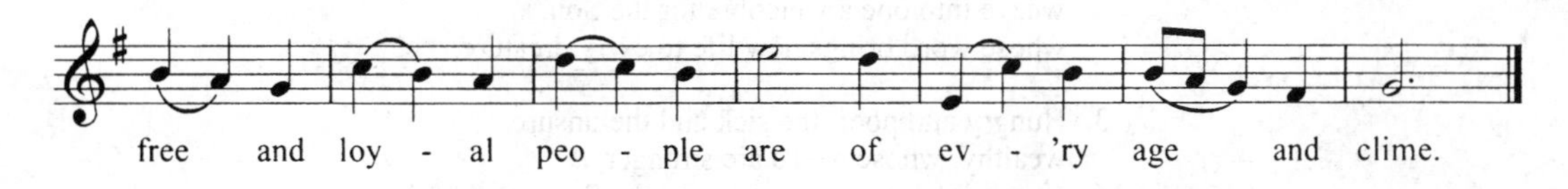

2. One holy Church, one mighty throng,
one steadfast, high intent;
one working band, one harvest-song,
one King omnipotent.

3. How purely hath thy speech come down
from earth's primeval youth!
How grandly hath thine empire grown
of freedom, love and truth!

4. How gleam thy watch-fires through the night
with never-fainting ray!
How rise thy tow'rs, serene and bright,
to meet the dawning day!

5. In vain the surge's angry shock,
in vain the drifting sands;
unharmed upon th'eternal Rock
th'eternal city stands.

107 Cloth for the cradle

John L. Bell (b. 1949)
Graham Maule (b.1958)

Traditional Scottish melody

2. Claimant and queen, wage earners in between,
trader and travelling preacher,
weave into one a welcome for the Son,
whose word brings new life to ev'ry creature.

3. Hungry and poor, the sick and the unsure,
wealthy, whose needs are stranger,
weave into one a welcome for the Son,
leave excess and want beneath the manger.

4. Wrinkled or fair, carefree or full of care,
searchers of all the ages,
weave into one a welcome for the Son,
the Saviour of shepherds and of sages.

Text © Copyright 1987 WGRG, Iona Community, Glasgow G2 3DH, Scotland.
Used by permission from the *Heaven shall not wait* collection.

108 Colours of day

Light up the fire

Words and music: Sue McClellan (b.1951), John Paculabo (b.1946) and Keith Ryecroft (b.1949)

2. Go through the park, on into the town;
the sun still shines on; it never goes down.
The light of the world is risen again;
the people of darkness are needing our friend.

3. Open your eyes, look into the sky,
the darkness has come, the sun came to die.
The evening draws on, the sun disappears,
but Jesus is living, and his Spirit is near.

© Copyright 1974 Kingsway's Thankyou Music, P.O. Box 75, Eastbourne, East Sussex BN23 6NW, UK. (tym@kingsway.co.uk). Used by permission.

109 Come and see

We worship at your feet

Words and music: Graham Kendrick (b.1950)

2. Come and weep, come and mourn
for your sin that pierced him there;
so much deeper than the wounds
of thorn and nail.
All our pride, all our greed,
all our fallenness and shame;
and the Lord has laid the punishment on him.

3. Man of heav'n, born to earth
to restore us to your heaven.
Here we bow in awe beneath
your searching eyes.
From your tears comes our joy,
from your death our life shall spring;
by your resurrection power we shall rise.

© Copyright 1989 Make Way Music, P.O. Box 263, Croydon, Surrey CR9 5AP, UK.
International copyright secured. All rights reserved. Used by permission.

110 Come and see the shining hope

Christopher Idle (b.1948)
based on Revelation 4,5

Traditional American melody

MARCHING THROUGH GEORGIA 13 13 13 8 and Refrain

2. All the gifts you send us, Lord, are faithful, good, and true;
holiness and righteousness are shown in all you do:
who can see your greatest gift and fail to worship you?
Love has the vict'ry for ever!

3. Power and salvation all belong to God on high!
So the mighty multitudes of heaven make their cry,
singing Alleluia! where the echoes never die:
Love has the vict'ry for ever!

Text © Copyright Christopher Idle/Jubilate Hymns, 4 Thorne Park Road,
Chelston, Torquay TQ2 6RX, UK. Used by permission.

111 Come, build the Church

Brian Wren (b.1936) Peter Cutts (b.1937)

ADVENT NEW LM

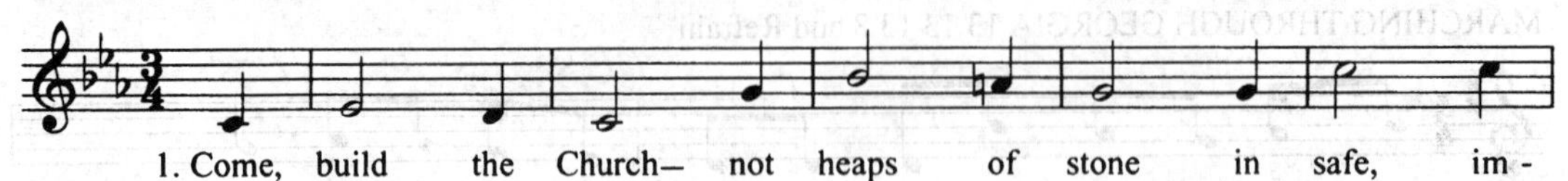

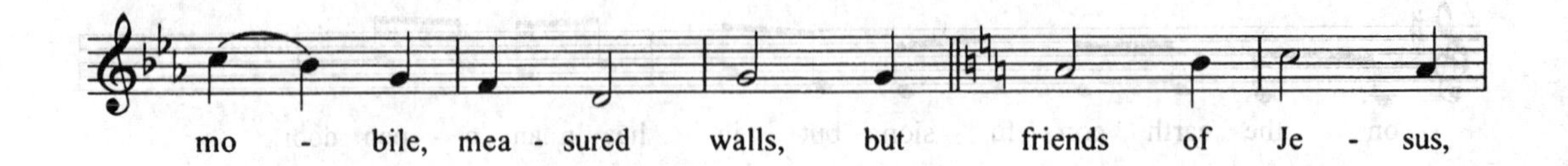

2. Come, occupy with glad dissent
where death and evil fence the ground,
and pitch a Resurrection-Tent
where peace is lived, and love is found.

3. Exposed upon the open ground
to screams of war in East and West,
our ears will catch a deeper sound:
the weeping of the world's oppressed.

4. In wearied face, or frightened child,
in all they know, and need to say,
the living Christ shall stand revealed.
Come, let us follow and obey!

© Copyright 1986 Stainer & Bell Ltd., P.O. Box 110, Victoria House,
23 Gruneison Road, Finchley, London N3 1DZ. Used by permission.

112 Come, come, come to the manger

Unknown, alt. Traditional melody
adapted by S.P. Waddington

COME TO THE MANGER Irregular

Refrain

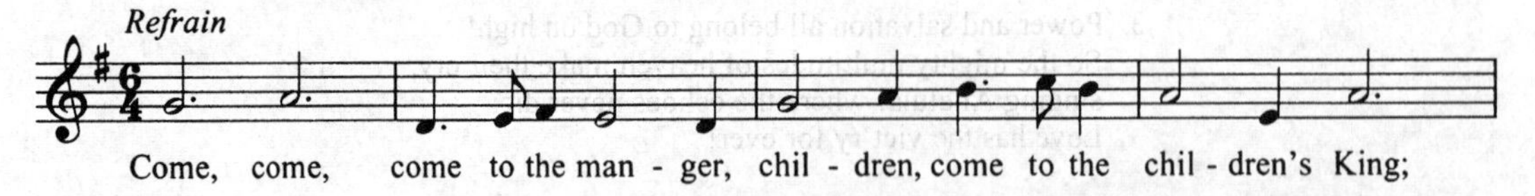

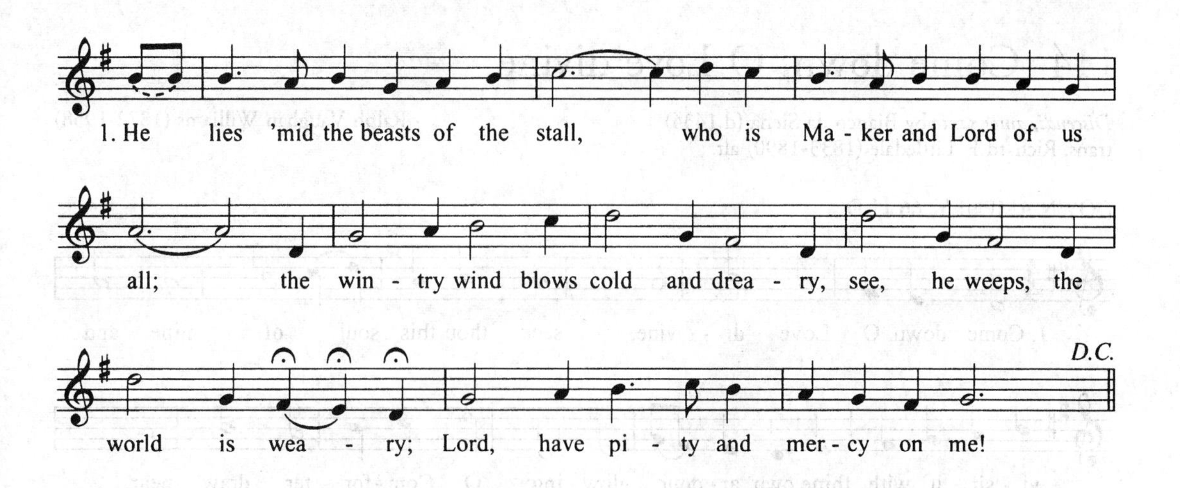

2. He leaves all his glory behind,
to be Saviour of all humankind,
with grateful beasts his cradle chooses,
thankless world his love refuses;
Lord, have pity and mercy on me!

3. To the manger of Bethlehem come,
to the Saviour Emmanuel's home;
the heav'nly hosts above are singing,
set the Christmas bells a-ringing;
Lord, have pity and mercy on me!

113 Come, dearest Lord

Isaac Watts (1674-1748) Barry Rose (b.1934)

CROSS DEEP LM

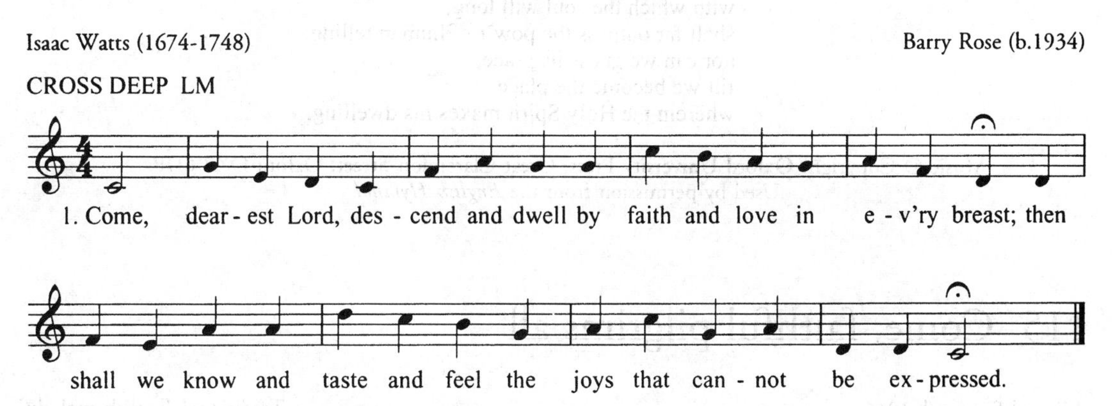

2. Come, fill our hearts with inward strength,
make our enlargèd souls possess
and learn the height and breadth and length
of thine unmeasurable grace.

3. Now to the God whose pow'r can do
more than our thoughts or wishes know,
be everlasting honours done
by all the Church, through Christ his Son.

Music © Copyright 1980 Barry Rose. Used by permission.

114 Come down, O Love divine

Discendi, amor santo by Bianco da Siena (d.1434)
trans. Richard F. Littledale (1833-1890) alt.

Ralph Vaughan Williams (1872-1958)

DOWN AMPNEY 66 11 D

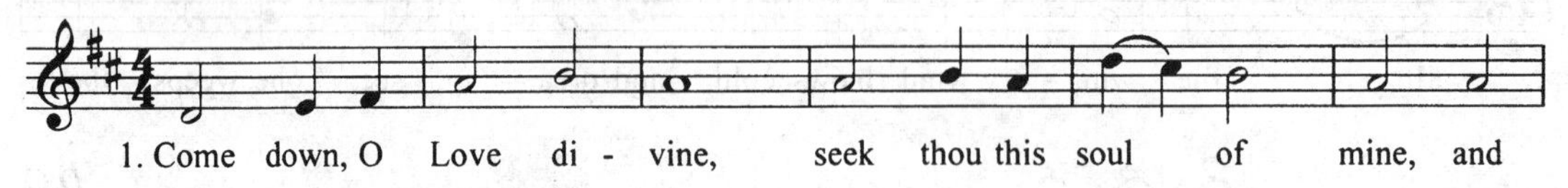

2. O let it freely burn,
till earthly passions turn
to dust and ashes in its heat consuming;
and let thy glorious light
shine ever on my sight,
and clothe me round, the while my path illuming.

3. Let holy charity
mine outward vesture be,
and lowliness become mine inner clothing;
true lowliness of heart,
which takes the humbler part,
and o'er its own shortcomings weeps with loathing.

4. And so the yearning strong,
with which the soul will long,
shall far outpass the pow'r of human telling;
nor can we guess its grace,
till we become the place
wherein the Holy Spirit makes his dwelling.

Music © Copyright Oxford University Press, Great Clarendon Street, Oxford OX2 6DP.
Used by permission from the *English Hymnal.*

115 Come, faithful pilgrims all

Michael Forster (b.1946)

Traditional English melody
collected by Ralph Vaughan Williams (1872-1958)

MONKS GATE 65 65 66 65

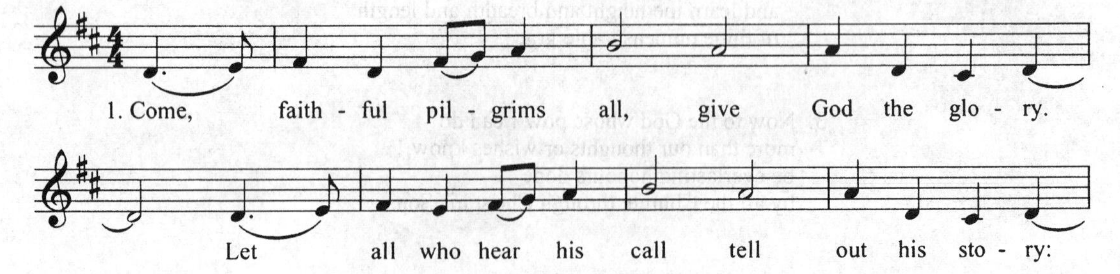

Text © Copyright 2000 Kevin Mayhew Ltd.
Music © Copyright Oxford University Press, Great Clarendon Street, Oxford OX2 6DP.
Used by permission from the *English Hymnal.*

2. Out on the desert way,
in all its starkness,
faith led them through the day,
and lit their darkness.
No written guarantee,
no easy certainty,
just God's great call to be
a pilgrim people.

3. Let all the world rejoice
in exultation
let ev'ry silent voice
sing of salvation.
Loose all the chains that bind,
set free both heart and mind,
and make all humankind
a pilgrim people.

See also No. 281 'He who would valiant be'.

116 Come, gracious Spirit

Simon Browne (1680-1732) and others

Henry John Gauntlett (1805-1876)

HAWKHURST LM

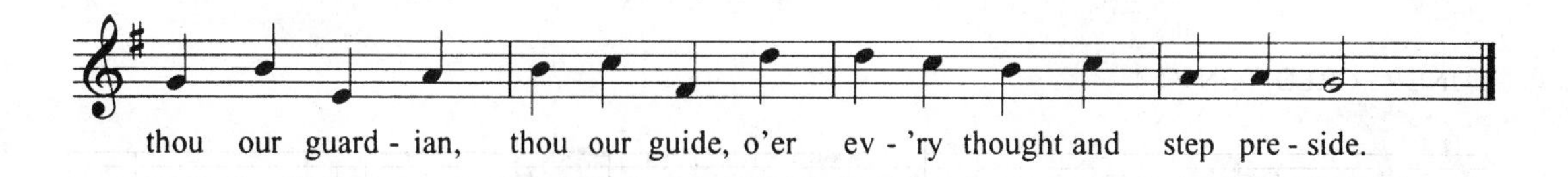

2. The light of truth to us display,
and make us know and choose thy way;
plant faith and love in ev'ry heart,
that we from God may ne'er depart.

3. Lead us to Christ, the living Way,
nor let us from our shepherd stray;
lead us to holiness, the road
that brings us to our home in God.

4. Lead us to heav'n, that we may share
fullness of joy for ever there;
lead us to God, the heart's true rest,
to dwell with him, for ever blest.

117 Come, Holy Ghost, our hearts inspire

Charles Wesley (1707-1788) From *Praxis Pietatis Melica* (1647)

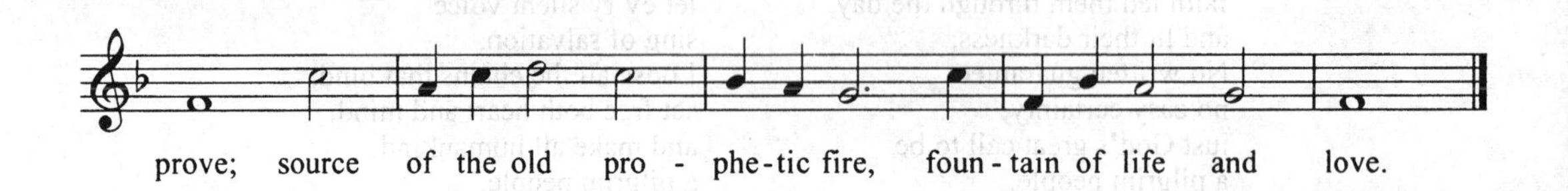

2. Come, Holy Ghost – for, moved by thee,
thy prophets wrote and spoke –
unlock the truth, thyself the key,
unseal the sacred book.

3. Expand thy wings, celestial Dove,
brood o'er our nature's night;
on our disordered spirits move,
and let there now be light.

4. God, through himself, we then shall know,
if thou within us shine;
and sound, with all thy saints below,
the depths of love divine.

Charles Wesley (1707-1788) Thomas Clark (1775-1859)

TUNE 2: CREDITON CM

118 Come, Holy Ghost, our souls inspire

vs. 1-3, 5: John Cosin (1594-1672)
after Rabanus Maurus (c.776-856) alt.
v.4: Michael Forster (b.1946)

Proper Sarum Melody

VENI, CREATOR SPIRITUS (MECHLIN) LM

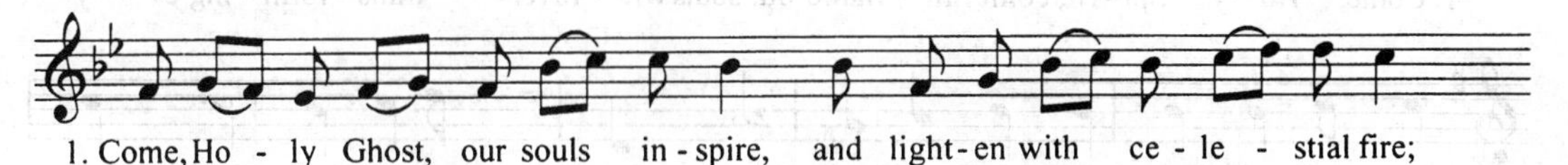

thou the a - noint - ing Spi - rit art, who dost thy sev'n - fold gifts im - part.

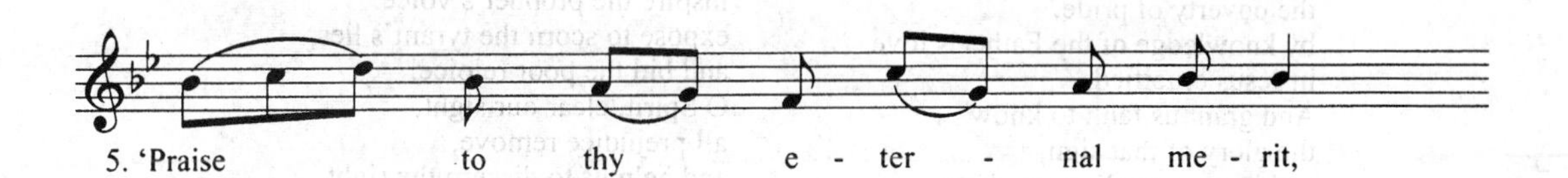

2. Thy blessèd unction from above
   is comfort, life, and fire of love;
   enable with perpetual light
   the dullness of our blinded sight.

3. Anoint and cheer our soilèd face
   with the abundance of thy grace:
   keep far our foes, give peace at home;
   where thou art guide no ill can come.

4. Show us the Father and the Son,
   in thee and with thee, ever one.
   Then through the ages all along,
   this shall be our unending song.

5. 'Praise to thy eternal merit,
   Father, Son and Holy Spirit.'
   Amen.

Text of verse 4 © Copyright 1993 Kevin Mayhew Ltd.

119 Come, Holy Spirit, come

Michael Forster (b.1946)
based on 1 Corinthians 12:4-11

Colin Mawby (b.1936)

DONNYBROOK DSM

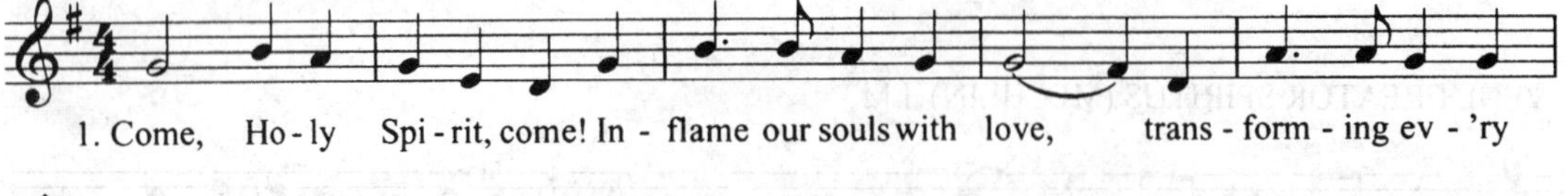

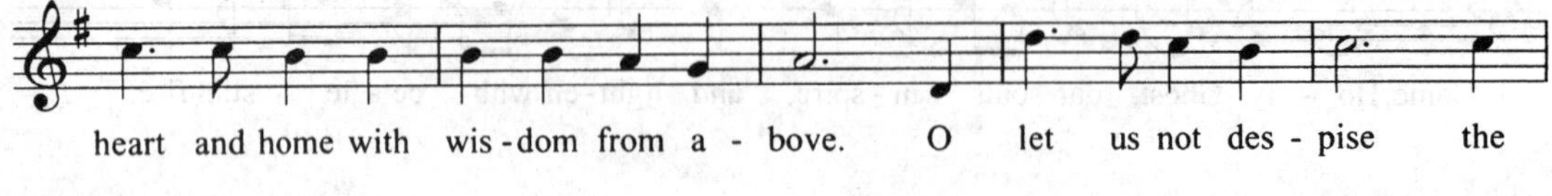

2. All-knowing Spirit, prove
the poverty of pride,
by knowledge of the Father's love
in Jesus crucified.
And grant us faith to know
the glory of that sign,
and in our very lives to show
the marks of love divine.

3. Come with the gift to heal
the wounds of guilt and fear,
and to oppression's face reveal
the kingdom drawing near.
Where chaos longs to reign,
descend, O holy Dove,
and free us all to work again
the miracles of love.

4. Spirit of truth, arise;
inspire the prophet's voice:
expose to scorn the tyrant's lies,
and bid the poor rejoice.
O Spirit, clear our sight,
all prejudice remove,
and help us to discern the right,
and covet only love.

5. Give us the tongues to speak,
in ev'ry time and place,
to rich and poor, to strong and weak,
the word of love and grace.
Enable us to hear
the words that others bring,
interpreting with open ear
the special song they sing.

6. Come, Holy Spirit, dance
within our hearts today,
our earthbound spirits to entrance,
our mortal fears allay.
And teach us to desire,
all other things above,
that self-consuming holy fire,
the perfect gift of love!

© Copyright 1992 Kevin Mayhew Ltd.

120 Come, let us join our cheerful songs

Isaac Watts (1674-1758) alt.

Henry Lahee (1826-1912)

NATIVITY CM

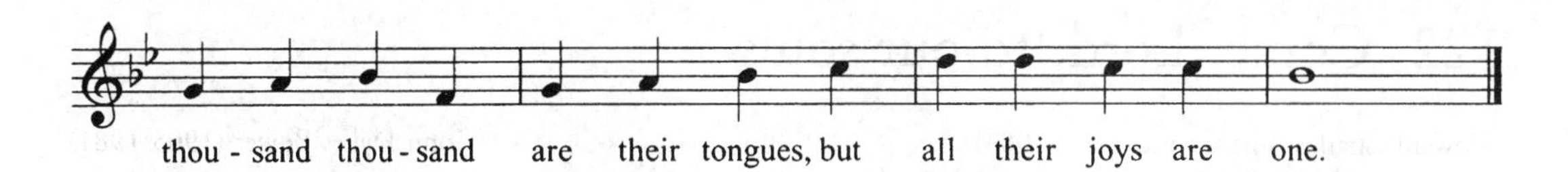

2. 'Worthy the Lamb that died,' they cry,
'to be exalted thus.'
'Worthy the Lamb,' our lips reply,
'for he was slain for us.'

3. Jesus is worthy to receive
honour and pow'r divine;
and blessings, more than we can give,
be, Lord, for ever thine.

4. Let all creation join in one
to bless the sacred name
of him that sits upon the throne,
and to adore the Lamb.

121 Come, let us sing

Robert Walmsley (1831-1905) F.L. Wiseman (1858-1944)

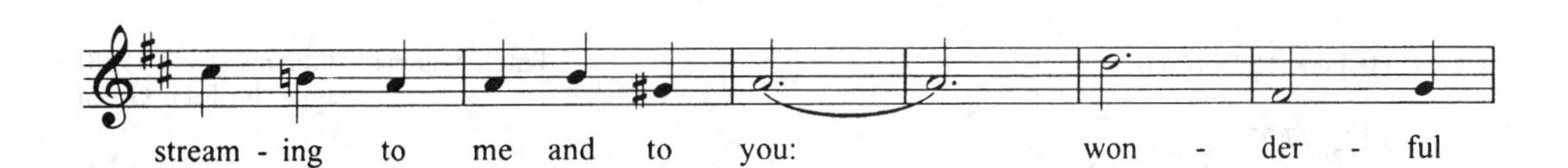

2. Jesus, the Saviour, this gospel to tell,
joyfully came;
came with the helpless and hopeless to dwell,
sharing their sorrow and shame;
seeking the lost,
saving, redeeming at measureless cost.

3. Jesus is seeking the wanderers yet;
why do they roam?
Love only waits to forgive and forget;
home! weary wanderer, home!
Wonderful love
dwells in the heart of the Father above.

4. Come to my heart, O thou wonderful love,
come and abide,
lifting my life till it rises above
envy and falsehood and pride;
seeking to be
lowly and humble, a learner of thee.

Music © Copyright Trustees for Methodist Church Purposes, Methodist Publishing House,
20 Ivatt Way, Peterborough PE3 7PG. Used by permission.

122 Come, Lord, to our souls

Howard Charles Adie Gaunt (1902-1983) John Dykes Bower (1905-1981)

QUEDGELEY 76 76

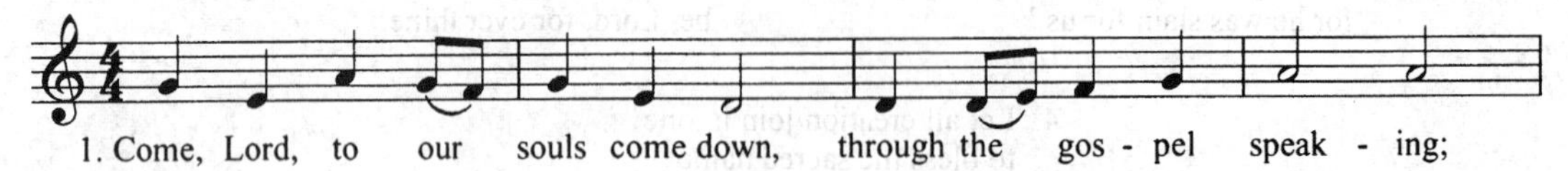

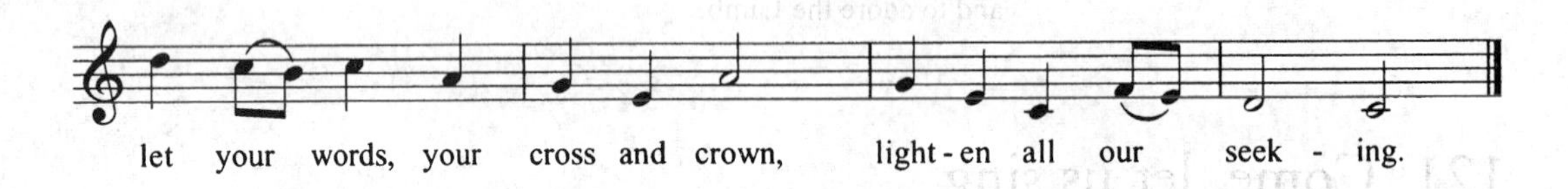

2. Drive out darkness from the heart,
banish pride and blindness;
plant in ev'ry inward part
truthfulness and kindness.

3. Eyes be open, spirits stirred,
minds new truth receiving;
lead us, Lord, by your own Word;
strengthen our believing.

Text © Copyright Oxford University Press, Great Clarendon Street, Oxford OX2 6DP.
Music © Copyright Hymns Ancient & Modern, St Mary's Works,
St Mary's Plain, Norwich NR3 3BH. Used by permission.

123 Come, my Way, my Truth, my Life

George Herbert (1593-1633) Ralph Vaughan Williams (1872-1958)
adapted by E.H. Green

THE CALL 77.77

2. Come, my Light, my Feast, my Strength:
such a light as shows a feast;
such a feast as mends in length;
such a strength as makes his guest.

3. Come, my Joy, my Love, my Heart:
such a joy as none can move;
such a love as none can part;
such a heart as joys in love.

Music © Copyright 1911 Stainer & Bell Ltd., P.O. Box 110, Victoria House,
23 Gruneison Road, Finchley, London N3 1DZ. Used by permission.

124 Come, O Lord, inspire us

Words and music: Frances M. Kelly

2. When the hungry want no more
and when the sick are healed,
we have the right to sing 'Alleluia!'
When the darkness holds no fear
and each new dawn brings hope,
we have the right to sing 'Alleluia!'

3. When the pow'r of hate lies crushed
and there's no ground for war,
we have the right to sing 'Alleluia!'
When the lion and the lamb
lie peaceful, all is calm,
we have the right to sing 'Alleluia!'

© Copyright 1999 Kevin Mayhew Ltd.

125 Come on and celebrate *Celebrate*

Words and music: Patricia Morgan
and Dave Bankhead

© Copyright 1984 Kingsway's Thankyou Music, P.O. Box 75, Eastbourne, East Sussex BN23 6NW, UK. (tym@kingsway.co.uk). Used by permission.

126 Come, risen Lord

George Wallace Briggs (1875-1959) | Orlando Gibbons (1583-1625)

SONG 4 10 10 10 10

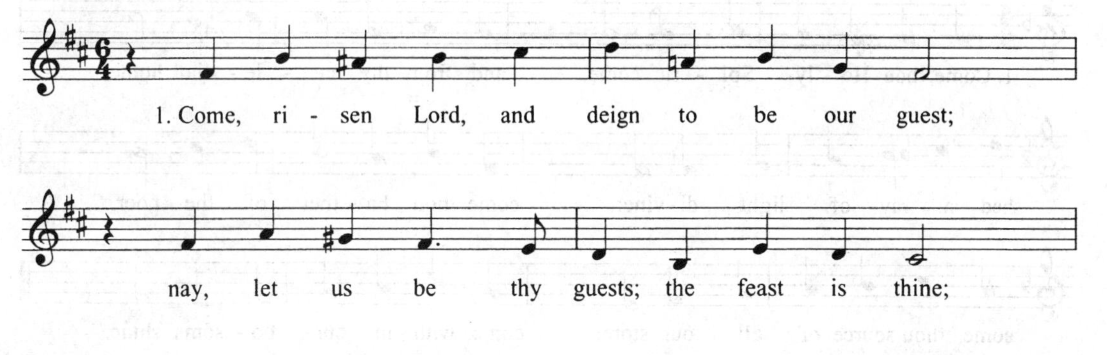

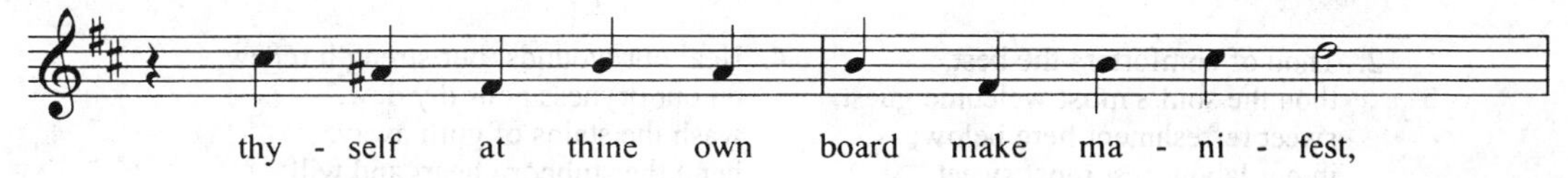

2. We meet, as in that upper room they met;
thou at thy table, blessing, yet dost stand:
'This is my body' – so thou givest yet;
faith still receives the cup as from thy hand.

3. One body we, one body who partake,
one Church united in communion blest;
one name we bear, one bread of life we break,
with all thy saints on earth and saints at rest.

4. One with each other, Lord, for one in thee,
who art one Saviour and one living Head;
then open thou our eyes, that we may see:
be known to us in breaking of the bread.

Text © Copyright Oxford University Press, Great Clarendon Steet, Oxford OX2 6DP.
Used by permission.

127 Come, thou Holy Spirit, come

Stephen Langton (d.1228)
trans. Edward Caswall (1814-1878) alt.

Samuel Webbe (1740-1816)

VENI, SANCTE SPIRITUS 777 D

2. Thou of comforters the best,
thou the soul's most welcome guest,
sweet refreshment here below;
in our labour rest most sweet,
grateful coolness in the heat,
solace in the midst of woe.

3. O most blessèd Light divine,
shine within these hearts of thine,
and our inmost being fill;
where thou art not, we have naught,
nothing good in deed or thought,
nothing free from taint of ill.

4. Heal our wounds; our strength renew;
on our dryness pour thy dew;
wash the stains of guilt away;
bend the stubborn heart and will;
melt the frozen, warm the chill;
guide the steps that go astray.

5. On the faithful, who adore
and confess thee, evermore
in thy sev'nfold gifts descend:
give them virtue's sure reward,
give them thy salvation, Lord,
give them joys that never end.

128 Come, thou long-expected Jesus

Charles Wesley (1707-1788)

John Stainer (1840-1901)

TUNE 1: CROSS OF JESUS 87 87

2. Israel's strength and consolation,
hope of all the earth thou art;
dear desire of ev'ry nation,
joy of ev'ry longing heart.

3. Born thy people to deliver;
born a child and yet a king;
born to reign in us for ever;
now thy gracious kingdom bring.

4. By thine own eternal Spirit,
rule in all our hearts alone:
by thine all-sufficient merit,
raise us to thy glorious throne.

Charles Wesley (1707-1788)

Version of a melody by William Boyce (1711-1779)
in S.S. Wesley's *European Psalmist* (1872)

TUNE 2: HALTON HOLGATE 87 87

129 Come to me, come, my people *Be humble of heart*

Words and music: Gerard Markland (b.1953)

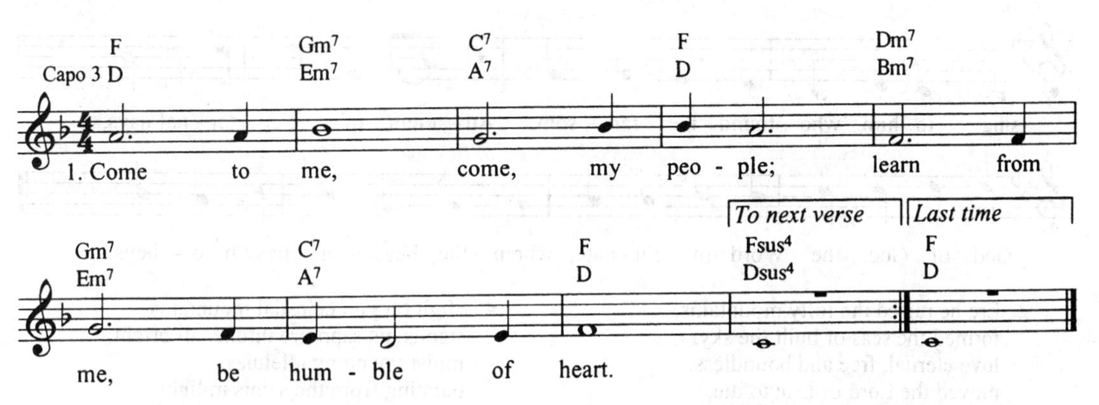

2. I your Lord, I your master;
learn from me, be humble of heart.

3. Follow me to my Father;
learn from me, be humble of heart.

4. In my death, in my rising;
learn from me, be humble of heart.

5. Be transformed by my Spirit;
learn from me, be humble of heart.

6. Glory be to my Father;
learn from me, be humble of heart.

© Copyright 1998 Kevin Mayhew Ltd.

130 Come, wounded Healer

Martin Leckebusch (b.1962) | Traditional Irish melody

SLANE 10 11 11 11

2. Come, hated Lover, and gather us near,
your welcome, your teaching, your challenge to hear:
where scorn and abuse cause rejection and pain,
your loving acceptance makes hope live again!

3. Come, broken Victor, condemned to a cross –
how great are the treasures we gain from your loss!
Your willing agreement to share in our strife
transforms our despair into fullness of life.

131 Come, ye faithful, raise the anthem

Job Hupton (1762-1849)
John Mason Neale (1818-1866) alt.

Joachim Neander (1640-1680)

NEANDER (UNSER HERRSCHER) 87 87 87

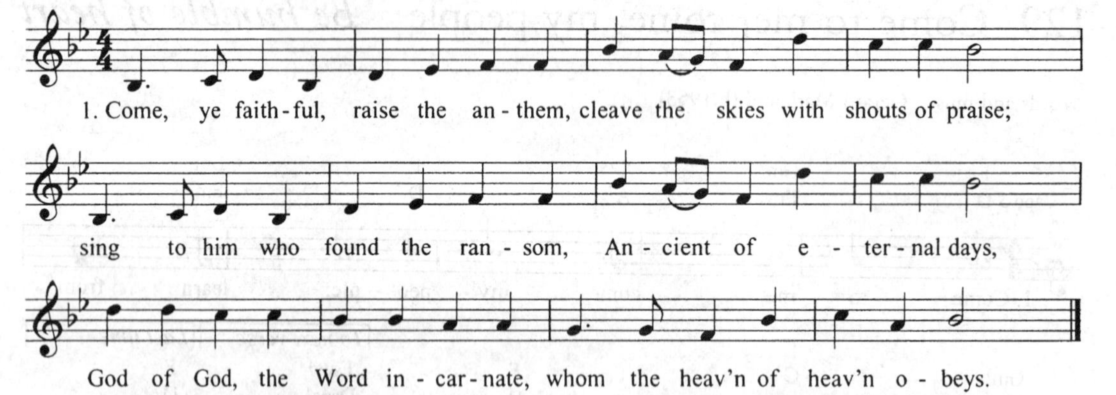

2. Ere he raised the lofty mountains,
formed the seas or built the sky,
love eternal, free and boundless,
moved the Lord of Life to die,
fore-ordained the Prince of princes
for the throne of Calvary.

3. There, for us and our redemption,
see him all his life-blood pour!
There he wins our full salvation,
dies that we may die no more;
then arising, lives for ever,
reigning where he was before.

4. High on yon celestial mountains
stands his sapphire throne, all bright,
midst unending alleluias
bursting from the saints in light;
Sion's people tell his praises,
victor after hard-won fight.

5. Bring your harps, and bring your incense,
sweep the string and pour the lay;
let the earth proclaim his wonders,
King of that celestial day;
he the Lamb once slain is worthy,
who was dead and lives for ay.

Text © Copyright 1999 Kevin Mayhew Ltd.

6. Laud and honour to the Father,
laud and honour to the Son,
laud and honour to the Spirit,
ever Three and ever One,
consubstantial, co-eternal,
while unending ages run.

132 Come, ye faithful, raise the strain

St John of Damascus (d. c. 754)
trans. John Mason Neale (1816-1866) alt.

Arthur Henry Brown (1830-1926)

TUNE 1: ST JOHN DAMASCENE 76 76 D

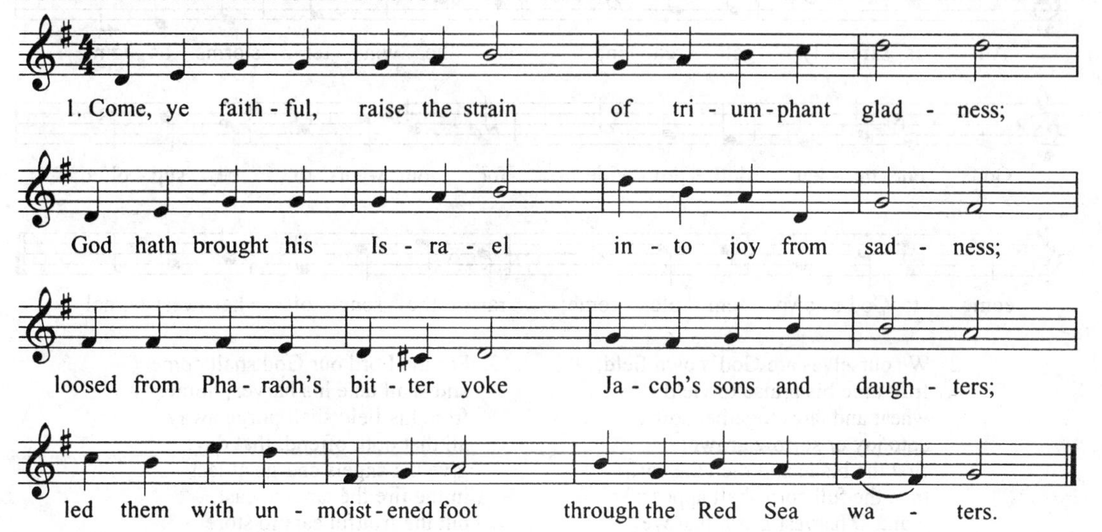

2. 'Tis the spring of souls today;
Christ hath burst his prison,
and from three days' sleep in death
as a sun hath risen:
all the winter of our sins,
long and dark, is flying
from his light, to whom we give
laud and praise undying.

3. Now the queen of seasons, bright
with the day of splendour,
with the royal feast of feasts,
comes its joy to render;
comes to glad Jerusalem,
who with true affection
welcomes in unwearied strains
Jesu's resurrection.

4. Alleluia now we cry
to our King immortal,
who triumphant burst the bars
of the tomb's dark portal;
Alleluia, with the Son,
God the Father praising;
Alleluia yet again
to the Spirit raising.

St John of Damascus (d.c. 754)
trans. John Mason Neale (1816-1866) alt.

Traditional melody from Johannes Leisentritt's *Catholicum Hymnologium Germanicum* Cologne (1584)

TUNE 2: AVE VIRGO VIRGINUM 76 76 D

1. Come, ye faith - ful, raise the strain of tri - um - phant glad - ness;
God hath brought his Is - ra - el in - to joy from sad - ness;
loosed from Pha - raoh's bit - ter yoke Ja - cob's sons and daugh - ters;
led them with un - moist - ened foot through the Red Sea wa - ters.

133 Come, ye thankful people, come

Henry Alford (1810-1871) alt. — George Job Elvey (1816-1893)

ST GEORGE'S WINDSOR 77 77 D

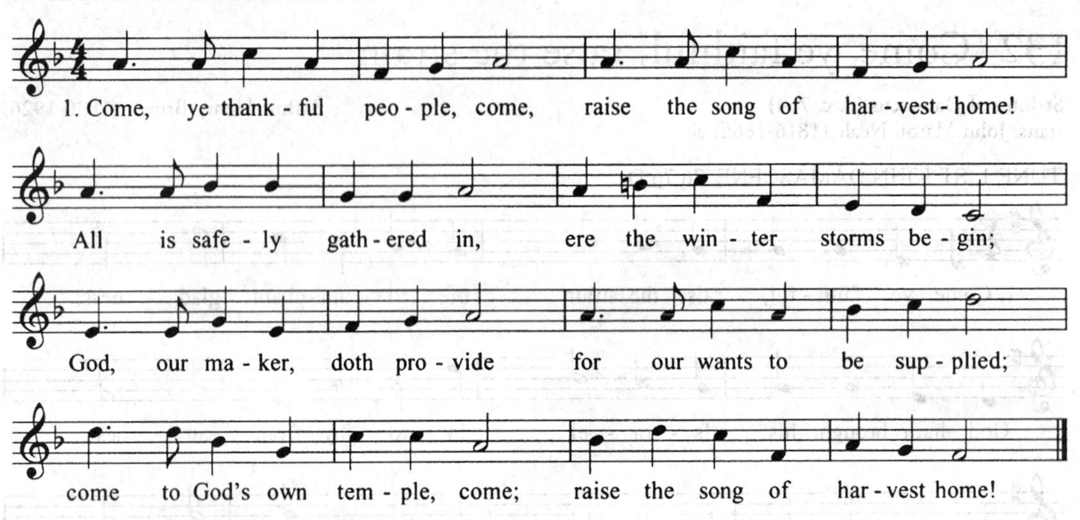

2. We ourselves are God's own field,
fruit unto his praise to yield;
wheat and tares together sown,
unto joy or sorrow grown;
first the blade and then the ear,
then the full corn shall appear:
grant, O harvest Lord, that we
wholesome grain and pure may be.

3. For the Lord our God shall come,
and shall take his harvest home,
from his field shall purge away
all that doth offend, that day;
give his angels charge at last
in the fire the tares to cast,
but the fruitful ears to store
in his garner evermore.

4. Then, thou Church triumphant, come,
raise the song of harvest-home;
all be safely gathered in,
free from sorrow, free from sin,
there for ever purified
in God's garner to abide:
come, ten thousand angels, come,
raise the glorious harvest-home!

134 Creating God, we bring our song of praise

Jan Berry (b.1953) — Andrew Moore (b.1954)

AD LIMINA 10 10 10 10

1. Cre - at - ing God, we bring our song of praise for life and
work that ce - le - brate your ways: the skill of hands, our liv - ing with the
earth, the joy that comes from know - ing our own worth.

© Copyright 1999 Kevin Mayhew Ltd.

2. Forgiving God, we bring our cries of pain
for all that shames us in our search for gain:
the hidden wounds, the angry scars of strife,
the emptiness that saps and weakens life.

3. Redeeming God, we bring our trust in you,
our fragile hope that all may be made new:
our dreams of truth, of wealth that all may share,
of work and service rooted deep in prayer.

4. Renewing God, we offer what shall be
a world that lives and works in harmony:
when peace and justice, once so long denied,
restore to all their dignity and pride.

135 Creator of the starry height

7th century
trans. John Mason Neale (1818-1866) alt.

Plainsong melody

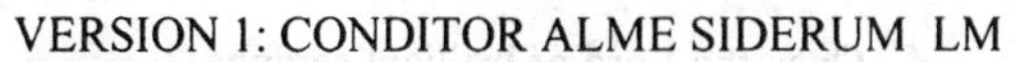
VERSION 1: CONDITOR ALME SIDERUM LM

2. Thou, grieving at the helpless cry
of all creation doomed to die,
didst come to save our fallen race
by healing gifts of heav'nly grace.

3. When earth was near its evening hour,
thou didst, in love's redeeming pow'r,
like bridegroom from his chamber, come
forth from a Virgin-mother's womb.

4. At thy great name, exalted now,
all knees in lowly homage bow;
all things in heav'n and earth adore,
and own thee King for evermore.

5. To thee, O Holy One, we pray,
our judge in that tremendous day,
ward off, while yet we dwell below,
the weapons of our crafty foe.

6. To God the Father, God the Son
and God the Spirit, Three in One,
praise, honour, might and glory be
from age to age eternally.

An alternative plainsong setting

VERSION 2: CONDITOR ALME SIDERUM

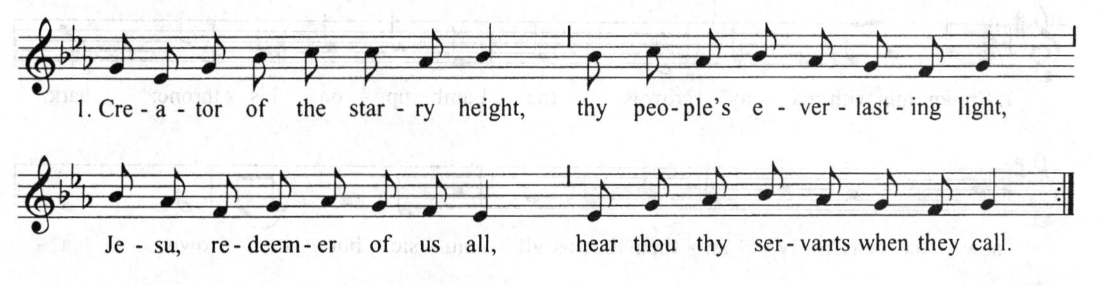

136 Cross of Jesus

William Sparrow-Simpson (1859-1952) John Stainer (1840-1901)

CROSS OF JESUS 87 87

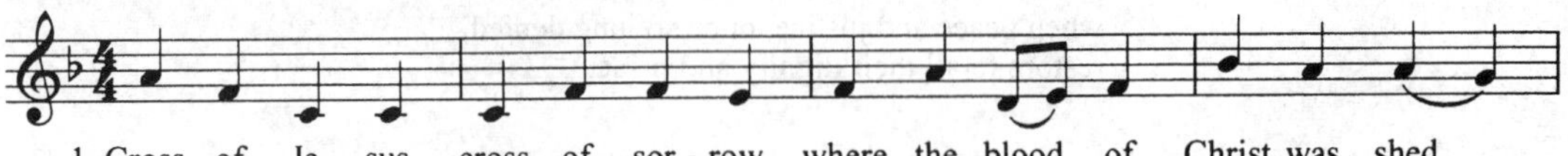

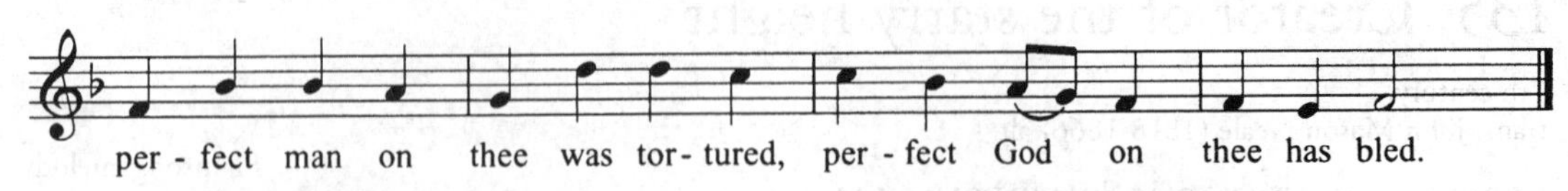

2. Here the King of all the ages,
throned in light ere worlds could be,
robed in mortal flesh is dying,
crucified by sin for me.

3. O, mysterious condescending!
O, abandonment sublime!
Very God himself is bearing
all the sufferings of time!

4. Evermore for human failure
by his Passion we can plead;
God has borne all mortal anguish,
surely he will know our need.

5. This - all human thought surpassing -
this is earth's most awful hour,
God has taken mortal weakness!
God has laid aside his pow'r!

6. Once the Lord of brilliant seraphs,
winged with love to do his will,
now the scorn of all his creatures,
and the aim of ev'ry ill.

7. Up in heav'n, sublimest glory
circled round him from the first;
but the earth finds none to serve him,
none to quench his raging thirst.

8. Who shall fathom that descending,
from the rainbow-circled throne,
down to earth's most base profaning
dying desolate, alone.

9. From the 'Holy, Holy, Holy,
we adore thee, O most High,'
down to earth's blaspheming voices
and the shout of 'Crucify'.

10. Cross of Jesus, cross of sorrow,
where the blood of Christ was shed,
perfect man on thee was tortured,
perfect God on thee has bled.

© Copyright 1887, 1915 Novello & Co. Ltd., 8/9 Frith Street, London W1D 3JB.
All rights reserved. International copyright secured. Used by permission.

137 Crown him with many crowns

Matthew Bridges (1800-1894) Richard Runciman Terry (1865-1938)

TUNE 1: CORONA DSM

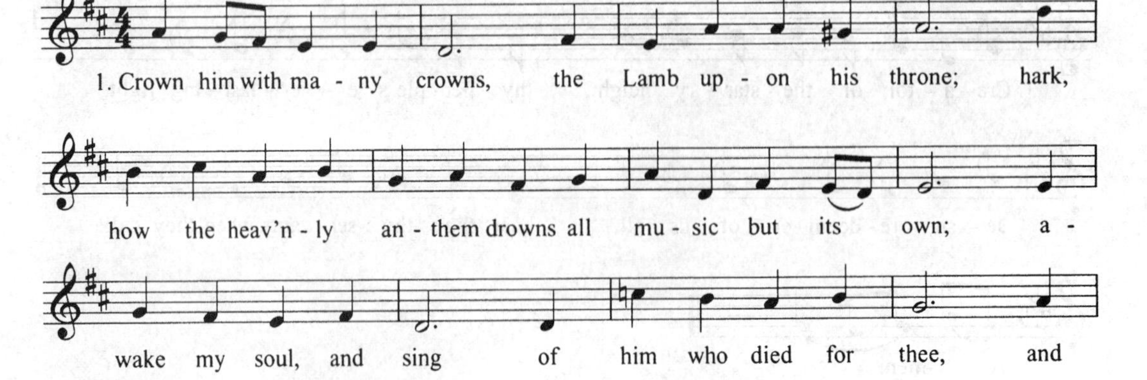

Tune 1 © Copyright Control.

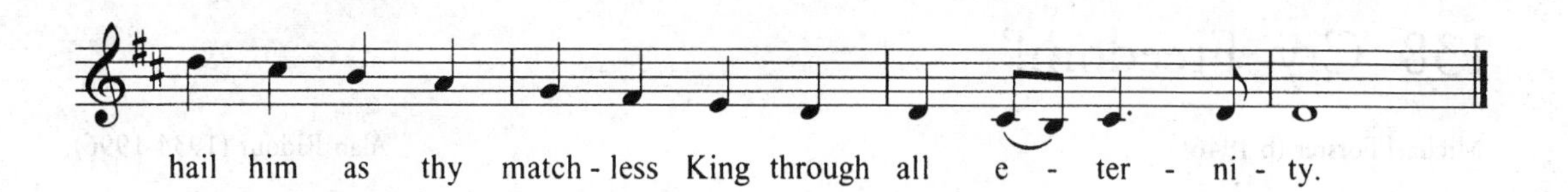

2. Crown him the Virgin's Son,
the God incarnate born,
whose arm those crimson trophies won
which now his brow adorn;
fruit of the mystic Rose,
as of that Rose the Stem,
the Root, whence mercy ever flows,
the Babe of Bethlehem.

3. Crown him the Lord of love;
behold his hands and side,
rich wounds, yet visible above,
in beauty glorified:
no angel in the sky
can fully bear that sight,
but downward bends each burning eye
at mysteries so bright.

4. Crown him the Lord of peace,
whose pow'r a sceptre sways
from pole to pole, that wars may cease,
absorbed in prayer and praise:
his reign shall know no end,
and round his piercèd feet
fair flow'rs of paradise extend
their fragrance ever sweet.

5. Crown him the Lord of years,
the Potentate of time,
Creator of the rolling spheres,
ineffably sublime.
All hail, Redeemer, hail!
for thou hast died for me;
thy praise shall never, never fail
throughout eternity.

Matthew Bridges (1800-1894) George Job Elvey (1816-1893)

TUNE 2: DIADEMATA DSM

138 Cry 'Freedom!'

Michael Forster (b.1946)

Alan Ridout (1934-1996)

THATCHER 14 14 14 and Refrain

2. Cry 'Freedom!' for the victims
of the earthquake and the rain:
where wealthy folk find shelter
and the poor must bear the pain;
where weapons claim resources
while the famine strikes again.

3. Cry 'Freedom!' for dictators
in their fortresses confined,
who hide behind their bodyguards
and fear the open mind,
and bid them find true freedom
in the good of humankind.

4. Cry 'Freedom!' in the church when
honest doubts are met with fear;
when vacuum-packed theology
makes questions disappear;
when journeys end before they start
and mystery is clear!

5. Cry 'Freedom!' when we find ourselves
imprisoned in our greed,
to live in free relationship
and meet each other's need.
From self released for others' good
we should be free indeed!

© Copyright 1992 Kevin Mayhew Ltd.

139 Dance and sing

John L. Bell (b.1949)
Graham Maule (b.1958)

Traditional Scottish melody

PULLING BRACKEN Irregular

2. Deserts stretch and torrents roar
in contrast and confusion;
treetops shake and mountains soar
and nothing is illusion.

3. All that flies and swims and crawls
displays an animation;
none can emulate or change
for each has its own station.

4. Brother man and sister woman,
born of dust and passion,
praise the one who calls you friends
and makes you in his fashion.

5. Kiss of life and touch of death
suggest our imperfection:
crib and womb and cross and tomb
cry out for resurrection.

Text © Copyright 1987 WGRG, Iona Community, Glasgow G2 3DH, Scotland.
Used by permission from the *Heaven shall not wait* collection.

140 Dance in your Spirit

Words and music: Mike Anderson (b.1956)

2. Jesus, you opened your arms for us,
but we nailed them to a cross;
but you are risen and now we live,
free from, free from ev'ry fear.

3. Your Spirit brings peace and gentleness,
kindness, self-control and love,
patience and goodness and faith and joy,
Spirit, Spirit fill us now.

© Copyright 1999 Kevin Mayhew Ltd.

141 Day of wrath and day of wonder

Michael Forster (b.1946)

Traditional Welsh melody

AR HYD Y NOS 84 84 88 84

2. Day of hope and day of glory,
though unperceived!
See redemption's dreadful story,
long, long conceived.
Evil pow'rs, in downfall lying,
knowing death itself is dying,
hear the voice triumphant crying,
'All is achieved!'

3. Day of majesty and splendour,
here ends the race!
Christ, our Priest, our soul's defender,
us will embrace.
He who walked this earth before us,
tried and tempted, yet victorious,
calls us to the kingdom glorious,
O perfect grace!

Text © Copyright 1993 Kevin Mayhew Ltd.

142 Dear Christ, uplifted from the earth

Brian A. Wren (b.1936)
from John 12:32,33
and Romans 15:7

Leonard Blake (1907-1989)

TUNE 1: WINCHCOMBE CM

2. Still east and west your love extends
and always, near and far,
you call and claim us as your friends
and loves us as we are.

3. Where age and gender, class and race,
divide us to our shame,
you see a person and a face,
a neighbour with a name.

4. May we, accepted as we are,
yet called in grace to grow,
reach out to others, near and far,
your healing love to show.

Brian A. Wren (b.1936)
from John 12:32,33
and Romans 15:7

Traditional English melody adapted by
Ralph Vaughan Williams (1872-1958)

TUNE 2: RODMELL CM

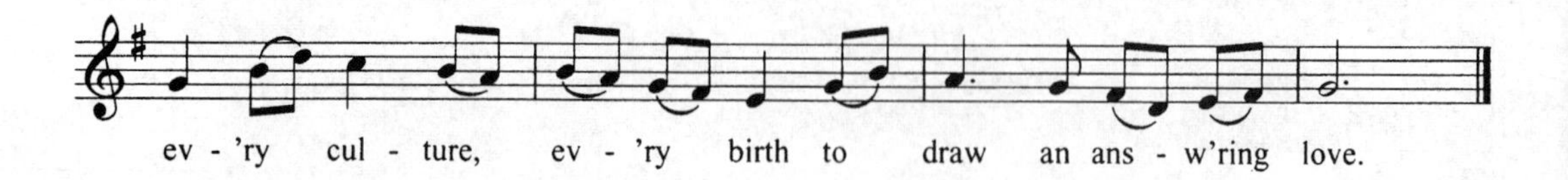

Text © Copyright 1973, 1996 Stainer & Bell Ltd., P.O. Box 110, Victoria House,
23 Gruneison Road, Finchley, London N3 1DZ. Used by permission.
Tune 1 © Copyright Lady Dunbar of Hempriggs.
Tune 2 © Copyright Oxford University Press, Great Clarendon Street, Oxford OX2 6DP.
Used by permission from the *English Hymnal*.

143 Dearest Jesu, we are here

George Ratcliffe Woodward (1848-1934)
after T. Clausnitzer (1619-1684)

Johann Rodolph Ahle (1625-1673)

LIEBSTER JESU 78 78 88

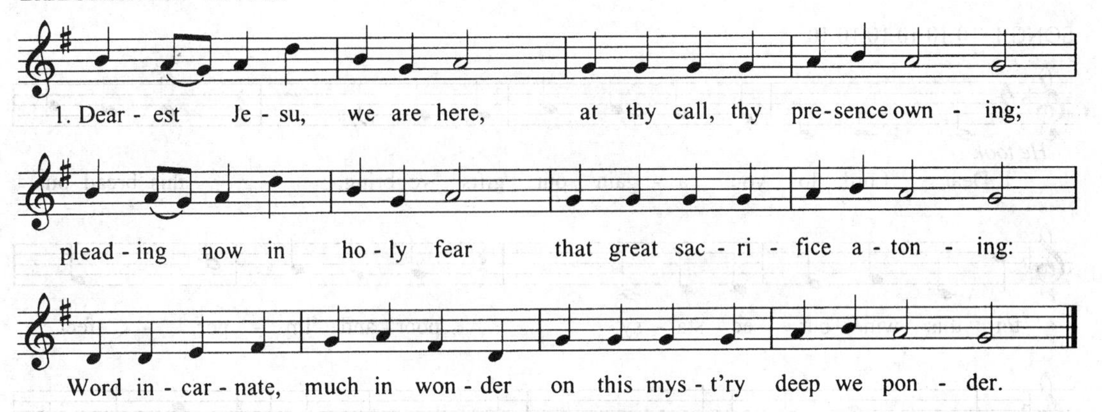

2. Jesu, strong to save – the same
yesterday, today, for ever –
make us fear and love thy name,
serving thee with best endeavour:
in this life, O ne'er forsake us,
but to bliss hereafter take us.

Text © Copyright Control.

144 Dear Lord and Father of mankind

John Greenleaf Whittier (1807-1892)

Charles Hubert Hastings Parry (1848-1918)

REPTON 86 88 6

2. In simple trust like theirs who heard,
beside the Syrian sea,
the gracious calling of the Lord,
let us, like them, without a word,
rise up and follow thee,
rise up and follow thee.

3. O Sabbath rest by Galilee!
O calm of hills above,
where Jesus knelt to share with thee
the silence of eternity,
interpreted by love!
Interpreted by love!

4. Drop thy still dews of quietness,
till all our strivings cease;
take from our souls the strain and stress,
and let our ordered lives confess
the beauty of thy peace,
the beauty of thy peace.

5. Breathe through the heats of our desire
thy coolness and thy balm;
let sense be dumb, let flesh retire;
speak through the earthquake, wind and fire,
O still small voice of calm!
O still small voice of calm!

145 Dear Lord, to you again

Henry Charles Adie Gaunt (1902-1983) | Orlando Gibbons (1583-1625)

He blessed

2. Yes, you will take and bless, and grace impart
to make again what once your goodness gave,
what we half crave, and half refuse to have,
a sturdier will, a more repentant heart.
You have on earth no hands, no hearts but ours;
bless them as yours, ourselves, our will, our pow'rs.

He broke

3. Break bread, O Lord, break down our wayward wills,
break down our prized possessions, break them down;
let them be freely given as your own
to all who need our gifts, to heal their ills.
Break this, the bread we bring, that all may share
in your one living body, everywhere.

He gave

4. Our lips receive your wine, our hands your bread;
you give us back the selves we offered you,
won by the cross, by Calvary made new,
a heart enriched, a life raised from the dead.
Grant us to take and guard your treasure well,
that we in you, and you in us may dwell.

Text © Copyright Oxford University Press, Great Clarendon Street, Oxford OX2 6DP.
Used by permission.

146 Deck thyself, my soul, with gladness

Johann Franck (1618-1677)
trans. Catherine Winkworth (1827-1878)

Johann Crüger (1598-1662)

2. Now I sink before thee lowly,
filled with joy most deep and holy,
as with trembling awe and wonder
on thy mighty works I ponder:
how, by mystery surrounded,
depth no mortal ever sounded,
none may dare to pierce unbidden
secrets that with thee are hidden.

PART TWO

3. Sun, who all my life dost brighten,
Light, who dost my soul enlighten,
Joy, which through my spirit floweth,
Fount, which life and health bestoweth,
at thy feet I cry, my Maker,
let me be a fit partaker
of this blessèd food from heaven,
for our good, thy glory, given.

4. Jesus, Bread of Life, I pray thee,
let me gladly here obey thee;
never to my hurt invited,
be thy love with love requited:
from this banquet let me measure,
Lord, how vast and deep its treasure;
through the gifts thou here dost give me,
as thy guest in heav'n receive me.

147 Deep within my heart

Words and music: Mike Anderson (b.1956)

2. Deep within my heart I know I'm forgiven,
deep within my heart I know that I'm free.
Free from sin, a new life to begin,
and I'm alive now.
Deep within my heart I know that I'm free.

3. Deep within my heart Jesus' love is healing,
deep within my heart he is healing me.
Tears like rain are flooding out the pain,
and I'm alive now.
Deep within my heart he is healing me.

© Copyright 1999 Kevin Mayhew Ltd.

148 Ding dong, merrily on high!

George Ratcliffe Woodward (1848-1934)

Traditional French melody

BRANSLE DE L'OFFICIAL 77 77 and Refrain

2. E'en so here below, below,
let steeple bells be swungen,
and io, io, io,
by priest and people sungen.

3. Pray you, dutifully prime
your matin chime, ye ringers;
may you beautifully rhyme
your evetime song, ye singers.

149 Disposer supreme

J.B. de Santeuil (1630-1697)
trans. Isaac Williams (1802-1865) alt.

Thomas Ravencroft
Psalms (1621)

OLD 104TH 10 10 11 11

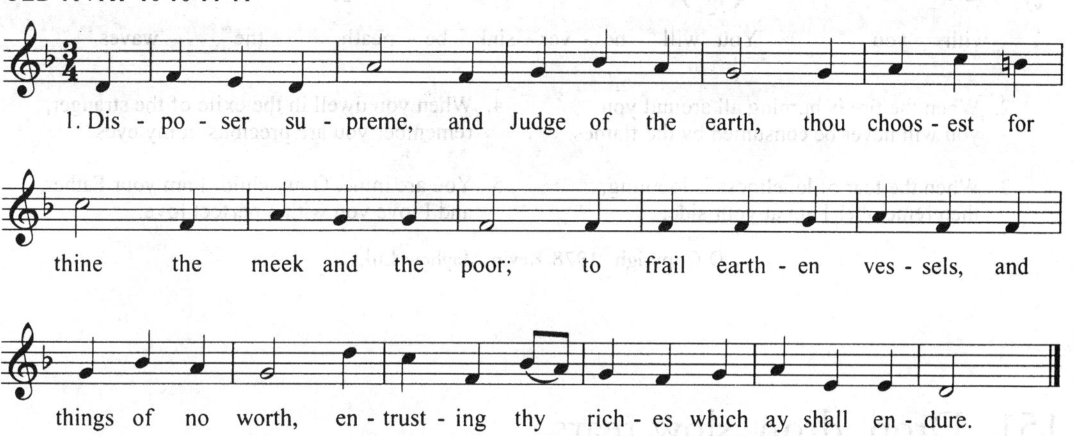

2. Those vessels are frail, though full of thy light,
and many, once made, are broken and gone;
thence brightly appeareth thy truth in its might,
as through the clouds riven the lightnings have shone.

3. Like clouds are they borne to do thy great will,
and swift as the winds about the world go:
the Word with his wisdom their spirits doth fill;
they thunder, they lighten, the waters o'erflow.

4. Their sound goeth forth, 'Christ Jesus the Lord!'
then Satan doth fear, his citadels fall;
as when the dread trumpets went forth at thy word,
and one long blast shattered the Canaanites' wall.

5. O loud be their cry, and stirring their sound,
to rouse us, O Lord, from slumber of sin:
the lights thou hast kindled in darkness around,
O may they awaken our spirits within.

6. All honour and praise, dominion and might,
to God, Three in One, eternally be,
who round us hath shed his own marvellous light,
and called us from darkness his glory to see.

Text © Copyright SPCK, Holy Trinity Church, Marylebone Road, London NW1 4DU.
Used by permission.

150 Do not be afraid

Words and music: Gerard Markland (b.1953)
based on Isaiah 43:1-4

2. When the fire is burning all around you,
you will never be consumed by the flames.

3. When the fear of loneliness is looming,
then remember I am at your side.

4. When you dwell in the exile of the stranger,
remember you are precious in my eyes.

5. You are mine, O my child, I am your Father,
and I love you with a perfect love.

© Copyright 1978 Kevin Mayhew Ltd.

151 Drop, drop, slow tears

Phineas Fletcher (1582-1650) Orlando Gibbons (1583-1625)

SONG 46 10 10

1. Drop, drop, slow tears, and bathe those beau - teous
feet, which brought from heav'n the news and Prince of Peace.

2. Cease not, wet eyes,
his mercies to entreat;
to cry for vengeance
sin doth never cease.

3. In your deep floods
drown all my faults and fears;
nor let his eye
see sin, but through my tears.

152 Earth has many a noble city

Aurelius Clemens Prudentius (348-c.413)
trans. Edward Caswall (1814-1878) alt.

German melody

STUTTGART 87 87

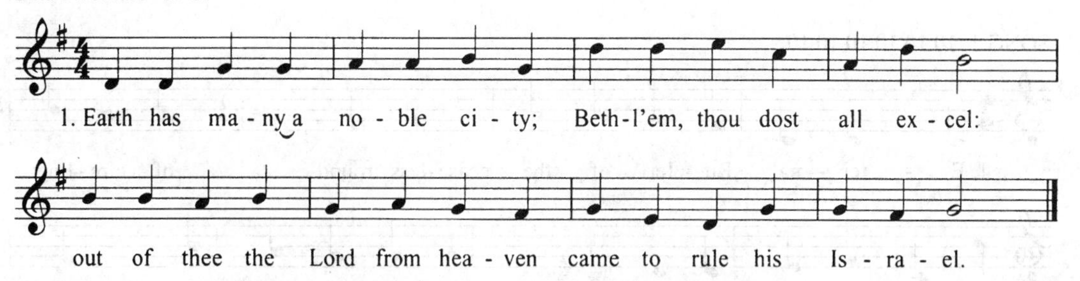

2. Fairer than the sun at morning
was the star that told his birth,
to the world its God announcing,
seen in fleshly form on earth.

3. Eastern sages at his cradle
make oblations rich and rare;
see them give in deep devotion
gold and frankincense and myrrh.

4. Sacred gifts of mystic meaning:
incense doth their God disclose,
gold the King of kings proclaimeth,
myrrh his sepulchre foreshows.

5. Jesu, whom the Gentiles worshipped
at thy glad Epiphany,
unto thee with God the Father
and the Spirit glory be.

153 Eternal Father, strong to save

William Whiting (1825-1878) alt.

John Bacchus Dykes (1823-1876)

MELITA 88 88 88

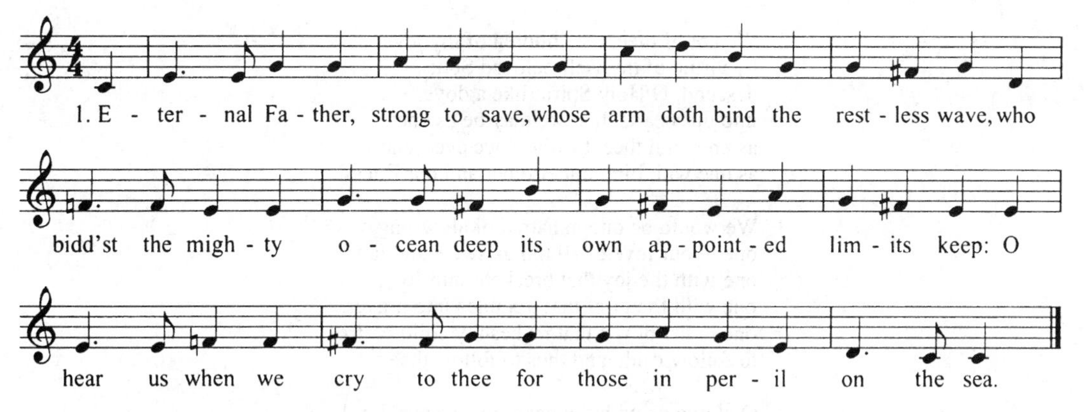

2. O Saviour, whose almighty word
the winds and waves submissive heard,
who walkedst on the foaming deep,
and calm, amid its rage, didst sleep:
O hear us when we cry to thee
for those in peril on the sea.

3. O sacred Spirit, who didst brood
upon the waters dark and rude,
and bid their angry tumult cease,
and give, for wild confusion, peace:
O hear us when we cry to thee
for those in peril on the sea.

4. O Trinity of love and pow'r,
our brethren shield in danger's hour.
From rock and tempest, fire and foe,
protect them whereso'er they go,
and ever let there rise to thee
glad hymns of praise from land and sea.

154 Eternal Ruler of the ceaseless round

John White Chadwick (1840-1904) alt. Orlando Gibbons (1583-1625)

2. We are of thee, the children of thy love,
by virtue of thy well-belovèd Son;
descend, O Holy Spirit, like a dove,
into our hearts, that we may be as one:
as one with thee, to whom we ever tend;
as one with him, our Brother and our Friend.

3. We would be one in hatred of all wrong,
one in our love of all things sweet and fair,
one with the joy that breaketh into song,
one with the grief that trembles into prayer,
one in the pow'r that makes thy children free
to follow truth, and thus to follow thee.

4. O clothe us with thy heav'nly armour, Lord,
thy trusty shield, thy sword of love divine;
our inspiration be thy constant word;
we ask no victories that are not thine:
give or withhold, let pain or pleasure be;
enough to know that we are serving thee.

155 Fair waved the golden corn

John Hampden Gurney (1802-1862) — James Watson (1816-1880)

HOLYROOD SM

2. To God so good and great
their cheerful thanks they pour;
then carry to his temple-gate
the choicest of their store.

3. Like Israel, Lord, we give
our earliest fruits to thee,
and pray that, long as we shall live,
we may thy children be.

4. Thine is our youthful prime,
and life and all its pow'rs;
be with us in our morning time,
and bless our evening hours.

5. In wisdom let us grow,
as years and strength are giv'n,
that we may serve thy Church below,
and join thy saints in heav'n.

156 Faithful Shepherd, feed me

Thomas Benson Pollock (1836-1896) — Friedrich Silcher (1789-1860)

PASTOR PASTORUM 65 65

2. Hold me fast, and guide me
in the narrow way;
so, with thee beside me,
I shall never stray.

3. Daily bring me nearer
to the heav'nly shore;
may my faith grow clearer,
may I love thee more.

4. Hallow ev'ry pleasure,
ev'ry gift and pain;
be thyself my treasure,
though none else I gain.

5. Day by day prepare me
as thou seest best,
then let angels bear me
to thy promised rest.

157 Faithful vigil ended

Timothy Dudley-Smith (b.1926)
based on Luke 2:29-32

Friedrich Silcher (1789-1860)

PASTOR PASTORUM 65 65

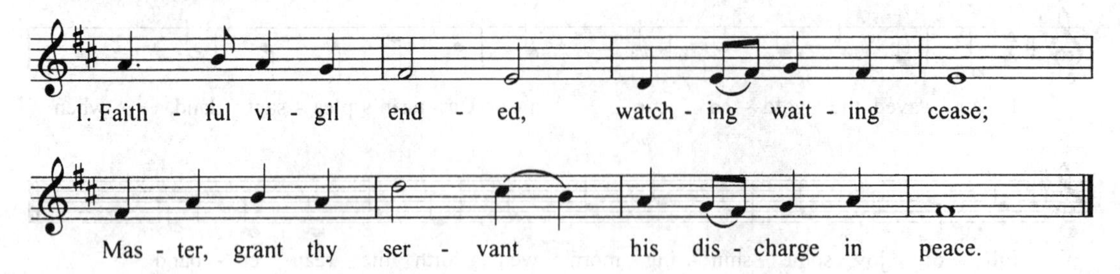

2. All the Spirit promised,
all the Father willed,
now these eyes behold it
perfectly fulfilled.

3. This thy great deliv'rance
sets thy people free;
Christ, their light, uplifted
all the nations see.

4. Christ, thy people's glory!
watching, doubting, cease;
grant to us thy servants
our discharge in peace.

Text © Copyright Timothy Dudley-Smith, 9 Ashlands, Ford, Salisbury, Wiltshire SP4 6DY.
Used by permission.

158 Father God, gentle Father God

Words and music: Gerard Markland (b.1953)
based on Psalm 139

© Copyright 1998 Kevin Mayhew Ltd.

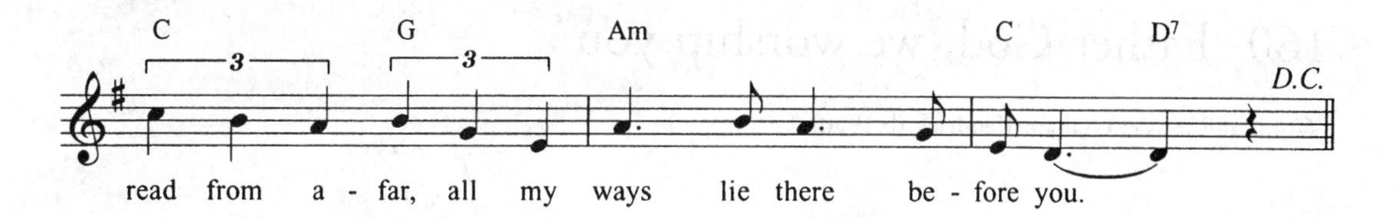

2. My heart, my innermost being
was made by you.
My body, secretly formed in the womb,
was always with you.

3. What place, what heavens could
hide me away from you.
Were I to fly to the ends of the sea,
your hand would guide me.

4. Your works, your knowledge, your love
are beyond my mind.
My Lord, I thank you for these
and the wonder of my being.

5. O Lord, come search me, come find
what is in my heart,
that I may never stray far
from your path of life eternal.

159 Father God, I wonder *I will sing your praises*

Words and music: Ian Smale

© Copyright 1984 Kingsway's Thankyou Music, P.O. Box 75, Eastbourne,
East Sussex BN23 6NW, UK. (tym@kingsway.co.uk). Used by permission.

160 Father God, we worship you

Words and music: Graham Kendrick (b.1950)

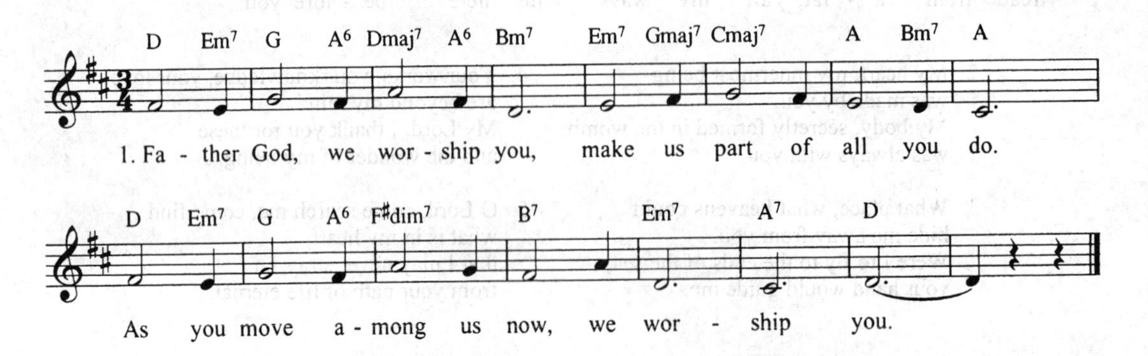

2. Jesus King, we worship you,
help us listen now to you.
As you move among us now,
we worship you.

3. Spirit pure, we worship you,
with your fire our zeal renew.
As you move among us now,
we worship you.

© Copyright 1981 Kingsway's Thankyou Music, P.O. Box 75, Eastbourne, East Sussex BN23 6NW, UK. (tym@kingsway.co.uk). Used by permission.

161 Father, hear the prayer we offer

Maria Willis (1824-1908)

Traditional English melody adapted by Ralph Vaughan Williams (1872-1958)

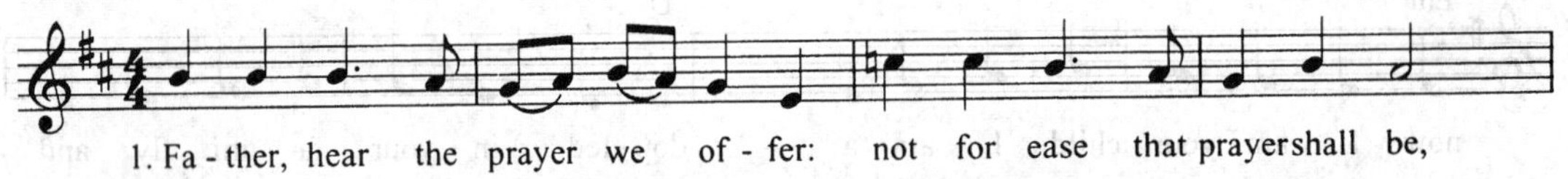

2. Not for ever in green pastures
do we ask our way to be;
but the steep and rugged pathway
may we tread rejoicingly.

3. Not for ever by still waters
would we idly rest and stay;
but would smite the living fountains
from the rocks along our way.

4. Be our strength in hours of weakness,
in our wand'rings be our guide;
through endeavour, failure, danger,
Father, be thou at our side.

Tune 1 © Copyright Oxford University Press, Great Clarendon Street, Oxford, OX2 6DP. Used by permission.
Tune 2 © Copyright Martin Shaw. Exclusively licensed to and reproduced by permission of J. Curwen & Sons Ltd., 8/9 Frith Street, London W1D 3JB. All rights reserved. International copyright secured. Used by permission.

Maria Willis (1824-1908) Martin Shaw (1875-1958)

TUNE 2: MARCHING 87 87

162 Father, I place into your hands

Words and music: Jenny Hewer (b.1945)

2. Father, I place into your hands
my friends and family.
Father, I place into your hands
the things that trouble me.
Father I place into your hands
the person I would be,
for I know I always can trust you.

3. Father, we love to see your face,
we love to hear your voice,
Father, we love to sing your praise
and in your name rejoice.
Father, we love to walk with you
and in your presence rest,
for we know we always can trust you.

4. Father, I want to be with you
and do the things you do.
Father, I want to speak the words
that you are speaking too.
Father, I want to love the ones
that you will draw to you,
for I know that I am one with you.

© Copyright 1975 Kingsway's Thankyou Music, P.O. Box 75, Eastbourne, East Sussex BN23 6NW, UK. (tym@kingsway.co.uk). Used by permission.

163 Father, Lord of all creation

Stewart Cross (1928-1989) — Cyril Vincent Taylor (1907-1991)

2. Jesus Christ, the Man for Others,
we, your people, make our prayer:
help us love – as sisters, brothers –
all whose burdens we can share.
Where your name binds us together
you, Lord Christ, will surely be;
where no selfishness can sever
there your love the world may see.

3. Holy Spirit, rushing, burning
wind and flame of Pentecost,
fire our hearts afresh with yearning
to regain what we have lost.
May your love unite our action,
nevermore to speak alone:
God, in us abolish faction,
God, through us your love make known.

Text © Copyright Mrs M. Cross. Used by kind permission.
Music © Copyright Oxford University Press, Great Clarendon Street, Oxford OX2 6DP.
Reproduced by permission from *The BBC Hymn Book.*

164 Father most holy, merciful and loving

Latin (c.10th century)
trans. Alfred E. Alston (1862-1927)

Melody from *Chartres Antiphoner* (1784)

CHARTRES (ANGERS) 11 11 11 5

2. Three in a wondrous Unity unbroken,
One perfect Godhead, love that never faileth,
light of the angels, succour of the needy,
hope of all living.

3. All thy creation serveth its Creator,
thee ev'ry creature praiseth without ceasing;
we too would sing thee psalms of true devotion:
hear, we beseech thee.

4. Lord God Almighty, unto thee be glory,
One in Three Persons, over all exalted.
Thine, as is meet, be honour, praise and blessing
now and for ever.

165 Father of heaven, whose love profound

Edward Cooper (1770-1833)

John Bacchus Dykes (1823-1876)

RIEVAULX LM

2. Almighty Son, incarnate Word,
our Prophet, Priest, Redeemer, Lord,
before thy throne we sinners bend,
to us thy saving grace extend.

3. Eternal Spirit, by whose breath
the soul is raised from sin and death,
before thy throne we sinners bend,
to us thy quick'ning pow'r extend.

4. Thrice Holy! Father, Spirit, Son;
mysterious Godhead, Three in One,
before thy throne we sinners bend,
grace, pardon, life, to us extend.

166 Father, we adore you

Words and music: Terrye Coelho (b.1952)

This may be sung as a round, with entries at A, B *and* C

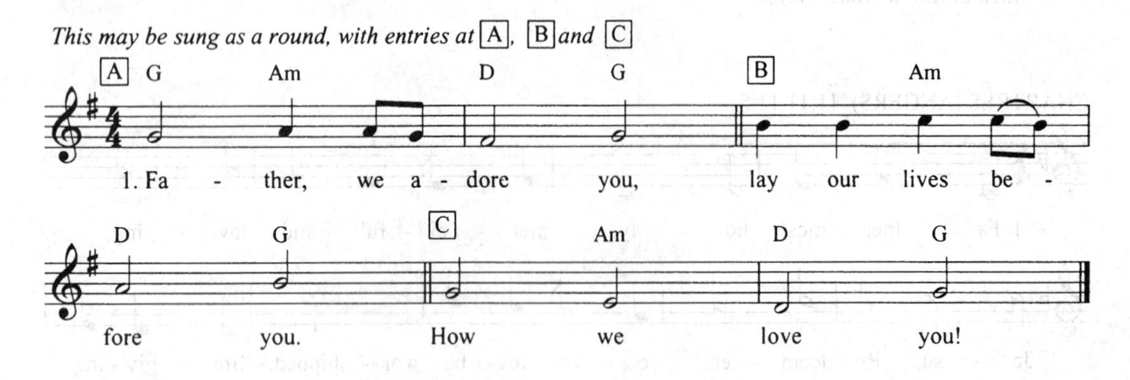

2. Jesus, we adore you,
lay our lives before you.
How we love you!

3. Spirit, we adore you,
lay our lives before you.
How we love you!

© Copyright 1972 Maranatha! Music. Administered by CopyCare, P.O. Box 77, Hailsham, East Sussex BN27 3EF, UK. (music@copycare.com). Used by permission.

167 Father, we love you *Glorify your name*

Words and music: Donna Adkins (b.1940)

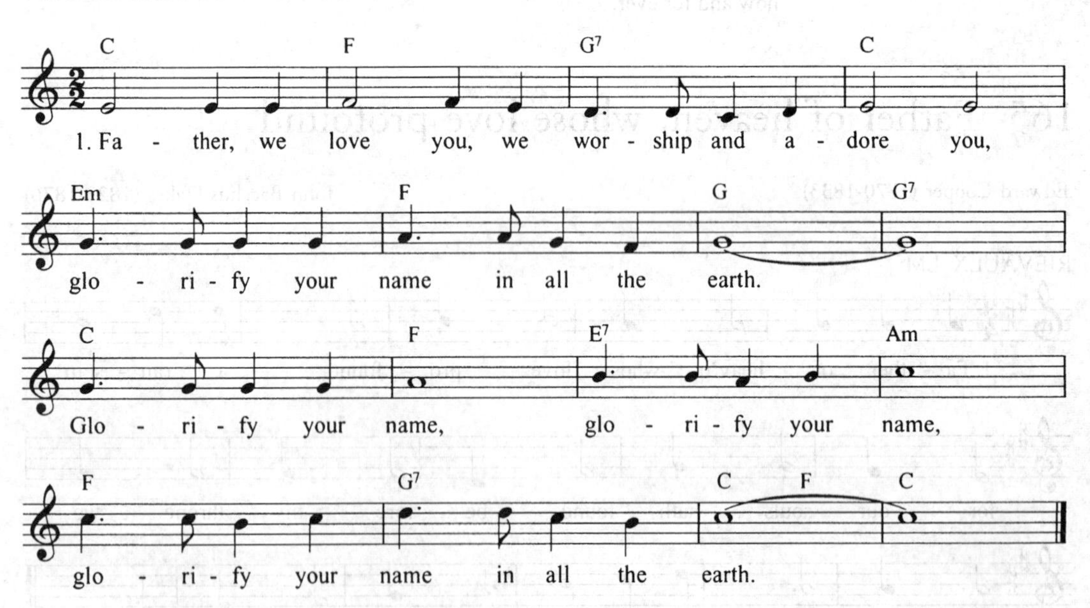

2. Jesus, we love you,
we worship and adore you,
glorify your name in all the earth.
Glorify your name, glorify your name,
glorify your name in all the earth.

3. Spirit, we love you,
we worship and adore you,
glorify your name in all the earth.
Glorify your name, glorify your name,
glorify your name in all the earth.

© Copyright 1976 Maranatha! Music. Administered by CopyCare, P.O. Box 77, Hailsham, East Sussex BN27 3EF, UK. (music@copycare.com). Used by permission.

168 Father, who in Jesus found us

Fred Kaan (b.1929)

German carol melody (14th century)

QUEM PASTORES 88 87

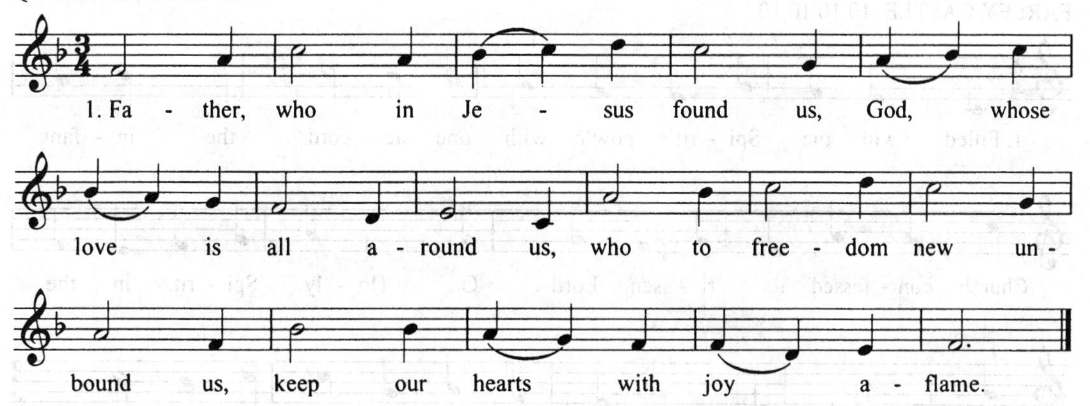

2. For the sacramental breaking,
for the honour of partaking,
for your life our lives remaking,
young and old, we praise your name.

3. From the service of this table
lead us to a life more stable,
for our witness make us able;
blessings on our work we claim.

4. Through our calling closely knitted,
daily to your praise committed,
for a life of service fitted,
let us now your love proclaim.

Text © Copyright 1968 Stainer & Bell Ltd., P.O. Box 110, Victoria House,
23 Gruneison Road, Finchley, London N3 1DZ. Used by permission.

169 Fight the good fight

John Samuel Bewley Monsell (1811-1875) alt.

Attributed to John Hatton (d.1793)

DUKE STREET LM

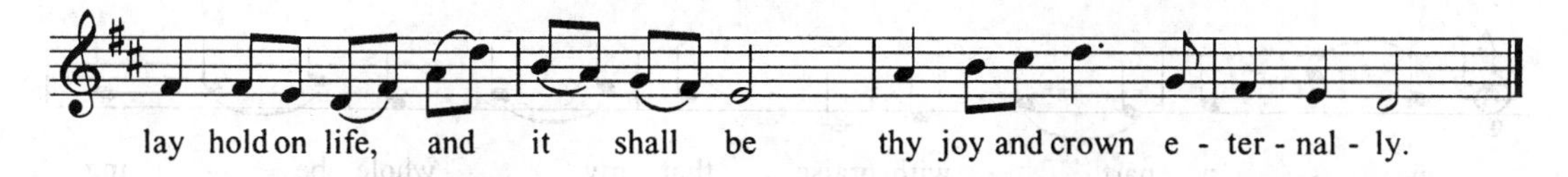

2. Run the straight race through God's good grace,
lift up thine eyes and seek his face;
life with its way before us lies;
Christ is the path, and Christ the prize.

3. Cast care aside, lean on thy guide;
his boundless mercy will provide;
trust, and thy trusting soul shall prove
Christ is its life, and Christ its love.

4. Faint not nor fear, his arms are near;
he changeth not, and thou art dear;
only believe, and thou shalt see
that Christ is all in all to thee.

170 Filled with the Spirit's power

John Raphael Peacey (1896-1971)

Henry Lawes (1596-1662)

FARLEY CASTLE 10 10 10 10

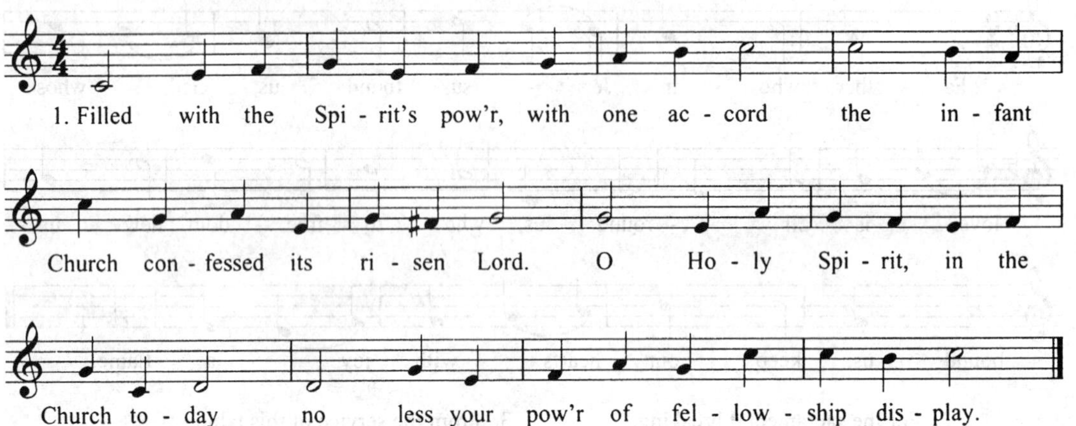

2. Now with the mind of Christ set us on fire,
that unity may be our great desire.
Give joy and peace; give faith to hear your call,
and readiness in each to work for all.

3. Widen our love, good Spirit, to embrace
in your strong care the people of each race.
Like wind and fire with life among us move,
till we are known as Christ's, and Christians prove.

171 Fill thou my life, O Lord my God

Horatius Bonar (1808-1889) alt.

Adapted from
Thomas Haweis (1734-1820)

RICHMOND CM

Text © Copyright the Revd. Mary Hancock.
Used by kind permission.

2. Not for the lip of praise alone,
nor e'en the praising heart,
I ask, but for a life made up
of praise in ev'ry part.

3. Praise in the common things of life,
its goings out and in;
praise in each duty and each deed,
however small and mean.

4. Fill ev'ry part of me with praise:
let all my being speak
of thee and of thy love, O Lord,
poor though I be and weak.

5. So shalt thou, Lord, receive from me
the praise and glory due;
and so shall I begin on earth
the song for ever new.

6. So shall each fear, each fret, each care,
be turnèd into song;
and ev'ry winding of the way
the echo shall prolong.

7. So shall no part of day or night
unblest or common be;
but all my life, in ev'ry step,
be fellowship with thee.

172 Fill your hearts with joy and gladness

Timothy Dudley-Smith (b.1926)

Ludwig van Beethoven (1770-1827)

Great the Lord in love and wis - dom, might and ma - jes - ty di-vine!

He who framed the star - ry hea - vens knows and names them as they shine.

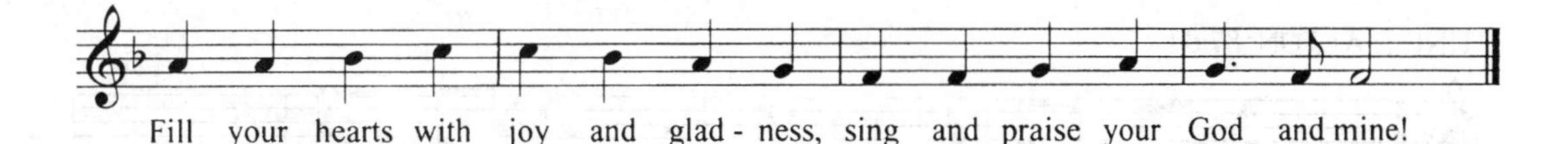

2. Praise the Lord, his people, praise him!
Wounded souls his comfort know.
Those who fear him find his mercies,
peace for pain and joy for woe;
humble hearts are high exalted,
human pride and pow'r laid low.
Praise the Lord, his people, praise him!
Wounded souls his comfort know.

3. Praise the Lord for times and seasons,
cloud and sunshine, wind and rain;
spring to melt the snows of winter
till the waters flow again;
grass upon the mountain pastures,
golden valleys thick with grain.
Praise the Lord for times and seasons,
cloud and sunshine, wind and rain.

4. Fill your hearts with joy and gladness,
peace and plenty crown your days!
Love his laws, declare his judgements,
walk in all his words and ways;
he the Lord and we his children,
praise the Lord, all people, praise!
Fill your hearts with joy and gladness,
peace and plenty crown your days!

Text © Copyright Timothy Dudley-Smith, 9 Ashlands, Ford, Salisbury, Wiltshire SP4 6DY.
Used by permission.

173 Finished the strife

Unknown
trans. John Mason Neale (1818-1866) alt.

Gregory Murray (1905-1992)

SURREXIT 8 8 8 and Alleluias

2. After the death that him befell,
Jesus Christ has harrowed hell;
songs of praising we are raising:
Alleluia, alleluia!

3. On the third morning he arose,
shining with vict'ry o'er his foes;
earth is singing, heav'n is ringing:
Alleluia, alleluia!

4. Lord, by your wounds on you we call,
you, by your death, have freed us all;
may our living be thanksgiving:
Alleluia, alleluia!

Music © Copyright the Estate of Gregory Murray.
Reproduced by permission of the Trustees, Downside Abbey, Stratton-on-the-Fosse, Bath BA3 4RH.

174 Firmly I believe and truly

John Henry Newman (1801-1890) alt.

Patrick Appleford (b.1925)

TUNE 1: ALTON 87 87

Tune 1 © Copyright 1960 Josef Weinberger Ltd., 12-14 Mortimer Street, London W1N 7RD.
Used by permission.

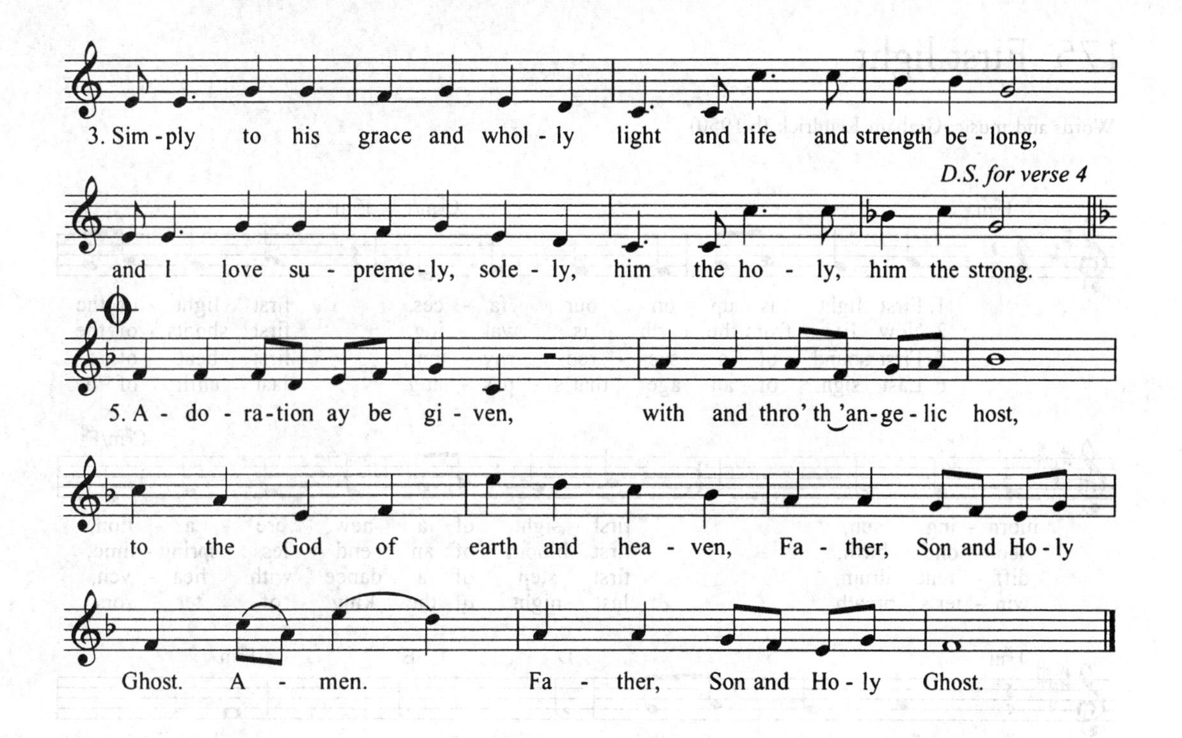

John Henry Newman (1801-1890) alt. | Warwickshire ballad

TUNE 2: SHIPSTON 87 87

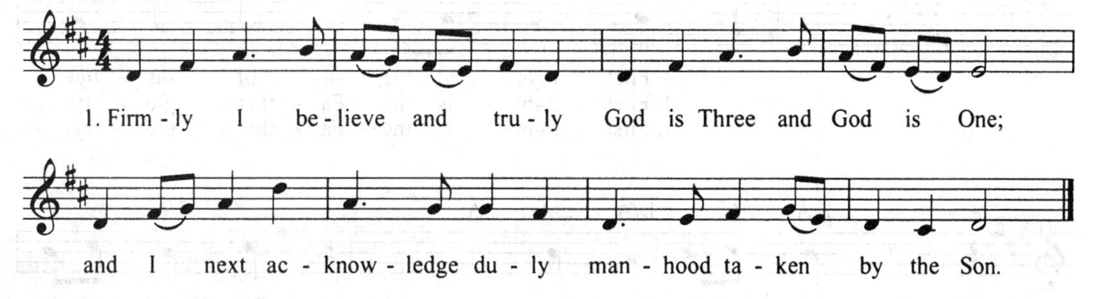

John Henry Newman (1801-1890) alt. | Version of a melody by William Boyce (1711-1779) in S.S. Wesley's *European Psalmist* (1872)

TUNE 3: HALTON HOLGATE 87 87

175 First light

Words and music: Graham Kendrick (b.1950)

© Copyright 1998 Ascent Music, P.O. Box 263, Croydon, Surrey CR9 5AP, UK. International copyright secured. All rights reserved. Used by permission. Taken from *The Millennium Chorus*.

176 Follow me

Michael Cockett (b.1938) Madeleine Cuddy

2. If you would follow me,
you must leave old ways behind.
You must take my cross and
follow on my path.
You may be far from loved ones,
you may be far from home,
but my Father will welcome you at last.

3. Although I go away
you will never be alone,
for the Spirit will be
there to comfort you.
Though all of you may scatter,
each follow his own path,
still the Spirit of love will lead you home.

© Copyright 1978 Kevin Mayhew Ltd.

177 For all the saints

William Walsham How (1823-1897) Ralph Vaughan Williams (1872-1958)

SINE NOMINE 10 10 10 4

2. Thou wast their rock, their fortress and their might;
thou, Lord, their captain in the well-fought fight;
thou in the darkness drear their one true light.
Alleluia, alleluia!

3. O may thy soldiers, faithful, true and bold,
fight as the saints who nobly fought of old,
and win, with them, the victor's crown of gold.
Alleluia, alleluia!

4. O blest communion! fellowship divine!
we feebly struggle, they in glory shine;
yet all are one in thee, for all are thine.
Alleluia, alleluia!

5. And when the strife is fierce, the warfare long,
steals on the ear the distant triumph song,
and hearts are brave again, and arms are strong.
Alleluia, alleluia!

6. The golden evening brightens in the west;
soon, soon to faithful warriors cometh rest;
sweet is the calm of paradise the blest.
Alleluia, alleluia!

7. But lo! There breaks a yet more glorious day;
the saints triumphant rise in bright array:
the King of glory passes on his way.
Alleluia, alleluia!

8. From earth's wide bounds, from ocean's farthest coast,
through gates of pearl streams in the countless host,
singing to Father, Son and Holy Ghost.
Alleluia, alleluia!

For alternative text see No. 178

Music © Copyright Oxford University Press, Great Clarendon Street, Oxford OX2 6DP.
Reproduced by permission from *The English Hymnal*.

178 For all the saints

William Walsham How (1823-1897)
adapted by Michael Forster (b.1946)

Ralph Vaughan Williams (1872-1958)

SINE NOMINE 10 10 10 4

2. Thou wast their rock, their refuge and their might,
thou, Lord, the vision ever in their sight;
thou in the darkness drear their one true light.
Alleluia, alleluia!

3. O may thy servants, faithful, true and bold,
strive for thy kingdom as the saints of old,
and win with them the glorious crown of gold:
Alleluia, alleluia!

4. O blest communion, fellowship divine!
We feebly struggle, they in glory shine,
yet all are one in thee, for all are thine:
Alleluia, alleluia!

5. And when the road is steep, the journey long,
steals on the ear the distant welcome song,
and hope is bright again, and faith is strong:
Alleluia, alleluia!

6. The golden evening brightens in the west,
soon, soon to faithful pilgrims cometh rest:
sweet is the calm of Paradise the blest:
Alleluia, alleluia!

7. But lo! There breaks a yet more glorious day,
the saints triumphant rise in bright array:
the King of glory passes on his way:
Alleluia, alleluia!

8. From earth's wide bounds, from ocean's farthest coast,
through gates of pearl streams in the countless host,
singing to Father, Son and Holy Ghost.
Alleluia, alleluia!

For alternative text see No. 177

Music © Copyright Oxford University Press, Great Clarendon Street, Oxford OX2 6DP.
Reproduced by permission from the *English Hymnal*.

179 For all thy saints

Richard Mant (1776-1848)　　Benjamin Milgrove (1731-1810)

MOUNT EPHRAIM SM

2. For all thy saints, O Lord,
who strove in thee to die,
and found in thee a full reward,
accept our thankful cry.

3. Thine earthly members fit
to join thy saints above,
in one communion ever knit,
one fellowship of love.

4. Jesu, thy name we bless,
and humbly pray that we
may follow them in holiness,
who lived and died for thee.

5. All might, all praise, be thine,
Father, co-equal Son,
and Spirit, bond of love divine,
while endless ages run.

180 Forgive our sins as we forgive

Rosamond E. Herklots (1905-1987) alt.　　Charles Wesley (1757-1834)

EPWORTH CM

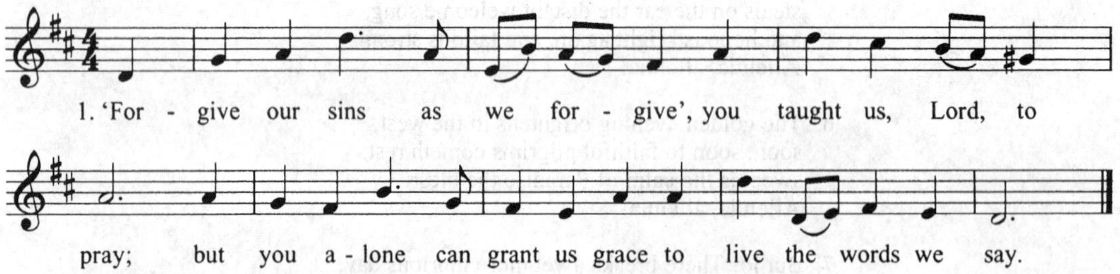

2. How can your pardon reach and bless
the unforgiving heart
that broods on wrongs, and will not let
old bitterness depart?

3. In blazing light your Cross reveals
the truth we dimly knew:
what trivial debts are owed to us,
how great our debt to you!

4. Lord, cleanse the depths within our souls,
and bid resentment cease.
Then, bound to all in bonds of love,
our lives will spread your peace.

Text: © Copyright Oxford University Press, Great Clarendon Street, Oxford OX2 6DP.
Reproduced by permission from *Enlarged Songs of Praise.*

181 For I'm building a people of power

Words and music: Dave Richards

© Copyright 1977 Kingsway's Thankyou Music, P.O. Box 75, Eastbourne, East Sussex BN23 6NW, UK. (tym@kingsway.co.uk). Used by permission.

182 For Mary, mother of our Lord

John Raphael Peacey (1896-1971)

Gordon Slater (1896-1979)

TUNE 1: ST BOTOLPH CM

first the Son of God a - dored, as on her child she gazed.

2. The angel Gabriel brought the word
she should Christ's mother be;
Our Lady, handmaid of the Lord,
made answer willingly.

3. The heav'nly call she thus obeyed,
and so God's will was done;
the second Eve love's answer made
which our redemption won.

4. She gave her body for God's shrine,
her heart to piercing pain,
and knew the cost of love divine
when Jesus Christ was slain.

5. Dear Mary, from your lowliness
and home in Galilee,
there comes a joy and holiness
to ev'ry family.

6. Hail, Mary, you are full of grace,
above all women blest;
and blest your Son, whom your embrace
in birth and death confessed.

John Raphael Peacey (1896-1971)

Neil Dougall (1776-1862)

TUNE 2: KILMARNOCK CM

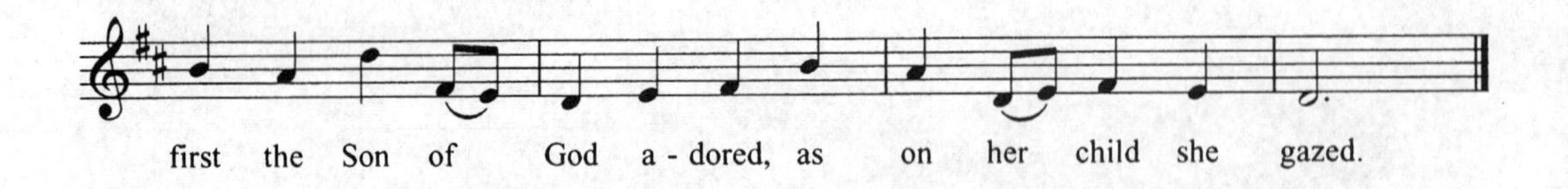

Text © Copyright the Revd. Mary J. Hancock. Reproduced by kind permission.
Tune 1 © Copyright Oxford University Press, Great Clarendon Street, Oxford OX2 6DP.
Reproduced by permission.

183 For ourselves no longer living

Fred Kaan (b.1929)

Geistreiches Gesangbuch, Darmstadt (1698)
adapted by William Henry Monk (1823-1889)

ALL SAINTS 87 87 77

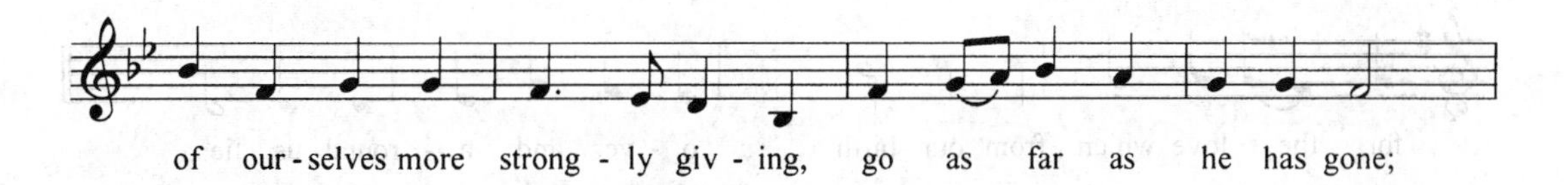

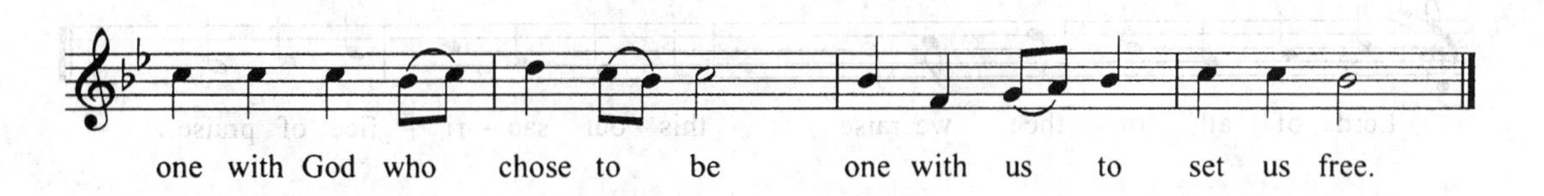

2. If we are to live for others,
share as equals human worth,
join the round of sisters, brothers,
that encircles all the earth:
all the fullness earth affords,
is the people's, is the Lord's.

3. Fighting fear and exploitation
is our daily common call;
finding selfhood, building nations,
sharing what we have with all.
As the birds that soar in flight,
let us rise towards the light.

4. Let us rise and join the forces
that combine to do God's will,
wisely using earth's resources,
human energy and skill.
Let us now, by love released,
celebrate the future's feast!

Text © Copyright 1975, 1988 Stainer & Bell Ltd., P.O. Box 110, Victoria House,
23 Gruneison Road, Finchley, London N3 1DZ. Used by permission.

184 For the beauty of the earth

Folliot Sandford Pierpoint (1835-1917)

Adapted from Conrad Kocher (1786-1872)
by William Henry Monk (1823-1889)

2. For the beauty of each hour
of the day and of the night,
hill and vale and tree and flow'r,
sun and moon and stars of light:

3. For the joy of human love,
brother, sister, parent, child,
friends on earth, and friends above,
pleasures pure and undefiled:

4. For each perfect gift of thine,
to our race so freely giv'n,
graces human and divine,
flow'rs of earth and buds of heav'n:

5. For thy Church which evermore
lifteth holy hands above,
off'ring up on ev'ry shore
her pure sacrifice of love:

Folliot Sandford Pierpoint (1835-1917)

Geoffrey Shaw (1879-1943)
adapted from a folk song

Tune 2 © Copyright Oxford University Press, Great Clarendon Street, Oxford OX2 6DP.
Used by permission.

185 For the fruits of his creation

Fred Pratt Green (1903-2000) Francis Jackson (b.1917)

EAST ACKLAM 84 84 888 4

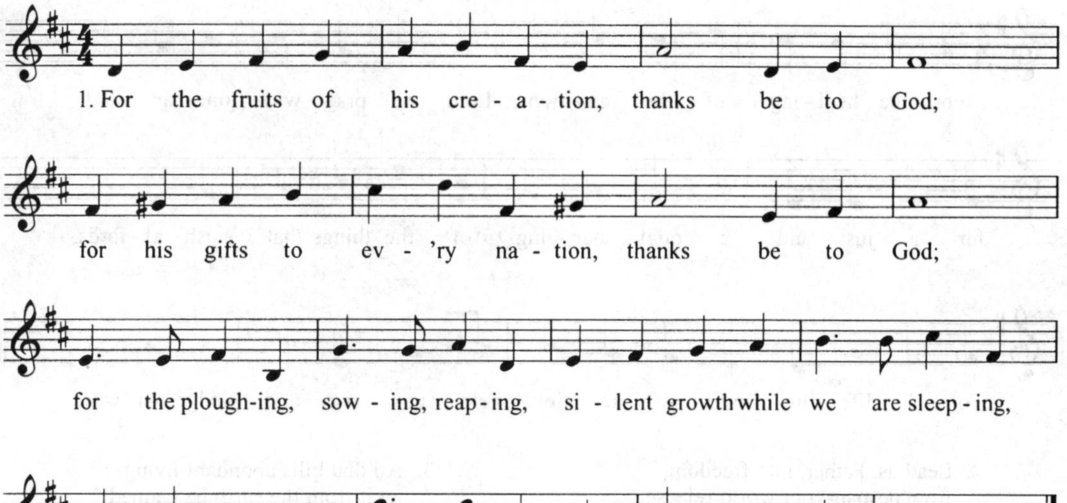

2. In the just reward of labour,
God's will is done;
in the help we give our neighbour,
God's will is done;
in our world-wide task of caring
for the hungry and despairing,
in the harvests we are sharing,
God's will is done.

3. For the harvests of his Spirit,
thanks be to God;
for the good we all inherit,
thanks be to God;
for the wonders that astound us,
for the truths that still confound us,
most of all, that love has found us,
thanks be to God.

Text © Copyright 1970 Stainer & Bell Ltd., P.O. Box 110, Victoria House, 23 Gruneison Road, Finchley, London N3 1DZ. Used by permission.
Music © Copyright Dr. Francis Jackson. Used by permission of the composer.

186 For the healing of the nations

Fred Kaan (b.1929) *Essay on the Church Plain Chant* (1782)

2. Lead us, Father, into freedom,
from despair your world release;
that, redeemed from war and hatred,
all may come and go in peace.
Show us how through care and goodness
fear will die and hope increase.

3. All that kills abundant living,
let it from the earth be banned;
pride of status, race or schooling
dogmas that obscure your plan.
In our common quest for justice
may we hallow life's brief span.

4. You, creator-God, have written
your great name on humankind;
for our growing in your likeness
bring the life of Christ to mind;
that by our response and service
earth its destiny may find.

Fred Kaan (b.1929) Traditional French melody

TUNE 2: PICARDY 87 87 87

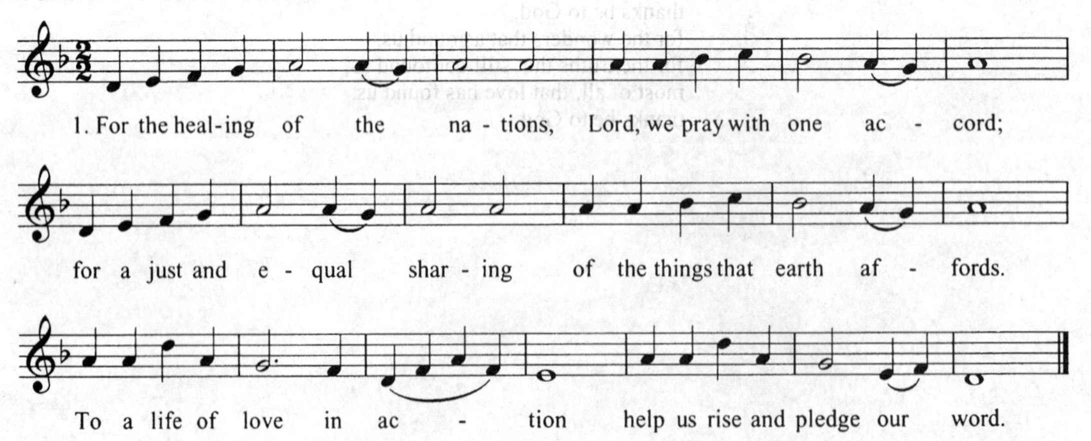

Text © Copyright 1968 Stainer & Bell Ltd., P.O. Box 110, Victoria House,
23 Gruneison Road, Finchley, London N3 1DZ. Used by permission.

187 Forth in the peace of Christ we go

James Quinn (b.1919) 15th century English melody

2. King of our hearts, Christ makes us kings;
kingship with him his servants gain;
with Christ, the Servant-Lord of all,
Christ's world we serve to share Christ's reign.

3. Priests of the world, Christ sends us forth
this world of time to consecrate,
our world of sin by grace to heal,
Christ's world in Christ to re-create.

4. Prophets of Christ, we hear his Word:
he claims our minds to search his ways;
he claims our lips to speak his truth;
he claims our hearts to sing his praise.

5. We are his Church, he makes us one:
here is one hearth for all to find;
here is one flock, one Shepherd-King;
here is one faith, one heart, one mind.

Text © Copyright 1969 Geoffrey Chapman/Continuum Publishers, The Tower Building,
11 York Road, London SE1 7NX.

188 Forth in thy name, O Lord, I go

Charles Wesley (1707-1788) alt.

Orlando Gibbons (1583-1625)

SONG 34 (ANGELS' SONG) LM

2. The task thy wisdom hath assigned
O let me cheerfully fulfil;
in all my works thy presence find,
and prove thy good and perfect will.

3. Thee may I set at my right hand,
whose eyes my inmost substance see,
and labour on at thy command,
and offer all my works to thee.

4. Give me to bear thy easy yoke,
and ev'ry moment watch and pray,
and still to things eternal look,
and hasten to thy glorious day.

5. For thee delightfully employ
whate'er thy bounteous grace hath giv'n,
and run my course with even joy,
and closely walk with thee to heav'n.

189 For thy mercy and thy grace

Henry Downton (1818-1885)

Johann Scheffler
Heilige Seelenlust (1657)

CULBACH 67 67

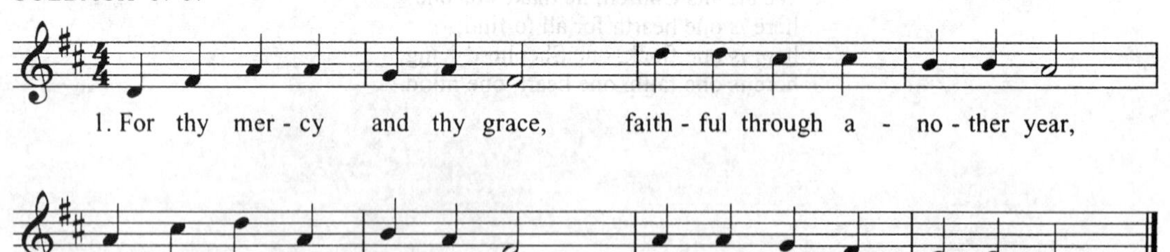

2. In our weakness and distress,
Rock of Strength, be thou our stay;
in the pathless wilderness
be our true and living Way.

3. Keep us faithful, keep us pure,
keep us evermore thine own.
Help, O help us to endure,
fit us for thy promised crown.

4. So within thy palace gate
we shall praise on golden strings
thee, the only potentate,
Lord of lords and King of kings.

190 Forty days and forty nights

George Hunt Smyttan (1822-1870)
adapted by Michael Forster (b.1946)

Nürnbergisches Gesangbuch (1676)

AUS DER TIEFE (HEINLEIN) 77 77

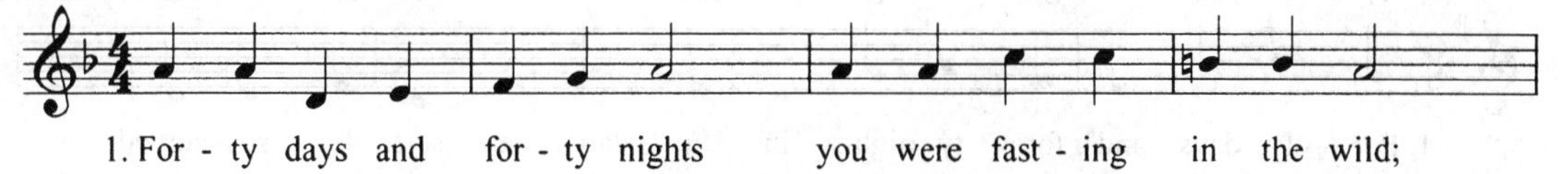

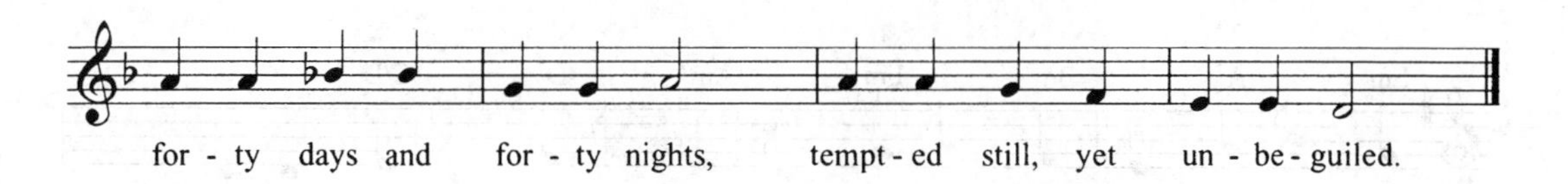

2. Sunbeams scorching all the day,
chilly dew-drops nightly shed,
prowling beasts about your way,
stones your pillow, earth your bed.

3. Let us your endurance share,
and from earthly greed abstain,
with you vigilant in prayer,
with you strong to suffer pain.

4. Then if evil on us press,
flesh or spirit to assail,
Victor in the wilderness,
help us not to swerve or fail.

5. So shall peace divine be ours;
holy gladness, pure and true:
come to us, angelic powers,
such as ministered to you.

6. Keep, O keep us, Saviour dear,
ever constant by your side,
that with you we may appear
at th'eternal Eastertide.

Another version

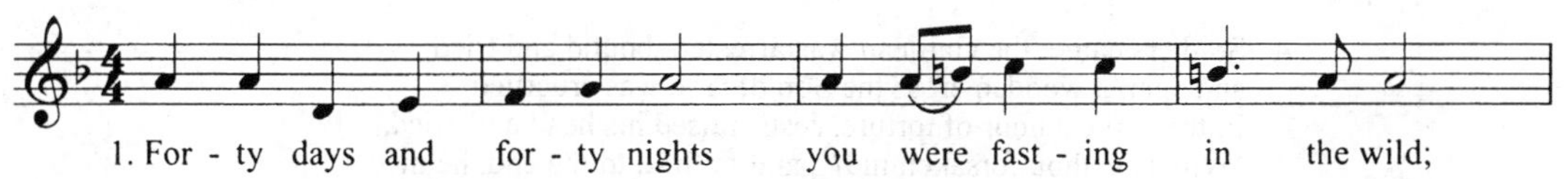

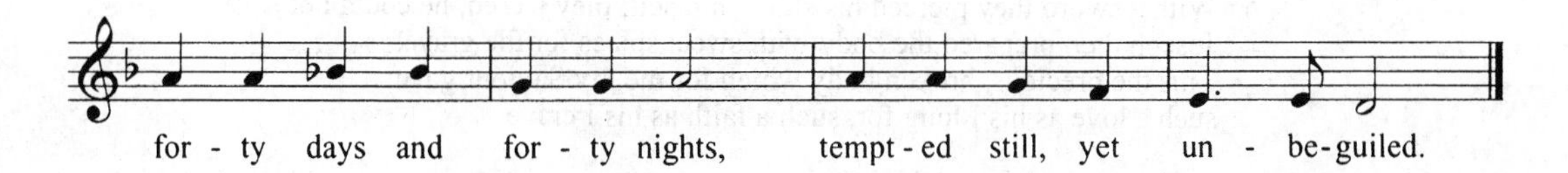

This version of text © Copyright 1999 Kevin Mayhew Ltd.

191 Forty days and forty nights in Judah's desert

Jean Holloway (b.1939) Evelyn Danzig (1901-1996)

SCARLET RIBBONS 15 15 15 15

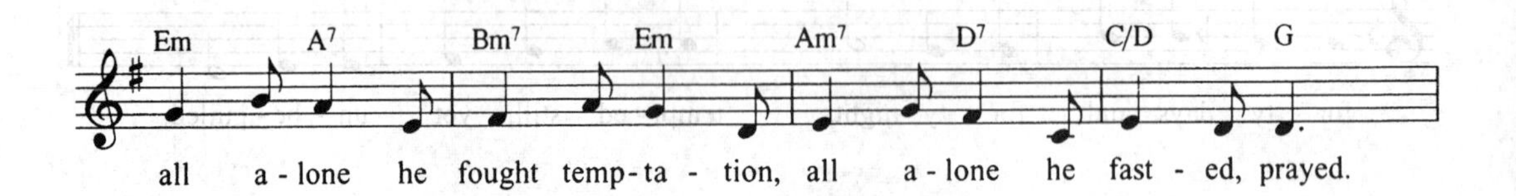

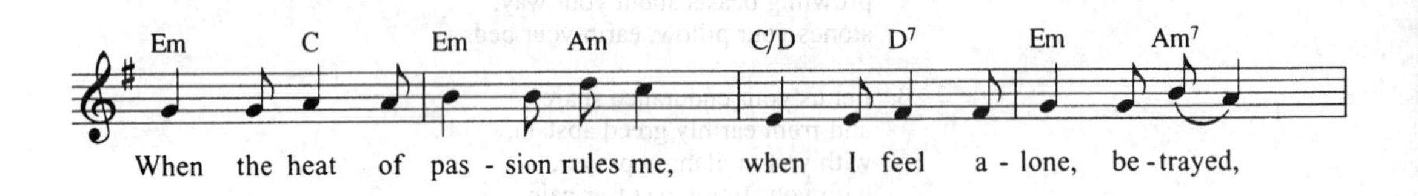

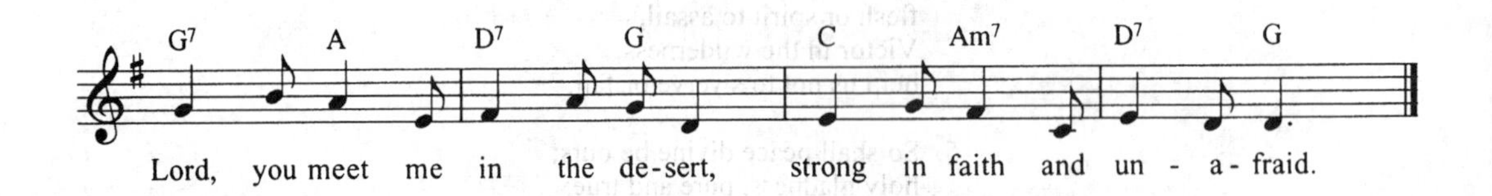

2. In the garden, his disciples slept the darkest hours away,
but our Lord did not condemn them when they would not watch or pray.
Make me constant in your service, keeping watch both night and day.
Give me grace that I may never such a love as yours betray.

3. When the rooster crowed at daybreak, Peter's fear and panic grew.
He denied three times the charge that Jesus was a man he knew.
When my love for you is challenged, when the faithful ones are few,
give me courage and conviction to proclaim my Lord anew.

4. Soldiers came, the Galilean was arrested, bound and tried,
and upon a wooden cross the Son of God was crucified.
In the darkest hour of torture, Jesus raised his head and cried,
'Why hast thou forsaken me?', and faithful to the end, he died.

5. With a sword they pierced his side – himself, they jeered, he could not save;
Joseph then prepared the body with sweet spices for the grave.
This the precious, broken body which for me my Saviour gave;
such a love as his I long for, such a faith as his I crave.

Text © Copyright 1995 Kevin Mayhew Ltd.
Music © Copyright 1949 EMI Mills Music Inc, USA.
Worldwide print rights controlled by Warner Bros. Publications Inc./IMP Ltd.
Used by permission of IMP Ltd., Griffin House, 161 Hammersmith Road, London W6 8BS.

192 From all that dwell below the skies

Isaac Watts (1674-1748)
based on Psalm 117

John Bishop (1665-1737)

ILLSLEY (BISHOP) LM

2. Eternal are thy mercies, Lord;
eternal truth attends thy word:
thy praise shall sound from shore to shore,
till suns shall rise and set no more.

193 From east to west

Translated from the Latin of
Caelius Sedulius (c.450)
by John Ellerton (1826-1893)

From Schumann's
Geistliche Lieder (1539)

VOM HIMMEL HOCH LM

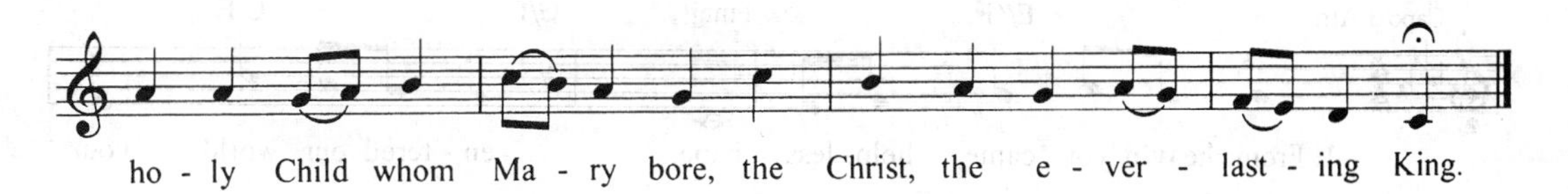

2. Behold, the world's creator wears
the form and fashion of a slave,
our very flesh our Maker shares,
his fallen creature, man, to save.

3. For this how wondrously he wrought!
A maiden, in her lowly place,
became, in ways beyond all thought,
the chosen vessel of his grace.

4. She bowed her to the angel's word
declaring what the Father willed,
and suddenly the promised Lord
that pure and hallowed temple filled.

5. He shrank not from the oxen's stall,
he lay within the manger-bed,
and he whose bounty feedeth all,
at Mary's breast himself was fed.

6. And while the angels in the sky
sang praise above the silent field,
to shepherds poor, the Lord most high,
the one great Shepherd was revealed.

7. All glory for that blessèd morn
to God the Father ever be,
all praise to thee, O virgin-born,
and praise, blest Spirit, unto thee.

194 From glory to glory advancing

Liturgy of St James
trans. Charles William Humphreys (1840-1921)

Gustav Holst (1874-1934)

SHEEN 14 14 14 15

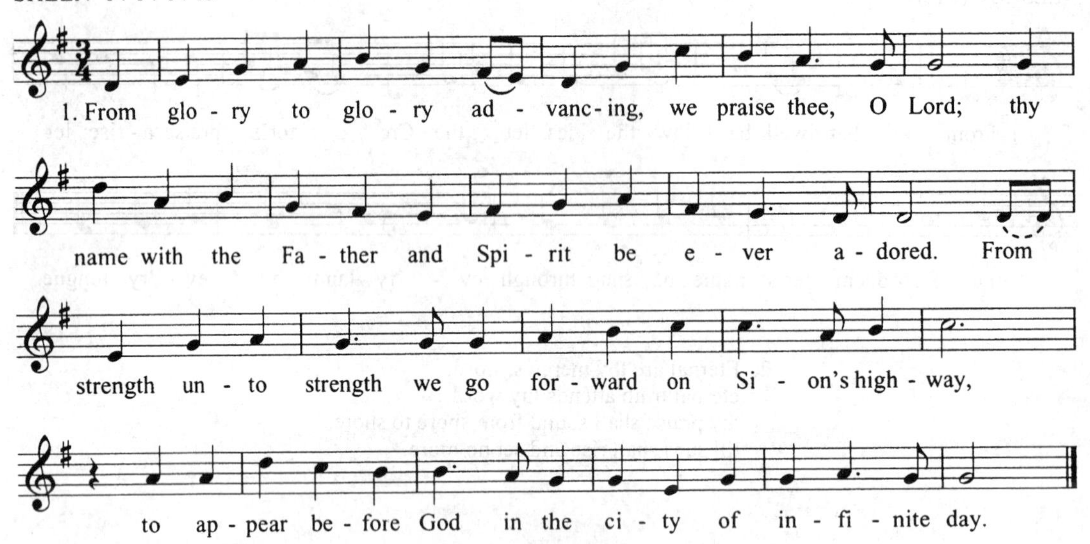

2. Thanksgiving and glory and worship and blessing and love,
one heart and one song have the saints upon earth and above.
Evermore, O Lord, to thy servants thy presence be nigh;
ever fit us by service on earth for thy service on high.

Music © Copyright Oxford University Press, Great Clarendon Street, Oxford OX2 6DP.
Used by permission.

195 From heaven you came *The Servant King*

Words and music: Graham Kendrick (b.1950)

© Copyright 1983 Kingsway's Thankyou Music, P.O. Box 75, Eastbourne,
East Sussex BN23 6NW, UK. (tym@kingsway.co.uk). Used by permission.

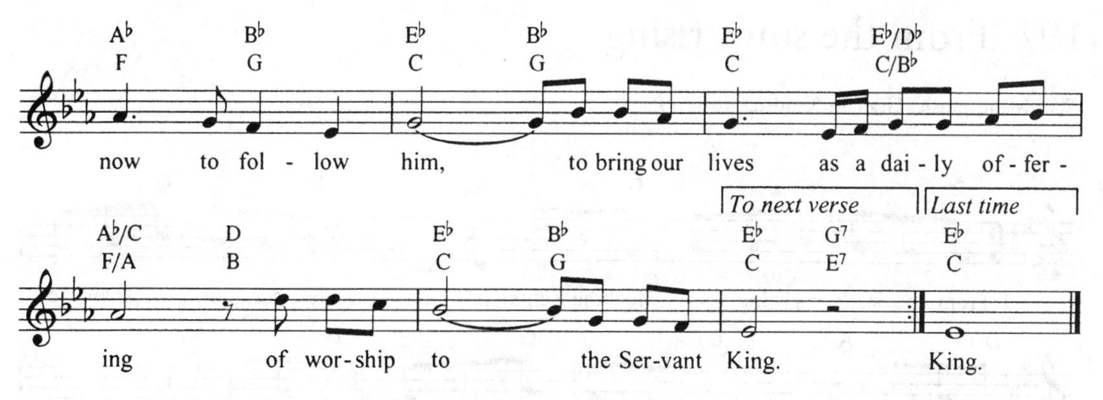

2. There in the garden of tears,
my heavy load he chose to bear;
his heart with sorrow was torn.
'Yet not my will but yours,' he said.

3. Come see his hands and his feet,
the scars that speak of sacrifice,
hands that flung stars into space,
to cruel nails surrendered.

4. So let us learn how to serve,
and in our lives enthrone him;
each other's needs to prefer,
for it is Christ we're serving.

196 From many grains

Michael Forster (b.1946)
based on the Didaché

Orlando Gibbons (1583-1625)

SONG 1 10 10 10 10 10 10

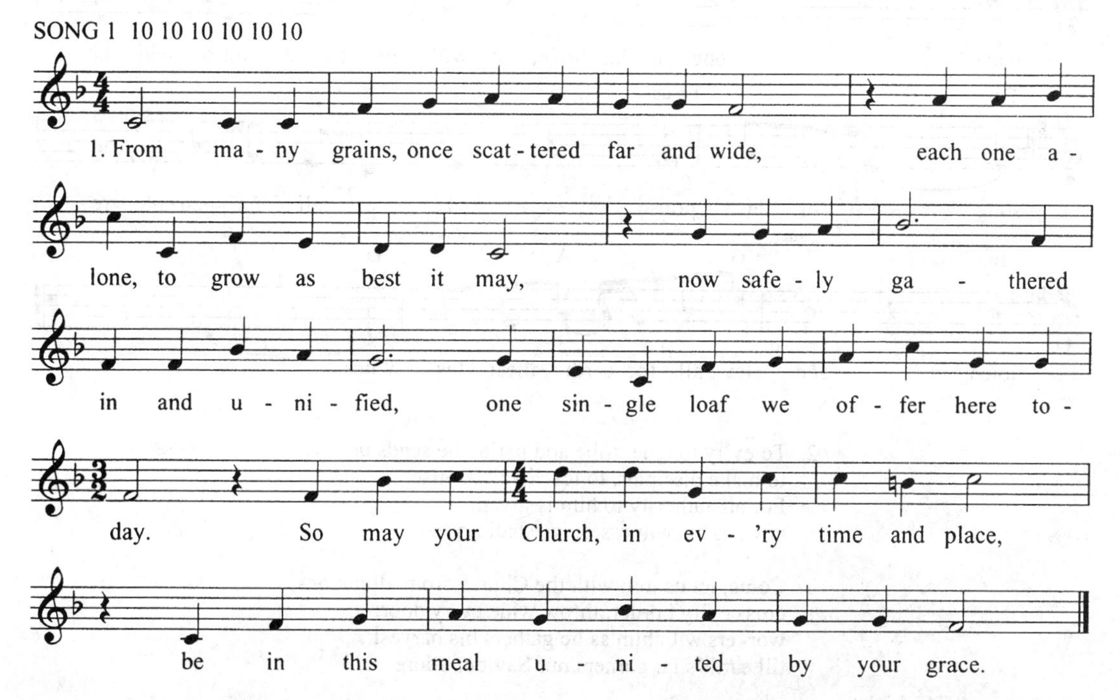

2. From many grapes, once living on the vine,
now crushed and broken under human feet,
we offer here this single cup of wine:
the sign of love, unbroken and complete.
So may we stand among the crucified,
and live the risen life of him who died.

3. From many places gathered, we are here,
each with a gift that we alone can bring.
O Spirit of the living God, draw near,
make whole by grace our broken offering.
O crush the pride that bids us stand alone;
let flow the love that makes our spirits one.

Text © Copyright 1992 Kevin Mayhew Ltd.

197 From the sun's rising

Words and music: Graham Kendrick (b.1950)

2. To ev'ry tongue, tribe and nation he sends us,
to make disciples, to teach and baptise.
For all authority to him is given;
now, as his witnesses, we shall arise.

3. Come, let us join with the Church from all nations,
cross ev'ry border, throw wide ev'ry door;
workers with him as he gathers his harvest,
till earth's far corners our Saviour adore.

© Copyright 1988 Make Way Music, P.O. Box 263, Croydon, Surrey CR9 5AP, UK.
International copyright secured. All rights reserved. Used by permission.

198 From the very depths of darkness

Michael Forster (b.1946) | Christopher Tambling (b.1964)

2. Jesus meets us at the dawning
of the resurrection day;
speaks our name with love, and gently
says that here we may not stay:
'Do not cling to me, but go to all
the fearful ones and say,
"The Lord is risen indeed!" '

3. So proclaim it in the high-rise,
in the hostel let it ring;
make it known in Cardboard City,
let the homeless rise and sing:
'He is Lord of life abundant,
and he changes everything;
the Lord is risen indeed!'

4. In the heartlands of oppression,
sound the cry of liberty;
where the poor are crucified,
behold the Lord of Calvary;
from the fear of death and dying,
Christ has set his people free;
the Lord is risen indeed!

5. To the tyrant, tell the gospel
of a love that can't be known
in a guarded palace-tomb,
condemned to live and die alone:
'Take the risk of love and freedom;
Christ has rolled away the stone!
The Lord is risen indeed!'

6. When our spirits are entombed
in mortal prejudice and pride;
when the gates of hell itself
are firmly bolted from inside;
at the bidding of his Spirit,
we may fling them open wide;
The Lord is risen indeed!.

Text and Tune 1 © Copyright 1992 Kevin Mayhew Ltd.

Michael Forster (b.1946) Traditional American melody

TUNE 2: BATTLE HYMN 15 15 15 7 and Refrain

2. Jesus meets us at the dawning
of the resurrection day;
speaks our name with love, and gently
says that here we may not stay:
'Do not cling to me, but go to all
the fearful ones and say,
"The Lord is risen indeed!" '

3. So proclaim it in the high-rise,
in the hostel let it ring;
make it known in Cardboard City,
let the homeless rise and sing:
'He is Lord of life abundant,
and he changes everything;
the Lord is risen indeed!'

4. In the heartlands of oppression,
sound the cry of liberty;
where the poor are crucified,
behold the Lord of Calvary;
from the fear of death and dying,
Christ has set his people free;
the Lord is risen indeed!

5. To the tyrant, tell the gospel
of a love that can't be known
in a guarded palace-tomb,
condemned to live and die alone:
'Take the risk of love and freedom;
Christ has rolled away the stone!
The Lord is risen indeed!'

6. When our spirits are entombed
in mortal prejudice and pride;
when the gates of hell itself
are firmly bolted from inside;
at the bidding of his Spirit,
we may fling them open wide;
The Lord is risen indeed!.

199 Gather around, for the table is spread

Jean Holloway (b.1939) Traditional Scottish melody

Text © 1994 Kevin Mayhew Ltd.

200 Gifts of bread and wine

Words and music: Christine McCann (b.1951)

2. Christ our Saviour, living presence here,
as he promised while on earth:
'I am with you for all time,
I am with you in this bread and wine.'

3. To the Father, with the Spirit,
one in union with the Son,
for God's people, joined in prayer,
faith is strengthened by the food we share.

© 1978 Kevin Mayhew Ltd.

201 Give me joy in my heart *Sing hosanna*

Words and music: traditional

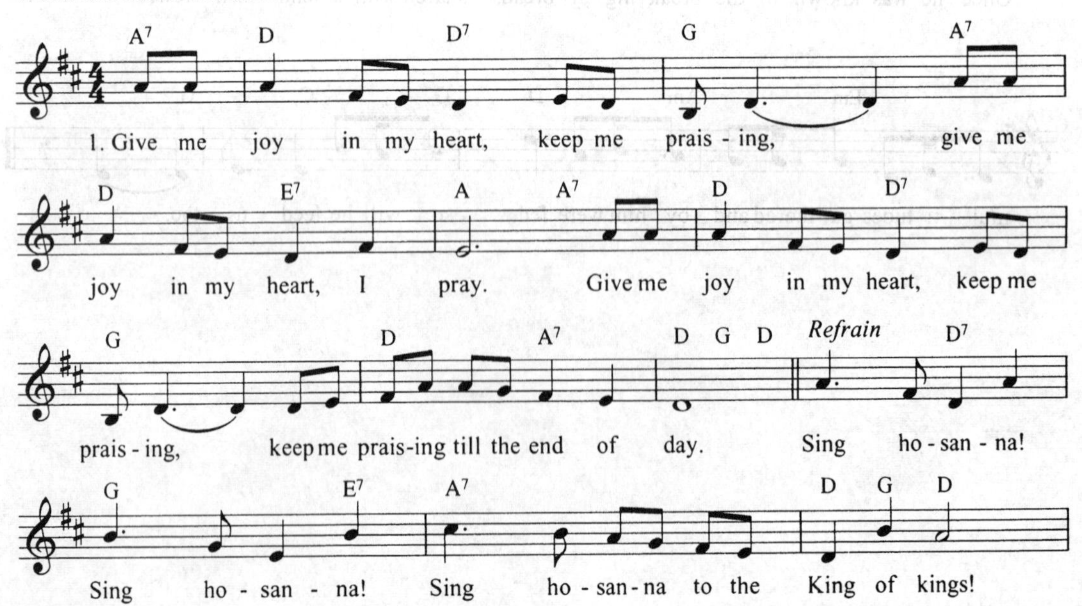

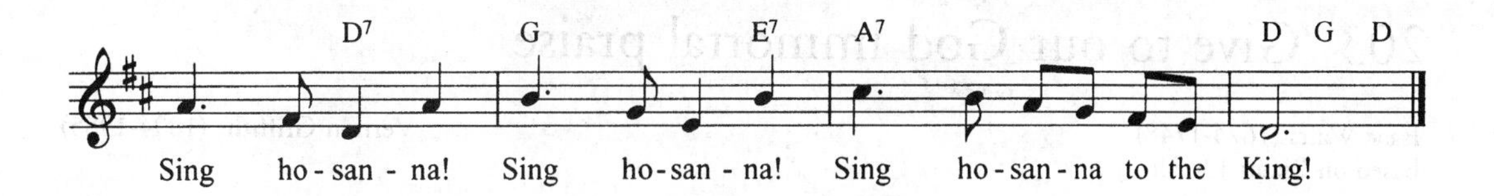

2. Give me peace in me heart,
keep me resting...

3. Give me love in my heart,
keep me serving...

4. Give me oil in my lamp,
keep me burning...

202 Give thanks with a grateful heart

Words and music: Henry Smith

© Copyright 1978 Integrity's Hosanna! Music/Sovereign Music UK, P.O. Box 356, Leighton Buzzard, LU7 3WP, UK. Used by permission.

203 Give to our God immortal praise

Isaac Watts (1674-1748)
based on Psalm 136 alt.

Vernon Griffiths (1894-1985)

DUNEDIN LM

2. Give to the Lord of lords renown,
the King of kings with glory crown:
his mercies ever shall endure
when earthly pow'rs are known no more.

3. He sent his Son with pow'r to save
from guilt and darkness and the grave:
wonders of grace to God belong,
repeat his mercies in your song.

4. Through earthly life he guides our feet,
and leads us to his heav'nly seat:
his mercies ever shall endure
when earthly pow'rs are known no more.

Music © Copyright 1971 Faber Music Ltd., 3 Queen Square, London WC1N 3AU.
Reproduced by permission from the *New Catholic Hymnal.*

204 Give us the wings of faith

Isaac Watts (1674-1748) alt.

From E. Prys, *Psalms* (1621)

SONG 67 CM

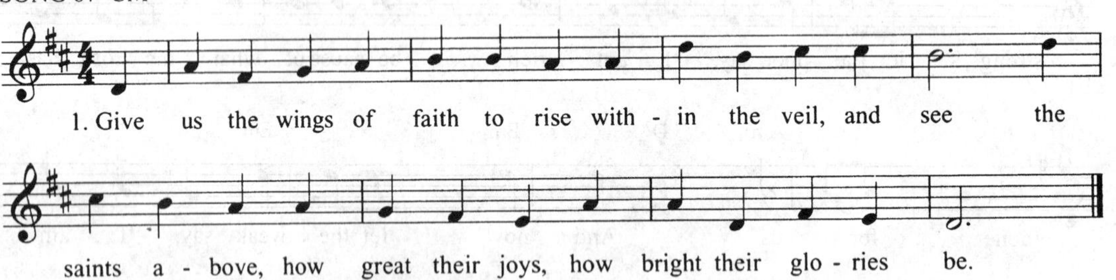

2. Once they were mourning here below,
their couch was wet with tears;
they wrestled hard, as we do now,
with sins and doubts and fears.

3. We ask them whence their vict'ry came:
they, with united breath,
ascribe the conquest to the Lamb,
their triumph to his death.

4. They marked the footsteps that he trod,
his zeal inspired their breast,
and, foll'wing their incarnate God,
they reached the promised rest.

5. Our glorious Leader claims our praise
for his own pattern giv'n;
while the great cloud of witnesses
show the same path to heav'n.

205 Glorious things of thee are spoken

John Newton (1725-1807)
based on Isaiah 33:20-21 alt.

Croatian folk melody adapted by
Franz Joseph Haydn (1732-1809)

TUNE 1: AUSTRIA 87 87 D

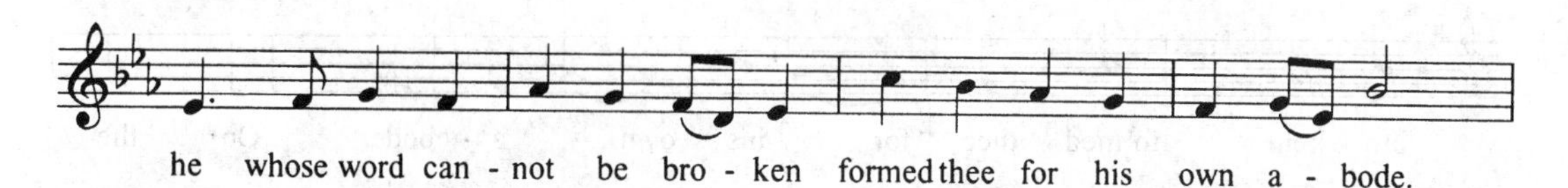

2. See, the streams of living waters,
springing from eternal love,
well supply thy sons and daughters,
and all fear of want remove.
Who can faint while such a river
ever flows their thirst to assuage?
Grace which, like the Lord, the giver,
never fails from age to age.

3. Round each habitation hov'ring,
see the cloud and fire appear
for a glory and a cov'ring,
showing that the Lord is near.
Thus they march, the pillar leading,
light by night and shade by day;
daily on the manna feeding
which he gives them when they pray.

4. Saviour, if of Zion's city
I through grace a member am,
let the world deride or pity,
I will glory in thy name.
Fading is the worldling's pleasure,
boasted pomp and empty show;
solid joys and lasting treasure
none but Zion's children know.

Tune 2 will be found overleaf

Tune 2 © Copyright Oxford University Press, Great Clarendon Street, Oxford OX2 6DP.
Reproduced by permission from *The BBC Hymn Book.*

John Newton (1725-1807)
based on Isaiah 33:20-21 alt.

Cyril Vincent Taylor (1907-1991)

TUNE 2: ABBOT'S LEIGH 87 87 D

2. See, the streams of living waters,
springing from eternal love,
well supply thy sons and daughters,
and all fear of want remove.
Who can faint while such a river
ever flows their thirst to assuage?
Grace which, like the Lord, the giver,
never fails from age to age.

3. Round each habitation hov'ring,
see the cloud and fire appear
for a glory and a cov'ring,
showing that the Lord is near.
Thus they march, the pillar leading,
light by night and shade by day;
daily on the manna feeding
which he gives them when they pray.

4. Saviour, if of Zion's city
I through grace a member am,
let the world deride or pity,
I will glory in thy name.
Fading is the worldling's pleasure,
boasted pomp and empty show;
solid joys and lasting treasure
none but Zion's children know.

206 Glory be to Jesus

Viva, viva, Gesù (18th century)
trans. Edward Caswall (1814-1878) alt.

Friedrich Filitz (1804-1876)

CASWALL 65 65

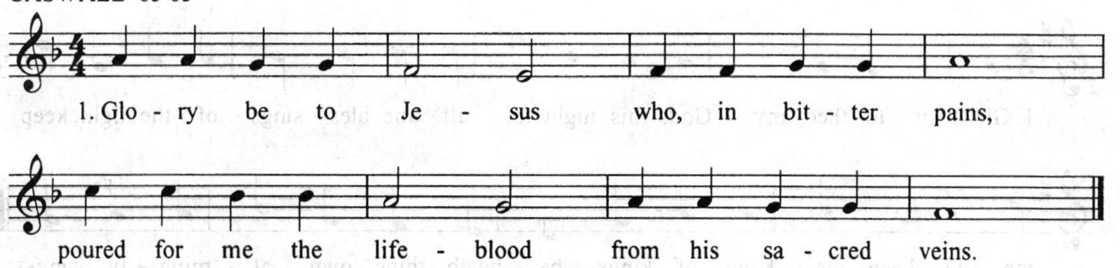

2. Grace and life eternal
in that blood I find:
blest be his compassion,
infinitely kind.

3. Blest, through endless ages,
be the precious stream
which, from endless torment,
did the world redeem.

4. There the fainting spirit
drinks of life her fill;
there, as in a fountain,
laves herself at will.

5. Abel's blood for vengeance
pleaded to the skies,
but the blood of Jesus
for our pardon cries.

6. Oft as it is sprinkled
on our guilty hearts
Satan in confusion
terror-struck departs.

7. Oft as earth exulting
wafts its praise on high
angel hosts rejoicing,
make their glad reply.

8. Lift, then, all your voices,
swell the mighty flood;
louder still and louder,
praise the precious blood.

207 Glory, love, and praise, and honour

Charles Wesley (1707-1788) alt.

Francis Brotherton Westbrook (1903-1975)

BENIFOLD 83 36 D

2. Thankful for our ev'ry blessing,
let us sing Christ the Spring,
never, never ceasing.
Source of all our gifts and graces
Christ we own; Christ alone
calls for all our praises.

3. He dispels our sin and sadness,
life imparts, cheers our hearts,
fills with food and gladness.
Who himself for all hath given,
us he feeds, us he leads
to a feast in heaven.

Music © Copyright Oxford University Press, Great Clarendon Street, Oxford OX2 6DP.
Used by permission.

208 Glory to thee, my God, this night

Thomas Ken (1637-1710) | Thomas Tallis (c.1505-1585)

TALLIS' CANON LM

2. Forgive me, Lord, for thy dear Son,
the ill that I this day have done,
that with the world, myself and thee,
I, ere I sleep, at peace may be.

3. Teach me to live, that I may dread
the grave as little as my bed;
teach me to die, that so I may
rise glorious at the aweful day.

4. O may my soul on thee repose,
and with sweet sleep mine eyelids close;
sleep that may me more vig'rous make
to serve my God when I awake.

5. Praise God, from whom all blessings flow;
praise him, all creatures here below;
praise him above, ye heav'nly host;
praise Father, Son and Holy Ghost.

209 Glory to thee, O God

Howard Charles Adie Gaunt (1902-1983) | John Ireland (1879-1962)

LOVE UNKNOWN 66 66 44 44

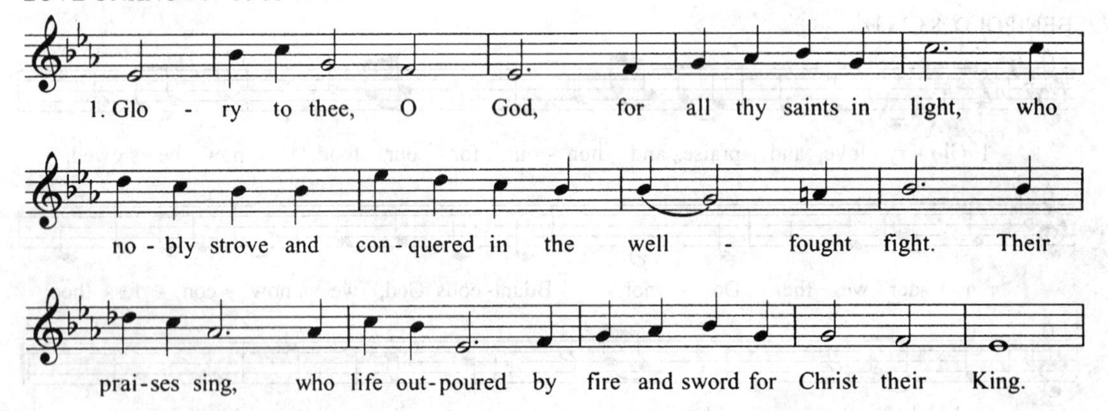

2. Thanks be to thee, O Lord,
for saints thy Spirit stirred
in humble paths to live thy life and
speak thy word.
Unnumbered they,
whose candles shine
to lead our footsteps after thine.

3. Lord God of truth and love,
'thy kingdom come', we pray;
give us thy grace to know thy truth and
walk thy way:
that here on earth
thy will be done,
till saints in earth and heav'n are one.

Text © Copyright Oxford University Press, Great Clarendon Street, Oxford OX2 6DP.
Music © Copyright The John Ireland Trust, 36 St Mary's Mansions, St Mary's Terrace, London W2 1SQ. UK.
Used by permission.

210 God! As with silent hearts

Fred Kaan (b.1929) Charles Harris (1865-1936)

THE SUPREME SACRIFICE 10 10 10

2. Hallow our will as humbly we recall
the lives of those who gave and give their all.
We thank you, Lord, for women, children, men
who seek to serve in love, today as then.

3. Give us deep faith to comfort those who mourn,
high hope to share with all the newly born,
strong love in our pursuit of human worth:
'lest we forget' the future of this earth.

4. So, Prince of Peace, disarm our trust in pow'r,
teach us to coax the plant of peace to flow'r.
May we, impassioned by your living Word,
remember forward to a world restored.

Text © Copyright 1997 Stainer & Bell Ltd., P.O. Box 110, Victoria House,
23 Gruneison Road, Finchley, London N3 1DZ.

211 God be in my head

Book of Hours (1514) Henry Walford Davies (1869-1941)

GOD BE IN MY HEAD Irregular

Music © Copyright Oxford University Press, Great Clarendon Street, Oxford OX2 6DP.
Used by permission.

212 God forgave my sin *Freely, freely*

Words and music: Carol Owens

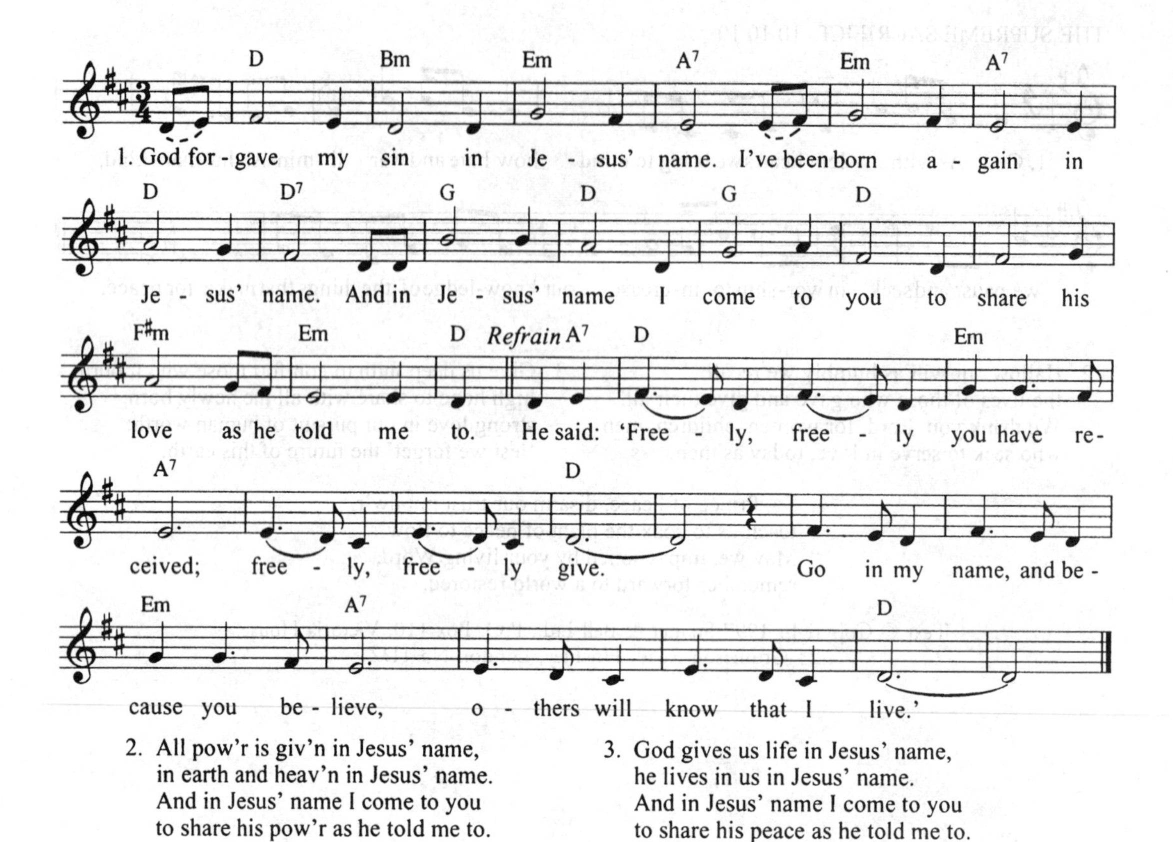

2. All pow'r is giv'n in Jesus' name,
in earth and heav'n in Jesus' name.
And in Jesus' name I come to you
to share his pow'r as he told me to.

3. God gives us life in Jesus' name,
he lives in us in Jesus' name.
And in Jesus' name I come to you
to share his peace as he told me to.

© Copyright 1972 Bud John Songs/EMI Christian Music Publishing. Administered by CopyCare Ltd., P.O. Box 77, Hailsham, East Sussex BN27 3EF, UK. (music@copycare.com). Used by permission.

213 God, in the planning *Bridegroom and bride*

John L. Bell (b.1949)
Graham Maule (b.1958)

Traditional Irish melody

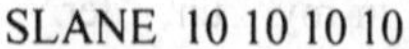
SLANE 10 10 10 10

Text © Copyright 1989 WGRG, Iona Community, Glasgow G2 3DH, Scotland.
Used by permission from *Love from Below* (Wild Goose Publications, 1989).

2. Jesus was found, at a similar feast,
taking the roles of both waiter and priest,
turning the worldly towards the divine,
tears into laughter and water to wine.

3. Therefore we pray that his Spirit preside
over the wedding of bridegroom and bride,
fulfilling all that they've hoped will come true,
lighting with love all they dream of and do.

4. Praise then the Maker, the Spirit, the Son,
source of the love through which two are made one.
God's is the glory, the goodness and grace
seen in this marriage and known in this place.

214 God is good

Words and music: Graham Kendrick (b.1950)

© Copyright 1985 Kingsway's Thankyou Music, P.O. Box 75, Eastbourne, East Sussex BN23 6NW, UK. (tym@kingsway.co.uk). Used by permission.

215 God is love

Words and music: Marie Lydia Pereira (b.1920)

2. God is life, God is life,
God is life for us.
His life keeps us from sin and strife,
and his sun comes shining through.

3. God is food, God is food,
God is food for us.
He is our food, our saving good,
and his sun comes shining through.

4. God is light, God is light,
God is light for us.
His light shines out through the darkest night,
and his sun comes shining through.

5. God is peace, God is peace.
God is peace for us.
And through his peace all quarrels cease,
and his sun comes shining through.

6. God is joy, God is joy,
God is joy for us.
The purest joy, the deepest joy,
and his sun comes shining through.

7. God is strength, God is strength,
God is strength for us.
The greatest strength, unfailing strength,
and his sun comes shining through.

8. God is truth, God is truth,
God is truth for us.
The surest truth, unchanging truth,
and his sun comes shining through.

© Copyright 1999 Kevin Mayhew Ltd.

216 God is love: his the care

Percy Dearmer (1867-1936) alt.

From *Piae Cantiones* (1582)

VERSION 1: PERSONENT HODIE (THEODORIC) 666 66 and Refrain

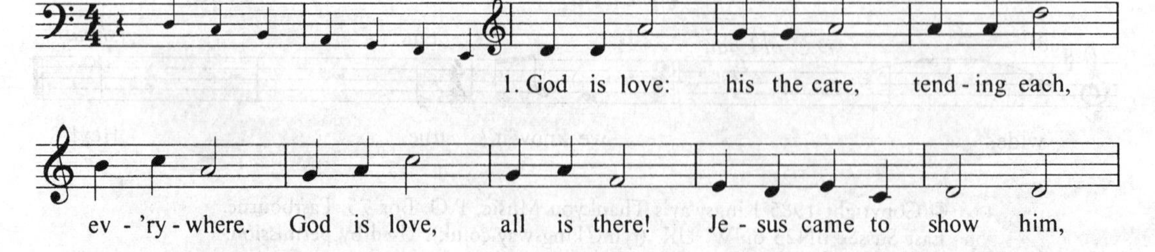

Text © Copyright Oxford University Press, Great Clarendon Street, Oxford OX2 6DP. Used by permission.

2. None can see God above;
we can share life and love;
thus may we Godward move,
seek him in creation,
holding ev'ry nation.

3. Jesus lived on the earth,
hope and life brought to birth
and affirmed human worth,
for he came to save us
by the truth he gave us.

4. To our Lord praise we sing,
light and life, friend and King,
coming down, love to bring,
pattern for our duty,
showing God in beauty.

Percy Dearmer (1867-1936) alt.

From *Piae Cantiones* (1582)

VERSION 2: PERSONENT HODIE (THEODORIC) 666 66 and Refrain

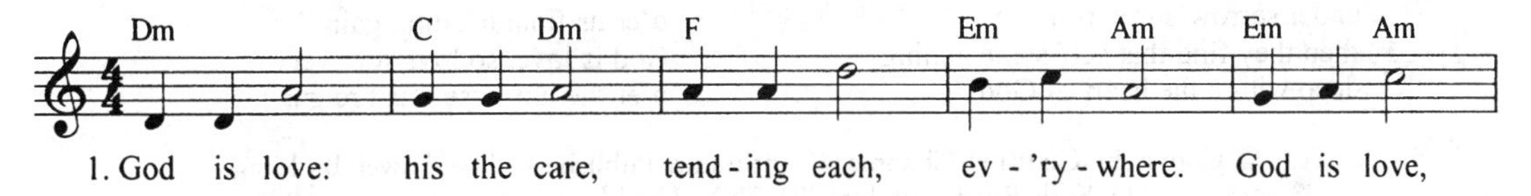

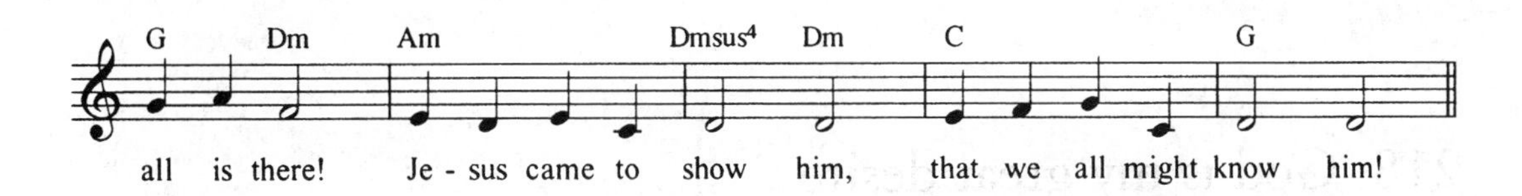

217 God is love: let heaven adore him

Timothy Rees (1874-1939) alt. | Samuel Sebastian Wesley (1810-1876)

ALLELUIA 87 87 D

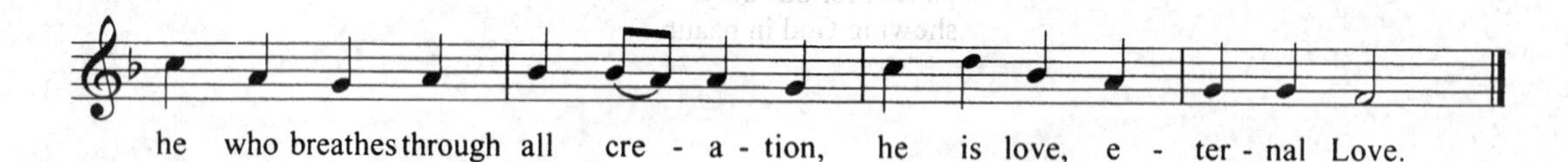

2. God is love: and he enfoldeth
all the world in one embrace;
with unfailing grasp he holdeth
ev'ry child of ev'ry race.
And when human hearts are breaking
under sorrow's iron rod,
then they find that self-same aching
deep within the heart of God.

3. God is love: and though with blindness
sin afflicts the human soul,
God's eternal loving-kindness
guides and heals and makes us whole.
Sin and death and hell shall never
o'er us final triumph gain;
God is love, so love for ever
o'er the universe must reign.

Text © Copyright Geoffrey Chapman/Continuum Publishers, The Tower Building, 11 York Road, London SE1 7NX. Used by permission.

218 God is my great desire

Timothy Dudley-Smith (b.1926)
based on Psalm 63

Transcribed from the *Yigdal*
by Meyer Lyon (c.1751-1797)

LEONI 66 84 D

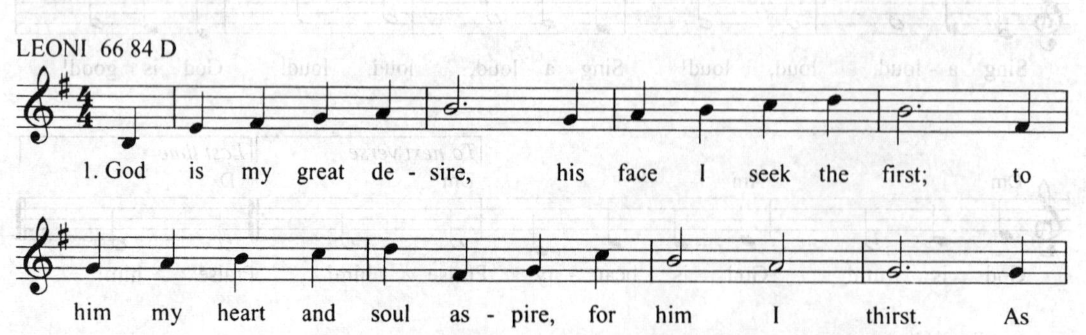

Text © Copyright Timothy Dudley-Smith, 9 Ashlands, Ford, Salisbury, Wiltshire SP4 6DY. Used by permission.

2. God is my true delight,
my richest feast his praise,
through silent watches of the night,
through all my days.
To him my spirit clings,
on him my soul is cast;
beneath the shadow of his wings
he holds me fast.

3. God is my strong defence
in ev'ry evil hour;
in him I face with confidence
the tempter's pow'r.
I trust his mercy sure,
with truth and triumph crowned:
my hope and joy for evermore
in him are found.

219 God is our strength and refuge

Richard Bewes
from Psalm 46

Eric Coates (1886-1958)

DAMBUSTERS' MARCH 77 76 77 11

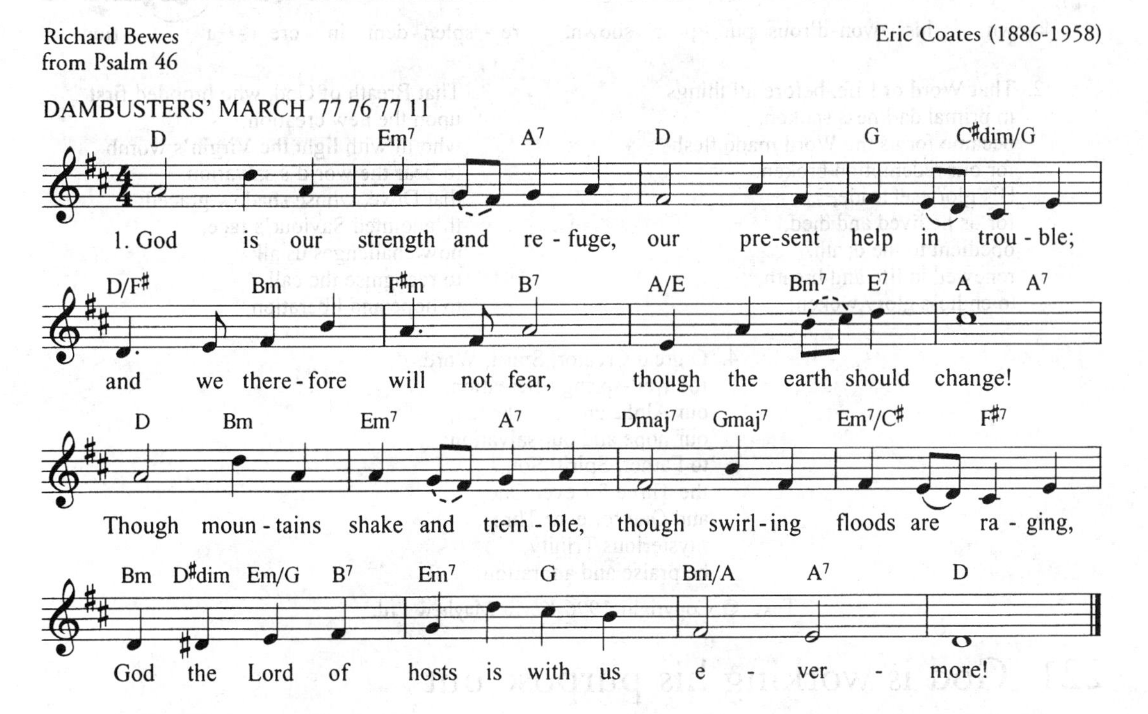

2. There is a flowing river,
within God's holy city;
God is in the midst of her –
she shall not be moved!
God's help is swiftly given,
thrones vanish at his presence
God the Lord of hosts is with us evermore!

3. Come, see the works of our maker,
learn of his deeds all-powerful;
wars will cease across the world
when he shatters the spear!
Be still and know your creator,
uplift him in the nations –
God the Lord of hosts is with us evermore!

Text © Copyright Richard Bewes/Jubilate Hymns, 4 Thorne Park Road,
Chelston, Torquay TQ2 6RX. Used by permission.
Music © Copyright 1954 Warner/Chappell Music Ltd., London W6 8BS.
Used by permission of IMP Ltd., Griffin House, 161 Hammersmith Road, London W6 8BS.

220 God is our strength from days of old

Michael Forster (b.1946) — Martin Luther (1483-1546)

EIN' FESTE BURG 87 87 66 667

2. That Word of Life, before all things
in primal darkness spoken,
became for us the Word made flesh
for our redemption broken.
His glory set aside,
for us he lived and died,
obedient to the death,
renewed in life and breath,
to endless glory woken!

3. That Breath of God, who brooded first
upon the new creation,
who lit with light the Virgin's womb
to bear the world's salvation;
that Dove, whose shadow graced
th'anointed Saviour's face,
now challenges us all
to recognise the call
to hope and liberation.

4. O great Creator, Spirit, Word,
the well-spring of creation,
our Alpha and our Omega,
our hope and our salvation;
to Father, Spirit, Son,
the Three for ever One,
and One for ever Three,
mysterious Trinity,
be praise and adoration.

Text © Copyright 1996 Kevin Mayhew Ltd.

221 God is working his purpose out

Arthur Campbell Ainger (1841-1919)
adapted by Michael Forster (b.1946) — Millicent Kingham (1866-1894) in *Church Hymns* (1903)

BENSON 86 87 87 12 8

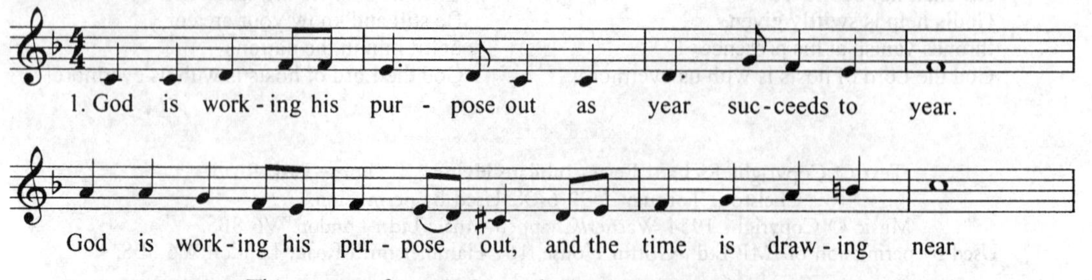

This version of text © Copyright 1996 Kevin Mayhew Ltd.

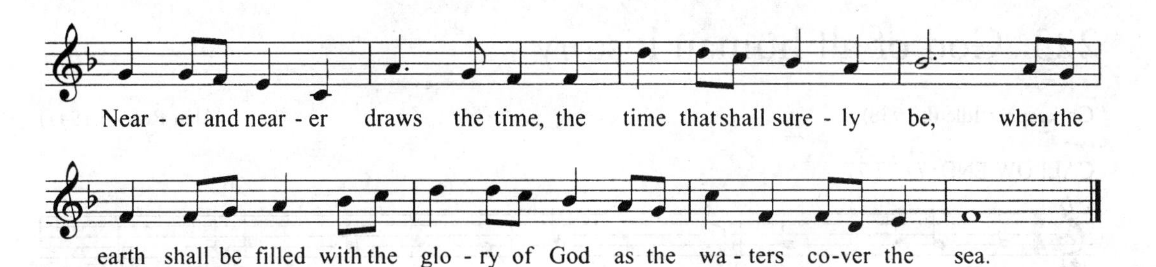

2. From the east to the utmost west
wherever foot has trod,
through the mouths of his messengers
echoes forth the voice of God:
'Listen to me, ye continents,
ye islands, give ear to me,
that the earth shall be filled
with the glory of God
as the waters cover the sea.'

3. How can we do the work of God,
how prosper and increase
harmony in the human race,
and the reign of perfect peace?
What can we do to urge the time,
the time that shall surely be,
when the earth shall be filled
with the glory of God
as the waters cover the sea?

4. March we forth in the strength of God,
his banner is unfurled;
let the light of the gospel shine
in the darkness of the world:
strengthen the weary, heal the sick
and set ev'ry captive free,
that the earth shall be filled
with the glory of God
as the waters cover the sea.

5. All our efforts are nothing worth
unless God bless the deed;
vain our hopes for the harvest tide
till he brings to life the seed.
Yet ever nearer draws the time,
the time that shall surely be,
when the earth shall be filled
with the glory of God
as the waters cover the sea.

222 God moves in a mysterious way

William Cowper (1731-1800)

From the *Scottish Psalter* (1635)
adapted by John Playford

LONDON NEW CM

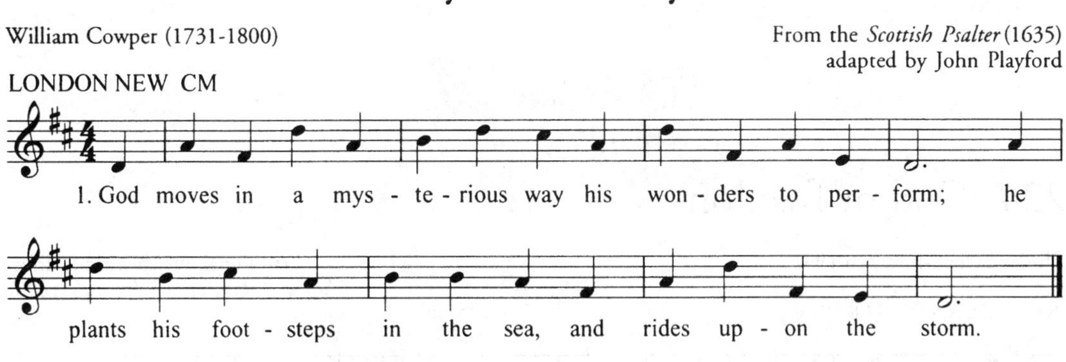

2. Deep in unfathomable mines
of never-failing skill,
he treasures up his bright designs,
and works his sov'reign will.

3. Ye fearful saints, fresh courage take;
the clouds ye so much dread
are big with mercy, and shall break
in blessings on your head.

4. Judge not the Lord by feeble sense,
but trust him for his grace;
behind a frowning providence
he hides a shining face.

5. His purposes will ripen fast,
unfolding ev'ry hour;
the bud may have a bitter taste,
but sweet will be the flow'r.

6. Blind unbelief is sure to err,
and scan his work in vain;
God is his own interpreter,
and he will make it plain.

223 God of all human history

Christopher Idle (b.1938) Alan Rees (b.1941)

CALLOW END 77 77 77

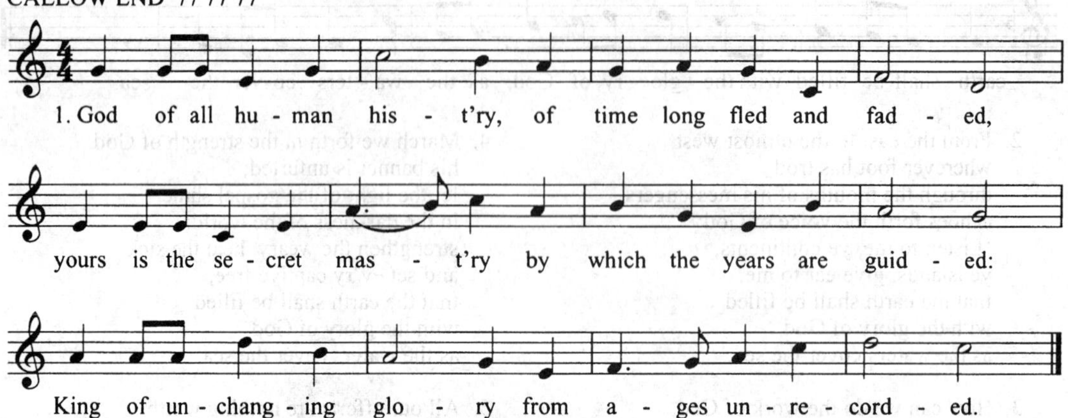

2. God of the hidden future
unfolding life for ever,
hope of each ransomed creature
as time speeds ever faster:
raise us to our full stature
in Christ, our one Redeemer.

3. God of this present moment
requiring our decision,
now is the hour of judgement
for ruin or salvation:
give us complete commitment
to your most urgent mission.

Text © Copyright Christopher Idle/Jubilate Hymns, 4 Thorne Park Road, Chelston, Torquay TQ2 6RX. Used by permission.
Music © Copyright 1999 Kevin Mayhew Lrd.

224 God of freedom

Shirley Erena Murray (b.1931) Traditional Welsh melody from *Musical Relicks of Welsh Bards* (1800)

RHUDDLAN 87 87 87

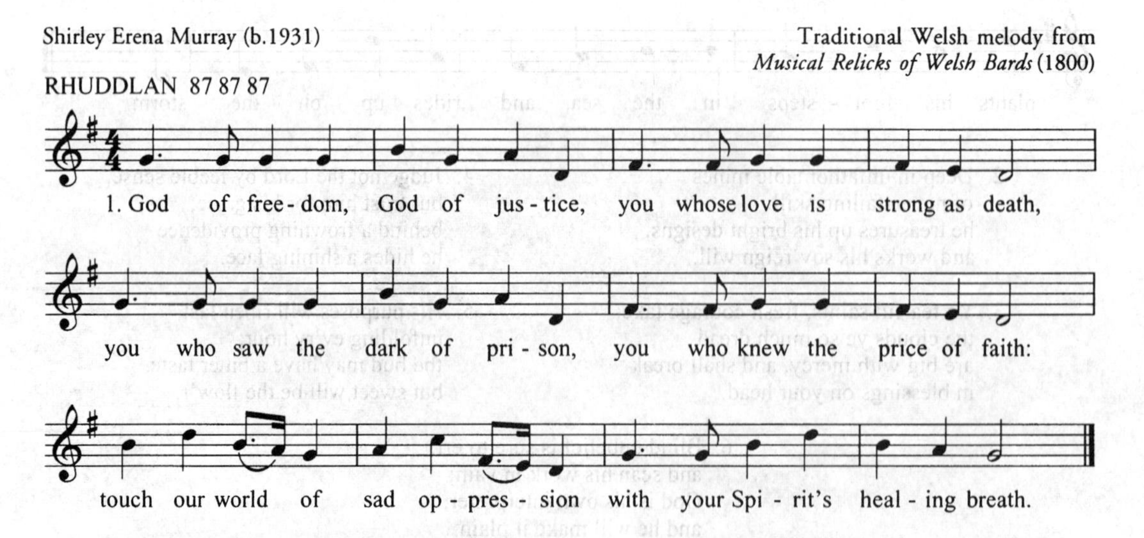

Text © Copyright 1992 Hope Publishing. Administered by CopyCare, P.O. Box 77, Hailsham, East Sussex BN27 3EF, UK. (music@copycare.com). Used by permission.

2. Rid the earth of torture's terror,
you whose hands were nailed to wood:
hear the cries of pain and protest,
you who shed the tears and blood;
move in us the pow'r of pity,
restless for the common good.

3. Make in us a captive conscience
quick to hear, to act, to plead;
make us truly sisters, brothers,
of whatever race or creed:
teach us to be fully human,
open to each other's need.

225 God of grace and God of glory

Harry Emerson Fosdick (1878-1969) alt.

Henry Smart (1813-1879)

REGENT SQUARE 87 87 87

2. Lo, the hosts of evil round us
scorn thy Christ, assail his ways;
from the fears that long have bound us
free our hearts to faith and praise.
Grant us wisdom, grant us courage,
for the living of these days.

3. Cure thy children's warring madness,
bend our pride to thy control;
shame our wanton selfish gladness,
rich in goods and poor in soul.
Grant us wisdom, grant us courage,
lest we miss thy kingdom's goal.

4. Set our feet on lofty places,
gird our lives that they may be
armoured with all Christlike graces
as we set your people free.
Grant us wisdom, grant us courage,
lest we fail the world or thee.

Text © Copyright The Estate of the late H.E. Fosdick.
Used by permission of Dr Elinor Fosdick Downs.

226 God of love

Jean Holloway (b.1939)

Robert Schumann (1810-1865)
adapted Richard Lloyd

SCHUMANN 87 87 D

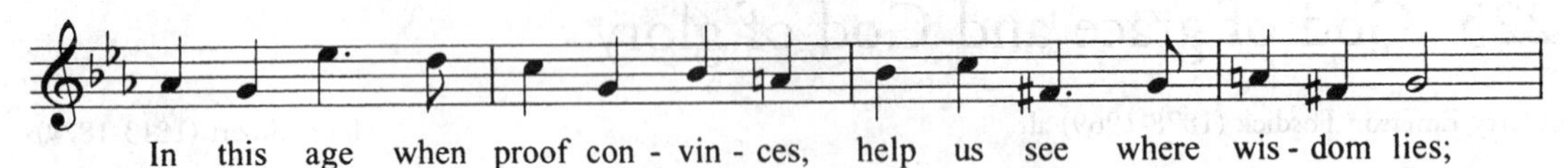

2. Son incarnate, yours the presence
which can heal an aching heart;
over death you reign triumphant,
you alone new life impart.
From your birth so long awaited,
to the cross on Calvary,
you will serve as our example,
let us, Lord, your servants be.

3. Holy Spirit, inspiration
day by day, yet mystery;
with the Son and the Creator
you form mystic unity.
Draw us into your communion,
with the love that sets us free;
bind our hearts to you for ever,
holy, blessèd Trinity.

Text © Copyright 1999 Kevin Mayhew Ltd.

227 God of mercy, God of grace

Henry Francis Lyte (1793-1847)
based on Psalm 67, alt.

Henry Smart (1813-1879)

HEATHLANDS 77 77 77

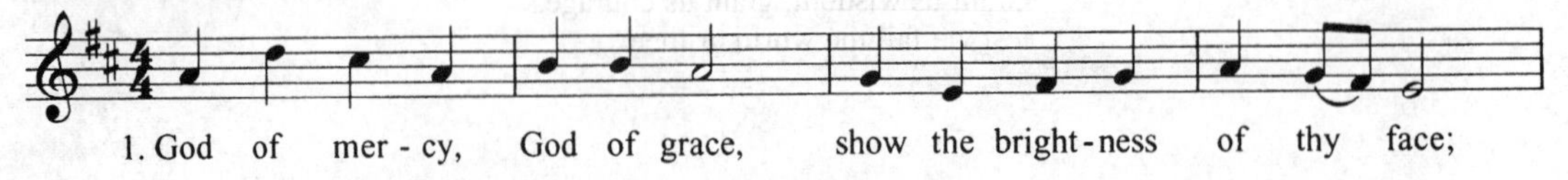

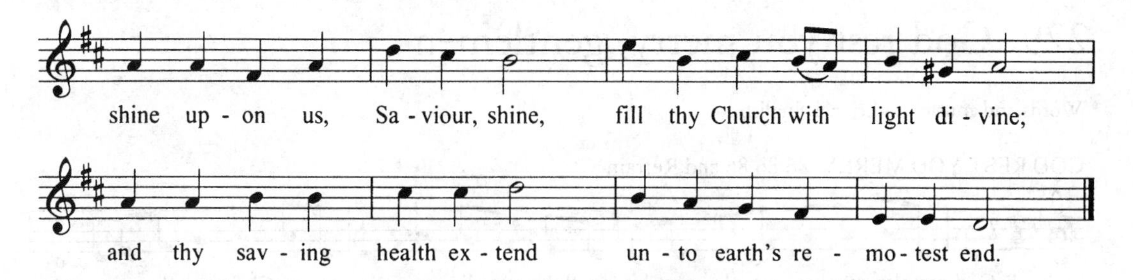

2. Let the people praise thee, Lord;
be by all that live adored;
let the nations shout and sing
glory to their Saviour King;
at thy feet their tribute pay,
and thy holy will obey.

3. Let the people praise thee, Lord;
earth shall then her fruits afford;
God to us his blessing give,
we to God devoted live;
all below, and all above,
one in joy and light and love.

228 God of the Passover

Michael Forster (b.1946)

Melody from
Praxis Pietatis Melica (1668)

LOBE DEN HERREN 14 14 4 7 8

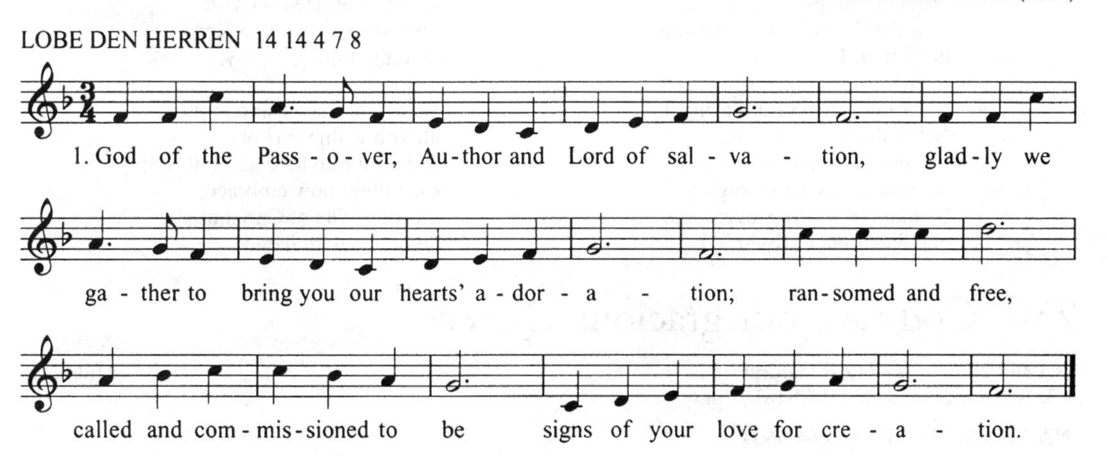

2. Here we remember that evening of wonder enthralling,
myst'ry of passion divine, and betrayal appalling.
Breaking the bread,
'This is my body,' he said,
'do this, my passion recalling.'

3. God of the Eucharist, humbly we gather before you
and, at your table, for pardon and grace we implore you.
Under the cross,
counting as profit our loss,
safe in its shade, we adore you.

Text © Copyright 1993 Kevin Mayhew Ltd.

229 God rest you merry, gentlemen

Words and music: traditional English

GOD REST YOU MERRY 86 86 86 and Refrain

2. In Bethlehem, in Jewry,
this blessèd babe was born,
and laid within a manger,
upon this blessèd morn;
at which his mother Mary
did nothing take in scorn.

3. From God, our heav'nly Father,
a blessèd angel came,
and unto certain shepherds
brought tidings of the same,
how that in Bethlehem was born
the Son of God by name.

4. 'Fear not,' then said the angel,
'let nothing you affright,
this day is born a Saviour,
of virtue, pow'r and might;
by him the world is overcome
and Satan put to flight.'

5. The shepherds at those tidings
rejoicèd much in mind,
and left their flocks a-feeding,
in tempest, storm and wind,
and went to Bethlehem straightway
this blessèd babe to find.

6. But when to Bethlehem they came,
whereat this infant lay,
they found him in a manger,
where oxen feed on hay;
his mother Mary kneeling,
unto the Lord did pray.

7. Now to the Lord sing praises,
all you within this place,
and with true love and fellowship
each other now embrace;
this holy tide of Christmas
all others doth deface.

230 God save our gracious Queen

vs.1 and 2: unknown (17th century) Unknown
v.3: William E. Hickson (1803-1870) alt.

NATIONAL ANTHEM 664 6664

2. Thy choicest gifts in store
on her be pleased to pour,
long may she reign:
may she defend our laws,
and ever give us cause
to sing with heart and voice
God save the Queen!

3. Not on this land alone,
but be God's mercies known
on ev'ry shore.
Lord, make the nations see
that all humanity
should form one family
the wide world o'er.

231 God's Spirit is in my heart *Go, tell everyone*

Alan Dale
Hubert J. Richards

Hubert J. Richards

2. Just as the Father sent me,
so I'm sending you out to be
my witnesses throughout the world,
the whole of the world.

3. Don't carry a load in your pack,
you don't need two shirts on your back.
A workman can earn his own keep,
can earn his own keep.

4. Don't worry what you have to say,
don't worry because on that day
God's Spirit will speak in your heart,
will speak in your heart.

© Copyright 1982 Kevin Mayhew Ltd.

232 God that madest earth and heaven

v.1: Reginald Heber (1783-1826)
v.2: Richard Whately (1787-1863)

Traditional Welsh melody

AR HYD Y NOS 84 84 88 84

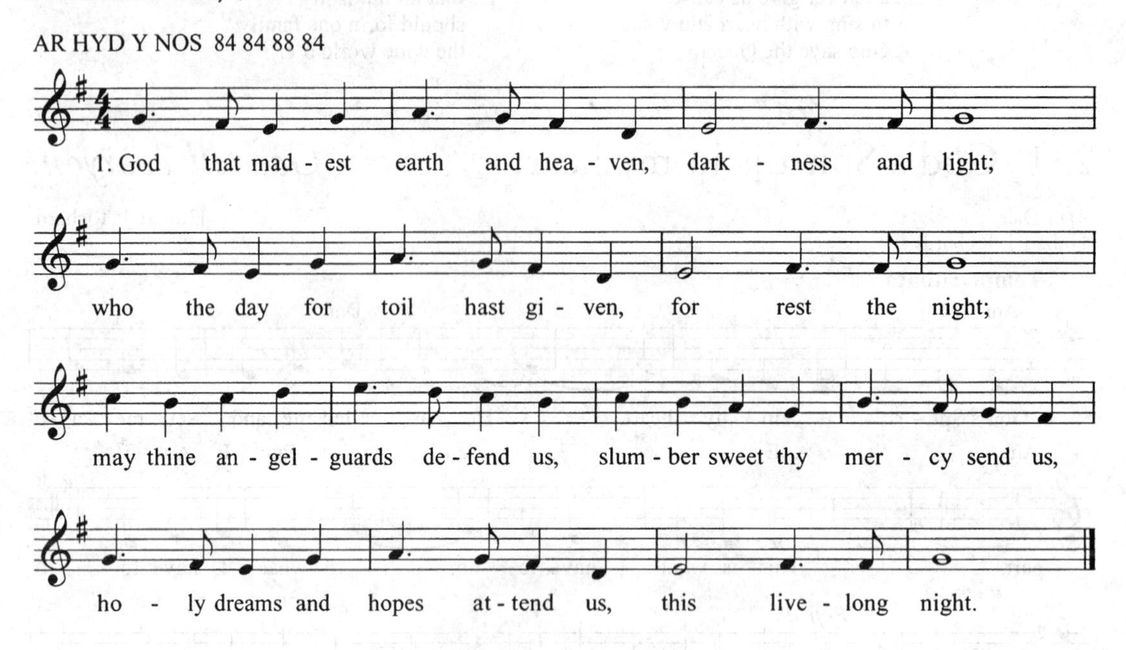

2. Guard us waking, guard us sleeping,
and, when we die,
may we in thy mighty keeping
all peaceful lie:
when the last dread call shall wake us,
do not thou our God forsake us,
but to reign in glory take us
with thee on high.

233 God, the source and goal of being

Ronald H. Green

Henry Smart (1813-1879)

REGENT SQUARE 87 87 87

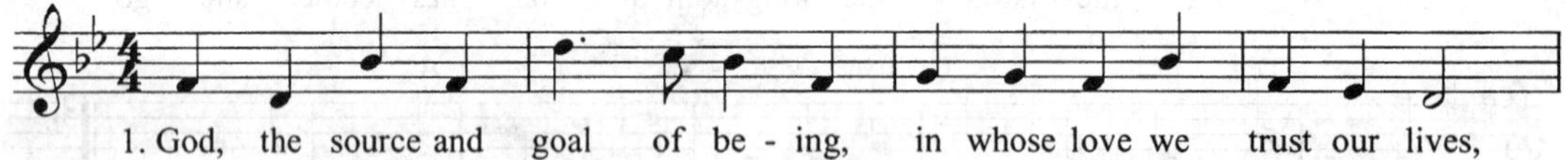

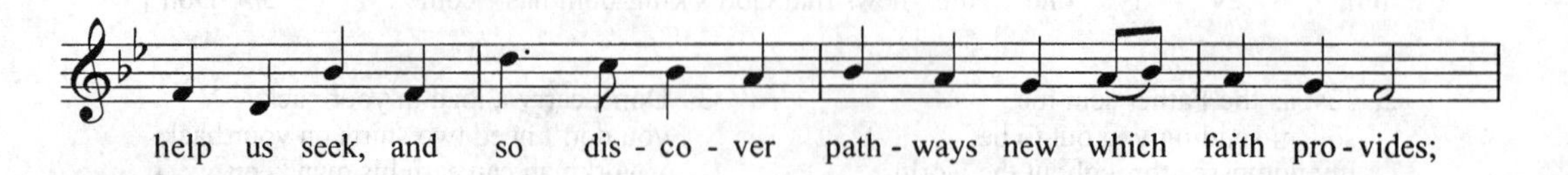

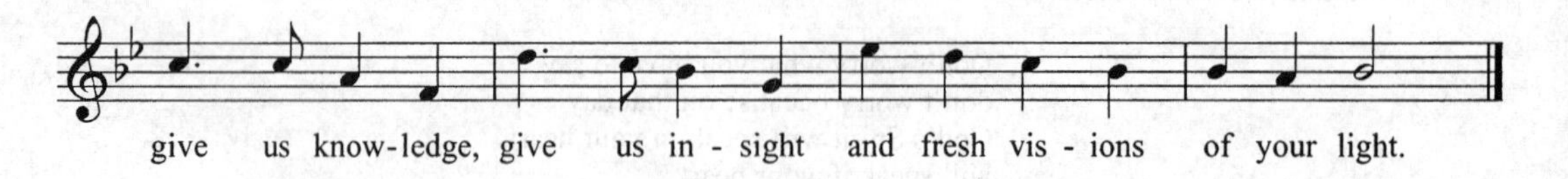

Text © Ronald H. Green. Used by permission.

2. God, whose touch brings hope to people,
who are lost without your love,
hear the prayers and praise we offer
from our dark to light above;
teach us how to share your glory
that your presence all may see.

3. God of love, of pow'r and action
from our bondage set us free;
take our lives and in them fashion
what you destine each shall be:
live in us who stand before you
and through us your world renew.

4. God the Father, God the Saviour,
God the Holy Spirit – One;
while we sing your praise to heav'nward
may on earth your will be done:
let the world accept our off'ring
of your song of love we bring.

234 God! When human bonds are broken

Fred Kaan (b.1929) | Edward Elgar (1857-1934)

DRAKES BROUGHTON 87 87

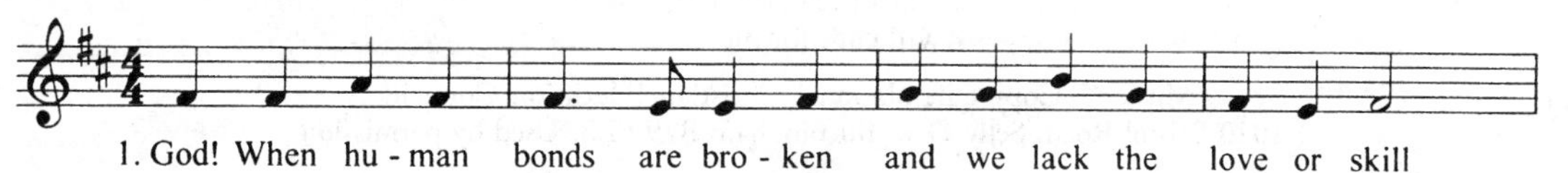

2. Through that stillness, with your Spirit
come into our world of stress,
for the sake of Christ forgiving
all the failures we confess.

3. You in us are bruised and broken:
hear us as we seek release
from the pain of earlier living;
set us free and grant us peace.

4. Send us, God of new beginnings,
humbly hopeful into life.
Use us as a means of blessing:
make us stronger, give us faith.

5. Give us faith to be more faithful,
give us hope to be more true,
give us love to go on learning:
God! Encourage and renew!

Text © Copyright 1989 Stainer & Bell Ltd., P.O. Box 110, Victoria House,
23 Gruneison Road, Finchley, London N3 1DZ. Used by permission.
Music © Copyright Control.

235 God who made the earth

Sarah Betts Rhodes (1824-1904) Carey Bonner (1859-1938)

SOMMERLIED 56 54

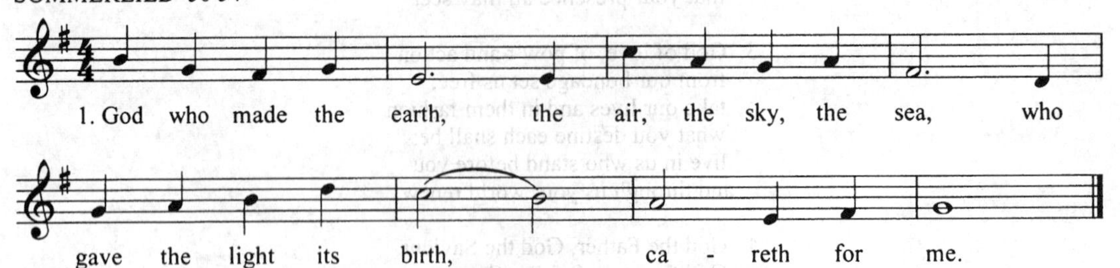

2. God who made the grass,
   the flow'r, the fruit, the tree,
   the day and night to pass,
   careth for me.

3. God who made the sun,
   the moon, the stars, is he
   who, when life's clouds come on,
   careth for me.

4. God who sent his Son
   to die on Calvary,
   he, if I lean on him,
   will care for me.

Music © Copyright National Christian Education Council,
1020 Bristol Road, Selly Oak, Birmingham B29 6LB. Used by permission.

236 God, whose farm is all creation

John Arlott (1914-1991) alt. Johann Ludwig Steiner (1688-1761)

GOTT WILL'S MACHEN 87 87

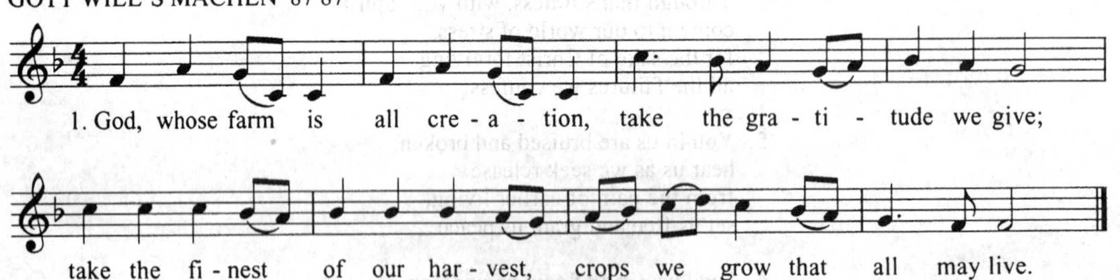

2. Take our ploughing, seeding, reaping,
   hopes and fears of sun and rain,
   all our thinking, planning, waiting,
   ripened in this fruit and grain.

3. All our labour, all our watching,
   all our calendar of care,
   in these crops of your creation,
   take, O God: they are our prayer.

Text © Copyright The Estate of the late L.T.J. Arlott.
Reproduced by kind permission of the Executors,
The old Presbytery, Les Rocquettes, Alderney, Guernsey GY9 3TF.

237 God, you meet us in our weakness

Glen Baker (b.1932) V. Earle Copes (b.1921)

KINGDOM 87 87

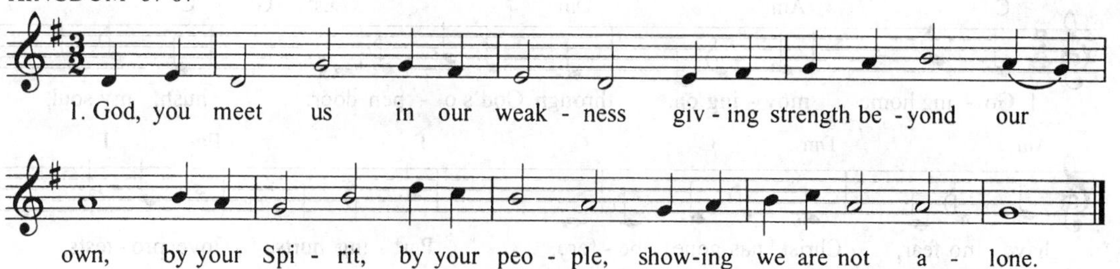

2. God, you meet us in our sorrows
with the comfort of your voice,
by your Spirit, by your people,
helping crying hearts rejoice.

3. God, you meet us in our neighbours,
when your strength and voice we need.
Yours the Spirit, we your people,
sharing love in word and deed!

Text © Copyright Glen W. Baker. Used by permission.
Music © Copyright Abingdon Press. Administered by CopyCare, P.O. Box 77,
Hailsham, East Sussex BN27 3EF, UK. (music@copycare.com). Used by permission.

238 Go forth and tell

James Edward Seddon (1915-1983) John Barnard (b. 1948)

YANWORTH 10 10 10 10

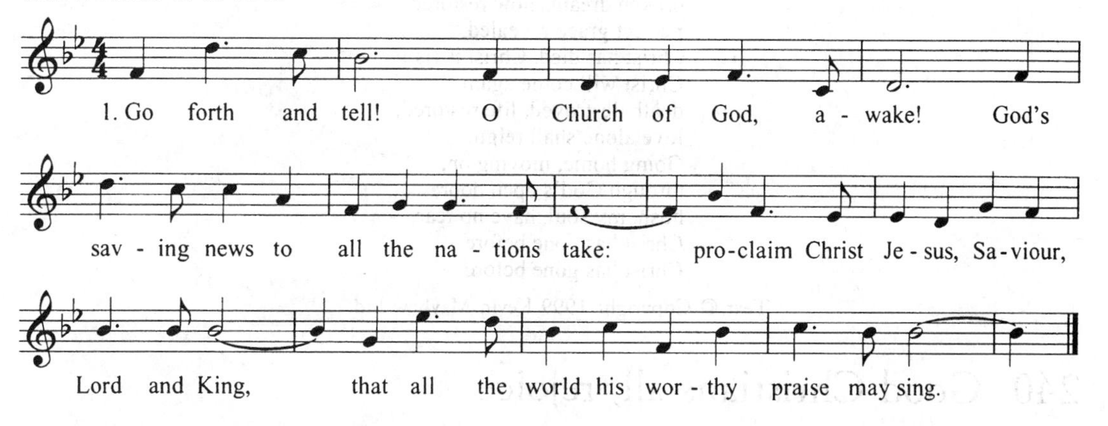

2. Go forth and tell! God's love embraces all;
he will in grace respond to all who call;
how shall they call if they have never heard
the gracious invitation of his word?

3. Go forth and tell! where still the darkness lies;
in wealth or want, the sinner surely dies:
give us, O Lord, concern of heart and mind,
a love like yours which cares for all mankind.

4. Go forth and tell! the doors are open wide:
share God's good gifts – let no-one be denied;
live out your life as Christ your Lord shall choose,
your ransomed pow'rs for his sole glory use.

5. Go forth and tell! O Church of God, arise!
Go in the strength which Christ your Lord supplies;
go till all nations his great name adore
and serve him, Lord and King, for evermore.

Text © Copyright Mrs M. Seddon/Jubilate Hymns.
Music © Copyright John Barnard/Jubilate Hymns, 4 Thorne Park Road, Chelston, Torquay TQ2 6RX.
Used by permission.

239 Going home

Michael Forster (b.1946)

Adapted from Dvořák's
New World Symphony

2. No more guilt, no more fear,
all the past is healed:
broken dreams now restored,
perfect grace revealed.
Christ has died, Christ is ris'n,
Christ will come again:
death destroyed, life restored,
love alone shall reign.
Going home, moving on,
through God's open door;
hush, my soul, have no fear,
Christ has gone before,
Christ has gone before.

Text © Copyright 1999 Kevin Mayhew Ltd.

240 Good Christians all, rejoice

John Mason Neale (1818-1866) alt.

14th century German carol melody

IN DULCI JUBILO Irregular

1. Good Christ - ians all, re - joice with heart and soul and voice!

Give ye heed to what we say: News! News! Je - sus Christ is

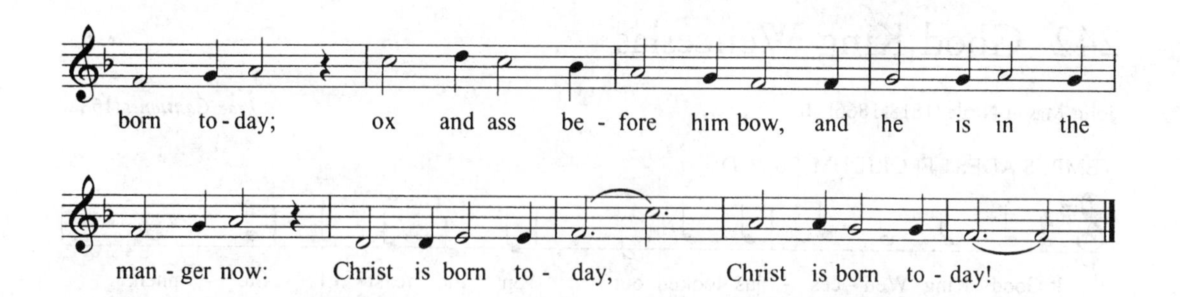

2. Good Christians all, rejoice
with heart and soul and voice!
Now ye hear of endless bliss:
Joy! Joy! Jesus Christ was born for this.
He hath opened heaven's door,
and we are blest for evermore:
Christ was born for this,
Christ was born for this.

3. Good Christians all, rejoice
with heart and soul and voice!
Now ye need not fear the grave:
Peace! Peace! Jesus Christ was born to save;
calls you one, and calls you all,
to gain his everlasting hall:
Christ was born to save,
Christ was born to save.

241 Good Christians all, rejoice and sing

Cyril Argentine Alington (1872-1955) alt.

Melody from Melchior Vulpius' *Gesangbuch* (1609)

GELOB'T SEI GOTT (VULPIUS) 888 and Alleluias

2. The Lord of Life is ris'n for ay:
bring flow'rs of song to strew his way;
let all mankind rejoice and say:
Alleluia!

3. Praise we in songs of victory
that Love, that Life, which cannot die
and sing with hearts uplifted high:
Alleluia!

4. Thy name we bless, O risen Lord,
and sing today with one accord
the life laid down, the life restored:
Alleluia!

Text © Copyright Hymns Ancient and Modern, St Mary's Works, St Mary's Plain, Norwich NR3 3BH.
Used by permission.

242 Good King Wenceslas

John Mason Neale (1818-1866) alt.

Piae Cantiones (1582)

TEMPUS ADEST FLORIDUM 76 76 D

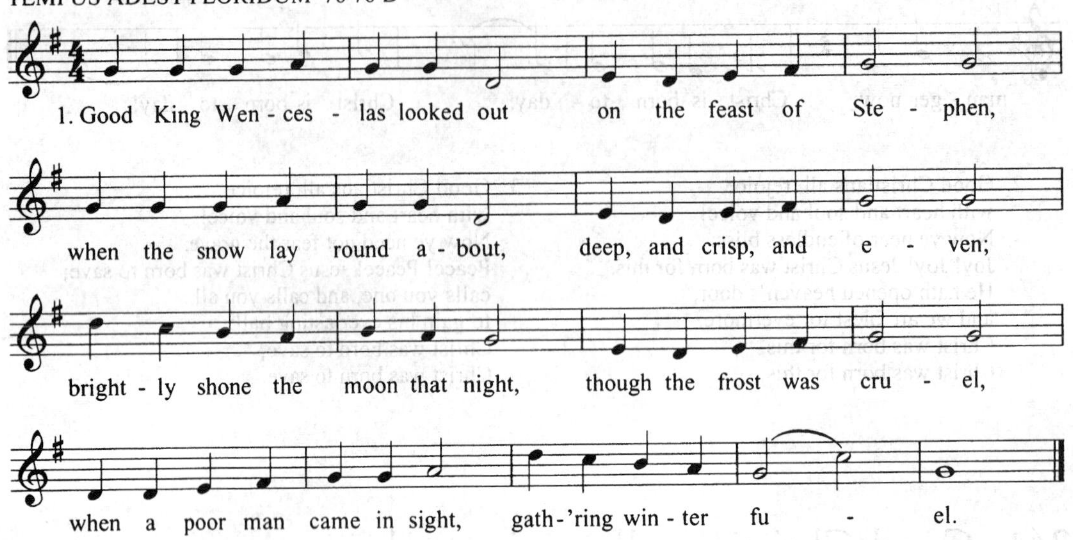

2. 'Hither, page, and stand by me,
if thou know'st it, telling,
yonder peasant, who is he,
where and what his dwelling?'
'Sire, he lives a good league hence,
underneath the mountain,
right against the forest fence,
by Saint Agnes' fountain.'

3. 'Bring me flesh, and bring me wine,
bring me pine logs hither:
thou and I will see him dine,
when we bring him thither.'
Page and monarch, forth they went,
forth they went together;
through the rude wind's wild lament,
and the bitter weather.

4. 'Sire, the night is darker now,
and the wind blows stronger;
fails my heart, I know not how;
I can go no longer.'
'Mark my footsteps good, my page;
tread thou in them boldly:
thou shalt find the winter's rage
freeze thy blood less coldly.'

5. In his master's steps he trod,
where the snow lay dinted;
heat was in the very sod
which the Saint had printed.
Therefore, Christians all, be sure,
wealth or rank possessing,
ye who now will bless the poor,
shall yourselves find blessing.

243 Go, tell it on the mountain

Words and music: traditional

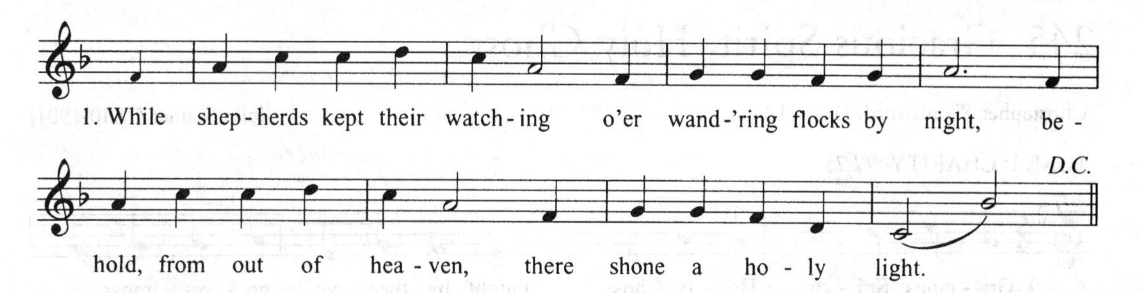

2. And lo, when they had seen it,
they all bowed down and prayed;
they travelled on together
to where the babe was laid.

3. When I was a seeker,
I sought both night and day:
I asked my Lord to help me
and he showed me the way.

4. He made me a watchman
upon the city wall,
and, if I am a Christian,
I am the least of all.

244 Gracious God, in adoration

Basil Bridge (b.1927) — Malcolm Archer (b.1952)

GOULDSBROOK 87 87 87

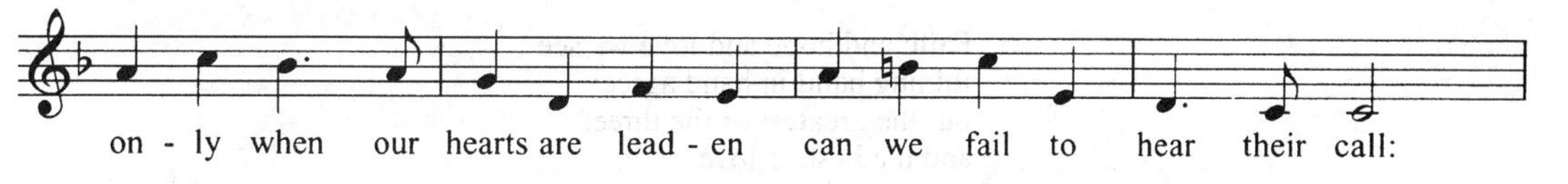

2. Earth and sky in silent praises
speak to those with eyes to see;
all earth's living creatures echo
'God has made us!' So may we
come with wonder, serve with gladness
him through whom they came to be.

3. You have made us in your image,
breathed your Spirit, given us birth;
Jesus calls, whose cross has given
ev'ry life eternal worth,
'Come with wonder, serve with gladness,
let God's will be done on earth!'

4. Earth by war and want is threatened;
deep the roots of fear and greed;
let your mercy be our measure
as we see our neighbour's need,
come with wonder, serve with gladness,
share your gift of daily bread.

5. Holy Spirit, urging, striving,
give us love that casts out fear,
courage, seeking peace with justice,
faith to make this message clear –
'Come with wonder, serve with gladness,
live in hope; the Lord is near!'

© Copyright 1999 Kevin Mayhew Ltd.

245 Gracious Spirit, Holy Ghost

Christopher Wordsworth (1807-1885) John Stainer (1840-1901)

TUNE 1: CHARITY 77 75

2. Love is kind, and suffers long,
love is meek, and thinks no wrong,
love than death itself more strong;
therefore give us love.

3. Prophecy will fade away,
melting in the light of day;
love will ever with us stay;
therefore give us love.

4. Faith will vanish into sight;
hope be emptied in delight;
love in heav'n will shine more bright;
therefore give us love.

5. Faith and hope and love we see
joining hand in hand agree;
but the greatest of the three,
and the best, is love.

6. From the overshadowing
of thy gold and silver wing
shed on us, who to thee sing,
holy, heav'nly love.

Christopher Wordsworth (1807-1885) Friedrich Filitz (1804-1876) alt.

TUNE 2: CAPETOWN 77 75

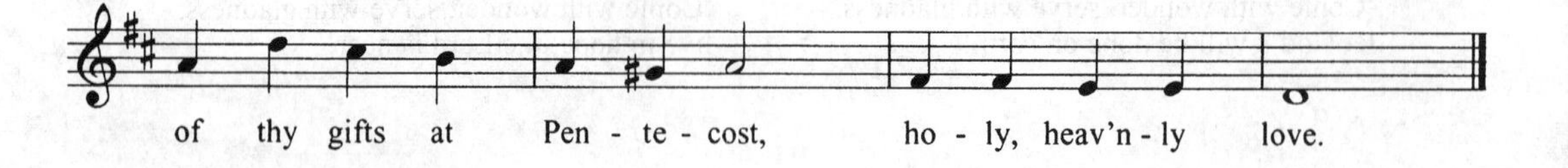

246 Great God, your love has called us

Brian Wren (b.1936)

Erik Routley (1917-1982)

ABINGDON 88 88 88

2. We come with self-inflicted pains
of broken trust and chosen wrong,
half-free, half-bound by inner chains,
by social forces swept along,
by pow'rs and systems close confined
yet seeking hope for humankind.

3. Great God, in Christ you call our name
and then receive us as your own,
not through some merit, right or claim
but by your gracious love alone.
We strain to glimpse your mercy-seat
and find you kneeling at our feet.

4. Then take the tow'l, and break the bread,
and humble us, and call us friends.
Suffer and serve till all are fed,
and show how grandly love intends
to work till all creation sings,
to fill all worlds, to crown all things.

5. Great God, in Christ you set us free
your life to live, your joy to share.
Give us your Spirit's liberty
to turn from guilt and dull despair
and offer all that faith can do
while love is making all things new.

Text © Copyright 1975, 1995 Stainer & Bell Ltd., P.O. Box 110, Victoria House,
23 Gruneison Road, Finchley, London N3 1DZ. Used by permission.
Music © Copyright Oxford University Press, Great Clarendon Street, Oxford OX2 6DP.
Used by permission.

247 Great indeed are your works, O Lord

Words and music: Aniceto Nazareth,
based on the Psalms.

2. You are the path which we tread,
   you will lead us onward.
   From ev'ry corner of earth
   all the nations gather.

3. You lead them all by the hand
   to the heav'nly kingdom.
   Then, at the end of all times,
   you will come in glory.

© Copyright 1984 Kevin Mayhew Ltd.

248 Great is the Lord and most worthy of praise

Words and music: Steve McEwan

© Copyright 1985 Body Songs. Administered by CopyCare, P.O. Box 77, Hailsham, East Sussex BN27 3EF, UK. (music@copycare.com). Used by permission.

249 Great is thy faithfulness

Thomas Obadiah Chilsholm (1866-1960) William Marion Runyan (1870-1957)

FAITHFULNESS (RUNYAN) 11 10 11 10 and Refrain

Refrain

been thou for e - ver wilt be. Great is thy faith - ful - ness! Great is thy faith - ful - ness!

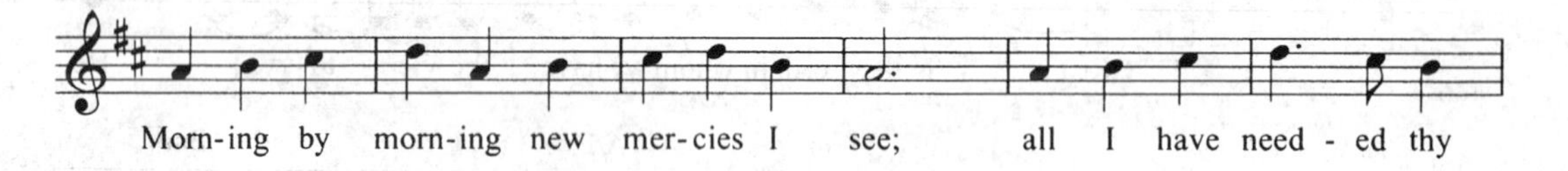

2. Summer and winter, and springtime and harvest,
sun, moon and stars in their courses above,
join with all nature in manifold witness
to thy great faithfulness, mercy and love.

3. Pardon for sin and a peace that endureth,
thine own dear presence to cheer and to guide;
strength for today and bright hope for tomorrow,
blessings all mine, with ten thousand beside!

© Copyright 1923, renewal 1951 by Hope Publishing Co. Administered by CopyCare, P.O. Box 77, Hailsham, East Sussex BN27 3EF, UK. (music@copycare.com). Used by permission.

250 Great Shepherd of thy people

John Newton (1725-1807) Henry Walford Davies (1869-1941)

OSWALD'S TREE CM

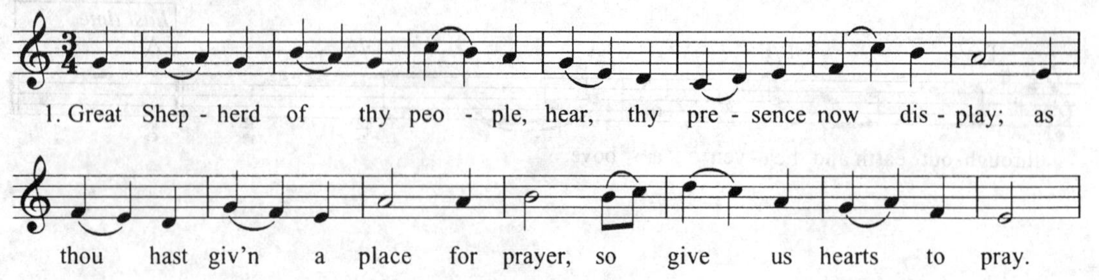

Music © Copyright Oxford University Press, Great Clarendon Street, Oxford OX2 6DP.
Used by permission.

2. Within these walls let holy peace
and love and concord dwell;
here give the troubled conscience ease,
the wounded spirit heal.

3. May we in faith receive thy word,
in faith present our pray'rs,
and in the presence of our Lord
unburden all our cares.

4. The hearing ear, the seeing eye,
the contrite heart, bestow;
and shine upon us from on high,
that we in grace may grow.

251 Great Son of God

Edwin Le Grice (1911-1992) | Orlando Gibbons (1583-1625)

TUNE 1: SONG 1 10 10 10 10 10 10

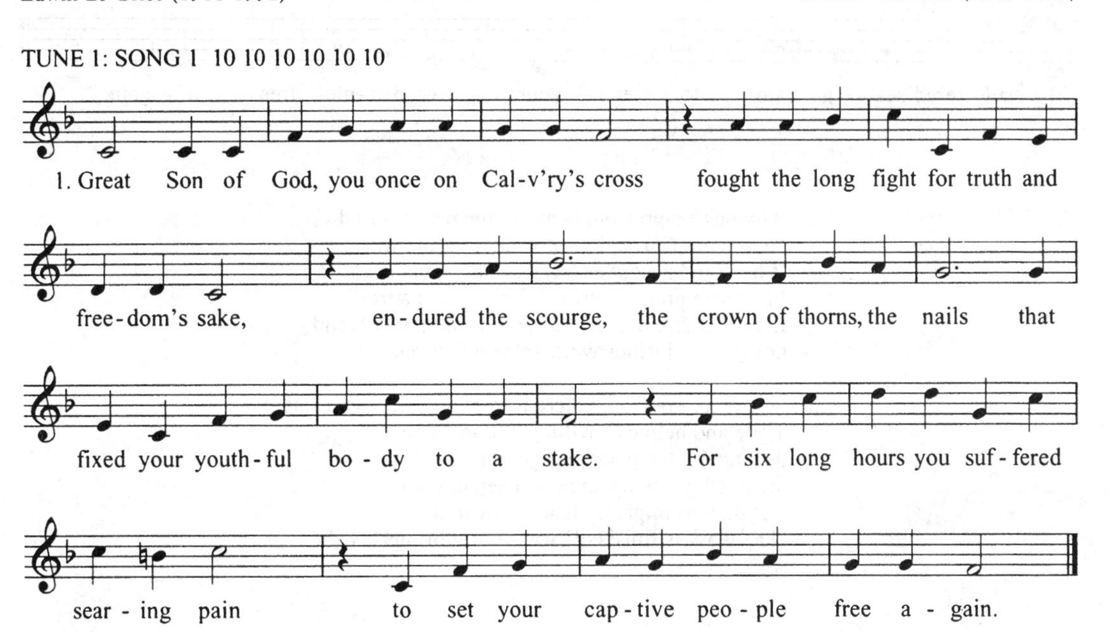

2. 'Give us a sign from heav'n,' the people cried.
'If you are Christ, leap down, alive and free.
Who could accept as Saviour one who died
like some poor miscreant skewered to a tree?'
Lord Christ, our Saviour, you would not descend
until your glorious work achieved its end.

3. 'My God, my God, where have you gone?' you called,
alone and helpless, willing still to share
through all the gath'ring gloom of Calvary,
the depth of dying sinners' deep despair.
But then triumphant, ready now to die,
'The work is finished!' was your glorious cry.

Text and Tune 2 © Copyright 1995 Kevin Mayhew Ltd.

Edwin Le Grice (1911-1992) Malcolm Archer (b.1952)

TUNE 2: EDDLESTON 10 10 10 10 10 10

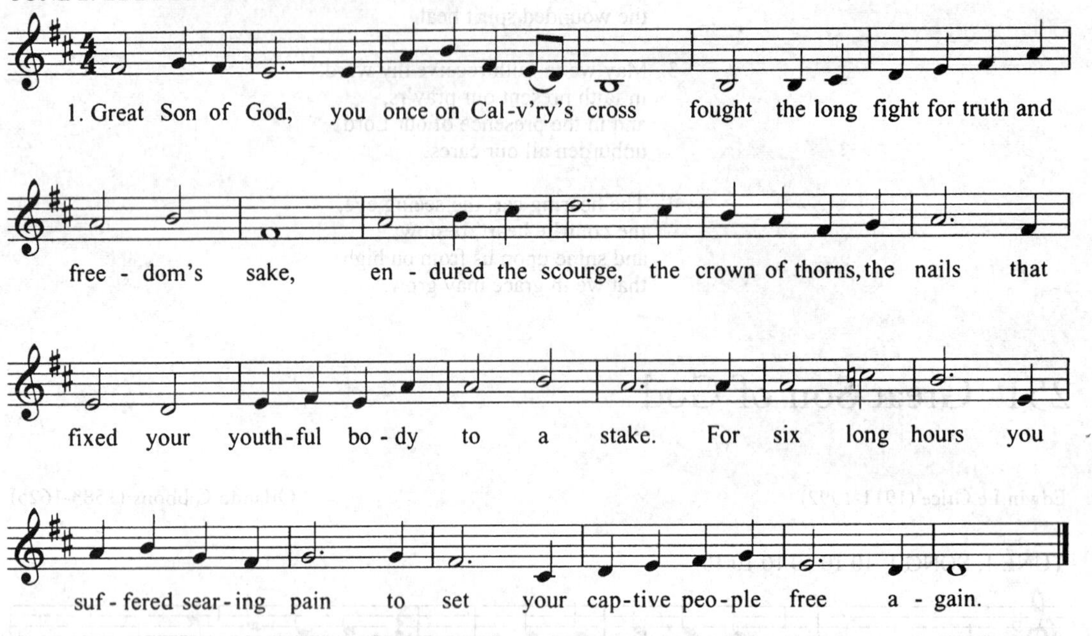

2. 'Give us a sign from heav'n,' the people cried.
'If you are Christ, leap down, alive and free.
Who could accept as Saviour one who died
like some poor miscreant skewered to a tree?'
Lord Christ, our Saviour, you would not descend
until your glorious work achieved its end.

3. 'My God, my God, where have you gone?' you called,
alone and helpless, willing still to share
through all the gath'ring gloom of Calvary,
the depth of dying sinners' deep despair.
But then triumphant, ready now to die,
'The work is finished!' was your glorious cry.

252 Guide me, O thou great Redeemer

William Williams (1717-1791)
trans. Peter Williams (1727-1796) and others

John Hughes (1873-1932)

CWM RHONDDA 87 87 47

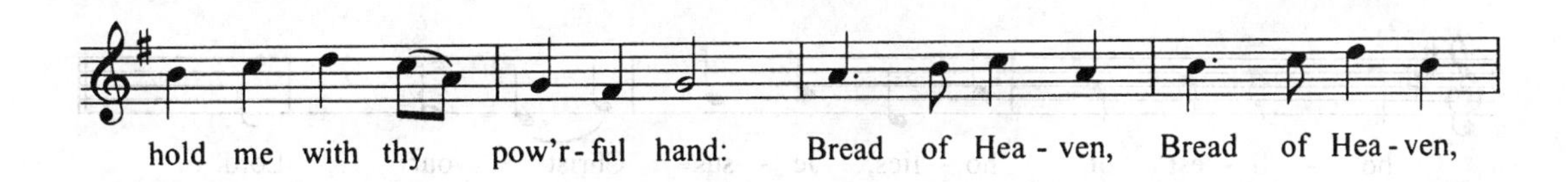

2. Open now the crystal fountain,
whence the healing stream doth flow;
let the fire and cloudy pillar
lead me all my journey through;
strong deliv'rer, strong deliv'rer,
be thou still my strength and shield,
be thou still my strength and shield.

3. When I tread the verge of Jordan,
bid my anxious fears subside;
death of death, and hell's destruction,
land me safe on Canaan's side;
songs of praises, songs of praises,
I will ever give to thee,
I will ever give to thee.

Music © Copyright Control

253 Hail, gladdening Light

Greek (3rd century or earlier)
trans. John Keble (1792-1866)

John Stainer (1840-1901)

254 Hail, O Star that pointest

Latin (c.9th century)
trans. Athelstan Riley (1858-1945)

Arundel Hymns (1896),
composed or arranged by
John Richardson (1816-1879)

AVE MARIS STELLA 66 66

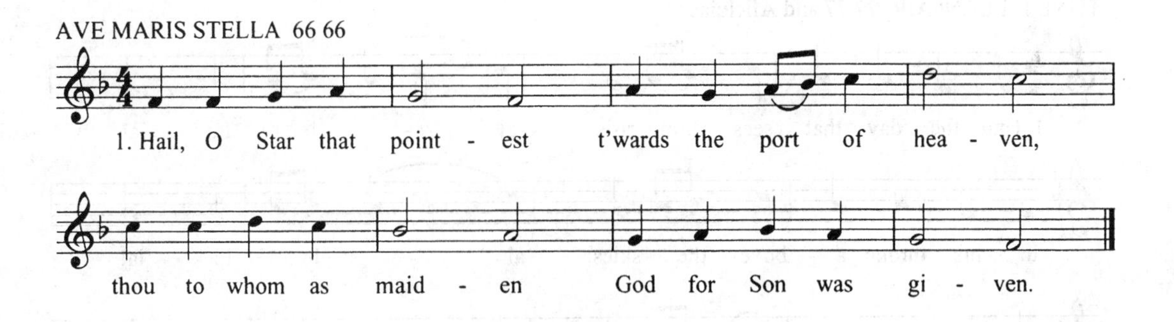

2. When the salutation
Gabriel had spoken,
peace was shed upon us,
Eva's bonds were broken.

3. Bound by Satan's fetters,
health and vision needing,
God will aid and light us
at thy gentle pleading.

4. Jesu's tender mother,
make the supplication
unto him who chose thee
at his incarnation.

5. That, O matchless maiden,
passing meek and lowly,
thy dear son may make us
blameless, chaste and holy.

6. So, as now we journey,
aid our weak endeavour
till we gaze on Jesus,
and rejoice for ever.

7. Father, Son and Spirit,
Three in One confessing,
give we equal glory,
equal praise and blessing.

Text © Copyright Oxford University Press, Great Clarendon Street, Oxford OX2 6DP.
Used by permission from the *English Hymnal*.

255 Hail the day that sees him rise

Charles Wesley (1707-1788),
Thomas Cotterill (1779-1823)
and others, alt.

Robert Williams (1781-1821)

TUNE 1: LLANFAIR 77 77 and Alleluias

2. There for him high triumph waits;
lift your heads, eternal gates!
He hath conquered death and sin;
take the King of Glory in!

3. Circled round with angel-pow'rs,
their triumphant Lord and ours;
wide unfold the radiant scene,
take the King of Glory in!

4. Lo, the heav'n its Lord receives,
yet he loves the earth he leaves;
though returning to his throne,
calls the human race his own.

5. See, he lifts his hands above;
see, he shows the prints of love;
hark, his gracious lips bestow
blessings on his Church below.

6. Still for us he intercedes,
his prevailing death he pleads;
near himself prepares our place,
he the first-fruits of our race.

7. Lord, though parted from our sight,
far above the starry height,
grant our hearts may thither rise,
seeking thee above the skies.

8. Ever upward let us move,
wafted on the wings of love;
looking when our Lord shall come,
longing, sighing after home.

Tune 3 © Copyright Hymns Ancient & Modern, St Mary's Works,
St Mary's Plain, Norwich NR3 3BH. Used by permission.

Charles Wesley (1707-1788),
Thomas Cotterill (1779-1823)
and others, alt.

William Henry Monk (1823-1889)

TUNE 2: ASCENSION 77 77 and Alleluias

Charles Wesley (1707-1788),
Thomas Cotterill (1779-1823)
and others, alt.

Sydney Hugo Nicholson (1875-1947)

TUNE 3: CHISLEHURST 77 77 and Alleluias

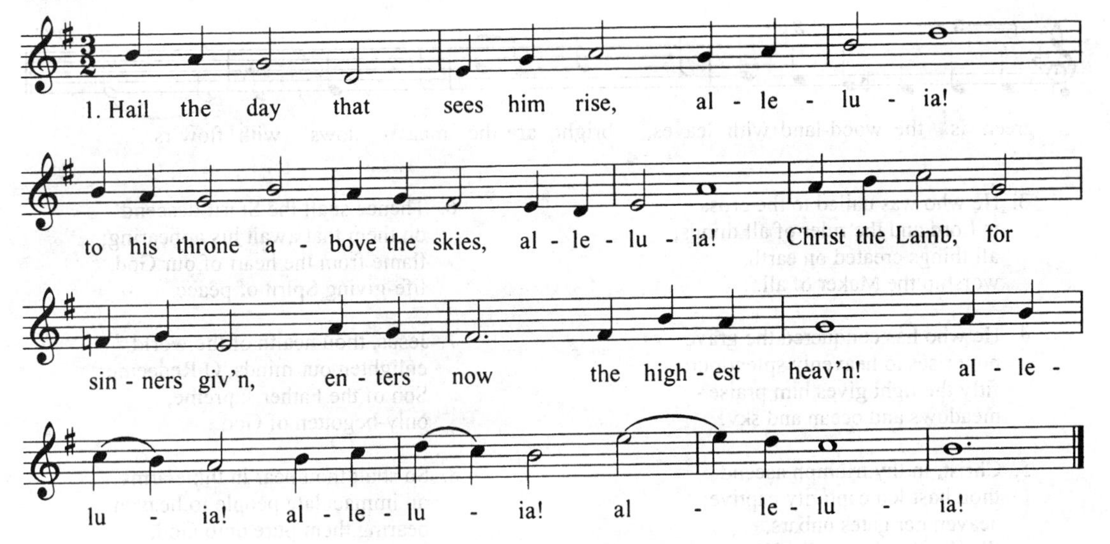

256 Hail thee, Festival Day (Ascension version)

The editors of *The New English Hymnal*
based on the Latin of
Venantius Fortunatus (530-609)

Ralph Vaughan Williams (1872-1958)

SALVE FESTA DIES Irregular and Refrain

3. He who was nailed to the cross
is Lord and the ruler of all things;
all things created on earth,
worship the Maker of all.

4. He who has conquered the grave
now rises to heavenly splendour;
fitly the light gives him praise -
meadows and ocean and sky.

5. Christ, in thy triumph ascend:
thou hast led captivity captive;
heaven her gates unbars,
flinging her increase of light.

6. Thence shall the Spirit descend
on them that await his appearing;
flame from the heart of our God,
life-giving Spirit of peace.

7. Jesus, thou health of the world,
enlighten our minds, O Redeemer,
Son of the Father supreme,
only-begotten of God.

8. So shalt thou bear in thine arms
an immaculate people to heaven,
bearing them pure unto God,
pledge of thy victory here.

9. Equal art thou, co-eternal,
in fellowship One with the Father,
and with the Spirit of truth,
God evermore to be blest!

Text © Copyright Hymns Ancient & Modern, St Mary's Works,
St Mary's Plain, Norwich NR3 3BH. Used by permission.
Music © Copyright Oxford University Press, Great Clarendon Street, Oxford OX2 6DP.
Used by permission from *The English Hymnal*.

257 Hail thee, Festival Day (Easter version)

The editors of *The New English Hymnal* based on the Latin of Venantius Fortunatus (530-609)

Ralph Vaughan Williams (1872-1958)

SALVE FESTA DIES Irregular and Refrain

3. He who was nailed to the cross
is Lord and the ruler of all things;
all things created on earth,
worship the Maker of all.

4. Ill it beseemeth that thou,
by whose hand all things are encompassed,
captive and bound should remain,
deep in the gloom of the rock.

5. Rise now, O Lord from the grave
and cast off the shroud that enwrapped thee;
leaving the caverns of death,
show us the light of thy face.

6. God of all pity and pow'r,
let thy word be assured to the doubting;
lo, he breaks from the tomb!
See, he appears to his own!

7. Jesus, thou health of the world,
enlighten our minds, O redeemer,
Son of the Father supreme,
only-begotten of God.

8. So shalt thou bear in thine arms
an immaculate people to heaven,
bearing them pure unto God,
pledge of thy victory here.

9. Equal art thou, co-eternal,
in fellowship One with the Father,
and with the Spirit of truth,
God evermore to be blest!

Text © Copyright Hymns Ancient & Modern, St Mary's Works,
St Mary's Plain, Norwich NR3 3BH. Used by permission.
Music © Copyright Oxford University Press, Great Clarendon Street, Oxford OX2 6DP.
Used by permission from *The English Hymnal*.

258 Hail, thou once despisèd Jesus

John Bakewell (1721-1819) alt. Arthur Seymour Sullivan (1842-1900)

LUX EOI 87 87 D

2. Paschal Lamb, by God appointed,
all our sins on thee were laid;
by almighty love anointed,
thou hast full atonement made.
All thy people are forgiven
through the virtue of thy blood;
opened is the gate of heaven,
we are reconciled to God.

3. Jesus, hail! enthroned in glory,
there for ever to abide;
all the heav'nly hosts adore thee,
seated at thy Father's side:
there for sinners thou art pleading,
there thou dost our place prepare;
ever for us interceding,
till in glory we appear.

4. Worship, honour, pow'r and blessing,
thou art worthy to receive;
loudest praises, without ceasing,
it is right for us to give:
help, ye bright angelic spirits!
bring your sweetest, noblest lays;
help to sing our Saviour's merits,
help to chant Immanuel's praise.

259 Hail to the Lord's anointed

Paraphrase of Psalm 72
by James Montgomery (1771-1854)

From a melody in Johann Crüger's *Gesangbuch*
adapted by William Henry Monk (1823-1889)

CRÜGER 76 76 D

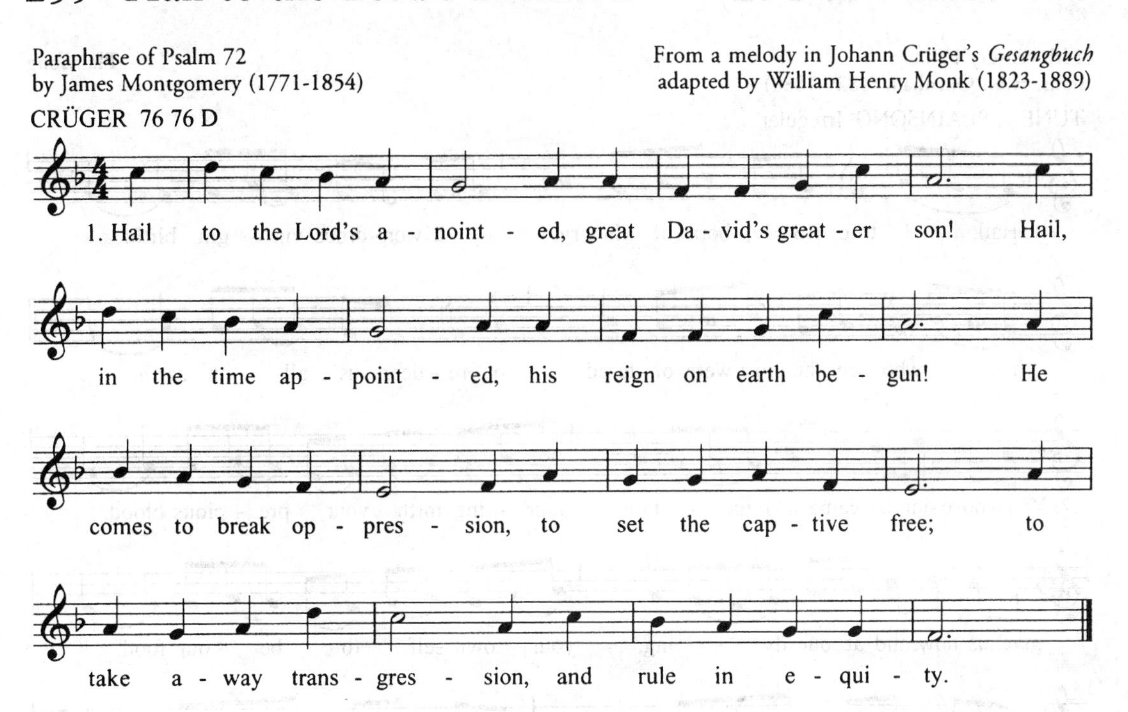

2. He comes with succour speedy
to those who suffer wrong;
to help the poor and needy,
and bid the weak be strong;
to give them songs for sighing,
their darkness turn to light,
whose souls, condemned and dying,
were precious in his sight.

3. He shall come down like showers
upon the fruitful earth,
and love, joy, hope, like flowers,
spring in his path to birth:
before him on the mountains
shall peace the herald go;
and righteousness in fountains
from hill to valley flow.

4. Kings shall fall down before him,
and gold and incense bring;
all nations shall adore him,
his praise all people sing;
to him shall prayer unceasing
and daily vows ascend;
his kingdom still increasing,
a kingdom without end.

5. O'er ev'ry foe victorious,
he on his throne shall rest,
from age to age more glorious,
all-blessing and all-blest;
the tide of time shall never
his covenant remove;
his name shall stand for ever;
that name to us is love.

260 Hail, true Body

Tune 2 © Copyright Hymns Ancient & Modern, St Mary's Works,
St Mary's Plain, Norwich NR3 3BH. Used by permission

261 Hallelujah, my Father

Tim Cullen alt. | Tim Cullen

© Copyright 1975 Celebration/Kingsway's Thankyou Music, P.O. Box 75, Eastbourne, East Sussex BN23 6NW, UK. (tym@kingsway.co.uk) Europe and Commonwealth (excl. Canada, Australasia & Africa). Used by permission

262 Happy are they, they that love God

Robert Bridges (1844-1930)
based on *O quam juvat*,
Charles Coffin (1676-1749) alt.

William Croft (1678-1727)

BINCHESTER CM

2. Glad is the praise, sweet are the songs,
when they together sing;
and strong the prayers that bow the ear
of heav'n's eternal King.

3. Christ to their homes giveth his peace,
and makes their loves his own:
but ah, what tares the evil one
hath in his garden sown!

4. Sad were our lot, evil this earth,
did not its sorrows prove
the path whereby the sheep may find
the fold of Jesus' love.

5. Then shall they know, they that love him,
how hope is wrought through pain;
their fellowship, through death itself,
unbroken will remain.

263 Hark! a herald voice is calling

Vox clara ecce intonat (6th century)
trans. Edward Caswall (1814-1878)

William Henry Monk (1823-1889)

MERTON 87 87

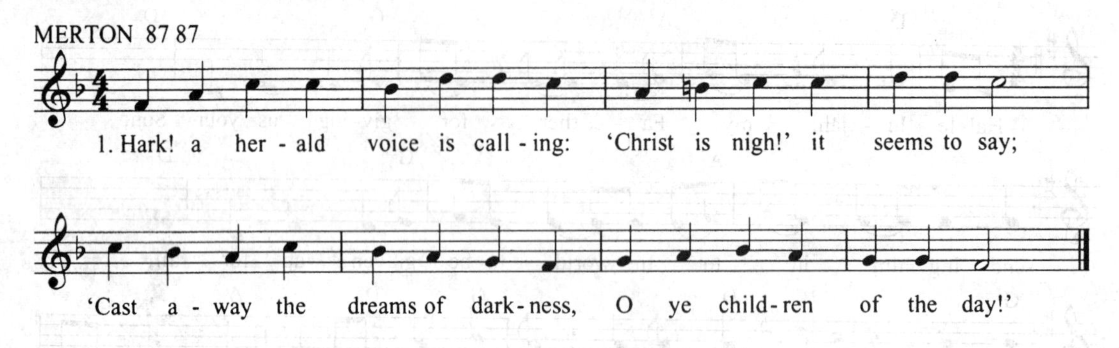

2. Startled at the solemn warning,
let the earth-bound soul arise;
Christ, her sun, all sloth dispelling,
shines upon the morning skies.

3. Lo, the Lamb, so long expected,
comes with pardon down from heav'n;
let us haste, with tears of sorrow,
one and all to be forgiv'n.

4. So when next he comes with glory,
wrapping all the earth in fear,
may he then, as our defender,
on the clouds of heav'n appear.

5. Honour, glory, virtue, merit,
to the Father and the Son,
with the co-eternal Spirit,
while unending ages run.

264 Hark, my soul, it is the Lord

William Cowper (1731-1800)
based on John 21:16

John Bacchus Dykes (1823-1876)

ST BEES 77 77

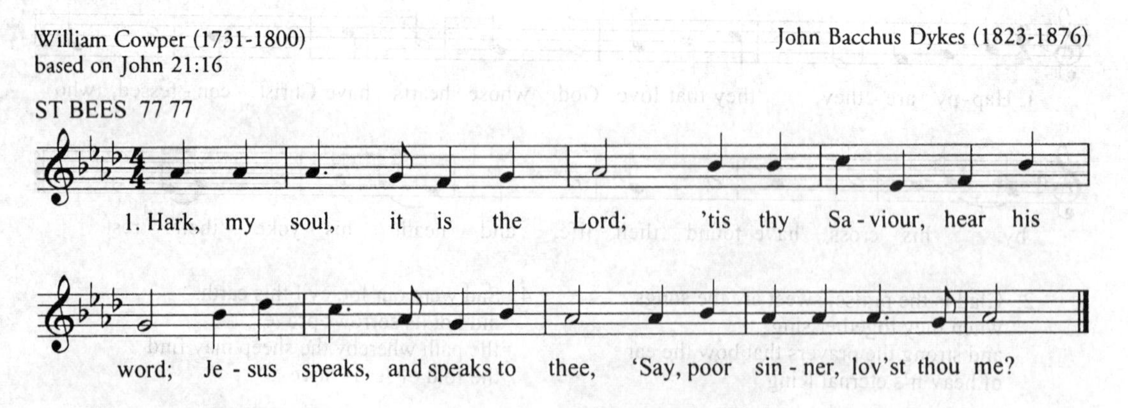

2. 'I delivered thee when bound,
and, when wounded, healed thy wound;
sought thee wand'ring, set thee right,
turned thy darkness into light.

3. 'Can a woman's tender care
cease towards the child she bare?
Yes, she may forgetful be,
yet will I remember thee.

4. 'Mine is an unchanging love,
higher than the heights above,
deeper than the depths beneath,
free and faithful, strong as death.

5. 'Thou shalt see my glory soon,
when the work of grace is done;
partner of my throne shalt be:
say, poor sinner, lov'st thou me?'

6. Lord, it is my chief complaint
that my love is weak and faint;
yet I love thee, and adore;
O for grace to love thee more!

265 Hark, the glad sound!

Thomas Ravenscroft (c.1582-c.1633),
Psalms (1621)

Philip Doddridge (1702-1751)
based on Luke 4:18-19

BRISTOL CM

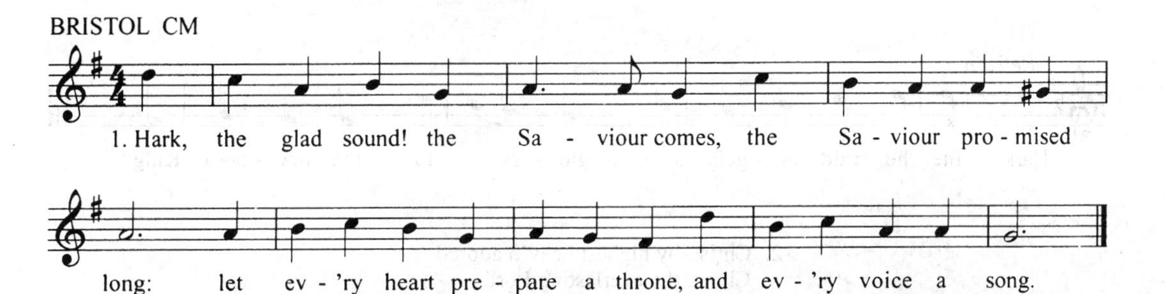

2. He comes, the pris'ners to release
in Satan's bondage held;
the gates of brass before him burst,
the iron fetters yield.

3. He comes, the broken heart to bind,
the bleeding soul to cure,
and with the treasures of his grace
to bless the humble poor.

4. Our glad hosannas, Prince of Peace,
thy welcome shall proclaim;
and heav'n's eternal arches ring
with thy belovèd name.

266 Hark, the herald-angels sing

Charles Wesley (1707-1788),
George Whitefield (1714-1770),
Martin Madan (1726-1790) and others, alt.

Adapted from Felix Mendelssohn (1809-1847)
by William Hayman Cummings (1831-1915)

MENDELSSOHN 77 77 D and Refrain

2. Christ, by highest heav'n adored,
Christ, the everlasting Lord,
late in time behold him come,
offspring of a virgin's womb!
Veiled in flesh the Godhead see,
hail, th'incarnate Deity!
Pleased as man with us to dwell,
Jesus, our Emmanuel.

3. Hail, the heav'n-born Prince of Peace!
Hail, the Sun of Righteousness!
Light and life to all he brings,
ris'n with healing in his wings;
mild he lays his glory by,
born that we no more may die,
born to raise us from the earth,
born to give us second birth.

267 Hark! the sound of holy voices

Christopher Wordsworth (1807-1885) alt.

James Langran (1835-1909)

DEERHURST 87 87 D

2. Patriarch and holy prophet,
   who prepared the way of Christ,
   king, apostle, saint, confessor,
   martyr and evangelist,
   saintly maiden, godly matron,
   widows who have watched in prayer,
   joined in holy concert, singing
   to the Lord of all, are there.

3. They have come from tribulation,
   and have washed their robes in blood,
   washed them in the blood of Jesus;
   tried they were, and firm they stood;
   gladly, Lord, with thee they suffered;
   gladly, Lord, with thee they died,
   and by death to life immortal
   they were born and glorified.

4. Now they reign in heav'nly glory,
   now they walk in golden light,
   now they drink, as from a river,
   holy bliss and infinite;
   love and peace they taste for ever,
   and all truth and knowledge see
   in the beatific vision
   of the blessèd Trinity.

5. God of God, the one-begotten,
   Light of Light, Emmanuel,
   in whose body joined together
   all the saints for ever dwell;
   pour upon us of thy fullness,
   that we may for evermore
   Father, Son and Holy Spirit
   truly worship and adore.

268 Have faith in God, my heart

Bryn Austin Rees (1911-1983)

Samuel Wesley (1766-1837)

DONCASTER SM

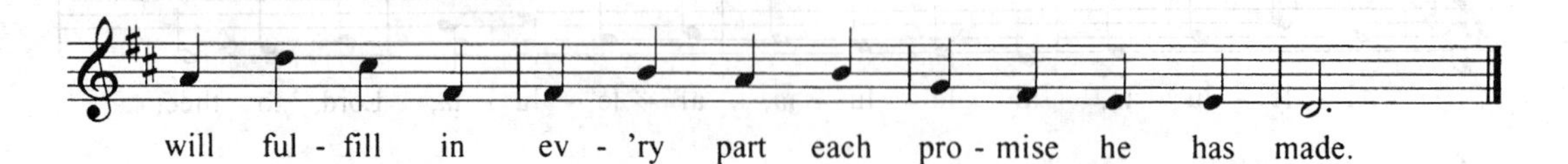

2. Have faith in God, my mind,
though oft thy light burns low;
God's mercy holds a wiser plan
than thou canst fully know.

3. Have faith in God, my soul,
his Cross for ever stands;
and neither life nor death can pluck
his children from his hands.

4. Lord Jesus, make me whole;
grant me no resting-place,
until I rest, heart, mind and soul,
the captive of thy grace.

Text © Copyright Alexander Scott. Used by kind permission.

269 Have mercy on us, O Lord

Susan Sayers (b.1946)
based on Psalm 51

Alan Ridout (1934-1996)

© Copyright 1989 Kevin Mayhew Ltd.

2. For all my offences I know very well,
I cannot escape from the sight of my sin.
Against you, O Lord, only you, have I sinned,
and done what is wrong in your eyes.

3. A pure heart create in your servant, O Lord;
a steadfast and trustworthy spirit in me.
O cast me not out from your presence, I pray,
and take not your spirit from me.

4. Restore to me, Lord, all the joy of your help;
sustain me with fervour, sustain me with zeal.
Then open my lips, and my mouth shall declare
the praise of my Lord and my God.

270 Healer of the sick

Francesca Leftley (b.1955)

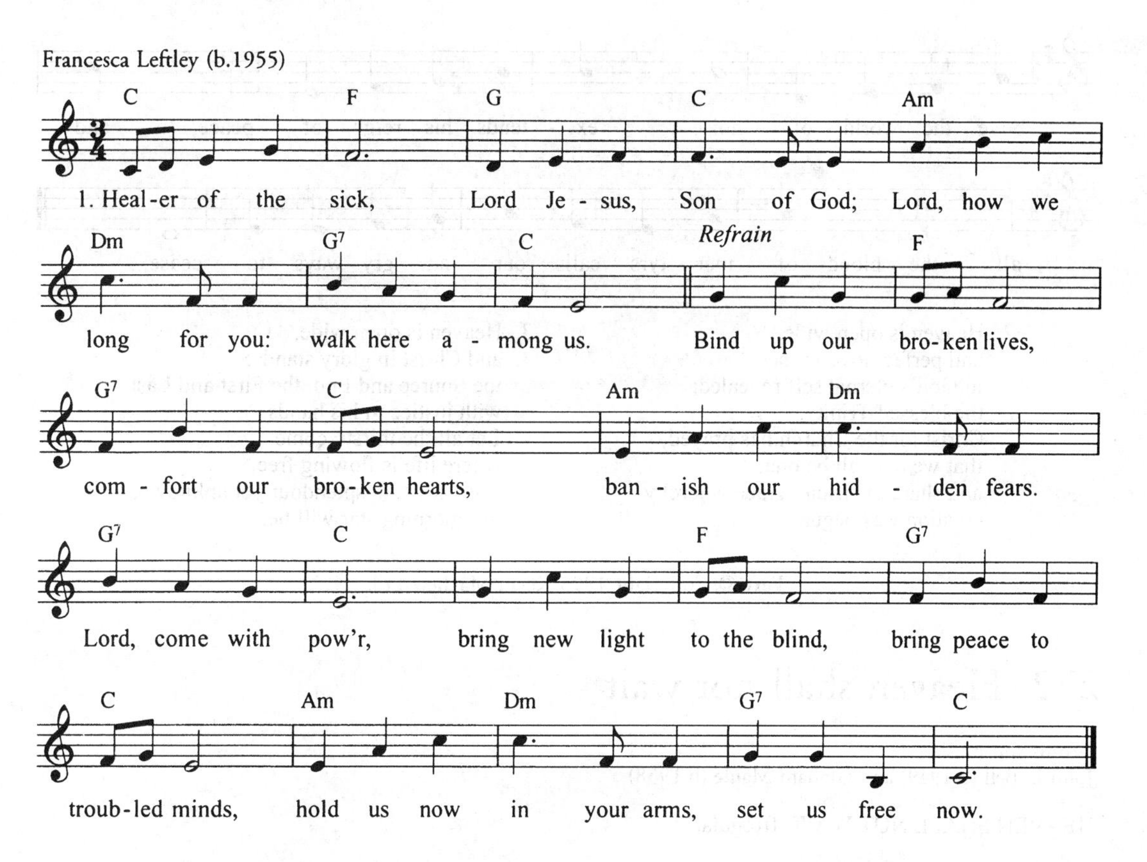

2. Bearer of our pain,
Lord Jesus, Lamb of God;
Lord, how we cry to you:
walk here among us.

3. Calmer of our fears,
Lord Jesus, Prince of Peace;
Lord, how we yearn for you:
walk here among us.

4. Saviour of the world,
Lord Jesus, mighty God;
Lord, how we sing to you:
walk here among us.

© Copyright 1999 Kevin Mayhew Ltd.

271 Heaven is open wide

Michael Forster (b.1946) George Job Elvey (1816-1893)

DIADEMATA DSM

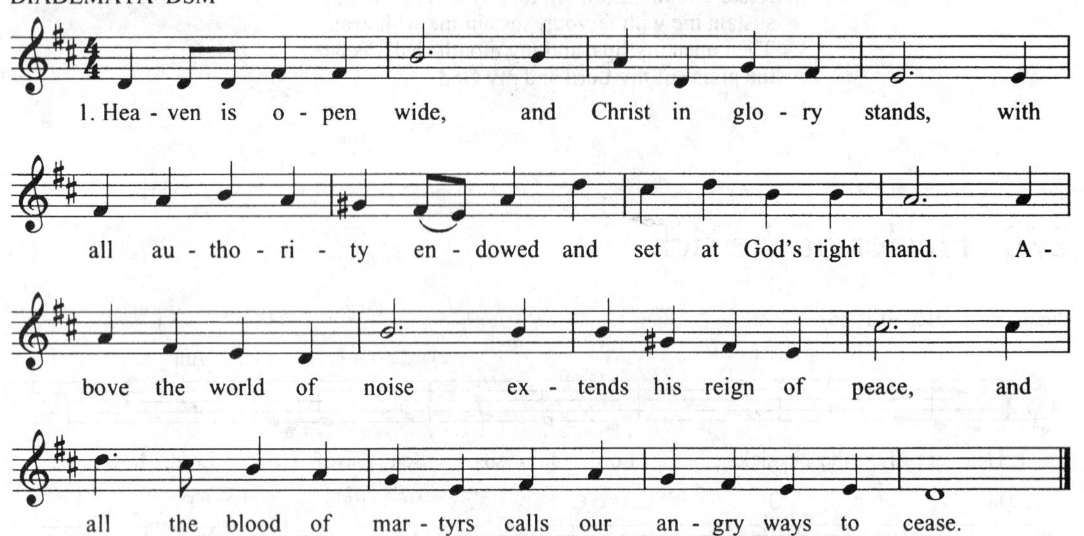

2. Heaven is open wide,
and perfect love we see
in God's eternal self revealed:
the blessèd Trinity.
Christ for the Church has prayed,
that we may all be one,
and share the triune grace whereby
creation was begun.

3. Heaven is open wide,
and Christ in glory stands:
the Source and End, the First and Last,
with justice in his hands.
Let all the thirsty come
where life is flowing free,
and Christ, in splendour yet unknown,
our morning star will be.

Text © Copyright 1993 Kevin Mayhew Ltd.

272 Heaven shall not wait

Words and music:
John L. Bell (b.1949) and Graham Maule (b.1958)

HEAVEN SHALL NOT WAIT Irregular

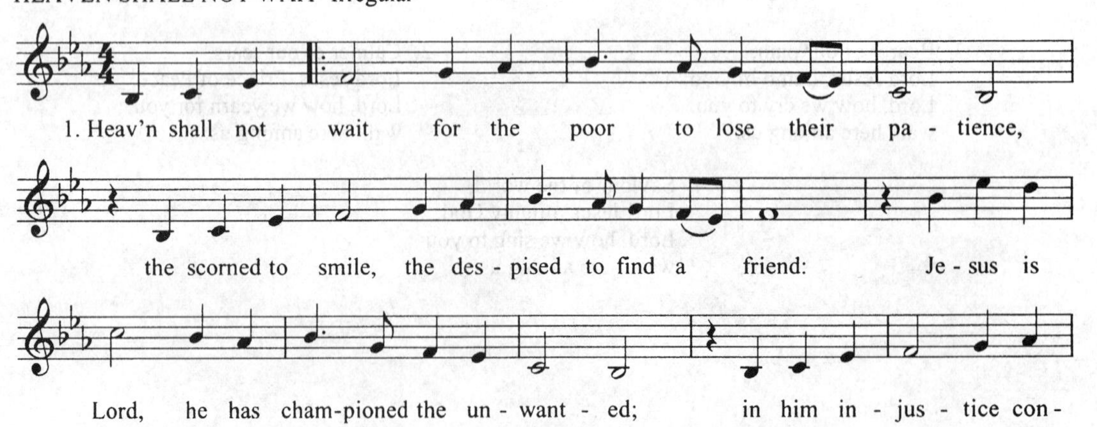

© Copyright 1987 WGRG, Iona Community, Glasgow G2 3DH, Scotland.
Used by permission from the *Heaven shall not wait* collection. (Wild Goose Publications, 1987).

2. Heav'n shall not wait for the rich to share their fortunes,
the proud to fall, the élite to tend the least:
Jesus is Lord; he has shown the masters' priv'lege –
to kneel and wash servants' feet before they feast.

3. Heav'n shall not wait for the dawn of great ideas,
thoughts of compassion divorced from cries of pain:
Jesus is Lord; he has married word and action;
his cross and company make his purpose plain.

4. Heav'n shall not wait for our legalised obedience,
defined by statute, to strict conventions bound:
Jesus is Lord; he has hallmarked true allegiance –
goodness appears where his grace is sought and found.

5. Heav'n shall not wait for triumphant hallelujahs,
when earth has passed and we reach another shore:
Jesus is Lord in our present imperfection;
his pow'r and love are for now and then for evermore.

273 He is exalted

Words and music: Twila Paris

© Copyright 1985 Straightway/Mountain Spring/EMI Christian Music Publishing. Administered by CopyCare, P.O. Box 77, Hailsham, East Sussex BN27 3EF, UK. (music@copycare.com). Used by permission.

274 He is Lord

Words and music: unknown

2. He is King, he is King.
He is risen from the dead and he is King.
Ev'ry knee shall bow, ev'ry tongue confess
that Jesus Christ is King.

3. He is love, he is love.
He is risen from the dead and he is love.
Ev'ry knee shall bow, ev'ry tongue confess
that Jesus Christ is love.

275 Help us to help each other, Lord

Charles Wesley (1707-1788) alt. *Scottish Psalter* (1615)

DUNFERMLINE CM

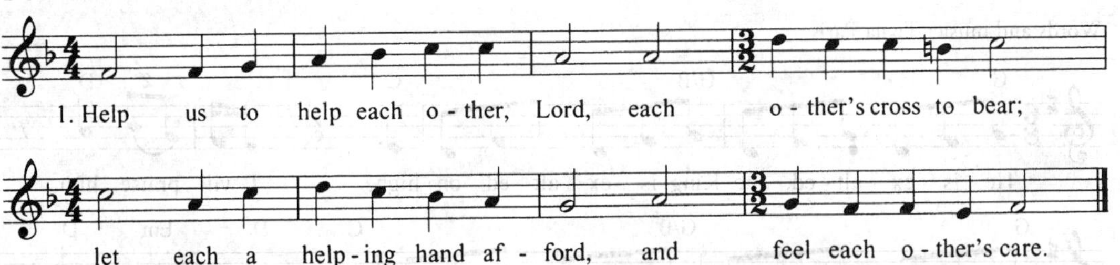

2. Up into thee, our living head,
let us in all things grow,
and by thy sacrifice be led
the fruits of love to show.

3. Drawn by the magnet of thy love
let all our hearts agree;
and ever t'wards each other move,
and ever move t'wards thee.

4. This is the bond of perfectness,
thy spotless charity.
O let us still we pray, possess
the mind that was in thee.

276 Here hangs a man discarded

Brian Wren (b.1936) Henry John Gauntlett (1805-1876)

ST ALPHEGE 76 76

Text © Copyright 1975, 1995 Stainer & Bell Ltd., P.O. Box 110, Victoria House,
23 Gruneison Road, Finchley, London N3 1DZ. Used by permission.

2. Can such a clown of sorrows
still bring a useful word
when faith and love seem phantoms
and ev'ry hope absurd?

3. Yet here is help and comfort
for lives by comfort bound,
when drums of dazzling progress
give strangely hollow sound:

4. Life, emptied of all meaning,
drained out in bleak distress,
can share in broken silence
our deepest emptiness;

5. And love that freely entered
the pit of life's despair
can name our hidden darkness
and suffer with us there.

6. Christ, in our darkness risen,
help all who long for light
to hold the hand of promise,
till faith receives its sight.

277 Here is bread

Words and music: Graham Kendrick (b.1950)

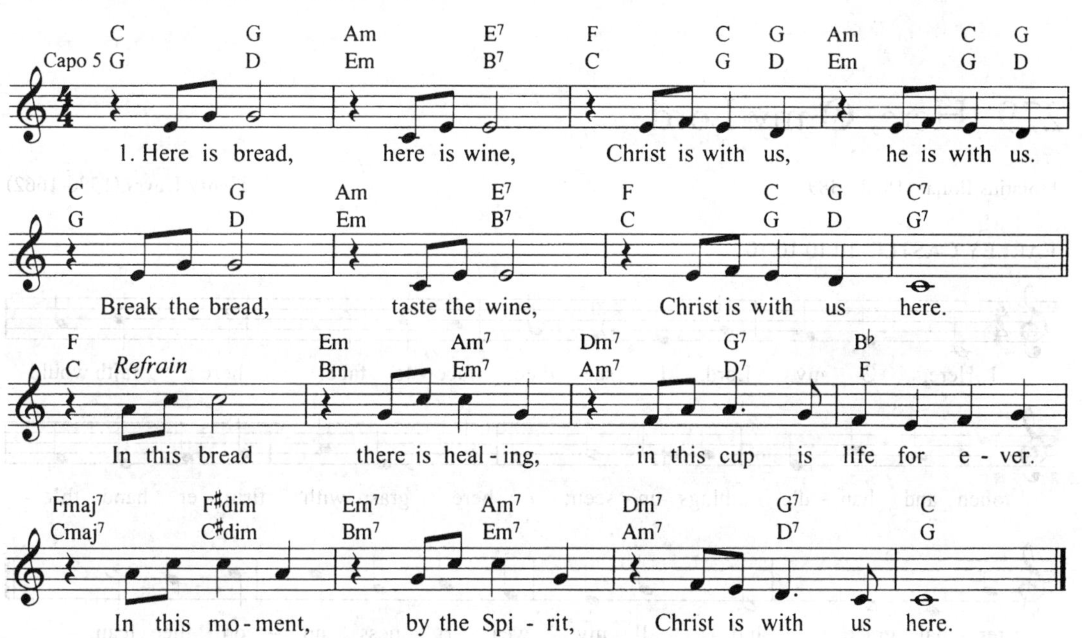

2. Here is grace, here is peace,
Christ is with us, he is with us;
know his grace, find his peace,
feast on Jesus here.

3. Here we are, joined in one,
Christ is with us, he is with us;
we'll proclaim, till he comes,
Jesus crucified.

© Copyright 1991 Make Way Music, P.O. Box 263, Croydon, Surrey CR9 5AP, UK.
International copyright secured. All rights reserved. Used by permission.

278 Here, Lord, we take the broken bread

Charles Venn Pilcher (1879-1961)

Irish melody (Petrie Collection)

ST COLUMBA 87 87

2. As you have giv'n, so we would give
ourselves for others' healing;
and as you lived, so we would live,
the Father's love revealing.

Text © Copyright 1935 Mrs I.E.V. Pilcher. Used by permission.

279 Here, O my Lord

Horatius Bonar (1808-1889)

Henry Lawes (1596-1662)

FARLEY CASTLE 10 10 10 10

2. Here would I feed upon the bread of God;
here drink with thee the royal wine of heav'n;
here would I lay aside each earthly load;
here taste afresh the calm of sin forgiv'n.

3. I have no help but thee; nor do I need
another arm save thine to lean upon:
it is enough, my Lord, enough indeed,
my strength is in thy might, thy might alone.

280 Here on the threshold of a new beginning

Timothy Dudley-Smith (b.1926) Malcolm Archer (b.1952)

ADVENIT 11 10 11 10 D

1. Here on the thres - hold of a new be - gin - ning, by grace for -
gi - ven, now we leave be - hind our long-re - pen - ted sel - fish-ness and
sin - ning, and all our bles-sings call a - gain to mind: Christ to re -
deem us, ran - som and re - store us, the love that holds us
in a Sa-viour's care, faith strong to wel - come all that lies be -
fore us, our un - known fu - ture, know - ing God is there.

2. May we, your children, feel with Christ's compassion
an earth disordered, hungry and in pain;
then, at your calling, find the will to fashion
new ways where freedom, truth and justice reign;
where wars are ended, ancient wrongs are righted,
and nations value human life and worth;
where in the darkness lamps of hope are lighted
and Christ is honoured over all the earth.

3. So may your wisdom shine from scripture's pages
to mould and make us stones with which to build
God's holy temple, through eternal ages,
one church united, strong and Spirit-filled;
heirs to the fullness of your new creation
in faith we follow, pledged to be your own;
yours is the future, ours the celebration,
for Christ is risen! God is on the throne!

Text © Copyright Timothy Dudley-Smith, 9 Ashlands,
Ford, Salisbury, Wiltshire SP4 6DY. Used by permission.
Music © Copyright 1999 Kevin Mayhew Ltd.

281 He who would valiant be

Percy Dearmer (1867-1936)
after John Bunyan (1628-1688)

Traditional English melody collected by
Ralph Vaughan Williams (1872-1958)

2. Who so beset him round
with dismal stories,
do but themselves confound –
his strength the more is.
No foes shall stay his might,
though he with giants fight:
he will make good his right
to be a pilgrim.

3. Since, Lord, thou dost defend
us with thy Spirit,
we know we at the end
shall life inherit.
Then fancies flee away!
I'll fear not what men say,
I'll labour night and day
to be a pilgrim.

© Copyright Oxford University Press, Great Clarendon Street, Oxford OX2 6DP.
Used by permission from the *English Hymnal*.

282 Hills of the north, rejoice

Charles Edward Oakley (1832-1865), adapted
Martin Shaw (1875-1958)

LITTLE CORNARD 66 66 88

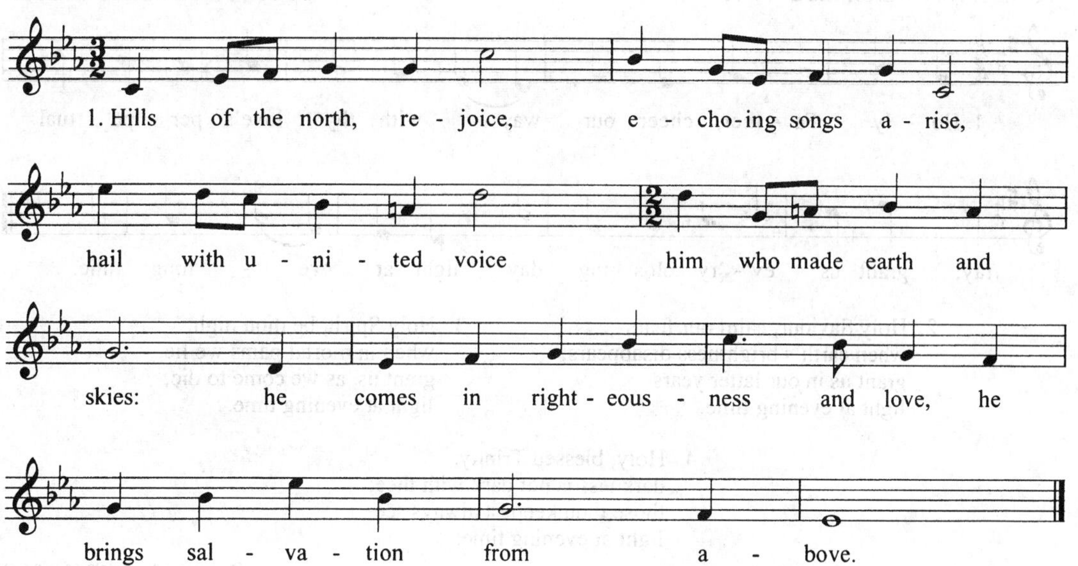

2. Isles of the southern seas
sing to the list'ning earth,
carry on ev'ry breeze
hope of a world's new birth:
in Christ shall all be made anew,
his word is sure, his promise true.

3. Lands of the east, arise,
he is your brightest morn,
greet him with joyous eyes,
praise shall his path adorn:
the God whom you have longed to know
in Christ draws near, and calls you now.

4. Shores of the utmost west,
lands of the setting sun,
welcome the heav'nly guest
in whom the dawn has come:
he brings a never-ending light
who triumphed o'er our darkest night.

5. Shout, as you journey on,
songs be in ev'ry mouth,
lo, from the north they come,
from east and west and south:
in Jesus all shall find their rest,
in him the longing earth be blest.

© Copyright Martin Shaw. Exclusively licensed to and reproduced by permission of J. Curwen & Sons Ltd., 8/9 Frith Street, London W1D 3JB. All rights reserved. International copyright secured. Used by permission.

283 Holy Father, cheer our way

Richard Robinson (1842-1892) | Walter Parratt (1841-1924)

TUNE 1: HUDDERSFIELD 77 75

ray; grant us ev - 'ry clos - ing day light at eve - ning time.

2. Holy Saviour, calm our fears
when earth's brightness disappears;
grant us in our latter years
light at evening time.

3. Holy Spirit, be thou nigh
when in mortal pains we lie;
grant us, as we come to die,
light at evening time.

4. Holy, blessed Trinity,
darkness is not dark with thee;
those thou keepest always see
light at evening time.

Richard Robinson (1842-1892) | John Stainer (1840-1901)

TUNE 2: VESPER 77 75

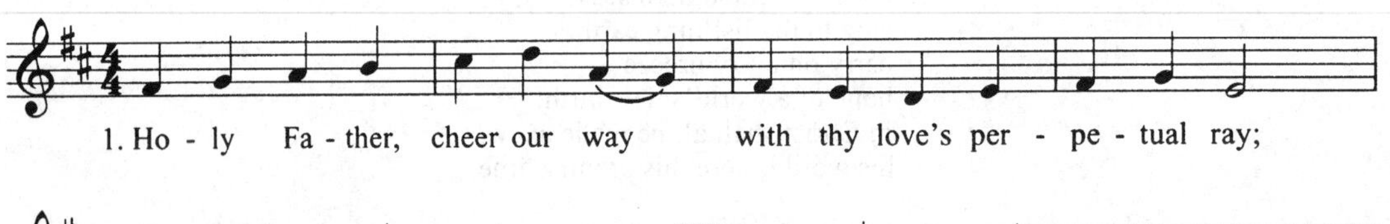

284 Holy, holy, holy

Words and music: Jimmy Owens

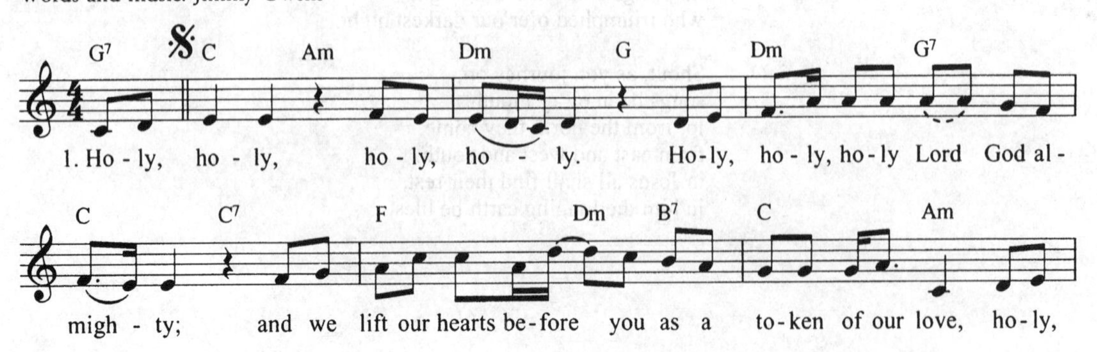

© Copyright 1972 Bud John Songs/EMI Christian Music Publishing. Administered by CopyCare, P.O. Box 77, Hailsham, East Sussex BN27 3EF, UK. (music@copycare.com). Used by permission.

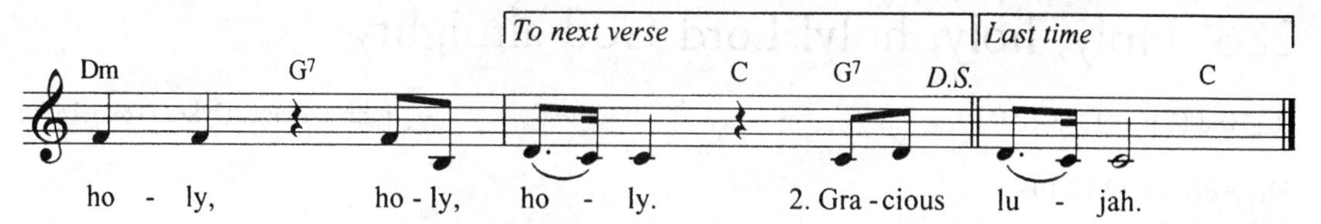

2. Gracious Father, gracious Father,
we are glad to be your children, gracious Father;
and we lift our heads before you as a token of our love,
gracious Father, gracious Father.

3. Risen Jesus, risen Jesus,
we are glad you have redeemed us, risen Jesus;
and we lift our hands before you as a token of our love,
risen Jesus, risen Jesus.

4. Holy Spirit, Holy Spirit,
come and fill our hearts anew, Holy Spirit;
and we lift our voice before you as a token of our love,
Holy Spirit, Holy Spirit.

5. Hallelujah, hallelujah,
hallelujah, hallelujah, hallelujah;
and we lift our hearts before you as a token of our love,
hallelujah, hallelujah.

285 Holy, holy, holy is the Lord

Words and music: unknown

2. Jesus, Jesus, Jesus is the Lord,
Jesus is the Lord God almighty.
Jesus, Jesus, Jesus is the Lord,
Jesus is the Lord God almighty:
who was, and is, and is to come;
Jesus, Jesus, Jesus is the Lord.

3. Worthy, worthy, worthy is the Lord,
worthy is the Lord God almighty.
Worthy, worthy, worthy is the Lord,
worthy is the Lord God almighty:
who was, and is and is to come;
worthy, worthy, worthy is the Lord.

4. Glory, glory, glory to the Lord,
glory to the Lord God almighty.
Glory, glory, glory to the Lord,
glory to the Lord God almighty:
who was, and is, and is to come;
glory, glory, glory to the Lord.

286 Holy, holy, holy! Lord God almighty

Reginald Heber (1783-1826) | John Bacchus Dykes (1823-1876)

NICAEA 11 12 12 10

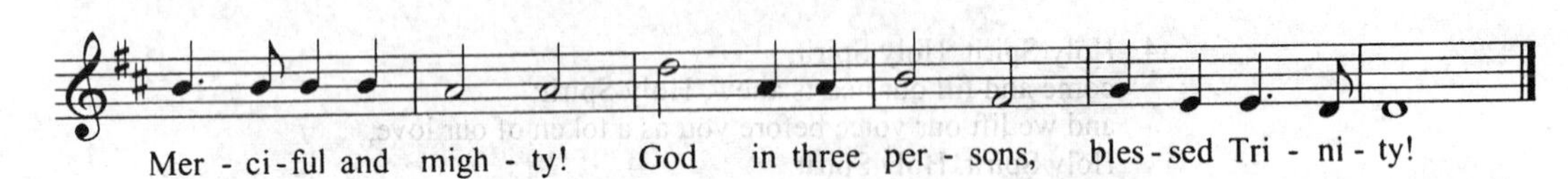

* 2. Holy, holy, holy! All the saints adore thee,
casting down their golden crowns around the glassy sea;
cherubim and seraphim falling down before thee,
which wert, and art, and evermore shall be.

3. Holy, holy, holy! Though the darkness hide thee,
though the sinful mortal eye thy glory may not see,
only thou art holy, there is none beside thee,
perfect in pow'r, in love, and purity.

4. Holy, holy, holy! Lord God almighty!
All thy works shall praise thy name, in earth and sky and sea;
holy, holy, holy! Merciful and mighty!
God in three persons, blessèd Trinity!

* *May be omitted*

287 Holy Jesu, by thy passion

William John Sparrow-Simpson (1859-1952) | John Stainer (1840-1901)

HOLY JESU 87 87 and Refrain

Text © Copyright 1887, 1915 Novello & Co. Ltd., 8/9 Frith Street, London W1D 3JB.
All rights reserved. International copyright secured. Used by permission.

2. By the treachery and trial,
by the blows and sore distress,
by desertion and denial,
by thine awful loneliness:

3. By thy look so sweet and lowly,
while they smote thee on the face,
by thy patience, calm and holy,
in the midst of keen disgrace:

4. By the hour of condemnation,
by the blood which trickled down,
when, for us and our salvation,
thou didst wear the robe and crown:

5. By the path of sorrows dreary,
by the cross, thy dreadful load,
by the pain, when, faint and weary,
thou didst sink upon the road:

6. By the Spirit which could render
love for hate and good for ill,
by the mercy, sweet and tender,
poured upon thy murd'rers still:

288 Holy Spirit, come, confirm us

Brian Foley (b.1919) — Richard Redhead (1820-1901)

TUNE 1: LAUS DEO (REDHEAD NO. 46) 87 87

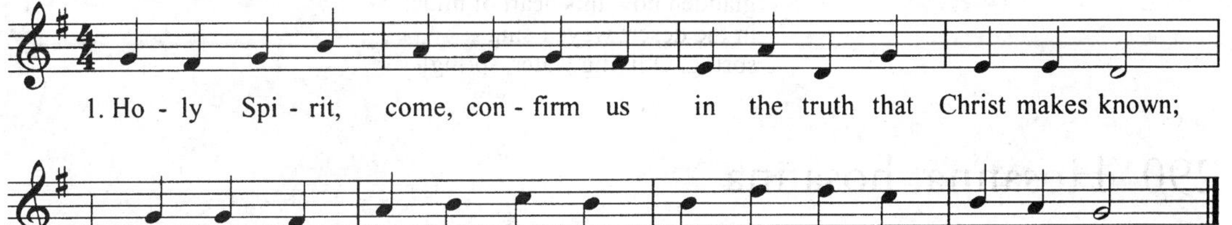

2. Holy Spirit, come, console us,
come as Advocate to plead;
loving Spirit from the Father,
grant in Christ the help we need.

3. Holy Spirit, come, renew us,
come yourself to make us live;
holy through your loving presence,
holy through the gifts you give.

4. Holy Spirit, come, possess us,
you the love of Three in One,
Holy Spirit of the Father,
Holy Spirit of the Son.

Brian Foley (b.1919) — John Stainer (1840-1901)

TUNE 2: ALL FOR JESUS 87 87

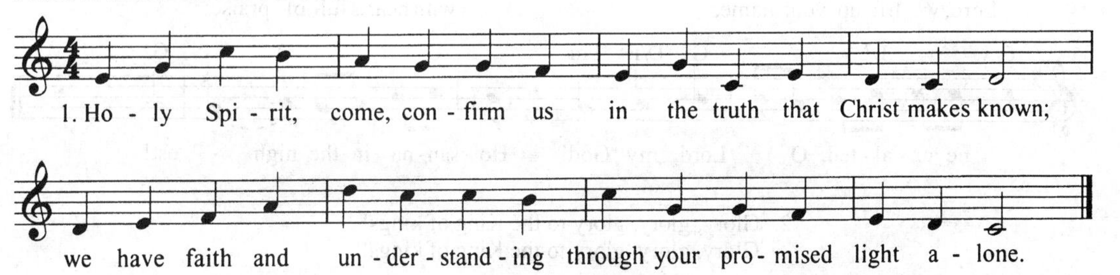

Text © Copyright 1971 Faber Music Ltd., 3 Queen Square, London WC1N 3AU.
Used by permission from the *New Catholic Hymnal*.

289 Holy Spirit, truth divine

Samuel Longfellow (1819-1892) | Orlando Gibbons (1583-1625)

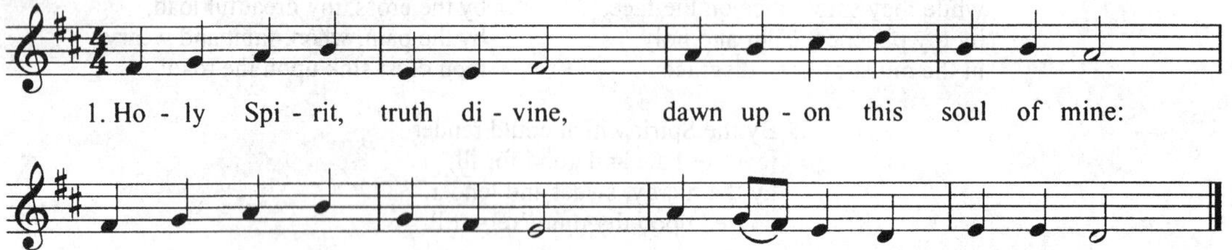

2. Holy Spirit, love divine,
glow within this heart of mine:
kindle ev'ry high desire,
purify me with your fire.

3. Holy Spirit, pow'r divine,
fill and nerve this will of mine:
boldly may I always live,
bravely serve and gladly give.

4. Holy Spirit, law divine,
reign within this soul of mine:
be my law, and I shall be
firmly bound, for ever free.

5. Holy Spirit, peace divine,
still this restless heart of mine:
speak to calm this tossing sea,
grant me your tranquillity.

6. Holy Spirit, joy divine,
gladden now this heart of mine:
in the desert ways I sing -
spring, O living water, spring!

290 Hosanna, hosanna

Words and music: Carl Tuttle

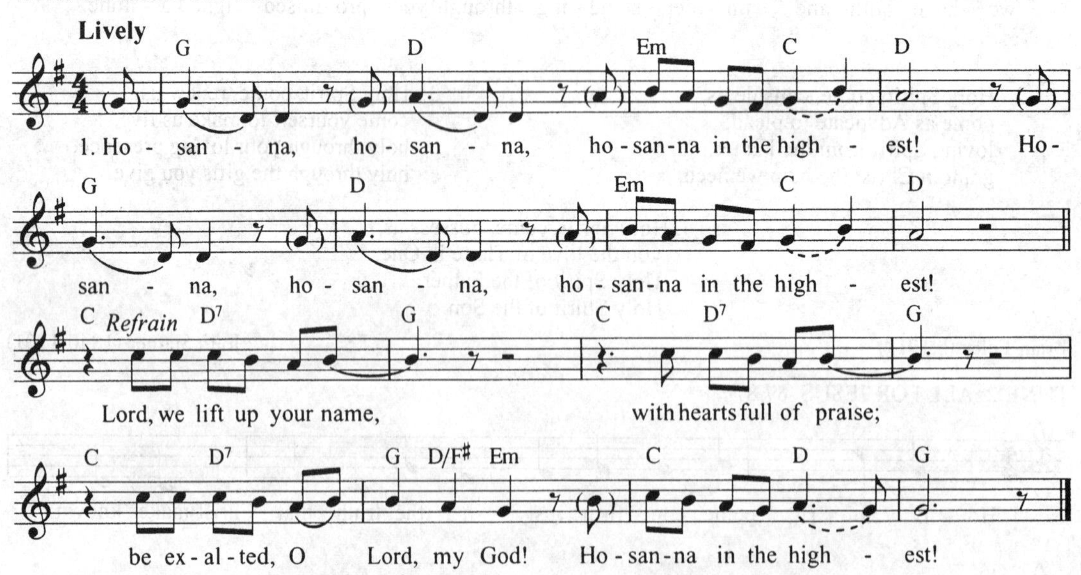

2. Glory, glory, glory to the King of kings!
Glory, glory, glory to the King of kings!

© Copyright 1985 Mercy/Vineyard Publishing. Administered by CopyCare, P.O. Box 77, Hailsham, East Sussex BN27 3EF, UK. (music@copycare.com). Used by permission.

291 How brightly shines the Morning Star!

German text of Philipp Nicolai
trans. William Mercer (1811-1873)

Philipp Nicolai (1556-1608)

WIE SCHÖN LEUCHTET 887 887 48 48

2. Though circled by the hosts on high,
he deigns to cast a pitying eye
upon his helpless creature;
the whole creation's Head and Lord,
by highest seraphim adored,
assumes our very nature.
Jesu, grant us,
through thy merit, to inherit
thy salvation;
hear, O hear our supplication.

3. Rejoice, ye heav'ns; thou earth, reply;
with praise, ye sinners, fill the sky,
for this his incarnation.
Incarnate God, put forth thy pow'r,
ride on, ride on, great Conqueror,
till all know thy salvation.
Amen, amen!
Alleluya, alleluya!
Praise be given
evermore by earth and heaven.

292 How firm a foundation

Richard Keen (c.1787) *Magdalen Hospital Hymns* (c.1760)

MONTGOMERY 11 11 11 11

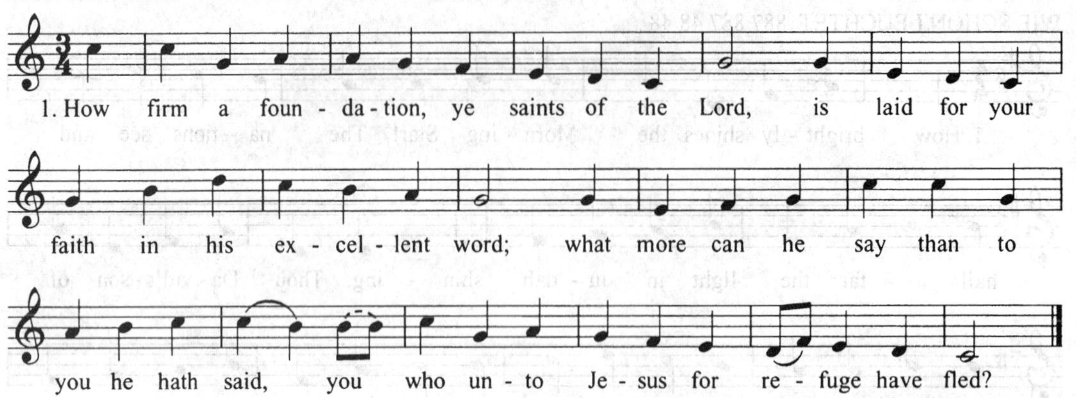

2. Fear not, he is with thee, O be not dismayed;
for he is thy God, and will still give thee aid:
he'll strengthen thee, help thee, and cause thee to stand,
upheld by his righteous, omnipotent hand.

3. In ev'ry condition, in sickness, in health,
in poverty's vale, or abounding in wealth;
at home and abroad, on the land, on the sea,
as thy days may demand shall thy strength ever be.

4. When through the deep waters he calls thee to go,
the rivers of grief shall not thee overflow;
for he will be with thee in trouble to bless,
and sanctify to thee thy deepest distress.

5. When through fiery trials thy pathway shall lie,
his grace all-sufficient shall be thy supply;
the flame shall not hurt thee, his only design
thy dross to consume and thy gold to refine.

6. The soul that on Jesus has leaned for repose
he will not, he cannot, desert to its foes;
that soul, though all hell should endeavour to shake,
he never will leave,he will never forsake.

293 How good is the God we adore

Joseph Hart (1712-1768) *Lancashire Sunday School Songs* (1857)

CELESTE LM

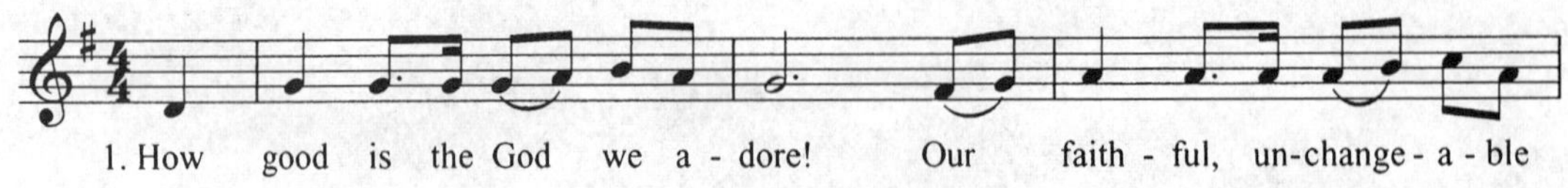

2. For Christ is the first and the last;
his Spirit will guide us safe home;
we'll praise him for all that is past
and trust him for all that's to come.

294 How lovely, Lord, how lovely

Arlo D. Duba,
based on Psalm 84

Hal H. Hopson

MERLE'S TUNE 76 76 D

2. In your blest courts to worship,
O God, a single day
is better than a thousand
if I from you should stray.
I'd rather keep the entrance
and claim you as my Lord,
than revel in the riches
the ways of sin afford.

3. A sun and shield for ever
are you, O God most high;
you shower us with blessings,
no good will you deny.
The saints, your grace receiving,
from strength to strength shall go,
and from their life shall rivers
of blessing overflow.

Text © Copyright 1986 Hope Publishing Co.
Music © Copyright 1983 Hope Publishing Co. Administered by CopyCare,
P.O. Box 77, Hailsham, East Sussex BN27 3EF. (music@copycare.com). Used by permission.

295 How lovely on the mountains *Our God reigns*

v.1 Leonard E. Smith Jnr.
based on Isaiah 52:7-10
vs. 2-4 unknown

Leonard E. Smith Jnr. (b.1942)

2. You watchmen, lift your voices
joyfully as one,
shout for your King, your King!
See eye to eye,
the Lord restoring Zion:
our God reigns, our God reigns.

3. Wasteplaces of Jerusalem,
break forth with joy!
We are redeemed, redeemed.
The Lord has saved
and comforted his people:
our God reigns, our God reigns.

4. Ends of the earth, see
the salvation of our God!
Jesus is Lord, is Lord!
Before the nations,
he has bared his holy arm:
our God reigns, our God reigns.

© Copyright 1974 Kingsway's Thankyou Music, P.O. Box 75, Eastbourne,
East Sussex BN23 6NW, UK. (tym@kingsway.co.uk). Europe only. Used by permission.

296 How shall I sing that majesty

John Mason (c.1645-1694)

Corner's *Geistliche Nachtigall* (1649)

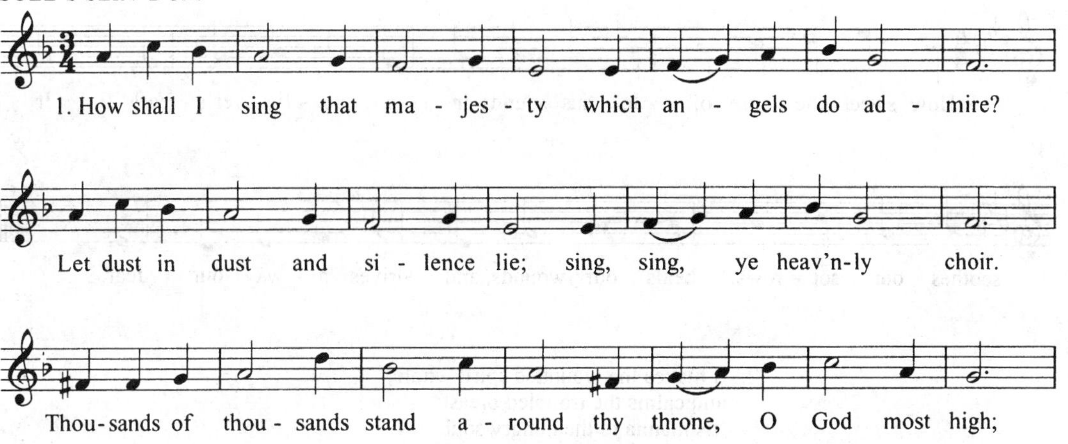

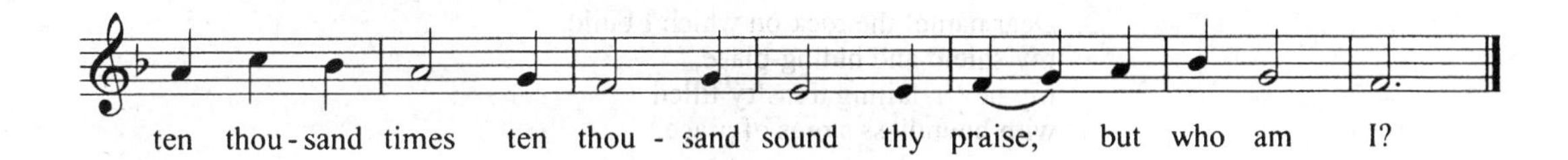

2. Thy brightness unto them appears,
whilst I thy footsteps trace;
a sound of God comes to my ears,
but they behold thy face.
They sing because thou art their Sun;
Lord, send a beam on me;
for where heav'n is but once begun
there alleluias be.

3. How great a being, Lord, is thine,
which doth all beings keep!
Thy knowledge is the only line
to sound so vast a deep.
Thou art a sea without a shore,
a sun without a sphere;
thy time is now and evermore,
thy place is ev'rywhere.

297 How sweet the name of Jesus sounds

John Newton (1725-1807)

Alexander Robert Reinagle (1799-1877)

ST PETER CM

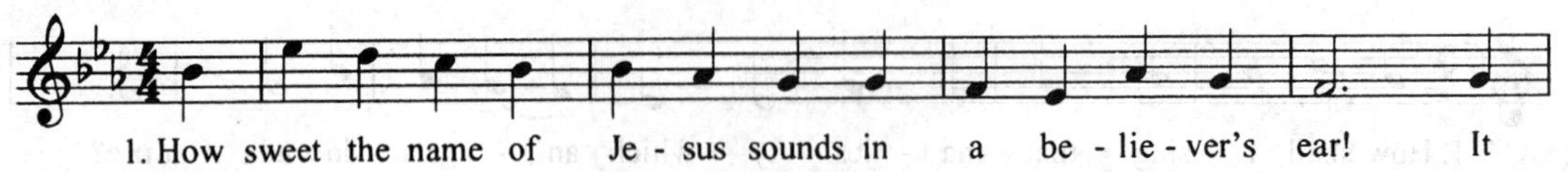

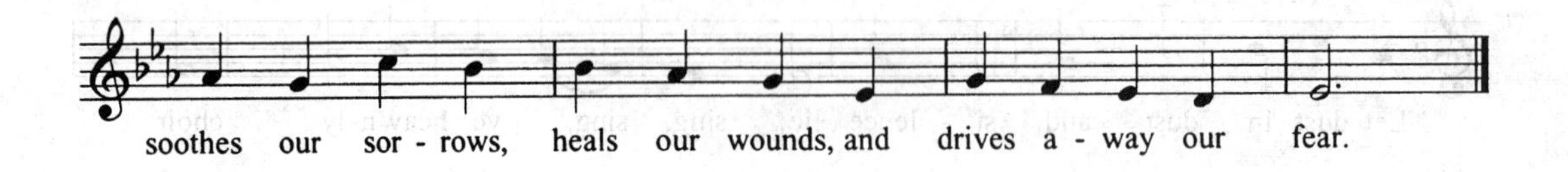

2. It makes the wounded spirit whole,
and calms the troubled breast;
'tis manna to the hungry soul,
and to the weary rest.

3. Dear name! the rock on which I build,
my shield and hiding-place,
my never-failing treas'ry filled
with boundless stores of grace.

4. Jesus! my shepherd, brother, friend,
my prophet, priest, and king,
my Lord, my life, my way, my end,
accept the praise I bring.

5. Weak is the effort of my heart,
and cold my warmest thought;
but when I see thee as thou art,
I'll praise thee as I ought.

6. Till then I would thy love proclaim
with ev'ry fleeting breath;
and may the music of thy name
refresh my soul in death.

298 I am a new creation

Words and music: Dave Bilbrough

© Copyright 1983 Kingsway's Thankyou Music, P.O. Box 75, Eastbourne, East Sussex BN23 6NW, UK. (tym@kingsway.co.uk). Used by permission.

299 I am the bread of life (Toolan)

Words and music: Suzanne Toolan (b.1927)

© Copyright 1966 GIA Publications Inc., 7404 S. Mason Avenue,
Chicago, Illinois 60638, USA. All rights reserved. Used by permission.

A C♯m D Esus4 E
4. I am the re - sur - rec -tion, I am the life. If you be -
A C♯m D A D Bm Esus4 D.S.
lieve in me, e - ven though you die, you shall live for e - ver.
A C♯m D Esus4 E
5. Yes, Lord, I be - lieve that you are the Christ, the
A C♯m D A D Bm Esus4 D.S.
Son of God, who has come in - to the world.

300 I am trusting thee, Lord Jesus

Frances Ridley Havergal (1836-1879) Ethelbert William Bullinger (1837-1913)

BULLINGER 85 83

2. I am trusting thee for pardon,
at thy feet I bow;
for thy grace and tender mercy,
trusting now.

3. I am trusting thee for cleansing
in the crimson flood;
trusting thee to make me holy
by thy blood.

4. I am trusting thee to guide me;
thou alone shalt lead,
ev'ry day and hour supplying
all my need.

5. I am trusting thee for power,
thine can never fail;
words which thou thyself shalt give me
must prevail.

6. I am trusting thee, Lord Jesus;
never let me fall;
I am trusting thee for ever,
and for all.

301 I believe in Jesus

Words and music: Marc Nelson

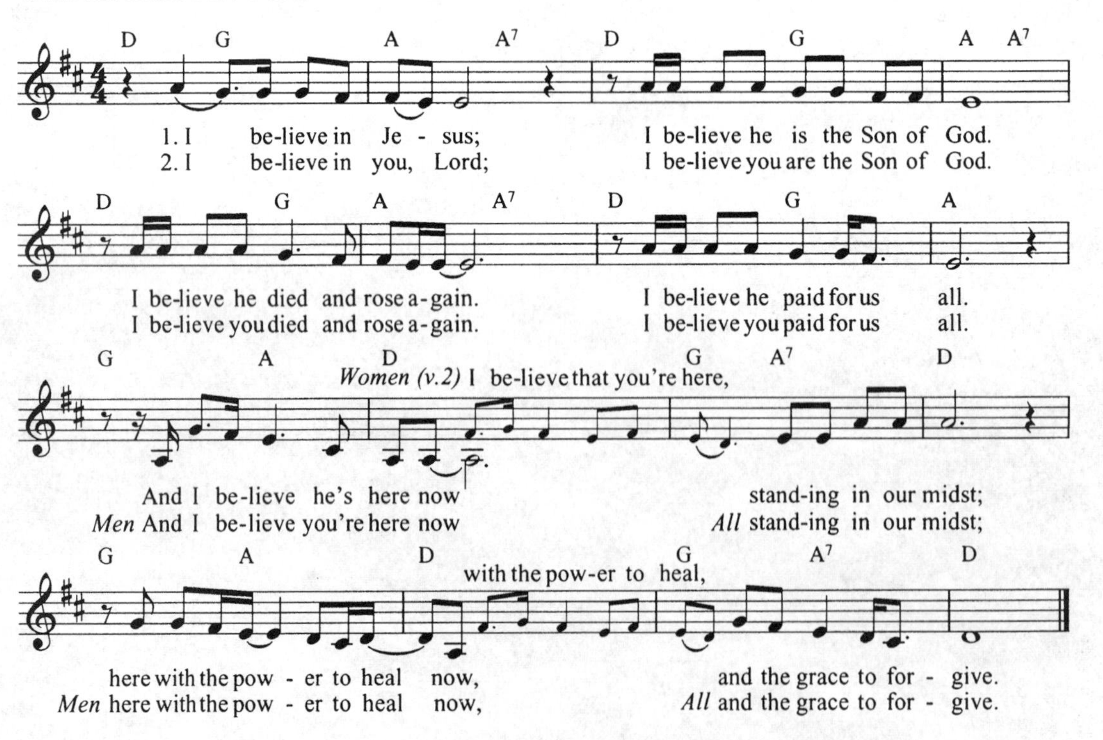

© Copyright 1987 Mercy/Vineyard Publishing. Administered by CopyCare, P.O. Box 77, Haisham, East Sussex BN27 3EF, UK. (music@copycare.com). Used by permission.

302 I bind unto myself today

Ascribed to St Patrick (373-463)
trans. Cecil Frances Alexander (1818-1895) alt.

Traditional Irish melodies

ST PATRICK'S BREASTPLATE Irregular

1. I bind un - to my - self to - day the strong name of the Tri - ni - ty, by in - vo - ca - tion of the same, the Three in One and One in Three.

2. I bind this day to me for e - ver, by pow'r of faith, Christ's in - car - na - tion, his bap - tism in the Jor - dan ri - ver, his death on cross for my sal - va - tion; his burst - ing from the spi - cèd tomb, his rid - ing up the heav'n - ly way, his com - ing at the day of doom, I bind un - to my - self to - day.

3. I bind un - to my - self the pow'r of the great love of che - ru - bim; the sweet 'Well done!' in judge - ment hour; the ser - vice of the se - ra - phim, con - fes - sors' faith, a - pos - tles'

word, the pat - riarch's prayers, the pro - phets' scrolls, all good deeds done un -
to the Lord, and pu - ri - ty of faith - ful souls.
PART II
4. Christ be with me, Christ with - in me, Christ be - hind me, Christ be - fore me,
Christ be - side me, Christ to win me, Christ to com - fort and re - store me.
Christ be - neath me, Christ a - bove me, Christ in qui - et, Christ in dan - ger,
Christ in hearts of all that love me, Christ in mouth of friend and stran - ger.
DOXOLOGY
5. I bind un - to my - self the name, the strong name of the
Tri - ni - ty, by in - vo - ca - tion of the same, the
Three in One and One in Three, of whom all
na - ture hath cre - a - tion, e - ter - nal Fa - ther, Spi - rit,
Word. Praise to the Lord of my sal - va - tion: sal - va - tion
is of Christ the Lord. A - men.

303 I cannot tell

William Young Fullerton (1857-1932) alt.

Traditional Irish melody

LONDONDERRY AIR 11 10 11 10 11 10 11 12

2. I cannot tell how silently he suffered,
as with his peace he graced this place of tears,
or how his heart upon the cross was broken,
the crown of pain to three and thirty years.
But this I know, he heals the broken-hearted,
and stays our sin, and calms our lurking fear,
and lifts the burden from the heavy laden,
for yet the Saviour, Saviour of the world, is here.

3. I cannot tell how he will win the nations,
how he will claim his earthly heritage,
how satisfy the needs and aspirations
of east and west, of sinner and of sage.
But this I know, all flesh shall see his glory,
and he shall reap the harvest he has sown,
and some glad day his sun shall shine in splendour
when he the Saviour, Saviour of the world, is known.

4. I cannot tell how all the lands shall worship,
when, at his bidding, ev'ry storm is stilled,
or who can say how great the jubilation
when ev'ry heart with perfect love is filled.
But this I know, the skies will thrill with rapture,
and myriad, myriad human voices sing,
and earth to heav'n, and heav'n to earth, will answer:
'At last the Saviour, Saviour of the world, is King!'

Text © Copyright Control

304 I come with joy

Brian A. Wren (b.1936) Gordon Slater (1896-1979)

ST BOTOLPH CM

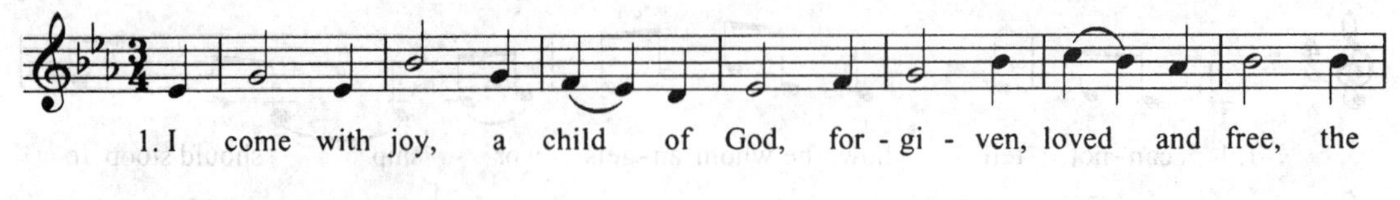

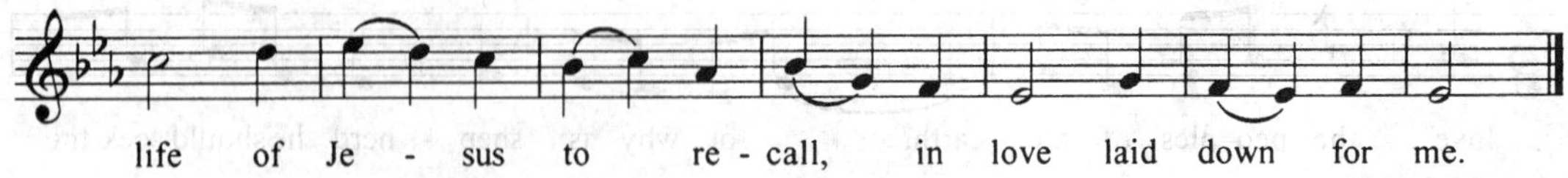

2. I come with Christians far and near
to find, as all are fed,
the new community of love
in Christ's communion bread.

3. As Christ breaks bread, and bids us share,
each proud division ends.
The love that made us, makes us one,
and strangers now are friends.

4. The Spirit of the risen Christ,
unseen, but ever near,
is in such friendship better known,
alive among us here.

5. Together met, together bound
by all that God has done,
we'll go with joy, to give the world
the love that makes us one.

Text © Copyright 1971, 1995 Stainer & Bell Ltd., P.O. Box 110,
Victoria House, 23 Gruneison Road, Finchley, London N3 1DZ.
Music © Copyright Oxford University Press, Great Clarendon Street, Oxford OX2 6DP.
Used by permission.

305 I danced in the morning *Lord of the dance*

Sydney Carter Traditional American melody adapted by Sydney Carter (b.1915)

© Copyright 1963 Stainer & Bell Ltd., P.O. Box 110, Victoria House, 23 Gruneison Road,
Finchley, London N3 1DZ, UK. Used by permission.

2. I danced for the scribe and the Pharisee,
   but they would not dance and they wouldn't follow me.
   I danced for the fishermen, for James and John –
   they came with me and the dance went on.

3. I danced on the Sabbath and I cured the lame;
   the holy people, they said it was a shame.
   They whipped and they stripped and they hung me on high,
   and they left me there on a cross to die.

4. I danced on a Friday when the sky turned black –
   it's hard to dance with the devil on your back.
   They buried my body, and they thought I'd gone,
   but I am the dance, and I still go on.

5. They cut me down and I leapt up high;
   I am the life that'll never, never die;
   I'll live in you if you'll live in me –
   I am the Lord of the Dance, said he.

306 I do not know the man

Michael Forster (b.1946) Richard Lloyd (b.1933)

MELMERBY SM

2. The great disciple failed;
his weakness we may own,
and stand with him where judgement meets
with grace, at Calv'ry's throne,
with grace, at Calv'ry's throne.

3. Christ stands among us still,
in those the world denies,
and in the faces of the poor,
we see his grieving eyes,
we see his grieving eyes.

4. We cannot cleanse our hands
of that most shameful spot,
since of our brother we have said,
'His keeper, I am not!'
'His keeper, I am not!'

5. And yet, what love is this?
Forgiveness all divine!
Christ says of our poor faithless souls,
'I know them, they are mine.'
'I know them, they are mine.'

© Copyright 1992 Kevin Mayhew Ltd.

307 If we only seek peace *Story of love*

Words and music: Susan Sayers (b.1946)

© Copyright 1984 Kevin Mayhew Ltd.

2. If we try to avoid
inconvenient giving,
or if love is destroyed
by our failure to serve,
then let the wide, unflinching, selfless giving
of the God who walked this earth
nourish our roots until we fruit
in the joy of the Lord.

3. If we start to object
to the path we are given
and decide to select
other ways of our own,
then let the full acceptance, firm obedience
of the God who walked this earth
nourish our roots until we fruit
in the joy of the Lord.

308 I give you all the honour *I worship you*

Words and music: Carl Tuttle

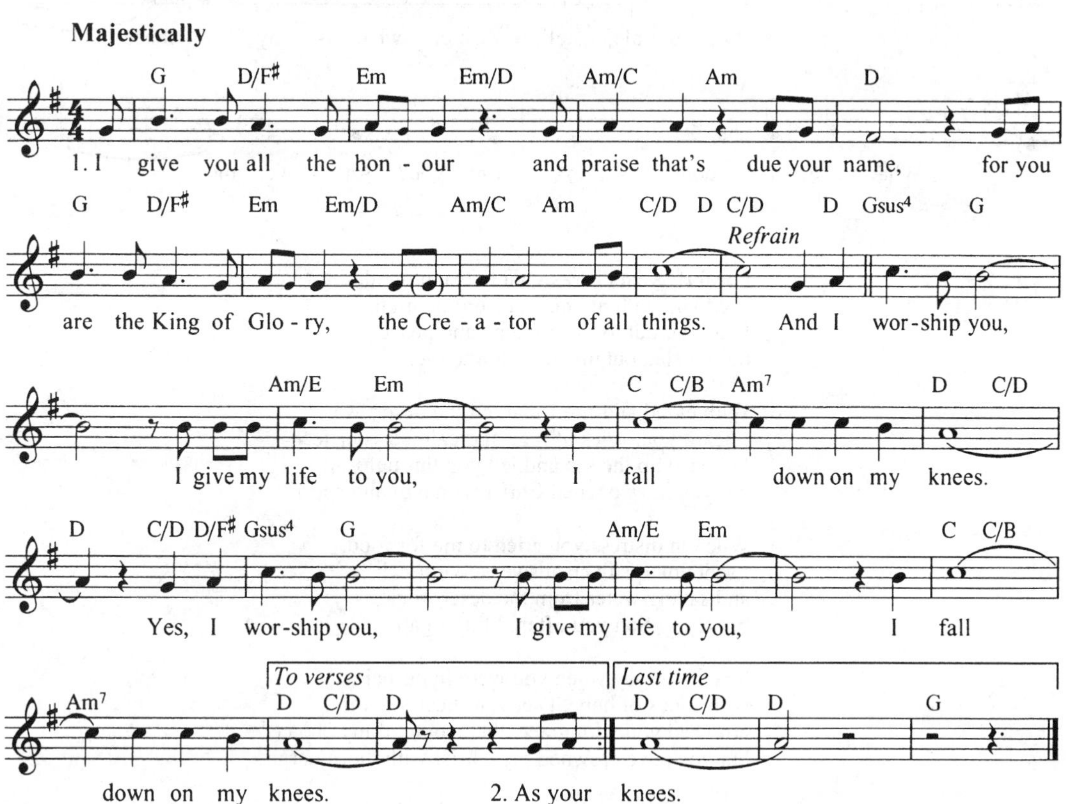

2. As your Spirit moves upon me now,
you meet my deepest need,
and I lift my hands up to your throne,
your mercy I've received.

3. You have broken chains that bound me,
you've set this captive free,
I will lift my voice to praise your name
for all eternity.

© Copyright 1982 Mercy/Vineyard Publishing. Administered by CopyCare, P.O. Box 77, Hailsham, East Sussex BN27 3EF, UK. (music@copycare.com). Used by permission.

309 I give you love

Reproaches

Michael Forster (b.1946)
based on the Good Friday *Reproaches*

Jean Sibelius (1865-1957)

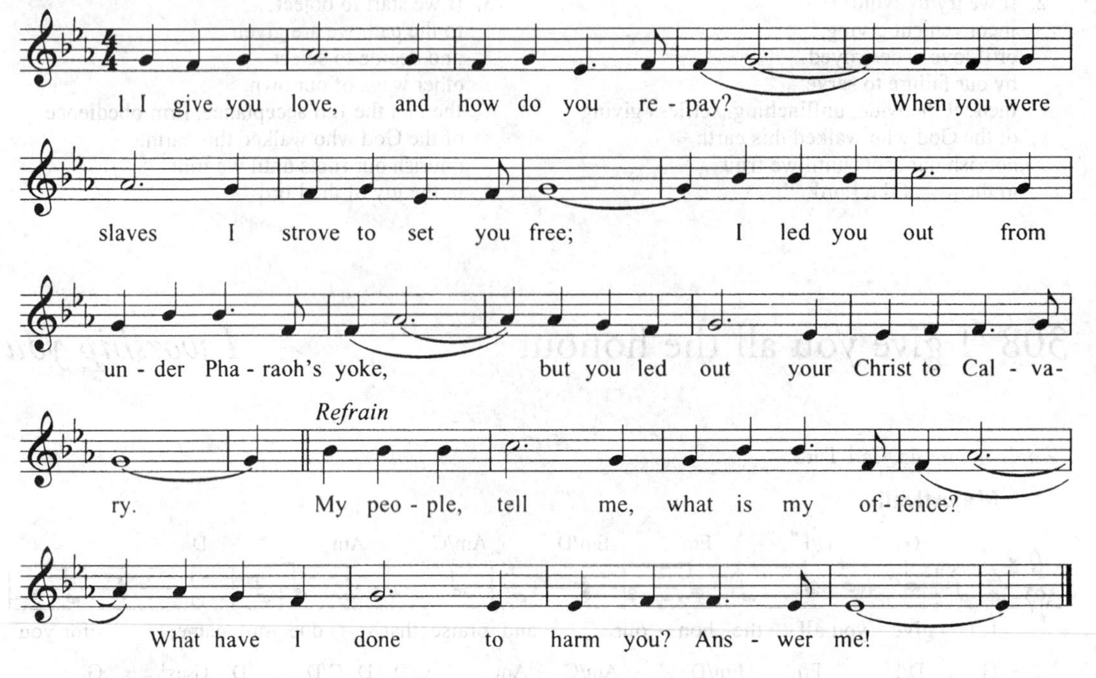

2. For forty years I was your constant guide.
I fed you with my manna from on high.
I led you out to live in hope and peace,
but you led out my only Son to die.

3. With cloud and fire I marked the desert way,
I heard your cries of rage and calmed your fear.
I opened up the sea and led you through,
but you have opened Christ with nail and spear.

4. When in distress you cried to me for food,
I sent you quails in answer to your call,
and saving water from the desert rock,
but to my Son you offered bitter gall.

5. I gave you joy when you were in despair,
with songs of hope, I set your hearts on fire;
crowned you with grace, the people of my choice,
but you have crowned my Christ with thorny briar.

6. When you were weak, exploited and oppressed,
I heard you cry and listened to your plea.
I raised you up to honour and renown,
but you have raised me on a shameful tree.

Text © Copyright 1996 Kevin Mayhew Ltd.
Music © Copyright Breitkopf and Härtel, Walkmühlstrasse 52, D-65195 Wiesbaden, Germany.
Used by permission.

310 I heard the voice of Jesus say

Horatius Bonar (1808-1889) — Traditional English melody

TUNE 1: KINGSFOLD DCM

2. I heard the voice of Jesus say,
'Behold, I freely give
the living water, thirsty one;
stoop down and drink and live.'
I came to Jesus, and I drank
of that life-giving stream;
my thirst was quenched, my soul revived,
and now I live in him.

3. I heard the voice of Jesus say,
'I am this dark world's light;
look unto me, thy morn shall rise,
and all thy day be bright.'
I looked to Jesus, and I found
in him my star, my sun;
and in that light of life I'll walk
till trav'lling days are done.

Horatius Bonar (1808-1889) — John Bacchus Dykes (1823-1876)

TUNE 2: VOX DILECTI DCM

311 I know that my Redeemer lives

Samuel Medley (1738-1799) alt. James William Elliot (1833-1915)

TUNE 1: CHURCH TRIUMPHANT LM

2. He lives, to bless me with his love;
he lives, to plead for me above;
he lives, my hungry soul to feed;
he lives, to help in time of need.

3. He lives, and grants me daily breath;
he lives – for me he conquered death;
he lives, my mansion to prepare;
he lives, to lead me safely there.

4. He lives, all glory to his name;
he lives, my Saviour, still the same;
what joy the blest assurance gives!
I know that my Redeemer lives!

Samuel Medley (1738-1799) alt. Robert Edwin Roberts (1878-1940)

TUNE 2: PHILIPPINE LM

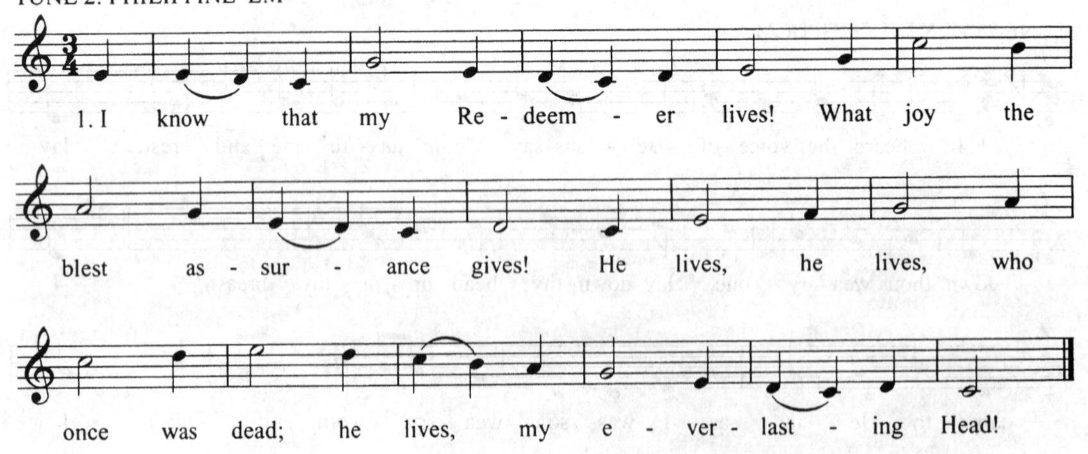

Tune 2: Music © Copyright Oxford University Press, Great Clarendon Street, Oxford OX2 6DP.
Used by permission.

312 I lift my eyes to the quiet hills

Timothy Dudley-Smith (b.1926)
from Psalm 121

Michael Baughen (b.1930)
and Elisabeth Crocker

DAVOS 458 457

2. I lift my eyes
to the quiet hills
to a calm that is mine to share;
secure and still
in the Father's will
and kept by the Father's care.

3. I lift my eyes
to the quiet hills
with a prayer as I turn to sleep;
by day, by night,
through the dark and light
my Shepherd will guard his sheep.

4. I lift my eyes
to the quiet hills
and my heart to the Father's throne;
in all my ways
to the end of days
the Lord will preserve his own.

Text © Copyright Timothy Dudley-Smith, 9 Ashlands, Ford, Salisbury, Wiltshire SP4 6DY. Used by permission.
Music © Copyright Michael Baughen/Jubilate Hymns, 4 Thorne Park Road, Chelston, Torquay TQ2 6RX. Used by permission.

313 I love you, Lord, and I lift my voice

Words and music: Laurie Klein

© Copyright 1978 Maranatha! Music. Administered by CopyCare, P.O. Box 77, Hailsham, East Sussex BN27 3EF, UK. (music@copycare.com). Used by permission.

314 Immortal, invisible, God only wise

Walter Chalmers Smith (1824-1908)
based on 1 Timothy 1:17

Adapted from a traditional Welsh hymn melody
in John Roberts' *Caniadu y Cyssegr* (1839)

ST DENIO 11 11 11 11

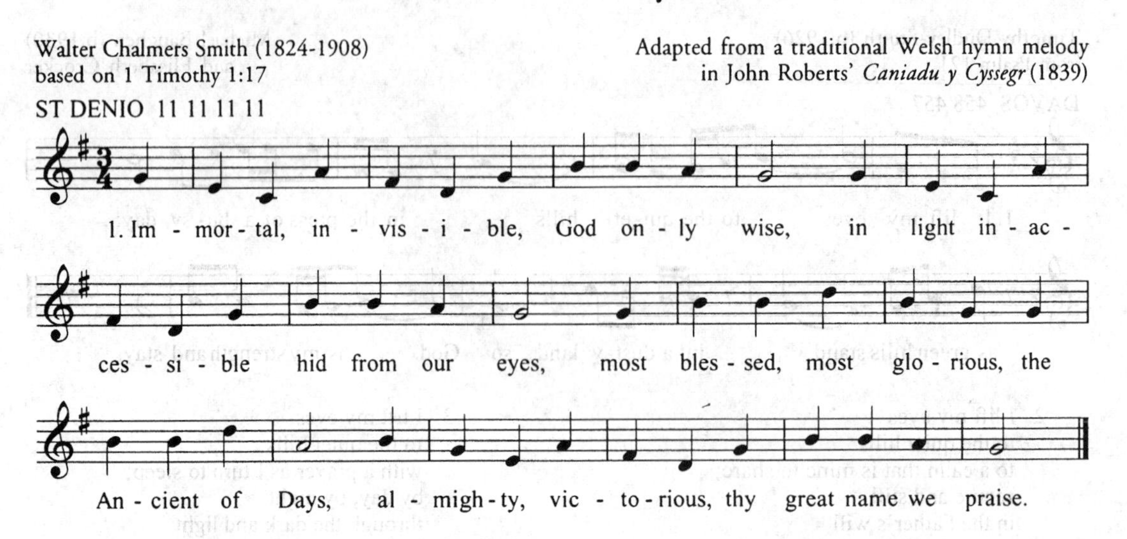

2. Unresting, unhasting, and silent as light,
nor wanting, nor wasting, thou rulest in might;
thy justice like mountains high soaring above
thy clouds which are fountains of goodness and love.

3. To all life thou givest, to both great and small;
in all life thou livest, the true life of all;
we blossom and flourish as leaves on the tree,
and wither and perish; but naught changeth thee.

4. Great Father of glory, pure Father of light,
thine angels adore thee, all veiling their sight;
all laud we would render, O help us to see
'tis only the splendour of light hideth thee.

315 Immortal love, for ever full

John Greenleaf Whittier (1807-1892)

Probably by Jeremiah Clarke (c.1674-1707)

BISHOPTHORPE CM

2. Our outward lips confess the name
all other names above;
love only knoweth whence it came
and comprehendeth love.

3. O warm, sweet, tender, even yet
a present help is he;
and faith has still its Olivet,
and love its Galilee.

4. The healing of his seamless dress
is by our beds of pain;
we touch him in life's throng and press,
and we are whole again.

5. Through him the first fond prayers are said
our lips of childhood frame;
the last low whispers of our dead
are burdened with his name.

6. Alone, O love ineffable,
thy saving name is giv'n;
to turn aside from thee is hell,
to walk with thee is heav'n.

316 I'm not ashamed to own my Lord

Isaac Watts (1674-1748) Thomas Jackson (1715-1781)

TUNE 1: JACKSON CM

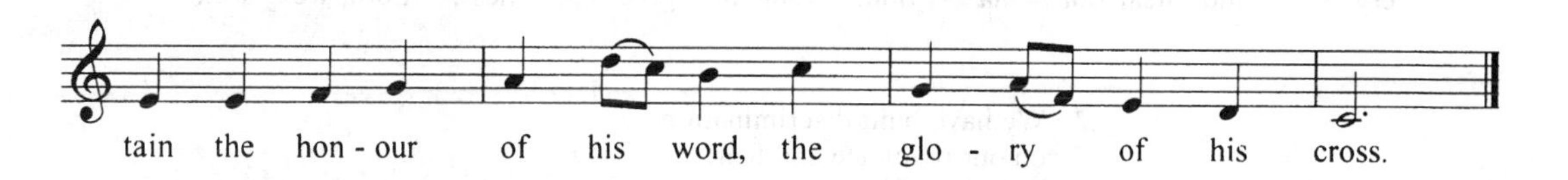

2. Jesus, my God, I know his name;
his name is all my trust;
nor will he put my soul to shame,
nor let my hope be lost.

3. Firm as his throne his promise stands;
and he can well secure
what I've committed to his hands,
till the decisive hour.

4. Then will he own my worthless name
before his Father's face;
and in the new Jerusalem
appoint my soul a place.

Isaac Watts (1674-1748) Neil Dougall (1776-1862)

TUNE 2: KILMARNOCK CM

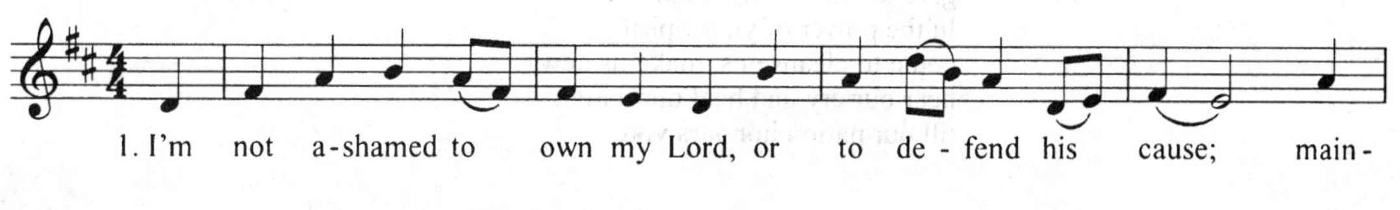

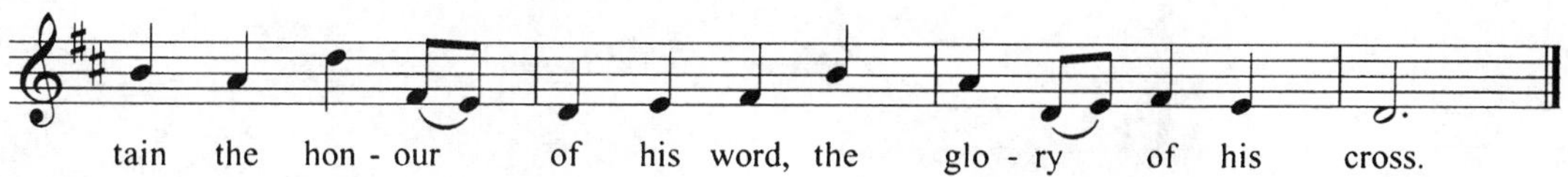

317 In an age of twisted values

Heal our nation

Martin E. Leckebusch (b.1962)

John Marsh (b.1939)

KILVE 87 87 D

2. We have built discrimination
on our prejudice and fear;
hatred swiftly turns to cruelty
if we hold resentments dear.
For communities divided
by the walls of class and race
hear our cry and heal our nation:
show us, Lord, your love and grace.

3. When our families are broken;
when our homes are full of strife;
when our children are bewildered,
when they lose their way in life;
when we fail to give the aged
all the care we know we should –
hear our cry and heal our nation
with your tender fatherhood.

4. We who hear your word so often
choose so rarely to obey;
turn us from our wilful blindness,
give us truth to light our way.
In the power of your Spirit
come to cleanse us, make us new:
hear our cry and heal our nation
till our nation honours you.

© Copyright 1999 Kevin Mayhew Ltd.

318 In bread we bring you, Lord

Words and music: Kevin Nichols (b.1929)

2. The bread we offer you is blessed and broken,
and it becomes for us our spirits' food.
Over the cup we bring your Word is spoken;
make it your gift to us, your healing blood.
Take all that daily toil plants in our hearts' poor soil,
take all we start and spoil, each hopeful dream,
the chances we have missed, the graces we resist,
Lord, in thy Eucharist, take and redeem.

© Copyright 1976 Kevin Mayhew Ltd.

319 In Christ there is no east or west

John Oxenham (1852-1941) alt.

Neil Dougall (1776-1862)

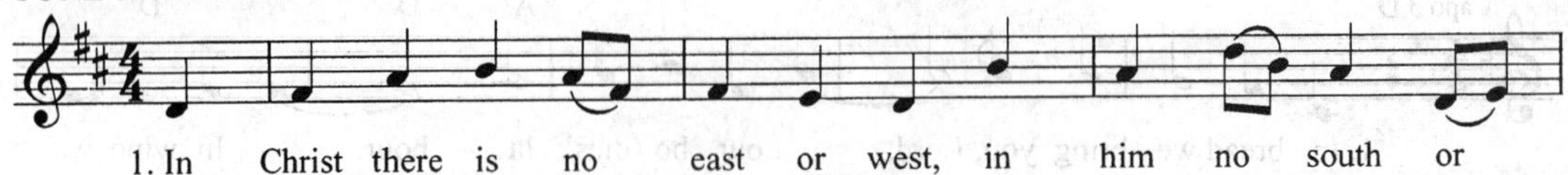

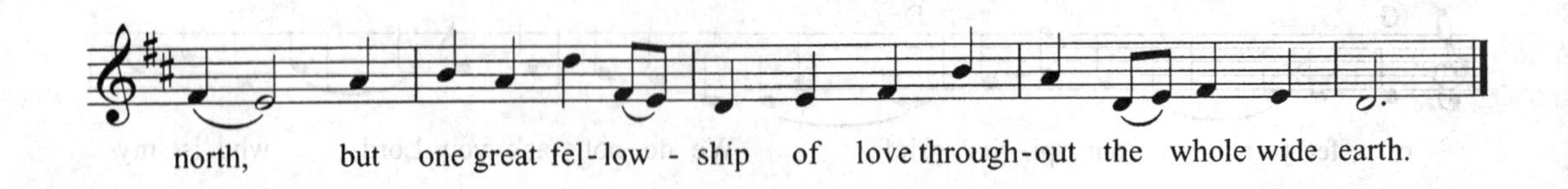

2. In him shall true hearts ev'rywhere
their high communion find;
his service is the golden cord,
close binding humankind.

3. Join hands, united in the faith,
whate'er your race may be;
who serve my Father as their own
are surely kin to me.

4. In Christ now meet both east and west,
in him meet south and north;
all Christlike souls are one in him,
throughout the whole wide earth.

John Oxenham (1852-1941) alt.

Robert Wainwright (1748-1782)
in *Divine Harmony* (1774)

TUNE 2: MANCHESTER CM

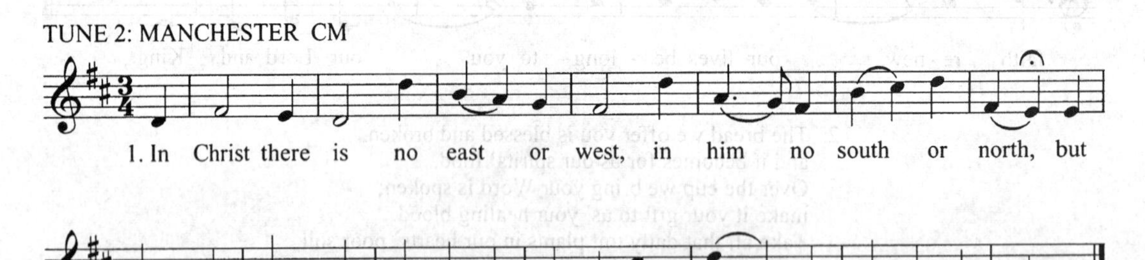

Text © Copyright Desmond Dunkerley.
Used by permission.

320 I need thee every hour

Annie Sherwood Hawks (1835-1918) | Robert Lowry (1826-1899)

2. I need thee ev'ry hour;
stay thou near by;
temptations lose their pow'r
when thou art nigh.

3. I need thee ev'ry hour,
in joy or pain;
come quickly and abide,
or life is vain.

4. I need thee ev'ry hour;
teach me thy will,
and thy rich promises
in me fulfill.

5. I need thee ev'ry hour,
most Holy One;
O make me thine indeed,
thou blessèd Son!

321 Infant holy, infant lowly

Traditional Polish
trans. Edith Margaret Gellibrand Reed (1885-1933) | Traditional Polish melody

WZLOBIE LEZY 87 87 88 77

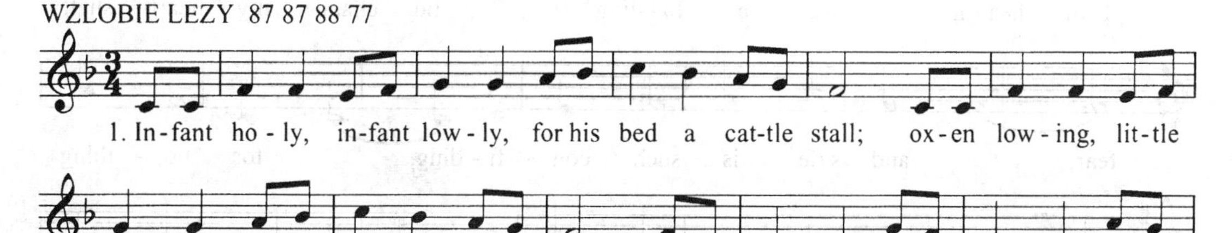

2. Flocks were sleeping, shepherds keeping
vigil till the morning new;
saw the glory, heard the story,
tidings of a gospel true.
Thus rejoicing, free from sorrow,
praises voicing, greet the morrow,
Christ the babe was born for you,
Christ the babe was born for you.

Text © Copyright Control.

322 In full and glad surrender

Frances Ridley Havergal (1836-1879) Henry John Gauntlett (1805-1876)

ST ALPHEGE 76 76

2. O Son of God, who lov'st me,
I will be thine alone;
and all I have and am, Lord,
shall henceforth be thine own!

3. Reign over me, Lord Jesus,
O make my heart thy throne;
it shall be thine, dear Saviour,
it shall be thine alone.

4. O come and reign, Lord Jesus,
rule over ev'rything!
And keep me always loyal
and true to thee, my King.

323 In heavenly love abiding

Anna Laetitia Waring (1820-1910)
based on Psalm 23

David Jenkins (1848-1915)

PENLAN 76 76 D

2. Wherever he may guide me,
no want shall turn me back;
my Shepherd is beside me,
and nothing can I lack.
His wisdom ever waketh,
his sight is never dim,
he knows the way he taketh,
and I will walk with him.

3. Green pastures are before me,
which yet I have not seen;
bright skies will soon be o'er me,
where the dark clouds have been.
My hope I cannot measure,
my path to life is free,
my Saviour has my treasure,
and he will walk with me.

324 In our day of thanksgiving

William Henry Draper (1855-1933) alt. From *Rheinhardt MS*, Üttingen (1754)

WAS LEBET Irregular

2. In the morning of life, and at noon, and at even,
he called them away from our worship below;
but not till his love, at the font and the altar,
supplied them with grace for the way they should go.

3. These stones that have echoed their praises are holy,
and dear is the ground where their feet have once trod;
yet here they confessed they were strangers and pilgrims,
and still they were seeking the city of God.

4. Sing praise, then, for all who here sought and here found him,
whose journey is ended, whose perils are past:
they believed in the light; and its glory is round them,
where the clouds of earth's sorrow are lifted at last.

Text © Copyright J. Curwen & Sons Ltd., 8/9 Frith Street, London W1D 3JB.
All rights reserved. International copyright secured. Used by permission.

325 Inspired by love and anger

John L. Bell (b.1949)
Graham Maule (b.1958)

Traditional Irish melody

2. From those for ever victims of heartless human greed,
their cruel plight composes a litany of need:
'Where are the fruits of justice? Where are the signs of peace?
When is the day when pris'ners and dreams find their release?'

3. From those for ever shackled to what their wealth can buy,
the fear of lost advantage provokes the bitter cry:
'Don't query our position! Don't criticise our wealth!
Don't mention those exploited by politics and stealth!'

4. To God, who through the prophets proclaimed a diff'rent age,
we offer earth's indiff'rence, its agony and rage:
'When will the wronged be righted? When will the kingdom come?
When will the world be gen'rous to all instead of some?'

5. God asks: 'Who will go for me? Who will extend my reach?
And who, when few will listen, will prophesy and preach?
And who, when few bid welcome, will offer all they know?
And who, when few dare follow, will walk the road I show?'

6. Amused in someone's kitchen, asleep in someone's boat,
attuned to what the ancients exposed, proclaimed and wrote,
a Saviour without safety, a tradesman without tools
has come to tip the balance with fishermen and fools.

Text © Copyright 1987 WGRG, Iona Community, Glasgow G2 3DH, Scotland.
Used by permission from *Heaven shall not wait.* collection (Wild Goose Publications, 1987).

326 In the bleak mid-winter

Christina Georgina Rossetti (1830-1894)

Gustav Holst (1874-1934)

Music © Copyright Oxford University Press, Great Clarendon Street, Oxford OX2 6DP.
Used by permission from the *English Hymnal*.

327 In the Cross of Christ I glory

John Bowring (1792-1872)
based on Galatians 6:14

Walter G. Whinfield (1865-1919)

TUNE 1: WYCHBOLD 87 87

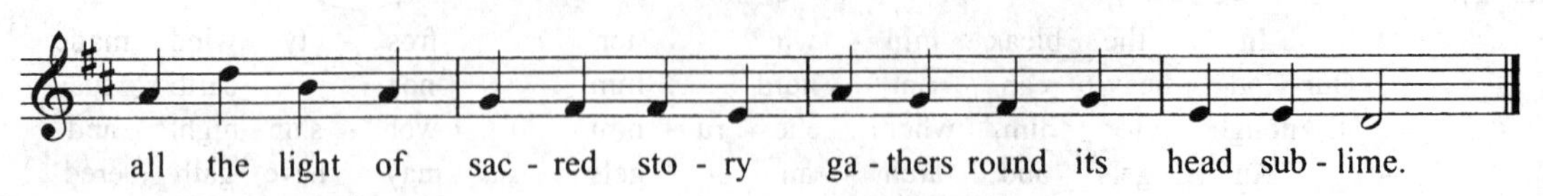

2. When the woes of life o'ertake me,
hopes deceive, and fears annoy,
never shall the Cross forsake me;
Lo! it glows with peace and joy.

3. When the sun of bliss is beaming
light and love upon my way,
from the Cross the radiance streaming
adds more lustre to the day.

4. Bane and blessing, pain and pleasure,
by the Cross are sanctified;
peace is there that knows no measure,
joys that through all time abide.

John Bowring (1792-1872)
based on Galatians 6:14

John Bacchus Dykes (1823-1876)

TUNE 2: ST OSWALD 87 87

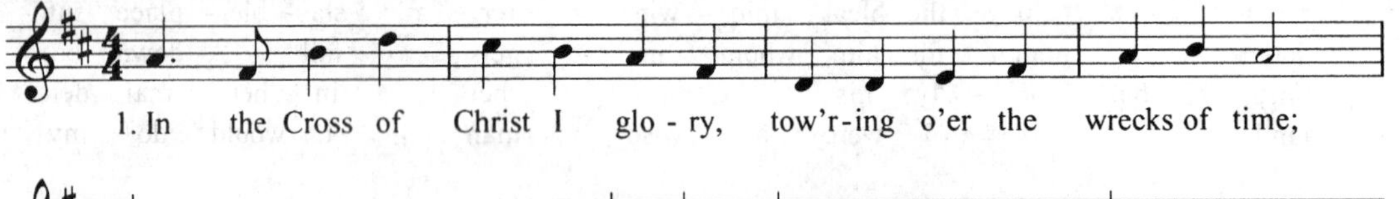

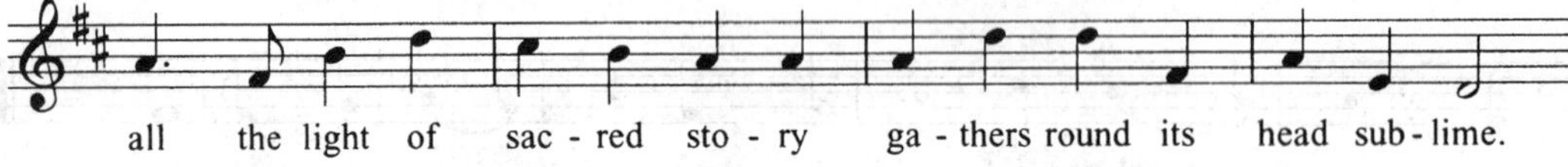

328 In you, my God

Words and music: Francesca Leftley (b.1955)

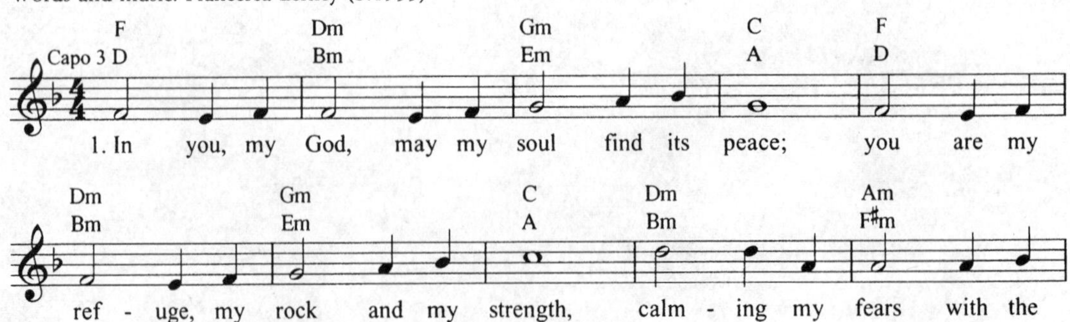

© Copyright 1978 Kevin Mayhew Ltd.

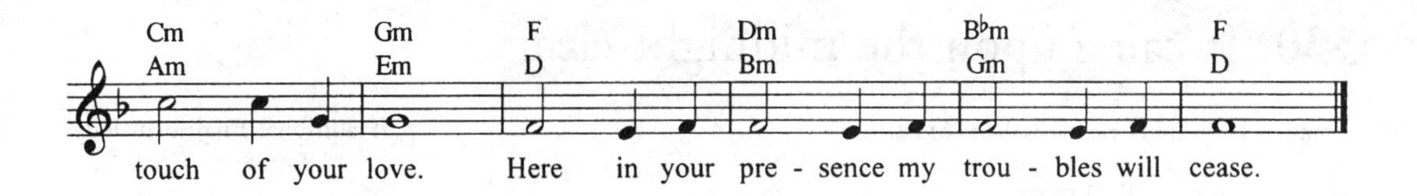

2. In you, my God, may my soul find its joy;
you are the radiance, the song of my heart,
drying my tears with the warmth of your love.
Here in your presence my troubles will cease.

3. In you, my God, may my soul find its rest;
you are the meaning, the purpose of life,
drawing me near to the fire of your love,
safe in your presence my yearning will cease.

329 I stand amazed in the presence *How marvellous*

Words and music: Charles H. Gabriel (d.1932)

2. For me it was in the garden
he prayed – 'Not my will, but thine';
he had no tears for his own griefs,
but sweat drops of blood for mine.

3. In pity angels beheld him,
and came from the world of light,
to comfort him in the sorrows
he bore for my soul that night.

4. He took my sins and my sorrows,
he made them his very own;
he bore the burden to Calvary,
and suffered, and died alone.

5. When with the ransomed in glory
his face I at last shall see,
'twill be my joy through the ages
to sing of his love for me.

© Copyright The Rodeheaver Company/Word Music. Administered by CopyCare, P.O. Box 77, Hailsham, East Sussex BN27 3EF, UK. (music@copycare.com). Used by permission.

330 It came upon the midnight clear

Edmund Hamilton Sears (1810-1876) alt. | Traditional English melody

NOEL DCM

2. Still through the cloven skies they come,
with peaceful wings unfurled;
and still their heav'nly music floats
o'er all the weary world:
above its sad and lowly plains
they bend on hov'ring wing;
and ever o'er its Babel-sounds
the blessèd angels sing.

3. Yet with the woes of sin and strife
the world has suffered long;
beneath the angel-strain have rolled
two thousand years of wrong;
and warring humankind hears not
the love-song which they bring;
O hush the noise of mortal strife,
and hear the angels sing!

4. And ye, beneath life's crushing load,
whose forms are bending low,
who toil along the climbing way
with painful steps and slow:
look now! for glad and golden hours
come swiftly on the wing;
O rest beside the weary road,
and hear the angels sing.

5. For lo, the days are hast'ning on,
by prophets seen of old,
when with the ever-circling years
comes round the age of gold;
when peace shall over all the earth
its ancient splendours fling,
and all the world give back the song
which now the angels sing.

331 It fell upon a summer day

Stopford Augustus Brooke (1832-1916) alt.

University of Wales (1923)

CHILDHOOD 88 86

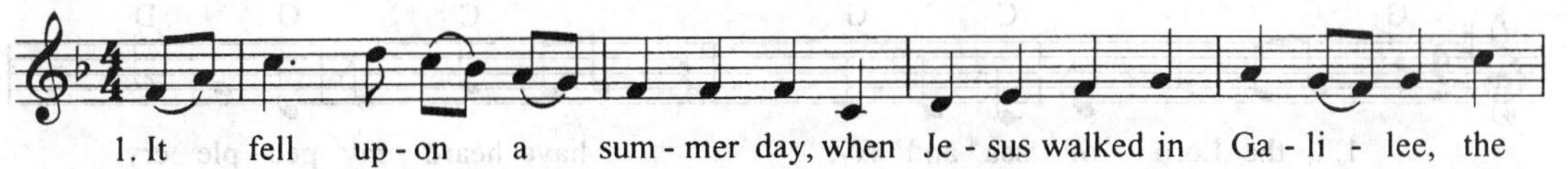

2. He took them in his arms, and laid
his hands on each remembered head;
'Allow these little ones to come
to me,' he gently said.

3. 'Forbid them not: unless ye bear
the childlike heart your hearts within,
unto my kingdom ye may come,
but may not enter in.'

4. My Lord, I fain would enter there;
O let me follow thee, and share
thy meek and lowly heart, and be
freed from all worldly care.

5. O happy thus to live and move,
and sweet this world, where I shall find
God's beauty everywhere, his love,
his good in humankind.

6. Then, Father, grant this childlike heart,
that I may come to Christ, and feel
his hands on me in blessing laid,
love-giving, strong to heal.

332 I, the Lord of sea and sky *Here I am, Lord*

Words and music: Dan Schutte
based on Isaiah 6

2. I, the Lord of snow and rain,
   I have borne my people's pain.
   I have wept for love of them.
   They turn away.
   I will break their hearts of stone,
   give them hearts for love alone.
   I will speak my word to them.
   Whom shall I send?

3. I, the Lord of wind and flame,
   I will tend the poor and lame.
   I will set a feast for them.
   My hand will save.
   Finest bread I will provide
   till their hearts be satisfied.
   I will give my life to them.
   Whom shall I send?

© Copyright 1981 Daniel L. Schutte and New Dawn Music, 5536 NE Hassalo, Portland, Oregon 97213, USA.
All rights reserved. Used by permission.

333 It is a thing most wonderful

William Walsham How (1823-1897)

Traditional English melody collected by
Ralph Vaughan Williams (1872-1958)

TUNE 1: HERONGATE LM

2. And yet I know that it is true:
he chose a poor and humble lot,
and wept and toiled, and mourned and died,
for love of those who loved him not.

3. I cannot tell how he could love
a child so weak and full of sin;
his love must be most wonderful,
if he could die my love to win.

4. I sometimes think about the cross,
and shut my eyes, and try to see
the cruel nails and crown of thorns,
and Jesus crucified for me.

5. But even could I see him die,
I could but see a little part
of that great love which, like a fire,
is always burning in his heart.

6. It is most wonderful to know
his love for me so free and sure;
but 'tis more wonderful to see
my love for him so faint and poor.

7. And yet I want to love thee, Lord;
O light the flame within my heart,
and I will love thee more and more,
until I see thee as thou art.

William Walsham How (1823-1897)

Thomas Bishop Southgate (1814-1868)

TUNE 2: BROOKFIELD LM

Tune 1: Music © Copyright Oxford University Press, Great Clarendon Street, Oxford OX2 6DP.
Used by permission from the *English Hymnal.*

334 I watch the sunrise *Close to you*

John Glynn (b.1948) Colin Murphy

2. I watch the sunlight shine through the clouds,
warming the earth below.
And at the mid-day, life seems to say:
'I feel your brightness near me.'
For you are always . . .

3. I watch the sunset fading away,
lighting the clouds with sleep.
And as the evening closes its eyes,
I feel your presence near me.
For you are always . . .

4. I watch the moonlight guarding the night,
waiting till morning comes.
The air is silent, earth is at rest –
only your peace is near me.
Yes, you are always . . .

© Copyright 1976 Kevin Mayhew Ltd.

335 I will bless the Lord

Susan Sayers (b.1946)
based on Psalm 34

Andrew Moore (b.1954)

2. When I was in pain,
   when I lived in fear,
   I was calling out to him.
   He rescued me from death,
   he wiped my tears away,
   I will sing your praise, O Lord.

3. Trust him with your life,
   trust him with today,
   come and praise the Lord with me;
   O come and know his love,
   O taste and understand,
   let us sing your praise, O Lord.

© Copyright 1996 Kevin Mayhew Ltd.

336 I will enter his gates

He has made me glad

Words and music: Leona von Brethorst

© Copyright 1976 Maranatha! Music. Administered by CopyCare, P.O. Box 77, Hailsham, East Sussex BN27 3EF, UK. (music@copycare.com). Used by permission.

337 I will sing the wondrous story

Francis Harold Rawley (1854-1952) Rowland Huw Pritchard (1811-1887)

2. I was lost but Jesus found me,
found the sheep that went astray,
raised me up and gently led me
back into the narrow way.
Days of darkness still may meet me,
sorrow's path I oft may tread;
but his presence still is with me,
by his guiding hand I'm led.

3. He will keep me till the river
rolls its waters at my feet:
then he'll bear me safely over,
made by grace for glory meet.
Yes, I'll sing the wondrous story
of the Christ who died for me –
sing it with his saints in glory,
gathered by the crystal sea.

Text © HarperCollins Religious. Administered by CopyCare, P.O. Box 77,
Hailsham, East Sussex BN27 3EF, UK. (music@copycare.com). Used by permission.

338 James and Andrew, Peter and John

John L. Bell (b.1949)
Graham Maule (b.1958)

Traditional Irish melody

Text © Copyright 1987 WGRG, Iona Community, Glasgow G2 3DH, Scotland.
Used by permission from *Heaven shall not wait* collection . (Wild Goose Publications, 1987).

339 Jerusalem, my happy home

Based on verses by F.B.P.,
an unknown author (c.1600)

Herbert Stephen Irons (1834-1905)

SOUTHWELL (IRONS) CM

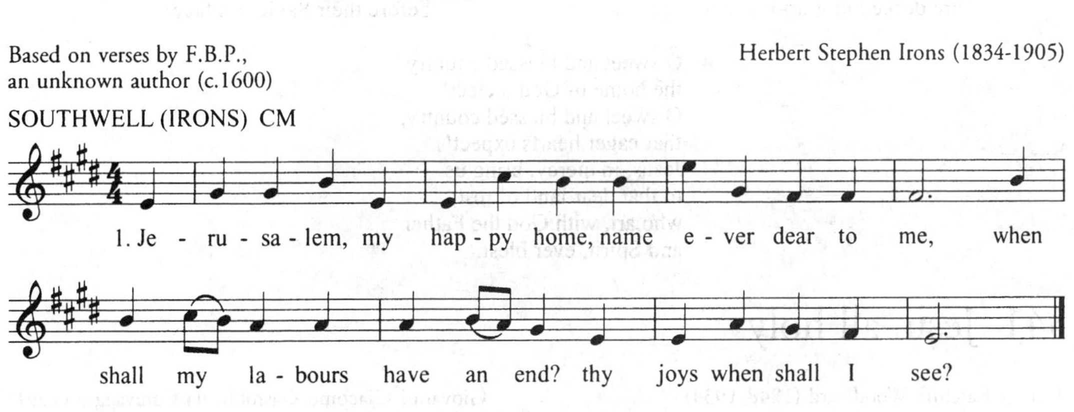

2. Apostles, martyrs, prophets, there
around my Saviour stand;
and all I love in Christ below
will join the glorious band.

3. Jerusalem, my happy home,
when shall I come to thee?
when shall my labours have an end?
thy joys when shall I see?

4. O Christ, do thou my soul prepare
for that bright home of love;
that I may see thee and adore,
with all thy saints above.

340 Jerusalem the golden

From *De Contemptu Mundi*
by St Bernard of Cluny (12th century)
trans. John Mason Neale (1818-1866) alt.

Alexander Ewing (1830-1895)

EWING 76 76 D

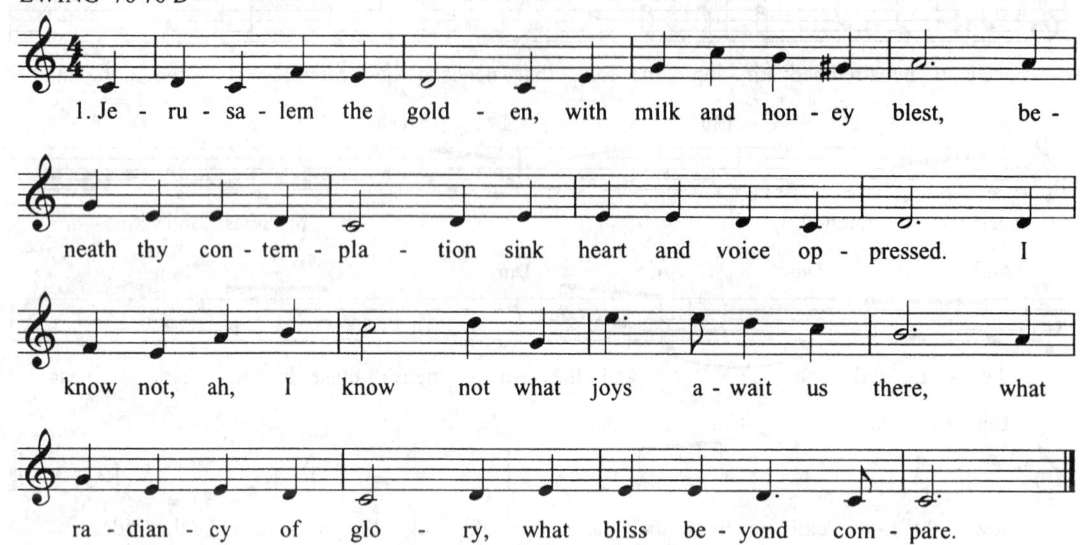

2. They stand, those halls of Zion,
all jubilant with song,
and bright with many angels,
and all the martyr throng;
the prince is ever with them,
the daylight is serene;
the pastures of the blessèd
are decked in glorious sheen.

3. There is the throne of David;
and there, from care released,
the shout of them that triumph,
the song of them that feast;
and they, who with their leader
have fully run the race,
are robed in white for ever
before their Saviour's face.

4. O sweet and blessèd country,
the home of God's elect!
O sweet and blessèd country,
that eager hearts expect!
Jesus, in mercy, bring us
to that dear land of rest;
who art, with God the Father
and Spirit, ever blest.

341 Jesu, all holy

George Ratcliffe Woodward (1848-1934)

Giovanni Giacomo Gastoldi, da Caravaggio (1591)

A LIETA VITA (IN DIR IST FREUDE) 557 D 55559 D

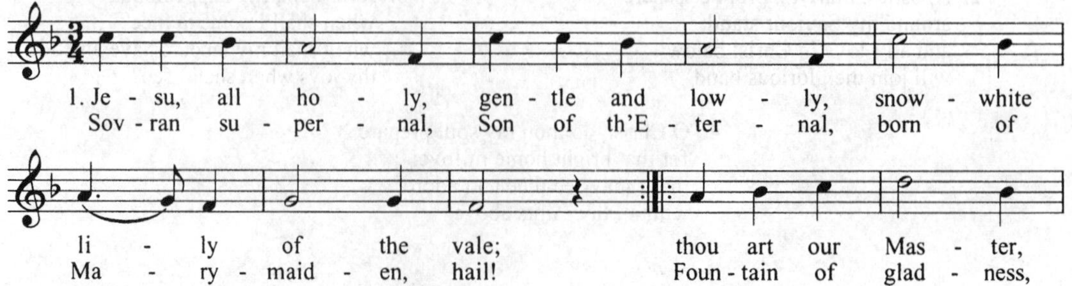

Text © Copyright Control

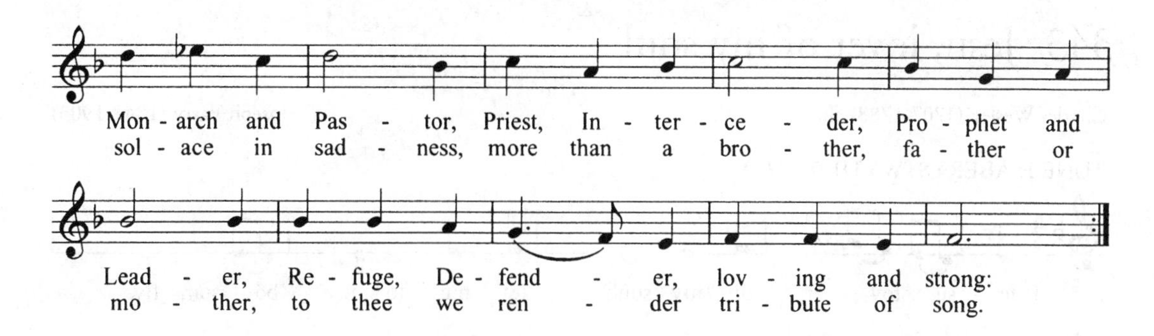

2. Jesu, we bless thee,
worship, confess thee:
Shepherd of the sheep thou art:
shelter, protect us,
tend and direct us,
strong of arm, and kind of heart:
shadow and moonlight
turn into noonlight;
soften the scorner,
comfort the mourner,
rule our behaviour, order our way:
bide with us, giving
grace to the living,
shrift to the dying
freely supplying,
be thou our Saviour ever and aye.

342 Jesu, grant me this, I pray

Latin (17th century)
trans. Henry Williams Baker (1821-1877)

Orlando Gibbons (1583-1625)

SONG 13 (CANTERBURY) 77 77

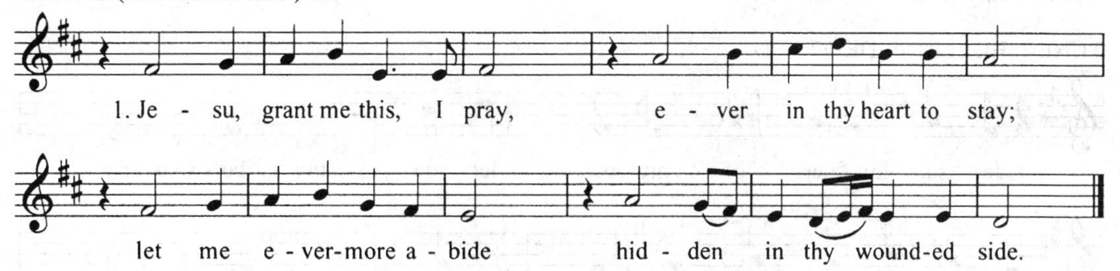

2. If the world or Satan lay
tempting snares about my way,
I am safe when I abide
in thy heart and wounded side.

3. If the flesh, more dang'rous still,
tempt my soul to deeds of ill,
naught I fear when I abide
in thy heart and wounded side.

4. Death will come one day to me;
Jesu, cast me not from thee:
dying let me still abide
in thy heart and wounded side.

343 Jesu, lover of my soul

Charles Wesley (1707-1788) alt. Joseph Parry (1841-1903)

TUNE 1: ABERYSTWYTH 77 77 D

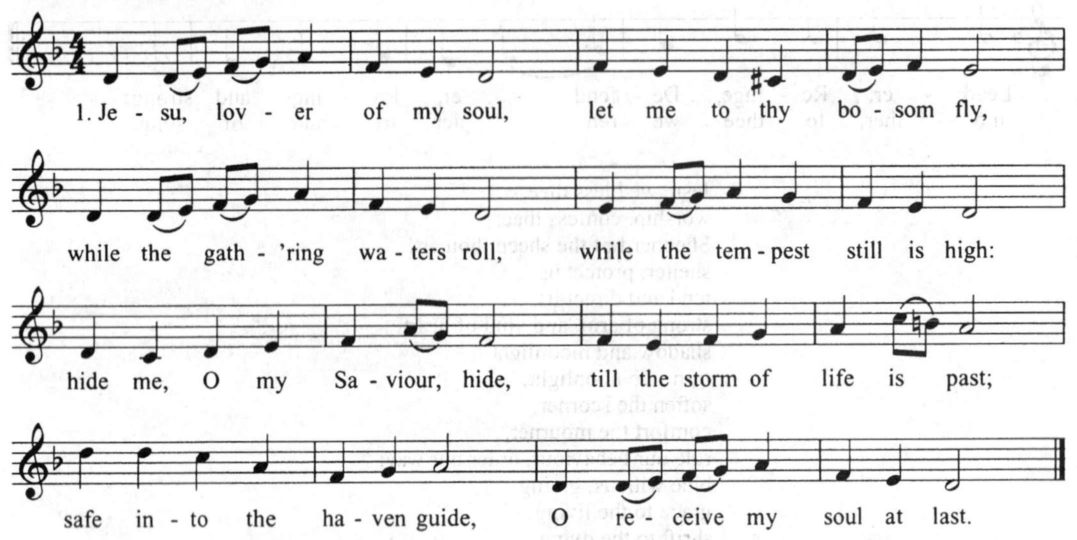

2. Other refuge have I none,
hangs my helpless soul on thee;
leave, ah, leave me not alone,
still support and comfort me.
All my trust on thee is stayed,
all my help from thee I bring;
cover my defenceless head
with the shadow of thy wing.

3. Plenteous grace with thee is found,
grace to cleanse from ev'ry sin;
let the healing streams abound,
make and keep me pure within.
Thou of life the fountain art,
freely let me take of thee,
spring thou up within my heart,
rise to all eternity.

Charles Wesley (1707-1788) alt. John Bacchus Dykes (1823-1876)

TUNE 2: HOLLINGSIDE 77 77 D

344 Jesu, priceless treasure

Johann Franck (1618-1677) alt.

Johann Crüger (1598-1662)

JESU, MEINE FREUDE 665 665 786

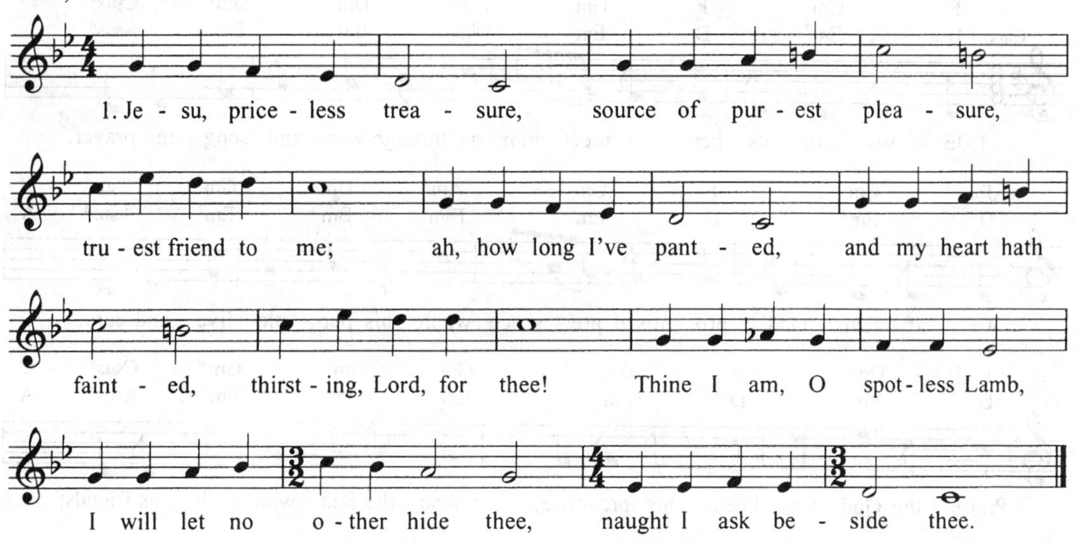

2. Hence, all fears and sadness,
for the Lord of gladness,
Jesus, enters in;
they who love the Father,
though the storms may gather,
still have peace within;
yea, whate'er I here must bear,
still in thee lies purest pleasure,
Jesu, priceless treasure.

345 Jesus, at your name

You are the Christ

Words and music: Chris Bowater

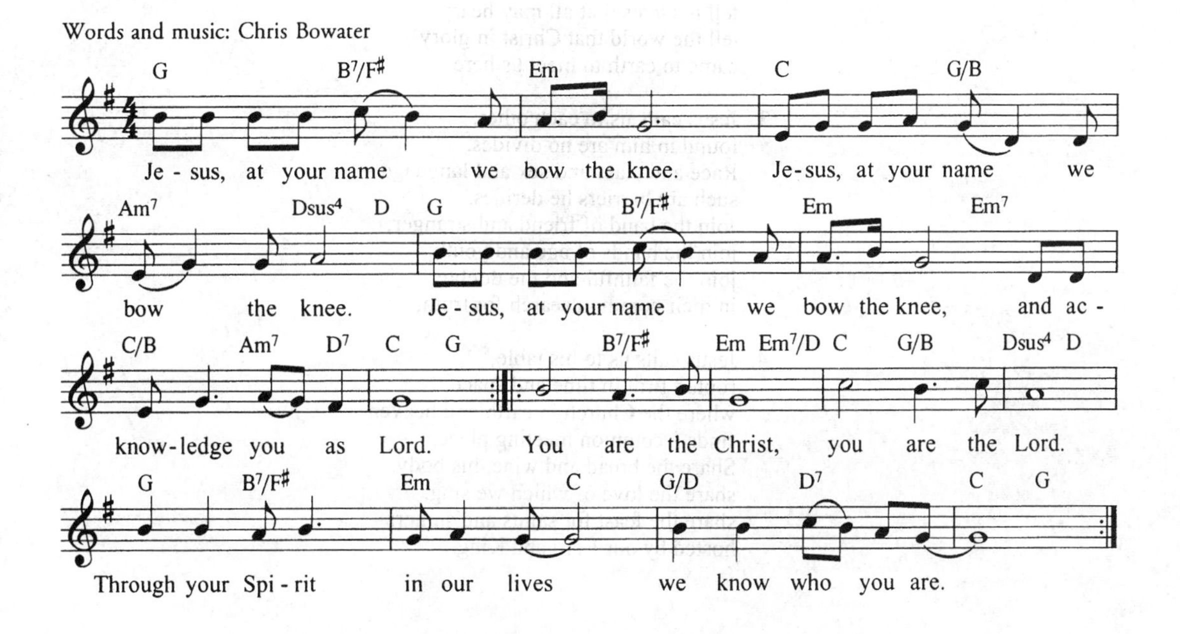

© Copyright 1982 Sovereign Lifestyle Music Ltd., P.O. Box 356,
Leighton Buzzard, Bedfordshire LU7 3WP, UK. Used by permission.

346 Jesus calls us

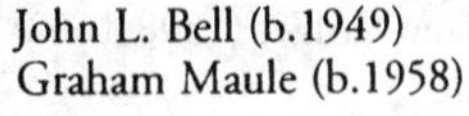

John L. Bell (b.1949)
Graham Maule (b.1958)

Gaelic air adapted by
John L. Bell and Graham Maule

2. Jesus calls us to confess him
Word of life and Lord of All,
sharer of our flesh and frailness
saving all who fail or fall.
Tell his holy human story;
tell his tales that all may hear;
tell the world that Christ in glory
came to earth to meet us here.

3. Jesus calls us to each other:
found in him are no divides.
Race and class and sex and language –
such are barriers he derides.
Join the hand of friend and stranger;
join the hands of age and youth;
join the faithful and the doubter
in their common search for truth.

4. Jesus calls us to his table,
rooted firm in time and space,
where the Church in earth and heaven
finds a common meeting place.
Share the bread and wine, his body;
share the love of which we sing;
share the feast for saints and sinners
hosted by our Lord and King.

© Copyright 1989 WGRG, Iona Community, Glasgow G2 3DH, Scotland.
Used by permission from *Love from below* collection. (Wild Goose Publications, 1989).

347 Jesus calls us: o'er the tumult

Cecil Frances Alexander (1818-1895) — Edward Henry Thorne (1834-1916)

TUNE 1: ST ANDREW 87 87

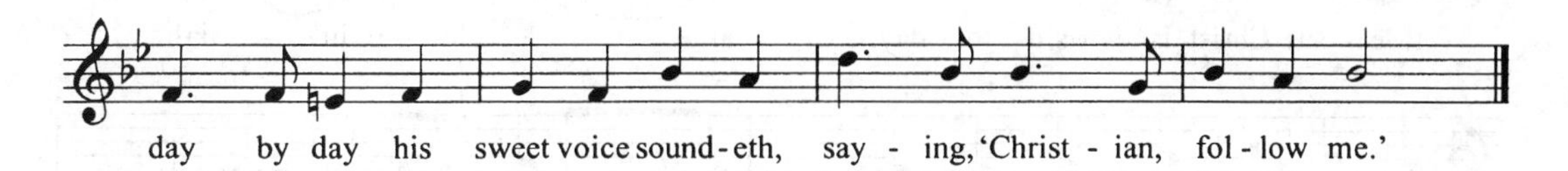

2. As of old Saint Andrew heard it
   by the Galilean lake,
   turned from home and toil and kindred,
   leaving all for his dear sake.

3. Jesus calls us from the worship
   of the vain world's golden store,
   from each idol that would keep us,
   saying, 'Christian, love me more.'

4. In our joys and in our sorrows,
   days of toil and hours of ease,
   still he calls, in cares and pleasures,
   that we love him more than these.

5. Jesus call us: by thy mercies,
   Saviour, make us hear thy call,
   give our hearts to thine obedience,
   serve and love thee best of all.

Cecil Frances Alexander (1818-1895) — William Henry Monk (1823-1889)

TUNE 2: MERTON 87 87

348 Jesus Christ is risen today

v.1 *Surrexit hodie* (14th century)
trans. anon as in *Lyra Davidica* (1708)
vs. 2-3 from J. Arnold's *Compleat Psalmodist* (1749)

Melody from *Lyra Davidica* (1708)

EASTER HYMN 77 77 and Alleluias

2. Hymns of praise then let us sing, alleluia!
unto Christ, our heav'nly King, alleluia!
who endured the cross and grave, alleluia!
sinners to redeem and save, alleluia!

3. But the pains that he endured, alleluia!
our salvation have procured; alleluia!
now above the sky he's King, alleluia!
where the angels ever sing, alleluia!

349 Jesus Christ is waiting

John L. Bell (b.1949)
Graham Maule (b.1958)

Traditional French melody

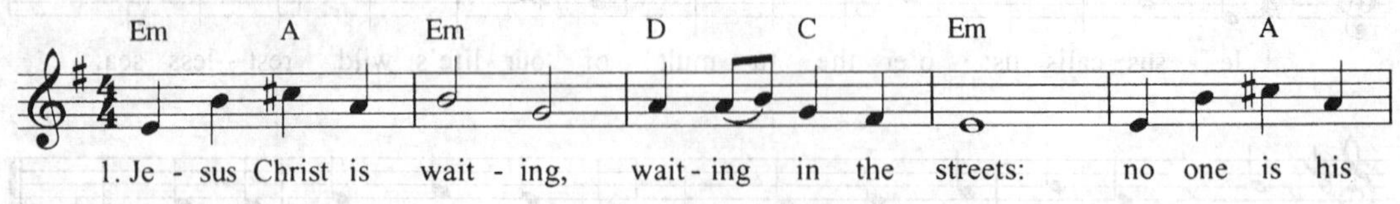

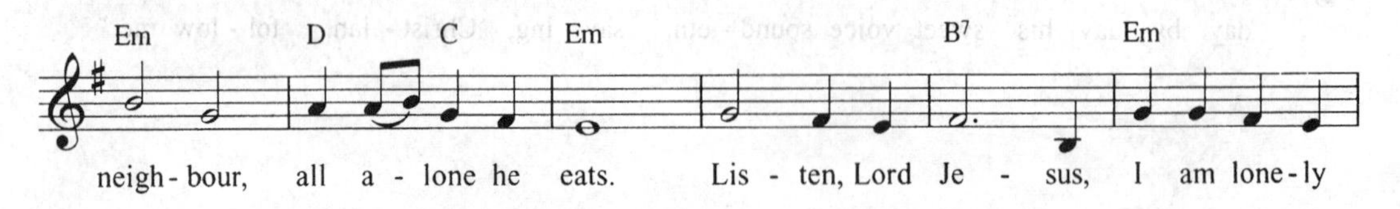

Text © Copyright 1988 WGRG, Iona Community, Glasgow G2 3DH, Scotland.
Used by permission from *Enemy of Apathy* Collection. (Wild Goose Publications, 1988).

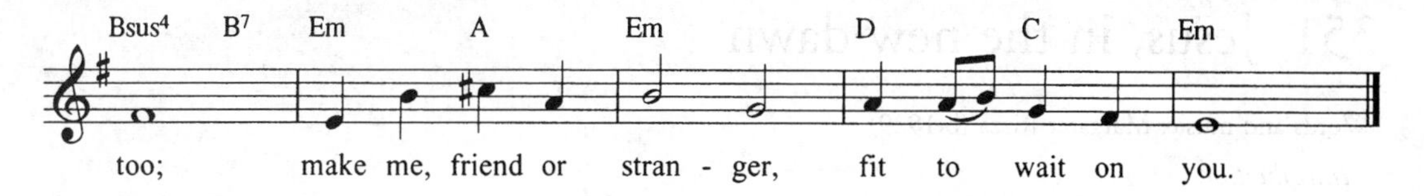

2. Jesus Christ is raging,
raging in the streets
where injustice spirals
and all hope retreats.
Listen, Lord Jesus,
I am angry too;
in the kingdom's causes
let me rage with you.

3. Jesus Christ is healing,
healing in the streets
curing those who suffer,
touching those he greets.
Listen, Lord Jesus,
I have pity too;
let my care be active,
healing just like you.

4. Jesus Christ is dancing,
dancing in the streets,
where each sign of hatred
his strong love defeats.
Listen, Lord Jesus,
I feel triumph too;
on suspicion's graveyard,
let me dance with you.

5. Jesus Christ is calling,
calling in the streets,
'Come and walk faith's tightrope,
I will guide your feet.'
Listen, Lord Jesus,
let my fears be few;
walk one step before me,
I will follow you.

350 Jesus, good above all other

Percy Dearmer (1867-1936)
after John Mason Neale (1818-1866) alt.

German Carol melody (14th century)

QUEM PASTORES 88 87

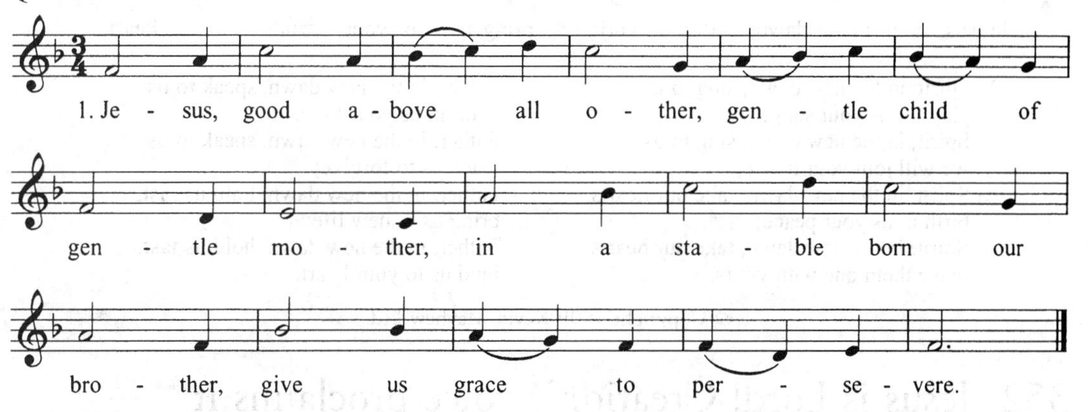

2. Jesus, cradled in a manger,
for us facing ev'ry danger,
living as a homeless stranger,
make we thee our King most dear.

3. Jesus, for thy people dying,
risen Master, death defying,
Lord in heav'n thy grace supplying,
keep us to thy presence near.

4. Jesus, who our sorrows bearest,
all our thoughts and hopes thou sharest,
thou to us the truth declarest;
help us all thy truth to hear.

5. Lord, in all our doings guide us;
pride and hate shall ne'er divide us;
we'll go on with thee beside us,
and with joy we'll persevere.

Text: © Copyright Oxford University Press, Great Clarendon Street, Oxford OX2 6DP.
Used by permission from the *English Hymnal.*

351 Jesus, in the new dawn

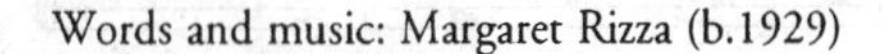

Words and music: Margaret Rizza (b.1929)

2. Spirit, in the new dawn, sing to us,
play for us your song;
Spirit, in the new dawn, sing to us,
we will join your dance;
Spirit, in the new dawn, take our hearts,
birth in us your peace;
Spirit, in the new dawn, take our hearts,
make them one with yours.

3. Father, in the new dawn, speak to us,
plant in us your love;
Father, in the new dawn, speak to us,
teach us to forgive;
Father, in the new dawn, hold us fast,
bring us to new life;
Father, in the new dawn, hold us fast,
bind us to your heart.

© Copyright 1999 Kevin Mayhew Ltd.

352 Jesus is Lord! Creation's voice proclaims it

Words and music: David J. Mansell

JESUS IS LORD 11 12 11 12 and Refrain

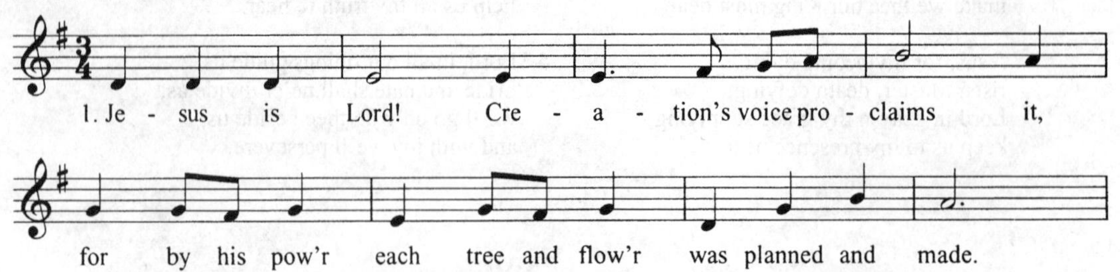

© Copyright 1982 Word's Spirit of Praise Music. Administered by CopyCare, P.O. Box 77, Hailsham, East Sussex BN27 3EF, UK. (music@copycare.com). Used by permission.

2. Jesus is Lord! Yet from his throne eternal
 in flesh he came to die in pain on Calv'ry's tree.
 Jesus is Lord! From him all life proceeding,
 yet gave his life as ransom thus setting us free.

3. Jesus is Lord! O'er sin the mighty conqu'ror,
 from death he rose and all his foes shall own his name.
 Jesus is Lord! God sends his Holy Spirit
 to show by works of power that Jesus is Lord.

353 Jesus, Jesus *Holy and anointed One*

Words and music: John Barnett

© Copyright 1980 Mercy/Vineyard Publishing. Administered by CopyCare, P.O. Box 77, Hailsham, East Sussex BN27 3EF, UK. (music@copycare.com). Used by permission.

354 Jesus lives! thy terrors now

Christian Fürchtegott Gellert (1715-1769)
trans. Frances Elizabeth Cox (1812-1897) alt.

Henry John Gauntlett (1805-1876)

ST ALBINUS 78 78 and Alleluia

2. Jesus lives! henceforth is death
but the gate of life immortal:
this shall calm our trembling breath,
when we pass its gloomy portal.
Alleluia.

3. Jesus lives! for us he died;
then, alone to Jesus living,
pure in heart may we abide,
glory to our Saviour giving.
Alleluia.

4. Jesus lives! our hearts know well
naught from us his love shall sever;
life nor death nor pow'rs of hell
tear us from his keeping ever.
Alleluia.

5. Jesus lives! to him the throne
over all the world is given:
may we go where he is gone,
rest and reign with him in heaven.
Alleluia.

355 Jesus, Name above all names

Words and music: Nadia Hearn (b.1944)

© Copyright 1974 Scripture in Song (a division of Integrity Music Inc.)/Sovereign Music UK, P.O. Box 356, Leighton Buzzard, LU7 3WP, UK. Used by permission.

356 Jesu, Son of Mary

Trans. from the Swahili
by Edmund S. Palmer (1856-1931)

Sabine Baring-Gould (1834-1924)

TUNE 1: EUDOXIA 65 65

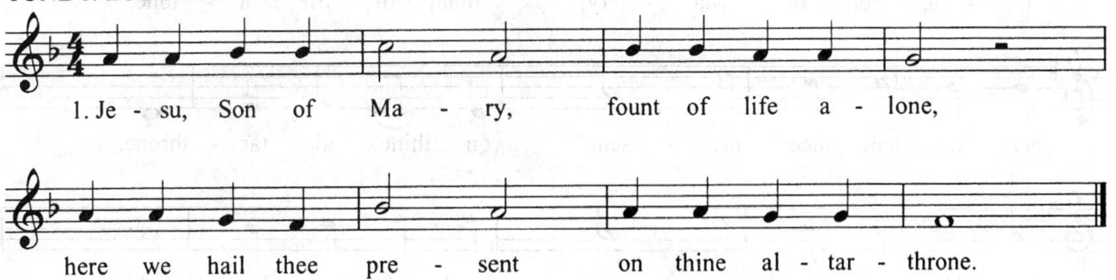

2. Humbly we adore thee,
Lord of endless might,
in the mystic symbols
veiled from earthly sight.

3. Think, O Lord, in mercy
on the souls of those
who, in faith gone from us,
now in death repose.

4. Here 'mid stress and conflict
toils can never cease;
there, the warfare ended,
bid them rest in peace.

5. Often were they wounded
in the deadly strife;
heal them, good Physician,
with the balm of life.

6. Ev'ry taint of evil,
frailty and decay,
good and gracious Saviour,
cleanse and purge away.

7. Rest eternal grant them,
after weary fight;
shed on them the radiance
of thy heav'nly light.

8. Lead them onward, upward,
to the holy place,
where thy saints made perfect
gaze upon thy face.

Trans. from the Swahili
by Edmund S. Palmer (1856-1931)

Friedrich Filitz (1804-1876)

TUNE 2: CASWALL 65 65

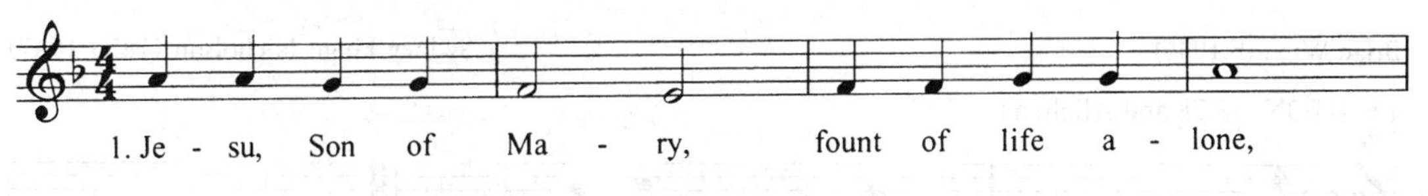

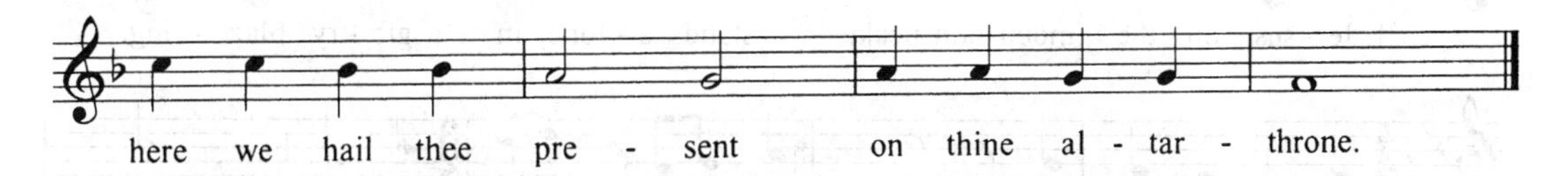

Trans. from the Swahili
by Edmund S. Palmer (1856-1931)

Johann Abraham Peter Schulz (1747-1800)
in *Lieder in Volkston*, Berlin (1785)

TUNE 3: SWAHILI 65 65 D

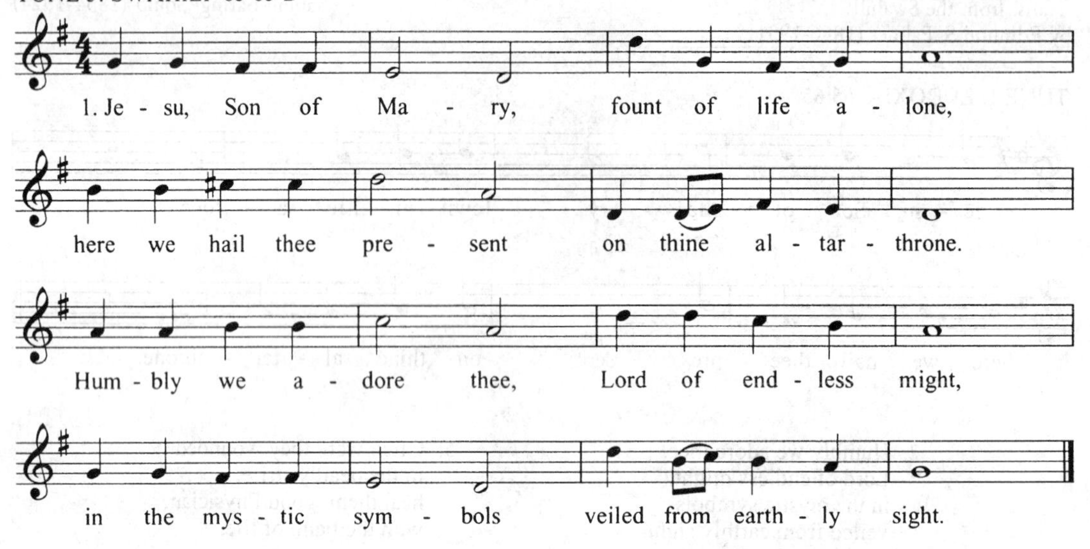

2. Think, O Lord, in mercy
on the souls of those
who, in faith gone from us,
now in death repose.
Here 'mid stress and conflict
toils can never cease;
there, the warfare ended,
bid them rest in peace.

3. Often were they wounded
in the deadly strife;
heal them, good Physician,
with the balm of life.
Ev'ry taint of evil,
frailty and decay,
good and gracious Saviour,
cleanse and purge away.

4. Rest eternal grant them,
after weary fight;
shed on them the radiance
of thy heav'nly light.
Lead them onward, upward,
to the holy place,
where thy saints made perfect
gaze upon thy face.

357 Jesus, on the mountain peak

Brian Wren (b.1936)

Sydney Hugo Nicholson (1875-1947)

FENITON 78 78 and Alleluias

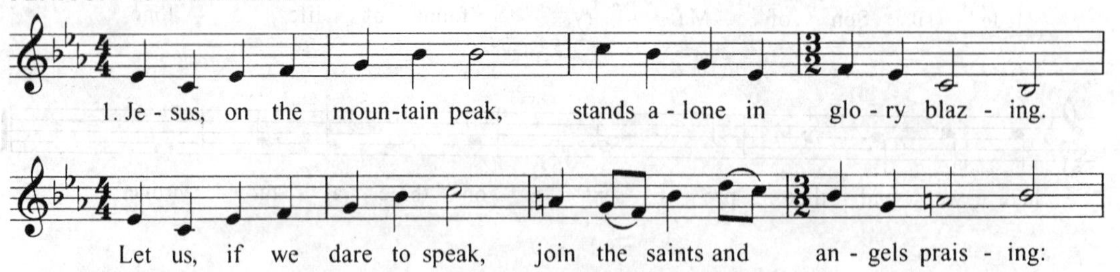

Text © Copyright 1977, 1995 Stainer & Bell Ltd., P.O. Box 110, Victoria House,
23 Gruneison Road, Finchley, London N3 1DZ.
Music © Copyright Hymns Ancient & Modern, St Mary's Works,
St Mary's Plain, Norwich NR3 3BH. Used by permission.

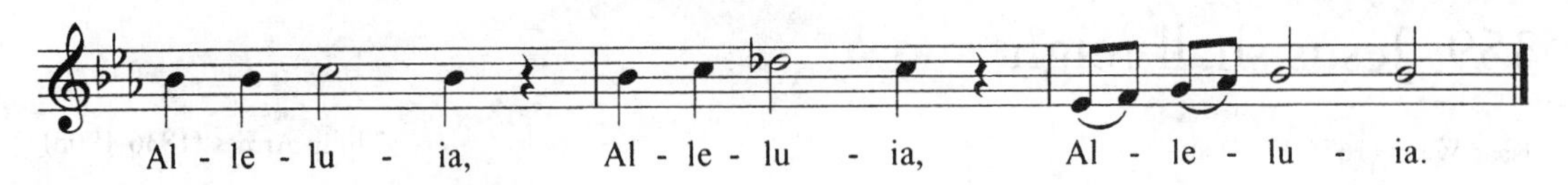

2. Trembling at his feet we saw
Moses and Elijah speaking.
All the Prophets and the Law
shout through them their joyful greeting:
Alleluia!

3. Swift the cloud of glory came,
God, proclaiming in the thunder,
Jesus as the Son by name!
Nations, cry aloud in wonder:
Alleluia!

4. Jesus is the chosen One,
living hope of ev'ry nation,
hear and heed him, everyone;
sing, with earth and all creation.
Alleluia!

358 Jesus, Prince and Saviour

Timothy Dudley-Smith (b.1926) Arthur Seymour Sullivan (1842-1900)

ST GERTRUDE 65 65 D and Refrain

2. In his pow'r and Godhead
ev'ry vict'ry won;
pain and passion ended,
all his purpose done.
Christ the Lord is risen!
sighs and sorrows past,
death's dark night is over,
morning comes at last!

3. Resurrection morning!
sinners' bondage freed;
Christ the Lord is risen —
he is ris'n indeed!
Jesus, Prince and Saviour,
Lord of life who died,
Christ the King of Glory
now is glorified!

Text © Copyright Timothy Dudley-Smith, 9 Ashlands, Ford,
Salisbury, Wiltshire SP4 6DY, UK. Used by permission.

359 Jesus shall reign

Isaac Watts (1674-1748) alt.

Philip Armes (1836-1908)

TUNE 1: GALILEE LM

2. People and realms of ev'ry tongue
dwell on his love with sweetest song,
and infant voices shall proclaim
their early blessings on his name.

3. Blessings abound where'er he reigns:
the pris'ners leap to lose their chains;
the weary find eternal rest,
and all the humble poor are blest.

4. To him shall endless prayer be made,
and praises throng to crown his head;
his name like incense shall arise
with ev'ry morning sacrifice.

5. Let ev'ry creature rise and bring
peculiar honours to our King;
angels descend with songs again,
and earth repeat the loud amen.

Isaac Watts (1674-1748) alt.

Melody from Thomas Williams' *Psalmodia Evangelica* (1789)

TUNE 2: TRURO LM

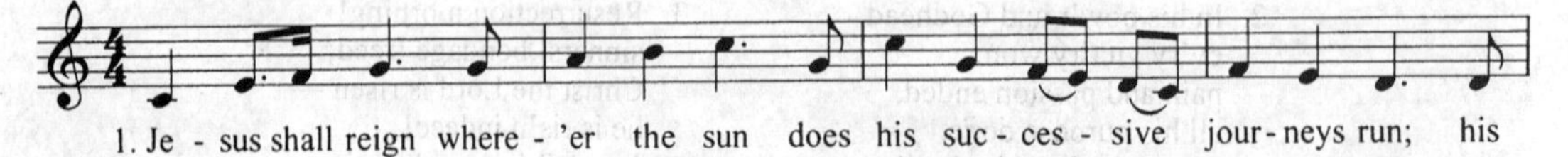

king - dom stretch from shore to shore, till moons shall wax and wane no more.

360 Jesus shall take the highest honour

© Copyright 1988 Sovereign Lifestyle Music Ltd., P.O Box 356, Leighton Buzzard, Bedfordshire LU7 3WP, UK. Used by permission.

361 Jesus, stand among us at the meeting of our lives

Words and music: Graham Kendrick (b.1950)

2. So to you we're gath'ring out of each and ev'ry land,
Christ the love between us at the joining of our hands.

Optional verse for Communion

3. Jesus stand among us at the breaking of the bread;
join us as one body as we worship you, our Head.

© Copyright 1977 Kingsway's Thankyou Music, P.O. Box 75,
Eastbourne, East Sussex BN23 6NW, UK. (tym@kingsway.co.uk). Used by permission.

362 Jesus, stand among us in thy risen power

William Pennefather (1816-1873) — Friedrich Filitz (1804-1876)

CASWALL 65 65

2. Breathe the Holy Spirit
into ev'ry heart;
bid the fears and sorrows
from each soul depart.

3. Thus with quickened footsteps
we'll pursue our way,
watching for the dawning
of eternal day.

363 Jesus, the broken bread

Nick Fawcett (b.1957) Noel Rawsthorne (b.1929)

HESWALL 10 10 10 10

2. Jesus, the poured out wine, we come with awe;
thirsty, we take the cup – quench and restore.
Teach us to seek your kingdom and your will,
reach out in love, we pray, our lives to fill.

3. Jesus, the crucified, we come with shame;
greedy, we've sought reward – made that our aim.
Teach us to worship now through word and deed,
reach out in love, we pray, to all in need.

4. Jesus, the risen Lord, we come with praise;
gladly, we sing of you, our hearts ablaze.
Teach us to glimpse new life beyond the grave,
reach out in love, we pray, to heal and save.

5. Jesus, the living one, we come with joy,
truly, no evil can your love destroy.
Teach us to walk in faith, though hope seems vain,
reach out in love, we pray, renew again.

6. Jesus, the King of kings, we come to serve,
freely give all for you as you deserve.
Teach us to share the love you daily show,
reach out in love, we pray, and bid us go.

© Copyright 1999 Kevin Mayhew Ltd.

364 Jesus, the name high over all

Charles Wesley (1707-1788)

Thomas Phillips (1735-1807)

LYDIA CM extended

2. Jesus, the name to sinners dear,
the name to sinners giv'n;
it scatters all their guilty fear,
it turns their hell to heav'n.

3. Jesus, the pris'ner's fetters breaks,
and bruises Satan's head;
pow'r into strengthless souls he speaks,
and life into the dead.

4. O, that the world might taste and see
the riches of his grace!
The arms of love that compass me,
hold all the human race.

5. His only righteousness I show,
his saving grace proclaim:
'tis all my business here below
to cry: 'Behold the Lamb!'

6. Happy, if with my latest breath
I may but gasp his name:
preach him to all, and cry in death:
'Behold, behold the Lamb!'

365 Jesus, these eyes have never seen

Ray Palmer (1808-1887)
based on John 20:29 and 1 Peter 1:8

From *Praxis Pietatis Melica* (1647)

NUN DANKET ALL CM

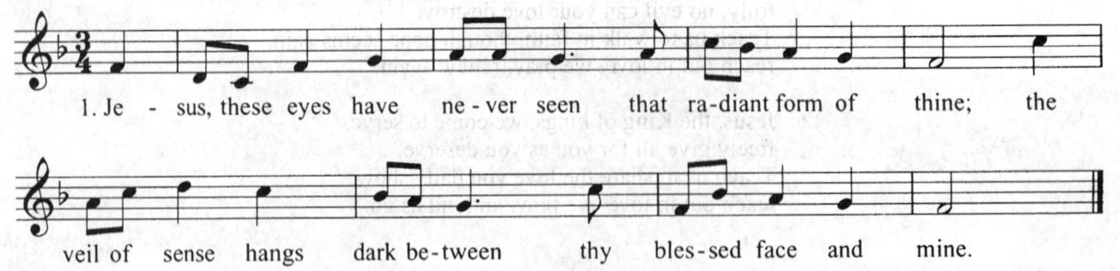

2. I see thee not, I hear thee not,
yet thou art oft with me;
and earth hath ne'er so dear a spot
as where I meet with thee.

3. Yet, though I have not seen, and still
must rest in faith alone,
I love thee, dearest Lord, and will,
unseen, but not unknown.

4. When death these mortal eyes shall seal,
and still this throbbing heart,
the rending veil shall thee reveal
all glorious as thou art.

366 Jesus took a piece of bread

Michael Forster (b.1946) Traditional English melody

ROYAL OAK 76 76 and Refrain

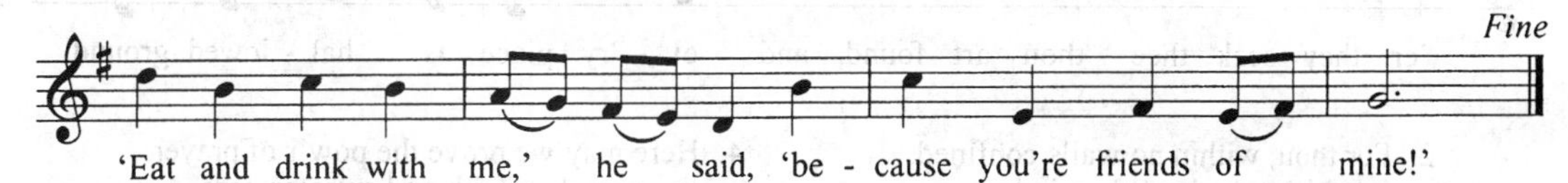

2. We share with one another
the bread and wine he gives,
and celebrate together
the special life he lives.

3. We rise up from the table,
and go where Jesus sends,
to tell the world the gospel
of love that never ends.

Text © Copyright 1996 Kevin Mayhew Ltd.

367 Jesus, where'er thy people meet

William Cowper (1731-1800) William Knapp (1698-1768)

TUNE 1: WAREHAM LM

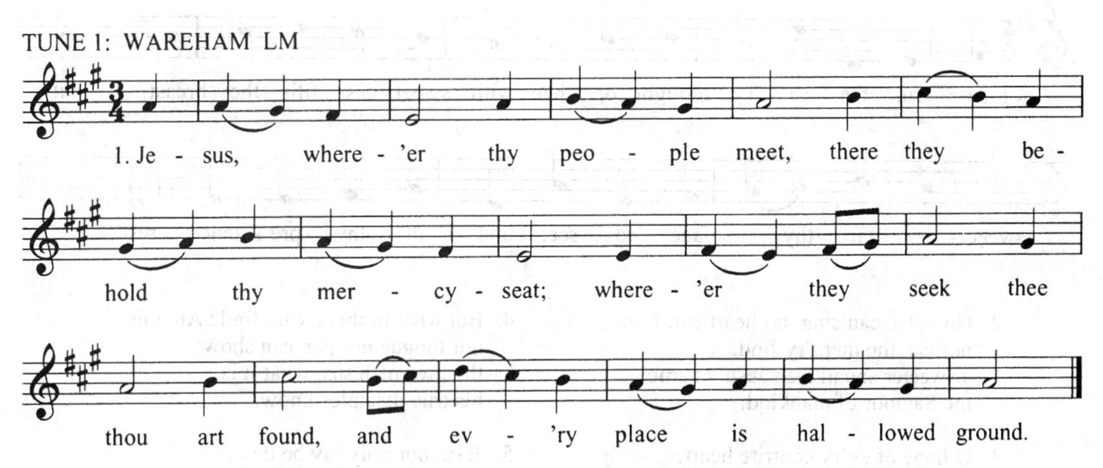

2. For thou, within no walls confined,
inhabitest the humble mind;
such ever bring thee when they come,
and, going, take thee to their home.

3. Dear Shepherd of thy chosen few,
thy former mercies here renew;
here to our waiting hearts proclaim
the sweetness of thy saving name.

4. Here may we prove the pow'r of prayer
to strengthen faith and sweeten care,
to teach our faint desires to rise,
and bring all heav'n before our eyes.

5. Lord, we are few, but thou art near;
nor short thine arm, nor deaf thine ear;
O rend the heav'ns, come quickly down,
and make a thousand hearts thine own.

Tune 2 will be found overleaf

William Cowper (1731-1800) George Cooper (1820-1876)

TUNE 2: ST SEPULCHRE LM

2. For thou, within no walls confined,
inhabitest the humble mind;
such ever bring thee when they come,
and, going, take thee to their home.

3. Dear Shepherd of thy chosen few,
thy former mercies here renew;
here to our waiting hearts proclaim
the sweetness of thy saving name.

4. Here may we prove the pow'r of prayer
to strengthen faith and sweeten care,
to teach our faint desires to rise,
and bring all heav'n before our eyes.

5. Lord, we are few, but thou art near;
nor short thine arm, nor deaf thine ear;
O rend the heav'ns, come quickly down,
and make a thousand hearts thine own.

368 Jesu, the very thought of thee

St Bernard of Clairvaux (1091-1153)
trans. Edward Caswall (1814-1878) alt. Richard Redhead (1820-1901)

TUNE 1: METZLER'S REDHEAD CM

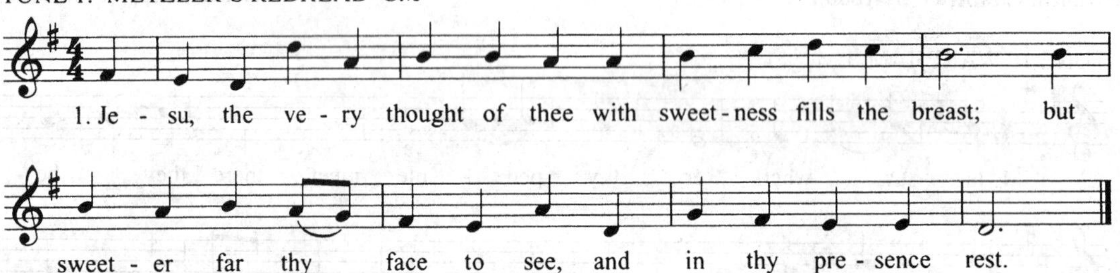

2. No voice can sing, no heart can frame,
nor can the mem'ry find,
a sweeter sound than Jesu's name,
the Saviour of mankind.

3. O hope of ev'ry contrite heart,
O joy of all the meek,
to those who ask how kind thou art,
how good to those who seek!

4. But what to those who find? Ah, this
nor tongue nor pen can show;
the love of Jesus, what it is
his true disciples know.

5. Jesu, our only joy be thou,
as thou our prize wilt be;
in thee be all our glory now,
and through eternity.

St Bernard of Clairvaux (1091-1153)
trans. Edward Caswall (1814-1878) alt.

John Bacchus Dykes (1823-1876)

TUNE 2: ST AGNES (DYKES) CM

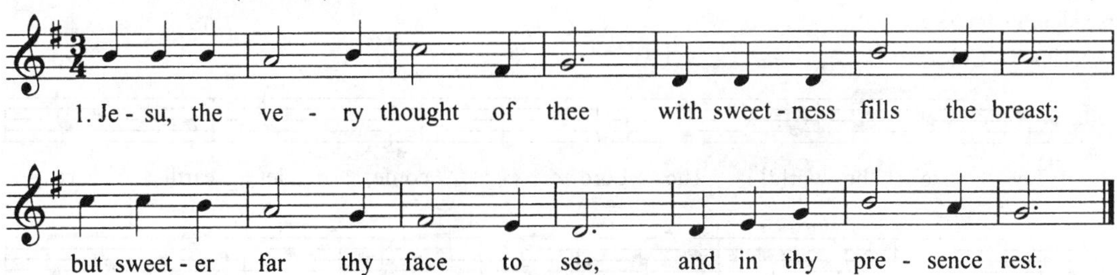

369 Jesu, thou joy of loving hearts

Jesu, dulcis memoria (12th century)
trans. Ray Palmer (1808-1887) alt.

Herbert Stanley Oakeley (1830-1903)

TUNE 1: EALING LM

2. Thy truth unchanged hath ever stood;
thou savest those that on thee call;
to them that seek thee thou art good,
to them that find thee, all in all.

3. We taste thee, O thou living bread,
and long to feast upon thee still;
we drink of thee, the fountain-head,
and thirst our souls from thee to fill.

4. Our restless spirits yearn for thee,
where'er our changeful lot is cast,
glad when thy gracious smile we see,
blest when our faith is holding fast.

5. O Jesu, ever with us stay;
make all our moments calm and bright;
chase the dark night of sin away;
shed o'er the world thy holy light.

Jesu, dulcis memoria (12th century)
trans. Ray Palmer (1808-1887) alt.

Melody by Johann Hermann Schein (1586-1630)
in his revised *Cantional* (1645)

TUNE 2: EISENACH LM

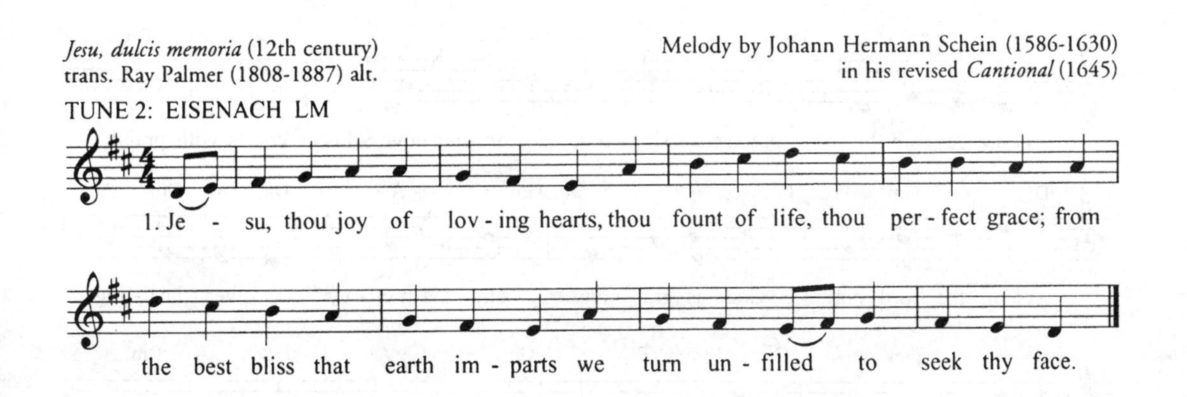

370 Joy to the world

Isaac Watts (1674-1748)
based on Psalm 98 alt.

George Frideric Handel (1685-1759)

ANTIOCH CM

2. Joy to the earth! The Saviour reigns;
let us our songs employ;
while fields and floods, rocks, hills and plains
repeat the sounding joy,
repeat the sounding joy,
repeat, repeat the sounding joy.

3. He rules the world with truth and grace,
and makes the nations prove
the glories of his righteousness,
and wonders of his love,
and wonders of his love,
and wonders, and wonders of his love.

371 Jubilate, everybody

Words and music: Fred Dunn (1907-1979)

JUBILATE DEO 88 87 88 86

© Copyright 1977 Kingsway's Thankyou Music, P.O. Box 75, Eastbourne,
East Sussex BN23 6NW, UK. (tym@kingsway.co.uk). Used by permission.

372 Judge eternal, throned in splendour

Henry Scott Holland (1847-1918) alt.

Traditional Welsh melody
from *Musical Relicks of Welsh Bards* (1800)

RHUDDLAN 87 87 87

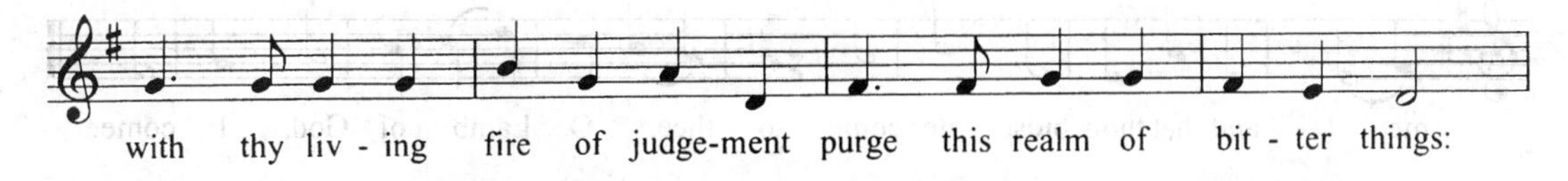

2. Still the weary folk are pining
for the hour that brings release:
and the city's crowded clangour
cries aloud for sin to cease;
and the homesteads and the woodlands
plead in silence for their peace.

3. Crown, O God, thine own endeavour;
cleave our darkness with thy sword;
feed thy people's hungry spirits
with the richness of thy word:
cleanse the body of this nation
through the glory of the Lord.

373 Just a closer walk with thee

Words and music: Traditional

JUST A CLOSER WALK 77 78

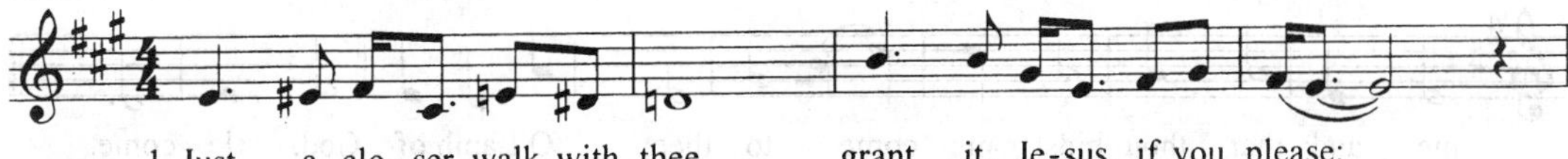

2. Through the day of toil that's near,
if I fall, dear Lord, who cares?
Who with me my burden shares?
None but thee, dear Lord, none but thee.

3. When my feeble life is o'er,
time for me will be no more.
Guide me gently, safely on
to the shore, dear Lord, to the shore.

374 Just as I am, without one plea

Charlotte Elliott (1789-1871) | Henry Smart (1813-1879)

TUNE 1: MISERICORDIA 88 86

2. Just as I am, though tossed about
with many a conflict, many a doubt,
fightings and fears within, without,
O Lamb of God, I come.

3. Just as I am, poor, wretched, blind;
sight, riches, healing of the mind,
yea, all I need, in thee to find,
O Lamb of God, I come.

4. Just as I am, thou wilt receive,
wilt welcome, pardon, cleanse, relieve:
because thy promise I believe,
O Lamb of God, I come.

5. Just as I am, thy love unknown
has broken ev'ry barrier down,
now to be thine, yea, thine alone,
O Lamb of God, I come.

6. Just as I am, of that free love
the breadth, length, depth and height to prove,
here for a season, then above,
O Lamb of God, I come.

Charlotte Elliott (1789-1871) | Arthur Henry Brown (1830-1926)

TUNE 2: SAFFRON WALDEN 88 86

Charlotte Elliott (1789-1871) | John Henry Maunder (1858-1920)

TUNE 3: MAUNDER 88 86 extended

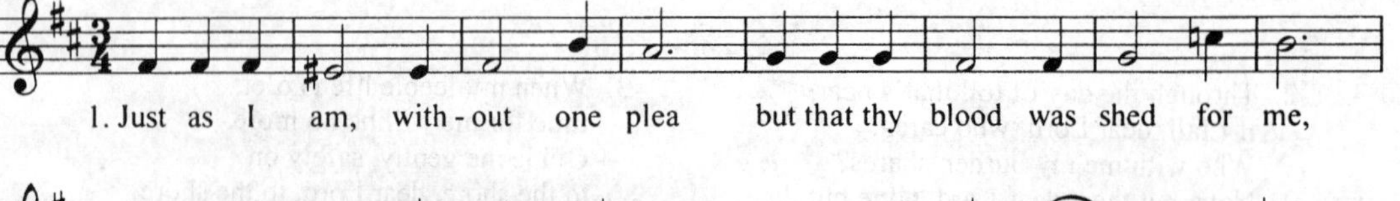

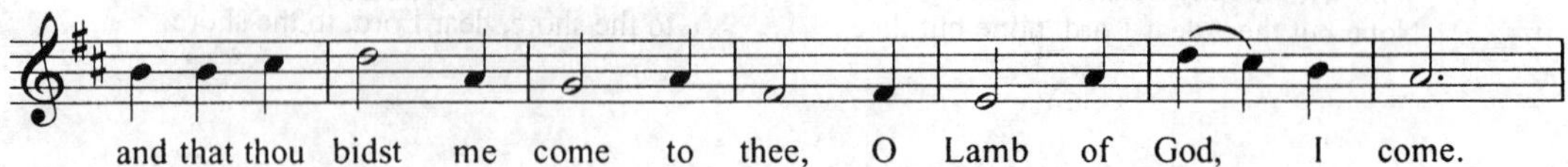

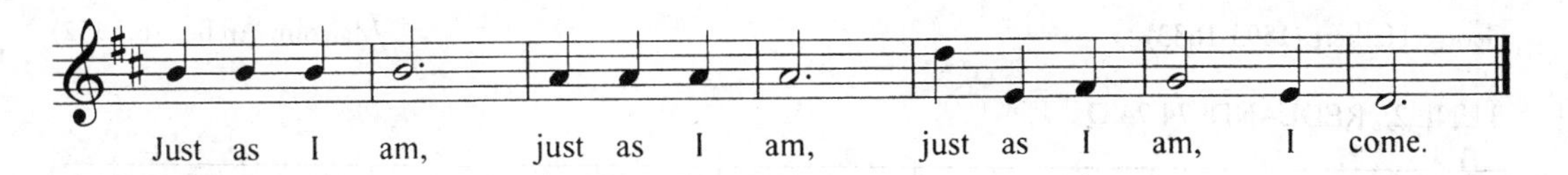

When the tune 'Maunder' is used this Refrain is added to each verse:

Just as I am, just as I am,
just as I am, I come.

375 King of glory, King of peace

George Herbert (1593-1633) John David Jones (1827-1870)

TUNE 1: GWALCHMAI 74 74 D

2. Wherefore with my utmost art,
   I will sing thee,
   and the cream of all my heart
   I will bring thee.
   Though my sins against me cried,
   thou didst clear me,
   and alone, when they replied,
   thou didst hear me.

3. Sev'n whole days, not one in sev'n,
   I will praise thee;
   in my heart, though not in heav'n,
   I can raise thee.
   Small it is, in this poor sort
   to enrol thee:
   e'en eternity's too short
   to extol thee.

Tune 2 will be found overleaf

George Herbert (1593-1633) Malcolm Archer (b.1952)

TUNE 2: REDLAND 74 74 D

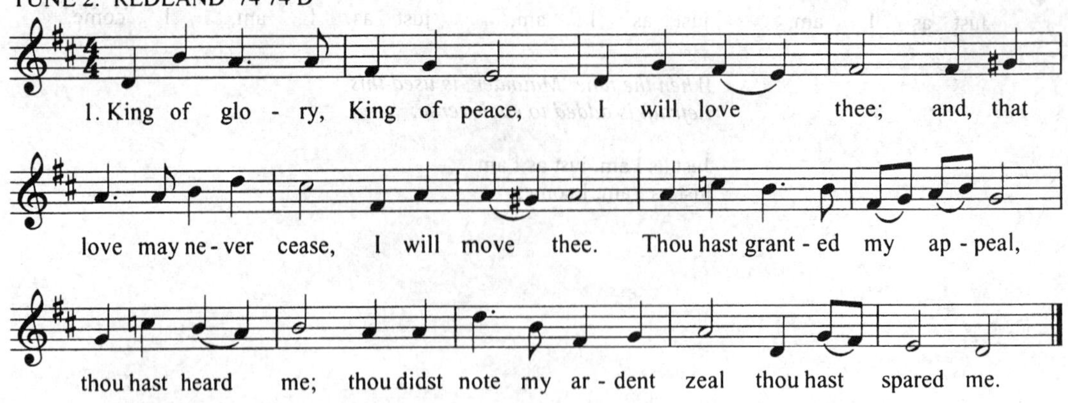

2. Wherefore with my utmost art,
I will sing thee,
and the cream of all my heart
I will bring thee.
Though my sins against me cried,
thou didst clear me,
and alone, when they replied,
thou didst hear me.

3. Sev'n whole days, not one in sev'n,
I will praise thee;
in my heart, though not in heav'n,
I can raise thee.
Small it is, in this poor sort
to enrol thee:
e'en eternity's too short
to extol thee.

Music © Copyright 1996 Kevin Mayhew Ltd.

376 King of kings and Lord of lords

Words and music: Naomi Batya and Sophie Conty

May be sung as a 2-part round, the second voices beginning when the first voices reach ⊕

© Copyright 1980 Maranatha! Music. Administered by CopyCare, P.O. Box 77, Hailsham, East Sussex BN27 3EF, UK. (music@copycare.com). Used by permission.

377 Lamb of God, Holy One

Words and music: Chris Bowater

© Copyright 1988 Sovereign Lifestyle Music, P.O. Box 356, Leighton Buzzard, Bedfordshire LU7 3WP, UK. Used by permission.

378 Lead, kindly light

John Henry Newman (1801-1890) | Charles Henry Purday (1799-1885)

TUNE 1: SANDON 10 4 10 4 10 10

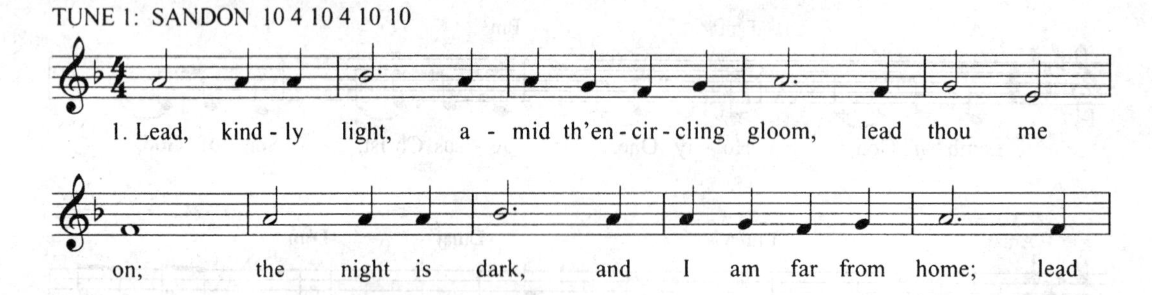

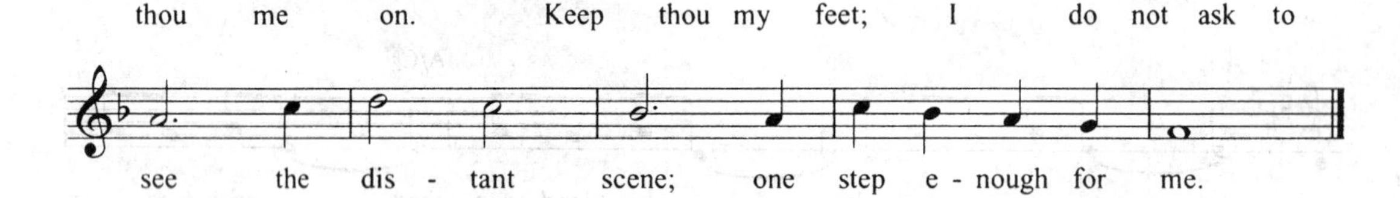

2. I was not ever thus, nor prayed that thou shouldst lead me on;
I loved to choose and see my path; but now lead thou me on.
I loved the garish day, and, spite of fears,
pride ruled my will: remember not past years.

3. So long thy pow'r hath blest me, sure it still will lead me on,
o'er moor and fen, o'er crag and torrent, till the night is gone;
and with the morn those angel faces smile,
which I have loved long since, and lost awhile.

John Henry Newman (1801-1890) | John Bacchus Dykes (1823-1876)

TUNE 2: LUX BENIGNA 10 4 10 4 10 10

Tune 3: Music © Copyright Oxford University Press, Great Clarendon Street,
Oxford OX2 6DP, UK. Used by permission.

John Henry Newman (1801-1890) William Henry Harris (1883-1973)

TUNE 3: ALBERTA 10 4 10 4 10 10

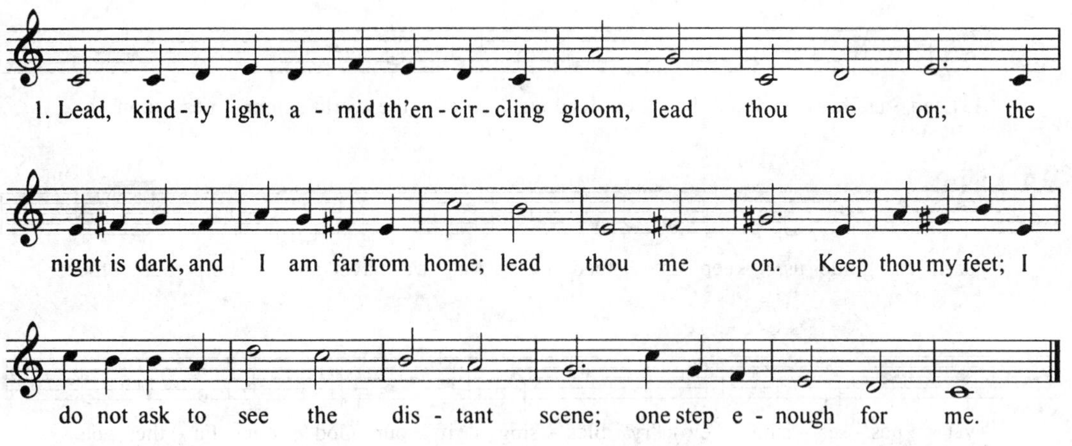

379 Lead us, heavenly Father, lead us

James Edmeston (1791-1867) Friedrich Filitz (1804-1876)

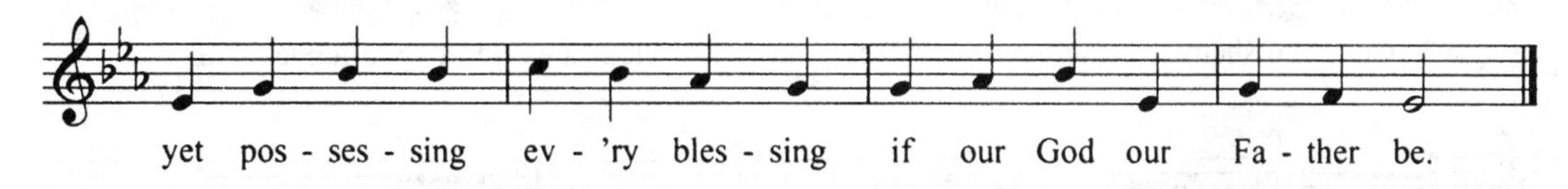

2. Saviour, breathe forgiveness o'er us,
all our weakness thou dost know,
thou didst tread this earth before us,
thou didst feel its keenest woe;
lone and dreary, faint and weary,
through the desert thou didst go.

3. Spirit of our God, descending,
fill our hearts with heav'nly joy,
love with ev'ry passion blending,
pleasure that can never cloy;
thus provided, pardoned, guided,
nothing can our peace destroy.

Tune 2 will be found overleaf

James Edmeston (1791-1867) Richard Lloyd (b.1933)

TUNE 2: RED WHARF BAY 87 87 87

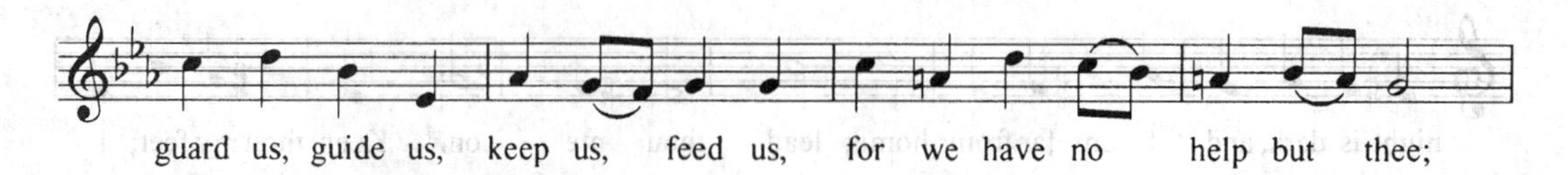

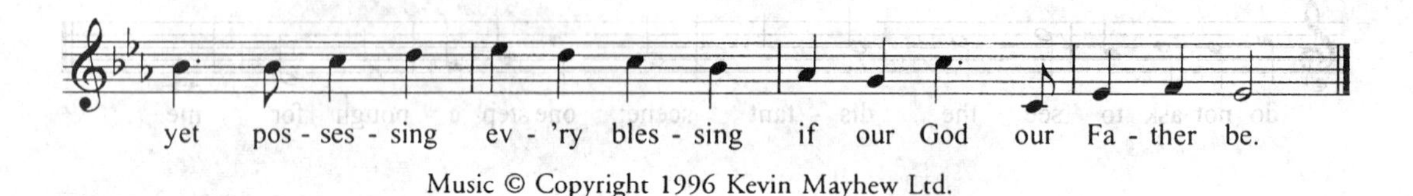

Music © Copyright 1996 Kevin Mayhew Ltd.

2. Saviour, breathe forgiveness o'er us,
all our weakness thou dost know,
thou didst tread this earth before us,
thou didst feel its keenest woe;
lone and dreary, faint and weary,
through the desert thou didst go.

3. Spirit of our God, descending,
fill our hearts with heav'nly joy,
love with ev'ry passion blending,
pleasure that can never cloy;
thus provided, pardoned, guided,
nothing can our peace destroy.

380 Led like a lamb *You're alive*

Words and music: Graham Kendrick (b.1950)

© Copyright 1983 Kingsway's Thankyou Music, P.O. Box 75, Eastbourne, East Sussex BN23 6NW, UK. (tym@kingsway.co.uk). Used by permission.

2. At break of dawn, poor Mary,
still weeping she came,
when through her grief she heard your voice
now speaking her name.
Mary, Master, Mary, Master.

3. At the right hand of the Father
now seated on high
you have begun your eternal reign
of justice and joy.
Glory, glory, glory, glory.

381 Let all mortal flesh keep silence

Liturgy of St James
trans. G. Moultrie (1829-1885)

Traditional French melody

PICARDY 87 87 87

2. King of kings, yet born of Mary,
as of old on earth he stood,
Lord of lords, in human vesture,
in the body and the blood.
He will give to all the faithful
his own self for heav'nly food.

3. Rank on rank the host of heaven
spreads its vanguard on the way,
as the Light of light descendeth
from the realms of endless day,
that the pow'rs of hell may vanish
as the darkness clears away.

4. At his feet the six-winged seraph;
cherubim, with sleepless eye,
veil their faces to the Presence,
as with ceaseless voice they cry,
alleluia, alleluia,
alleluia, Lord most high.

382 Let all the world in every corner sing

George Herbert (1593-1633) Basil Harwood (1859-1949)

LUCKINGTON 10 4 66 66 10 4

1. Let all the world in ev - 'ry cor - ner sing, my
God and King! The heav'ns are not too high, his praise may thi - ther
fly; the earth is not too low, his prai - ses there may grow. Let
all the world in ev - 'ry cor - ner sing, my God and King!

2. Let all the world in ev'ry corner sing,
my God and King!
The Church with psalms must shout,
no door can keep them out;
but, above all, the heart
must bear the longest part.
Let all the world in ev'ry corner sing,
my God and King!

Music © Copyright The Estate of Dr. Basil Harwood. Reproduced by permission of the Trustees of the Late Dr. Basil Harwood Settlement Trust, Public Trust Office, 24 Kingsway, London WC2B 6XJ, UK.

383 Let love be real

Michael Forster (b.1946) Christopher Tambling (b.1964)

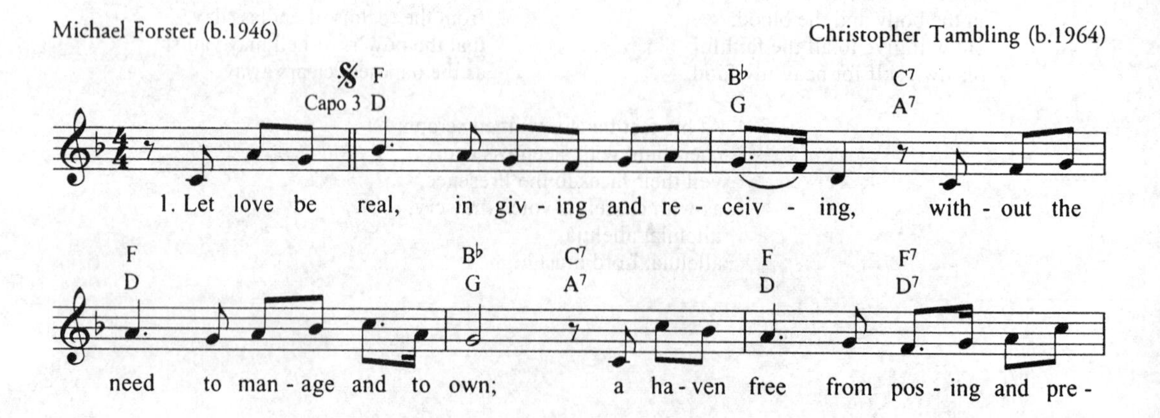

© Copyright 1995 Kevin Mayhew Ltd.

2. Let love be real, not grasping or confining,
   that strange embrace that holds yet sets us free;
   that helps us face the risk of truly living,
   and makes us brave to be what we might be.
   Give me your strength when all my words are weakness;
   give me your love in spite of all you know.

3. Let love be real, with no manipulation,
   no secret wish to harness or control;
   let us accept each other's incompleteness,
   and share the joy of learning to be whole.
   Give me your hope through dreams and disappointments;
   give me your trust when all my failings show.

384 Let saints on earth in concert sing

Charles Wesley (1707-1788)
and others, alt.

Melody from *Psalms,* Edinburgh (1615)

DUNDEE CM

1. Let saints on earth in con - cert sing with those whose work is done; for all the ser - vants of our King in heav'n and earth are one.

2. One family, we dwell in him,
one Church, above, beneath;
though now divided by the stream,
the narrow stream of death.

3. The people of the living God,
to his command we bow:
part of the host have crossed the flood,
and part are crossing now.

4. E'en now to their eternal home
there pass some spirits blest;
while others to the margin come,
waiting their call to rest.

5. Jesu, be thou our constant guide;
then, when the word is giv'n,
bid Jordan's narrow stream divide,
and bring us safe to heav'n.

385 Let the heavens declare

Words and music: Mike Anderson (b.1956)

© Copyright 1999 Kevin Mayhew Ltd.

2. Hanging on the cross for me
Jesus died in agony.
Blood and tears he shed for me,
that I might have life. *(x4)*

3. In the kingdom he revealed
broken hearts can all be healed,
through the covenant he sealed
with his holy blood. *(x4)*

386 Let there be love

Words and music: Dave Bilbrough

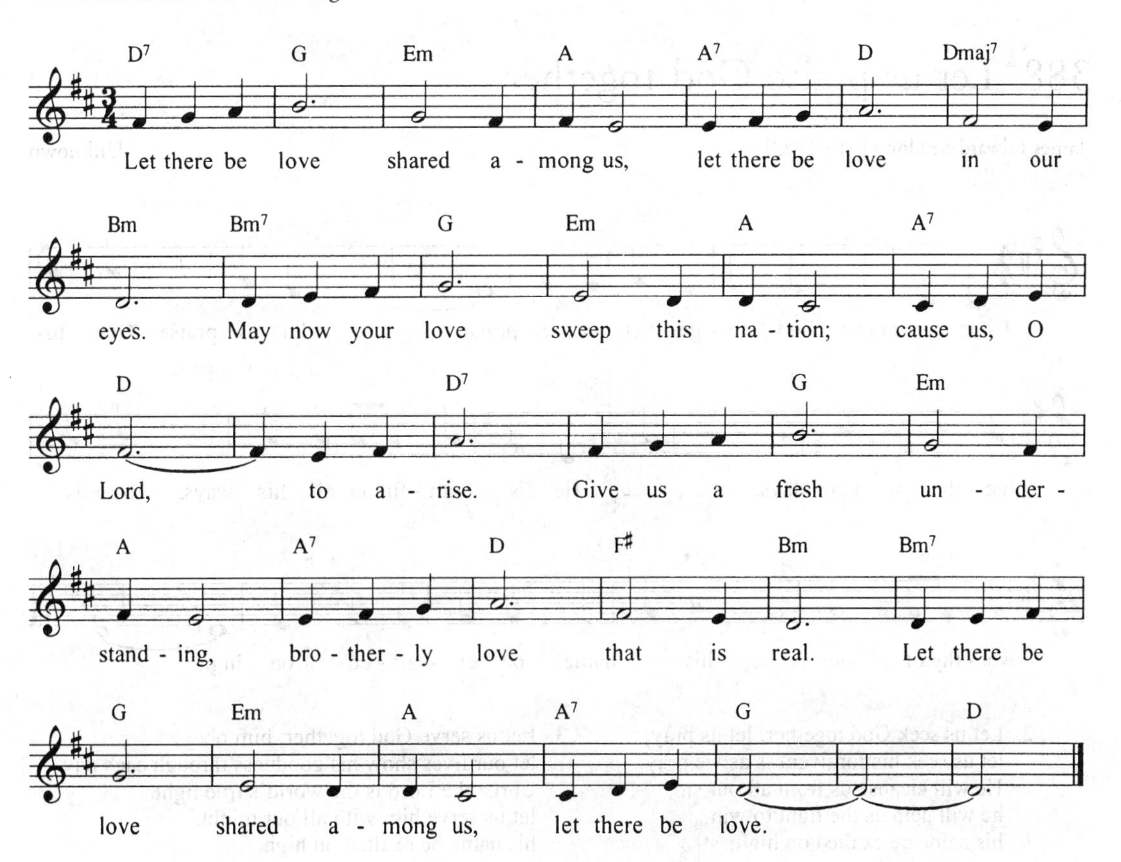

© Copyright 1979 Kingsway's Thankyou Music, P.O. Box 75, Eastbourne, East Sussex BN23 6NW, UK. (tym@kingsway.co.uk). Used by permission.

387 Let us break bread together

Words and music: Unknown

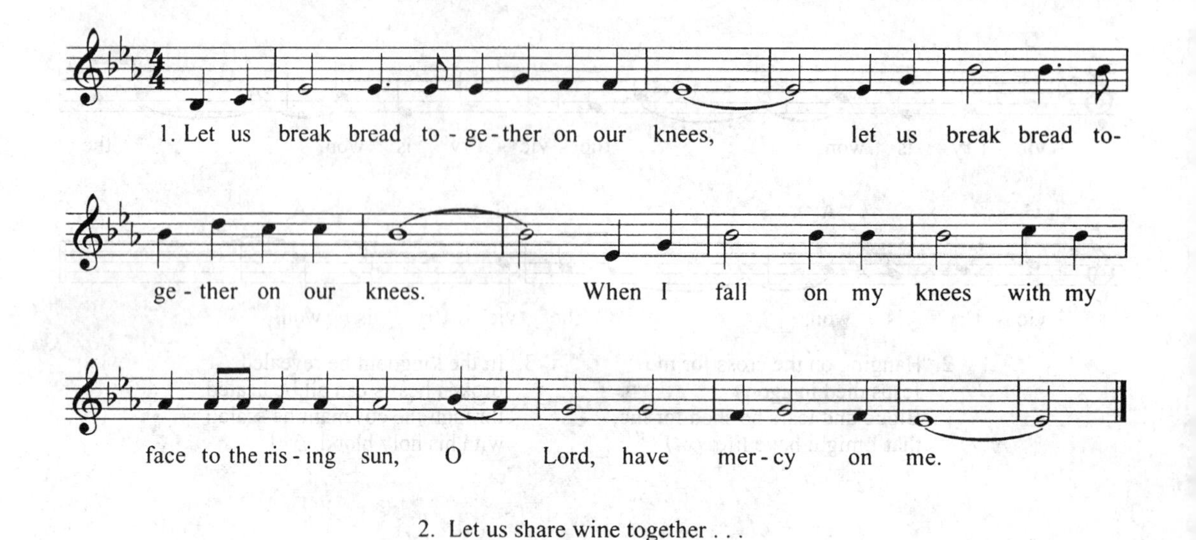

2. Let us share wine together . . .

3. Let us praise God together . . .

388 Let us praise God together

James Edward Seddon (1915-1983) Unknown

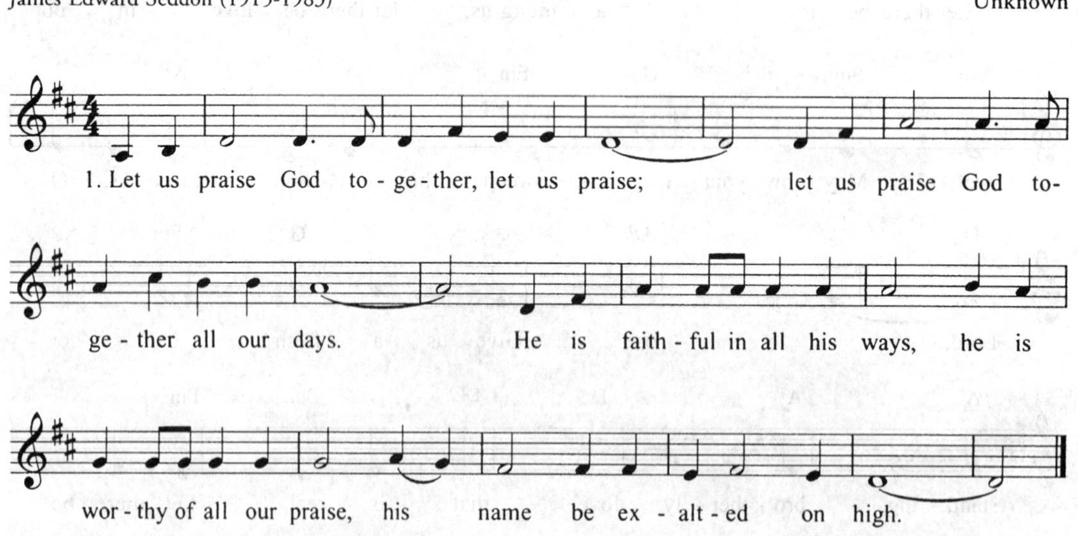

2. Let us seek God together, let us pray;
let us seek his forgiveness as we pray.
He will cleanse us from all our sin,
he will help us the fight to win,
his name be exalted on high.

3. Let us serve God together, him obey;
let our lives show his goodness through each day.
Christ the Lord is the world's true light,
let us serve him with all our might,
his name be exalted on high.

Text © Copyright Mrs M. Seddon/Jubilate Hymns, 4 Thorne Park Road,
Chelston, Torquay TQ2 6RX, UK. Used by permission.

389 Let us rejoice

Martin E. Leckebusch (b.1962)
based on Romans 5:1-5

Charles Villiers Stanford (1852-1924)

ENGELBERG 10 10 10 4

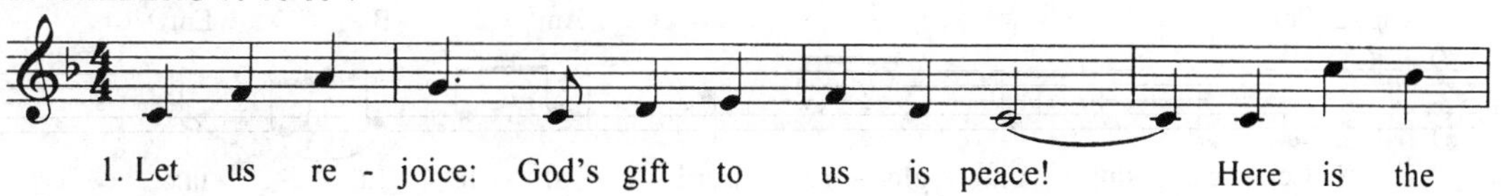

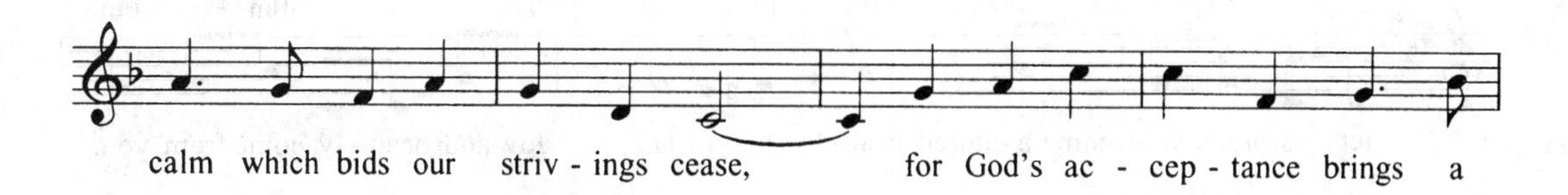

2. We can be strong, for now we stand by grace,
   held in his loving, fatherly embrace;
   his care remains, whatever trials we face:
   alleluia!

3. We trust in God – and shall not be dismayed,
   nor find our hopes of glory are betrayed,
   for all his splendour we shall see displayed:
   alleluia!

4. And come what may, we never need despair –
   God is at work through all the griefs we bear,
   that in the end his likeness we may share:
   alleluia!

5. Deep in our hearts the love of God is found;
   his precious gifts of life and joy abound –
   so let our finest songs of praise resound:
   alleluia!

Text © Copyright 1999 Kevin Mayhew Ltd.

390 Let us sing your glory

Words and music: Marie Lydia Pereira (b.1920)

2. Leaf that quivers on the tree, alleluia,
flowers that we delight to see, alleluia.
Planets as they reel in space, alleluia,
tell us of your pow'r and grace, alleluia.

3. All creation sings your praise, alleluia,
young and old their voices raise, alleluia.
Children as they laugh and sing, alleluia,
to your goodness homage bring, alleluia.

© Copyright 1999 Kevin Mayhew Ltd.

391 Let us talents and tongues employ

Fred Kaan (b.1929)

Jamaican Folk song
adapted by Doreen Potter (1925-1980)

LINSTEAD LM and Refrain

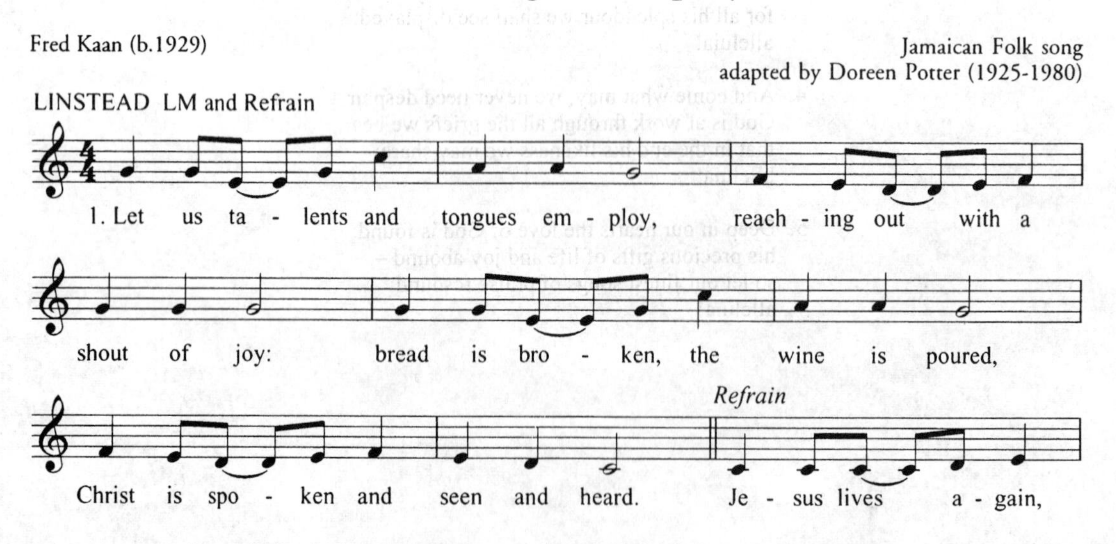

Text: © Copyright 1975 Stainer & Bell Ltd., P.O. Box 110, Victoria House,
23 Gruneisen Road, Finchley, London N3 1DZ, UK. Used by permission.
Music: © Copyright 1975 Hope Publishing Co. Administered by CopyCare,
P.O. Box 77, Hailsham, East Sussex BN27 3EF. (music@copycare.com). Used by permission.

2. Christ is able to make us one,
at his table he sets the tone,
teaching people to live to bless,
love in word and in deed express.

3. Jesus calls us in, sends us out
bearing fruit in a world of doubt,
gives us love to tell, bread to share:
God-Immanuel everywhere!

392 Let us, with a gladsome mind

John Milton (1608-1674)
based on Psalm 136

From *Hymn Tunes of the United Brethren*
adapt. by John Bernard Wilkes (1785-1869)

TUNE 1: MONKLAND 77 77

Refrain

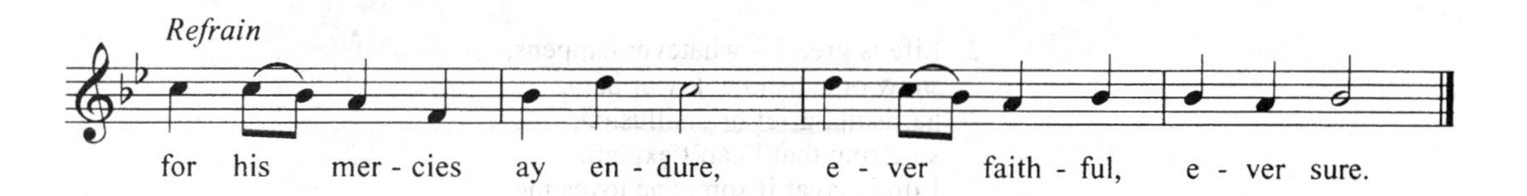

2. Let us blaze his name abroad,
for of gods he is the God;

3. He, with all-commanding might,
filled the new-made world with light;

4. He the golden-tressèd sun
caused all day his course to run;

5. And the moon to shine at night,
'mid her starry sisters bright;

6. All things living he doth feed,
his full hand supplies their need;

7. Let us, with a gladsome mind,
praise the Lord, for he is kind;

John Milton (1608-1674)
based on Psalm 136

Henry John Gauntlett (1805-1876)

TUNE 2: UNIVERSITY COLLEGE 77 77

1. Let us, with a glad - some mind, praise the Lord, for he is kind;

Refrain

393 Life is great! *A song of love and living*

Brian A. Wren (b.1936) Peter Cutts (b.1937)

LITHEROP 87 87 87

2. Life is great! – whatever happens,
snow or sunshine, joy or pain,
hardship, grief or disillusion,
suff'ring that I can't explain.
Life is great if someone loves me,
holds my hand and calls my name.

3. Love is great! – the love of lovers,
whispered words and longing eyes;
love that gazes at the cradle
where a child of loving lies;
love that lasts when youth has faded,
bends with age, but never dies.

4. Love is giving and receiving –
boy and girl, or friend with friend.
Love is bearing and forgiving
all the hurts that hate can send.
Love's the greatest way of living:
hoping, trusting to the end.

5. Great is God, who lived among us:
truth in Jesus seen and done,
healing, teaching, hate resisting,
loving where we scoff and shun,
dying, rising, joy surprising
reaching out to everyone.

© Copyright 1974, 1995 Stainer & Bell Ltd., P.O. Box 110, Victoria House,
23 Gruneisen Road, Finchley, London N3 1DZ, UK. Used by permission.

394 Lift high the Cross

George William Kitchin (1827-1912)
Michael Robert Newbolt (1874-1956) alt.

Sydney Hugo Nicholson (1875-1947)

CRUCIFER 10 10 and Refrain

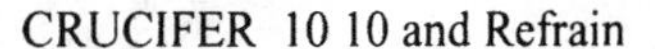

2. Led on their way by this triumphant sign,
   the hosts of God in joyful praise combine:

3. Each new disciple of the Crucified
   is called to bear the seal of him who died:

4. Saved by the Cross whereon their Lord was slain,
   now Adam's children their lost home regain:

5. From north and south, from east and west they raise
   in growing harmony their song of praise:

6. O Lord, once lifted on the glorious tree,
   as thou hast promised, draw us unto thee:

7. Let ev'ry race and ev'ry language tell
   of him who saves from fear of death and hell:

8. From farthest regions, let them homage bring,
   and on his Cross adore their Saviour King:

9. Set up thy throne, that earth's despair may cease
   beneath the shadow of its healing peace:

10. For thy blest Cross which doth for all atone,
    creation's praises rise before thy throne:

11. So let the world proclaim with one accord
    the praise of our ever-living Lord.

© Copyright Hymns Ancient & Modern Ltd., St Mary's Works, St Mary's Plain, Norwich NR3 3BH, UK.
Used by permission.

395 Lift up your hearts!

Henry Montagu Butler (1833-1918) alt.

Walter Greatorex (1877-1949)

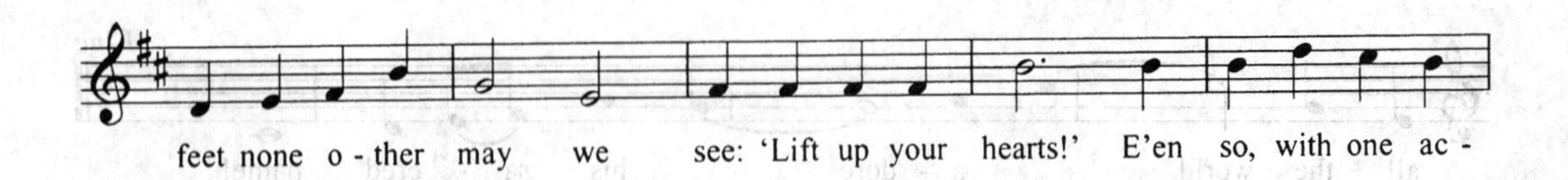

2. Above the swamps of subterfuge and shame,
the deeds, the thoughts, that honour may not name,
the halting tongue that dares not tell the whole,
O Lord of truth, lift ev'ry human soul.

3. Lift ev'ry gift that thou thyself hast giv'n:
low lies the best till lifted up to heav'n;
low lie the pounding heart, the teeming brain,
till, sent from God, they mount to God again.

4. Then, as the trumpet-call, in after years,
'Lift up your hearts!' rings pealing in our ears,
still shall those hearts respond, with full accord,
'We lift them up, we lift them to the Lord.'

Music © Copyright Oxford University Press, Great Clarendon Street, Oxford OX2 6DP. UK.
Used by permission from *Enlarged Songs of Praise*.

396 Light a candle for thanksgiving!

David Mowbray (b.1938) Martin Setchell (b.1949)

CANDLE 87 87 D

1. Light a can - dle for thanks - giv - ing! Sing to God for Christ the Lord! Born to Ma - ry, dy - ing, liv - ing; still the Spi - rit speaks his word. Wel-come ev - 'ry to - wer peal - ing, ce - le - brate two thou-sand years! Years of grace and years re - veal - ing Christ where Christ-like love ap - pears.

2. Light a candle for achievers!
Marvel at their range of thought:
artists, scientists, believers
famed for what their hands have wrought.
For the feats of engineering,
for each fresh, creative probe;
ev'ry benefit appearing,
spread across a shrinking globe.

3. Light a candle for the nation
and the future of its youth!
Build with them on this foundation:
love, security and truth.
Christ the Lord, by patience winning
many a household, many a heart,
set ablaze their faith's beginning,
journey with them from the start.

4. Light a candle for tomorrow!
Ask that countries may walk free:
truly free, not bound to borrow,
but released for jubilee.
One has come among us bearing
news that prisoners are restored:
let his voice move us to sharing –
sing to God for Christ the Lord!

Text © Copyright David Mowbray/Jubilate Hymns, 4 Thorne Park Road, Chelston, Torquay TQ2 6RX, UK. Used by permission.
Music © Copyright 1999 Kevin Mayhew Ltd.

397 Light of the minds that know him

Timothy Dudley-Smith (b.1926)
based on a prayer of St Augustine of Hippo (354-430)

Psalm 130 in the *Genevan Psalter* (1542) adapted

AU FORT DE MA DÉTRESSE 76 76 D

2. Life of the souls that love him:
may Christ be ours indeed!
the living bread from heaven
on whom our spirits feed;
who died for love of sinners
to bear our guilty load,
and make of life's brief journey
a new Emmaus road.

3. Strength of the wills that serve him:
may Christ be strength to me,
who stilled the storm and tempest,
who calmed the tossing sea;
his Spirit's pow'r to move me,
his will to master mine,
his cross to carry daily
and conquer in his sign.

4. May it be ours to know him
that we may truly love,
and loving, fully serve him
as serve the saints above;
till in that home of glory
with fadeless splendour bright,
we serve in perfect freedom
our strength, our life, our light.

Text © Copyright Timothy Dudley-Smith, 9 Ashlands, Ford, Salisbury,
Wiltshire SP4 6DY, UK. Used by permission.

398 Light's abode, celestial Salem

Ascribed to Thomas à Kempis (c.1379-1471)
trans. John Mason Neale (1818-1866)

Henry Smart (1813-1879)

REGENT SQUARE 87 87 87

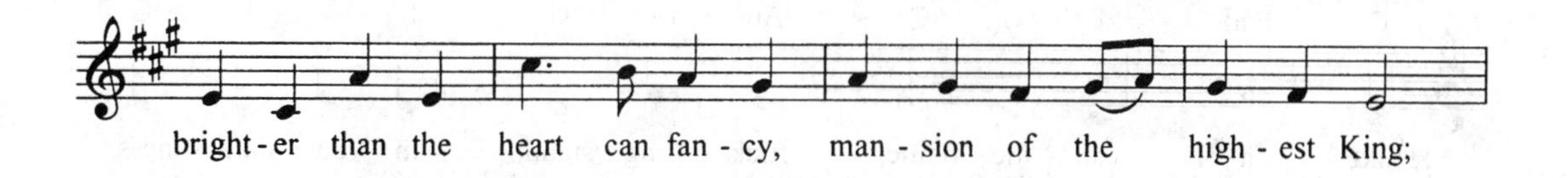

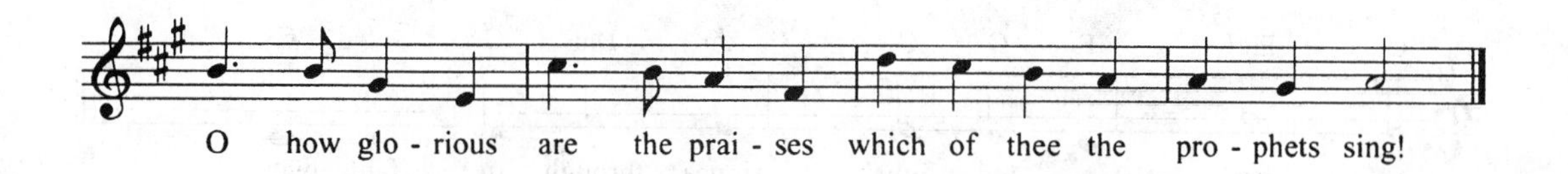

2. There for ever and for ever
alleluia is outpoured;
for unending, for unbroken
is the feast-day of the Lord;
all is pure and all is holy
that within thy walls is stored.

3. There no cloud or passing vapour
dims the brightness of the air;
endless noon-day, glorious noon-day,
from the Sun of suns is there;
there no night brings rest from labour,
for unknown are toil and care.

4. O how glorious and resplendent,
fragile body, shalt thou be,
when endued with so much beauty,
full of health and strong and free,
full of vigour, full of pleasure
that shall last eternally.

5. Now with gladness, now with courage,
bear the burden on thee laid,
that hereafter these thy labours
may with endless gifts be paid;
and in everlasting glory
thou with brightness be arrayed.

6. Laud and honour to the Father,
laud and honour to the Son,
laud and honour to the Spirit,
ever Three and ever One,
consubstantial, co-eternal,
while unending ages run.

399 Like a candle flame *The candle song*

Words and music: Graham Kendrick (b.1950)

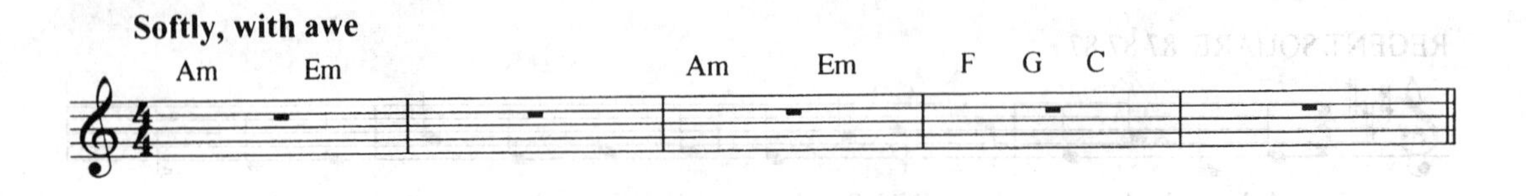

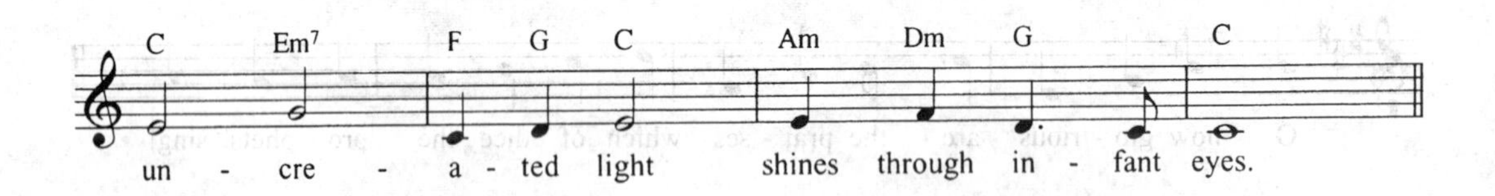

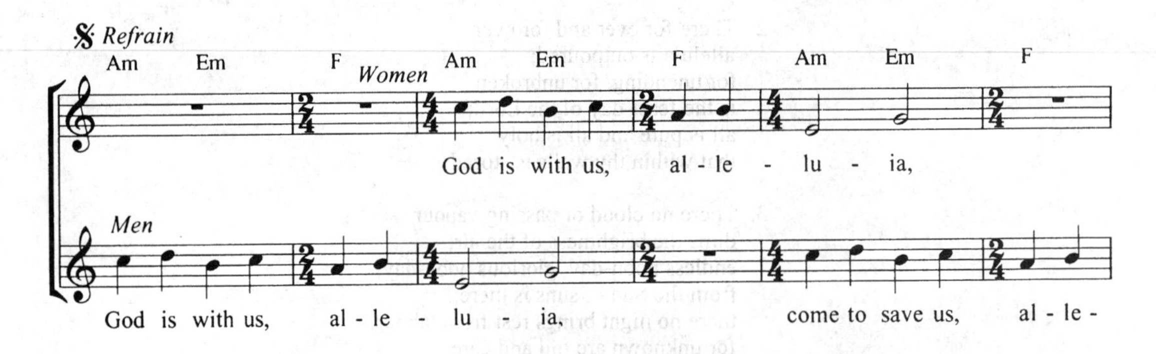

2. Stars and angels sing,
yet the earth
sleeps in shadows;
can this tiny spark
set a world on fire?

3. Yet his light shall shine
from our lives,
spirit blazing,
as we touch the flame
of his holy fire.

© Copyright 1988 Make Way Music, P.O. Box 263, Croydon, Surrey CR9 5AP, UK.
International copyright secured. All rights reserved. Used by permission.

400 Like a mighty river flowing

Michael Perry (1942-1996) Noël Harwood Tredinnick (b.1949)

OLD YEAVERING 88 87

2. Like the hills serene and even,
like the coursing clouds of heaven,
like the heart that's been forgiven
is the perfect peace of God.

3. Like the summer breezes playing,
like the tall trees softly swaying,
like the lips of silent praying
is the perfect peace of God.

4. Like the morning sun ascended,
like the scents of evening blended,
like a friendship never ended
is the perfect peace of God.

5. Like the azure ocean swelling,
like the jewel all-excelling,
far beyond our human telling
is the perfect peace of God.

Text © Copyright Mrs B. Perry/Jubilate Hymns.
Music © Copyright Noël Harwood Tredinnick/Jubilate Hymns, 4 Thorne Park Road, Chelston, Torquay TQ2 6RX, UK. Used by permission.

401 Listen, let your heart keep seeking

Words and music: Aniceto Nazareth

2. He's in the laughter of children,
in the patter of the rain.
Hear him in cries of the suff'ring,
in their moaning and their pain.

3. He's in the noise of the city,
in the singing of the birds.
And in the night-time the stillness
helps you listen to his word.

© Copyright 1984 Kevin Mayhew Ltd.

402 Listen to me, Yahweh

Mike Anderson
based on Psalm 86

Mike Anderson (b.1956)

© Copyright 1999 Kevin Mayhew Ltd.

2. Lord, in your goodness, please forgive me;
listen to me, hear my plea.

3. Lord, you are merciful and faithful;
turn to me now in my need.

4. Lord, give me strength, I am your servant;
show me that you really care.

403 Listen to my voice *A healing song*

Words and music: Francesca Leftley (b.1955)

2. Rest within my arms and let your fears depart,
feel my peace and joy bind up your broken heart.
I will wipe your tears and make you whole again:
come to me, my child, and turn away from sin.

3. Take my hand, and now we will begin once more,
I will walk beside you as I did before.
I have never left you, though your eyes were dim:
walk with me in light, and turn away from sin.

© Copyright 1999 Kevin Mayhew Ltd.

404 Living God, your word has called us

Jan Berry (b.1953) Malcolm Archer (b.1952)

TOR HILL 87 87 D

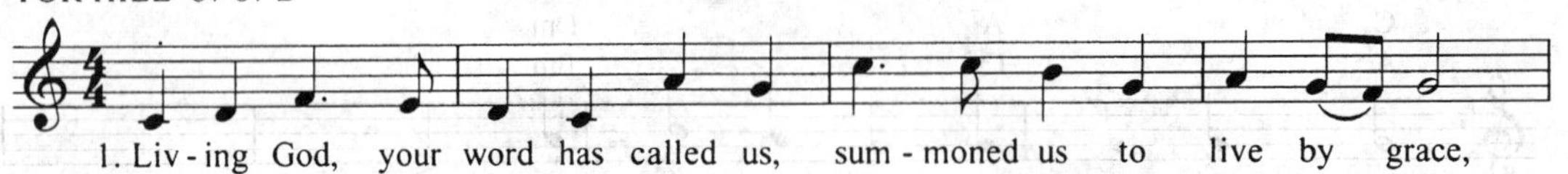

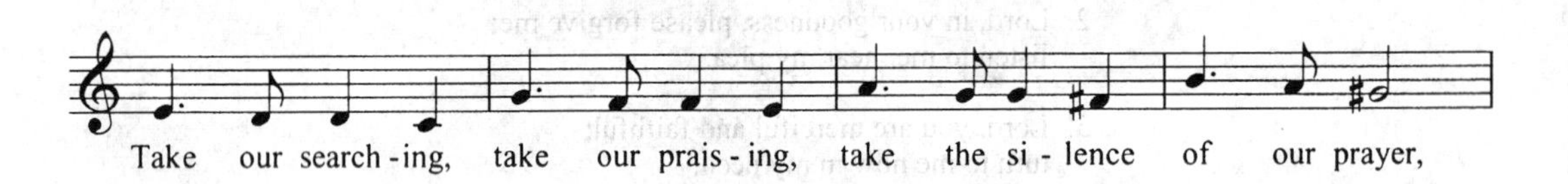

2. Living God, your love has called us
in the name of Christ your Son,
forming us to be his body,
by your Spirit making one.
Working, laughing, learning, growing,
old and young and black and white,
gifts and skills together sharing,
in your service all unite.

3. Living God, your hope has called us
to the world that you have made,
teaching us to live for others,
humble, joyful, unafraid.
Give us eyes to see your presence,
joy in laughter, hope in pain.
In our loving, in our living,
give us strength that Christ may reign.

© Copyright 1999 Kevin Mayhew Ltd.

405 Lo, he comes with clouds descending

Charles Wesley (1707-1788),
John Cennick (1718-1755)
and Martin Madan (1726-1790) alt.

From Charles Wesley's
Select Hymns with Tunes Annext (1765)

HELMSLEY 87 87 47

2. Ev'ry eye shall now behold him
robed in dreadful majesty;
we who set at naught and sold him,
pierced and nailed him to the tree,
deeply grieving, deeply grieving, deeply grieving,
shall the true Messiah see.

3. Those dear tokens of his passion
still his dazzling body bears,
cause of endless exultation
to his ransomed worshippers:
with what rapture, with what rapture, with what rapture
gaze we on those glorious scars!

4. Yea, amen, let all adore thee,
high on thine eternal throne;
Saviour, take the pow'r and glory,
claim the kingdom for thine own.
Alleluia! Alleluia! Alleluia!
Thou shalt reign, and thou alone.

406 Long ago, prophets knew

Fred Pratt Green (b.1903-2000) — From *Piae Cantiones*

PERSONENT HODIE (THEODORIC) 666 66 and Refrain

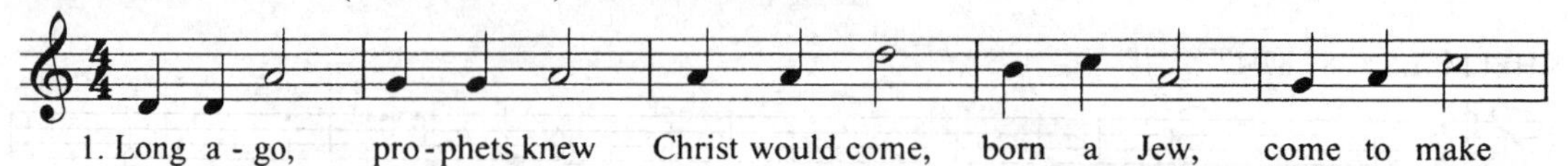

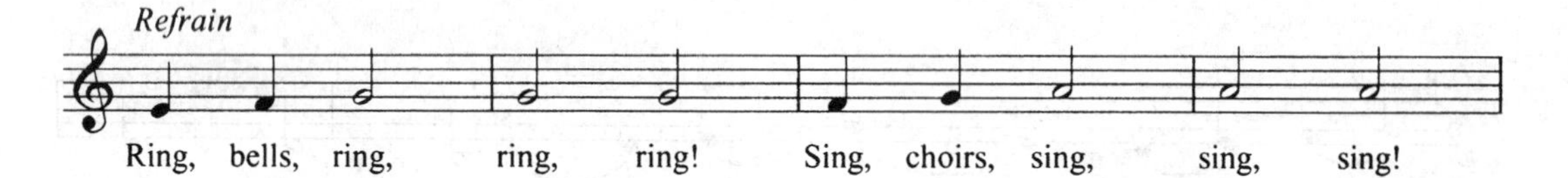

2. God in time, God in man,
this is God's timeless plan:
he will come, as a man,
born himself of woman,
God divinely human:

3. Mary, hail! Though afraid,
she believed, she obeyed.
In her womb God is laid:
till the time expected,
nurtured and protected:

4. Journey ends! Where afar
Bethlem shines, like a star,
stable door stands ajar.
Unborn Son of Mary,
Saviour, do not tarry.

Text © Copyright 1971 Stainer & Bell Ltd., P.O. Box 110, Victoria House,
23 Gruneisen Road, Finchley, London N3 1DZ, UK. Used by permission.

407 Lord Christ, who on thy heart

Arnold Thomas (1848-1924) alt. — Percy Carter Buck (1871-1947)

GONFALON ROYAL LM

Music © Copyright Oxford University Press, Great Clarendon Street, Oxford OX2 6DP, UK.
Used by permission.

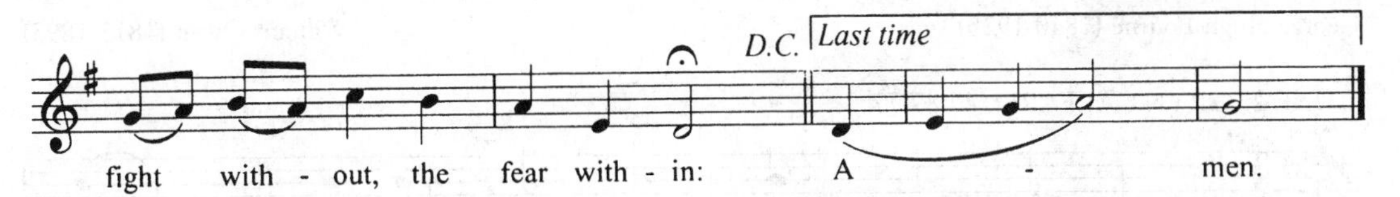

2. Thy patience cannot know defeat,
thy pity will not be denied,
thy loving-kindness still is great,
thy tender mercies still abide.

3. O brother Man, for this we pray,
thou brother Man and sov'reign Lord,
that we thy brethren, day by day,
may follow thee and keep thy word.

4. That we may care, as thou hast cared,
for sick and lame, for deaf and blind,
and freely share, as thou hast shared,
in all the woes of humankind.

5. That ours may be the holy task
to help and bless, to heal and save;
this is the happiness we ask,
and this the service that we crave.
Amen.

408 Lord, enthroned in heavenly splendour

George Hugh Bourne (1840-1925) | George Clement Martin (1844-1916)

TUNE 1: ST HELEN 87 87 87

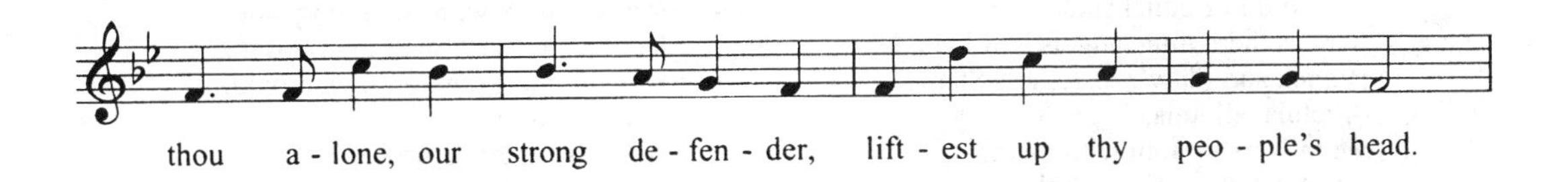

2. Here our humblest homage pay we,
here in loving rev'rence bow;
here for faith's discernment pray we,
lest we fail to know thee now.
Alleluia, alleluia,
thou art here, we ask not how.

3. Though the lowliest form doth veil thee
as of old in Bethlehem,
here as there thine angels hail thee,
Branch and Flow'r of Jesse's Stem.
Alleluia, alleluia,
we in worship join with them.

4. Paschal Lamb, thine off'ring, finished
once for all when thou wast slain,
in its fullness undiminished
shall for evermore remain.
Alleluia, alleluia,
cleansing souls from ev'ry stain.

5. Life-imparting heav'nly manna,
stricken rock with streaming side,
heav'n and earth with loud hosanna
worship thee, the Lamb who died.
Alleluia, alleluia,
ris'n, ascended, glorified!

Tune 2 will be found overleaf

George Hugh Bourne (1840-1925) William Owen (1813-1893)

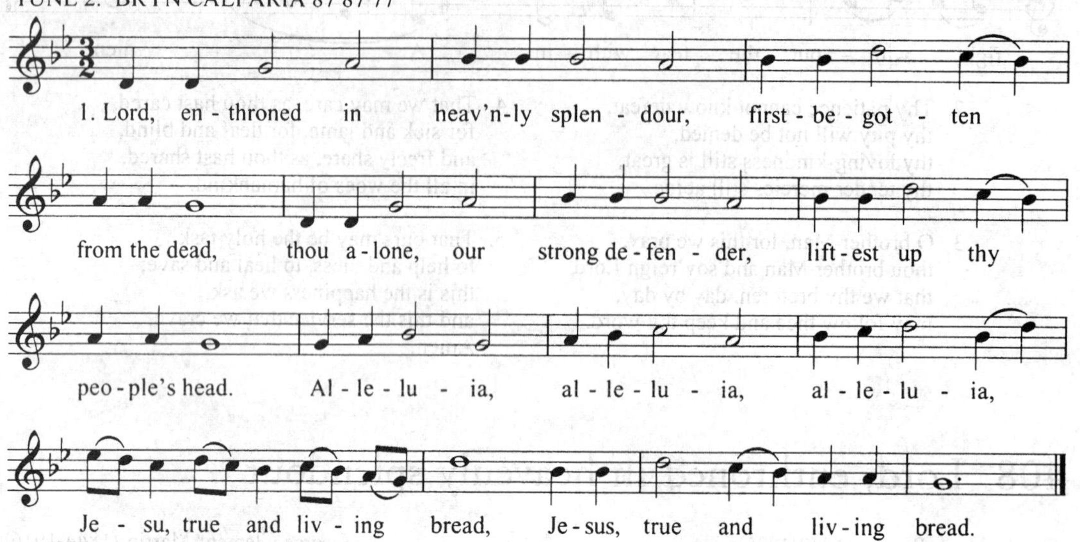

2. Here our humblest homage pay we,
here in loving rev'rence bow;
here for faith's discernment pray we,
lest we fail to know thee now.
Alleluia, alleluia,
thou art here, we ask not how,
thou art here, we ask not how.

3. Though the lowliest form doth veil thee
as of old in Bethlehem,
here as there thine angels hail thee,
Branch and Flow'r of Jesse's Stem.
Alleluia, alleluia,
we in worship join with them,
we in worship join with them.

4. Paschal Lamb, thine off'ring, finished
once for all when thou wast slain,
in its fullness undiminished
shall for evermore remain.
Alleluia, alleluia,
cleansing souls from ev'ry stain,
cleansing souls from ev'ry stain.

5. Life-imparting heav'nly manna,
stricken rock with streaming side,
heav'n and earth with loud hosanna
worship thee, the Lamb who died.
Alleluia, alleluia,
ris'n, ascended, glorified,
ris'n, ascended, glorified!

409 Lord, for the years

Timothy Dudley-Smith (b.1926) Michael Baughen (b.1930)

LORD OF THE YEARS 11 10 11 10

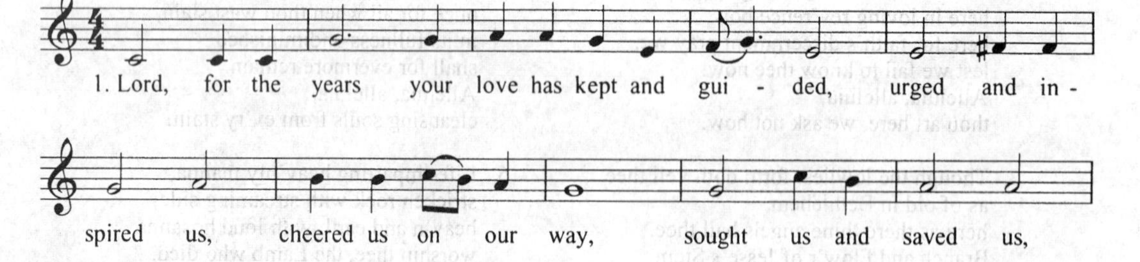

Text © Copyright Timothy Dudley-Smith, 9 Ashlands, Ford, Salisbury, Wiltshire SP4 6DY, UK.
Music © Copyright Michael Baughen/Jubilate Hymns, 4 Thorne Park Road,
Chelston, Torquay TQ2 6RX, UK. Used by permission.

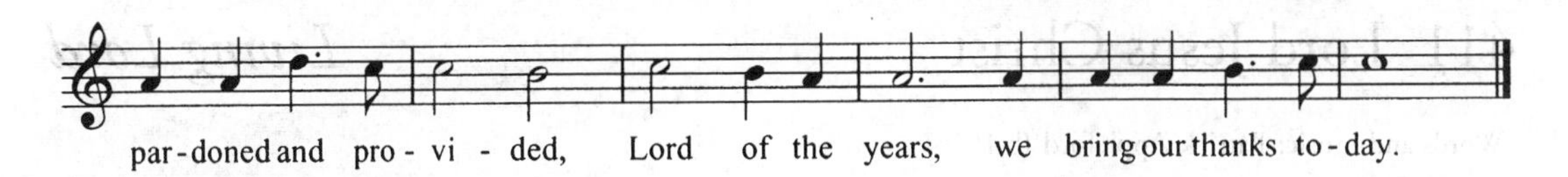

2. Lord, for that word, the word of life which fires us,
speaks to our hearts and sets our souls ablaze,
teaches and trains, rebukes us and inspires us:
Lord of the word, receive your people's praise.

3. Lord, for our land in this our generation,
spirits oppressed by pleasure, wealth and care:
for young and old, for commonwealth and nation,
Lord of our land, be pleased to hear our prayer.

4. Lord, for our world; when we disown and doubt you,
loveless in strength, and comfortless in pain,
hungry and helpless, lost indeed without you:
Lord of the world, we pray that Christ may reign.

5. Lord for ourselves; in living power remake us –
self on the cross and Christ upon the throne,
past put behind us, for the future take us:
Lord of our lives, to live for Christ alone.

410 Lord, for tomorrow and its needs

Sister M. Xavier — Richard Runciman Terry (1865-1938)

LORD FOR TOMORROW (PROVIDENCE) 84 84

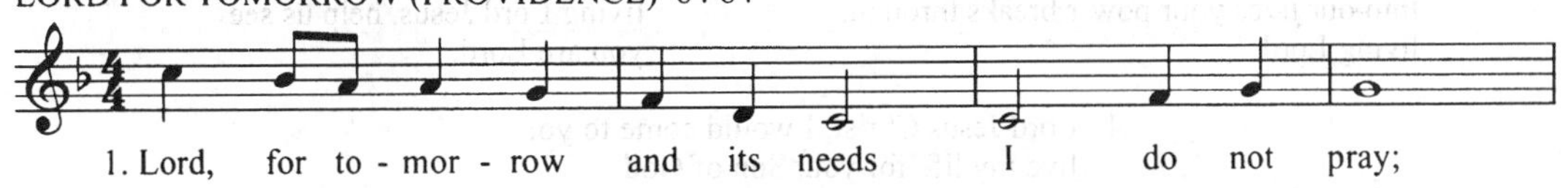

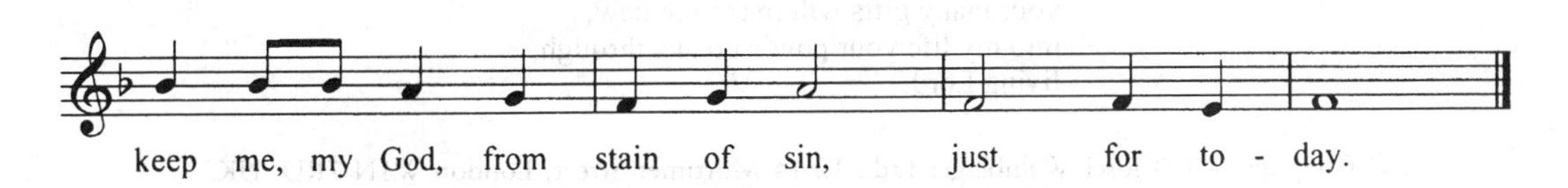

2. Let me both diligently work
and duly pray;
let me be kind in word and deed,
just for today.

3. Let me no wrong or idle word
unthinking say;
set thou a seal upon my lips,
just for today.

4. And if today my tide of life
should ebb away,
give me thy sacraments divine,
sweet Lord, today.

5. So, for tomorrow and its needs
I do not pray;
but keep me, guide me, love me, Lord,
just for today.

Music © Copyright Burns & Oates Ltd./Continuum Publishers, The Tower Building,
11 York Road, London SE1 7NX. Used by permission.

411 Lord Jesus Christ *Living Lord*

Words and music: Patrick Appleford (b.1925)

LIVING LORD 9 8 88 83

2. Lord Jesus Christ, now and ev'ry day
teach us how to pray, Son of God.
You have commanded us to do
this in remembrance, Lord, of you.
Into our lives your pow'r breaks through,
living Lord.

3. Lord Jesus Christ, you have come to us,
born as one of us, Mary's Son.
Led out to die on Calvary,
risen from death to set us free,
living Lord Jesus, help us see
you are Lord.

4. Lord Jesus Christ, I would come to you,
live my life for you, Son of God.
All your commands I know are true,
your many gifts will make me new,
into my life your pow'r breaks through,
living Lord.

© Copyright 1960 Josef Weinberger Ltd., 12-14 Mortimer Street, London W1N 7RD, UK.
All rights reserved. Used by permission.

412 Lord Jesus, think on me

Mñoeo Christe by
Bishop Synesius (375-430)
trans. Allen William Chatfield (1808-1896)

John Stainer (1840-1901)

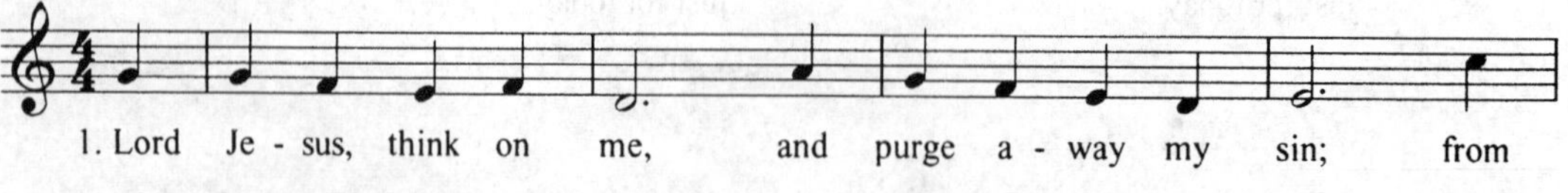

2. Lord Jesus, think on me,
with care and woe opprest;
let me thy loving servant be
and taste thy promised rest.

3. Lord Jesus, think on me
amid the battle's strife;
in all my pain and misery
be thou my health and life.

4. Lord Jesus, think on me,
nor let me go astray;
through darkness and perplexity
point thou the heav'nly way.

5. Lord Jesus, think on me,
when flows the tempest high:
when on doth rush the enemy,
O Saviour, be thou nigh.

6. Lord Jesus, think on me,
that, when the flood is past,
I may th'eternal brightness see,
and share thy joy at last.

Mñoeo Christe by
Bishop Synesius (375-430)
trans. Allen William Chatfield (1808-1896)

From *The Psalmes in English Metre* (1579)
adapted by William Damon (1540-1591)

TUNE 2: SOUTHWELL (DAMON) SM

413 Lord of all hopefulness

Jan Struther (1901-1953)

Traditional Irish melody

SLANE 10 11 11 12

2. Lord of all eagerness,
Lord of all faith,
whose strong hands were skilled
at the plane and the lathe,
be there at our labours,
and give us, we pray,
your strength in our hearts, Lord,
at the noon of the day.

3. Lord of all kindliness,
Lord of all grace,
your hands swift to welcome,
your arms to embrace,
be there at our homing,
and give us, we pray,
your love in our hearts, Lord,
at the eve of the day.

4. Lord of all gentleness,
Lord of all calm,
whose voice is contentment,
whose presence is balm,
be there at our sleeping,
and give us, we pray,
your peace in our hearts, Lord,
at the end of the day.

Text © Copyright Oxford University Press, Great Clarendon Street, Oxford OX2 6DP, UK.
Used by permission from *Enlarged Songs of Praise.*

414 Lord of all life and power

Timothy Dudley-Smith (b.1926) — Malcolm Archer (b.1952)

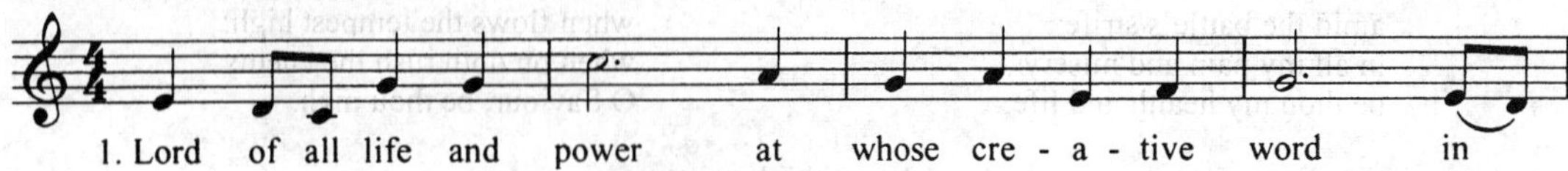

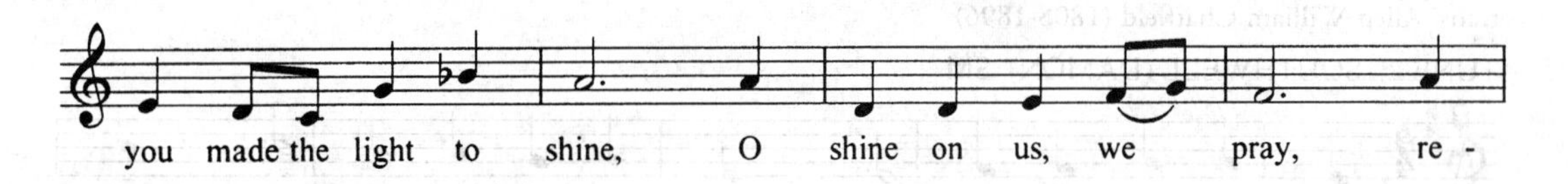

2. Lord of the fertile earth
who caused the world to be,
whose life alone can bring to birth
the fruits of land and sea,
teach us to use aright
and share the gifts you give,
to tend the earth as in your sight
that all the world may live.

3. Lord of the cross and grave
who died and lives again,
who came in love to seek and save
and then to rise and reign,
we share, as once you shared,
in mortal birth and breath,
and ours the risen life that dared
to vanquish sin and death.

4. Lord of the wind and flame,
the promised Spirit's sign,
possess our hearts in Jesus' name,
come down, O Love divine!
Help us in Christ to grow,
from sin and self to cease,
and daily in our lives to show
your love and joy and peace.

5. Lord of the passing years
whose changeless purpose stands,
our lives and loves, our hopes and fears,
we place within your hands;
we bring you but your own,
forgiven, loved and free,
to follow Christ, and Christ alone,
through all the days to be.

Text © Copyright Timothy Dudley-Smith, 9 Ashlands, Ford, Salisbury, Wiltshire SP4 6DY, UK. Used by permission.
Music © Copyright 1999 Kevin Mayhew Ltd.

415 Lord of beauty, thine the splendour

Cyril Argentine Alington (1872-1955)

Basil Harwood (1859-1949)

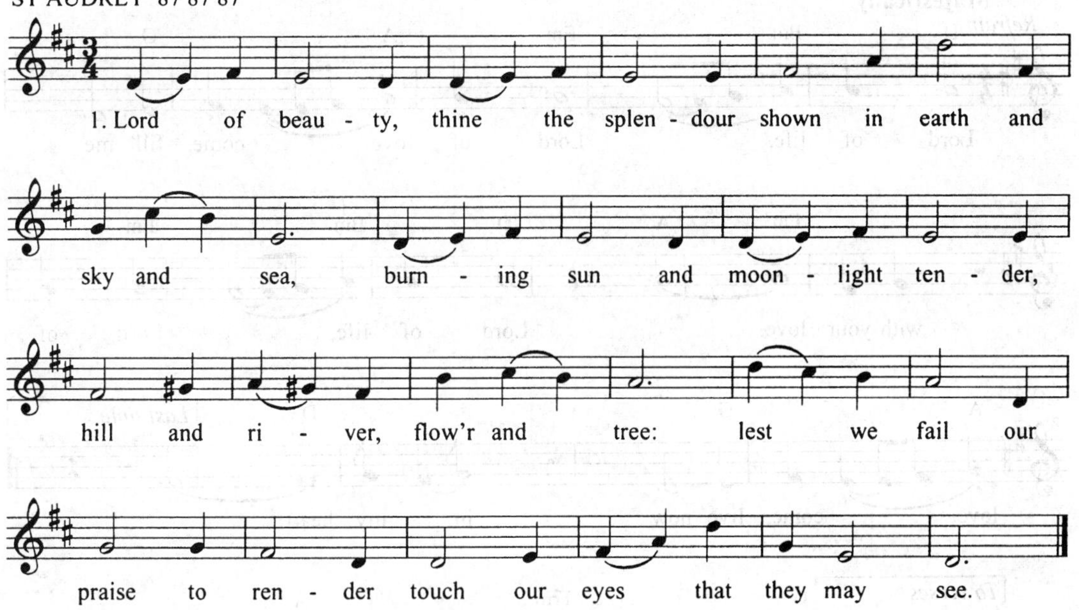

2. Lord of wisdom, whom obeying
mighty waters ebb and flow,
while unhasting, undelaying,
planets on their courses go:
in thy laws thyself displaying,
each our minds thyself to know.

3. Lord of life, alone sustaining
all below and all above,
Lord of love, by whose ordaining
sun and stars sublimely move:
in our earthly spirits reigning,
lift our hearts that we may love.

4. Lord of beauty, bid us own thee,
Lord of truth, our footsteps guide,
till as Love our hearts enthrone thee,
and, with vision purified,
Lord of all, when all have known thee,
thou in all art glorified.

Text © Copyright Hymns Ancient & Modern, St Mary's Works,
St Mary's Plain, Norwich NR3 3BH. Used by permission.
Music © Copyright The Executors of the late Dr. Basil Harwood. Reproduced by permission
of the Public Trust Office, Stewart House, 24 Kingsway, London WC2B 6JX.

416 Lord of life

Words and music: Mike Anderson (b.1956)

2. You are wrapped in radiant light,
you are the Lord of day and night,
come, lighten my life with your love.

3. All my sins you will forgive,
for you alone I want to live,
come, take me and fill me again.

© Copyright 1999 Kevin Mayhew Ltd.

417 Lord of our life, and God of our salvation

Philip Pusey (1799-1855) based on the German
of Matthäus Appelles von Löwenstern (1594-1648) alt.

Joseph Barnby (1838-1896)

TUNE 1: CLOISTERS 11 11 11 5

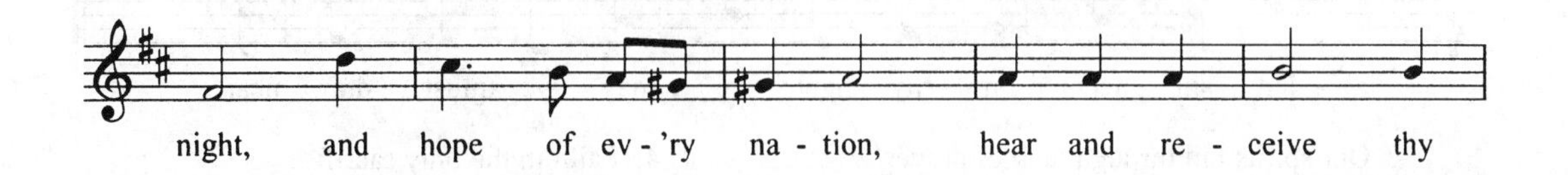

2. Lord, thou canst help when earthly armour faileth,
Lord, thou canst save when deadly sin assaileth;
Christ, o'er thy rock nor death nor hell prevaileth;
grant us thy peace, Lord.

3. Peace in our hearts, our evil thoughts assuaging;
peace in thy Church, where people are engaging;
peace, when the world its busy war is waging:
calm all our raging.

4. Grant us thy grace through trial and temptation,
grant us thy truth, thy promise of salvation,
grant us thy peace in ev'ry heart and nation,
and in thy heaven.

Philip Pusey (1799-1855) based on the German
of Matthäus Appelles von Löwenstern (1594-1648) alt.

Poitiers Antiphoner (1746)

TUNE 2: ISTE CONFESSOR 11 11 11 5

418 Lord, teach us how to pray aright

James Montgomery (1771-1854) alt. — Edward John Hopkins (1818-1901)

ST HUGH CM

2. Our spirits fail through lack of prayer:
O grant us pow'r to pray;
and, when to meet thee we prepare,
Lord, meet us by the way.

3. God of all grace, we bring to thee
a broken, contrite heart;
give what thine eye delights to see,
truth in the inward part;

4. Faith in the only sacrifice
that can for sin atone,
to cast our hopes, to fix our eyes,
on Christ, on Christ alone;

5. Patience to watch and wait and weep,
though mercy long delay;
courage our fainting souls to keep,
and trust in thee alway.

6. Give these, and then thy will be done;
thus, strengthened with all might,
we, through thy Spirit and thy Son,
shall pray, and pray aright.

This version of text © Copyright 1996 Kevin Mayhew Ltd.

419 Lord, the light of your love *Shine, Jesus, shine*

Words and music: Graham Kendrick (b.1950)

SHINE, JESUS, SHINE 9 9 10 10 6

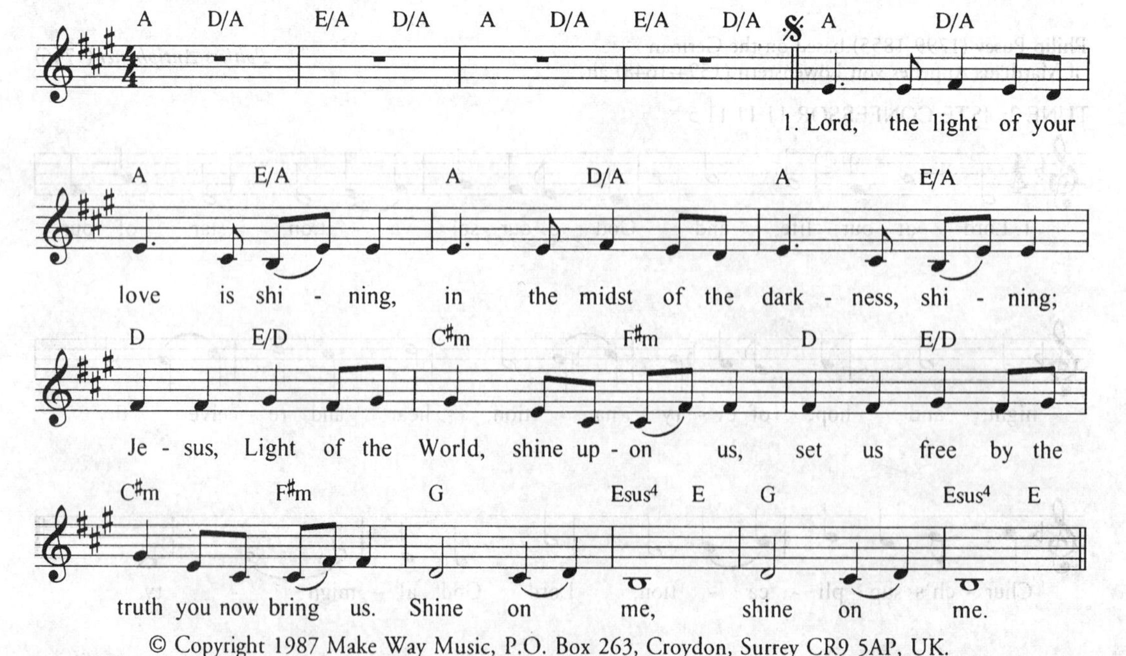

© Copyright 1987 Make Way Music, P.O. Box 263, Croydon, Surrey CR9 5AP, UK.
International copyright secured. All rights reserved. Used by permission.

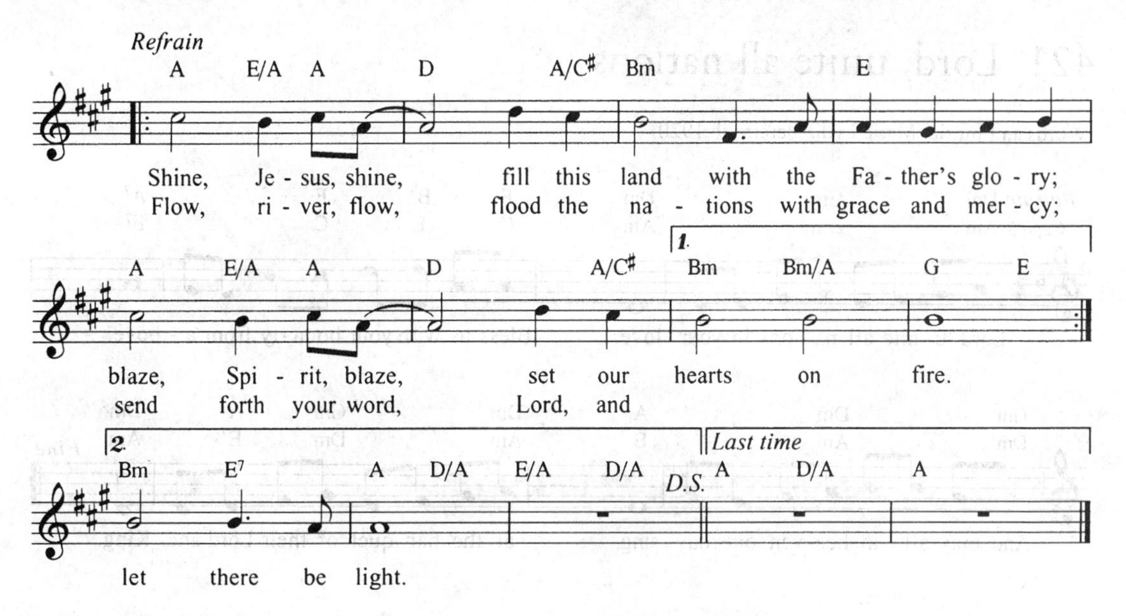

2. Lord, I come to your awesome presence,
from the shadows into your radiance;
by the blood I may enter your brightness,
search me, try me, consume all my darkness.
Shine on me, shine on me.

3. As we gaze on your kingly brightness,
so our faces display your likeness,
ever changing from glory to glory;
mirrored here may our lives tell your story.
Shine on me, shine on me.

(Refrain twice to end)

420 Lord, thy word abideth

Henry Williams Baker (1821-1877)

Melody from M. Weisse's *Neu Gesangbüchlein* (1531) adapted by William Henry Monk (1823-1889)

RAVENSHAW 66 66

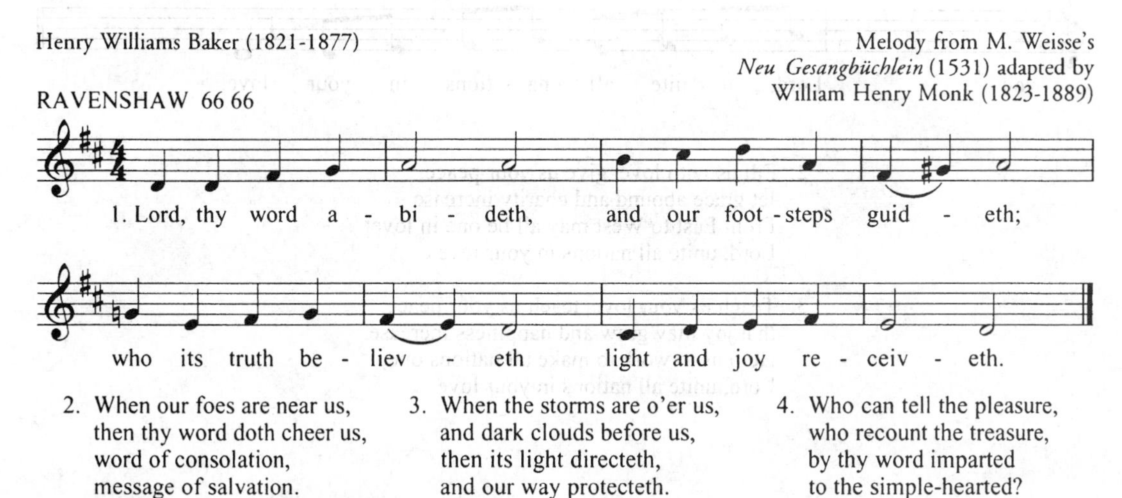

2. When our foes are near us,
then thy word doth cheer us,
word of consolation,
message of salvation.

3. When the storms are o'er us,
and dark clouds before us,
then its light directeth,
and our way protecteth.

4. Who can tell the pleasure,
who recount the treasure,
by thy word imparted
to the simple-hearted?

5. Word of mercy, giving
succour to the living;
word of life, supplying
comfort to the dying.

6. O that we, discerning
its most holy learning,
Lord, may love and fear thee,
evermore be near thee.

421 Lord, unite all nations

Words and music: Marie Lydia Pereira (b.1920)

2. Fill us with love, give us your peace,
let grace abound and charity increase.
From East to West may all be one in love:
Lord, unite all nations in your love.

3. Teach us your love, teach us your peace,
that joy may grow and happiness increase.
Help us to work to make all nations one;
Lord, unite all nations in your love.

© Copyright 1999 Kevin Mayhew Ltd.

422 Lord, we come to ask your healing

Jean Holloway (b.1939) Traditional Welsh melody

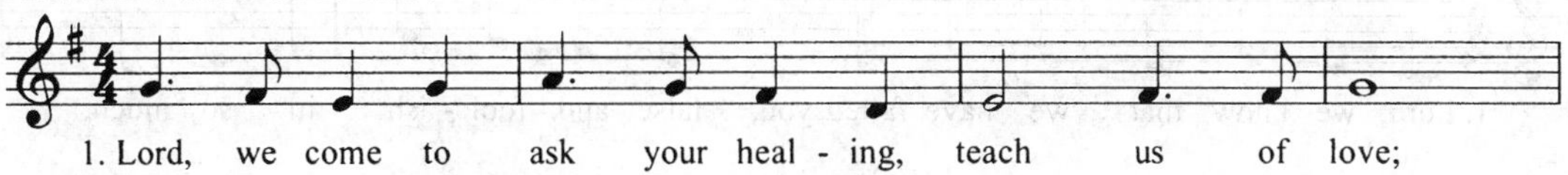

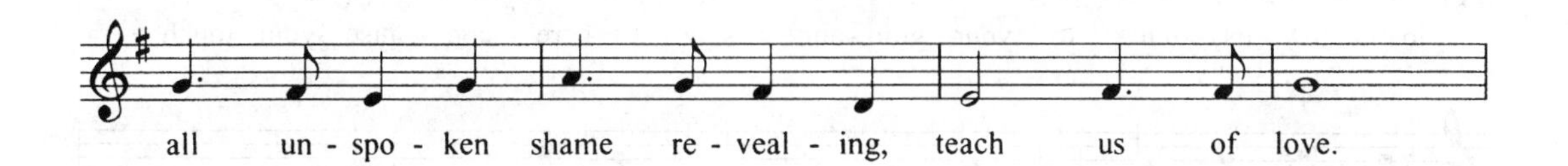

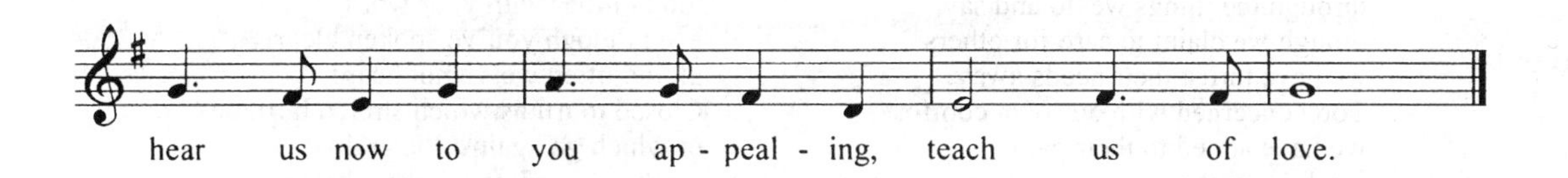

2. Soothe away our pain and sorrow,
hold us in love;
grace we cannot buy or borrow,
hold us in love.
Though we see but dark and danger,
though we spurn both friend and stranger,
though we often dread tomorrow,
hold us in love.

3. When the bread is raised and broken,
fill us with love;
words of consecration spoken,
fill us with love.
As our grateful prayers continue,
make the faith that we have in you
more than just an empty token,
fill us with love.

4. Help us live for one another,
bind us in love;
stranger, neighbour, father, mother –
bind us in love.
All are equal at your table,
through your Spirit make us able
to embrace as sister, brother,
bind us in love.

Text © Copyright 1995 Kevin Mayhew Ltd.

423 Lord, we know that we have failed you

Nick Fawcett (b.1957) | Noel Rawsthorne (b.1929)

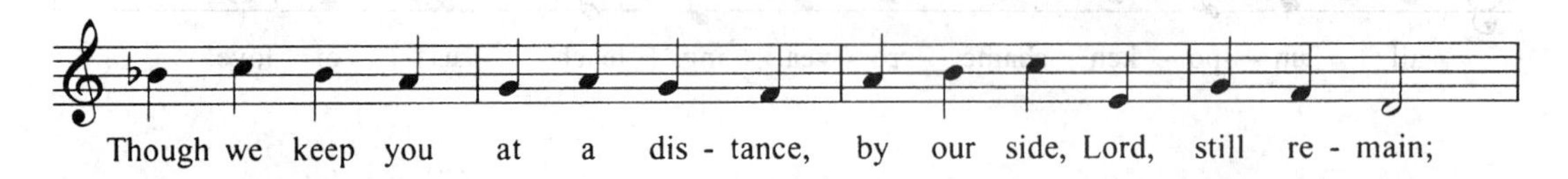

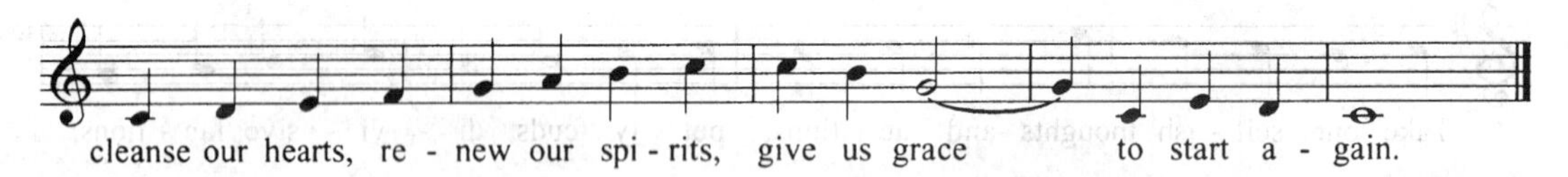

2. Lord, we know that we have failed you
through the things we do and say,
though we claim to care for others
we have thrust their needs away.
Too concerned with our own comfort
we have added to their pain;
teach us to show faith in action,
give us grace to start again.

3. Lord, we know that we have failed you,
full of doubt when life's been hard;
suffering has sapped our vision,
sorrow left our spirits scarred.
Faced by bitter disappointment
faith has buckled under strain;
help us know your hand upon us,
give us grace to start again.

4. Lord, we know that we have failed you,
too familiar with your word,
even though you've spoken clearly
all too often we've not heard.
Closed to truths which stretch horizons
or which go against the grain –
teach us, Lord, to stop and listen,
give us grace to start again.

5. Lord, we know that we have failed you,
lives too fraught to stop and stare;
dwelling always on the present –
what to eat or drink or wear.
Teach us first to seek your kingdom,
in our hearts for ever reign;
send us out, restored, forgiven,
give us grace to start again.

© Copyright 1999 Kevin Mayhew Ltd.

424 Lord, we thank you for the promise

Martin E. Leckebusch (b.1962) | Martin Setchell (b.1939)

THE PROMISE 87 87 D

© Copyright 1999 Kevin Mayhew Ltd.

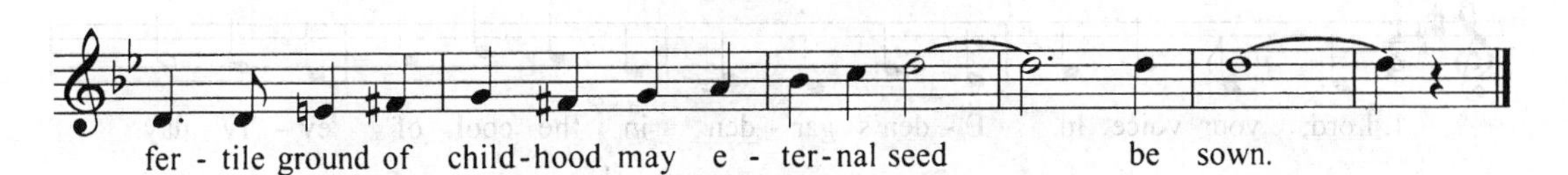

2. Lord, we thank you for the vigour
burning in the years of youth:
strength to face tomorrow's challenge,
zest for life and zeal for truth.
In the choice of friends and partners,
when ideas and values form,
may the message of your kingdom
be the guide, the goal, the norm.

3. Lord, we thank you for the harvest
of the settled, middle years:
times when work and home can prosper,
when life's richest fruit appears;
but when illness, stress and hardship
fill so many days with dread,
may your love renew the vision
of a clearer road ahead.

4. Lord, we thank you for the beauty
of a heart at last mature:
crowned with peace and rich in wisdom,
well-respected and secure;
but to those who face the twilight
frail, bewildered, lacking friends,
Lord, confirm your gracious offer:
perfect life which never ends.

425 Lord, when I turn my back on you *I need you, Lord*

Words and music: Susan Sayers (b.1946)

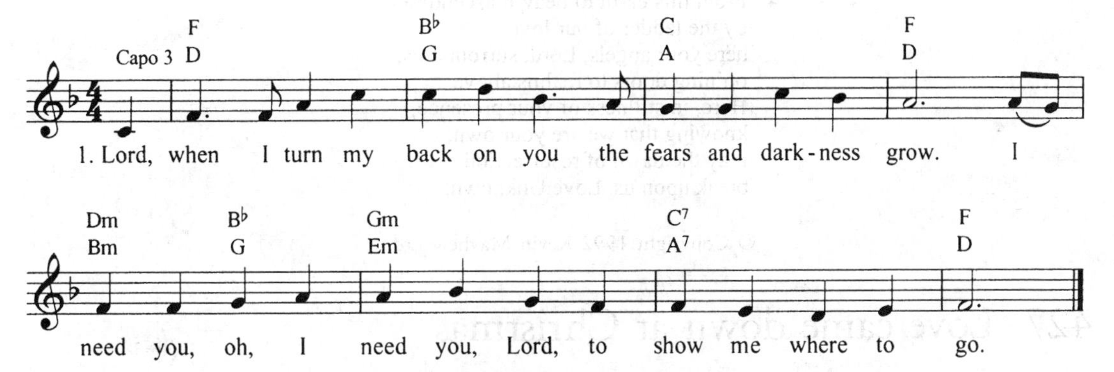

2. With you beside me, Lord, I find
the evils that I face
become instead a joyfulness,
a fountain of your grace.

3. So shape me to your purpose, Lord,
and tell me what to do;
and if I start to turn away,
then turn me back to you.

4. And when the world is over Lord,
or over just for me,
there is nowhere but with you, Lord,
that I would rather be.

© Copyright 1984 Kevin Mayhew Ltd.

426 Lord, your voice in Eden's garden

Edwin Le Grice (1911-1992)
from the Cantata *Love Unknown*

Malcolm Archer (b.1952)

GARDEN OF EDEN 87 87 D

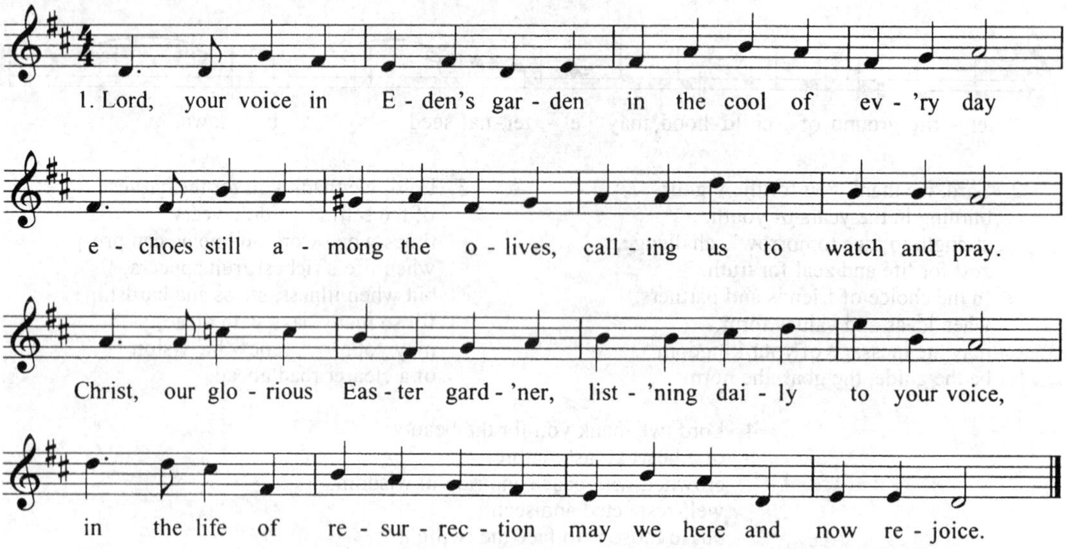

1. Lord, your voice in Eden's garden in the cool of ev-'ry day
e-choes still a-mong the o-lives, call-ing us to watch and pray.
Christ, our glo-rious Eas-ter gard-'ner, list-'ning dai-ly to your voice,
in the life of re-sur-rec-tion may we here and now re-joice.

Women

2. Here we meet you, risen Saviour,
in the marvels of your earth:
in the trust of little children
see the wonder of your birth:
here in sweat of daily labour,
here in love of man and wife,
here in strength of mind and body
share your resurrection life.

Men

3. In unlimited forgiveness
ready to receive and give,
open handed, open hearted,
show your servants how to live,
bearing sin, enduring suff'ring,
sharing joy, accepting pain,
learning, risen Lord and Master,
how to die and rise again.

4. From this earth to heav'n ascending
by the ladder of our love,
here your angels, Lord, surround us,
op'ning doors to realms above.
Here, in stillness of your presence,
knowing that we are your own,
may the dawn of resurrection
break upon us, Love Unknown.

© Copyright 1992 Kevin Mayhew Ltd.

427 Love came down at Christmas

Christina Georgina Rossetti (1830-1894)

Reginald Owen Morris (1886-1948)

TUNE 1: HERMITAGE 67 67

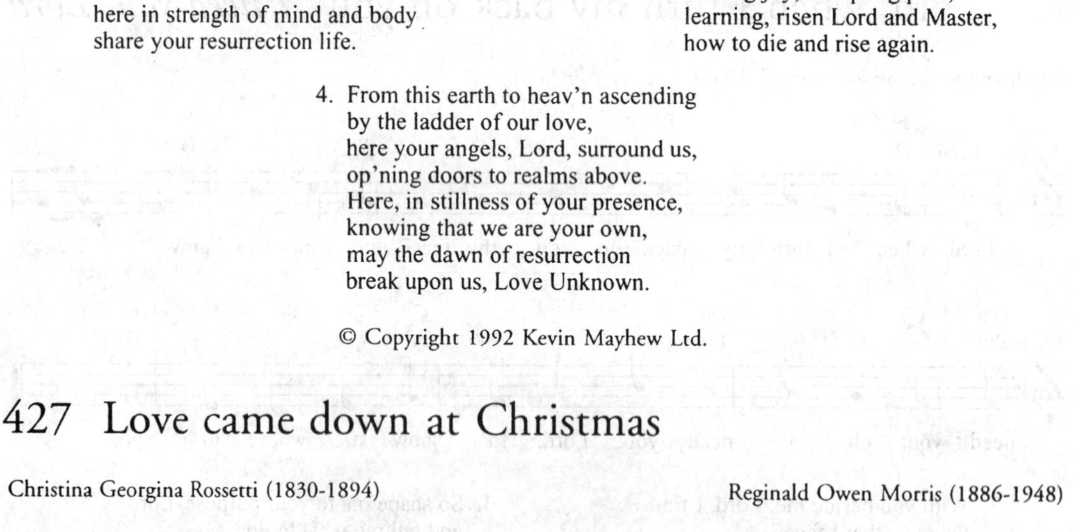

1. Love came down at Christ-mas, Love all love-ly, Love di-vine;
Love was born at Christ-mas, star and an-gels gave the sign.

2. Worship we the Godhead,
Love incarnate, Love divine;
worship we our Jesus:
but wherewith for sacred sign?

3. Love shall be our token,
love be yours and love be mine,
love to God and all men,
love for plea and gift and sign.

Christina Georgina Rossetti (1830-1894)

Malcolm Archer (b.1952)

TUNE 2: LOVE CAME DOWN 67 67

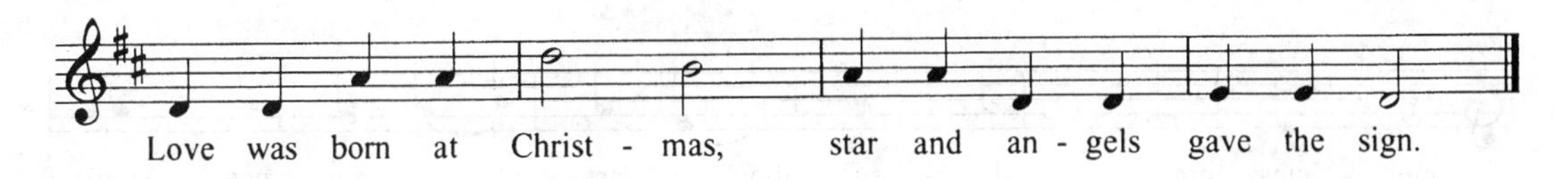

Music © Copyright 1991 Kevin Mayhew Ltd.

428 Love divine, all loves excelling

Charles Wesley (1707-1788) alt.

John Stainer (1840-1901)

TUNE 1: LOVE DIVINE 87 87

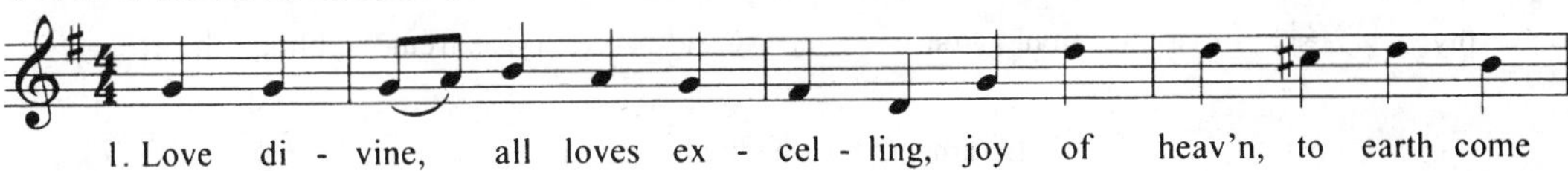

2. Jesu, thou art all compassion,
pure unbounded love thou art;
visit us with thy salvation,
enter ev'ry trembling heart.

3. Breathe, O breathe thy loving Spirit
into ev'ry troubled breast;
let us all in thee inherit,
let us find thy promised rest.

4. Take away the love of sinning,
Alpha and Omega be;
end of faith, as its beginning,
set our hearts at liberty.

5. Come, almighty to deliver,
let us all thy grace receive;
suddenly return, and never,
never more thy temples leave.

6. Thee we would be always blessing,
serve thee as thy hosts above;
pray, and praise thee without ceasing,
glory in thy perfect love.

7. Finish then thy new creation,
pure and spotless let us be;
let us see thy great salvation
perfectly restored in thee.

8. Changed from glory into glory,
till in heav'n we take our place,
till we cast our crowns before thee,
lost in wonder, love, and praise.

Tune 2 will be found overleaf

Charles Wesley (1707-1788) alt. William Penfro Rowlands (1860-1937)

TUNE 2: BLAENWERN 87 87 D

2. Breathe, O breathe thy loving Spirit
into ev'ry troubled breast;
let us all in thee inherit,
let us find thy promised rest.
Take away the love of sinning,
Alpha and Omega be;
end of faith, as its beginning,
set our hearts at liberty.

3. Come, almighty to deliver,
let us all thy grace receive;
suddenly return, and never,
never more thy temples leave.
Thee we would be always blessing,
serve thee as thy hosts above;
pray, and praise thee without ceasing,
glory in thy perfect love.

4. Finish then thy new creation,
pure and spotless let us be;
let us see thy great salvation
perfectly restored in thee.
Changed from glory into glory,
till in heav'n we take our place,
till we cast our crowns before thee,
lost in wonder, love, and praise.

Music © Copyright G.A. Gabe, Swansea.
Used by permission.

429 Love is his word

Luke Connaughton (1917-1979) alt.

Anthony Milner (b.1925)

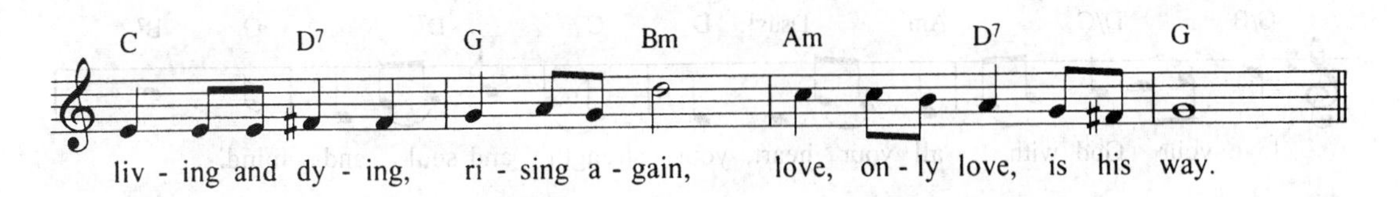

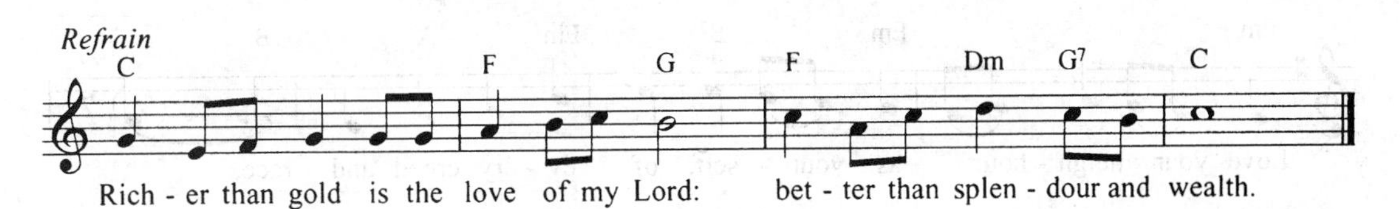

2. Love is his way, love is his mark,
sharing his last Passover feast,
Christ at the table, host to the twelve,
love, only love, is his mark.

3. Love is his mark, love is his sign,
bread for our strength, wine for our joy,
'This is my body, this is my blood.'
Love, only love, is his sign.

4. Love is his sign, love is his news,
'Do this,' he said, 'lest you forget
all my deep sorrow, all my dear blood.'
Love, only love, is his news.

5. Love is his news, love is his name,
we are his own, chosen and called,
family, brethren, cousins and kin.
Love, only love, is his name.

6. Love is his name, love is his law,
hear his command, all who are his,
'Love one another, I have loved you.'
Love, only love, is his law.

7. Love is his law, love is his word:
love of the Lord, Father and Word,
love of the Spirit, God ever one,
love, only love, is his word.

© Copyright McCrimmon Publishing Co. Ltd., 10-12 High Street, Great Wakering, Southend-on-Sea, Essex SS3 0EQ, UK. All rights reserved. Used by arrangement.

430 Love is the only law

Michael Forster (b.1946) — Andrew Moore (b.1954)

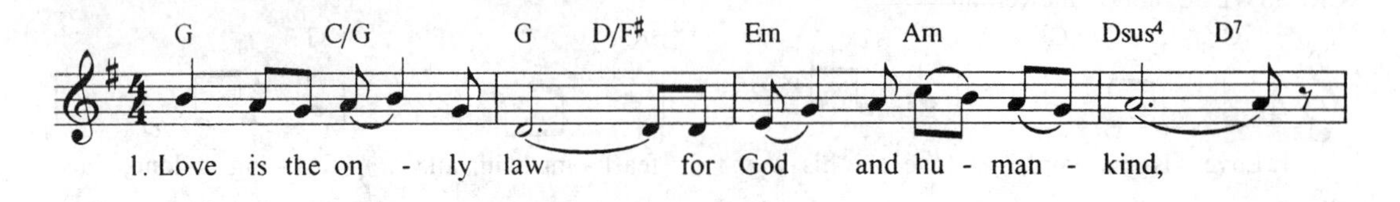

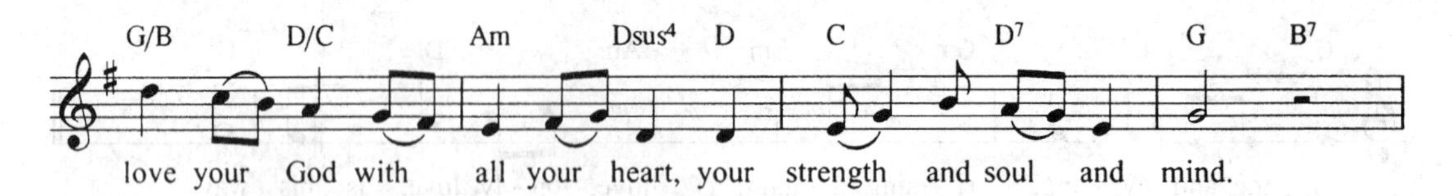

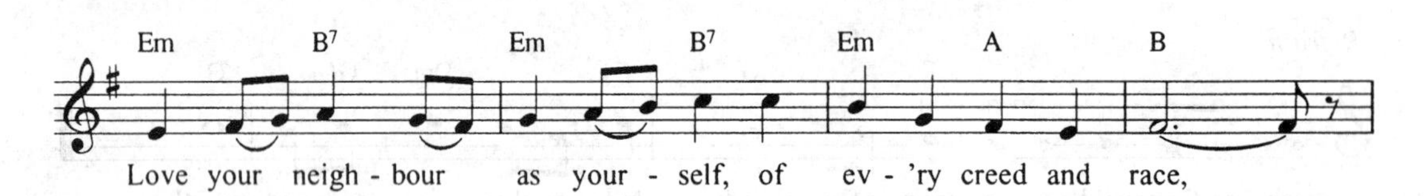

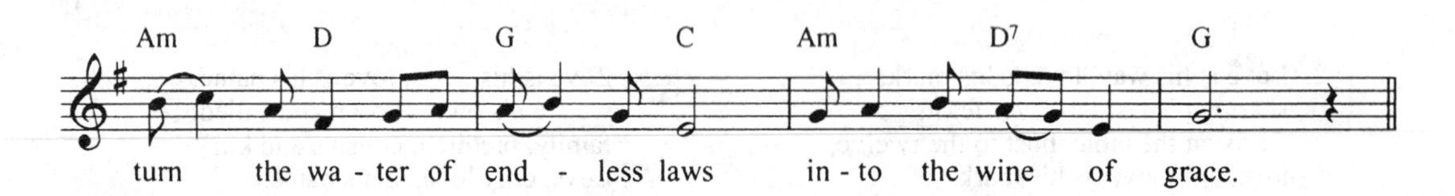

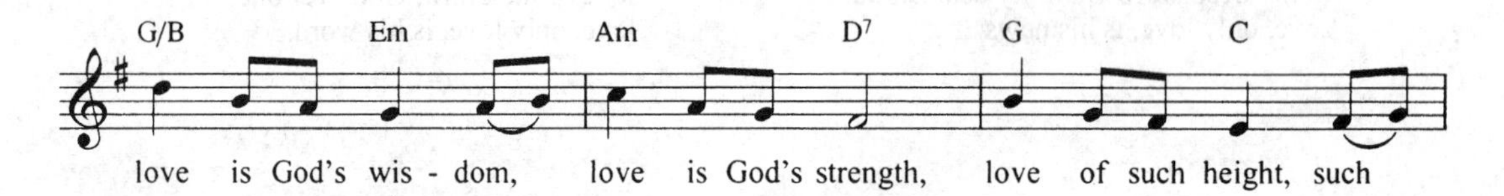

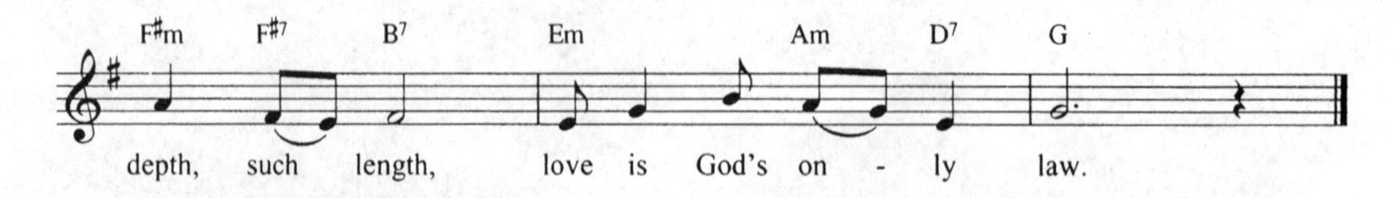

2. Give to the poor a voice
and help the blind to see,
feed the hungry, heal the sick
and set the captive free.
All that God requires of you
will then fall into place,
turn the water of endless laws
into the wine of grace.

3. Let love like fountains flow
and justice like a stream,
faith become reality
and hope your constant theme.
Then shall freedom, joy and peace
with righteousness embrace,
turn the water of endless laws
into the wine of grace.

© Copyright 1997 Kevin Mayhew Ltd.

431 Lovely in your littleness *Jesus is our joy*

Pamela Hayes Margaret Rizza (b.1929)

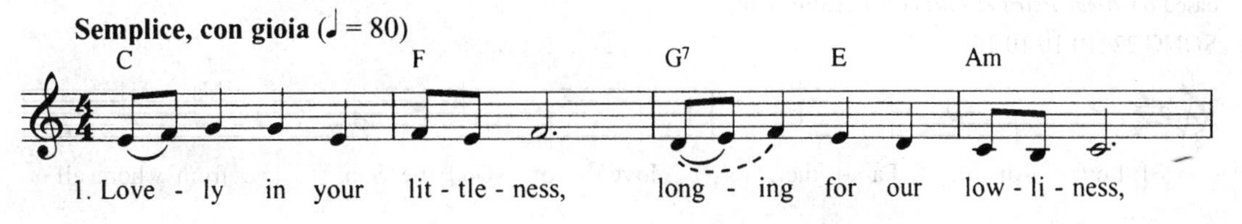

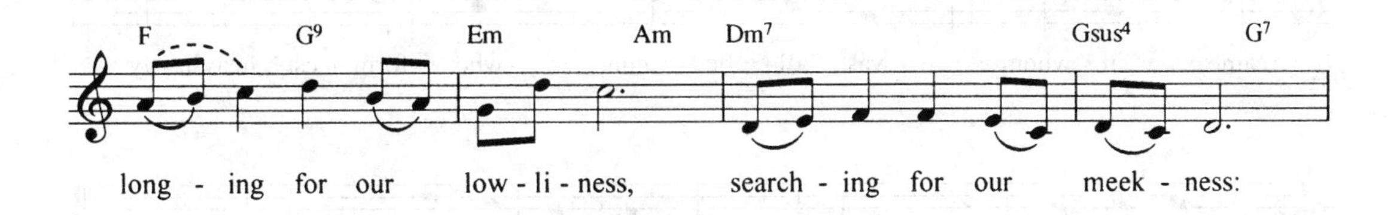

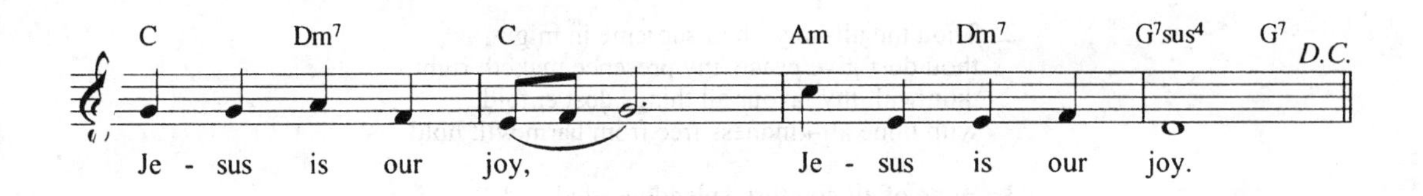

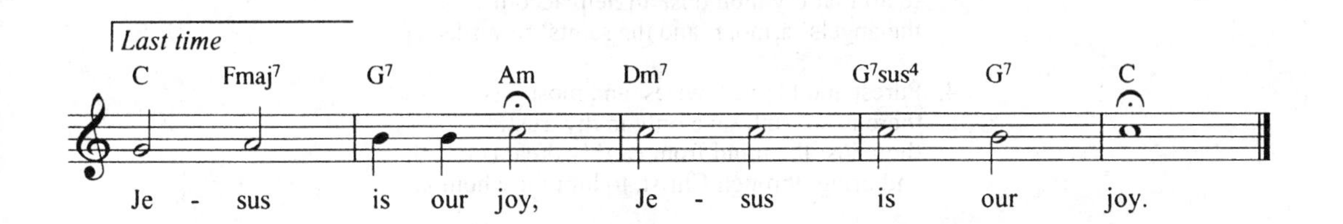

2. Peace within our powerlessness,
hope within our helplessness,
hope within our helplessness,
love within our loneliness:
Jesus is our joy, Jesus is our joy.

3. Held in Mary's tenderness,
tiny hands are raised to bless,
tiny hands are raised to bless,
touching us with God's caress:
Jesus is our joy, Jesus is our joy.

4. Joy, then, in God's graciousness,
peace comes with gentleness,
peace comes with gentleness,
filling hearts with gladness:
Jesus is our joy, Jesus is our joy.

© Copyright 1998 Kevin Mayhew Ltd.

432 Love of the Father

Robert Bridges (1844-1930)
based on *Amor Patris et Filii* (12th century) alt.

Orlando Gibbons (1583-1625)

SONG 22 10 10 10 10

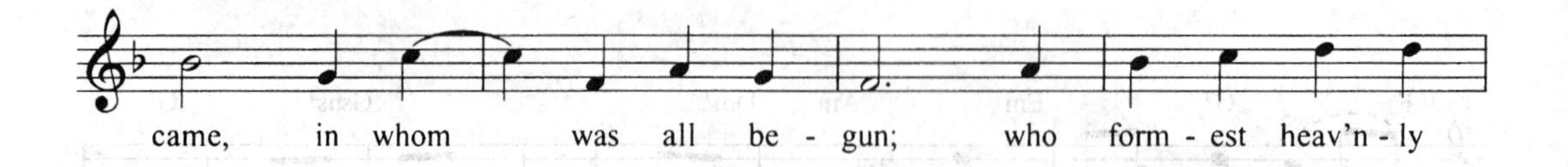

2. Thou the all-holy, thou supreme in might,
thou dost give peace, thy presence maketh right;
thou with thy favour all things dost enfold,
with thine all-kindness free from harm wilt hold.

3. Hope of all comfort, splendour of all aid,
that dost not fail nor leave the heart afraid:
to all that cry thou dost all help accord,
the angels' armour, and the saints' reward.

4. Purest and highest, wisest and most just,
there is no truth save only in thy trust;
thou dost the mind from earthly dreams recall,
and bring, through Christ, to him for whom are all.

5. Eternal glory, let the world adore,
who art and shalt be worshipped evermore:
us whom thou madest, comfort with thy might,
and lead us to enjoy thy heav'nly light.

433 Love's redeeming work is done

Charles Wesley (1707-1788)

John Wesley's *Foundery Collection* (1742)

SAVANNAH 77 77

2. Vain the stone, the watch, the seal;
Christ has burst the gates of hell;
death in vain forbids his rise;
Christ has opened paradise.

3. Lives again our glorious King;
where, O death, is now thy sting?
Dying once, he all doth save;
where thy victory, O grave?

4. Soar we now where Christ has led,
foll'wing our exalted Head;
made like him, like him we rise;
ours the cross, the grave, the skies.

5. Hail the Lord of earth and heav'n!
praise to thee by both be giv'n;
thee we greet triumphant now;
hail, the Resurrection thou!

434 Loving Shepherd of thy sheep

Jane Elizabeth Leeson (1809-1881)

Leighton George Hayne (1836-1883)

2. Loving shepherd, thou didst give
thine own life that I might live;
may I love thee day by day,
gladly thy sweet will obey.

3. Loving shepherd, ever near,
teach me still thy voice to hear;
suffer not my steps to stray
from the straight and narrow way.

4. Where thou leadest may I go,
walking in thy steps below;
then, before thy Father's throne,
Jesu, claim me for thine own.

Jane Elizabeth Leeson (1809-1881)

Adapted from Freylinghausen's *Geistreiches Gesangbuch* (1704)

TUNE 2: LÜBECK (GOTT SEI DANK) 77 77

435 Low in the grave he lay

Words and music: Robert Lowry (1826-1899)

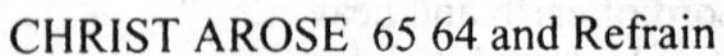
CHRIST AROSE 65 64 and Refrain

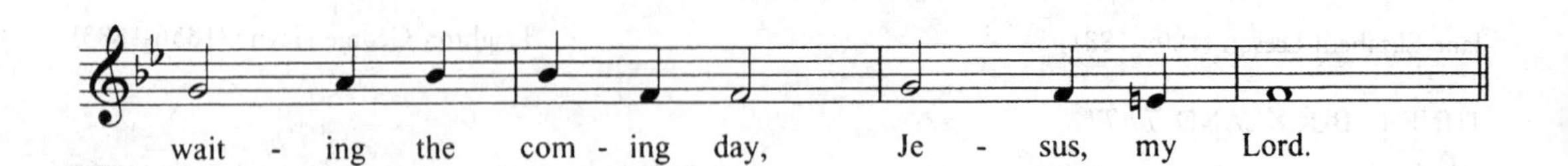

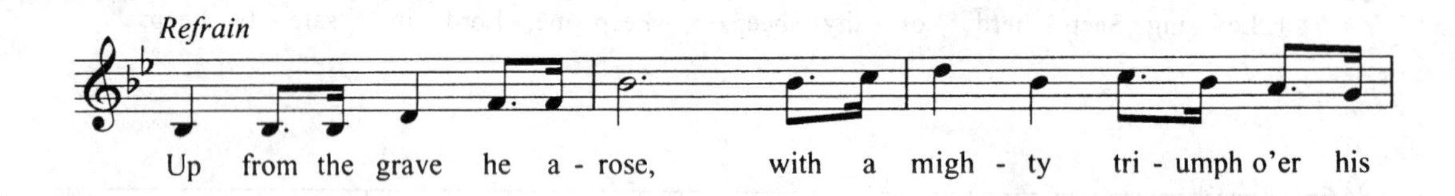

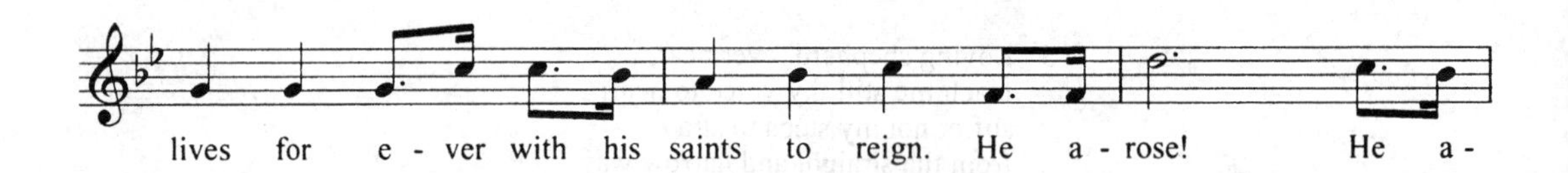

2. Vainly they watch his bed,
Jesus, my Saviour;
vainly they seal the dead,
Jesus, my Lord.

3. Death cannot keep its prey,
Jesus, my Saviour;
he tore the bars away,
Jesus, my Lord.

436 Majesty, worship his majesty

Words and music: Jack W. Hayford (b.1934)

© Copyright Rocksmith Music Inc, USA. Rights administered in the UK & Republic of Ireland by Bucks Music Ltd., Onward House, 11 Uxbridge Street, London W8 7TQ. Used by permission.

437 Make me a channel of your peace

Words and music: Sebastian Temple (1928-1997)
based on the prayer of St Francis

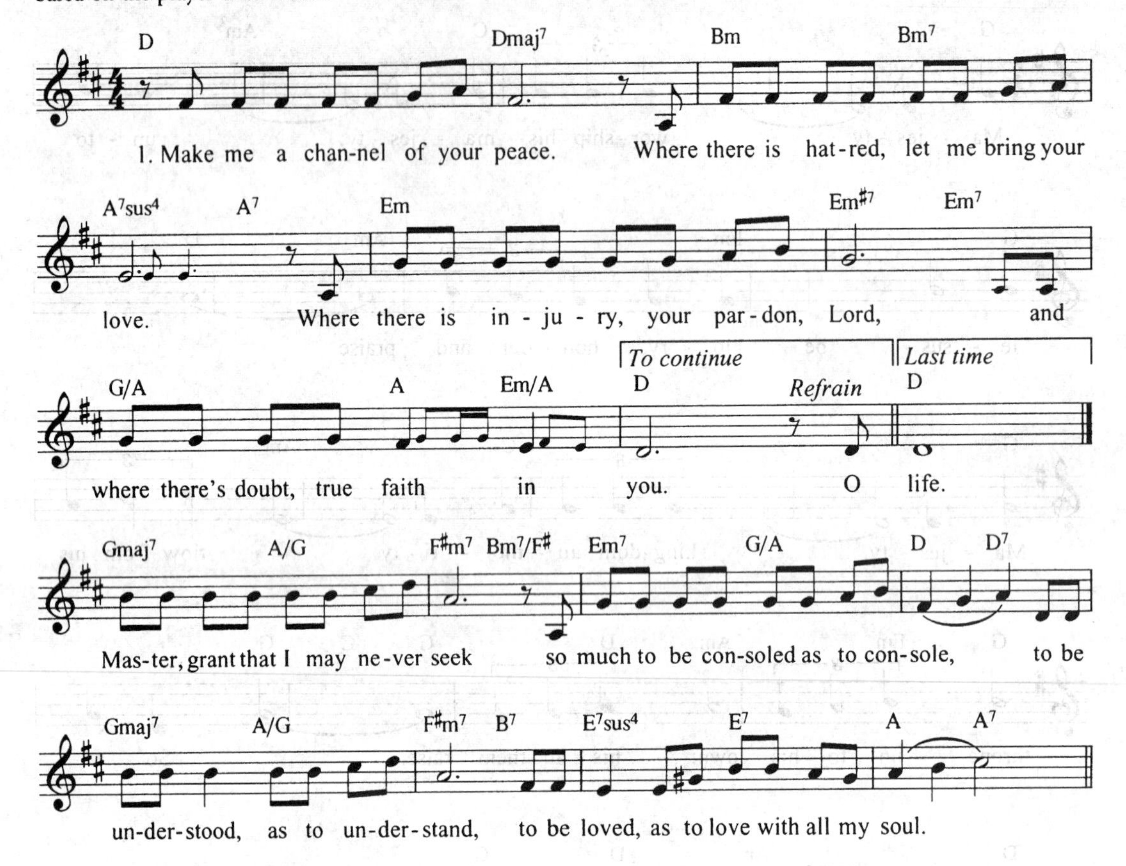

2. Make me a channel of your peace.
Where there's despair in life, let me bring hope.
Where there is darkness, only light,
and where there's sadness, ever joy.

3. Make me a channel of your peace.
It is in pardoning that we are pardoned,
in giving of ourselves that we receive,
and in dying that we're born to eternal life.

© Copyright 1967 OCP Publications, 5536 NE Hassalo, Portland, Oregon 97213, USA.
All rights reserved. Used by permission. Dedicated to Mrs Frances Tracy.
This song is not covered by a CCL Licence. Permission should be obtained from
Calamus, 30 North Terrace, Mildenhall, Suffolk IP28 7AB.

438 Make way, make way

Words and music: Graham Kendrick (b.1950)

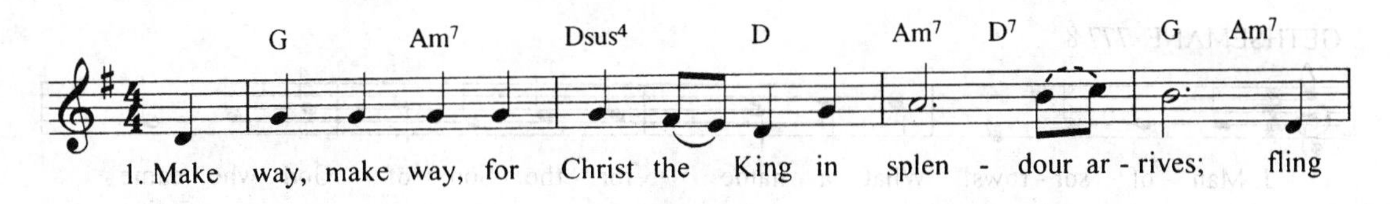

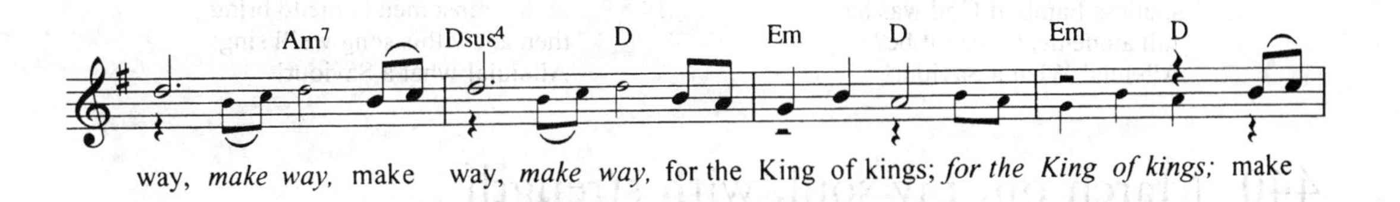

2. He comes the broken hearts to heal,
the pris'ners to free;
the deaf shall hear, the lame shall dance,
the blind shall see.

3. And those who mourn with heavy hearts,
who weep and sigh,
with laughter, joy and royal crown
he'll beautify.

4. We call you now to worship him
as Lord of all,
to have no gods before him,
their thrones must fall.

© Copyright 1986 Kingsway's Thankyou Music, P.O. Box 75, Eastbourne, East Sussex BN23 6NW, UK. (tym@kingsway.co.uk). Used by permission.

439 Man of sorrows

Words and music: Philipp Bliss (1838-1876) alt.

GETHSEMANE 777 8

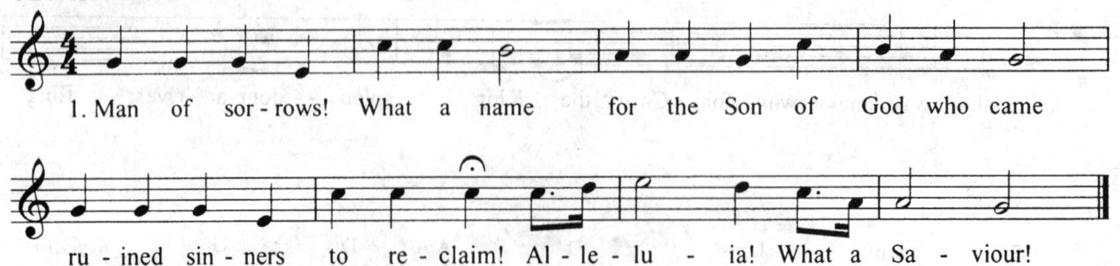

2. Bearing shame and scoffing rude,
in my place condemned he stood;
sealed my pardon with his blood;
Alleluia! What a Saviour!

3. Guilty, vile and helpless we;
spotless Lamb of God was he:
full atonement – can it be?
Alleluia! What a Saviour!

4. Lifted up was he to die:
'It is finished!' was his cry;
now in heav'n exalted high;
Alleluia! What a Saviour!

5. When he comes, our glorious King,
all his ransomed home to bring,
then anew this song we'll sing:
Alleluia! what a Saviour!

440 March on, my soul, with strength

William Wright (1859-1924) alt.

Charles Steggal (1826-1905)

CHRISTCHURCH 66 66 88

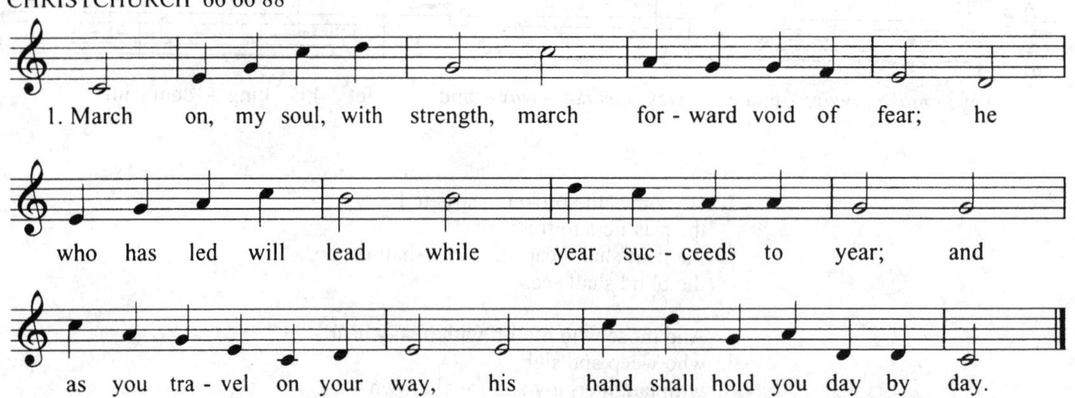

2. March on, my soul, with strength;
in ease you dare not dwell;
high duty calls you forth;
then up, and serve him well!
Take up your cross, take up your sword,
and fight the battles of your Lord!

3. March on, my soul, with strength,
with strength, but not your own;
the conquest you will gain
through Christ your Lord alone;
his grace shall nerve your feeble arm,
his love preserve you safe from harm.

4. March on, my soul, with strength,
from strength to strength march on;
warfare shall end at length,
all foes be overthrown.
And then, my soul, if faithful now,
the crown of life awaits your brow.

441 Mary, blessed grieving mother

Michael Forster (b.1946) Alan Ridout (1934-1996)

BLACK MADONNA 87 87 77

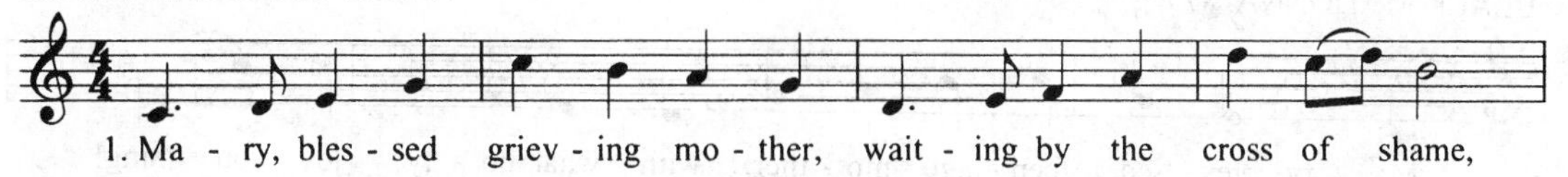

2. Where the crosses of the nations
darken still the noon-day skies,
see the sad madonna weeping
through a million mothers' eyes.
Holy Mary, full of grace,
all our tears with yours embrace.

3. Standing with the suff'ring Saviour,
still oppressed by hate and fear,
where the gentle still are murdered
and protesters disappear:
mother of the crucified,
call his people to your side!

4. Holy mother, watching, waiting,
for the saving of the earth;
in the loneliness of dying,
speak of hope and human worth,
there for all the world to see,
lifted up at Calvary!

© Copyright 1996 Kevin Mayhew Ltd.

442 Mary, blessed teenage mother

Alan Ridout (1934-1996)

Michael Forster (b.1946)

BLACK MADONNA 87 87 77

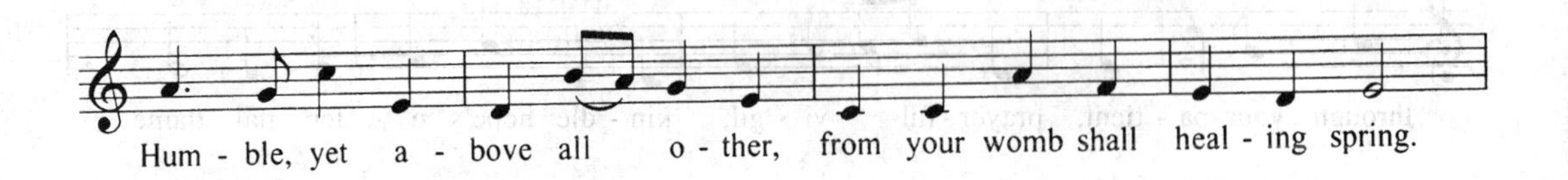

2. Mother of the homeless stranger
only outcasts recognise,
point us to the modern manger;
not a sight for gentle eyes!
Oh the joyful news we tell:
Even here, Immanuel!'

3. Now, throughout the townships ringing,
hear the black madonna cry,
songs of hope and freedom singing,
poor and humble lifted high.
Here the Spirit finds a womb
for the breaker of the tomb!

4. Holy mother, for the nations
bring to birth the child divine:
Israel's strength and consolation,
and the hope of Palestine!
All creation reconciled
in the crying of a child!

© Copyright 1996 Kevin Mayhew Ltd.

443 Mary had a baby

Words and music: West Indian Spiritual, alt.

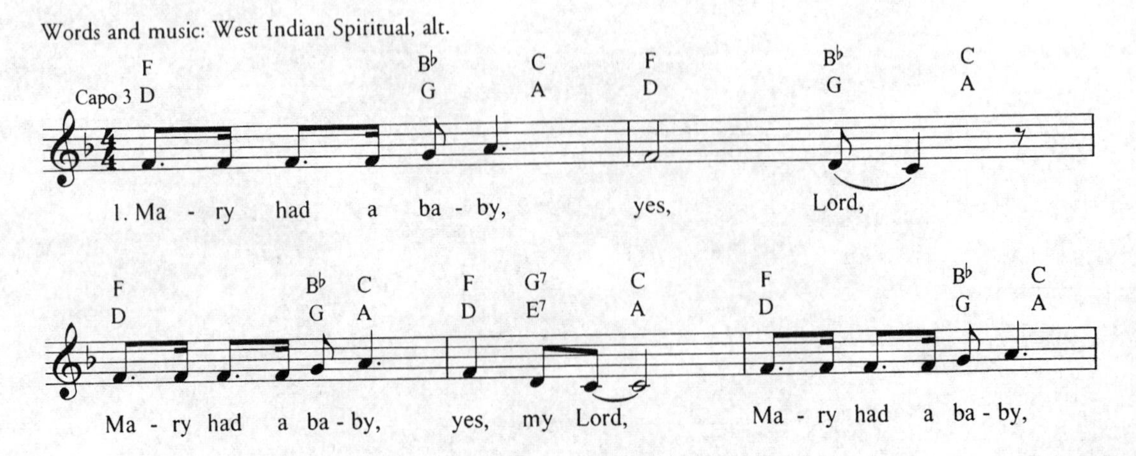

This versions of text © Copyright 1999 Kevin Mayhew Ltd.

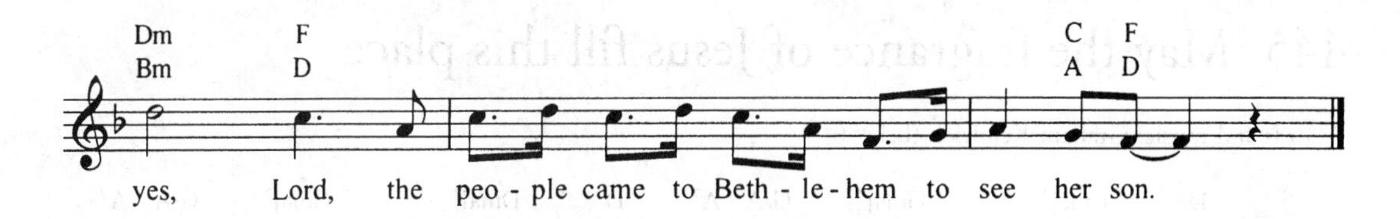

2. What did she name him, yes, Lord? *(x3)*
The people came to Bethlehem to see her son.
3. Mary named him Jesus, yes, Lord. *(x3)*
The people came to Bethlehem to see her son.
4. Where was he born, yes, Lord? *(x3)*
The people came to Bethlehem to see her son.
5. Born in a stable, yes, Lord. *(x3)*
The people came to Bethlehem to see her son.
6. Where did she lay him, yes, Lord? *(x3)*
The people came to Bethlehem to see her son.
7. Laid him in a manger, yes, Lord. *(x3)*
The people came to Bethlehem to see her son.

444 May God's blessing surround you

Words and music: Cliff Barrows

© Copyright 1982 Cliff Barrows.
Used by permission.

445 May the fragrance of Jesus fill this place

Words and music: Graham Kendrick (b.1950)

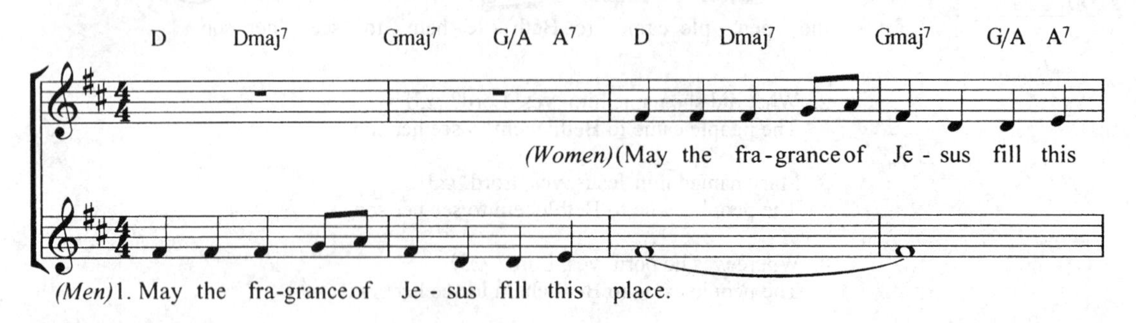

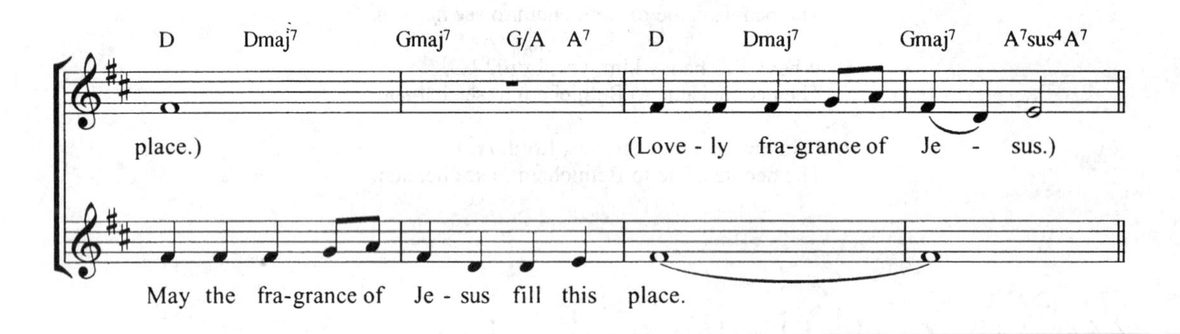

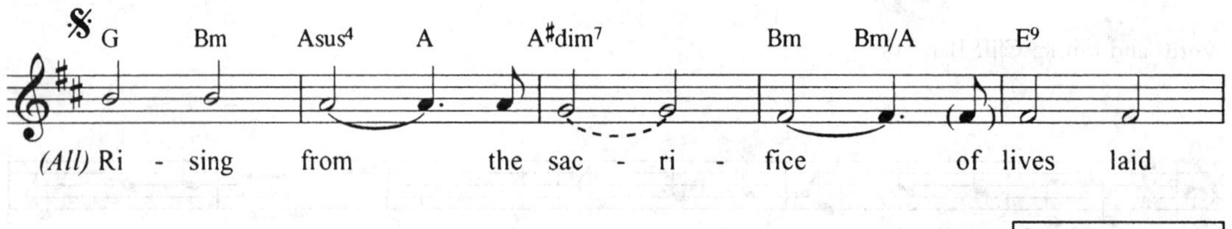

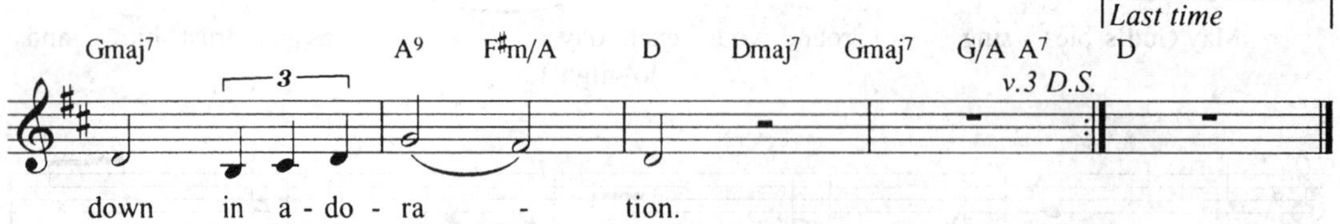

2. May the glory of Jesus fill his church
(may the glory of Jesus fill his church).
May the glory of Jesus fill his church.
(Radiant glory of Jesus),
shining from our faces
as we gaze in adoration.

3. May the beauty of Jesus fill my life.
(may the beauty of Jesus fill my life).
May the beauty of Jesus fill my life
(Perfect beauty of Jesus),
fill my thoughts, my words, my deeds;
may I give in adoration.
Fill my thoughts, my words, my deeds;
may I give in adoration.

© Copyright 1986 Kingsway's Thankyou Music, P.O. Box 75, Eastbourne, East Sussex BN23 6NW, UK. (tym@kingsway.co.uk). Used by permission.

446 May the grace of Christ our Saviour

John Newton (1725-1807)
based on 2 Corinthians 13:13

Melody by Heinrich Albert (1604-1651)
adapted by Charles Steggall (1826-1905)

TUNE 1: WALTHAM 87 87

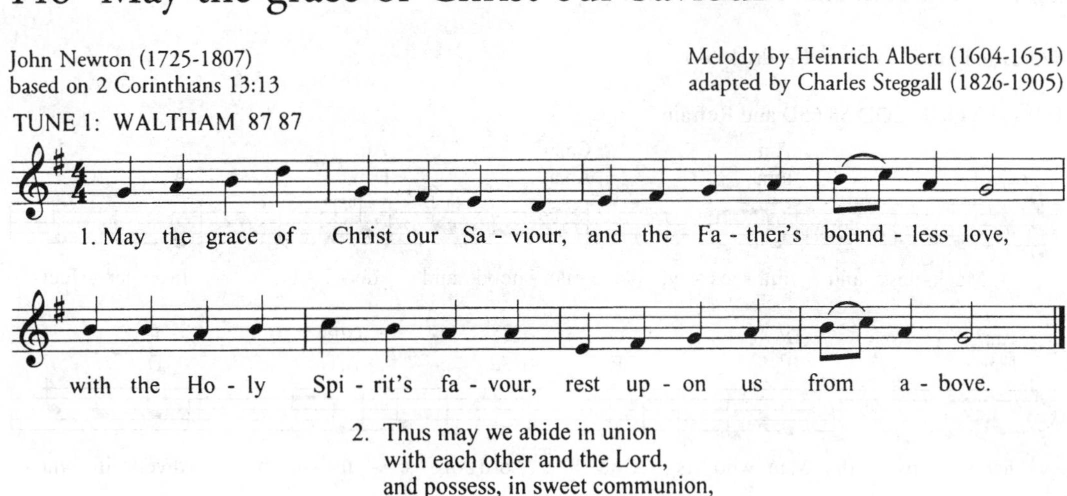

2. Thus may we abide in union
with each other and the Lord,
and possess, in sweet communion,
joys which earth cannot afford.

John Newton (1725-1807)
based on 2 Corinthians 13:13

Melody by Heinrich Albert (1604-1651)

TUNE 2: GOTT DES HIMMELS 87 87

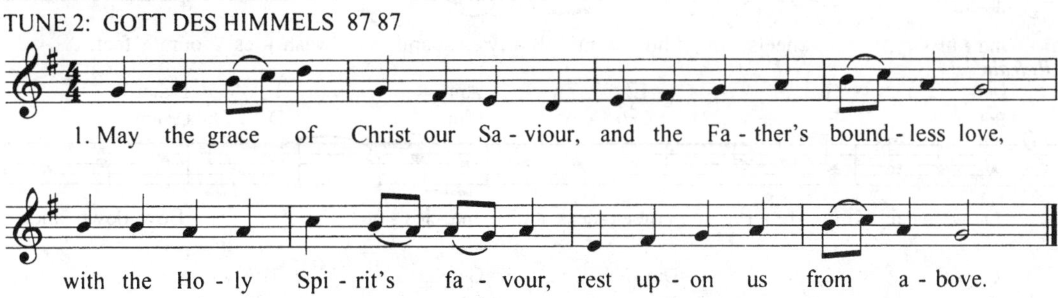

447 May the mind of Christ my Saviour

Kate Barclay Wilkinson (1859-1928)

Arthur Cyril Barham Gould (1891-1953)

ST LEONARD'S 87 75

2. May the word of God dwell richly
in my heart from hour to hour,
so that I may triumph only
in his saving pow'r.

3. May the peace of God my Father
rule my life in ev'rything,
that I may be calm to comfort
sick and sorrowing.

4. May the love of Jesus fill me,
as the waters fill the sea;
him exalting, self abasing,
this is victory.

5. May I run the race before me,
strong and brave to face the foe,
looking only unto Jesus,
as I onward go.

Music © Copyright the Executors of the late Arthur Cyril Barham Gould.
Used by permission of D.R. Gould Esq.

 Meekness and majesty *This is your God*

Words and music: Graham Kendrick (b.1950)

THIS IS YOUR GOD 66 65D and Refrain

2. Father's pure radiance,
perfect in innocence,
yet learns obedience
to death on a cross.
Suff'ring to give us life,
conqu'ring through sacrifice,
and as they crucify
prays: 'Father forgive.'

3. Wisdom unsearchable,
God the invisible,
love indestructible
in frailty appears.
Lord of infinity,
stooping so tenderly,
lifts our humanity
to the heights of his throne.

© Copyright 1986 Kingsway's Thankyou Music, P.O. Box 75, Eastbourne, East Sussex BN23 6NW, UK. (tym@kingsway.co.uk). Used by permission.

449 Mine eyes have seen the glory

Julia Ward Howe (1819-1910) alt. | Traditional American melody

BATTLE HYMN 14 15 15 6 and Refrain

2. I have seen him in the watchfires
of a hundred circling camps.
They have gilded him an altar
in the evening dews and damps.
I can read his righteous sentence
by the dim and flaring lamps.
His day is marching on.

3. He has sounded forth the trumpet
that shall never sound retreat.
He is sifting out all human hearts
before his judgement seat.
O, be swift my soul to answer him,
be jubilant my feet!
Our God is marching on.

4. In the beauty of the lilies
Christ was born across the sea,
with a glory in his bosom
that transfigures you and me.
As he died to make us holy,
let us live that all be free,
whilst God is marching on.

This version of text © Copyright 1992 Kevin Mayhew Ltd.

450 Morning has broken

Eleanor Farjeon (1881-1965) | Traditional Gaelic melody

BUNESSAN 55 54 D

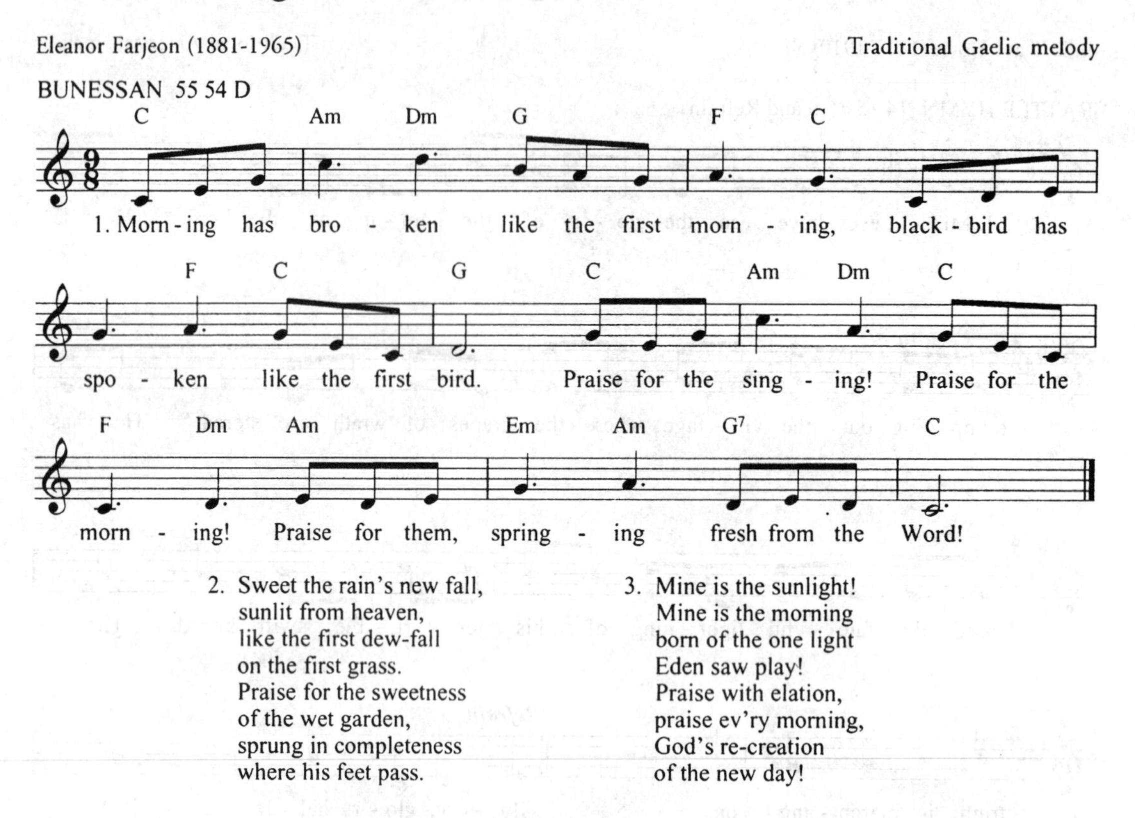

2. Sweet the rain's new fall,
sunlit from heaven,
like the first dew-fall
on the first grass.
Praise for the sweetness
of the wet garden,
sprung in completeness
where his feet pass.

3. Mine is the sunlight!
Mine is the morning
born of the one light
Eden saw play!
Praise with elation,
praise ev'ry morning,
God's re-creation
of the new day!

Text © Copyright David Higham Associates, 5-8 Lower John Street, Golden Square, London W1R 4HA, UK.
Used by permission from *The Children's Bells,* published by Oxford University Press.

451 Moses, I know you're the man *The people of God*

Words and music: Estelle White (b.1925)

© Copyright McCrimmon Publishing Co. Ltd., 10-12 High Street, Great Wakering,
Southend-on-Sea, Essex SS3 0EQ, UK. and Stainer & Bell Ltd. Used by arrangement.

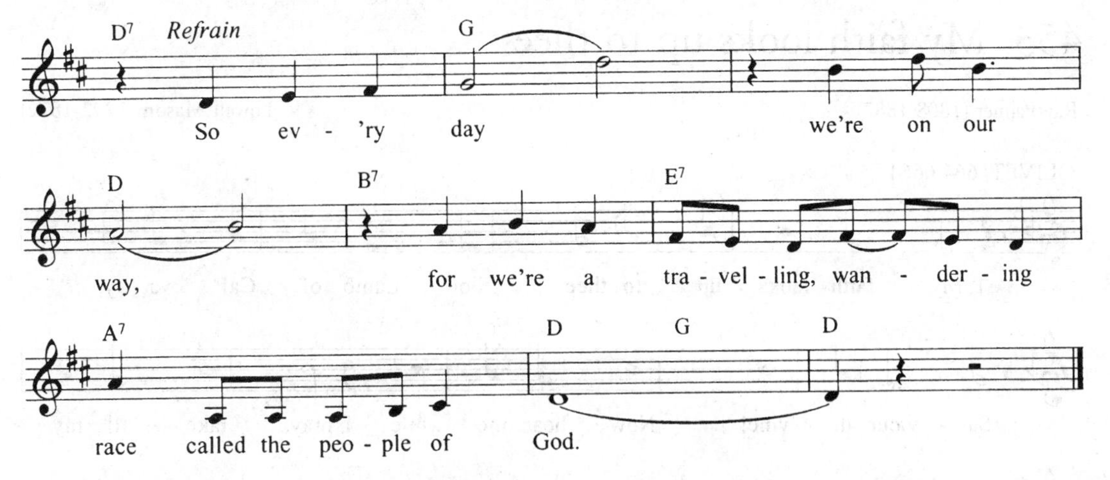

2. 'Don't get too set in your ways,' the Lord said.
'Each step is only a phase,' the Lord said.
'I'll go before you and I shall be a sign
to guide my travelling, wandering race.
You're the people of God.'

3. 'No matter what you may do,' the Lord said,
'I shall be faithful and true,' the Lord said.
'My love will strengthen you as you go along,
for you're my travelling, wandering race.
You're the people of God.'

4. 'Look at the birds in the air,' the Lord said.
'They fly unhampered by care,' the Lord said.
'You will move easier if you're trav'lling light,
for you're a wandering, vagabond race.'
You're the people of God.'

5. 'Foxes have places to go,' the Lord said.
'but I've no home here below,' the Lord said.
'So if you want to be with me all your days,
keep up the moving and travelling on.
You're the people of God.'

452 Most glorious Lord of life

Edmund Spenser (1552-1599)

Henry Lawes (1596-1662)

FARLEY CASTLE 10 10 10 10

2. This joyous day, dear Lord, with joy begin,
and grant that we for whom thou didst die,
being with thy dear blood clean washed from sin,
May live for ever in felicity:

3. And that thy love we weighing worthily,
may likewise love thee for the same again;
and for thy sake, that all like dear didst buy,
with love may one another entertain;

4. So let us love, dear Love, like as we ought;
love is the lesson which the Lord us taught.

453 My faith looks up to thee

Ray Palmer (1808-1887) Lowell Mason (1792-1872)

OLIVET 664 6664

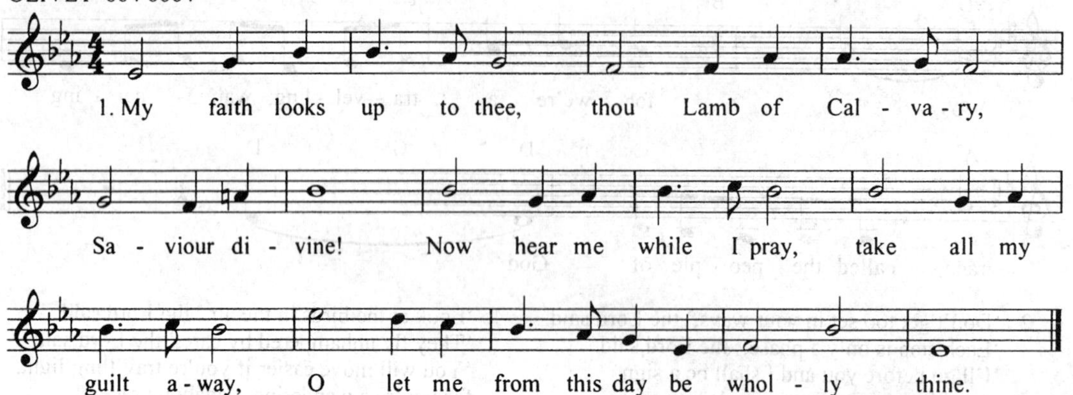

2. May thy rich grace impart
strength to my fainting heart,
my zeal inspire.
As thou hast died for me,
O may my love to thee
pure, warm and changeless be,
a living fire.

3. While life's dark maze I tread,
and griefs around me spread,
be thou my guide;
bid darkness turn to day,
wipe sorrow's tears away,
nor let me ever stray
from thee aside.

4. When ends life's transient dream,
when death's cold sullen stream
shall o'er me roll,
blest Saviour, then in love,
fear and distrust remove;
O bear me safe above,
a ransomed soul.

454 My Father, for another night

Words and music: Henry Williams Baker (1821-1877)

ST TIMOTHY CM

2. Now with the new-born day I give
myself anew to thee,
that as thou willest I may live,
and what thou willest be.

3. Whate'er I do, things great or small,
whate'er I speak or frame,
thy glory may I seek in all,
do all in Jesus' name.

4. My Father, for his sake, I pray,
thy child accept and bless;
and lead me by thy grace today
in paths of righteousness.

455 My God, accept my heart this day

Matthew Bridges (1800-1894)

Adapted from William Gardiner's *Sacred Melodies* (1812)

TUNE 1: BELMONT CM

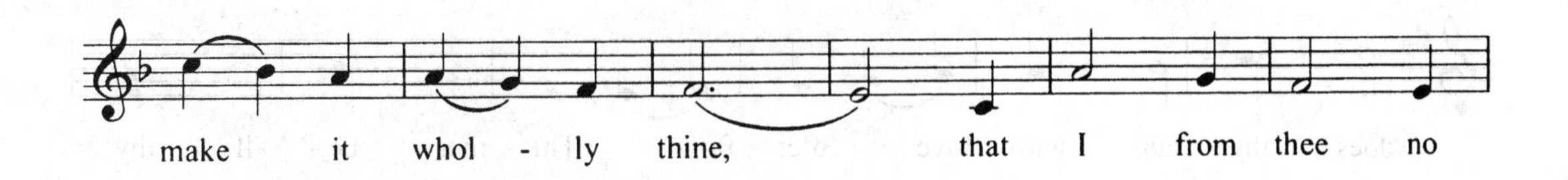

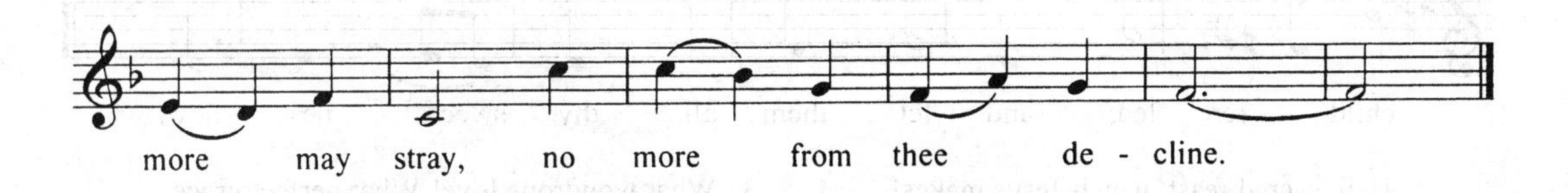

2. Before the cross of him who died,
behold, I prostrate fall;
let ev'ry sin be crucified,
and Christ be all in all.

3. Anoint me with thy heav'nly grace,
and seal me for thine own,
that I may see thy glorious face,
and worship at thy throne.

4. Let ev'ry thought and work and word
to thee be ever giv'n.
then life shall be thy service, Lord,
and death the gate of heav'n.

5. All glory to the Father be,
all glory to the Son,
all glory, Holy Ghost, to thee,
while endless ages run.

Matthew Bridges (1800-1894)

Raphael Courteville (c.1675-1772)

TUNE 2: ST JAMES CM

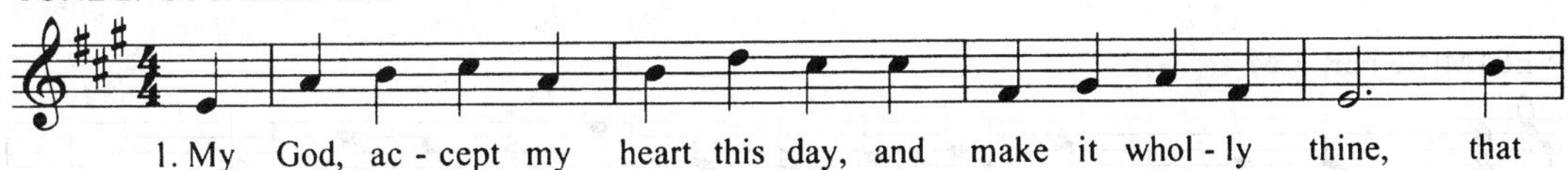

456 My God, and is thy table spread

Philip Doddridge (1702-1751) alt.
v.3: Michael Forster (b.1946)

From A. Williams' *Second Supplement to Psalmody in Miniature* (c.1780)
adapted by Edward Miller (1735-1807)

ROCKINGHAM LM

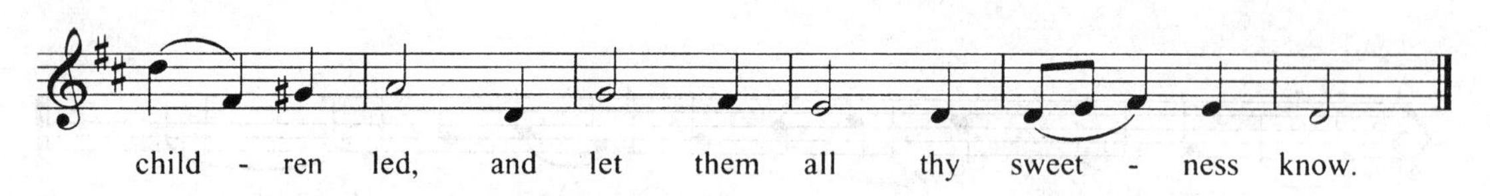

2. Hail, sacred feast, which Jesus makes!
Rich banquet of his flesh and blood!
Thrice happy all, who here partake
that sacred stream, that heav'nly food.

3. What wondrous love! What perfect grace,
for Jesus, our exalted host,
invites us to this special place
who offer least and need the most.

4. O let thy table honoured be,
and furnished well with joyful guests;
and may each soul salvation see,
that here its sacred pledges tastes.

Thie version of text © Copyright 1996 Kevin Mayhew Ltd.

457 My God, how wonderful you are

Frederick William Faber (1814-1863) alt.

James Turle (1802-1882)

WESTMINSTER CM

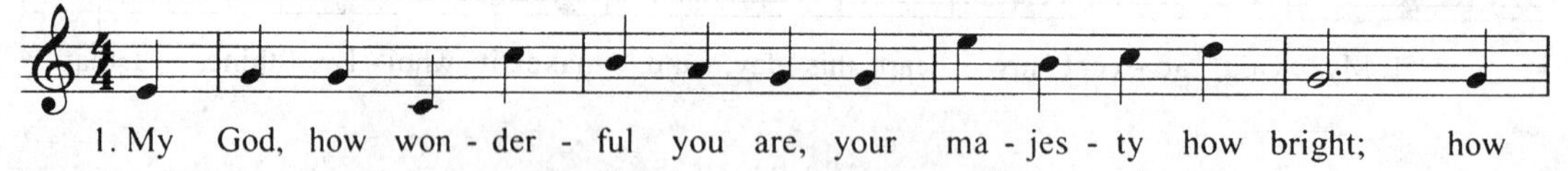

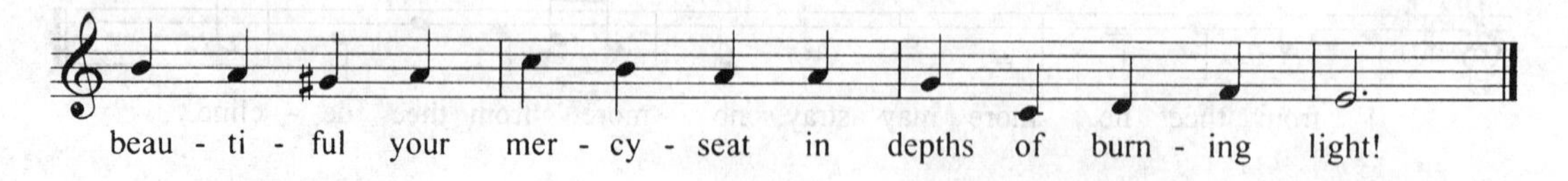

2. Creator from eternal years
and everlasting Lord,
by holy angels day and night
unceasingly adored!

3. How wonderful, how beautiful
the sight of you must be –
your endless wisdom, boundless power,
and awesome purity!

This version of text © Copyright Jubilate Hymns, 4 Thorne Park Road,
Chelston, Torquay TQ2 6RX, UK. Used by permission.

4. O how I fear you, living God,
with deepest, tenderest fears,
and worship you with trembling hope
and penitential tears!

5. But I may love you too, O Lord,
though you are all-divine,
for you have stooped to ask of me
this feeble love of mine.

6. Father of Jesus, love's reward,
great King upon your throne,
what joy to see you as you are
and know as I am known!

458 My God, I love thee

Latin (17th century)
trans. Edward Caswall (1814-1878)

John Stainer (1840-1901)

TUNE 1: ST FRANCIS XAVIER CM

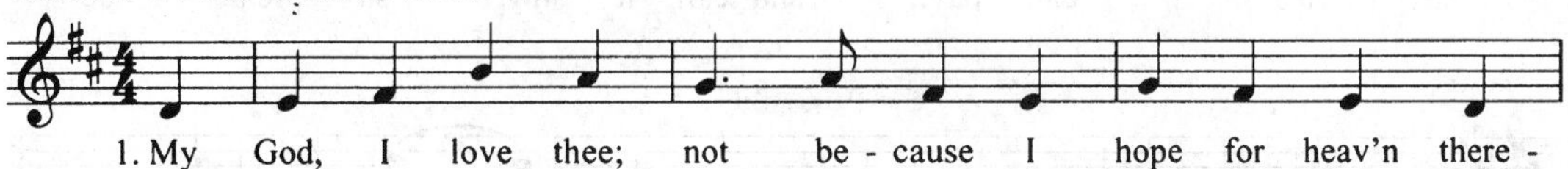

2. Thou, O my Jesus, thou didst me
upon the cross embrace;
for me didst bear the nails and spear,
and manifold disgrace.

3. And griefs and torments numberless,
and sweat of agony;
yea, death itself – and all for me
who was thine enemy.

4. Then why, O blessèd Jesu Christ,
should I not love thee well?
Not for the sake of winning heav'n,
nor of escaping hell.

5. Not from the hope of gaining aught,
not seeking a reward;
but as thyself hast lovèd me,
O ever-loving Lord.

6. So would I love thee, dearest Lord,
and in thy praise will sing;
solely because thou art my God,
and my most loving King.

Latin (17th century)
trans. Edward Caswall (1814-1878)

Adapted from an aria
in Handel's *Solomon* (1749)

TUNE 2: SOLOMON CM

459 My gracious Lord

Philip Doddridge (1702-1751) alt. Ralph Harrison (1748-1810)

2. What is my being but for thee,
its sure support, its noblest end,
thy ever-smiling face to see
and serve the cause of such a friend?

3. I would not breathe for worldly joy,
or to increase my worldly good,
nor future days or pow'rs employ
to spread a sounding name abroad;

4. But to my Saviour I would live,
to him who for my ransom died;
nor could untainted Eden give
such bliss as blossoms at his side.

5. His work my later years shall bless,
when youthful vigour is no more,
and my last hour of life confess
his love has animating pow'r.

460 My heart will sing to you *Great love*

Words and music: Robin Mark

2. When earthly wisdom dims the light of knowing you,
or if my search for understanding clouds your way,
to you I fly, my hiding-place,
where revelation is beholding face to face.

© Copyright 1996 Daybreak Music Ltd., Silverdale Road, Eastbourne, East Sussex BN20 7AB, UK.
All rights reserved. International copyright secured. Used by permission.

461 My Jesus, my Saviour *Shout to the Lord*

Words and music: Darlene Zschech

© Copyright 1993 Darlene Zschech/Hillsongs Australia/Kingsway's Thankyou Music, P.O. Box 75, Eastbourne, East Sussex BN23 6NW, UK. (tym@kingsway.co.uk). Used by permission.

462 My Lord, what love is this *Amazing love*

Words and music: Graham Kendrick (b.1950)

2. And so they watched him die,
despised, rejected;
but O, the blood he shed
flowed for me!

3. And now this love of Christ
shall flow like rivers;
come, wash your guilt away,
live again!

© Copyright 1989 Make Way Music, P.O. Box 263, Croydon, Surrey CR9 5AP, UK.
International copyright secured. All rights reserved. Used by permission.

463 My song is love unknown

Samuel Crossman (c.1624-1684) alt.

John Ireland (1879-1962)

LOVE UNKNOWN 66 66 44 44

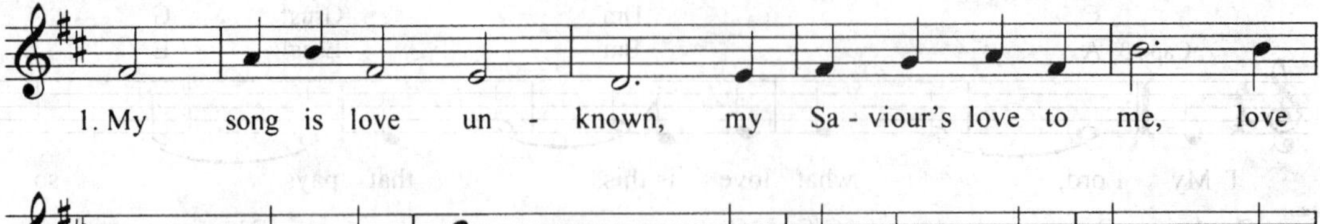

2. He came from his blest throne,
salvation to bestow;
but men refused, and none
the longed-for Christ would know.
But O, my friend, my friend indeed,
who at my need his life did spend!

3. Sometimes they strew his way,
and his sweet praises sing:
resounding all the day
hosannas to their King:
then 'Crucify!' is all their breath,
and for his death they thirst and cry.

4. Why what hath my Lord done?
What makes this rage and spite?
He made the lame to run,
he gave the blind their sight.
Sweet injuries! Yet they at these
themselves displease, and 'gainst him rise.

5. They rise, and needs will have
my dear Lord made away;
a murderer they save,
the Prince of Life they slay.
Yet cheerful he to suff'ring goes,
that he his foes from thence might free.

6. Here might I stay and sing,
no story so divine;
never was love, dear King,
never was grief like thine.
This is my friend in whose sweet praise
I all my days could gladly spend.

Music © Copyright The John Ireland Trust, 35 St Mary's Mansions, St Mary's Terrace, London W2 1SQ, UK.
Used by permission.

464 My soul, there is a country

Henry Vaughan (1622-1695)

Melody by M. Vulpius (c.1560-1615)

CHRISTUS DER IST MEIN LEBEN 76 76

2. There above noise, and danger,
sweet peace sits crowned with smiles,
and one born in a manger
commands the beauteous files.

3. He is thy gracious Friend,
and - O my soul, awake! -
did in pure love descend,
to die here for thy sake.

4. If thou canst get but thither,
there grows the flow'r of peace,
the Rose that cannot wither,
thy fortress and thy ease.

5. Leave then thy foolish ranges,
for none can thee secure,
but one who never changes,
thy God, thy life, thy cure.

465 Name of all majesty

Timothy Dudley-Smith (b.1926)

Malcolm Archer (b.1952)

NAME OF ALL MAJESTY 66 64 D

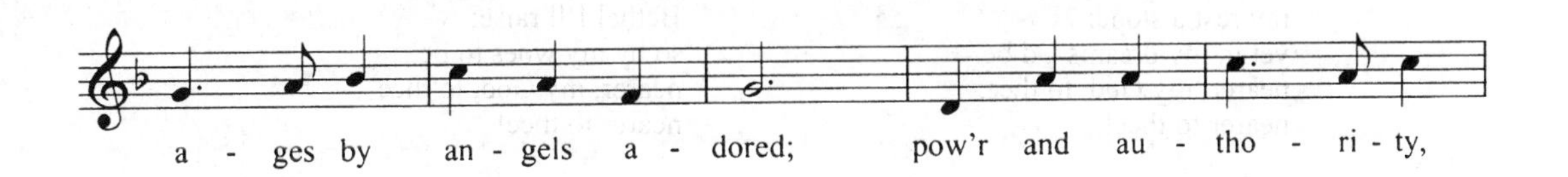

2. Child of our destiny,
God from eternity,
love of the Father
on sinners outpoured;
see now what God has done
sending his only Son,
Christ the belovéd One,
Jesus is Lord!

3. Saviour of Calvary,
costliest victory,
darkness defeated
and Eden restored;
born as a man to die,
nailed to a cross on high,
cold in the grave to lie,
Jesus is Lord!

4. Source of all sovereignty,
light, immortality,
life everlasting
and heaven assured;
so with the ransomed, we
praise him eternally,
Christ in his majesty,
Jesus is Lord!

Text © Copyright Timothy Dudley-Smith, 9 Ashlands, Ford, Salisbury, Wiltshire SP4 6DY, UK.
Used by permission. Music © Copyright 1999 Kevin Mayhew Ltd.

466 Nearer, my God, to thee

Sarah Flower Adams (1805-1848) — John Bacchus Dykes (1823-1876)

TUNE 1: HORBURY 64 64 664

2. Though, like the wanderer,
the sun gone down,
darkness be over me,
my rest a stone;
yet in my dreams I'd be
nearer, my God, to thee,
nearer to thee!

3. There let the way appear,
steps unto heav'n;
all that thou sendest me
in mercy giv'n:
angels to beckon me
nearer, my God, to thee,
nearer to thee!

4. Then, with my waking thoughts
bright with thy praise,
out of my stony griefs
Bethel I'll raise;
so by my woes to be
nearer, my God, to thee,
nearer to thee!

5. Or if on joyful wing
cleaving the sky,
sun, moon and stars forgot,
upwards I fly,
still all my song shall be,
'Nearer, my God, to thee,
nearer to thee.'

Sarah Flower Adams (1805-1848) — Arthur Seymour Sullivan (1842-1900)

TUNE 2: PROPIOR DEO 64 64 664 extended

467 New every morning is the love

John Kebe (1792-1866)
based on Lamentations 3:23

Samuel Webbe (1740-1816)

MELCOMBE LM

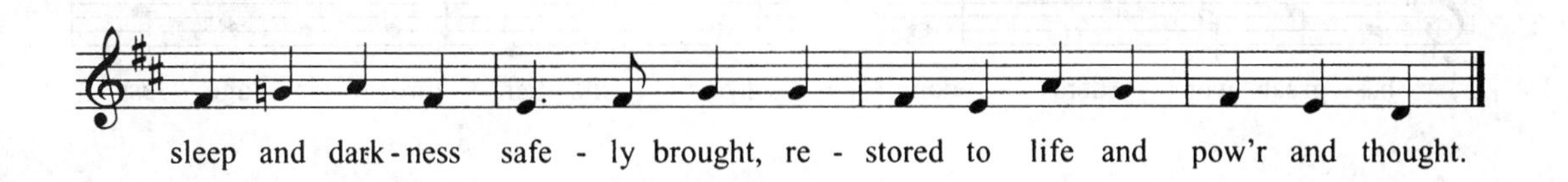

2. New mercies, each returning day,
   hover around us while we pray;
   new perils past, new sins forgiv'n,
   new thoughts of God, new hopes of heav'n.

3. If on our daily course our mind
   be set to hallow all we find,
   new treasures still, of countless price,
   God will provide for sacrifice.

4. Old friends, old scenes, will lovelier be,
   as more of heav'n in each we see;
   some soft'ning gleam of love and prayer
   shall dawn on ev'ry cross and care.

5. The trivial round, the common task,
   will furnish all we need to ask,
   room to deny ourselves, a road
   to bring us daily nearer God.

6. Only, O Lord, in thy dear love
   fit us for perfect rest above;
   and help us, this and ev'ry day,
   to live more nearly as we pray.

468 New songs of celebration render

Erik Routley (1917-1982)

Louis Bourgeois (c.1510-1561)
in the *Genevan Psalter*

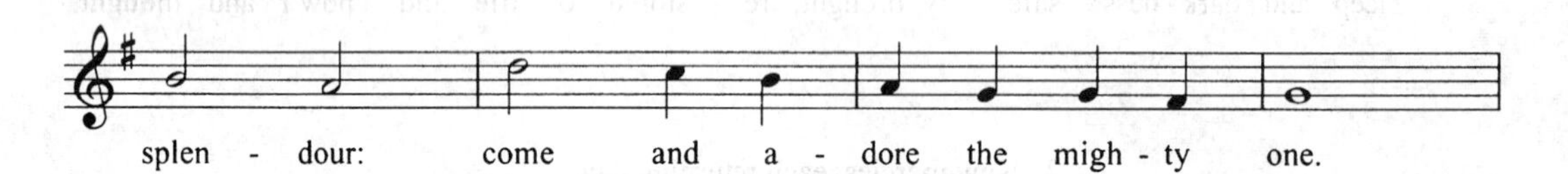

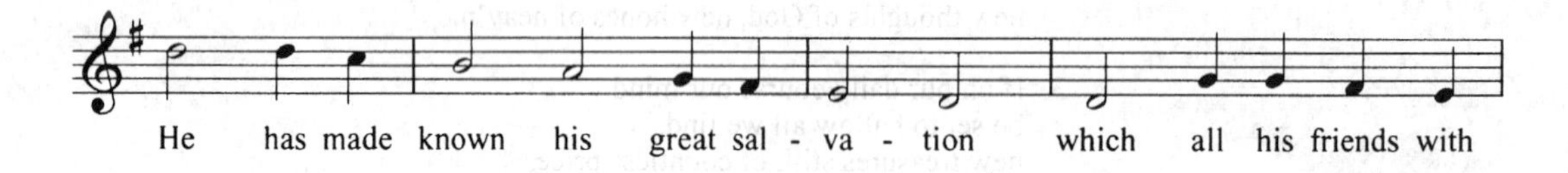

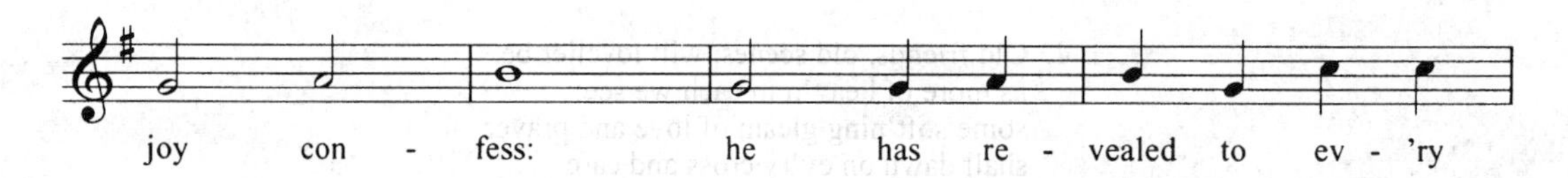

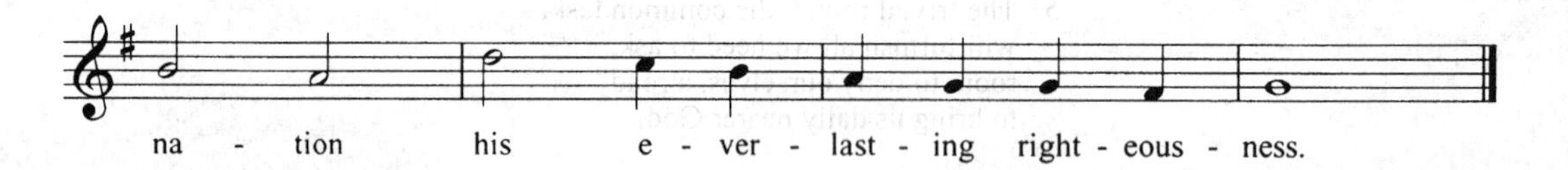

2. Joyfully, heartily resounding,
let ev'ry instrument and voice
peal out the praise of grace abounding,
calling the whole world to rejoice.
Trumpets and organs, set in motion
such sounds as make the heavens ring;
all things that live in earth and ocean,
make music for your mighty King.

3. Rivers and seas and torrents roaring,
honour the Lord with wild acclaim;
mountains and stones look up adoring
and find a voice to praise his name.
Righteous, commanding, ever glorious,
praises be his that never cease:
just is our God, whose truth victorious
establishes the world in peace.

Text © Copyright 1974 Hope Publishing Co.
Music © Copyright 1977 Hope Publishing Co. Administered by CopyCare, P.O. Box 77,
Hailsham, East Sussex BN27 3EF, UK. (music@copycare.com). Used by permission.

469 Now I know what love is

Words and music: Mike Anderson (b.1956)

2. Darkness will not hide your love,
shining like a star.

3. What could ever quench your love,
love that changes hearts.

© Copyright 1999 Kevin Mayhew Ltd.

470 Now is eternal life

George Wallace Briggs (1875-1959) alt.

Charles Steggall (1826-1905)

CHRISTCHURCH 66 66 88

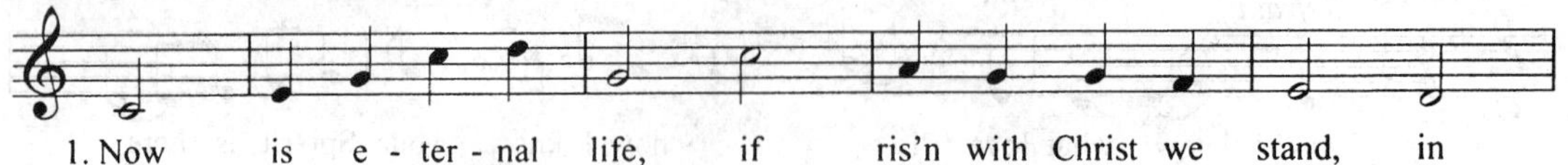

1. Now is e - ter - nal life, if ris'n with Christ we stand, in

him to life re - born, and held with - in his hand; no

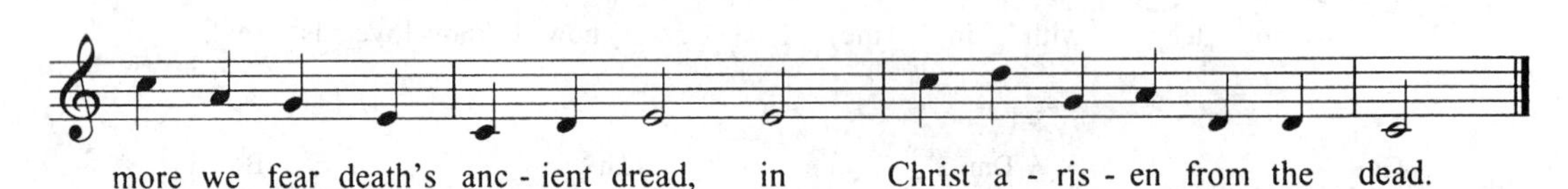

more we fear death's anc - ient dread, in Christ a - ris - en from the dead.

2. The human mind so long
brooded o'er life's brief span;
was it, O God, for naught,
for naught that life began?
Thou art our hope, our vital breath;
shall hope undying end in death?

3. And God, the living God,
stooped down to share our state;
by death destroying death,
Christ opened wide life's gate.
He lives, who died; he reigns on high;
who lives in him shall never die.

4. Unfathomed love divine,
reign thou within my heart;
from thee nor depth nor height,
nor life nor death can part;
my life is hid in God with thee,
now and through all eternity.

5. Thee will I love and serve
now in time's passing day;
thy hand shall hold me fast
when time is done away,
in God's unknown eternal spheres
to serve him through eternal years.

Text © Copyright Oxford University Press, Great Clarendon Street, Oxford OX2 6DP, UK.
Used by permission.

471 Now join we, to praise the Creator

Fred Kaan (b.1929)

Paul Bateman (b.1954)

CONWAY 98 98

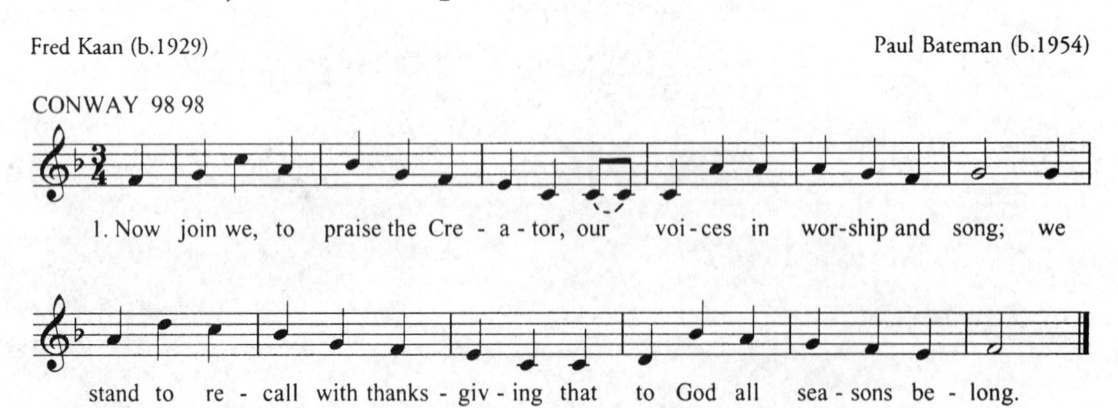

Text © Copyright 1968 Stainer & Bell Ltd., P.O. Box 110, Victoria House,
23 Gruneisen Road, Finchley, London N3 1DZ. Used by permission.
Music © Copyright Paul Bateman. Used by permission.

2. We thank you, O Source of all goodness,
for the joy and abundance of crops,
for food that is stored in our larders,
for all we can buy in the shops.

3. But also of need and starvation
we sing with concern and despair,
of skills that are used for destruction,
of land that is burnt and laid bare.

4. We cry for the plight of the hungry
while harvests are left on the field,
for orchards neglected and wasting,
for produce from markets withheld.

5. The song grows in depth and in wideness;
the earth and its people are one.
There can be no thanks without giving,
no words without deeds that are done.

6. Then teach us, O God of the harvest,
to be humble in all that we claim,
to share what we have with the nations,
to care for the world in your name.

472 Now let us from this table rise

Fred Kaan (b.1929)

Traditional Swiss melody

2. With minds alert, upheld by grace,
to spread the Word in speech and deed,
we follow in the steps of Christ,
at one with all in hope and need.

3. To fill each human house with love,
it is the sacrament of care;
the work that Christ began to do
we humbly pledge ourselves to share.

4. Then give us courage, living God,
to choose again the pilgrim way,
and help us to accept with joy
the challenge of tomorrow's day.

Text © Copyright 1968 Stainer & Bell Ltd., P.O. Box 110, Victoria House, 23 Gruneisen Road, Finchley, London N3 1DZ. Used by permission.

473 Now, my tongue, the mystery telling

St Thomas Aquinas (1227-1274)
trans. John Mason Neale (1818-1866),
Edward Caswall (1814-1878) and others

Plainsong mode iii

TUNE 1: PANGE LINGUA 87 87 87

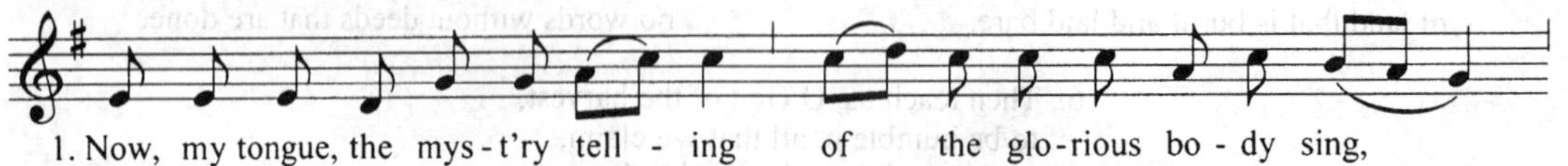

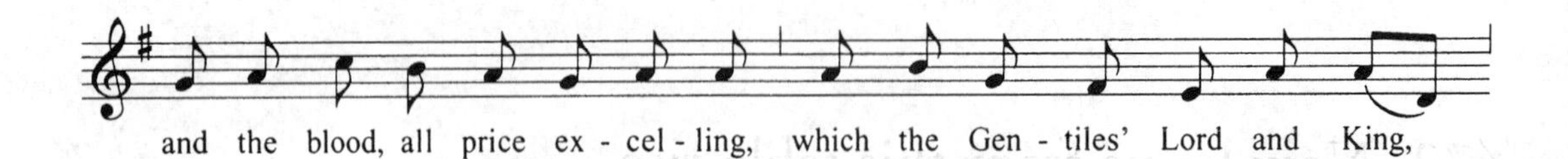

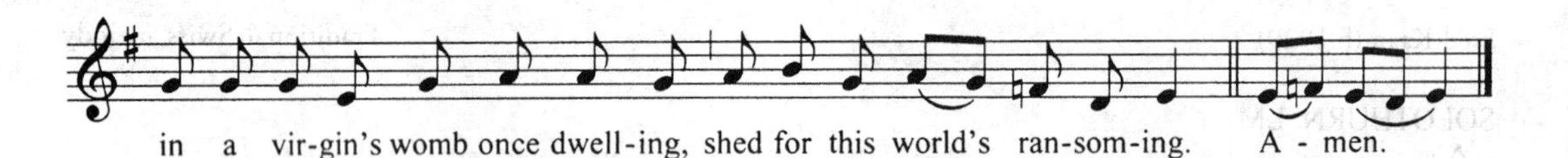

2. Giv'n for us, for us descending
of a virgin to proceed,
he, with us in converse blending,
scattered here the gospel seed,
till his sojourn drew to ending
which he closed with wondrous deed.

3. At the last great supper lying,
circled by his chosen band,
meekly with the law complying,
first he finished its command.
Then, immortal food supplying,
gave himself with his own hand.

4. Word made flesh, by word he maketh
very bread his flesh to be;
we, in wine, Christ's blood partaketh,
and if senses fail to see,
faith alone the true heart waketh,
to behold the mystery.

PART TWO

5. Therefore we, before him bending,
this great sacrament revere:
types and shadows have their ending,
for the newer rite is here;
faith, our outward sense befriending,
makes our inward vision clear.

6. Glory let us give and blessing
to the Father and the Son,
honour, might and praise addressing,
while eternal ages run;
ever too his love confessing,
who, from both, with both is one.
(Amen.)

St Thomas Aquinas (1227-1274)
trans. John Mason Neale (1818-1866),
Edward Caswall (1814-1878) and others

French melody (1881)

TUNE 2: TANTUM ERGO (GRAFTON) 87 87 87

474 Now thank we all our God

Nun danket alle Gott
by Martin Rinkart (1586-1649)
trans. Catherine Winkworth (1827-1878)

Melody by Johann Crüger (1598-1662)

TUNE 1: NUN DANKET 67 67 66 66

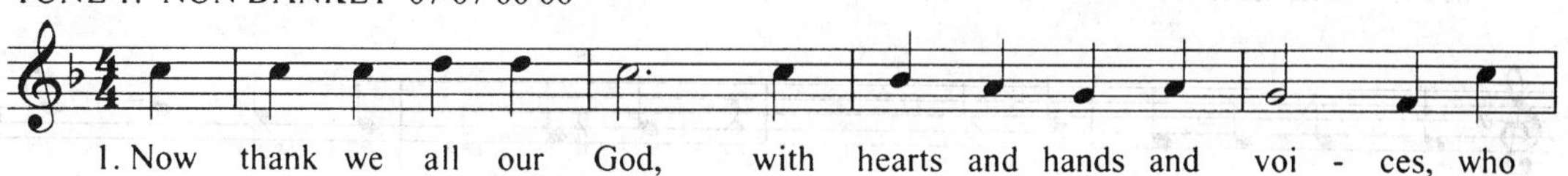

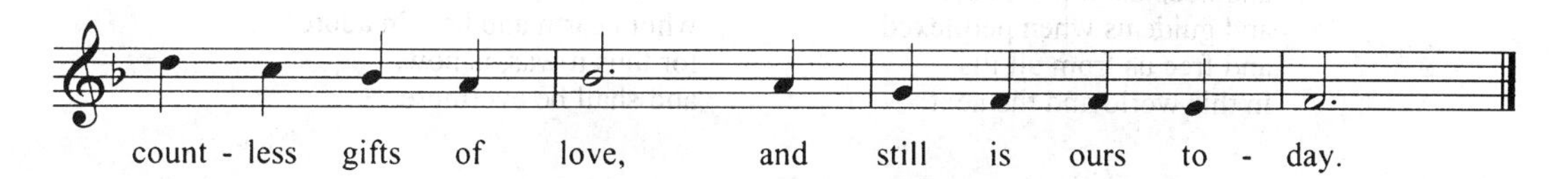

2. O may this bounteous God
through all our life be near us,
with ever joyful hearts
and blessèd peace to cheer us;
and keep us in his grace,
and guide us when perplexed,
and free us from all ills
in this world and the next.

3. All praise and thanks to God
the Father now be given,
the Son and him who reigns
with them in highest heaven,
the one eternal God,
whom earth and heav'n adore;
for thus it was, is now,
and shall be evermore.

Tune 2 will be found overleaf

Tune 2: Music © Copyright 1965 W. Paxton & Co. Ltd., 8/9 Frith Street,
London W1D 3JB. All rights reserved. Used by permission.

Nun danket alle Gott
by Martin Rinkart (1586-1649)
trans. Catherine Winkworth (1827-1878)

Geoffrey Beaumont (1903-1970)

TUNE 2: GRACIAS 67 67 66 66

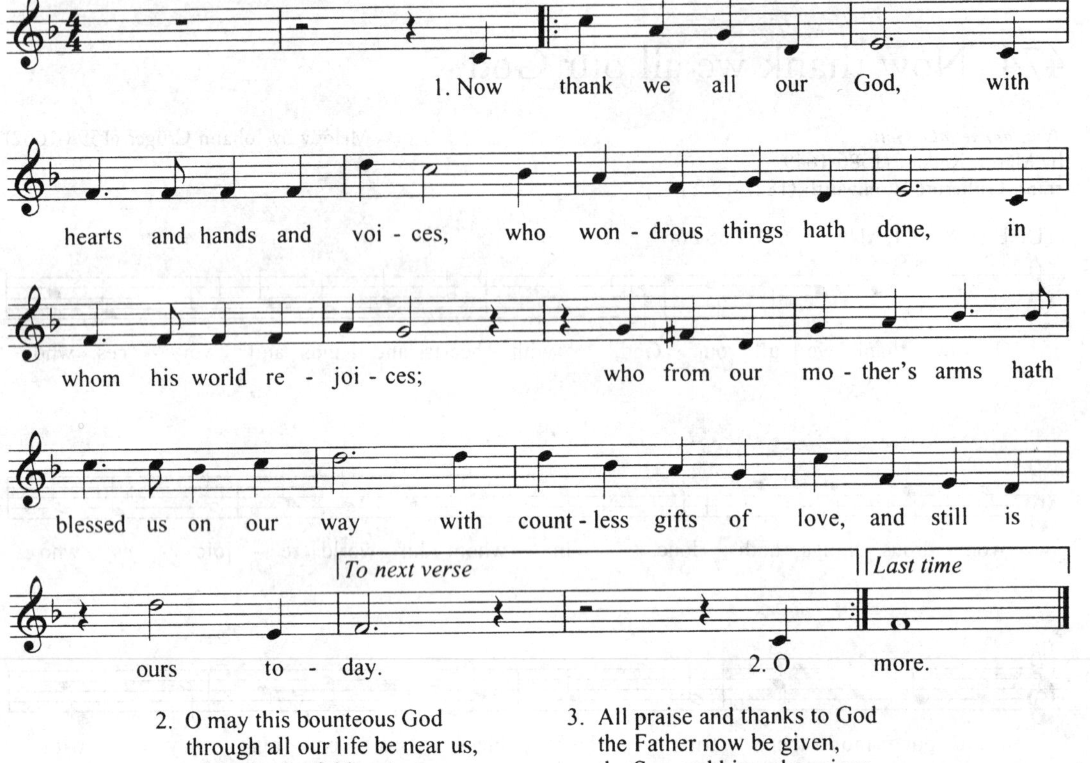

2. O may this bounteous God
through all our life be near us,
with ever joyful hearts
and blessèd peace to cheer us;
and keep us in his grace,
and guide us when perplexed,
and free us from all ills
in this world and the next.

3. All praise and thanks to God
the Father now be given,
the Son and him who reigns
with them in highest heaven,
the one eternal God,
whom earth and heav'n adore;
for thus it was, is now,
and shall be evermore.

475 Now the green blade riseth

John Macleod Campbell Crum (1872-1958) alt.

Traditional French melody

NOEL NOUVELET 11 11 10 11

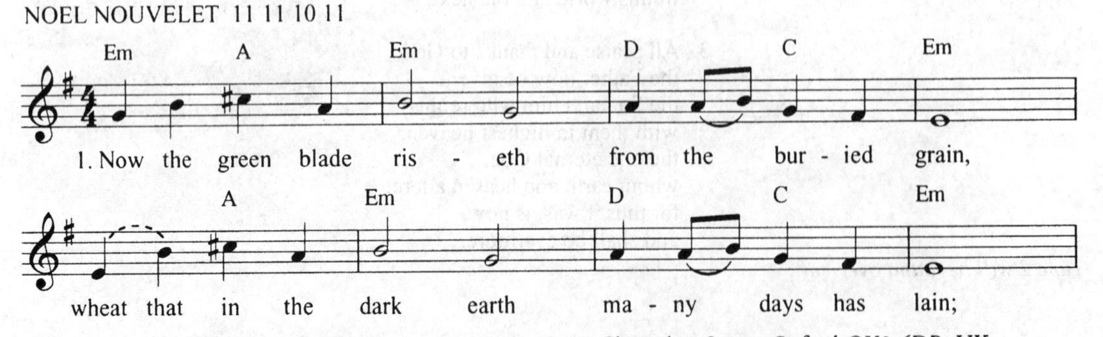

Text © Copyright 1928 Oxford University Press, Great Clarendon Street, Oxford OX2 6DP, UK.
Used by permission from *The Oxford Book of Carols*.

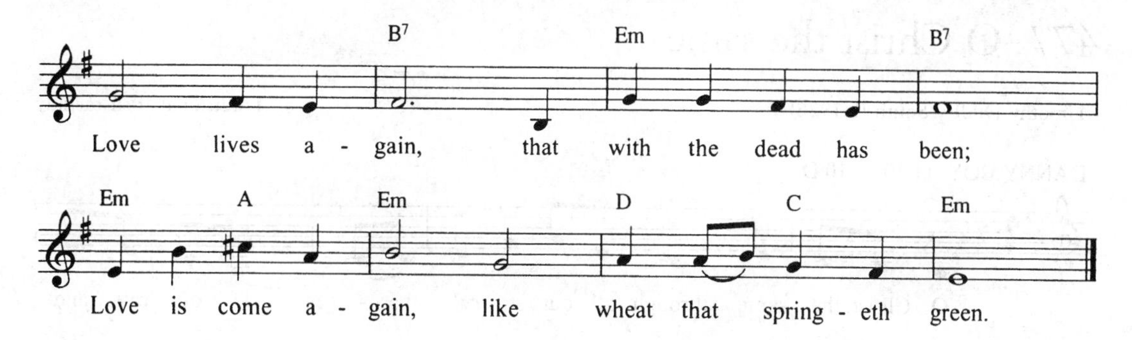

2. In the grave they laid him, Love by hatred slain,
thinking that never he would wake again,
laid in the earth like grain that sleeps unseen:
Love is come again, like wheat that springeth green.

3. Forth he came at Easter, like the risen grain,
he that for three days in the grave had lain;
quick from the dead, my risen Lord is seen:
Love is come again, like wheat that springeth green.

4. When our hearts are wintry, grieving or in pain,
thy touch can call us back to life again;
fields of our hearts, that dead and bare have been:
Love is come again, like wheat that springeth green.

476 O Breath of Life

Elizabeth Ann Porter Head (1850-1936) | Mary Jane Hammond (1878-1964)

SPIRITUS VITAE 98 98

Church with life and pow'r; O Breath of Life, come cleanse, re -

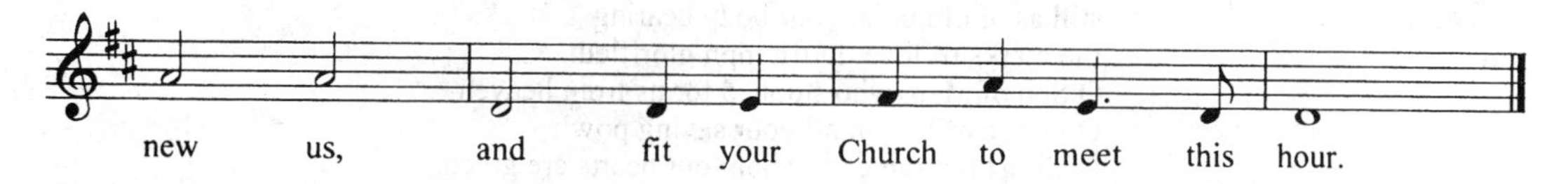

2. O Breath of Love, come breathe within us,
renewing thought and will and heart;
come, love of Christ, afresh to win us,
revive your Church in ev'ry part!

3. O Wind of God, come bend us, break us,
till humbly we confess our need;
then, in your tenderness remake us,
revive, restore – for this we plead.

4. Revive us, Lord; is zeal abating
while harvest fields are vast and white?
Revive us, Lord, the world is waiting –
equip thy Church to spread the light.

© Copyright Control.

477 O Christ the same

Timothy Dudley-Smith (b.1926) | Traditional Irish melody

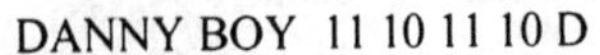

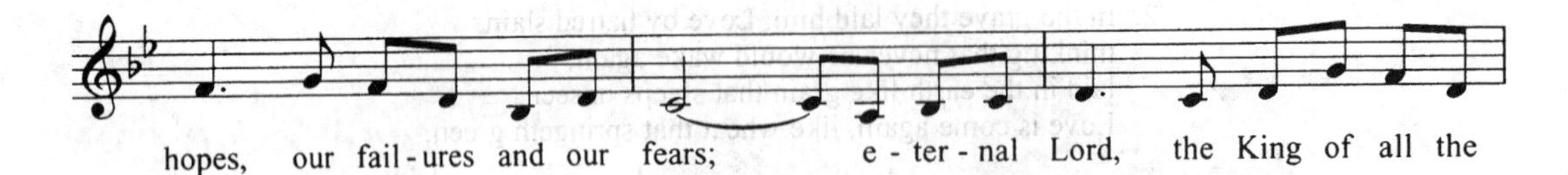

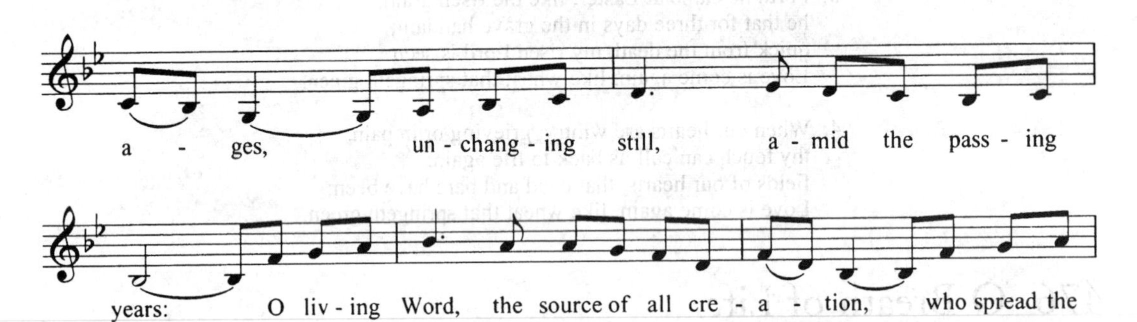

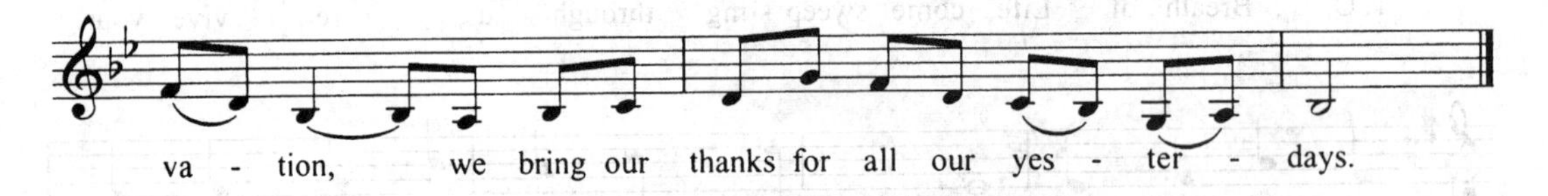

2. O Christ the same, the friend of sinners, sharing
our inmost thoughts, the secrets none can hide,
still as of old upon your body bearing
the marks of love, in triumph glorified:
O Son of Man, who stooped for us from heaven,
O Prince of life, in all your saving pow'r,
O Christ the same, to whom our hearts are given,
we bring our thanks for this the present hour.

3. O Christ the same, secure within whose keeping
our lives and loves, our days and years remain,
our work and rest, our waking and our sleeping,
our calm and storm, our pleasure and our pain:
O Lord of love, for all our joys and sorrows,
for all our hopes, when earth shall fade and flee,
O Christ the same, for all our brief tomorrows,
we bring our thanks for all that is to be.

Text © Copyright Timothy Dudley-Smith, 9 Ashlands, Ford, Salisbury, Wiltshire SP4 6DY, UK.
Used by permission.

478 O Christ, who art the Light and Day

Latin (6th century)
trans. William Copeland (1804-1887) and others

Plainsong mode ii

CHRISTE QUI LUX LM

2. All-holy Lord, we pray to thee,
keep us to-night from danger free;
grant us, dear Lord, in thee to rest,
so be our sleep in quiet blest.

3. And while the eyes soft slumber take,
still be the heart to thee awake;
be thy right hand upheld above
thy servants resting in thy love.

4. O strong defender, be thou nigh
to bid the pow'rs of darkness fly;
keep us from sin, and guide for good
thy servants purchased by the blood.

5. Remember us, dear Lord, we pray
while in this mortal flesh we stay:
'tis thou who dost the soul defend —
be present with us to the end.

6. Blest Three in One and One in Three,
almighty God, we pray to thee
that thou wouldst now vouchsafe to bless
our fast with fruits of righteousness.
Amen.

479 O come, all ye faithful

Original Latin attributed to John Francis Wade
trans. Frederick Oakeley (1802-1880)

Attributed to John Francis Wade (1711-1786)

ADESTE FIDELES Irregular and Refrain

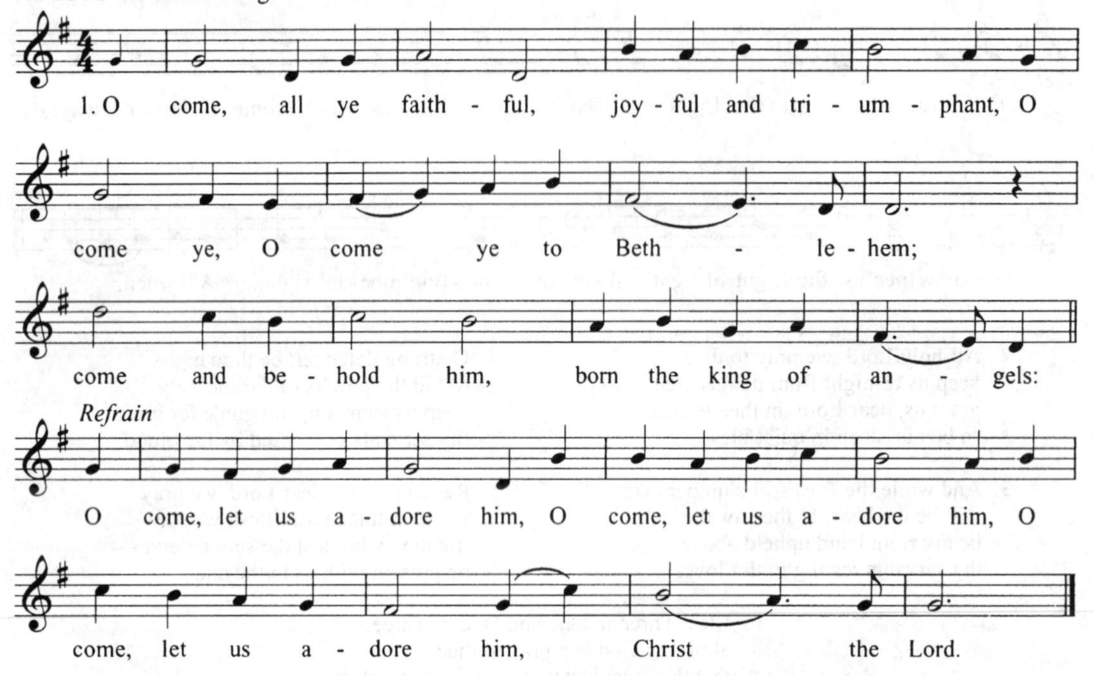

2. God of God,
Light of Light,
lo, he abhors not the Virgin's womb;
very God, begotten not created:

3. See how the shepherds,
summoned to his cradle,
leaving their flocks, draw nigh with lowly fear;
we too will thither bend our joyful footsteps:

4. Lo, star-led chieftains,
Magi, Christ adoring,
offer him incense, gold and myrrh;
we to the Christ-child bring our hearts' oblations:

5. Child, for us sinners
poor and in the manger,
fain we embrace thee, with love and awe;
who would not love thee, loving us so dearly?

6. Sing, choirs of angels,
sing in exultation,
sing, all ye citizens of heav'n above;
glory to God in the highest:

7. Yea, Lord, we greet thee,
born this happy morning,
Jesu, to thee be glory giv'n;
Word of the Father, now in flesh appearing:

480 O come, O come, Emmanuel

From the *Great O Antiphons* (12th-13th century)
trans. John Mason Neale (1818-1866)

Adapted by Thomas Helmore (1811-1890)
from a French Missal

VENI EMMANUEL LM and Refrain

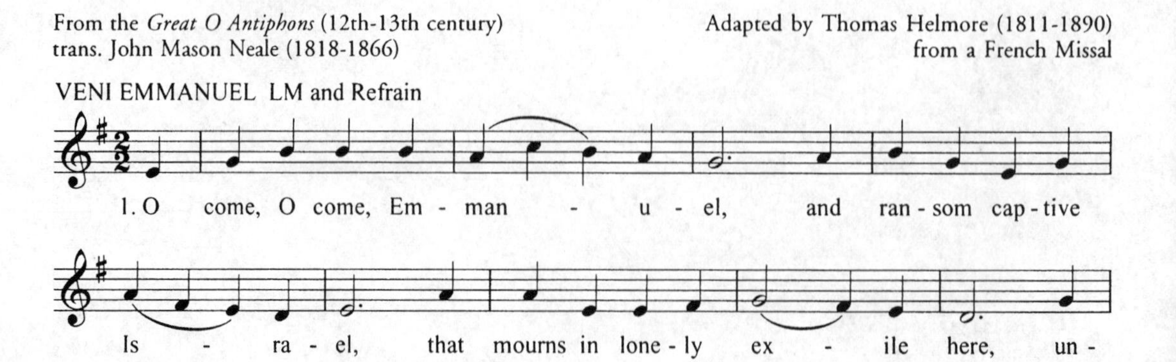

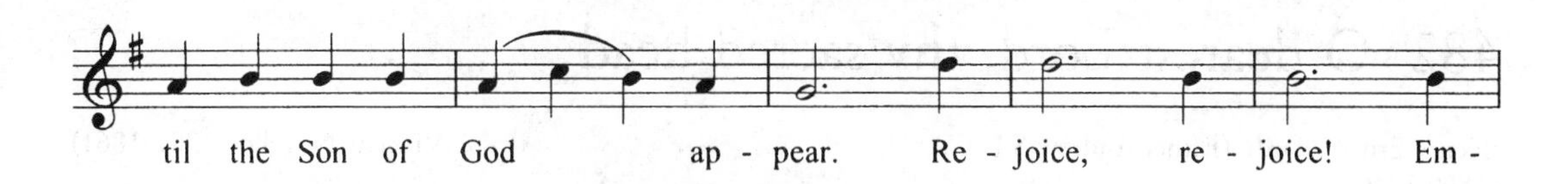

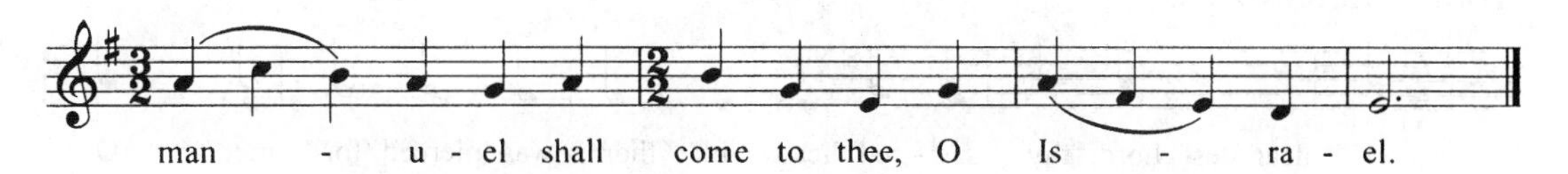

2. O come, thou rod of Jesse, free
thine own from Satan's tyranny;
from depths of hell thy people save,
and give them vict'ry o'er the grave.

3. O come, thou dayspring, come and cheer
our spirits by thine advent here;
disperse the gloomy clouds of night,
and death's dark shadows put to flight.

4. O come, thou key of David, come
and open wide our heav'nly home;
make safe the way that leads on high,
and close the path to misery.

5. O come, O come, thou Lord of might,
who to thy tribes on Sinai's height
in ancient times didst give the Law,
in cloud and majesty and awe.

481 O comfort my people

Chrysogonus Waddell
based on Isaiah 40

Traditional Irish melody

COMFORT 11 11 11 11

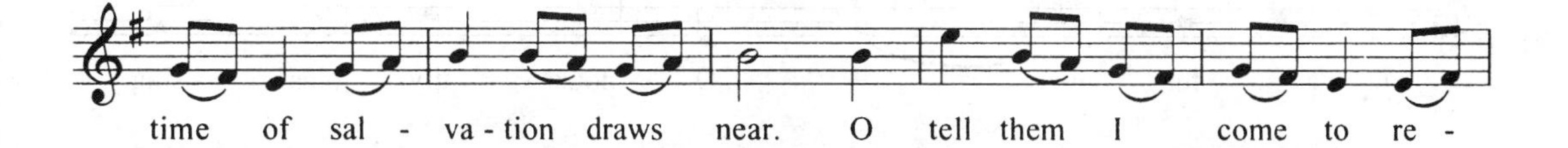

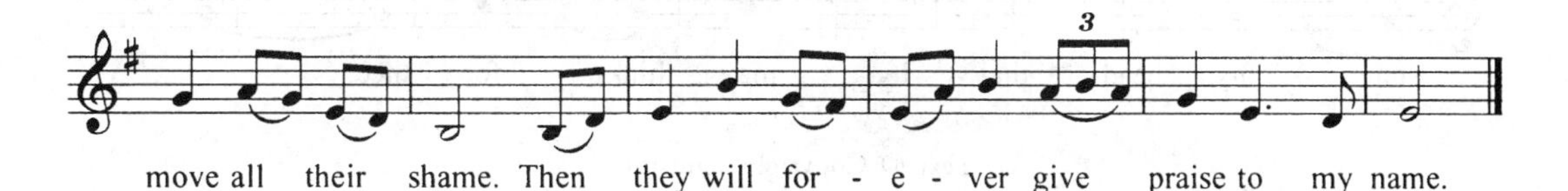

2. Proclaim to the cities
of Judah my word;
that 'gentle yet strong
is the hand of the Lord.
I rescue the captives,
my people defend,
and bring them to justice
and joy without end.'

3. 'All mountains and hills
shall become as a plain,
for vanished are mourning
and hunger and pain.
And never again shall
these war against you.
Behold I come quickly
to make all things new.'

Text © Copyright Chrysogonus Waddell.

482 O dearest Lord, thy sacred head

Henry Ernest Hardy (Father Andrew S.D.C.) (1869-1946) | Vincent Novello (1781-1861)

TUNE 1: ALBANO CM

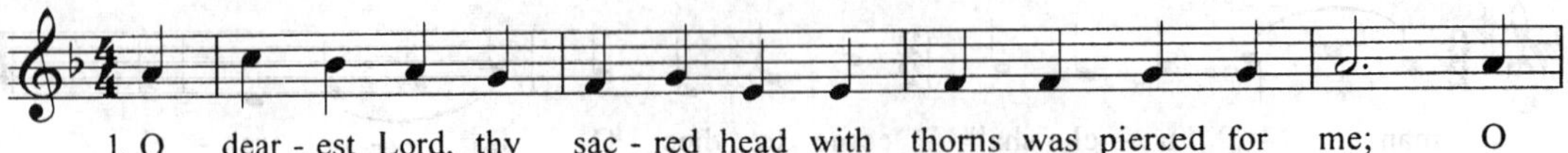

2. O dearest Lord, thy sacred hands
with nails were pierced for me;
O shed thy blessing on my hands
that they may work for thee.

3. O dearest Lord, thy sacred feet
with nails were pierced for me;
O pour thy blessing on my feet
that they may follow thee.

4. O dearest Lord, thy sacred heart
with spear was pierced for me;
O pour thy Spirit in my heart
that I may live for thee.

Henry Ernest Hardy (Father Andrew S.D.C.) (1869-1946) | Adapted from William Gardiner's *Sacred Melodies* (1812)

TUNE 2: BELMONT CM

Text © Copyright Control.

483 O for a closer walk with God

William Cowper (1731-1800) | Charles Hutcheson (1792-1860)

TUNE 1: STRACATHRO CM

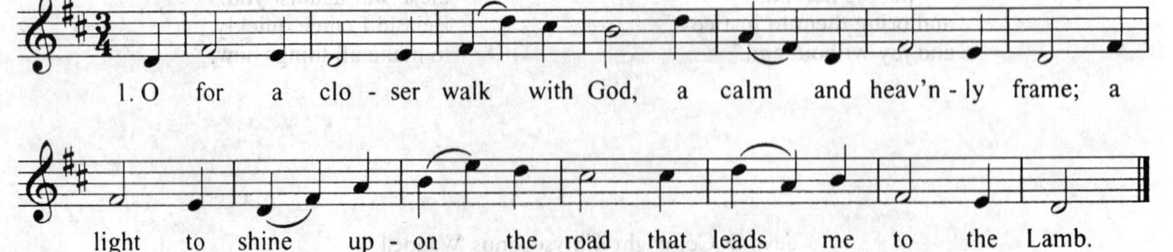

2. What peaceful hours I once enjoyed,
how sweet their mem'ry still!
But they have left an aching void
the world can never fill.

3. The dearest idol I have known,
whate'er that idol be,
help me to tear it from thy throne,
and worship only thee.

4. So shall my walk be close with God,
calm and serene my frame;
so purer light shall mark the road
that leads me to the Lamb.

William Cowper (1731-1800)

Melody from the *Scottish Psalter* (1635)

TUNE 2: CAITHNESS CM

484 O for a heart to praise my God

Charles Wesley (1707-1788)

Thomas Wright (1763-1829)

STOCKTON CM

2. A heart resigned, submissive, meek,
my great Redeemer's throne;
where only Christ is heard to speak,
where Jesus reigns alone.

3. A humble, lowly, contrite heart,
believing, true and clean,
which neither life nor death can part
from him that dwells within.

4. A heart in ev'ry thought renewed,
and full of love divine;
perfect and right and pure and good –
a copy, Lord, of thine.

5. Thy nature, gracious Lord, impart,
come quickly from above;
write thy new name upon my heart,
thy new best name of love.

485 O for a thousand tongues to sing

Charles Wesley (1707-1788)

Thomas Jarman (1776-1861)

TUNE 1: LYNGHAM 86 86 extended

2. Jesus! the name that charms our fears,
that bids our sorrows cease,
that bids our sorrows cease;
'tis music in the sinner's ears,
'tis life and health and peace. *(x3)*

3. He breaks the pow'r of cancelled sin,
he sets the pris'ner free,
he sets the pris'ner free;
his blood can make the foulest clean;
his blood availed for me. *(x3)*

4. He speaks; and, list'ning to his voice,
new life the dead receive,
new life the dead receive,
the mournful broken hearts rejoice,
the humble poor believe. *(x3)*

5. Hear him, ye deaf; his praise, ye dumb,
your loosened tongues employ,
your loosened tongues employ;
ye blind, behold your Saviour come;
and leap, ye lame, for joy! *(x3)*

6. My gracious Master and my God,
assist me to proclaim,
assist me to proclaim
and spread through all the earth abroad
the honours of thy name. *(x3)*

Charles Wesley (1707-1788)

Possibly by George Coombes (d.1769)
from Isaac Smith's *Psalmody* (1770)

TUNE 2: OXFORD NEW CM

2. Jesus! the name that charms our fears,
that bids our sorrows cease;
'tis music in the sinner's ears,
'tis life and health and peace.

3. He breaks the pow'r of cancelled sin,
he sets the pris'ner free;
his blood can make the foulest clean;
his blood availed for me.

4. He speaks; and, list'ning to his voice,
new life the dead receive,
the mournful broken hearts rejoice,
the humble poor believe,

5. Hear him, ye deaf; his praise, ye dumb,
your loosened tongues employ;
ye blind, behold your Saviour come;
and leap, ye lame, for joy!

6. My gracious Master and my God,
assist me to proclaim
and spread through all the earth abroad
the honours of thy name.

Charles Wesley (1707-1788)

Alfred James Eyre (1853-1919)

TUNE 3: SELBY CM

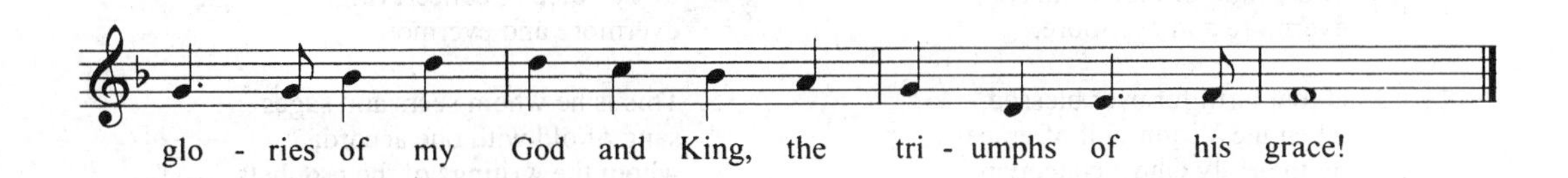

486 Of the Father's love begotten

Corde natus ex parentis by
Aurelius Clemens Prudentius (348-413)
trans. John Mason Neale (1818-1866) alt.

Plainsong melody (13th century)
adapted by Theodoricus Petrus
in *Piae Cantiones* (1582)

CORDE NATUS (DIVINUM MYSTERIUM) 87 87 87 7

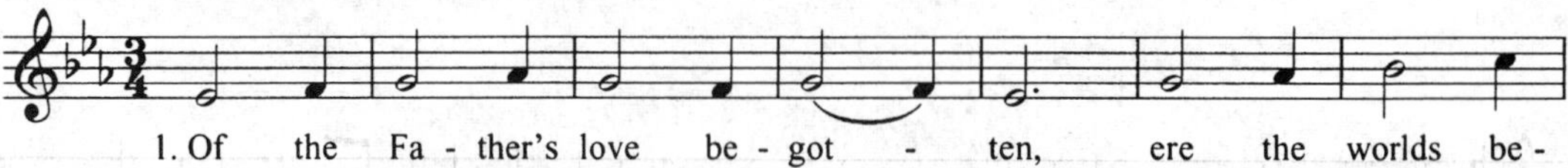

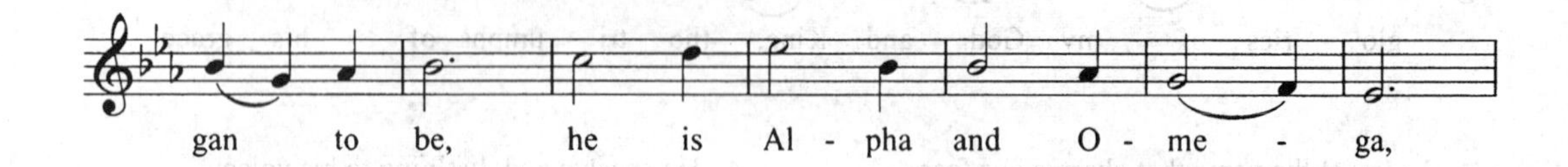

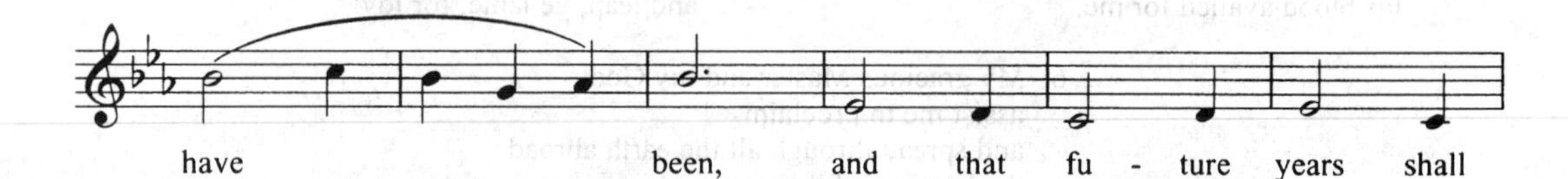

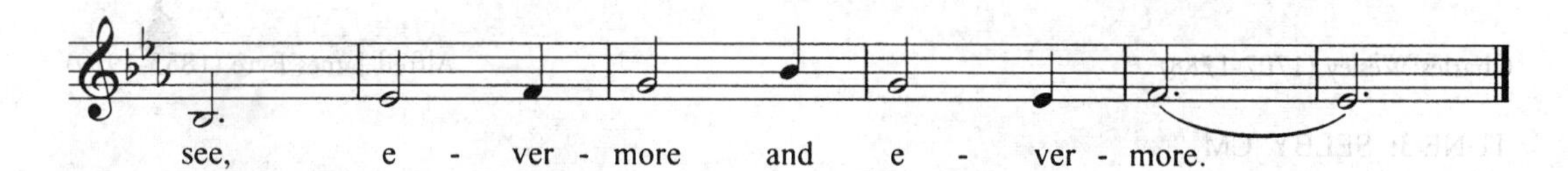

2. At his word they were created;
he commanded; it was done:
heav'n and earth and depths of ocean
in their threefold order one;
all that grows beneath the shining
of the light of moon and sun,
evermore and evermore.

3. O that birth for ever blessèd,
when the Virgin, full of grace,
by the Holy Ghost conceiving,
bore the Saviour of our race,
and the babe, the world's Redeemer,
first revealed his sacred face,
evermore and evermore.

4. O ye heights of heav'n, adore him;
angel hosts, his praises sing;
pow'rs, dominions, bow before him,
and extol our God and King:
let no tongue on earth be silent,
ev'ry voice in concert ring,
evermore and evermore.

5. This is he whom seers and sages
sang of old with one accord;
whom the writings of the prophets
promised in their faithful word;
now he shines, the long-expected;
let our songs declare his worth,
evermore and evermore.

6. Christ, to thee, with God the Father,
and, O Holy Ghost, to thee,
hymn and chant and high thanksgiving,
and unwearied praises be;
honour, glory, and dominion,
and eternal victory,
evermore and evermore.

487 Oft in danger, oft in woe

Henry Kirke White (1785-1806)
and others

Henry John Gauntlett (1805-1876)

UNIVERSITY COLLEGE 77 77

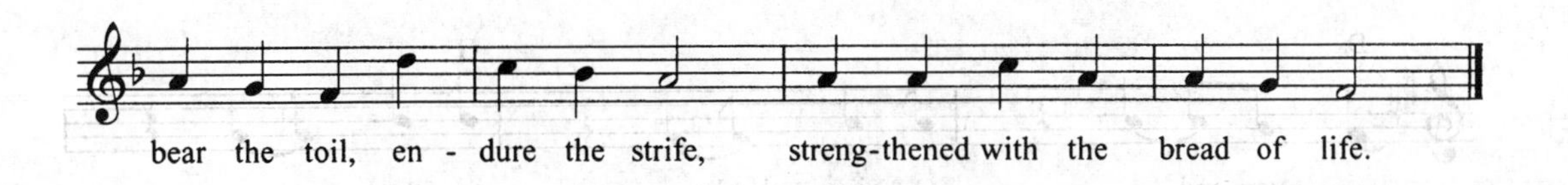

2. Onward through the desert night,
keeping faith and vision bright;
face the challenge of the hour
trusting in your Saviour's pow'r.

3. Let not sorrow dim your eye,
soon shall ev'ry tear be dry;
let not fears your course impede,
great your strength if great your need.

4. Let your drooping heart be glad;
march in faith and honour clad;
march, nor think the journey long,
march to hope's eternal song.

5. Onward then, undaunted, move;
more than faithful God will prove;
though the raging waters flow,
Christian pilgrims, onward go.

488 O give thanks

Words and music: Graham Kendrick (b.1950)

2. Give him thanks for the fruitful earth,
for the sun, the seasons, the rain.
For the joys of his good creation,
the life and breath he sustains.

3. Let the heavens rejoice before him,
the earth and all it contains.
All creation in jubilation,
join in the shout, 'The Lord reigns!'

4. Let the hearts of those who seek him
be happy now in his love.
Let their faces look up and gaze
at his gracious smile from above.

© Copyright 1991 Make Way Music, P.O. Box 263, Croydon, Surrey CR9 5AP, UK.
International copyright secured. All rights reserved. Used by permission.

489 O God beyond all praising

Michael Perry (1942-1996)

Gustav Holst (1874-1934)

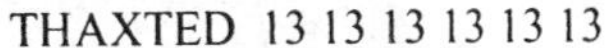

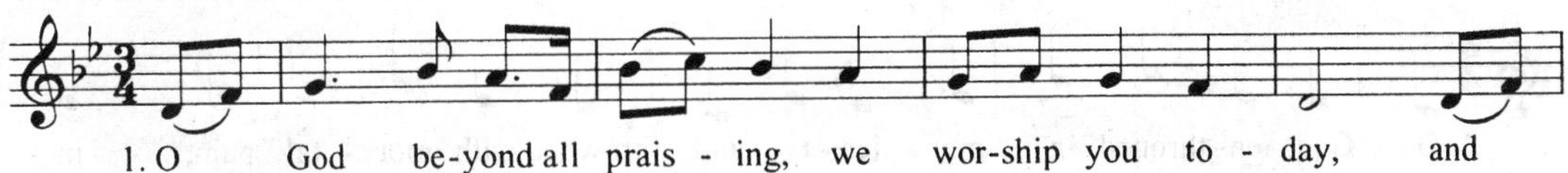

2. Then hear, O gracious Saviour,
accept the love we bring,
that we who know your favour
may serve you as our King;
and whether our tomorrows
be filled with good or ill,
we'll triumph through our sorrows
and rise to bless you still:
to marvel at your beauty
and glory in your ways,
and make a joyful duty
our sacrifice of praise.

Text © Copyright Mrs. B. Perry/Jubilate Hymns, 4 Thorne Park Road, Chelston,
Torquay TQ2 5RX. Used by permission.
Music © Copyright Control.

490 O God, enthroned in majesty

Michael Forster (b.1946) John Marsh (b.1939)

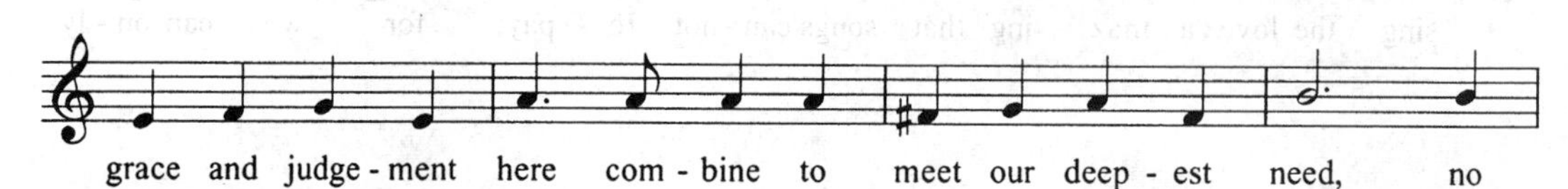

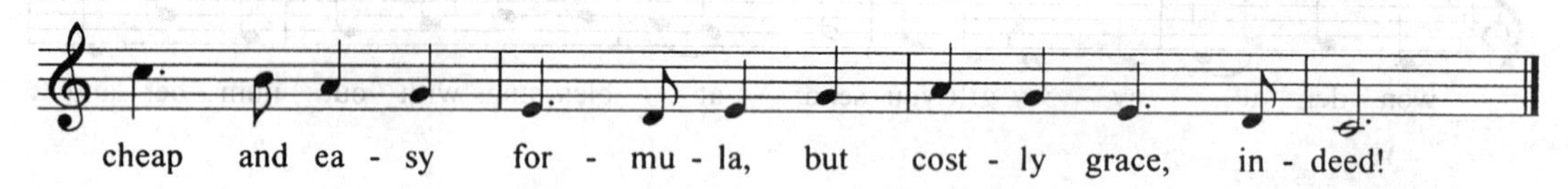

2. Confronted by the awesome truth,
we shrink away in fear:
all sin is death, the cross proclaims,
and none stands blameless here.
Yet through the pain, amazing love
assures us of your grace,
and gives us courage to return
and stand before your face.

3. Now give us grace to stand beneath
the crosses of the world,
that all may judge the power of sin,
yet see your love unfurled.
Let no more lives be crucified
by poverty or war,
but grace and judgement, hand in hand,
unite to cry, 'No more!'

4. Then let the world be freed from fear
to seek love's open way,
to journey from untimely night
toward a greater day:
to justice, hope and liberty,
the kingdom of your choice,
when all our praise is gathered up
in one united voice.

© Copyright 1999 Kevin Mayhew Ltd.

491 O God of Bethel, by whose hand

Philip Doddridge (1702-1751) and John Logan (1748-1788) alt. Hugh Wilson (1766-1824)

TUNE 1: MARTYRDOM CM

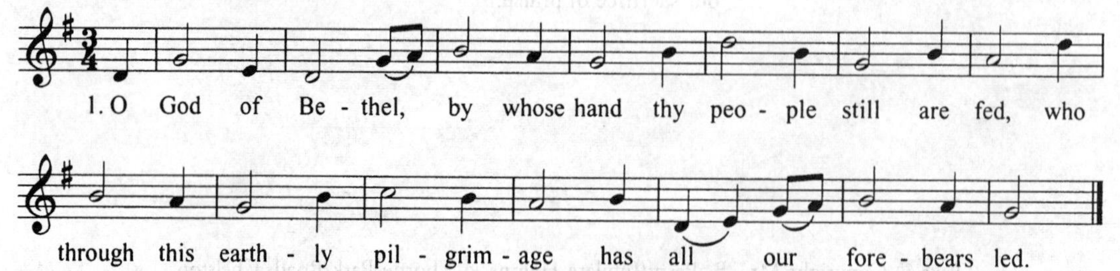

2. Our vows, our prayers, we now present
before thy throne of grace;
God of our forebears, be the God
of their succeeding race.

3. Through each mysterious path of life
be thou our constant guide;
give us each day our daily bread,
and raiment fit provide.

4. O spread thy cov'ring wings around,
till all our journeys cease,
and at our Father's loved abode
our souls arrive in peace.

Philip Doddridge (1702-1751) and
John Logan (1748-1788) alt.

From *Chetham's Psalmody* (1718)

TUNE 2: BURFORD CM

492 O God of earth and altar

Gilbert Keith Chesterton (1874-1936)

Traditional English melody collected
by Ralph Vaughan Williams (1872-1958)

TUNE 1: KING'S LYNN 76 76 D

2. From all that terror teaches,
from lies of tongue and pen,
from all the easy speeches
that comfort cruel men,
from sale and profanation
of honour and the sword,
from sleep and from damnation,
deliver us, good Lord!

3. Tie in a living tether
the prince and priest and thrall,
bind all our lives together,
smite us and save us all;
in ire and exultation
aflame with faith and free,
lift up a living nation,
a single sword to thee.

Tune 2 will be found overleaf

© Copyright Oxford University Press, Great Clarendon Street, Oxford OX2 6DP, UK.
Used by permission from the *English Hymnal.*

Gilbert Keith Chesterton (1874-1936) Robert Lucas de Pearsall (1795-1856)

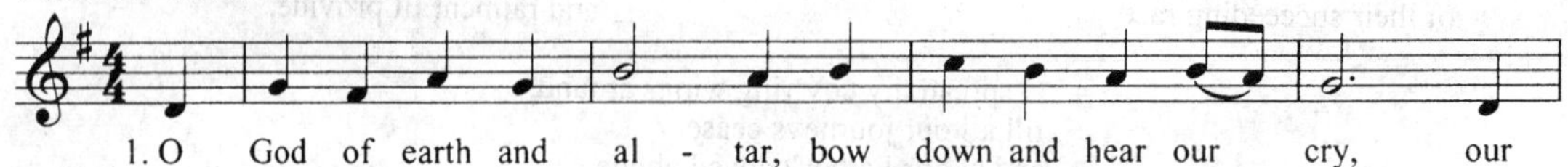

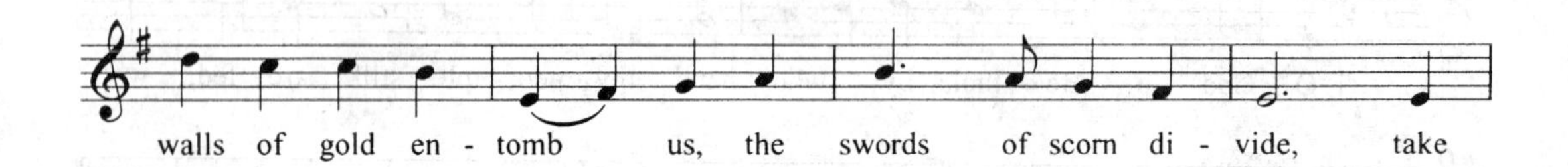

2. From all that terror teaches,
from lies of tongue and pen,
from all the easy speeches
that comfort cruel men,
from sale and profanation
of honour and the sword,
from sleep and from damnation,
deliver us, good Lord!

3. Tie in a living tether
the prince and priest and thrall,
bind all our lives together,
smite us and save us all;
in ire and exultation
aflame with faith and free,
lift up a living nation,
a single sword to thee.

493 O God of hope

Basil E. Bridge (b.1927) Charles Hubert Hastings Parry (1848-1918)

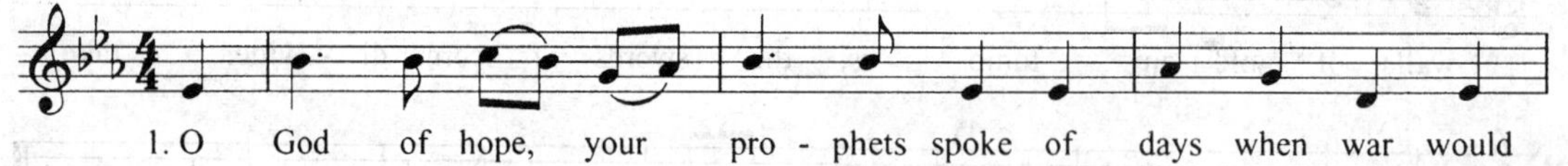

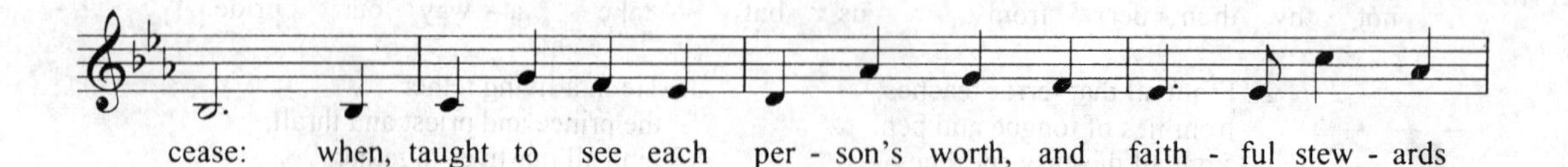

Text © Copyright 1999 Kevin Mayhew Ltd.

2. We pray that our divided world
may hear their words anew:
then lift for good the curse of war,
let bread with justice bless the poor,
and turn in hope to you.

3. Earth's fragile web of life demands
our reverence and our care,
lest in our folly, sloth and greed,
deaf both to you and others' need,
we lay our planet bare.

4. Earth's rich resources give us power
to build or to destroy:
your Spirit urges us to turn
from selfish, fear-bound ways, and learn
his selfless trust and joy.

5. The Prince of Peace is calling us
to shun the way of strife:
he brings us healing through his pain;
our shattered hope is born again
through his victorious life.

494 O God, our help in ages past

Isaac Watts (1674-1748) alt. William Croft (1678-1727)

ST ANNE CM

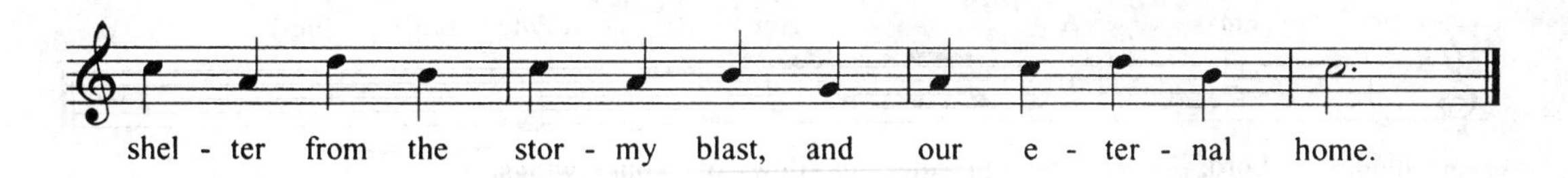

2. Beneath the shadow of thy throne,
thy saints have dwelt secure;
sufficient is thine arm alone,
and our defence is sure.

3. Before the hills in order stood,
or earth received her frame,
from everlasting thou art God,
to endless years the same.

4. A thousand ages in thy sight
are like an evening gone;
short as the watch that ends the night
before the rising sun.

5. Time, like an ever-rolling stream,
will bear us all away;
we fade and vanish, as a dream
dies at the op'ning day.

6. O God, our help in ages past,
our hope for years to come,
be thou our guard while troubles last,
and our eternal home.

495 O God, please listen

In the shadow of your wings

Frances M. Kelly
based on Psalm 95

Frances M. Kelly

2. If only I had wings to fly I would escape, Lord:
I'd fly as far as I could go to find some peace of mind.

3. I feel defeated by life's trials and disappointments.
My days and nights are spent in fear, with no one I can trust.

4. But all of this I can survive if you are with me:
my life is here, my life is now, and I must carry on.

5. Within the shadow of your wings I find my refuge.
You are the only one I have; I count on you, O Lord.

© Copyright 1999 Kevin Mayhew Ltd.

496 O God, unseen but ever near

Edward Osler (1798-1863)

From *Day's Psalter* (1562)

ST FLAVIAN CM

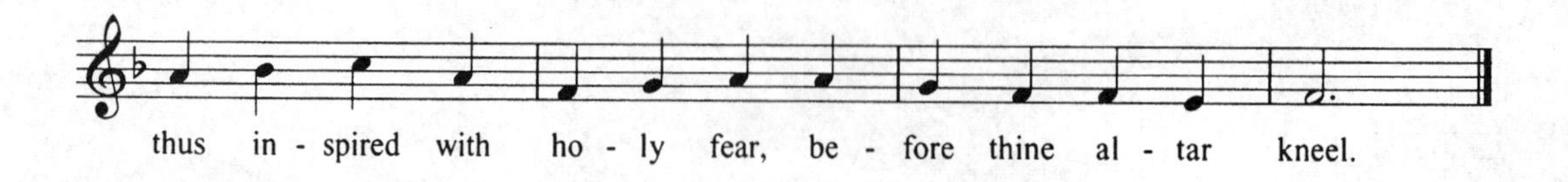

2. Here may thy faithful people know
the blessings of thy love,
the streams that through the desert flow,
the manna from above.

3. We come, obedient to thy word,
to feast on heav'nly food;
our meat the body of the Lord,
our drink his precious blood.

4. Thus may we all thy word obey,
for we, O God, are thine;
and go rejoicing on our way,
renewed with strength divine.

497 O happy band of pilgrims

John Mason Neale (1818-1866) alt. Justin Heinrich Knecht (1752-1817)

KNECHT (KOCHER) 76 76

2. The cross that Jesus carried
he carried as your due:
the crown that Jesus weareth
he weareth it for you.

3. The faith by which ye see him,
the hope in which ye yearn,
the love that through all troubles
to him alone will turn.

4. What are they but forerunners
to lead you to his sight,
the longed-for distant dawning
of uncreated light?

5. The trials that beset you,
the sorrows ye endure,
are known to Christ your Saviour,
whose perfect grace will cure.

6. O happy band of pilgrims,
let fear not dim your eyes,
remember, your afflictions
shall lead to such a prize!

Verse 6 © Copyright 1996 Kevin Mayhew Ltd.

498 O happy day

Philip Doddridge (1702-1751) alt.

Adapted from a melody in Freylinghausen's *Geistreiches Gesangbuch,* Halle (1704)

TUNE 1: FESTUS LM

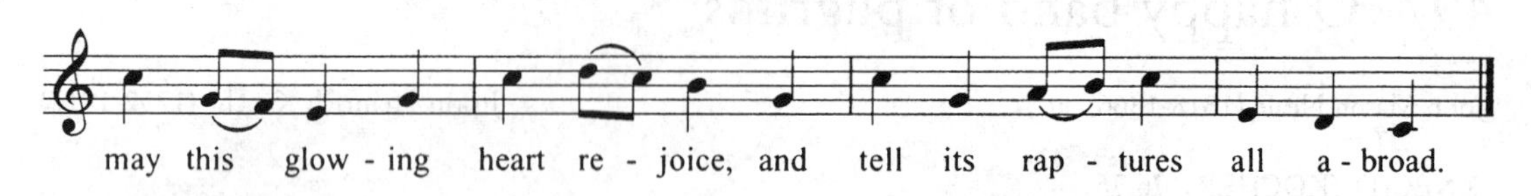

2. 'Tis done, the work of grace is done!
I am my Lord's, and he is mine!
He drew me, and I followed on,
glad to confess the voice divine.

3. Now rest, my long-divided heart,
fixed on this blissful centre, rest;
nor ever from thy Lord depart,
with him of ev'ry good possessed.

4. High heav'n, that heard the solemn vow,
that vow renewed shall daily hear;
till in life's latest hour I bow,
and bless in death a bond so dear.

Philip Doddridge (1702-1751)

Ron Jones

TUNE 2: O HAPPY DAY LM

Tune 2 © Copyright Ron Jones.

499 O, heaven is in my heart *Heaven is in my heart*

Words and music: Graham Kendrick (b.1950)

2. His precious life on me he spent,
heaven is in my heart.
To give me life without an end,
heaven is in my heart.
In Christ is all my confidence,
heaven is in my heart.
The hope of my inheritance,
heaven is in my heart.

3. We are a temple for his throne,
heaven is in my heart.
And Christ is the foundation stone,
heaven is in my heart.
He will return to take us home,
heaven is in my heart.
The Spirit and the Bride say, 'Come!',
heaven is in my heart.

© Copyright 1991 Make Way Music, P.O. Box 263, Croydon, Surrey CR9 5AP, UK.
International copyright secured. All rights reserved. Used by permission.

500 O Holy Ghost, thy people bless

Words and music: Henry Williams Baker (1821-1887)

ST TIMOTHY CM

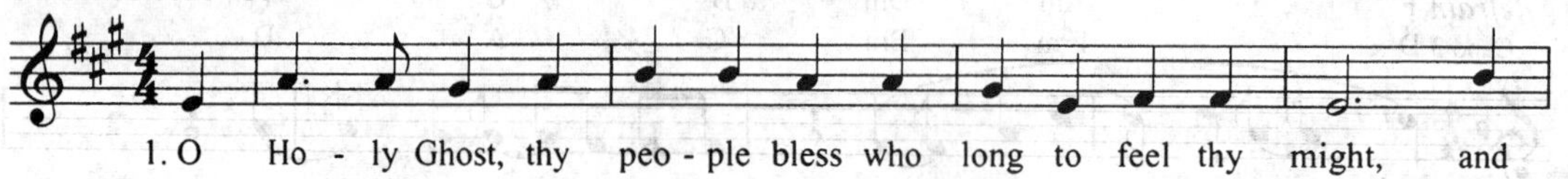

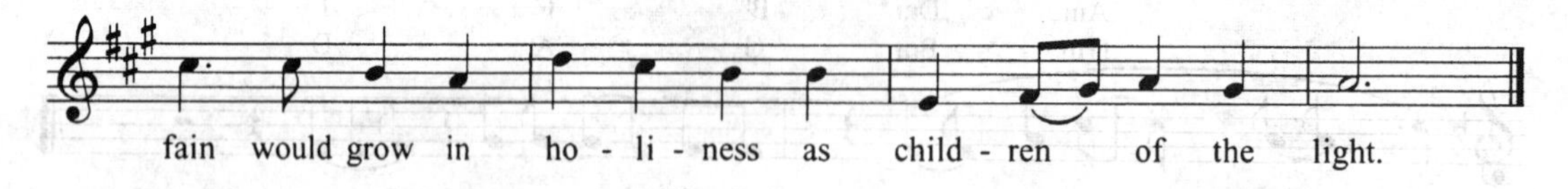

2. To thee we bring, who art the Lord,
ourselves to be thy throne;
let ev'ry thought and deed and word
thy pure dominion own.

3. Life-giving Spirit, o'er us move,
as on the formless deep;
give life and order, light and love,
where now is death or sleep.

4. Great gift of our ascended King,
his saving truth reveal;
our tongues inspire his praise to sing,
our hearts his love to feel.

5. True wind of heav'n, from south or north,
for joy or chast'ning, blow;
the garden-spices shall spring forth
if thou wilt bid them flow.

6. O Holy Ghost, of sev'nfold might,
all graces come from thee;
grant us to know and serve aright
One God in Persons Three.

501 O Holy Spirit, Lord of grace

Charles Coffin (1676-1749)
trans. John Chandler (1808-1876) alt.

Thomas Tallis (c.1505-1585)

TALLIS' ORDINAL CM

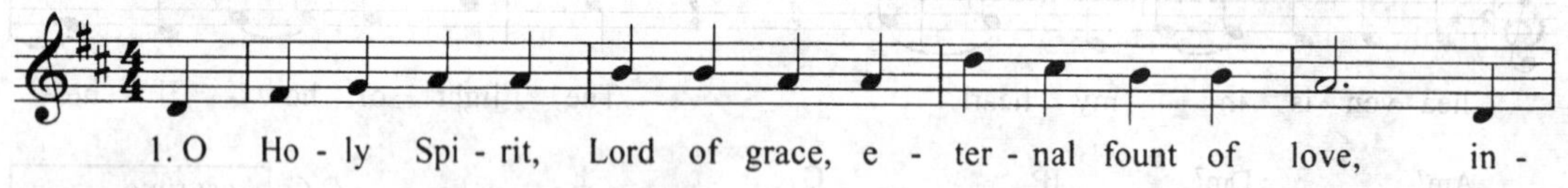

2. As thou dost join with holiest bonds
the Father and the Son,
so fill thy saints with mutual love
and link their hearts in one.

3. To God the Father, God the Son
and God the Holy Ghost,
be praise eternal from the earth,
and from the angel-host.

502 O, how good is the Lord

Words and music: Traditional

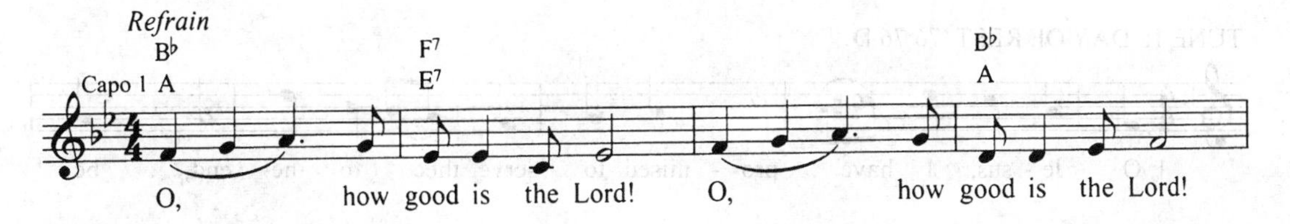

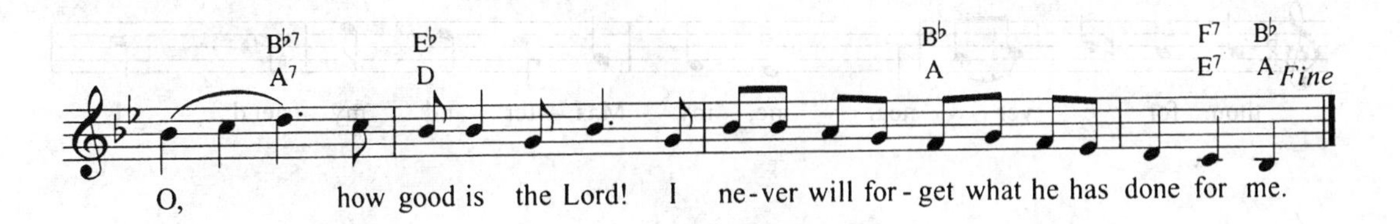

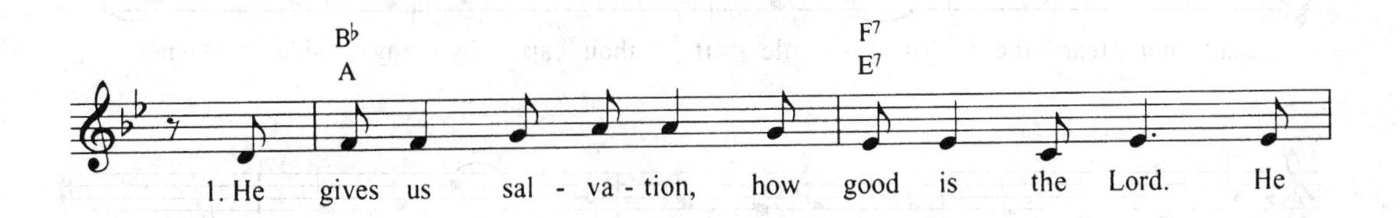

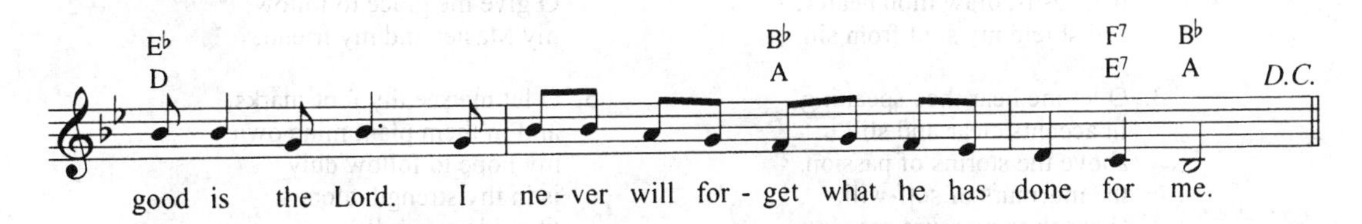

2. He gives us his Spirit, how good is the Lord. *(x3)*
I never will forget what he has done for me.

3. He gives us his healing, how good is the Lord. *(x3)*
I never will forget what he has done for me.

4. He gives us his body, how good is the Lord. *(x3)*
I never will forget what he has done for me.

5. He gives us his freedom, how good is the Lord. *(x3)*
I never will forget what he has done for me.

6. He gives us each other, how good is the Lord. *(x3)*
I never will forget what he has done for me.

7. He gives us his glory, how good is the Lord. *(x3)*
I never will forget what he has done for me.

503 O Jesus, I have promised

John Ernest Bode (1816-1874) — James William Elliott (1833-1915)

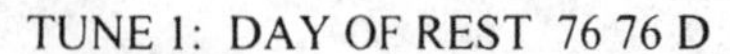
TUNE 1: DAY OF REST 76 76 D

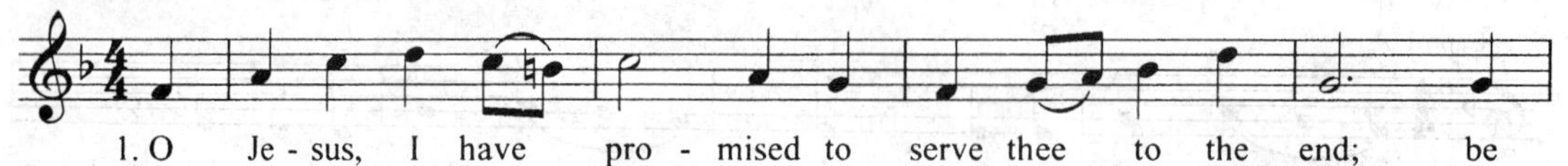

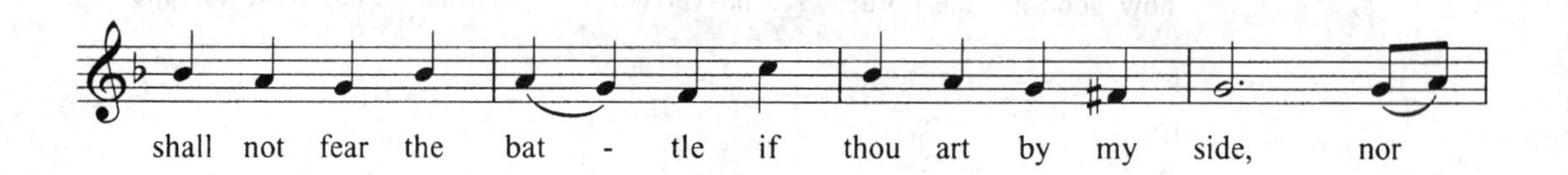

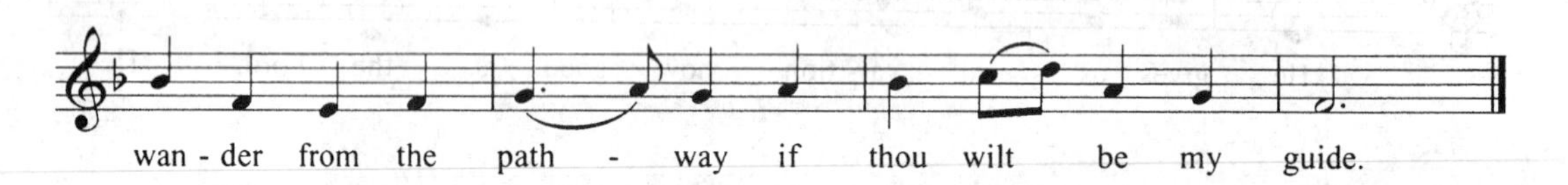

2. O let me feel thee near me;
the world is ever near;
I see the sights that dazzle,
the tempting sounds I hear;
my foes are ever near me,
around me and within;
but, Jesus, draw thou nearer,
and shield my soul from sin.

3. O let me hear thee speaking
in accents clear and still,
above the storms of passion,
the murmurs of self-will;
O speak to reassure me,
to hasten or control;
O speak and make me listen,
thou guardian of my soul.

4. O Jesus, thou hast promised,
to all who follow thee,
that where thou art in glory
there shall thy servant be;
and, Jesus, I have promised
to serve thee to the end:
O give me grace to follow,
my Master and my friend.

5. O let me see thy foot-marks,
and in them plant mine own;
my hope to follow duly
is in thy strength alone:
O guide me, call me, draw me,
uphold me to the end;
and then in heav'n receive me,
my Saviour and my friend.

John Ernest Bode (1816-1874) — William Harold Ferguson (1874-1950)

TUNE 2: WOLVERCOTE 76 76 D

Tune 2 © Copyright Oxford University Press, Great Clarendon Street, Oxford OX2 6DP, UK.
Used by permission.

John Ernest Bode (1816-1874) Geoffrey Beaumont (1903-1970)

TUNE 3: HATHEROP CASTLE 76 76 D

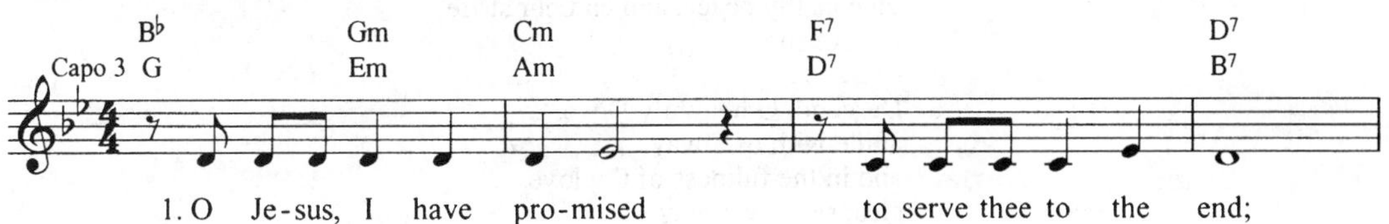

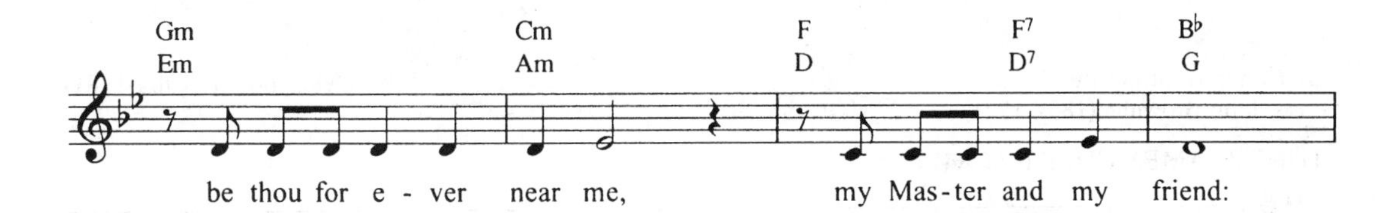

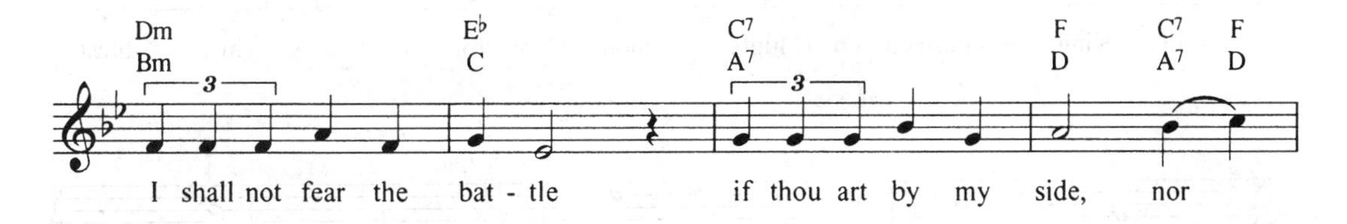

Tune 3 © Copyright 1960 Josef Weinberger Ltd., 12-14 Mortimer Street, London W1N 7RD, UK.
Used by permission.

504 O King enthroned on high

Greek hymn (8th century)
trans. John Brownlie (1857-1925)

Henry Walford Davies (1869-1941)

TUNE 1: TEMPLE 66 84

2. Thou art the source of life,
thou art our treasure-store;
give us thy peace, and end our strife
for evermore.

3. Descend, O heav'nly Dove,
abide with us alway;
and in the fullness of thy love
cleanse us, we pray.

Greek hymn (8th century)
trans. John Brownlie (1857-1925)

John Dykes Bower (1905-1981)

TUNE 2: AMEN COURT 66 84

Tune 1 © Copyright Oxford University Press, Great Clarendon Street,
Oxford OX2 6DP, UK. Used by permission.
Tune 2 © Copyright Hymns Ancient & Modern Ltd., St Mary's Works, St Mary's Plain,
Norwich NR3 3BH, UK. Used by permission.

505 O Lamb of God

Michael Forster (b.1946)
based on the German

Wolfgang Amadeus Mozart (1756-1791)

MOZART 76 76 D

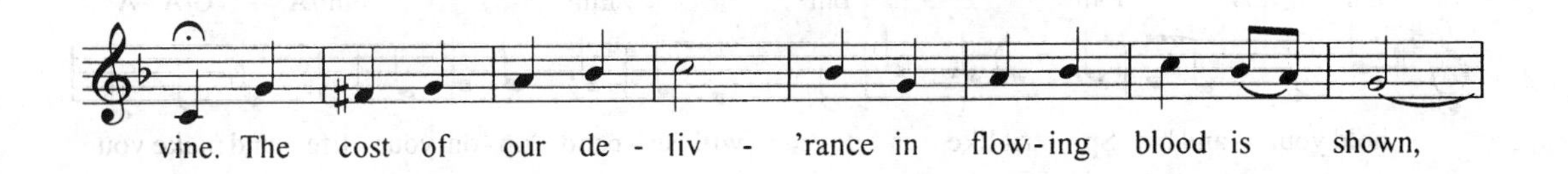

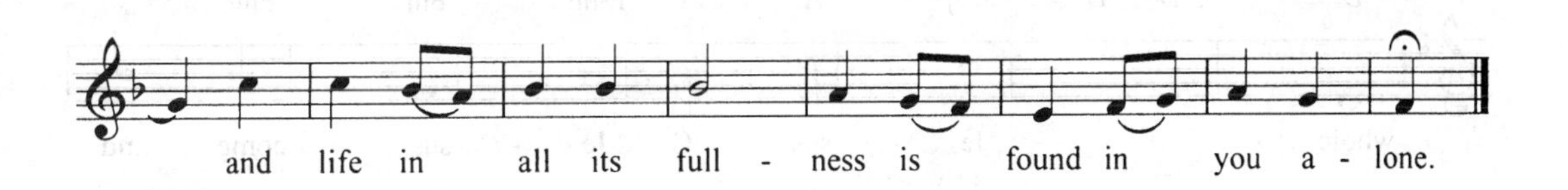

2. Upon the cross you carried
a universe of shame,
your dying breath atoning
for centuries of blame.
So now accept your servant,
who on your love relied,
to rest in peace eternal
redeemed and purified.

3. O draw us to your presence,
beyond the sundered veil,
to stand in silent wonder,
where words and senses fail.
In fellowship unbroken
with all who went before,
we join with saints and angels
to worship and adore.

Text © Copyright 1996 Kevin Mayhew Ltd.

506 O let the Son of God enfold you *Spirit song*

Words and music: John Wimber (1934-1997)

2. O come and sing this song with gladness
as your hearts are filled with joy,
lift your hands in sweet surrender to his name.
O give him all your tears and sadness,
give him all your years of pain,
and you'll enter into life in Jesus' name.

© Copyright 1979 Mercy/Vineyard Publishing. Administered by CopyCare, P.O. Box 77, Hailsham, East Sussex BN27 3EF, UK. (music@copycare.com). Used by permission.

507 O little one sweet, O little one mild

Translated from the German of Samuel Scheidt (1650)
by Percy Dearmer (1867-1936) alt.

From Samuel Scheidt's *Tabulaturbuch* (1650)

O JESULEIN SÜSS 10 9 88 10

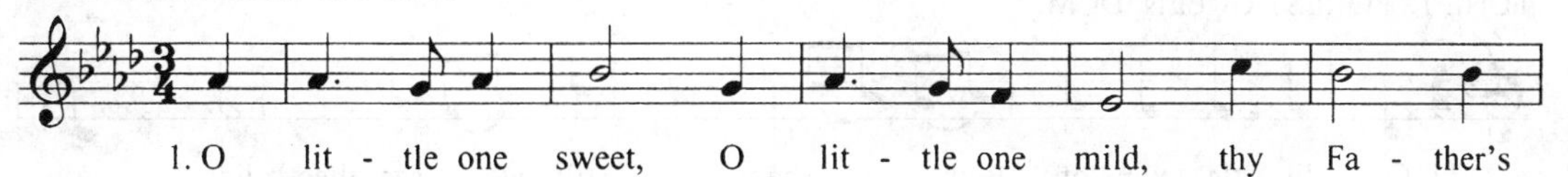

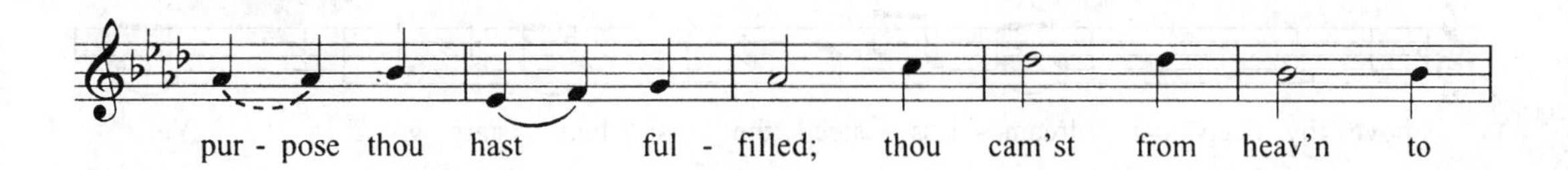

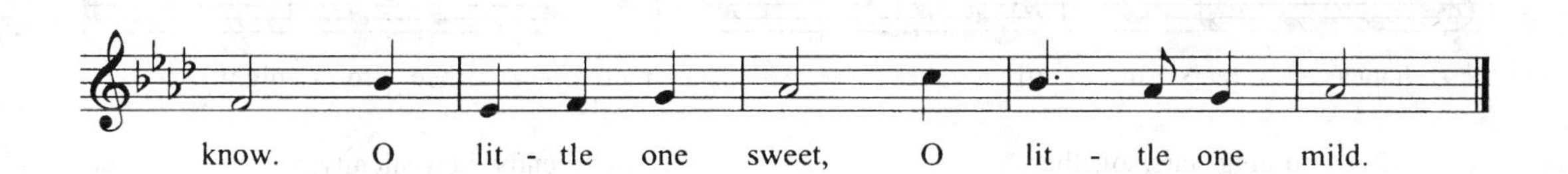

2. O little one sweet, O little one mild,
with joy thou hast the whole world filled;
thou camest here from heav'n's domain,
to bring us comfort in our pain,
O little one sweet, O little one mild.

3. O little one sweet, O little one mild,
in thee Love's beauties are all distilled;
then light in us thy love's bright flame,
that we may give thee back the same,
O little one sweet, O little one mild.

© Copyright Oxford University Press, Great Clarendon Street, Oxford OX2 6DP, UK.
Used by permission from the *Oxford Book of Carols*.

508 O little town of Bethlehem

Phillips Brooks (1835-1893) alt.

Traditional English melody collected by Ralph Vaughan Williams (1872-1958)

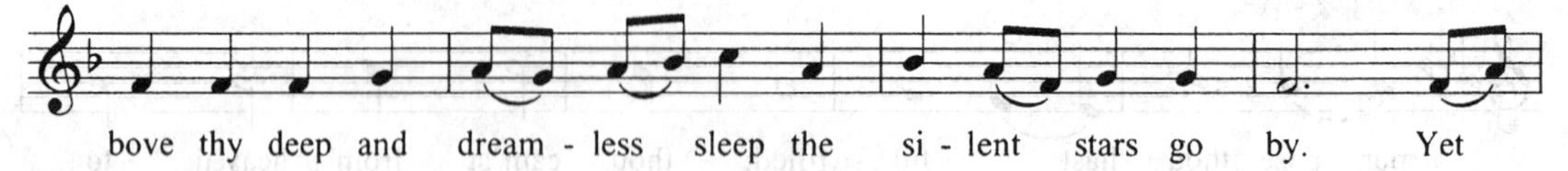

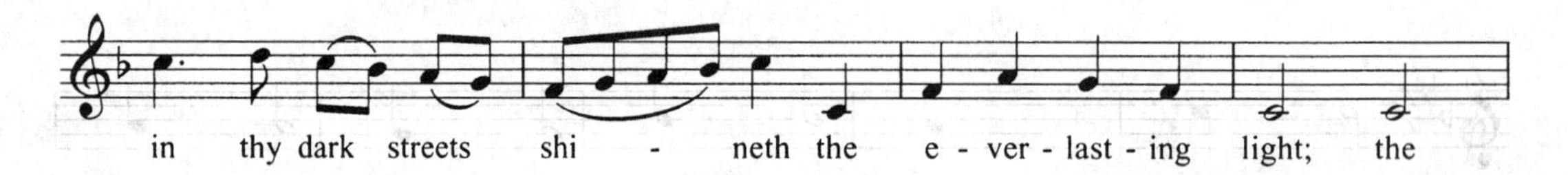

2. O morning stars, together
proclaim the holy birth,
and praises sing to God the King,
and peace to all the earth.
For Christ is born of Mary;
and, gathered all above,
while mortals sleep, the angels keep
their watch of wond'ring love;

3. How silently, how silently,
the wondrous gift is giv'n!
So God imparts to human hearts
the blessings of his heav'n.
No ear may hear his coming;
but in this world of sin,
where meek souls will receive him still,
the dear Christ enters in.

4. O holy child of Bethlehem,
descend to us, we pray;
cast out our sin, and enter in,
be born in us today.
We hear the Christmas angels
the great glad tidings tell:
O come to us, abide with us,
our Lord Emmanuel.

Phillips Brooks (1835-1893) alt.

Henry Walford Davies (1869-1941)

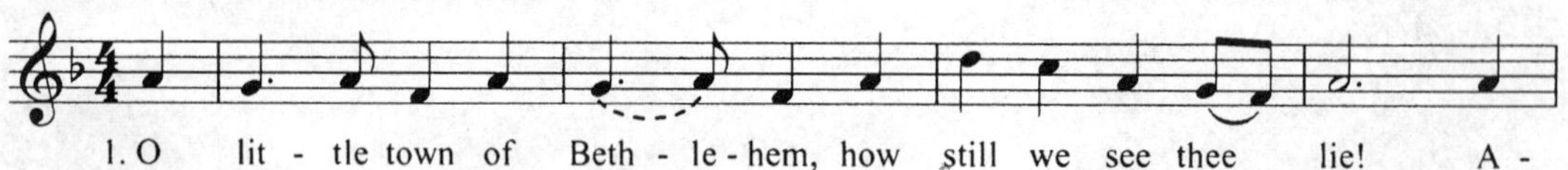

Tune 1 © Copyright Oxford University Press, Great Clarendon Street, Oxford OX2 6DP, UK.
Used by permission from the *English Hymnal.* Tune 2 © Copyright Oxford University Press. Used by permission.

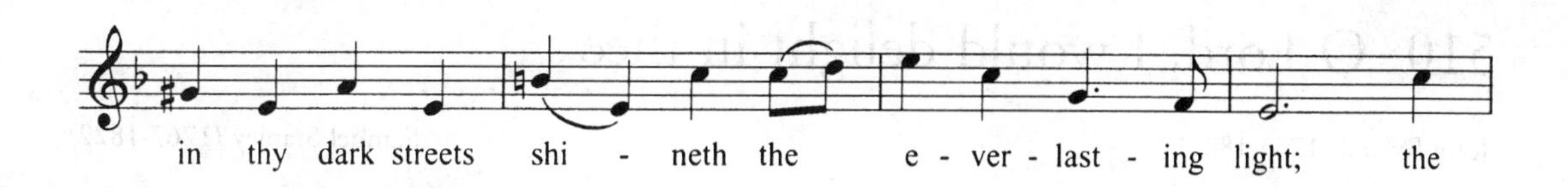

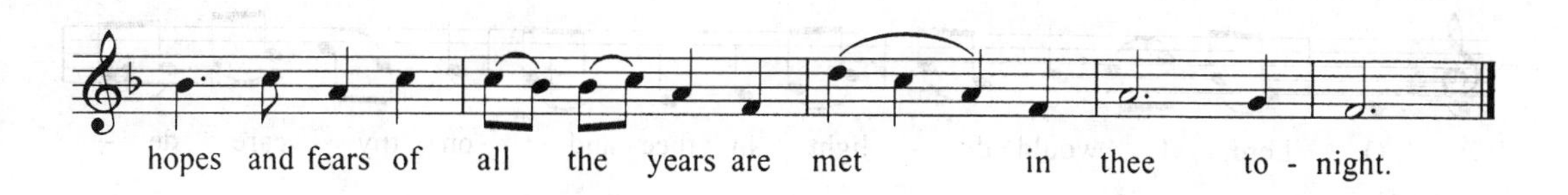

509 O Lord, all the world belongs to you

Words and music: Patrick Appleford (b.1925)

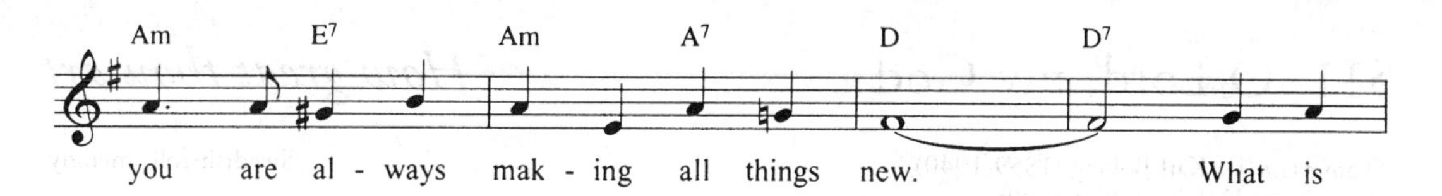

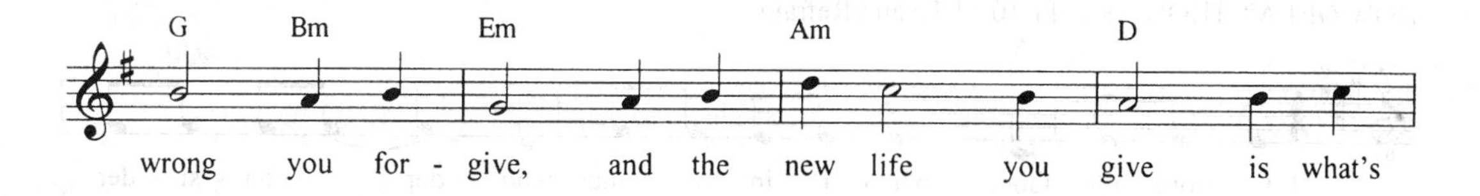

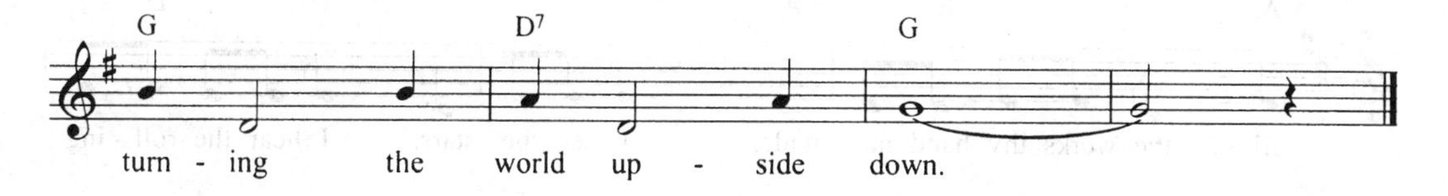

2. The world's only loving to its friends,
but you have brought us love that never ends;
loving enemies too,
and this loving with you
is what's turning the world upside down.

3. This world lives divided and apart.
You draw us all together and we start,
in your body, to see
that in a fellowship we
can be turning the world upside down.

4. The world wants the wealth to live in state,
but you show us a new way to be great:
like a servant you came,
and if we do the same,
we'll be turning the world upside down.

5. O Lord, all the world belongs to you,
and you are always making all things new.
Send your Spirit on all
in your Church, whom you call
to be turning the world upside down.

© Copyright 1965 Josef Weinberger Ltd., 12-14 Mortimer Street, London W1N 7RD, UK.
Used by permission.

510 O Lord, I would delight in thee

John Ryland (1753-1825) — Samuel Stanley (1767-1822)

2. When all created streams are dried,
thy fullness is the same:
may I with this be satisfied,
and glory in thy name.

3. No good in creatures can be found
but may be found in thee;
I must have all things and abound,
while God is God to me.

4. He that has made my heav'n secure
will here all good provide;
while Christ is rich can I be poor?
What can I want beside?

5. O Lord, I cast my care on thee;
I triumph and adore;
henceforth my great concern shall be
to love and please thee more.

511 O Lord, my God *How great thou art*

O Støre Gud by Karl Boberg (1859-1940)
trans. Stuart K. Hine (1899-1989) — Swedish folk melody

HOW GREAT THOU ART 11 10 11 10 and Refrain

© Copyright 1953 Stuart K. Hine. Administered by Kingsway's Thankyou Music, P.O. Box 75, Eastbourne, East Sussex BN23 6NW, UK. (tym@kingsway.co.uk). Worldwide (excl. USA and Canada). Used by permission.

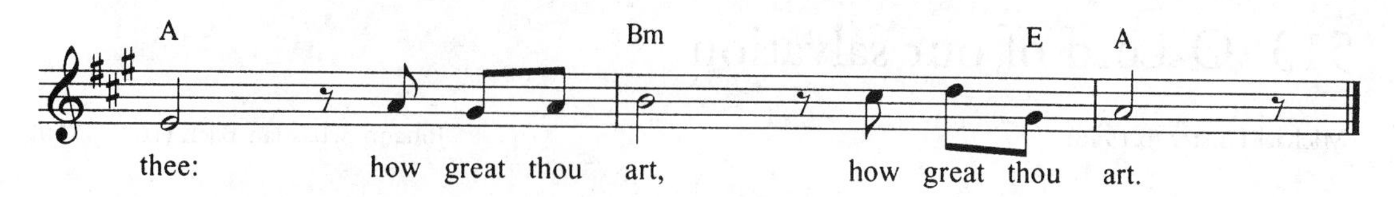

2. When through the woods and forest glades I wander
and hear the birds sing sweetly in the trees;
when I look down from lofty mountain grandeur,
and hear the brook, and feel the gentle breeze.

3. And when I think that God, his Son not sparing,
sent him to die, I scarce can take it in
that on the cross, my burden gladly bearing,
he bled and died to take away my sin.

4. When Christ shall come with shout of acclamation
and take me home, what joy shall fill my heart;
when I shall bow in humble adoration,
and there proclaim: my God, how great thou art.

512 O Lord of every shining constellation

Albert F. Bayly (1901-1984) Thomas Wood (1892-1950)

ST OSYTH 11 10 11 10

2. You, Lord, have made the atom's hidden forces,
your laws its mighty energies fulfil;
teach us, to whom you give such rich resources,
in all we use, to serve your holy will.

3. O Life, awaking life in cell and tissue,
from flow'r to bird, from beast to brain of man;
help us to trace, from birth to final issue,
the sure unfolding of your age-long plan.

4. You, Lord, have stamped your image on your creatures,
and, though they mar that image, love them still;
lift up our eyes to Christ, that in his features
we may discern the beauty of your will.

5. Great Lord of nature, shaping and renewing,
you made us more than nature's sons to be;
you help us tread, with grace our souls enduring,
the road to life and immortality.

Text © Copyright 1988 Oxford University Press, Great Clarendon Street, Oxford OX2 6DP, UK.
Music © Copyright Oxford University Press. Used by permission.

513 O Lord of our salvation

Michael Forster (b.1946) — Johann Sebastian Bach (1685-1750)

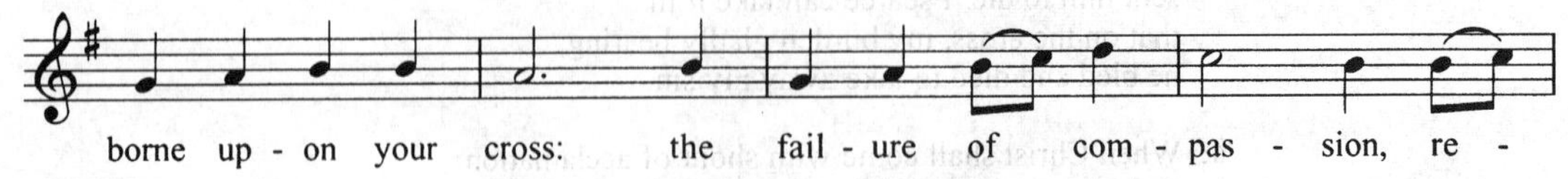

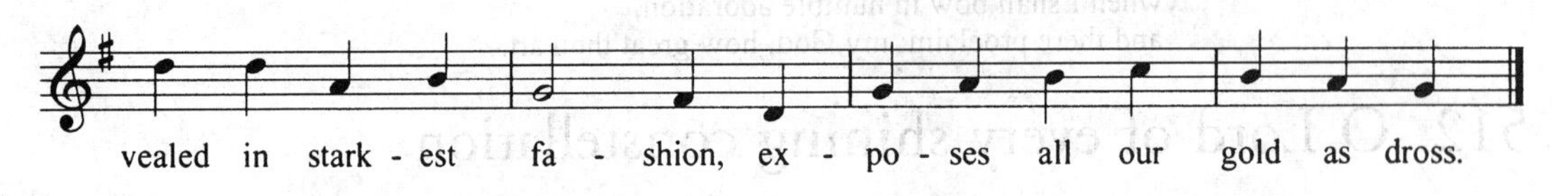

2. We hear your voice protesting,
to love and hope attesting,
where justice is denied.
Where innocents are dying,
where hate is crucifying,
you call us to your bleeding side.

3. O give us faith to stay here,
to wait, to watch and pray here,
and witness to your cry;
in scarred and tearful faces,
in countless painful places,
you give us hope that will not die.

Text © Copyright 1996 Kevin Mayhew Ltd.

514 O Lord, we long to see your face

Text © Copyright the Revd. Mary J. Hancock.
Used by kind permission.

2. O Lord, we do not know the way,
nor clearly see the path ahead;
so often, therefore, we delay
and doubt your pow'r to raise the dead.
Yet with you we will firmly stay;
you are the Truth, the Life, the Way.

3. We find it hard, Lord, to believe;
all habit makes us want to prove;
we would with eye and hand perceive
the truth and person whom we love.
Yet, as in fellowship we meet,
you come yourself each one to greet.

4. You come to us, our God, our Lord;
you do not show your hands and side;
but faith has its more blest reward;
in love's assurance we confide.
Now we believe, that we may know,
and in that knowledge daily grow.

515 O Lord, your tenderness

Words and music: Graham Kendrick (b.1950)

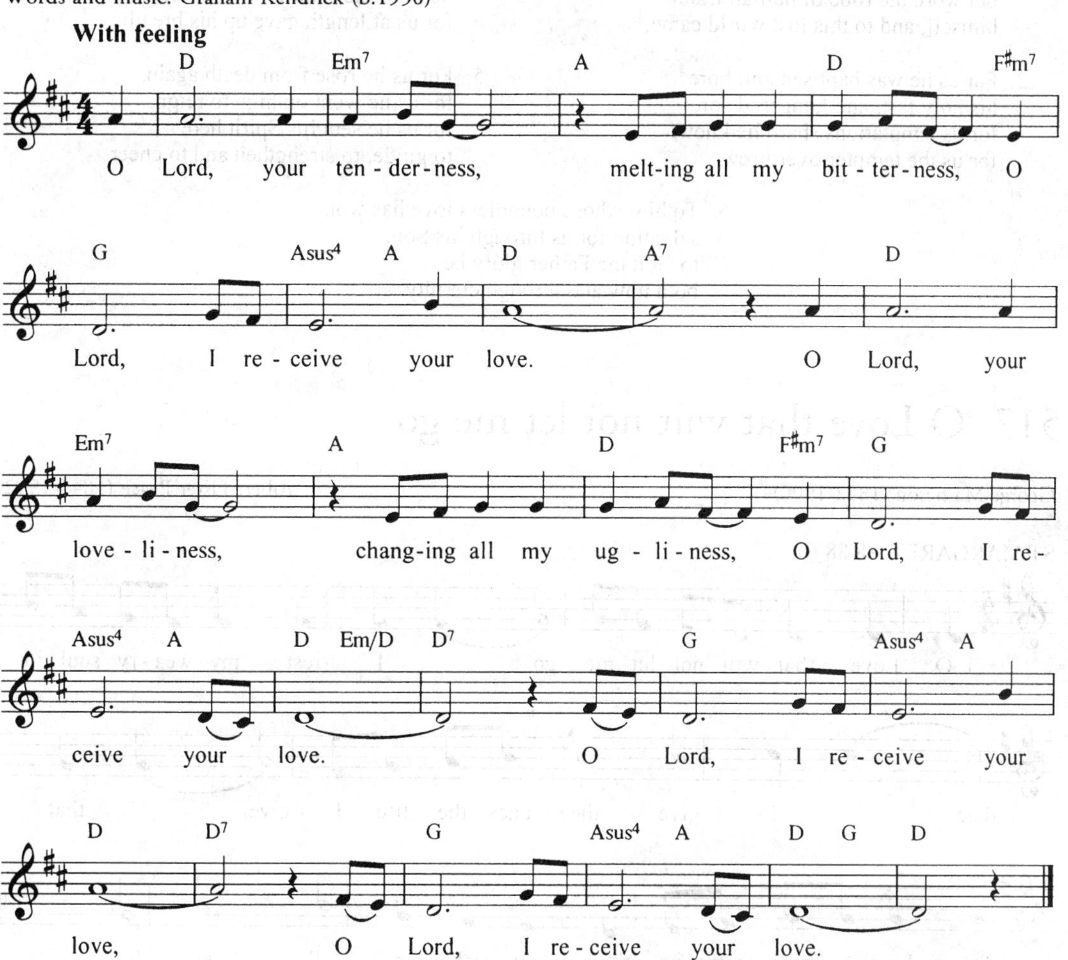

© Copyright 1986 Kingsway's Thankyou Music, P.O. Box 75, Eastbourne, East Sussex BN23 6NW, UK. (tym@kingsway.co.uk). Used by permission.

516 O love, how deep, how broad, how high

Benjamin Webb (1819-1885) alt,
from Thomas à Kempis (c.1379-1471)

Johann Herman Schein (1586-1630)
in his revised *Cantional* (1645)

EISENACH LM

2. He sent no angel to our race
   of higher or of lower place,
   but wore the robe of human frame
   himself, and to this lost world came.

3. For us he was baptised and bore
   his holy fast, and hungered sore;
   for us temptations sharp he knew;
   for us the tempter overthrew.

4. For us to wicked pow'rs betrayed,
   scourged, mocked, in purple robe arrayed,
   he bore the shameful cross and death;
   for us at length gave up his breath.

5. For us he rose from death again,
   for us he went on high to reign,
   for us he sent his Spirit here
   to guide, to strengthen and to cheer.

6. To him whose boundless love has won
   salvation for us through his Son,
   to God the Father glory be,
   both now and through eternity.

517 O Love that wilt not let me go

George Matheson (1842-1906)

Albert Lister Peace (1844-1912)

ST MARGARET 88 88 6

2. O Light that follow'st all my way,
   I yield my flick'ring torch to thee;
   my heart restores its borrowed ray,
   that in thy sunshine's blaze its day
   may brighter, fairer be.

3. O Joy that seekest me through pain,
   I cannot close my heart to thee;
   I trace the rainbow through the rain,
   and feel the promise is not vain
   that morn shall tearless be.

4. O Cross that liftest up my head,
I dare not ask to fly from thee:
I lay in dust life's glory dead,
and from the ground there blossoms red
life that shall endless be.

518 O most merciful

Reginald Heber (1783-1826) | From *Münster Gesangbuch* (1677)

SCHÖNSTER HERR JESU 10 7 10 7

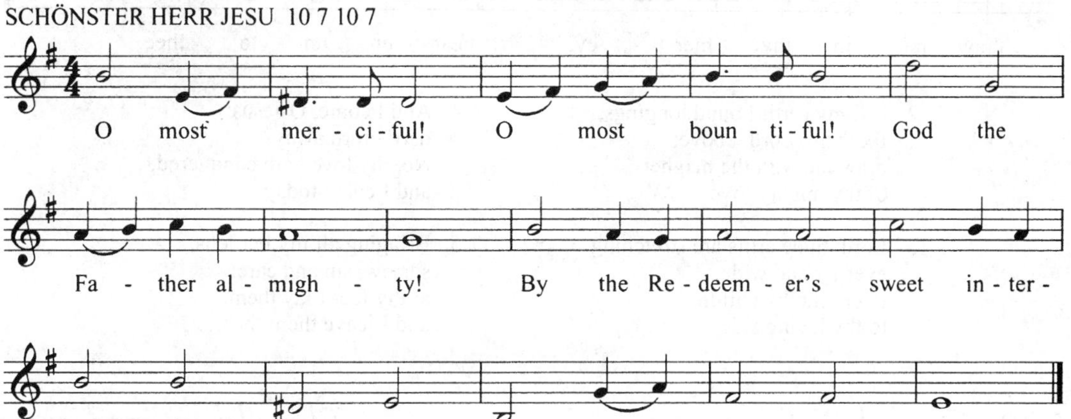

519 O my Saviour, lifted from the earth

William Walsham How (1823-1897) | Timothy Richard Matthews (1826-1910)

TUNE 1: NORTH COATES 65 65

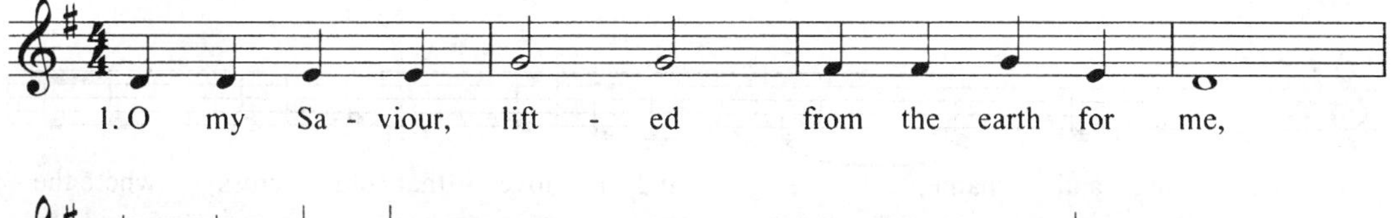

2. Lift my earth-bound longings,
fix them, Lord, above;
draw me with the magnet
of thy mighty love.

3. Lord, thine arms are stretching
ever far and wide,
to enfold thy children
to thy loving side.

4. And I come, O Jesus:
dare I turn away?
No, thy love hath conquered,
and I come today.

5. Bringing all my burdens,
sorrow, sin and care;
at thy feet I lay them,
and I leave them there.

Tune 2 will be found overleaf

William Walsham How (1823-1897) | Friedrich Filitz (1804-1876)

TUNE 2: CASWALL 65 65

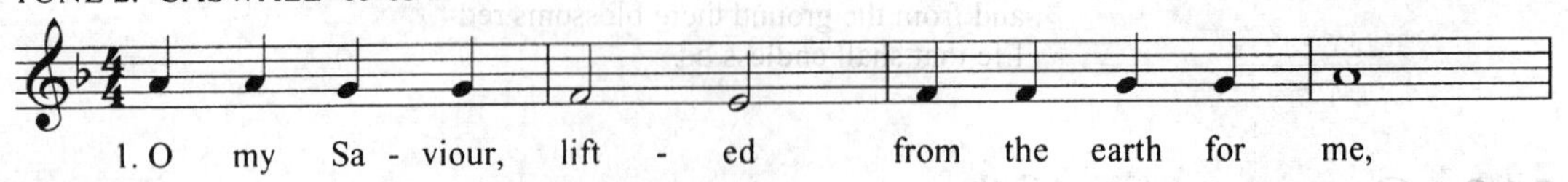

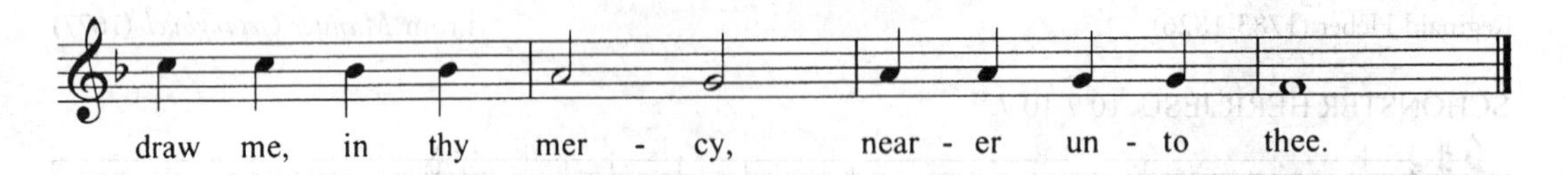

2. Lift my earth-bound longings,
fix them, Lord, above;
draw me with the magnet
of thy mighty love.

3. Lord, thine arms are stretching
ever far and wide,
to enfold thy children
to thy loving side.

4. And I come, O Jesus:
dare I turn away?
No, thy love hath conquered,
and I come today.

5. Bringing all my burdens,
sorrow, sin and care;
at thy feet I lay them,
and I leave them there.

520 On a hill far away — *The old rugged cross*

Words and music: George Bennard (1873-1958)

THE OLD RUGGED CROSS 66 8D and Refrain

© Copyright The Rodeheaver Co./Word Music. Administered by CopyCare, P.O. Box 77, Hailsham, East Sussex BN27 3EF, UK. (music@copycare.com). Used by permission.

2. O that old rugged cross,
so despised by the world,
has a wondrous attraction for me:
for the dear Lamb of God
left his glory above
to bear it to dark Calvary.

3. In the old rugged cross,
stained with blood so divine,
a wondrous beauty I see.
For t'was on that old cross
Jesus suffered and died
to pardon and sanctify me.

4. To the old rugged cross
I will ever be true,
its shame and reproach gladly bear.
Then he'll call me some day
to my home far away;
there his glory for ever I'll share.

521 Once in royal David's city

Cecil Frances Alexander (1818-1895) alt. — Henry John Gauntlett (1805-1876)

IRBY 87 87 77

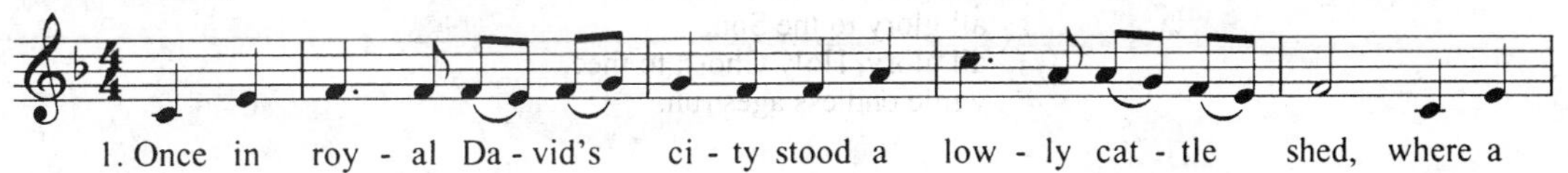

2. He came down to earth from heaven,
who is God and Lord of all,
and his shelter was a stable,
and his cradle was a stall;
with the needy, poor and lowly,
lived on earth our Saviour holy.

3. For he is our childhood's pattern,
day by day like us he grew;
he was little, weak and helpless,
tears and smiles like us he knew;
and he feeleth for our sadness,
and he shareth in our gladness.

4. And our eyes at last shall see him
through his own redeeming love,
for that child so dear and gentle
is our Lord in heav'n above;
and he leads his children on
to the place where he is gone.

This version of text © Copyright 1996 Kevin Mayhew Ltd.

522 Once, only once, and once for all

William Bright (1824-1901) — Vincent Novello (1781-1861)

ALBANO CM

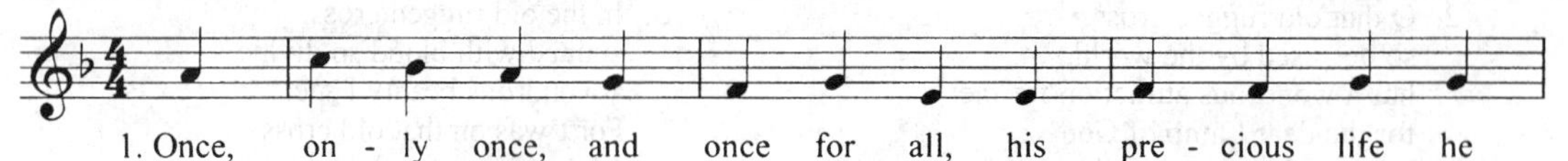

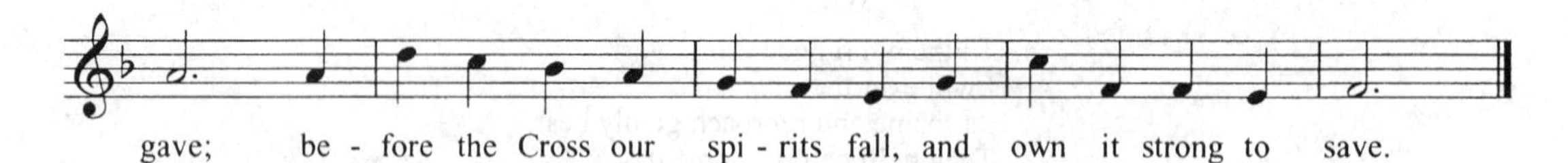

2. 'One off'ring, single and complete,'
with lips and heart we say;
but what he never can repeat
he shows forth day by day.

3. For, as the priest of Aaron's line
within the holiest stood,
and sprinkled all the mercy-shrine
with sacrificial blood;

4. So he who once atonement wrought,
our Priest of endless pow'r,
presents himself for those he bought
in that dark noontide hour.

5. And so we show thy death, O Lord,
till thou again appear;
and feel, when we approach thy board,
we have an altar here.

6. All glory to the Father be,
all glory to the Son,
all glory, Holy Ghost, to thee,
while endless ages run.

523 On Christmas night all Christians sing

Traditional English carol, alt. — Traditional English melody collected by Ralph Vaughan Williams (1872-1958)

Music © Copyright 1919 Stainer & Bell Ltd., P.O. Box 110, Victoria House, 23 Gruneisen Road, Finchley, London N3 1DZ, UK. Used by permission.

2. Then why should we on earth be so sad,
since our Redeemer made us glad,
then why should we on earth be so sad,
since our Redeemer made us glad,
when from our sin he set us free,
all for to gain our liberty?

3. When sin departs before his grace,
then life and health come in its place,
when sin departs before his grace,
then life and health come in its place,
angels and earth with joy may sing,
all for to see the new-born King.

4. All out of darkness we have light,
which made the angels sing this night:
all out of darkness we have light,
which made the angels sing this night:
'Glory to God and peace to men,
now and for evermore. Amen.'

524 One Father

One God

Words and music: Gerard Markland (b.1953)

2. Lord Jesus, now enthroned in glory,
what God is this who gives his life
to set me free?

3. O loving breath of God almighty,
what God is this who through my weakness
sings his praise?

© Copyright 1998 Kevin Mayhew Ltd.

525 One more step along the world I go

Words and music: Sydney Carter (b.1915)

SOUTHCOTE 99 79 and Refrain

2. Round the corners of the world I turn,
more and more about the world I learn.
All the new things that I see
you'll be looking at along with me.

3. As I travel through the bad and good,
keep me travelling the way I should.
Where I see no way to go,
you'll be telling me the way, I know.

4. Give me courage when the world is rough,
keep me loving though the world is tough.
Leap and sing in all I do,
keep me travelling along with you.

5. You are older than the world can be,
you are younger than the life in me.
Ever old and ever new,
keep me travelling along with you.

© Copyright 1971 Stainer & Bell Ltd., P.O. Box 110, Victoria House, 23 Gruneisen Road, Finchley, London N3 1DZ, UK. Used by permission.

526 One shall tell another *New Wine*

Words and music: Graham Kendrick (b.1950)

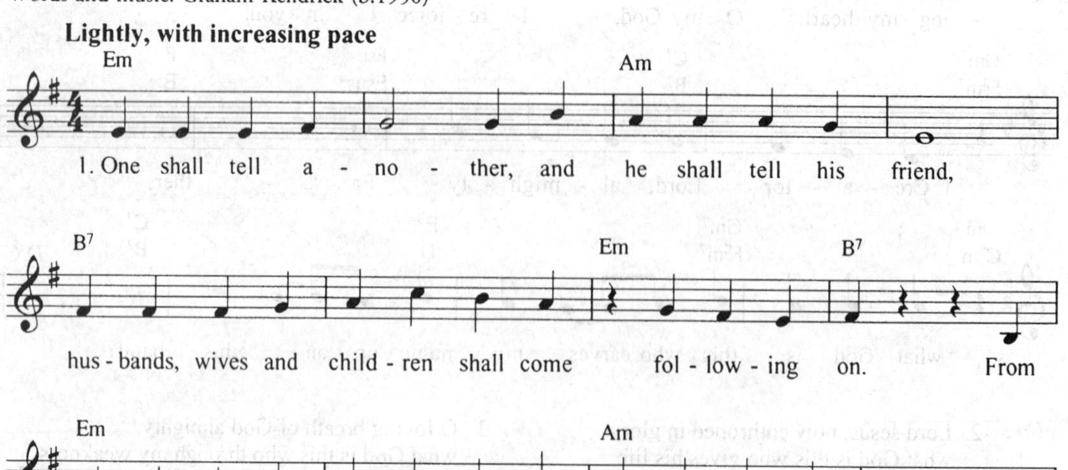

© Copyright 1981 Kingsway's Thankyou Music, P.O. Box 75, Eastbourne, East Sussex BN23 6NW, UK. (tym@kingsway.co.uk). Used by permission.

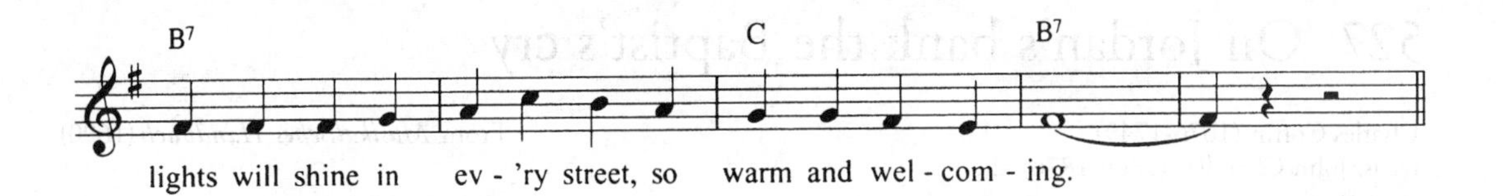

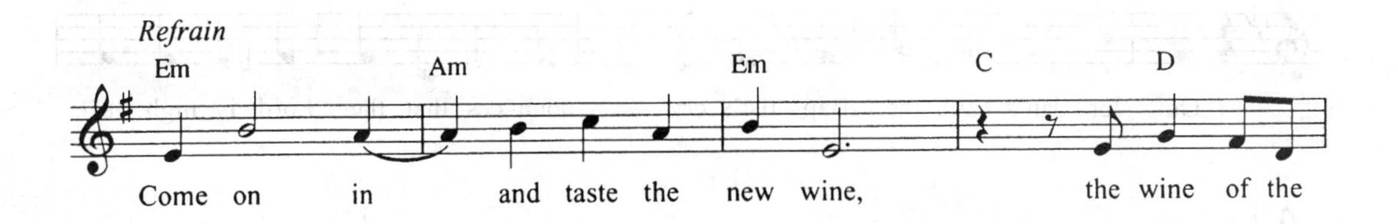

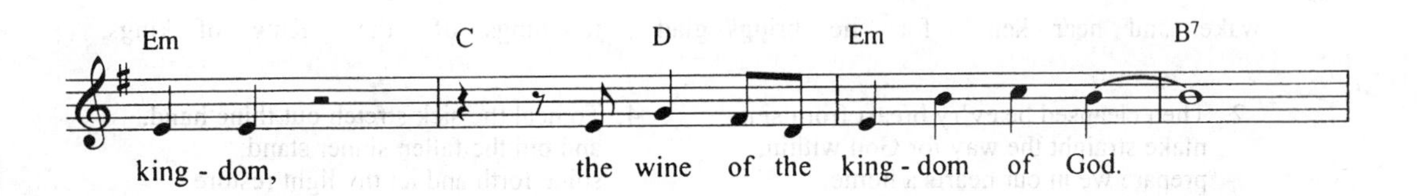

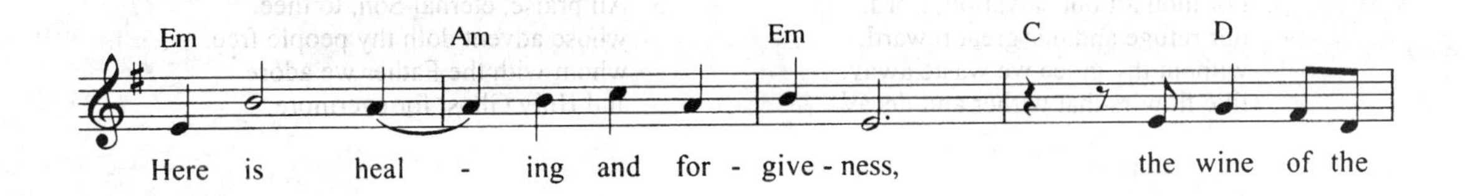

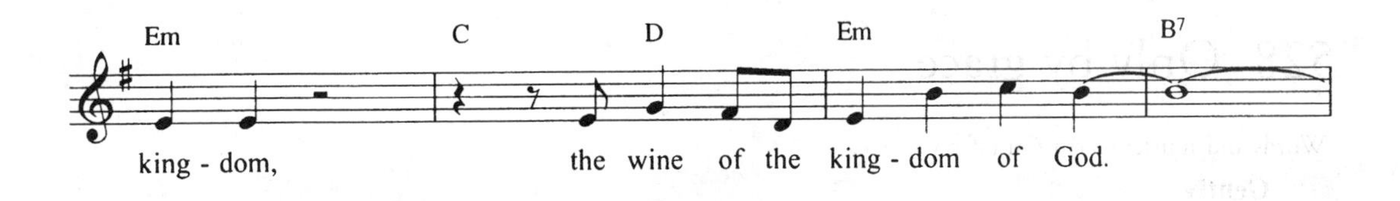

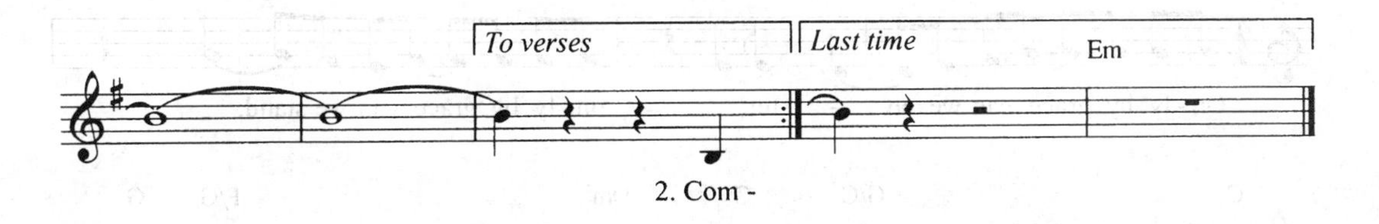

2. Compassion of the Father
is ready now to flow,
through acts of love and mercy
we must let it show.
He turns now from his anger
to show a smiling face,
and longs that all should stand beneath
the fountain of his grace.

3. He longs to do much more than
our faith has yet allowed,
to thrill us and surprise us
with his sovereign power.
Where darkness has been darkest
the brightest light will shine;
his invitation comes to us,
it's yours and it is mine.

527 On Jordan's bank the Baptist's cry

Charles Coffin (1676-1749)
trans. John Chandler (1806-1876) alt.

From *Musikalisches Handbuch* (1690)

WINCHESTER NEW LM

2. Then cleansed be ev'ry breast from sin;
make straight the way for God within;
prepare we in our hearts a home,
where such a mighty guest may come.

3. For thou art our salvation, Lord,
our refuge and our great reward;
without thy grace we waste away,
like flow'rs that wither and decay.

4. To heal the sick stretch out thine hand,
and bid the fallen sinner stand;
shine forth and let thy light restore
earth's own true loveliness once more.

5. All praise, eternal Son, to thee
whose advent doth thy people free,
whom with the Father we adore
and Holy Ghost for evermore.

528 Only by grace

Words and music: Gerrit Gustafson

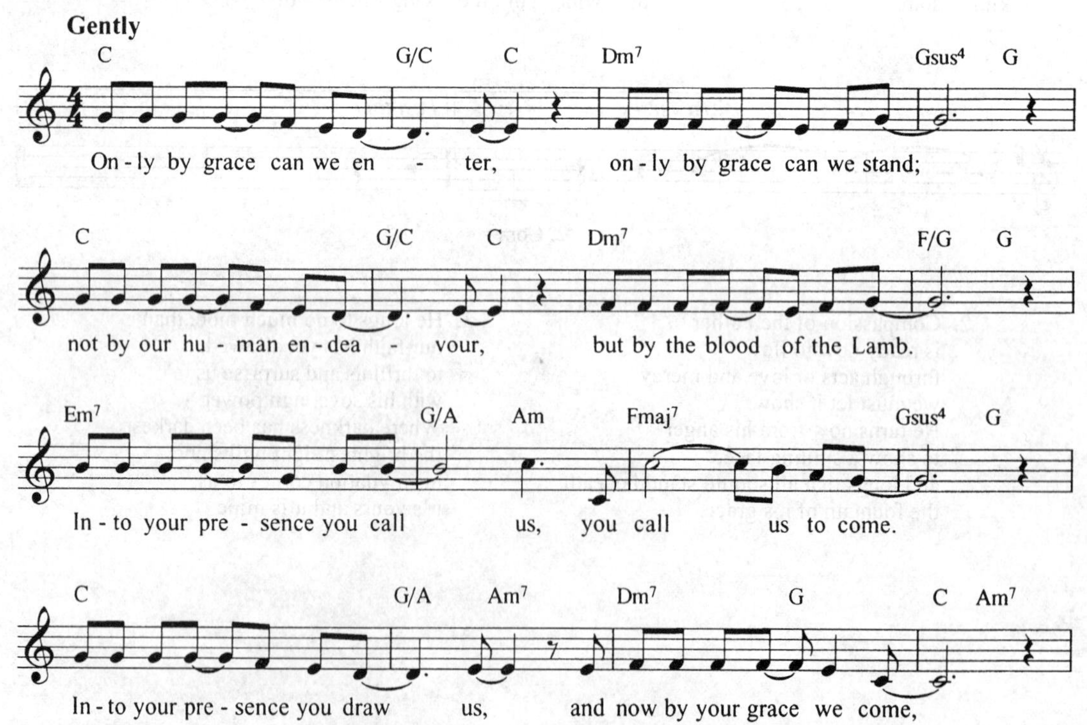

© Copyright 1990 Integrity's Hosanna! Music/Sovereign Music UK, P.O. Box 356,
Leighton Buzzard, LU7 3WP, UK. Used by permission.

529 On this day of joy

Words and music: Marie Lydia Pereira (b.1920)

2. Bread to be your body, Lord,
   wine to be your saving blood;
   on this day of joy, on this day of hope,
   we come to you in love.

© Copyright 1999 Kevin Mayhew Ltd.

530 On this day, the first of days

18th century, trans Henry Williams Baker (1821-1877)
adapted by the editors of *English Praise*

Freylinghausen's *Gesangbuch* (1704)

LÜBECK (GOTT SEI DANK) 77 77

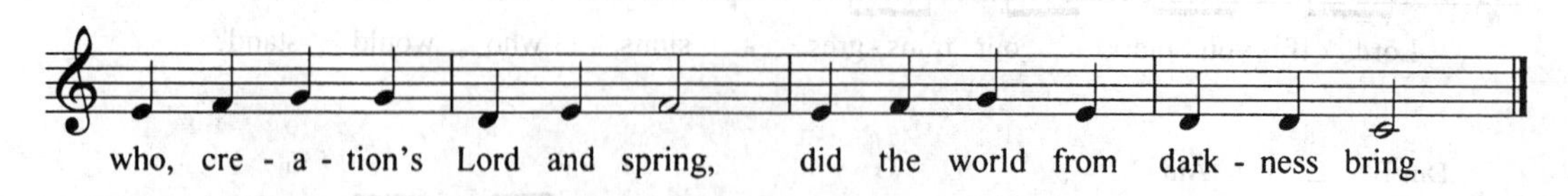

2. On this day his only Son
over death the triumph won;
on this day the Spirit came
with his gifts of living flame.

3. On this day his people raise
one pure sacrifice of praise,
and, with all the saints above,
tell of Christ's redeeming love.

4. Praise, O God, to thee be giv'n,
praise on earth and praise in heav'n,
praise to thy eternal Son,
who this day our vict'ry won.

Text © Copyright Oxford University Press, Great Clarendon Street, Oxford OX2 6DP, UK.
Used by permission.

531 Onward, Christian pilgrims

Michael Forster (b.1946)

Arthur Seymour Sullivan (1842-1900)

ST GERTRUDE 65 65 D and Refrain

1. On - ward, Christ - ian pil - grims, Christ will be our light;

see, the heav'n - ly vi - sion breaks up - on our sight!

Out of death's en - slave - ment Christ has set us free,

Text © Copyright 1996 Kevin Mayhew Ltd.

2. Onward, Christian pilgrims,
up the rocky way,
where the dying Saviour
bids us watch and pray.
Through the darkened valley
walk with those who mourn,
share the pain and anger,
share the promised dawn!

3. Onward, Christian pilgrims,
in the early dawn;
death's great seal is broken,
life and hope reborn!
Faith in resurrection
strengthens pilgrims' hearts,
ev'ry load is lightened,
ev'ry fear departs.

4. Onward, Christian pilgrims,
hearts and voices raise,
till the whole creation
echoes perfect praise;
swords are turned to ploughshares,
pride and envy cease,
truth embraces justice,
hope resolves in peace.

532 Open our eyes, Lord

Words and music: Robert Cull (b.1949)

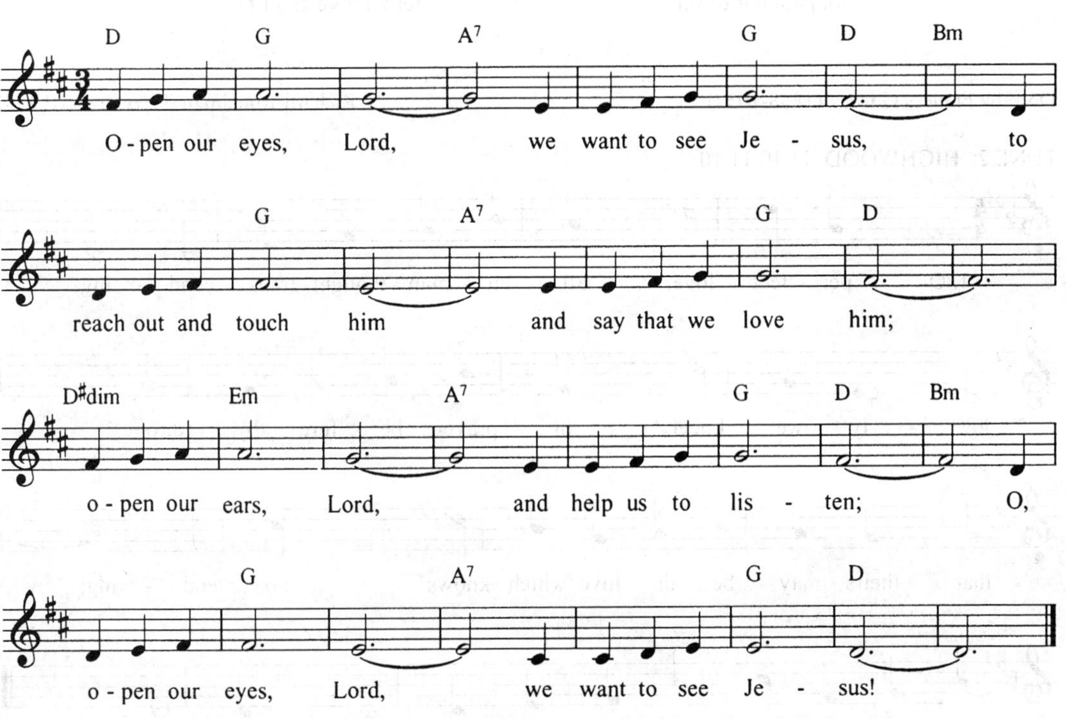

© Copyright 1976 Maranatha! Music. Administered by CopyCare, P.O. Box 77, Hailsham, East Sussex BN27 3EF, UK. (music@copycare.com). Used by permission.

533 O perfect love

Dorothy Frances Gurney (1858-1932) Joseph Barnby (1838-1896)

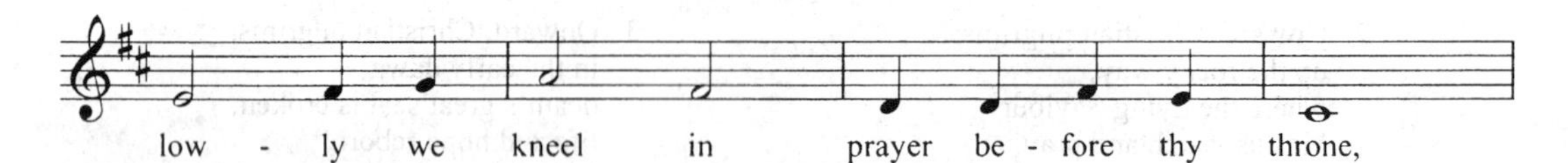

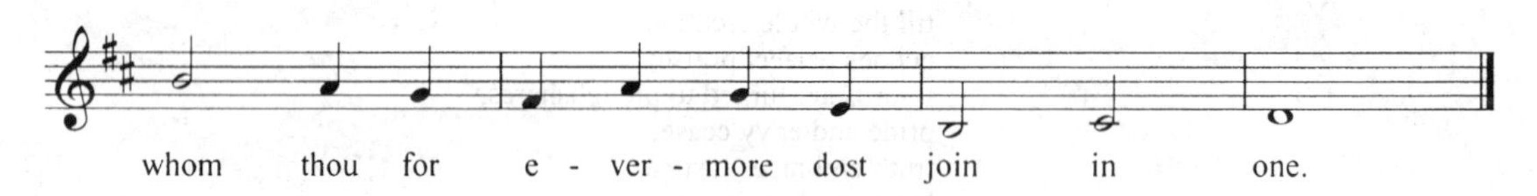

2. O perfect life,
be thou their full assurance
of tender charity
and steadfast faith,
of patient hope
and quiet, brave endurance,
with childlike trust that fears
not pain nor death.

3. Grant them the joy
which brightens earthly sorrow,
grant them the peace
which calms all earthly strife;
and to life's day
the glorious unknown morrow
that dawns upon
eternal love and life.

Dorothy Frances Gurney (1858-1932) Richard Runciman Terry (1865-1938)

Text © Copyright Control.
Tune 2 © Copyright Oxford University Press, Great Clarendon Street, Oxford OX2 6DP, UK. Used by permission.

534 O praise ye the Lord!

Henry Williams Baker (1821-1877)
based on Psalms 148 and 150 alt.

Charles Hubert Hastings Parry (1848-1918)

TUNE 1: LAUDATE DOMINUM (PARRY) 10 10 11 11

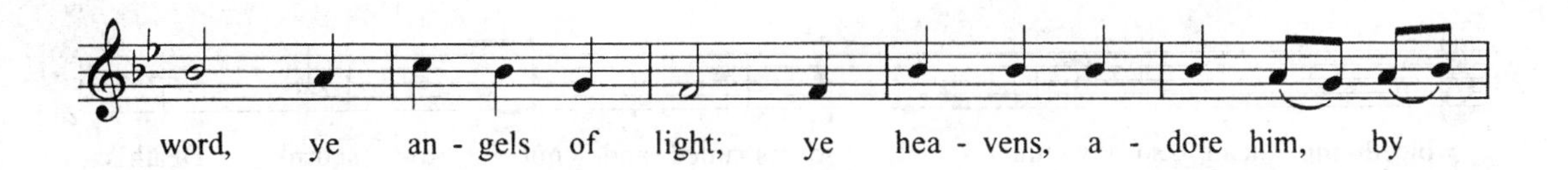

2. O praise ye the Lord! praise him upon earth,
in tuneful accord, all you of new birth;
praise him who hath brought you his grace from above,
praise him who hath taught you to sing of his love.

3. O praise ye the Lord! all things that give sound;
each jubilant chord re-echo around;
loud organs his glory forth tell in deep tone,
and, sweet harp, the story of what he hath done.

4. O praise ye the Lord! thanksgiving and song
to him be outpoured all ages along:
for love in creation, for heaven restored,
for grace of salvation, O praise ye the Lord!

Henry Williams Baker (1821-1877)
based on Psalms 148 and 150 alt.

Henry John Gauntlett (1805-1876)

TUNE 2: LAUDATE DOMINUM (GAUNTLETT) 10 10 11 11

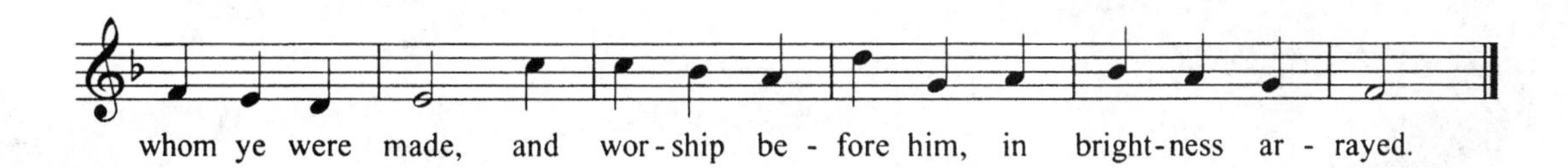

535 O sacred head, surrounded

Paul Gerhardt (1607-1676)
based on *Salve caput cruentatum*
trans. Henry Williams Baker (1821-1877)

Hans Leo Hassler (1564-1612)

PASSION CHORALE 76 76 D

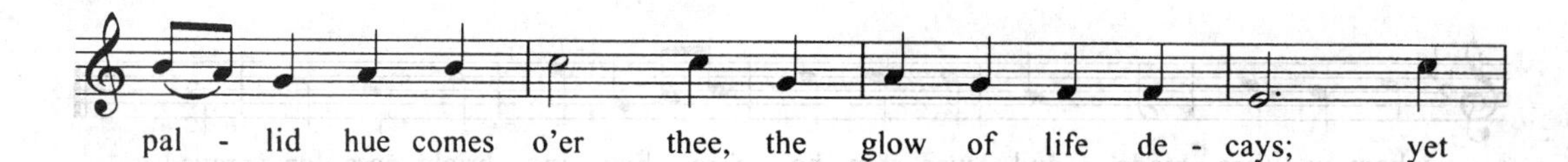

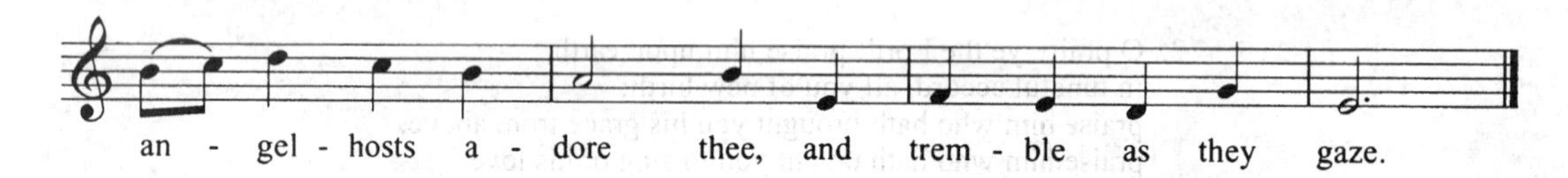

2. Thy comeliness and vigour
is withered up and gone,
and in thy wasted figure
I see death drawing on.
O agony and dying!
O love to sinners free!
Jesu, all grace supplying,
turn thou thy face on me.

3. In this thy bitter passion,
good Shepherd, think of me
with thy most sweet compassion,
unworthy though I be:
beneath thy cross abiding
for ever would I rest,
in thy dear love confiding,
and with thy presence blest.

536 O sing a song of Bethlehem

Louis F. Benson (1855-1930)

Traditional English melody adapted by
Ralph Vaughan Williams (1872-1958)

KINGSFOLD DCM

Music © Copyright Oxford University Press, Great Clarendon Street, Oxford OX2 6DP, UK.
Used by permission from the *English Hymnal.*

2. O sing a song of Nazareth,
of sunny days of joy,
O sing of fragrant flowers' breath
and of the sinless Boy:
for now the flow'rs of Nazareth
in ev'ry heart may grow;
now spreads the fame of his dear name
on all the winds that blow.

3. O sing a song of Galilee,
of lake and woods and hill,
of him who walked upon the sea
and bade its waves be still:
for though, like waves on Galilee,
dark seas of trouble roll,
when faith has heard the Master's word,
falls peace upon the soul.

4. O sing a song of Calvary,
its glory and dismay;
of him who hung upon the tree,
and took our sins away;
for he who died on Calvary
is risen from the grave,
and Christ our Lord, by heaven adored,
is mighty now to save.

537 O strength and stay

St Ambrose (c.340-397)
trans. John Ellerton (1826-1893)
and Fenton John Anthony Hort (1828-1892)

John Bacchus Dykes (1823-1876)

STRENGTH AND STAY 11 10 11 10

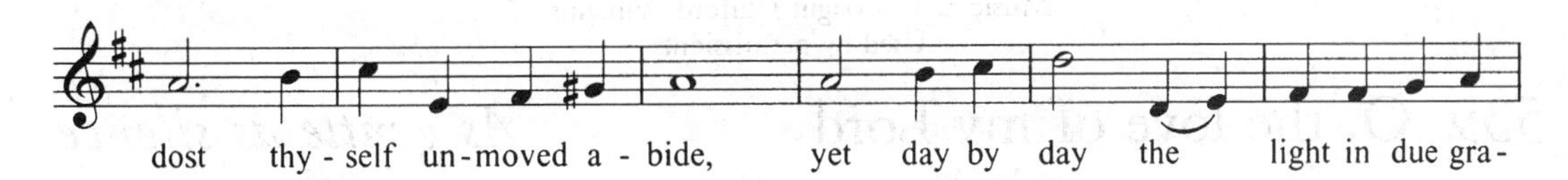

2. Grant to life's day a calm unclouded ending,
an eve untouched by shadows of decay,
the brightness of a holy death-bed blending
with dawning glories of th'eternal day.

3. Hear us, O Father, gracious and forgiving,
through Jesus Christ thy co-eternal Word,
who with the Holy Ghost by all things living
now and to endless ages art adored.

538 O the deep, deep love of Jesus!

Samuel Trevor Francis (1834-1925)

From an anthem by Thomas Williams (1869-1944)

EBENEZER (TON-Y-BOTEL) 87 87 D

2. O the deep, deep love of Jesus!
Spread his praise from shore to shore,
how he loveth, ever loveth,
changeth never, nevermore;
how he watches o'er his loved ones,
died to call them all his own;
how for them he intercedeth,
watcheth o'er them from the throne.

3. O the deep, deep love of Jesus!
Love of ev'ry love the best;
'tis an ocean vast of blessing,
'tis a haven sweet of rest.
O the deep, deep love of Jesus!
'Tis a heav'n of heav'ns to me;
and it lifts me up to glory,
for its lifts me up to thee.

Music © Copyright Clifford Williams.
Used by permission.

539 O, the love of my Lord

As gentle as silence

Words and music: Estelle White (b.1925)

AS GENTLE AS SILENCE 10 9 12 10

© Copyright McCrimmon Publishing Co. Ltd., 10-12 High Street, Great Wakering, Southend-on-Sea, Essex SS3 0EQ, UK. Used by arrangement.

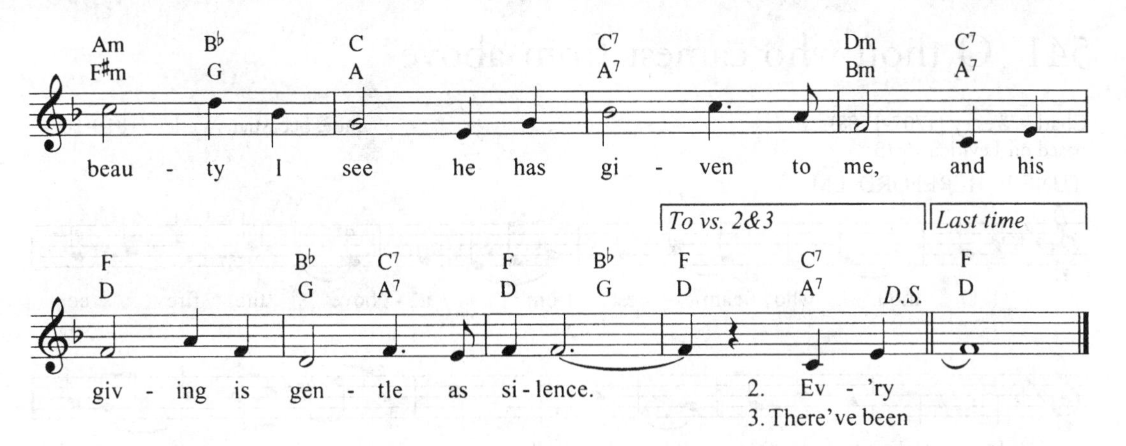

2. Ev'ry day, ev'ry hour, ev'ry moment
have been blessed by the strength of his love.
At the turn of each tide he is there at my side,
and his touch is as gentle as silence.

3. There've been times when I've turned from his presence,
and I've walked other paths, other ways;
but I've called on his name in the dark of my shame,
and his mercy was gentle as silence.

540 O thou, who at thy Eucharist didst pray

William Harry Turton (1856-1938)
based on John 17

Orlando Gibbons (1583-1625)

SONG 1 10 10 10 10 10 10

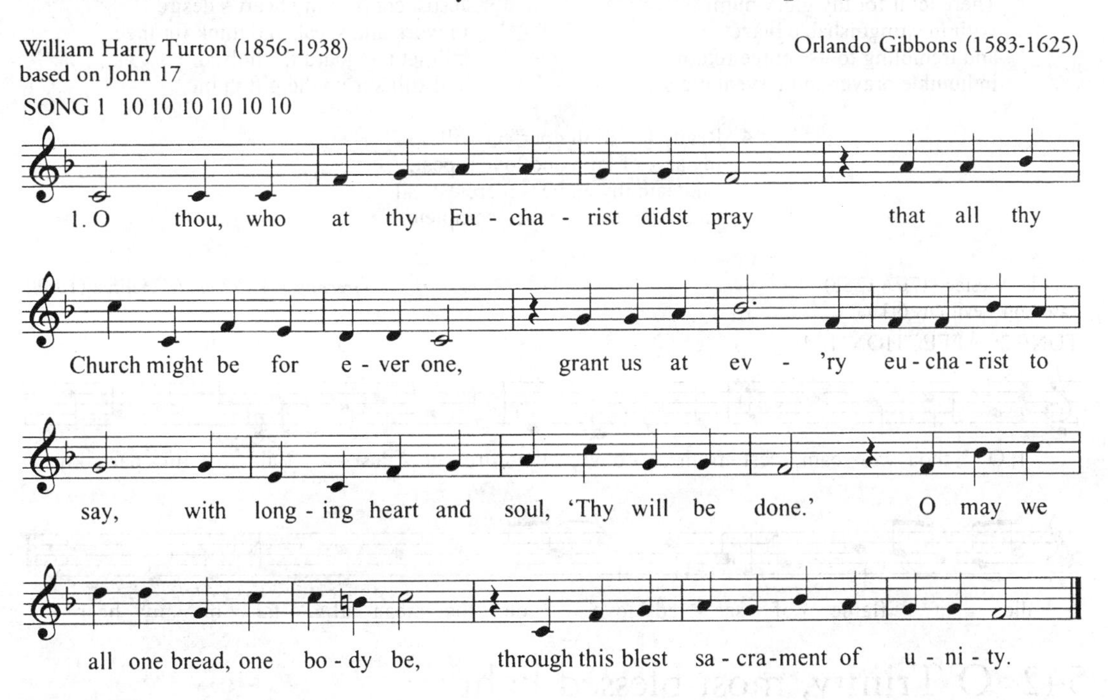

2. For all thy Church, O Lord, we intercede;
make thou our sad divisions soon to cease;
draw us the nearer each to each, we plead,
by drawing all to thee, O Prince of Peace:
thus may we all one bread, one body be,
through this blest sacrament of unity.

3. We pray thee too for wand'rers from thy fold;
O bring them back, good Shepherd of the sheep,
back to the faith which saints believed of old,
back to the Church which still that faith doth keep;
soon may we all one bread, one body be,
through this blest sacrament of unity.

4. So, Lord, at length when sacraments shall cease,
may we be one with all thy Church above,
one with thy saints in one unbroken peace,
one with thy saints in one unbounded love;
more blessèd still, in peace and love to be
one with the Trinity in unity.

Text © Copyright Control

541 O thou who camest from above

Charles Wesley (1707-1788)
based on Leviticus 6:13

Samuel Sebastian Wesley (1810-1876)

TUNE 1: HEREFORD LM

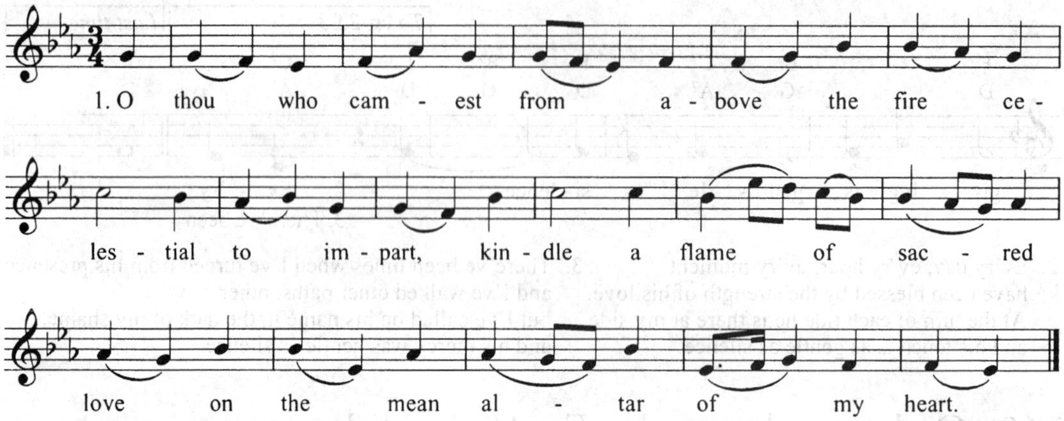

1. O thou who cam - est from a - bove the fire ce - les - tial to im - part, kin - dle a flame of sac - red love on the mean al - tar of my heart.

2. There let it for thy glory burn
with inextinguishable blaze,
and trembling to its source return
in humble prayer and fervent praise.

3. Jesus, confirm my heart's desire
to work and speak and think for thee;
still let me guard the holy fire
and still stir up the gift in me.

4. Ready for all thy perfect will,
my acts of faith and love repeat,
till death thy endless mercies seal,
and make the sacrifice complete.

Charles Wesley (1707-1788)
based on Leviticus 6:13

Greenwood's Psalmody, Halifax (1838)

TUNE 2: AFFECTION LM

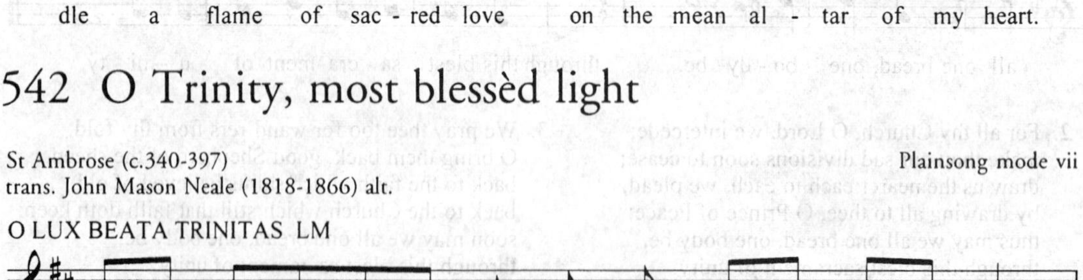

1. O thou who cam - est from a - bove, the fire ce - les - tial to im - part, kin - dle a flame of sac - red love on the mean al - tar of my heart.

542 O Trinity, most blessèd light

St Ambrose (c.340-397)
trans. John Mason Neale (1818-1866) alt.

Plainsong mode vii

O LUX BEATA TRINITAS LM

1. O Tri - ni - ty, most bles - sèd light,
O U - ni - ty of sov - 'reign might,

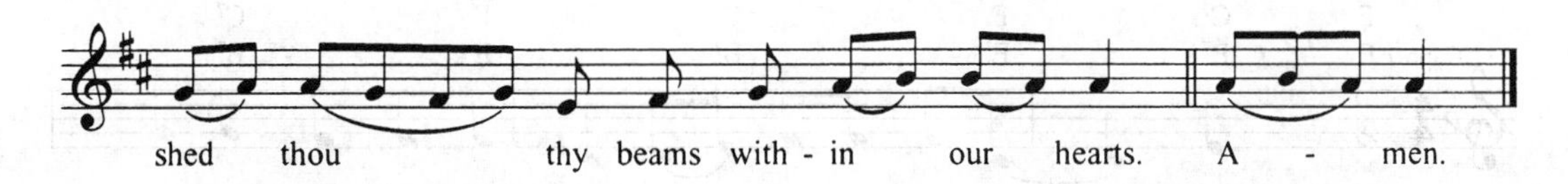

2. To thee our morning song of praise,
   to thee our evening prayer we raise;
   thee may our souls for evermore
   in lowly reverence adore.

3. All praise to God the Father be,
   all praise, eternal Son, to thee,
   whom with the Spirit we adore,
   for ever and for evermore. Amen.

543 Our blest Redeemer, ere he breathed

Harriet Auber (1773-1862) John Bacchus Dykes (1823-1876)

ST CUTHBERT 86 84

2. He came in tongues of living flame,
   to teach, convince, subdue;
   all-pow'rful as the wind he came,
   as viewless too.

3. He came sweet influence to impart,
   a gracious, willing guest,
   while he can find one humble heart
   wherein to rest.

4. And his that gentle voice we hear,
   soft as the breath of ev'n,
   that checks each fault, that calms each fear,
   and speaks of heav'n.

5. And ev'ry virtue we possess,
   and ev'ry vict'ry won,
   and ev'ry thought of holiness,
   are his alone.

6. Spirit of purity and grace,
   our weakness, pitying, see:
   O make our hearts thy dwelling-place,
   and worthier thee.

544 Our Father (Caribbean)

Traditional Caribbean
based on Matthew 6:9-13 and Luke 11:2-4

Traditional Caribbean melody

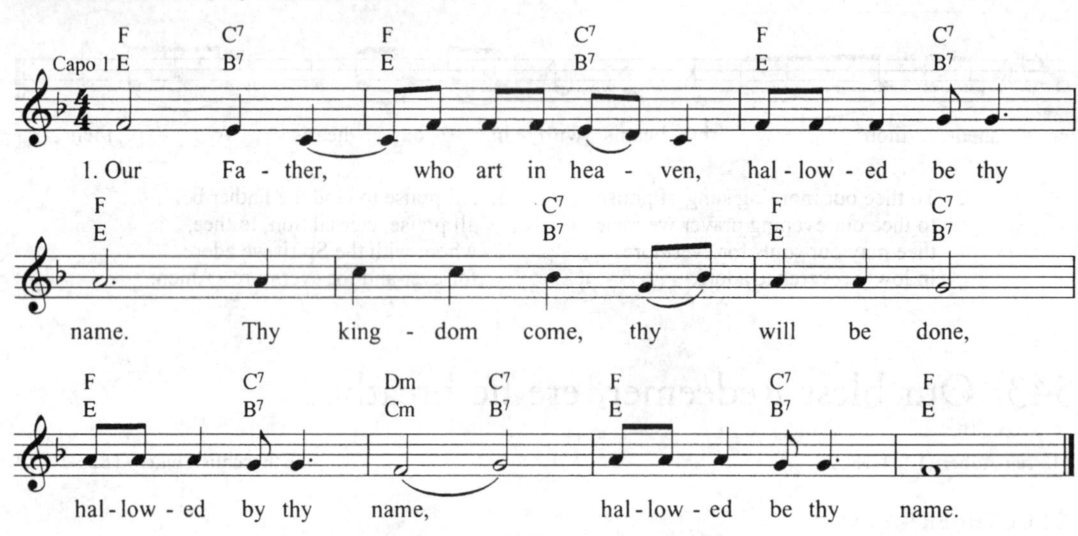

2. On earth as it is in heaven,
   hallowed be thy name.
   Give us this day our daily bread,
   hallowed be thy name. (x2)

3. Forgive us our trespasses,
   as we forgive those who trespass against us.

4. Lead us not into temptation,
   but deliver us from all that is evil.

5. For thine is the kingdom, the power, and the glory,
   for ever, and for ever and ever.

6. Amen, amen, it shall be so.
   Amen, amen, it shall be so.

545 Our Father (White)

Matthew 6:9-13 and Luke 11:2-4

Estelle White (b.1925)

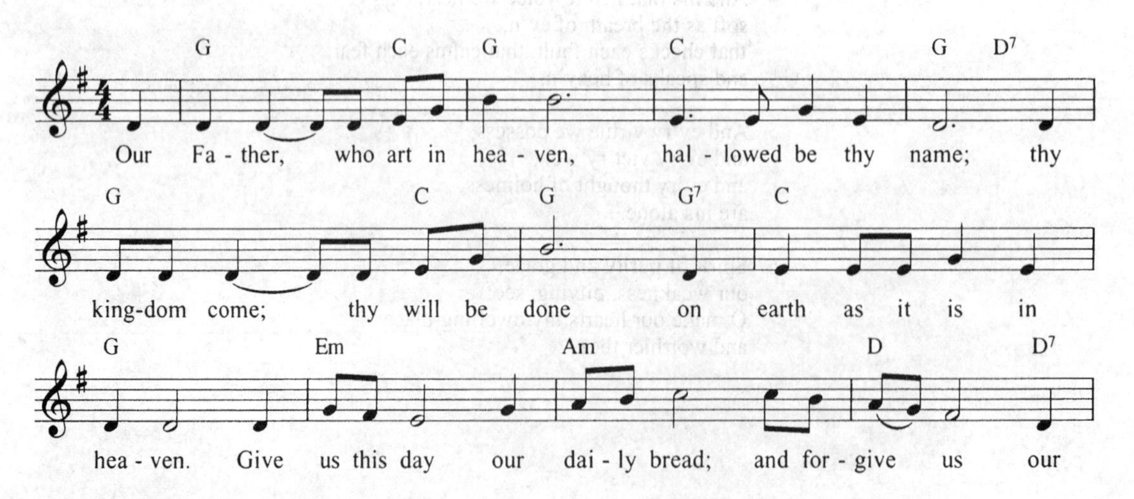

© Copyright 1974, 1976 Kevin Mayhew Ltd.

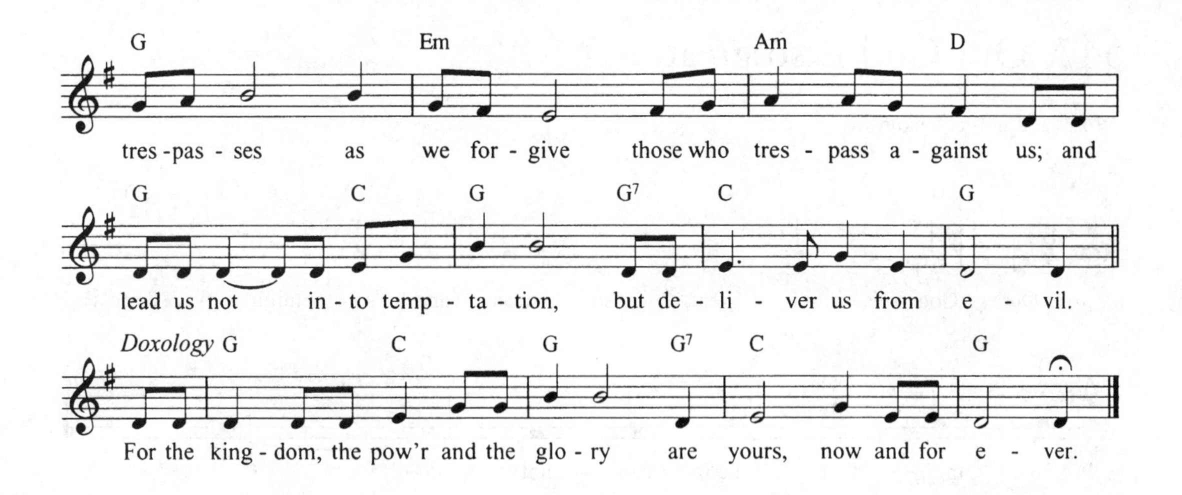

546 Our Father (Wiener)

Matthew 6:9-13 and Luke 11:2-4

Julian Wiener

© Copyright 1984 Kevin Mayhew Ltd.

547 Our God is so great

Words and music: Unknown

548 Our God loves us

v. 1: unknown
vs. 2-5: Sandra Joan Billington (b.1946)

Johann Martini (1741-1816)

PLAISIR D'AMOUR 4 6 6 5

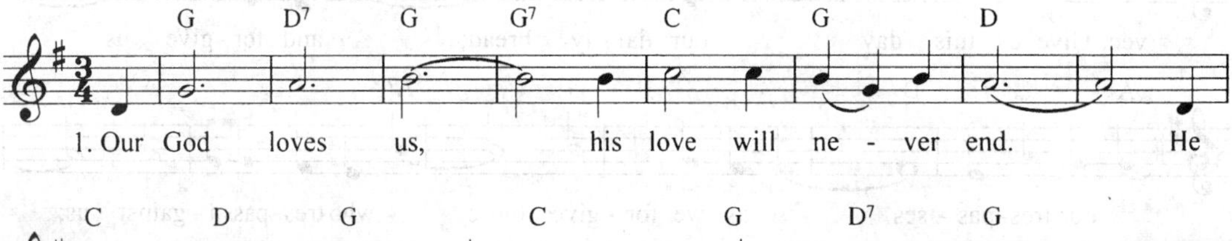

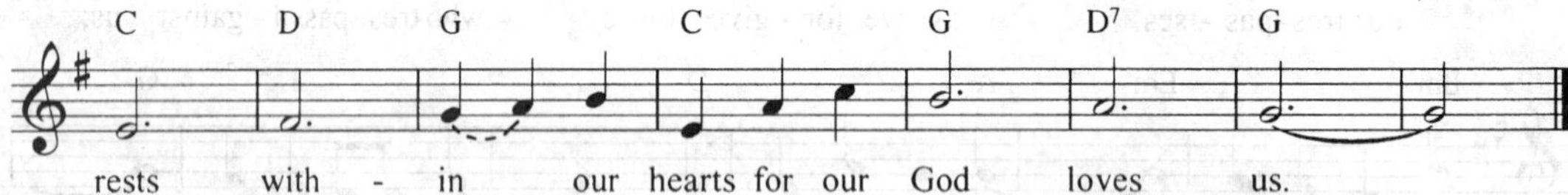

2. His gentle hand
he stretches over us.
Though storm-clouds threaten the day,
he will set us free.

3. He comes to us
in sharing bread and wine.
He brings us life that will reach
past the end of time.

4. Our God loves us,
his faithful love endures,
and we will live like his child
held in love secure.

5. The joys of love
as off'rings now we bring.
The pains of love will be lost
in the praise we sing.

Text © Copyright 1976, 1996 Kevin Mayhew Ltd.

549 Out of our failure to create

Fred Kaan (b.1929)

Later form of a melody from Holdroyd's *The Spiritual Man's Companion* (1753)

ST NICHOLAS CM

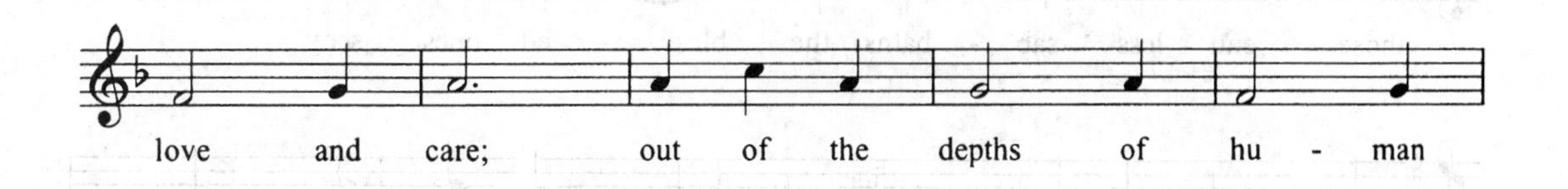

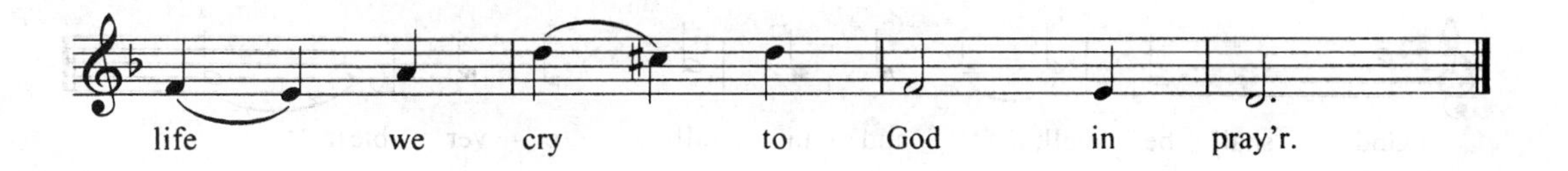

2. Out of the darkness of our time,
of days forever gone,
our souls are longing for the light,
like watchers for the dawn.

3. Out of the depths we cry to God
whose mercy ends our night.
Our human hole-and-corner ways
by God are brought to light.

4. Hope in the Lord whose timeless love
gives laughter where we wept;
who ev'ry time, at ev'ry point
his word has giv'n and kept.

Text © Copyright 1968 Stainer & Bell Ltd., P.O. Box 110, Victoria House, 23 Gruneisen Road, Finchley, London N3 1DZ, UK. Used by permission.

550 O what their joy and their glory must be

Peter Abelard (1079-1142)
trans. John Mason Neale (1818-1866) alt.

La Feilée, *Méthode* (1808)

O QUANTA QUALIA 10 10 10 10

1. O what their joy and their glo - ry must be,
those end - less sab - baths the bless - ed ones see;
crown for the va - liant, to wea - ry ones rest;
God shall be all, and in all e - ver blest.

2. What are the Monarch, his court, and his throne?
What are the peace and the joy that they own?
O that the blest ones, who in it have share,
all that they feel could as fully declare.

3. Truly Jerusalem name we that shore,
'Vision of peace,' that brings joy evermore.
Wish and fulfilment can severed be ne'er,
nor the thing prayed for come short of the prayer.

4. There, where no troubles distraction can bring,
we the sweet anthems of Sion shall sing,
while for thy grace, Lord, their voices of praise
thy blessèd people eternally raise.

5. There dawns no sabbath, no sabbath is o'er,
those sabbath-keepers have one evermore;
one and unending is that triumph-song
which to the angels and us shall belong.

6. Now in the meanwhile, with hearts raised on high,
we for that country must yearn and must sigh;
seeking Jerusalem, dear native land,
through our long exile on Babylon's strand.

7. Low before him with our praises we fall,
of whom, and in whom, and through whom are all:
of whom, the Father; and in whom, the Son;
through whom, the Spirit, with them ever One.

551 O worship the King

Robert Grant (1779-1838)
based on Psalm 104

William Croft (1678-1727)
in *A Supplement to the New Version* (1708)

HANOVER 10 10 11 11

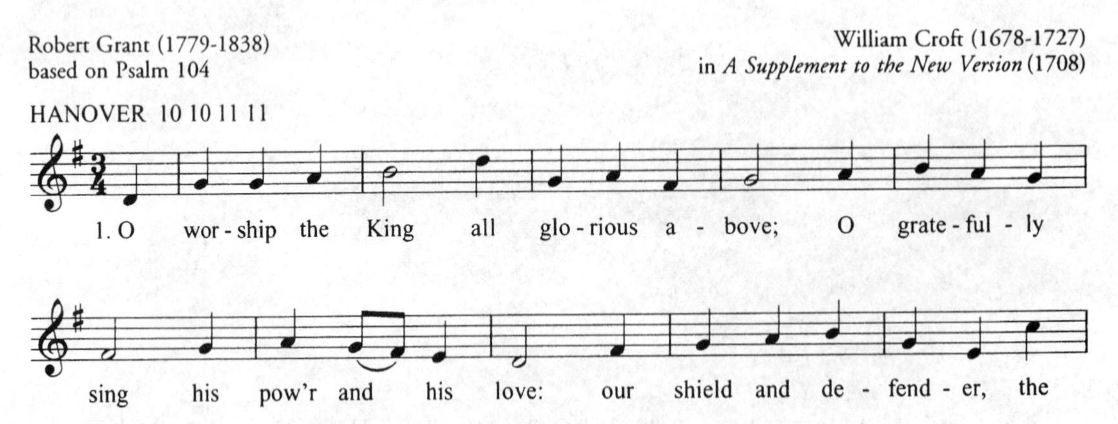

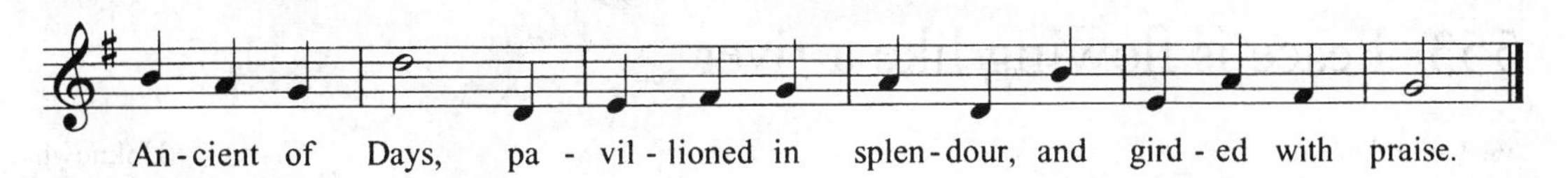

2. O tell of his might, O sing of his grace,
whose robe is the light, whose canopy space;
his chariots of wrath the deep thunder-clouds form,
and dark is his path on the wings of the storm.

3. This earth, with its store of wonders untold,
almighty, thy pow'r hath founded of old:
hath stablished it fast by a changeless decree,
and round it hath cast, like a mantle, the sea.

4. Thy bountiful care what tongue can recite?
It breathes in the air, it shines in the light;
it streams from the hills, it descends to the plain,
and sweetly distils in the dew and the rain.

5. Frail children of dust, and feeble as frail,
in thee do we trust, nor find thee to fail;
thy mercies how tender, how firm to the end!
Our maker, defender, redeemer, and friend.

6. O measureless might, ineffable love,
while angels delight to hymn thee above,
thy humbler creation, though feeble their lays,
with true adoration shall sing to thy praise.

552 O worship the Lord in the beauty of holiness

John Samuel Bewley Monsell (1811-1875)

Melody from the *Rheinhardt MS*, Üttingen (1754)

WAS LEBET 13 10 13 10

2. Low at his feet lay thy burden of carefulness:
high on his heart he will bear it for thee,
comfort thy sorrows, and answer thy prayerfulness,
guiding thy steps as may best for thee be.

3. Fear not to enter his courts in the slenderness
of the poor wealth thou wouldst reckon as thine:
truth in its beauty, and love in its tenderness,
these are the off'rings to lay on his shrine.

4. These, though we bring them in trembling and fearfulness,
he will accept for the name that is dear;
mornings of joy give for evenings of tearfulness,
trust for our trembling and hope for our fear.

553 Peace is flowing like a river

Verse 5 © Copyright 1999 Kevin Mayhew Ltd.

554 Peace, perfect peace in this dark world of sin

Edward Henry Bickersteth (1825-1906) — George Thomas Caldbeck (1852-1918) and Charles Vincent (1852-1934)

TUNE 1: PAX TECUM 10 10

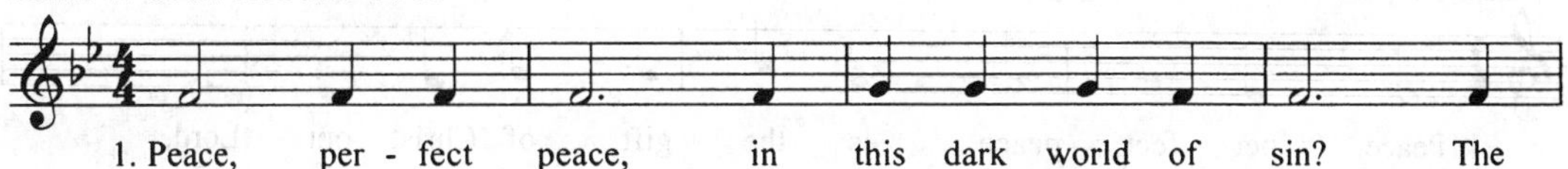

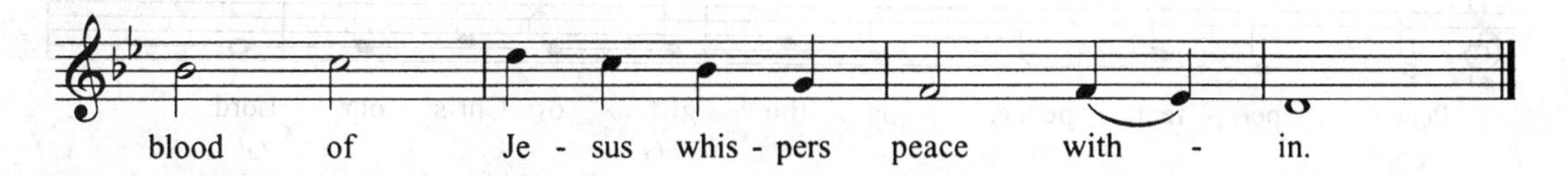

2. Peace, perfect peace, by thronging duties pressed?
   To do the will of Jesus, this is rest.

3. Peace, perfect peace, with sorrows surging round?
   In Jesus' presence naught but calm is found.

4. Peace, perfect peace, with loved ones far away?
   In Jesus' keeping we are safe, and they.

5. Peace, perfect peace, our future all unknown?
   Jesus we know, and he is on the throne.

6. Peace, perfect peace, death shad'wing us and ours?
   Jesus has vanquished death and all its pow'rs.

7. It is enough: earth's struggles soon shall cease,
   and Jesus call us to heav'n's perfect peace.

Edward Henry Bickersteth (1825-1906) — Orlando Gibbons (1583-1625)

TUNE 2: SONG 46 10 10

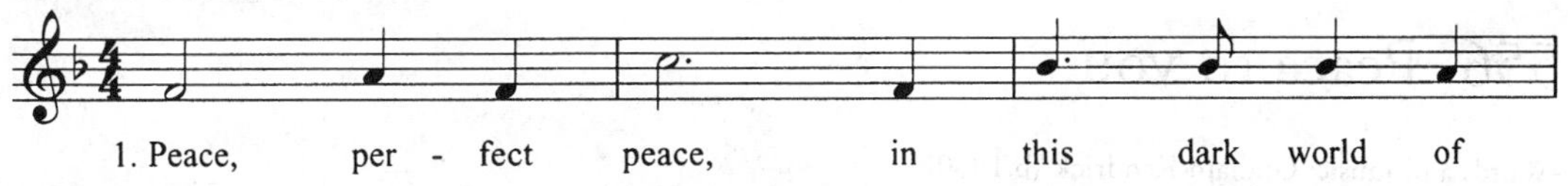

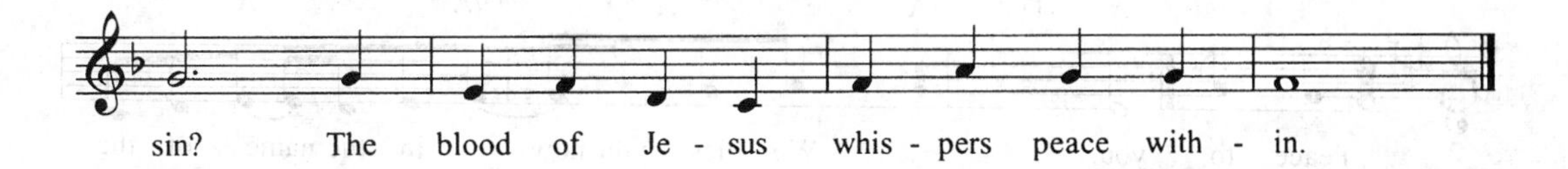

Tune 1 © Copyright Control.

555 Peace, perfect peace, is the gift

Words and music: Kevin Mayhew (b.1942)

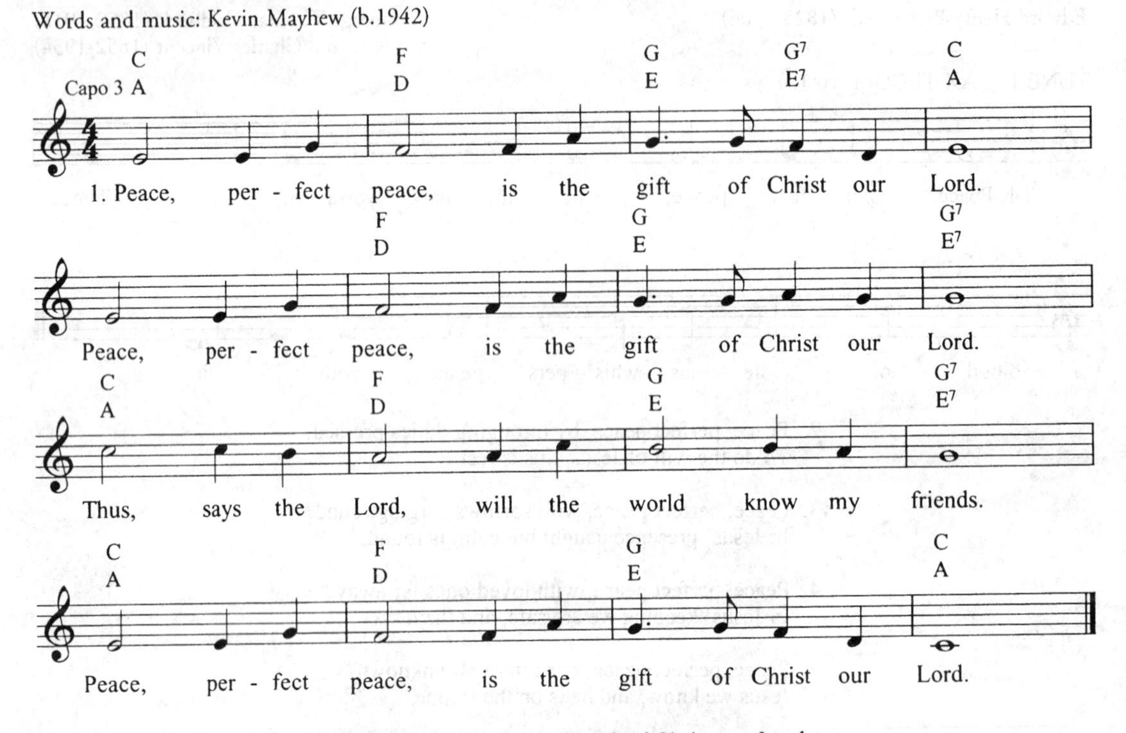

2. Love, perfect love, is the gift of Christ our Lord . . .

3. Faith, perfect faith, is the gift of Christ our Lord . . .

4. Hope, perfect hope, is the gift of Christ our Lord . . .

5. Joy, perfect joy, is the gift of Christ our Lord . . .

© Copyright 1976 Kevin Mayhew Ltd.

556 Peace to you

Words and music: Graham Kendrick (b.1950)

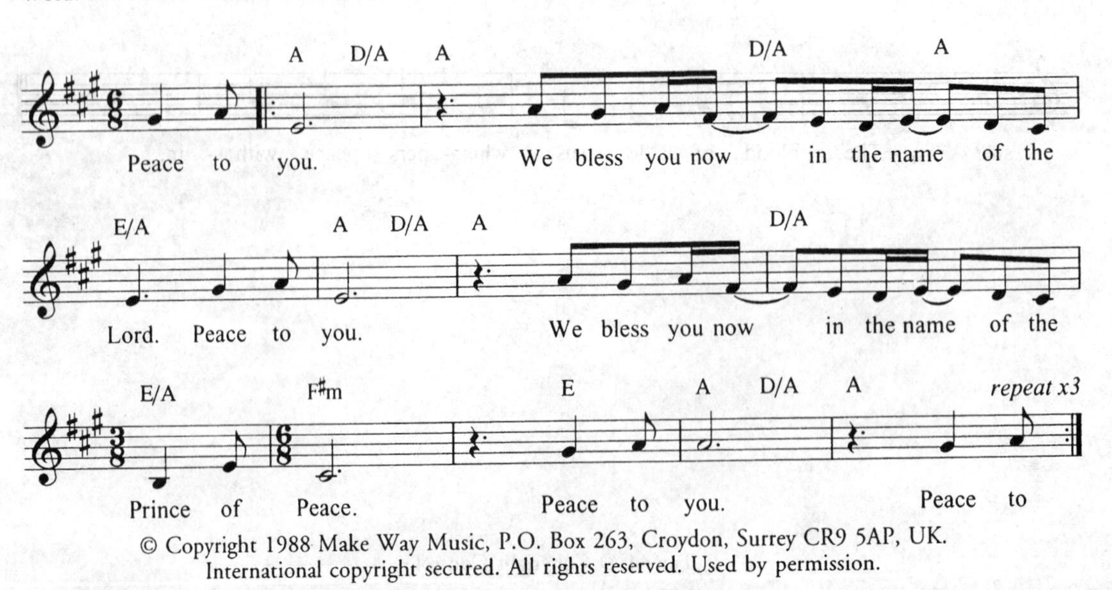

© Copyright 1988 Make Way Music, P.O. Box 263, Croydon, Surrey CR9 5AP, UK.
International copyright secured. All rights reserved. Used by permission.

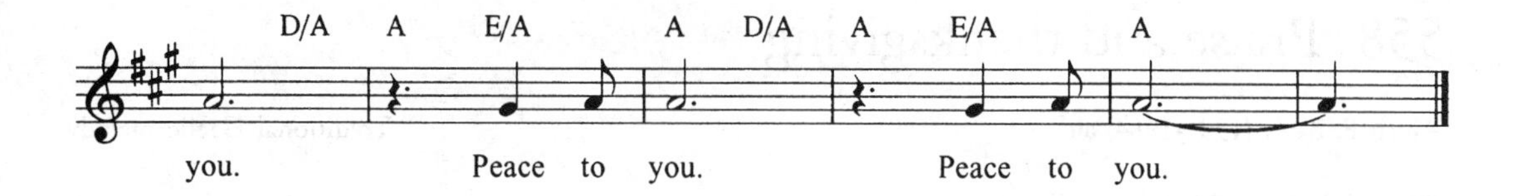

557 People, look east

Eleanor Farjeon (1881-1965)

Traditional Besançon melody

CAROL OF THE ADVENT 87 98 and Refrain

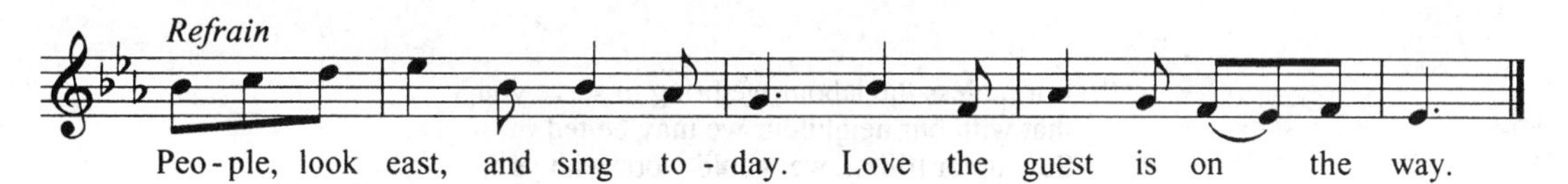

2. Furrows, be glad. Though the earth is bare,
one more seed is planted there:
give up your strength the seed to nourish,
that in course the flow'r may flourish.

People, look east, and sing today:
Love the rose is on the way.

3. Birds, though ye long have ceased to build,
guard the nest that must be filled.
Even the hour when wings are frozen
he for fledging-time has chosen.

People, look east, and sing today:
Love the bird is on the way.

4. Stars, keep the watch. When night is dim
one more light the bowl shall brim,
shining beyond the frosty weather,
bright as sun and moon together.

People, look east, and sing today:
Love the star is on the way.

5. Angels, announce to man and beast
him who cometh from the east.
Set ev'ry peak and valley humming
with the word, the Lord is coming.

People, look east, and sing today:
Love the Lord is on the way.

Text © Copyright David Higham Associates Ltd., 5-8 Lower John Street, Golden Square, London W1R 4HA, UK. Used by permission.

558 Praise and thanksgiving

Albert F. Bayly (1901-1984) alt.

Traditional Gaelic melody

BUNESSAN 55 54 D

liv - ing you have made good; har - vest of sown fields, fruits of the

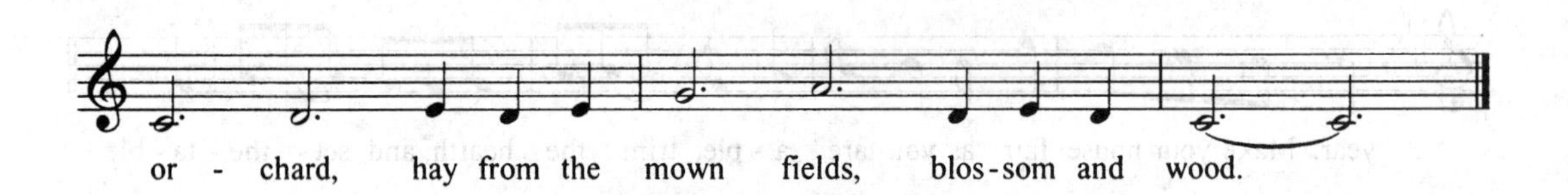

2. Lord, bless the labour we bring to serve you,
that with our neighbour we may be fed.
Sowing or tilling, we would work with you;
harvesting, milling, for daily bread.

3. Father, providing food for your children,
your wisdom guiding teaches us share
one with another, so that, rejoicing,
sister and brother may know your care.

4. Then will your blessing reach ev'ry people;
each one confessing your gracious hand:
where you are reigning no one will hunger,
your love sustaining fruitful the land.

Text © Copyright 1988 Oxford University Press, Great Clarendon Street,
Oxford OX2 6DP. UK. Used by permission.

559 Praise God for the harvest

Brian A. Wren (b.1936)

Traditional English melody

STOWEY 11 11 11 11

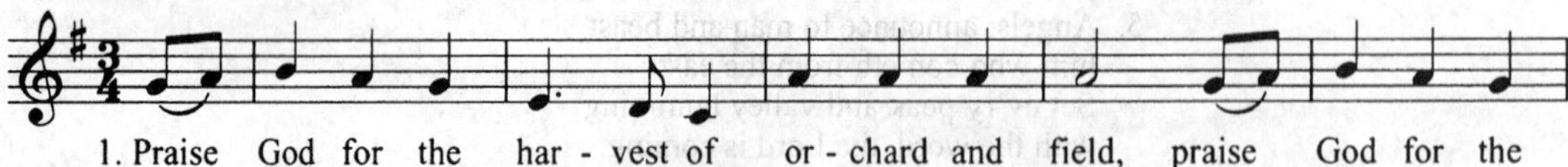

peo - ple who ga - ther their yield, the long hours of la - bour, the

Text © Copyright 1974, 1996 Stainer & Bell Ltd., P.O. Box 110, Victoria House, 23 Gruneisen Road,
Finchley, London N3 1DZ, UK. Used by permission.

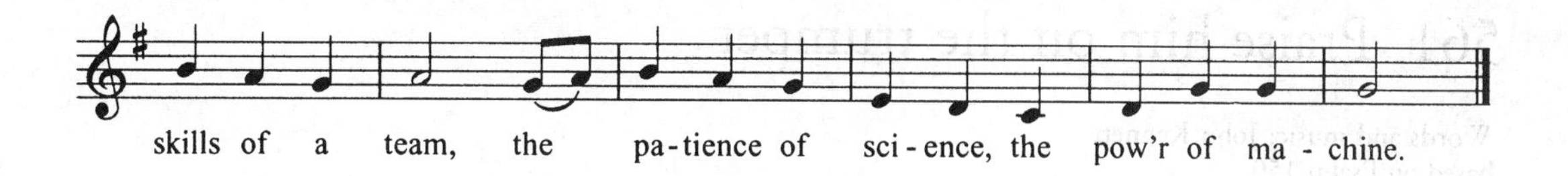

2. Praise God for the harvest that comes from afar,
from market and harbour, the sea and the shore:
foods packed and transported, and gathered and grown
by God-given neighbours, unseen and unknown.

3. Praise God for the harvest that's quarried and mined,
then sifted, and smelted, or shaped and refined:
for oil and for iron, for copper and coal,
praise God, who in love has provided them all.

4. Praise God for the harvest of science and skill,
the urge to discover, create and fulfil:
for dreams and inventions that promise to gain
a future more hopeful, a world more humane.

5. Praise God for the harvest of mercy and love
from leaders and peoples who struggle and serve
with patience and kindness, that all may be led
to freedom and justice, and all may be fed.

560 Praise God from whom all blessings flow *Doxologyy*

Thomas Ken (1637-1710)

Jimmy Owens

DOXOLOGY LM

Music © Copyright 1972 Bud John Songs/EMI Christian Music Publishing. Administered by CopyCare, P.O. Box 77, Hailsham, East Sussex BN27 3EF, UK. (music@copycare.com). Used by permission.

561 Praise him on the trumpet

Words and music: John Kennett
based on Psalm 150

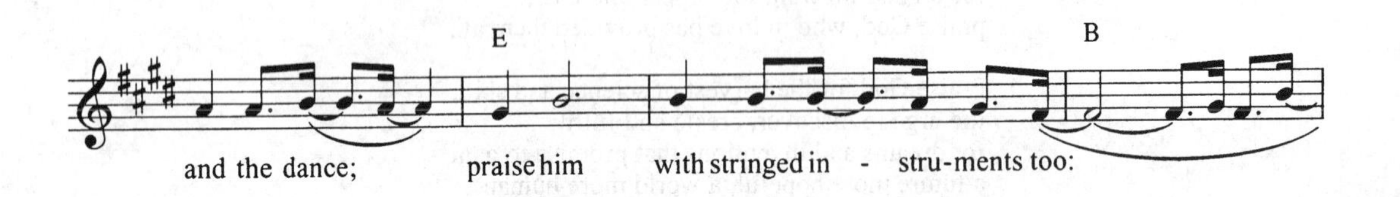

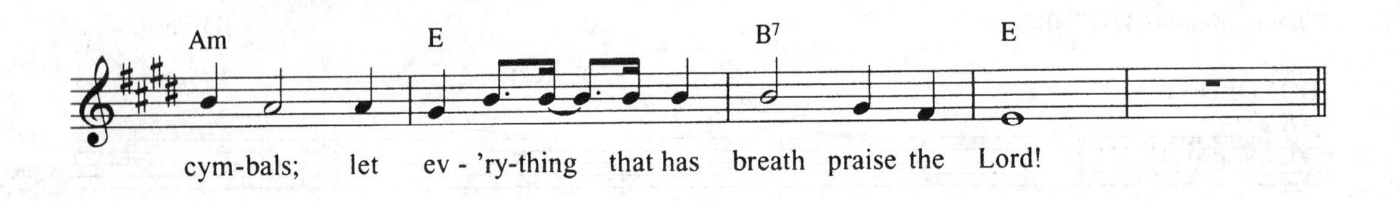

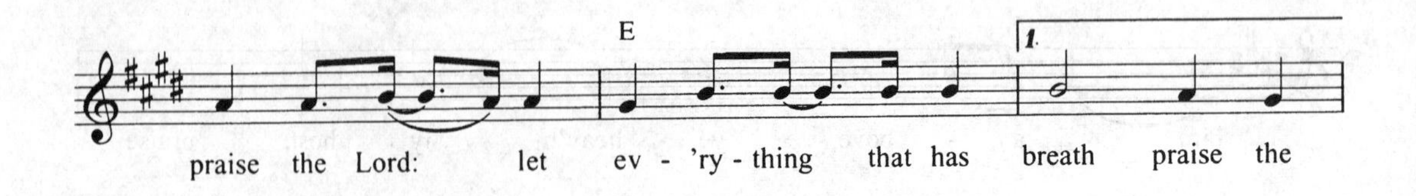

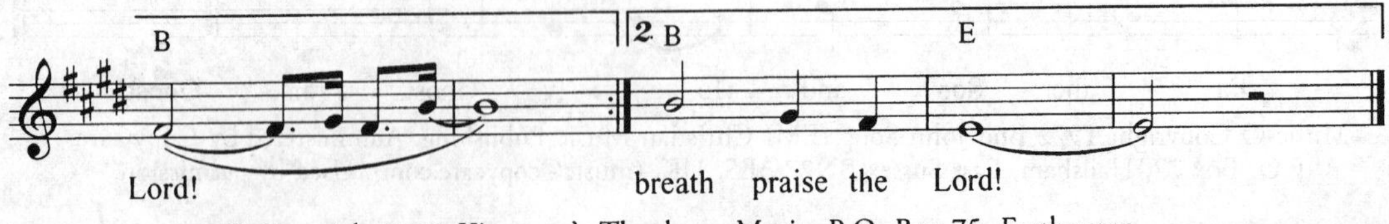

© Copyright 1981 Kingsway's Thankyou Music, P.O. Box 75, Eastbourne,
East Sussex BN23 6NW, UK. (tym@kingsway.co.uk). Used by permission.

562 Praise him, praise him

Frances Jane van Alstyne (Fanny J. Crosby) (1820-1915) | Chester G. Allen (1838-1878)

PRAISE HIM 12 10 12 10 11 10 12 10

2. Praise him, praise him! Jesus, our blessèd Redeemer!
For our sins he suffered, and bled, and died!
He – our rock, our hope of eternal salvation,
hail him, hail him! Jesus the crucified!
Sound his praises – Jesus who bore our sorrows,
love unbounded, wonderful, deep and strong.

3. Praise him, praise him! Jesus, our blessèd Redeemer!
Heav'nly portals, loud with hosannas ring!
Jesus, Saviour, reigneth for ever and ever:
crown him, crown him! Prophet, and Priest, and King!
Christ is coming, over the world victorious,
pow'r and glory unto the Lord belong.

563 Praise him, praise him, all his children

Percy Dearmer (1867-1936)
based on Carey Bonner (1859-1938)

Martin Shaw (1875-1958)

TUNE 1: MANOR STREET 10 6 10 6

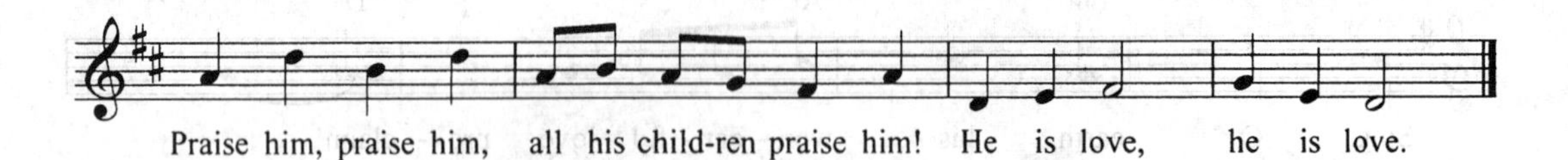

2. Thank him, thank him, all his children thank him!
He is love, he is love.
Thank him, thank him, all his children thank him!
He is love, he is love.

3. Love him, love him, all his children love him!
He is love, he is love.
Love him, love him, all his children love him!
He is love, he is love.

4. Crown him, crown him, all his children crown him!
He is love, he is love.
Crown him, crown him, all his children crown him!
He is love, he is love.

Percy Dearmer (1867-1936)
based on Carey Bonner

Carey Bonner (1859-1938)

TUNE 2: HE IS LOVE 10 6 10 6

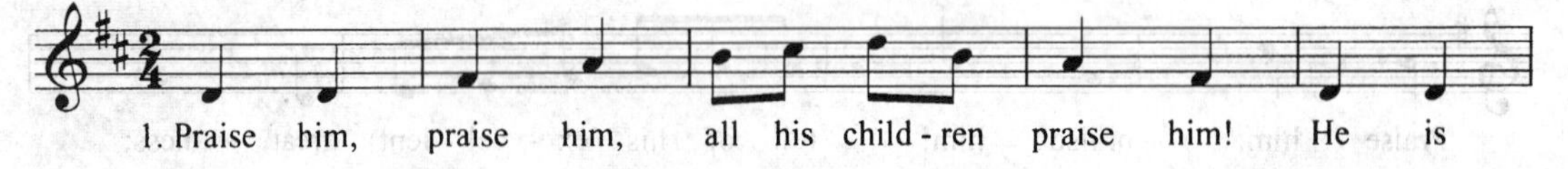

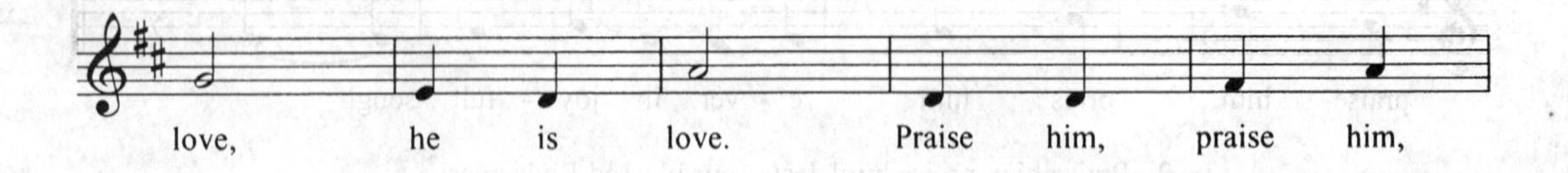

Text © Copyright Oxford University Press, Great Clarendon Street,
Oxford OX2 6DP, UK. Used by permission.
Tune 1 © Copyright J. Curwen & Sons, 8/9 Frith Street, London W1V 5TZ, UK. Used by permission.
Tune 2 ©Copyright Control.

564 Praise him, praise him, praise him

Words and music: Unknown

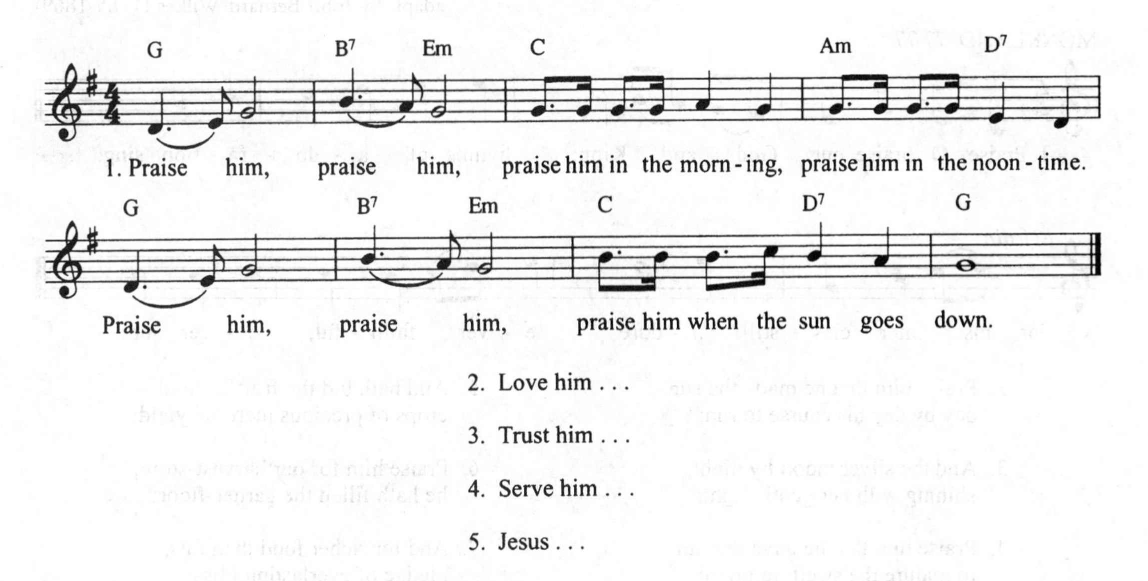

2. Love him . . .

3. Trust him . . .

4. Serve him . . .

5. Jesus . . .

565 Praise, my soul, the King of heaven

Henry Francis Lyte (1793-1847)
based on Psalm 103

John Goss (1800-1880)

PRAISE, MY SOUL 87 87 87

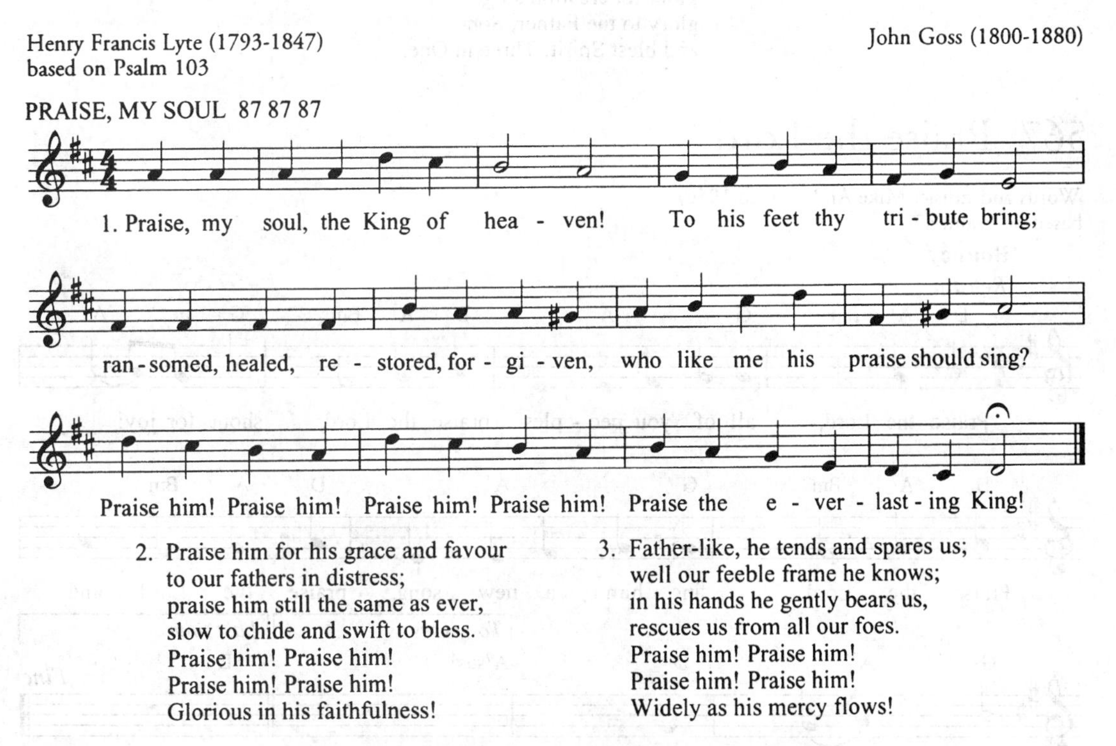

2. Praise him for his grace and favour
to our fathers in distress;
praise him still the same as ever,
slow to chide and swift to bless.
Praise him! Praise him!
Praise him! Praise him!
Glorious in his faithfulness!

3. Father-like, he tends and spares us;
well our feeble frame he knows;
in his hands he gently bears us,
rescues us from all our foes.
Praise him! Praise him!
Praise him! Praise him!
Widely as his mercy flows!

4. Angels, help us to adore him;
ye behold him face to face;
sun and moon, bow down before him,
dwellers all in time and space.
Praise him! Praise him!
Praise him! Praise him!
Praise with us the God of grace!

566 Praise, O praise our God and King

Henry Williams Baker (1821-1877)

From *Hymn Tunes of the United Brethren*
adapt. by John Bernard Wilkes (1785-1869)

MONKLAND 77 77

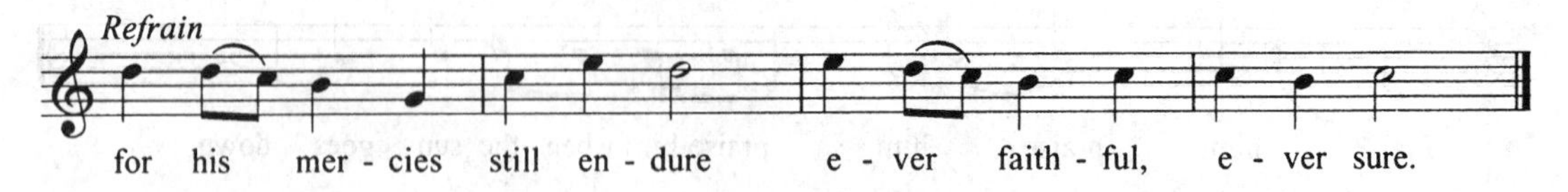

2. Praise him that he made the sun
day by day his course to run:

3. And the silver moon by night,
shining with her gentle light:

4. Praise him that he gave the rain
to mature the swelling grain:

5. And hath bid the fruitful field
crops of precious increase yield:

6. Praise him for our harvest-store;
he hath filled the garner-floor:

7. And for richer food than this,
pledge of everlasting bliss:

8. Glory to our bounteous King;
glory let creation sing:
glory to the Father, Son
and blest Spirit, Three in One.

567 Praise the Lord

Words and music: Mike Anderson (b.1956)
based on Psalm 47

Bouncy

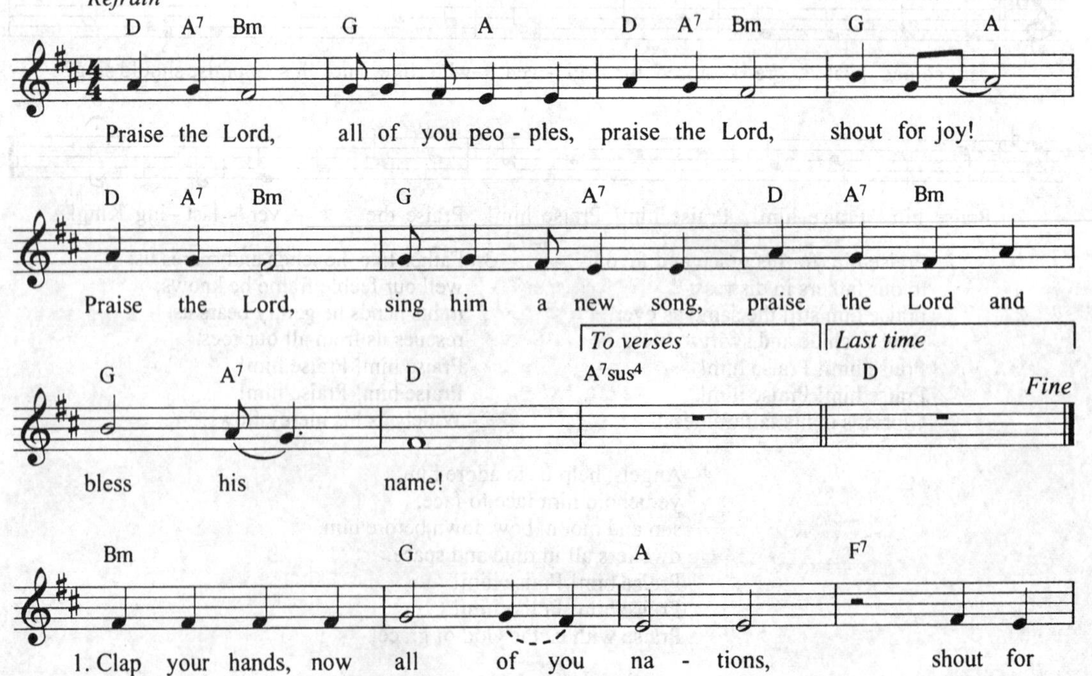

© Copyright 1999 Kevin Mayhew Ltd.

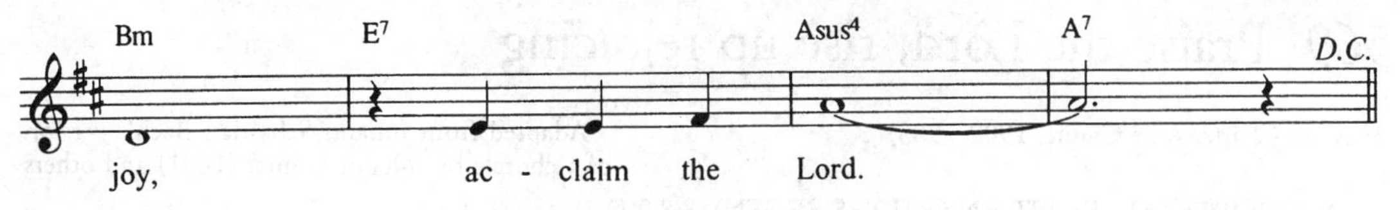

2. He goes up to shouts which acclaim him,
   he goes up to trumpet blast.

3. Let the music sound for the Lord, now;
   let your chords resound in praise.

4. He is King of all the nations;
   honour him by singing psalms.

568 Praise the Lord of heaven

Timothy Dudley-Smith (b.1926)
based on Psalm 148

Malcolm Archer (b.1952)

VICARS' CLOSE 76 76 D

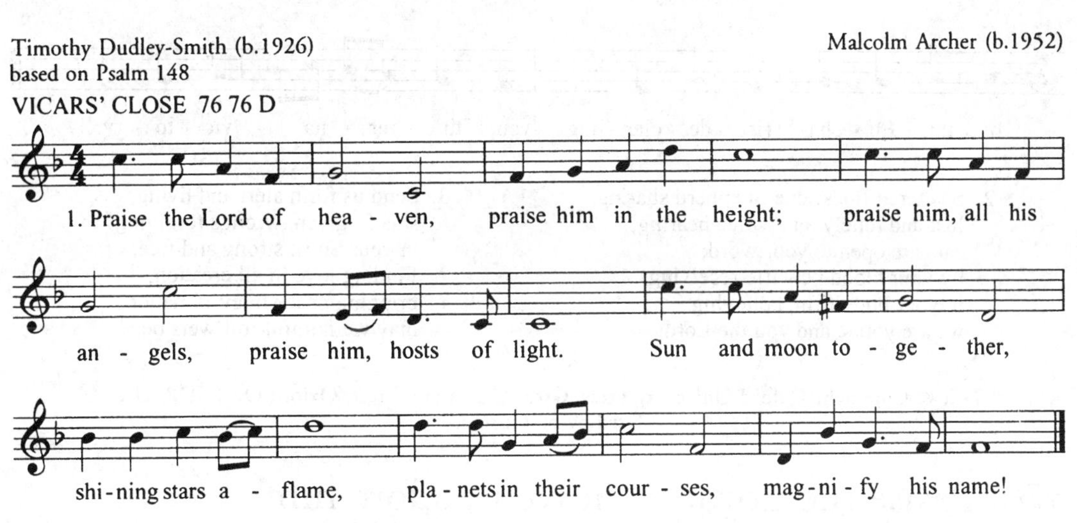

2. Earth and ocean praise him;
   mountains, hills and trees;
   fire and hail and tempest,
   wind and storm and seas.
   Praise him, fields and forests,
   birds on flashing wings,
   praise him, beasts and cattle,
   all created things.

3. Now by prince and people
   let his praise be told;
   praise him, men and maidens,
   praise him, young and old.
   He, the Lord of glory!
   We, his praise proclaim!
   High above all heavens
   magnify his name!

Optional descant

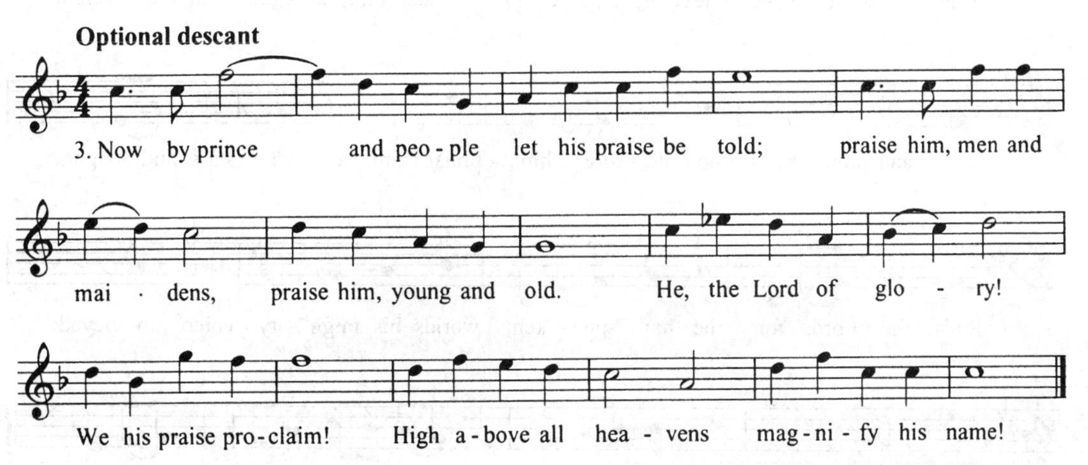

Text © Copyright Timothy Dudley-Smith, 9 Ashlands, Ford, Salisbury, Wiltshire SP4 6DY, UK.
Used by permission. Music © Copyright 1999 Kevin Mayhew Ltd.

569 Praise the Lord, rise up rejoicing

Howard Charles Adie Gaunt (1902-1983)

Adapted from Johann Sebastian Bach's version of a chorale by Johann Löhner (1691) and others

EVANGELISTS (ALLES IST AN GOTTES SEGEN) 8 8 7 D

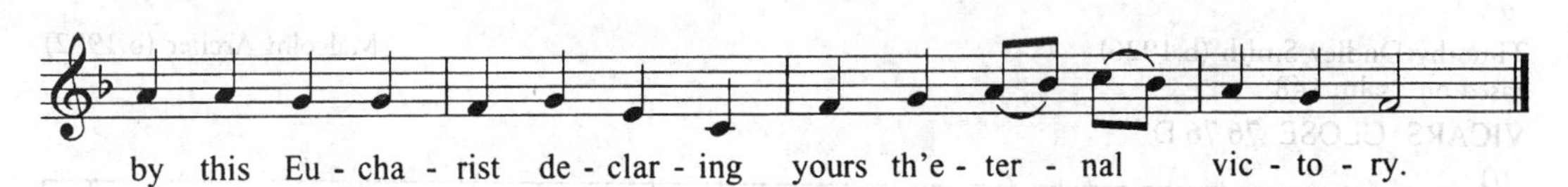

2. Scattered flock, one Shepherd sharing,
lost and lonely, one voice hearing,
ears are open to your word;
by your blood new life receiving,
in your body firm, believing,
we are yours, and you the Lord.

3. Send us forth alert and living,
sins forgiven, wrongs forgiving,
in your Spirit strong and free.
Finding love in all creation,
bringing peace in ev'ry nation,
may we faithful foll'wers be.

Text © Copyright Oxford University Press, Great Clarendon Street, Oxford OX2 6DP, UK. Used by permission.

570 Praise the Lord, ye heavens, adore him

vs. 1, 2: from *Foundling Hospital Collection* (1796)
v. 3: Edward Osler (1798-1863)

Croatian Folk melody adapted by Franz Joseph Haydn (1732-1809)

AUSTRIA 87 87 D

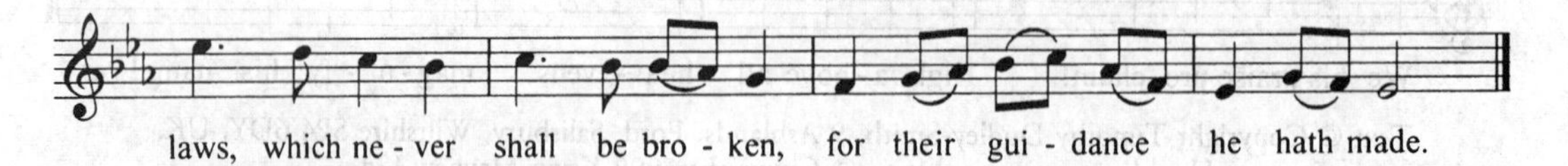

2. Praise the Lord, for he is glorious:
never shall his promise fail.
God hath made his saints victorious;
sin and death shall not prevail.
Praise the God of our salvation,
hosts on high, his pow'r proclaim;
heav'n and earth and all creation,
laud and magnify his name!

3. Worship, honour, glory, blessing,
Lord, we offer to thy name;
young and old, thy praise expressing,
join their Saviour to proclaim.
As the saints in heav'n adore thee,
we would bow before thy throne;
as thine angels serve before thee,
so on earth thy will be done.

571 Praise to God for saints and martyrs

Michael Forster (b.1946)

Traditional Dutch melody

TUNE 1: IN BABILONE 87 87 D

1. Praise to God for saints and mar - tyrs, in - spi - ra - tion to us all;

in the pre - sence of our Sa - viour, their ex - am - ple we re - call:

lives of ho - ly con - tem - pla - tion, sac - ri - fice or sim - ple love,

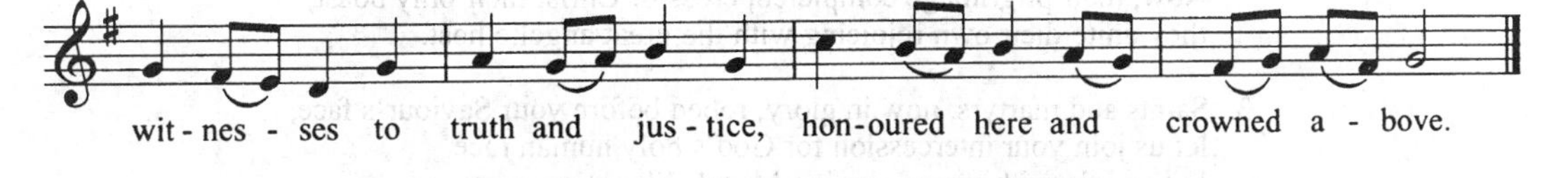

2. How we long to share their story, faithful in response to grace,
signs of God's eternal presence in the realm of time and space.
Now, their pilgrimage completed, cross of Christ their only boast,
they unite their own rejoicing with the great angelic host.

3. Saints and martyrs, now in glory, robed before your Saviour's face,
let us join your intercession for God's holy human race.
Let us join with you in singing Mary's liberation song,
till a just and free creation sings, with the angelic throng:

4. Praise and honour to the Father, adoration to the Son,
with the all-embracing Spirit wholly Three and holy One.
All the universe, united in complete diversity,
sings as one your endless praises, ever blessèd Trinity!

Tune 2 will be found overleaf

Text © Copyright 1999 Kevin Mayhew Ltd.

Michael Forster (b.1946)

From an anthem by Thomas Williams (1869-1944)

TUNE 2: EBENEZER (TON-Y-BOTEL) 87 87 D

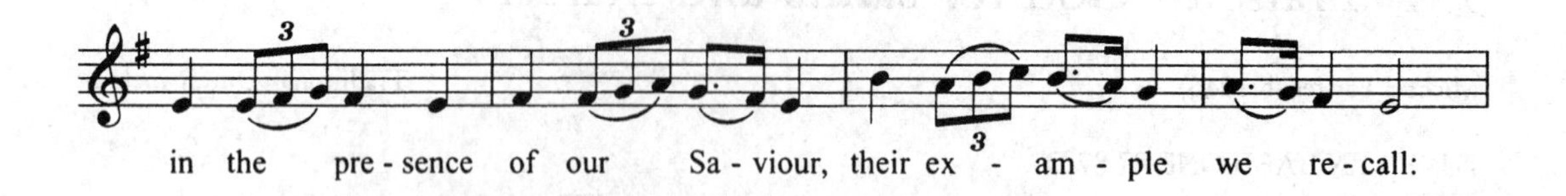

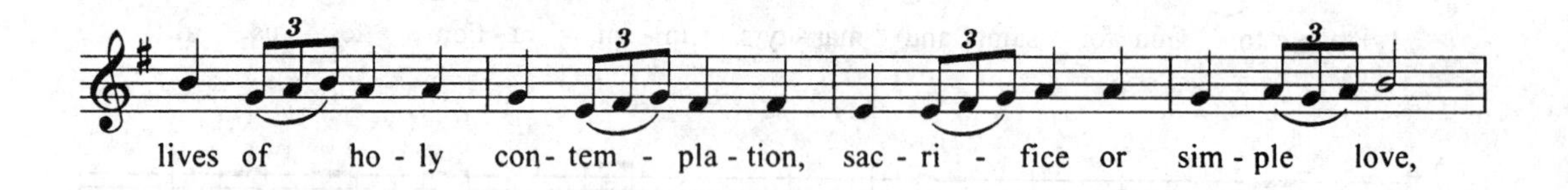

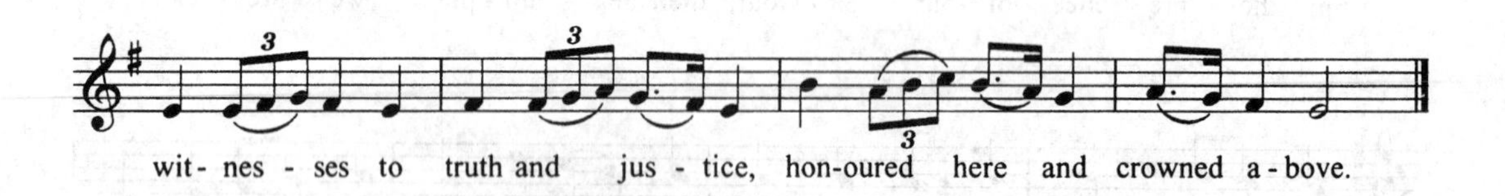

2. How we long to share their story, faithful in response to grace,
signs of God's eternal presence in the realm of time and space.
Now, their pilgrimage completed, cross of Christ their only boast,
they unite their own rejoicing with the great angelic host.

3. Saints and martyrs, now in glory, robed before your Saviour's face,
let us join your intercession for God's holy human race.
Let us join with you in singing Mary's liberation song,
till a just and free creation sings, with the angelic throng:

4. Praise and honour to the Father, adoration to the Son,
with the all-embracing Spirit wholly Three and holy One.
All the universe, united in complete diversity,
sings as one your endless praises, ever blessèd Trinity!

Text © Copyright 1999 Kevin Mayhew Ltd
Tune 2 © Copyright Clifford Williams. Used by permission.

572 Praise to the Holiest

John Henry Newman (1801-1890)

Melody adapted from
Thomas Haweis (1734-1820)

TUNE 1: RICHMOND CM

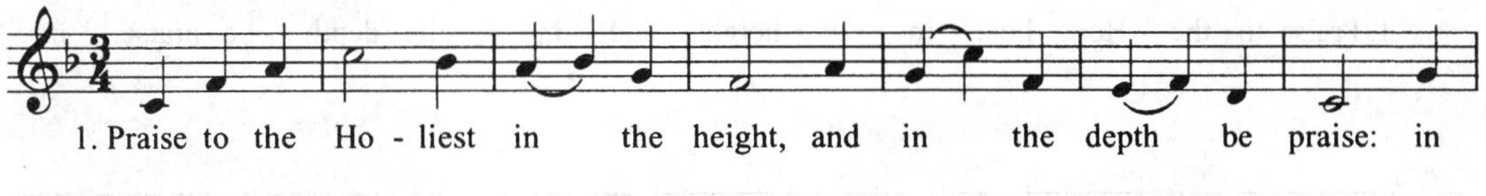

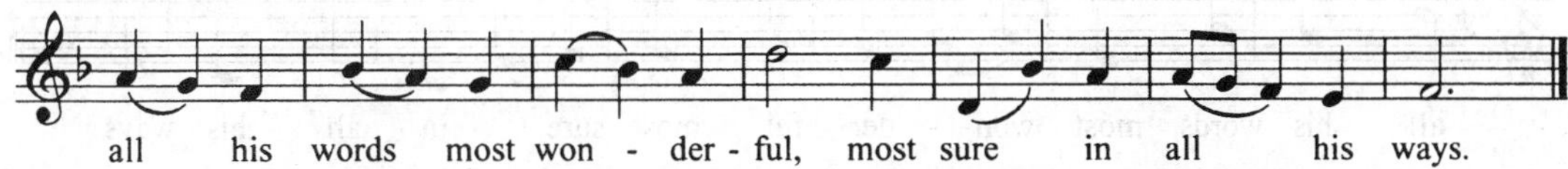

2. O loving wisdom of our God!
when all was sin and shame,
a second Adam to the fight,
and to the rescue came.

3. O wisest love! that flesh and blood,
which did in Adam fail,
should strive afresh against the foe,
should strive and should prevail.

4. And that a higher gift than grace
should flesh and blood refine,
God's presence and his very self,
and essence all-divine.

5. And in the garden secretly,
and on the cross on high,
should teach his brethren, and inspire
to suffer and to die.

6. Praise to the Holiest in the height,
and in the depth be praise;
in all his words most wonderful,
most sure in all his ways.

John Henry Newman (1801-1890)

John Bacchus Dykes (1823-1876)

TUNE 2: GERONTIUS CM

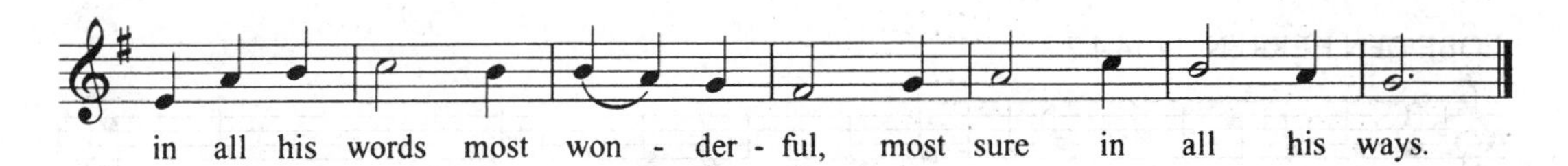

John Henry Newman (1801-1890)

Arthur Somervell (1863-1937)

TUNE 3: CHORUS ANGELORUM (SOMERVELL) CM

Tune 4 will be found overleaf

Tune 3 © Copyright Oxford University Press, Great Clarendon Street, Oxford OX2 6DP, UK.
Used by permission.

John Henry Newman (1801-1890) Richard Runciman Terry (1865-1938)

TUNE 4: BILLING CM

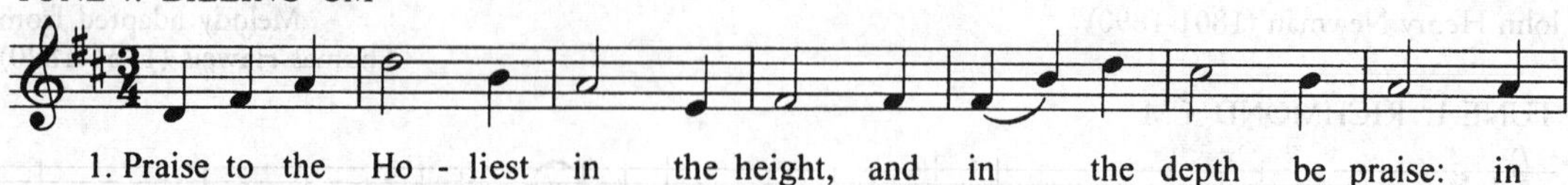

1. Praise to the Ho - liest in the height, and in the depth be praise: in

all his words most won - der - ful, most sure in all his ways.

2. O loving wisdom of our God!
when all was sin and shame,
a second Adam to the fight,
and to the rescue came.

3. O wisest love! that flesh and blood,
which did in Adam fail,
should strive afresh against the foe,
should strive and should prevail.

4. And that a higher gift than grace
should flesh and blood refine,
God's presence and his very self,
and essence all-divine.

5. And in the garden secretly,
and on the cross on high,
should teach his brethren, and inspire
to suffer and to die.

6. Praise to the Holiest in the height,
and in the depth be praise;
in all his words most wonderful,
most sure in all his ways.

573 Praise to the Lord, the Almighty

Joachim Neander (1650-1680)
trans. Catherine Winkworth (1827-1878)

From *Praxis Pietatis Melica* (1668)

LOBE DEN HERREN 14 14 4 7 8

1. Praise to the Lord, the Al - migh-ty, the King of cre - a - tion! O my soul,

praise him, for he is thy health and sal - va - tion. All ye who hear,

now to his tem - ple draw near; join - ing in glad a - do - ra - tion.

2. Praise to the Lord, who o'er all things so wondrously reigneth,
shieldeth thee gently from harm, or when fainting sustaineth:
hast thou not seen
how thy heart's wishes have been
granted in what he ordaineth?

3. Praise to the Lord, who doth prosper thy work and defend thee,
surely his goodness and mercy shall daily attend thee:
ponder anew
what the Almighty can do,
if to the end he befriend thee.

4. Praise to the Lord, O let all that is in us adore him!
All that hath life and breath, come now with praises before him.
Let the 'Amen'
sound from his people again,
gladly for ay we adore him.

574 Purify my heart *Refiner's fire*

Words and music: Brian Doerksen

2. Purify my heart,
cleanse me from within and make me holy.
Purify my heart,
cleanse me from my sin, deep within.

© Copyright 1990 Mercy/Vineyard Publishing. Administered by CopyCare, P.O. Box 77, Hailsham, East Sussex BN27 3EF, UK. (music@copycare.com). Used by permission.

575 Put peace into each other's hands

Fred Kaan (b.1929)

Irish melody
from the Petrie collection

TUNE 1: ST COLUMBA 87 87

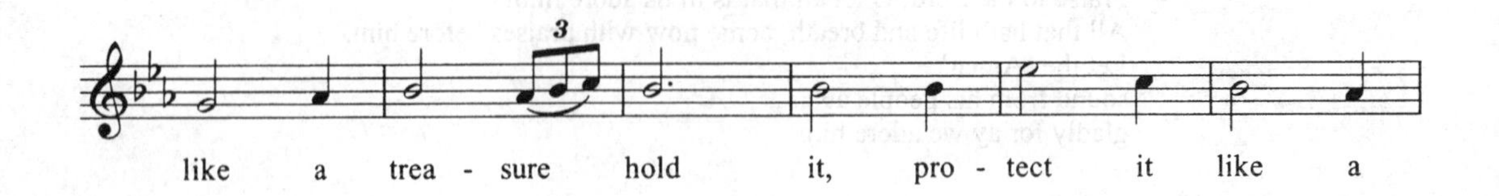

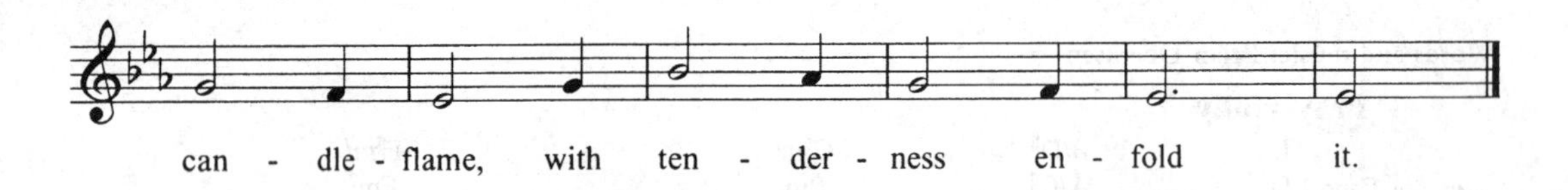

2. Put peace into each other's hands
with loving expectation;
be gentle in your words and ways,
in touch with God's creation.

3. Put peace into each other's hands
like bread we break for sharing;
look people warmly in the eye:
our life is meant for caring.

4. As at communion, shape your hands
into a waiting cradle;
the gift of Christ receive, revere,
united round the table.

5. Put Christ into each other's hands,
he is love's deepest measure;
in love make peace, give peace a chance,
and share it like a treasure.

Fred Kaan (b.1929)

Melody in *Neu-Leipziger Gesangbuch*
adapted by Johann Sebastian Bach (1685-1750)

TUNE 2: ACH GOTT UND HERR 87 87

1. Put peace in - to each o - ther's hands and like a trea - sure hold it, pro -

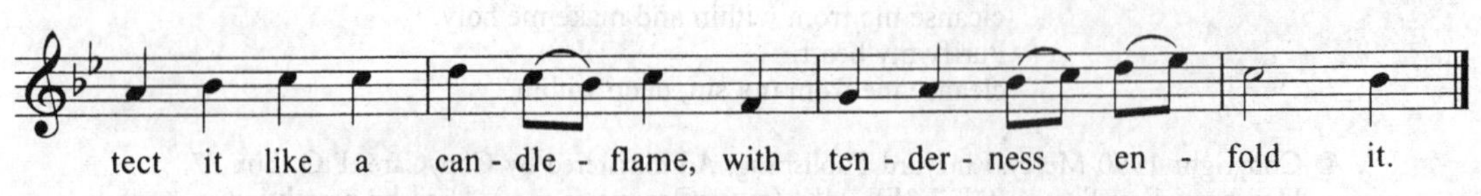

Text © Copyright 1989 Stainer & Bell Ltd., P.O. Box 110, Victoria House, 23 Gruneisen Road, Finchley, London N3 1DZ, UK. Used by permission.

576 Put thou thy trust in God

Paul Gerhardt (1607-1676)
trans. John Wesley (1703-1791) and others

Samuel Wesley (1766-1837)

DONCASTER SM

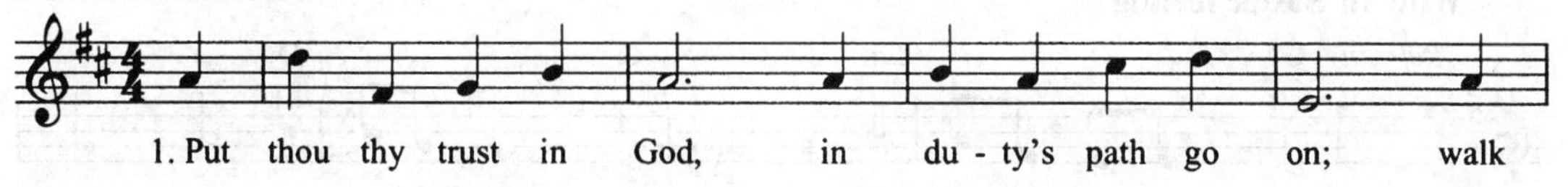

2. Commit thy ways to him,
thy works into his hands,
and rest on his unchanging word,
who heav'n and earth commands.

3. Though years on years roll on,
his cov'nant shall endure;
though clouds and darkness hide his path,
the promised grace is sure.

4. Give to the winds thy fears;
hope, and be undismayed:
God hears thy sighs and counts thy tears;
God shall lift up thy head.

5. Through waves and clouds and storms
his pow'r will clear thy way:
wait thou his time; the darkest night
shall end in brightest day.

6. Leave to his sov'reign sway
to choose and to command;
so shalt thou, wond'ring, own his way,
how wise, how strong his hand.

577 Rejoice, heavenly powers *Exsultet*

Words and music: Mike Anderson (b.1956)
based on the *Exsultet*

© Copyright 1999 Kevin Mayhew Ltd.

2. The price for Adam's sin is paid, (Rejoice! Rejoice!)
by Jesus' blood we have been saved; (Rejoice! Rejoice!)
he rose triumphant from the grave, (Rejoice! Rejoice!)
rejoice, rejoice, rejoice!

3. This night will be as clear as day, (Rejoice! Rejoice!)
the morning star is here to stay; (Rejoice! Rejoice!)
and he has washed all guilt away, (Rejoice! Rejoice!)
rejoice, rejoice, rejoice!

4. And now this Easter candle's light (Rejoice! Rejoice!)
dispels the darkness of the night; (Rejoice! Rejoice!)
rejoice in justice, peace and right, (Rejoice! Rejoice!)
rejoice, rejoice, rejoice!

578 Rejoice in the Lord always

Words and music: Unknown
based on Phlippians 4:4

This may be sung as a round, the second voice entering at the double bar.

G D7 G

Re - joice in the Lord al - ways and a - gain I say re - joice. Re -

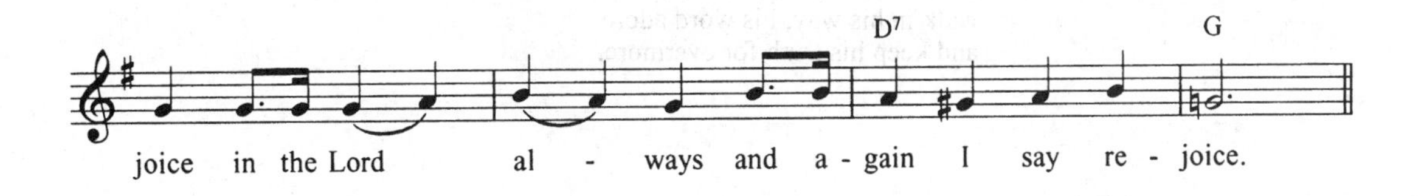

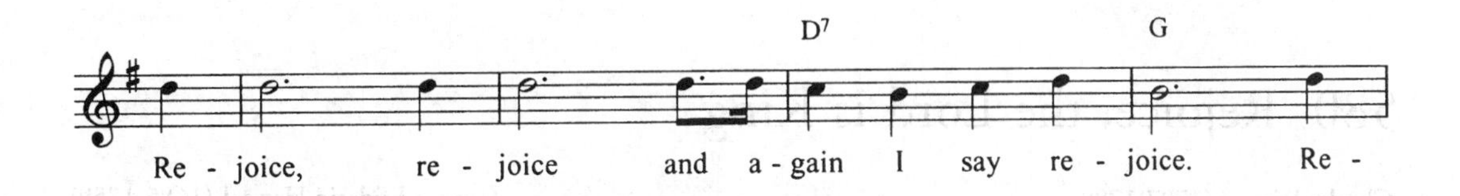

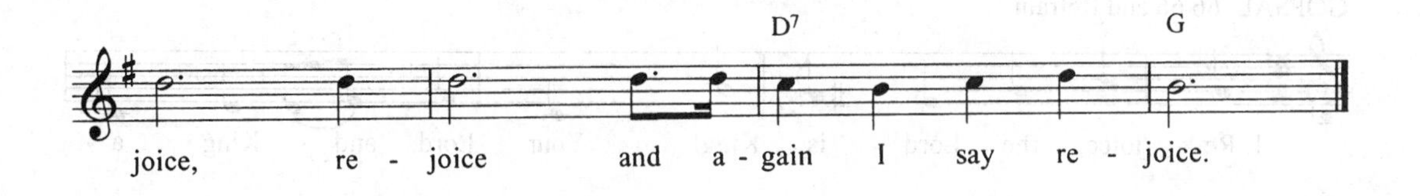

579 Rejoice, O land, in God thy might

Robert Bridges (1844-1930)

William Knapp (1698-1768)

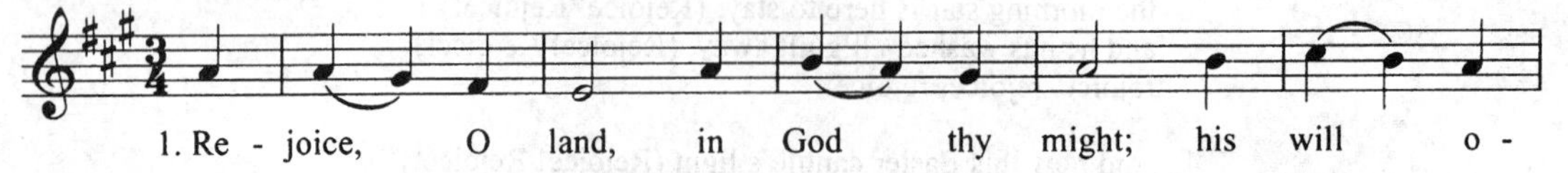

2. Glad shalt thou be, with blessing crowned,
with joy and peace thou shalt abound;
yea, love with thee shall make his home
until thou see God's kingdom come.

3. He shall forgive thy sins untold:
remember thou his love of old;
walk in his way, his word adore,
and keep his truth for evermore.

580 Rejoice, the Lord is King

Charles Wesley (1707-1788)

George Frideric Handel (1685-1759)

GOPSAL 66 66 and Refrain

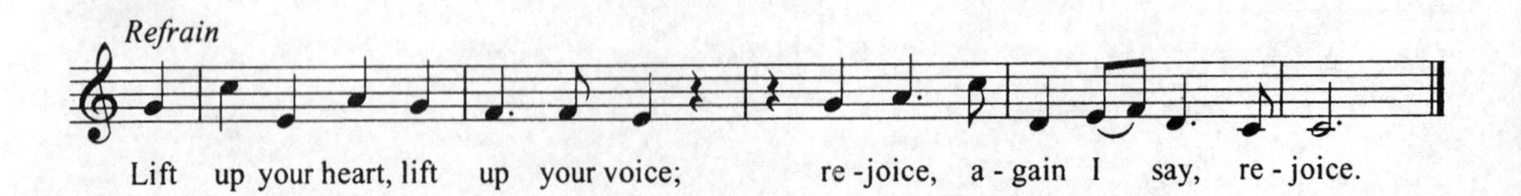

2. Jesus the Saviour reigns,
the God of truth and love;
when he had purged our stains,
he took his seat above.

3. His kingdom cannot fail;
he rules o'er earth and heav'n;
the keys of death and hell
are to our Jesus giv'n.

4. He sits at God's right hand
till all his foes submit,
and bow to his command,
and fall beneath his feet.

581 Rejoice, the year upon its way

Based on the Latin (c.4th century)
trans. the Editors of *The New English Hymnal*

Plainsong mode viii

TUNE 1: VENI, CREATOR SPIRITUS (MECHLIN) LM

2. From out the heav'ns a rushing noise
came like the tempest's sudden voice,
and mingled with th'Apostles' prayer,
proclaiming loud that God was there.

3. Like quiv'ring tongues of light and flame,
upon each one the Spirit came:
tongues, that the earth might hear their call,
and fire, that love might burn in all.

4. And so to all were spread abroad
the wonders of the works of God;
they knew the prophet's word fulfilled,
and owned the gift which God had willed.

5. Look down, most gracious God, this day
upon thy people as we pray;
and Christ the Lord upon us pour
the Spirit's gift for evermore.
Amen.

Tune 2 will be found overleaf

Text © Copyright The Canterbury Press, St Mary's Works, St Mary's Plain,
Norwich NR3 3BH, UK. Used by permission.
Tune 2 © Copyright the Executors of Kenneth Finlay. Used by permission of
Broomhill Church of Scotland, 74 Marlborough Avenue, Broomhill, Glasgow G117BH, Scotland.

Based on the Latin (c.4th century)
trans. the Editors of *The New English Hymnal*

Kenneth Finlay (1882-1974)

TUNE 2: FINNART LM

2. From out the heav'ns a rushing noise
came like the tempest's sudden voice,
and mingled with th'Apostles' prayer,
proclaiming loud that God was there.

3. Like quiv'ring tongues of light and flame,
upon each one the Spirit came:
tongues, that the earth might hear their call,
and fire, that love might burn in all.

4. And so to all were spread abroad
the wonders of the works of God;
they knew the prophet's word fulfilled,
and owned the gift which God had willed.

5. Look down, most gracious God, this day
upon thy people as we pray;
and Christ the Lord upon us pour
the Spirit's gift for evermore.
Amen.

582 Restore, O Lord

Words and music: Graham Kendrick (b.1950)
and Chris Rolinson (b.1958)

Steadily, with feeling

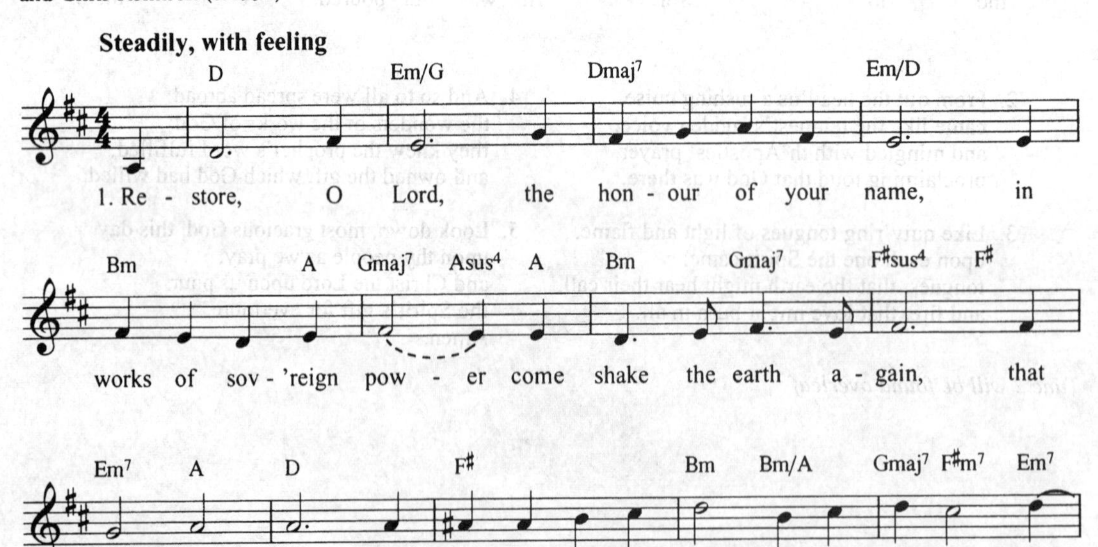

© Copyright 1981 Kingsway's Thankyou Music, P.O. Box 75, Eastbourne,
East Sussex BN23 6NW, UK. (tym@kingsway.co.uk). Used by permission.

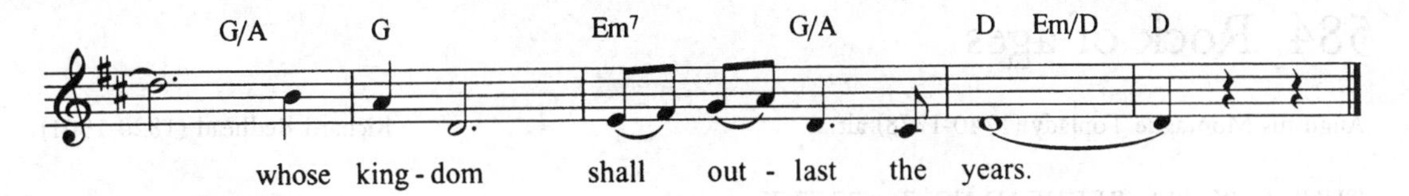

2. Restore, O Lord,
in all the earth your fame,
and in our time revive
the church that bears your name.
And in your anger,
Lord, remember mercy,
O living God,
whose mercy shall outlast the years.

3. Bend us, O Lord,
where we are hard and cold,
in your refiner's fire:
come purify the gold.
Though suff'ring comes
and evil crouches near,
still our living God
is reigning, he is reigning here.

4. *As verse 1*

583 Ride on, ride on in majesty

Henry Hart Milman (1791-1868) alt.

From *Musikalisches Handbuch* (1690)

TUNE 1: WINCHESTER NEW LM

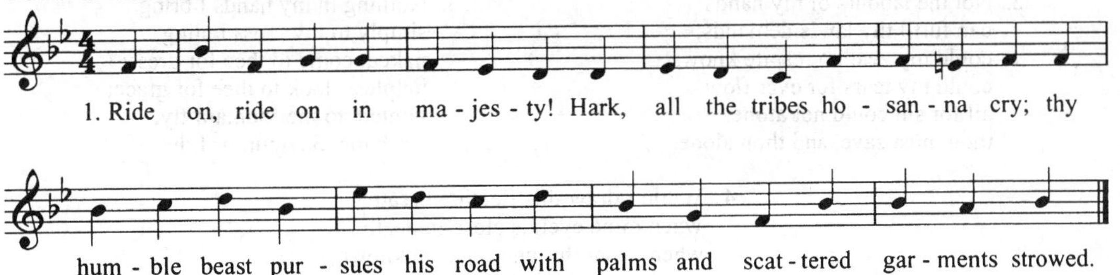

2. Ride on, ride on in majesty!
In lowly pomp ride on to die;
O Christ, thy triumphs now begin
o'er captive death and conquered sin.

3. Ride on, ride on in majesty!
The wingèd squadrons of the sky
look down with sad and wond'ring eyes
to see th'approaching sacrifice.

4. Ride on, ride on in majesty!
Thy last and fiercest strife is nigh;
the Father, on his sapphire throne,
awaits his own appointed Son.

5. Ride on, ride on in majesty!
In lowly pomp ride on to die;
bow thy meek head to mortal pain,
then take, O God, thy pow'r, and reign.

Henry Hart Milman (1791-1868) alt.

John Bacchus Dykes (1823-1876)

TUNE 2: ST DROSTANE LM

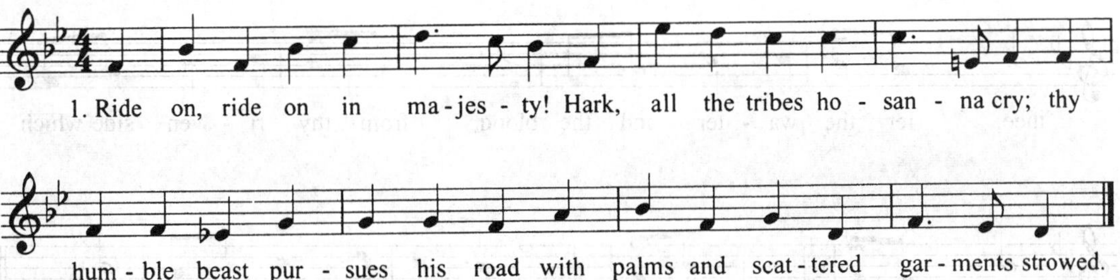

584 Rock of ages

Augustus Montague Toplady (1740-1778) alt. | Richard Redhead (1820-1901)

TUNE 1: PETRA (REDHEAD NO. 76) 77 77 77

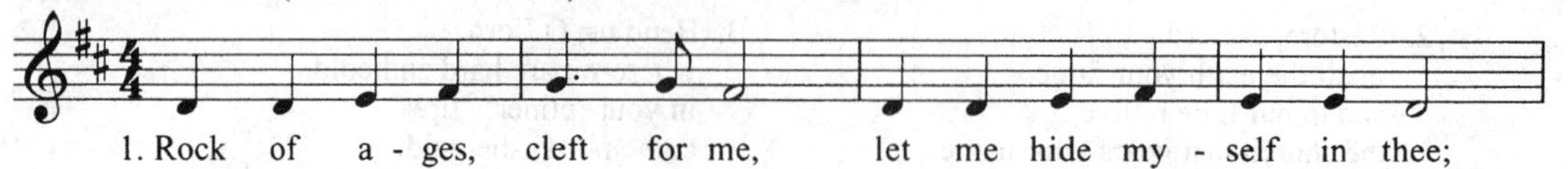

2. Not the labours of my hands
can fulfil thy law's demands;
could my zeal no respite know,
could my tears for ever flow,
all for sin could not atone:
thou must save, and thou alone.

3. Nothing in my hands I bring,
simply to thy cross I cling;
naked, come to thee for dress;
helpless, look to thee for grace;
tainted, to the fountain fly;
wash me, Saviour, or I die.

4. While I draw this fleeting breath,
when mine eyelids close in death,
when I soar through tracts unknown,
see thee on thy judgement throne;
Rock of ages, cleft for me,
let me hide myself in thee.

Augustus Montague Toplady (1740-1778) alt. | Thomas Hastings (1784-1872)

TUNE 2: TOPLADY 77 77 77

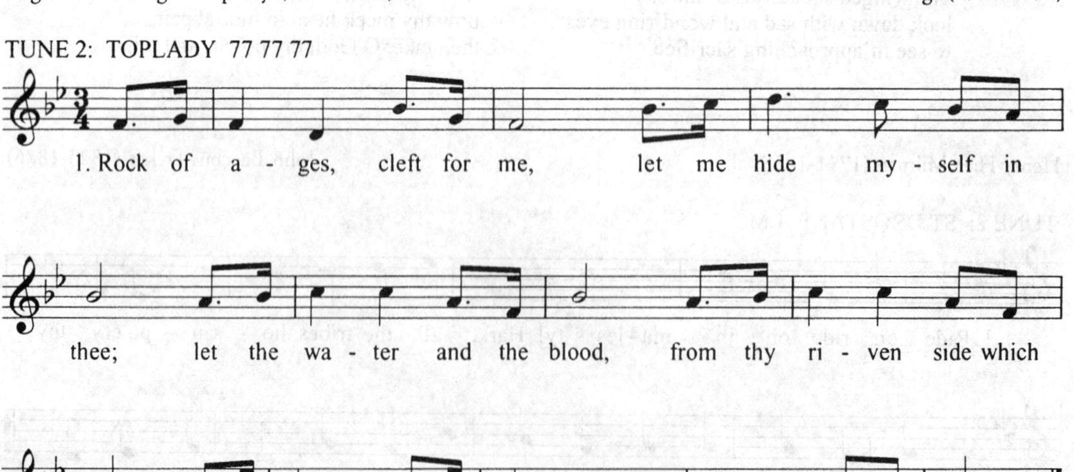

585 Round me falls the night

William Romanis (1824-1889)

Melody contributed to *Geistleiches Gesangbuch,* Darmstadt (1698) by A. Drese (1620-1710)

ARNSTADT (SEELENBRÄUTIGAM) 55 88 55

1. Round me falls the night; Sa - viour, be my light:

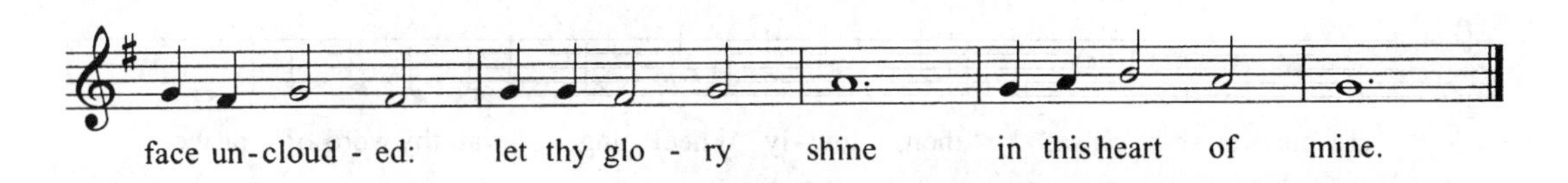

2. Earthly work is done,
earthly sounds are none;
rest in sleep and silence seeking,
let me hear thee softly speaking;
in my spirit's ear
whisper, 'I am near.'

3. Blessèd, heavenly light,
shining through earth's night;
voice, that oft of love hast told me,
arms, so strong to clasp and hold me;
thou thy watch wilt keep,
Saviour, o'er my sleep.

586 Save us, O Lord

The Office of Night Prayer

Kevin Mayhew (b.1942)

Music © Copyright 1996 Kevin Mayhew Ltd.

587 Saviour, again to thy dear name we raise

John Ellerton (1826-1893) Edward John Hopkins (1818-1901)

ELLERS 10 10 10 10

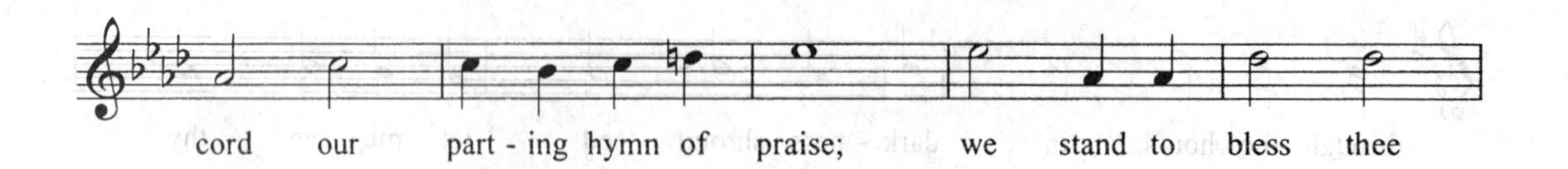

2. Grant us thy peace upon our homeward way;
with thee began, with thee shall end, the day:
guard thou the lips from sin, the hearts from shame,
that in this house have called upon thy name.

3. Grant us thy peace, Lord, through the coming night;
turn thou for us its darkness into light;
from harm and danger keep thy children free,
for dark and light are both alike to thee.

4. Grant us thy peace throughout our earthly life,
our balm in sorrow, and our stay in strife;
then, when thy voice shall bid our conflict cease,
call us, O Lord, to thine eternal peace.

588 See, amid the winter's snow

Edward Caswall (1814-1878) John Goss (1800-1880)

TUNE 1: HUMILITY (OXFORD) 77 77 and Refrain

Refrain

2. Lo, within a manger lies
   he who built the starry skies;
   he, who, throned in heights sublime,
   sits amid the cherubim.

3. Say, you holy shepherds, say,
   what your joyful news today?
   Wherefore have you left your sheep
   on the lonely mountain steep?

4. 'As we watched at dead of night,
   there appeared a wondrous light;
   angels, singing peace on earth,
   told us of the Saviour's birth.'

5. Sacred infant, all divine,
   what a tender love was thine,
   thus to come from highest bliss,
   down to such a world as this!

6. Virgin mother, Mary, blest,
   by the joys that fill thy breast,
   pray for us, that we may prove
   worthy of the Saviour's love.

Edward Caswall (1814-1878) — Traditional melody

TUNE 2: CHRISTMAS MORN 77 77 and Refrain

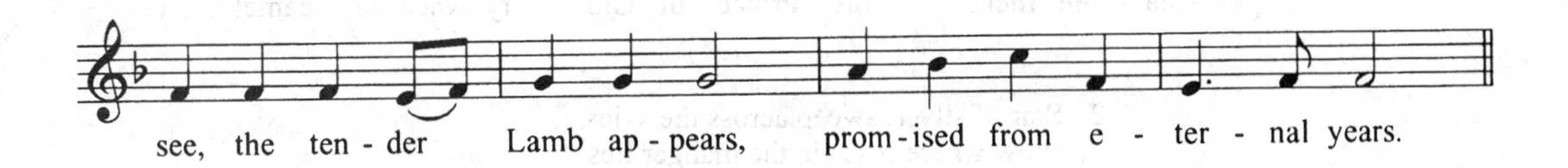

Refrain

589 See him lying on a bed of straw

Words and music: Michael Perry (1942-1996)

CALYPSO CAROL Irregular and Refrain

2. Star of silver, sweep across the skies,
show where Jesus in the manger lies;
shepherds, swiftly from your stupor rise
to see the Saviour of the world!

3. Angels, sing again the song you sang,
sing the glory of God's gracious plan;
sing that Bethlehem's little baby can
be the Saviour of us all.

4. Mine are riches, from your poverty;
from your innocence, eternity;
mine, forgiveness by your death for me,
child of sorrow for my joy.

© Copyright 1965 Mrs B. Perry/Jubilate Hymns, 4 Thorne Park Road, Chelston,
Torquay TQ2 6RX, UK. Used by permission.

590 Seek ye first

v. 1: Karen Lafferty
vs. 2&3: unknown, based on Matthew 6:33, 7:7

Karen Lafferty (b.1948)

This may be sung as a round, the second entry beginning at the double bar.

SEEK YE FIRST Irregular

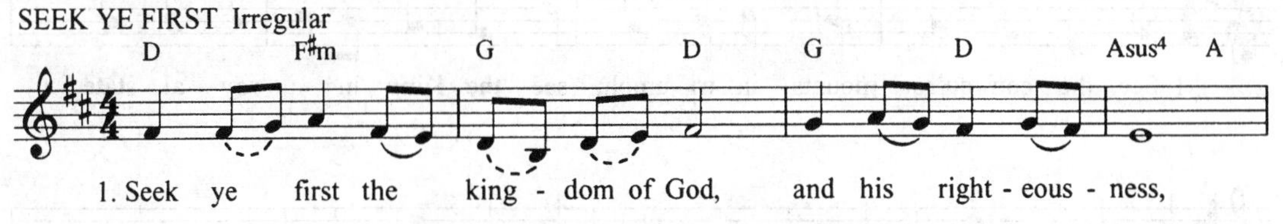

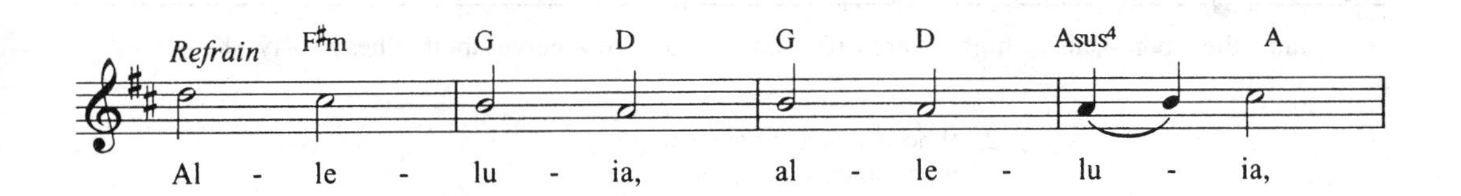

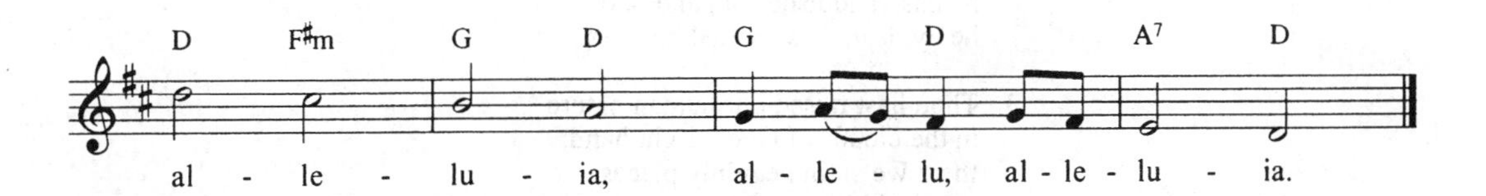

2. You shall not live by bread alone,
but by ev'ry word
that proceeds from the mouth of God;
allelu, alleluia.

3. Ask and it shall be given unto you,
seek and ye shall find;
knock, and it shall be opened unto you;
allelu, alleluia.

© Copyright 1972 Maranatha! Music. Administered by CopyCare, P.O. Box 77, Hailsham, East Sussex BN27 3EF, UK. (music@copycare.com). Used by permission.

591 See the conqueror mounts in triumph

Christopher Wordsworth (1807-1855) alt. | Henry Smart (1813-1879)

REX GLORIAE 87 87 D

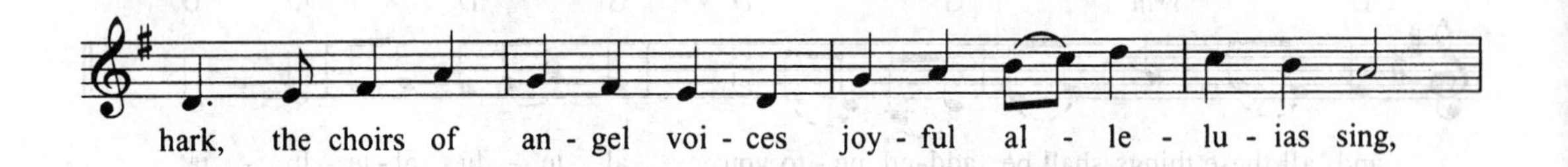

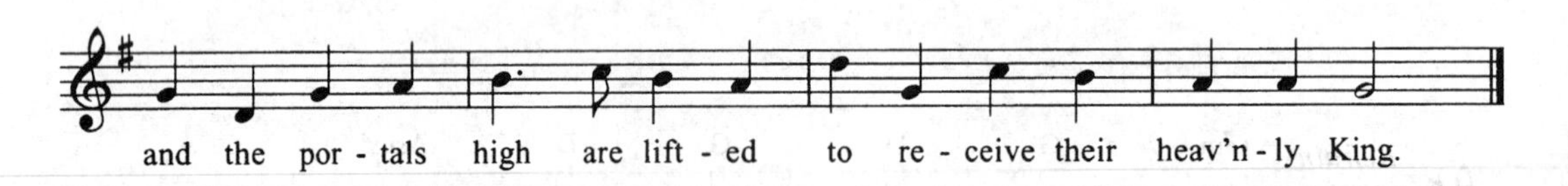

2. Who is this that comes in glory
with the trump of jubilee?
Lord of battles, God of armies,
he has gained the victory;
he who on the cross did suffer,
he who from the grave arose,
he has vanquished sin and Satan,
he by death has spoiled his foes.

3. Thou hast raised our human nature
in the clouds of God's right hand;
there we sit in heav'nly places,
there with thee in glory stand;
Jesus reigns, adored by angels,
takes our flesh to heaven's throne;
mighty Lord, in thine ascension,
we by faith behold our own.

4. Glory be to God the Father;
glory be to God the Son,
dying, ris'n, ascending for us,
who the heav'nly realm has won;
glory to the Holy Spirit;
to One God in persons Three;
glory both in earth and heaven,
glory, endless glory, be.

592 See the holy table, spread for our healing

Michael Forster (b.1946) John Bacchus Dykes (1823-1876)

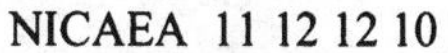

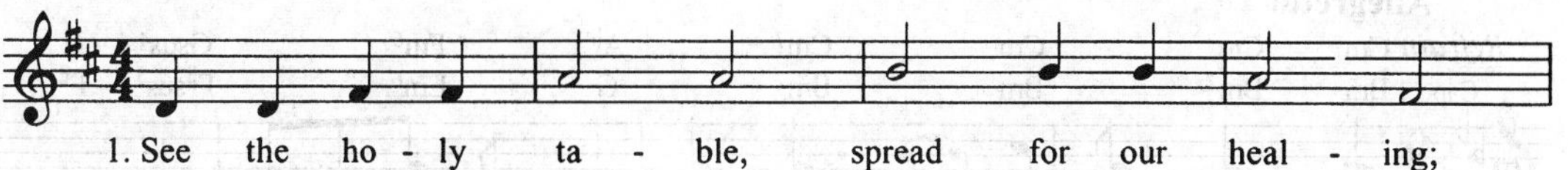

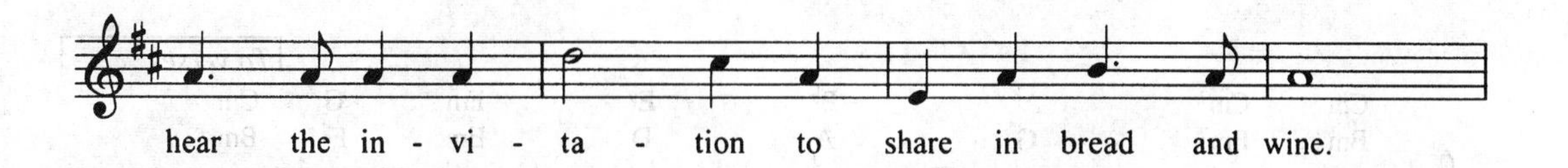

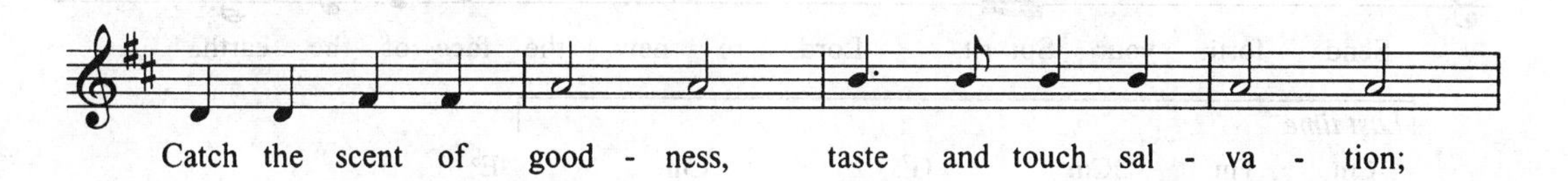

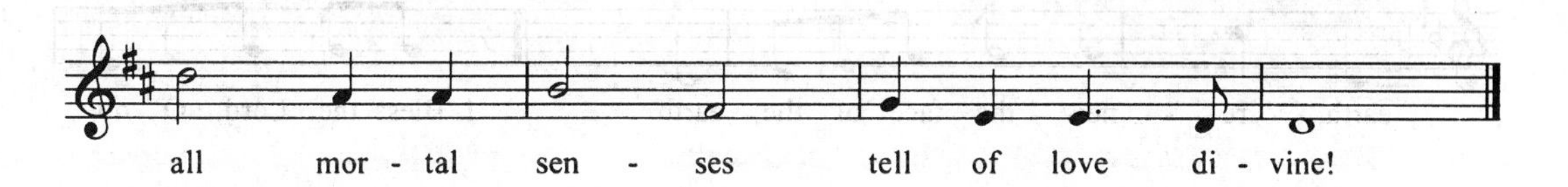

2. As the bread is broken, Christ is remembered;
as the wine is flowing, his passion we recall;
as redemption's story opens up before us,
hope is triumphant, Christ is all in all.

3. Tell again the story, wonder of wonders:
Christ, by grace eternal, transforms the simplest food!
Sign of hope and glory, life in all its fullness,
God's whole creation ransomed and renewed!

Text © Copyright 1993 Kevin Mayhew Ltd.

593 Send forth your Spirit, Lord

Adapted from Psalm 104
by Michael Forster (b.1946)

Margaret Rizza (b.1929)

2. Lord, how great are your works,
in wisdom you made them all;
all the earth is full of your creatures,
your hand always open to feed them.

3. May your wisdom endure,
rejoice in your works, O Lord.
I will sing for ever and ever,
in praise of my God and my King.

© Copyright 1997 Kevin Mayhew Ltd.

594 Shall we gather at the river

Words and music: Robert Lowry (1826-1899)

HANSON PLACE 87 87 and Refrain

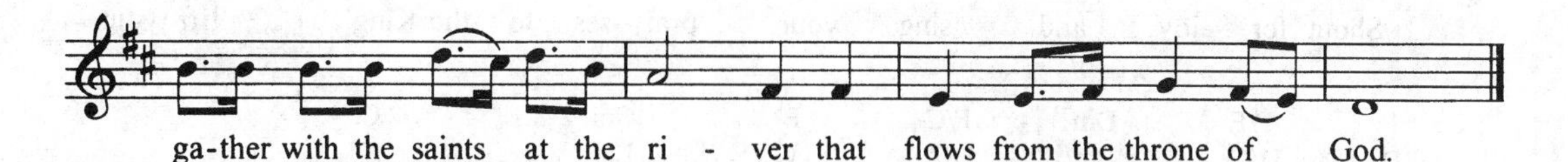

2. On the margin of the river,
washing up its silver spray,
we will walk and worship ever,
all the happy golden day.

3. Ere we reach the shining river,
lay we every burden down;
grace our spirits will deliver,
and provide a robe and crown.

4. At the smiling of the river,
mirror of the Saviour's face,
saints, whom death will never sever,
lift their songs of saving grace.

5. Soon we'll reach the shining river,
soon our pilgrimage will cease;
soon our happy hearts will quiver
with the melody of peace.

595 Shall we not love thee, Mother dear

Henry Williams Baker (1821-1877) — John Bacchus Dykes (1823-1876)

BEATITUDO CM

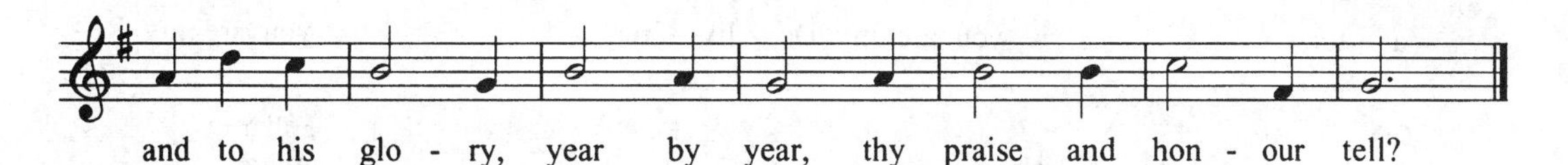

2. Thee did he choose from whom to take
true flesh, his flesh to be;
in it to suffer for our sake,
and by it make us free.

3. O wondrous depth of love divine,
that he should bend so low;
and, Mary, O what joy was thine
the Saviour's love to know.

4. Joy to be mother of the Lord,
yet thine the truer bliss,
in ev'ry thought and deed and word
to be for ever his.

5. Now in the realm of life above
close to thy Son thou art,
while on thy soul glad streams of love
flow from his sacred heart.

6. Jesu, the Virgin's holy Son,
praise we thy mother blest;
grant when our earthly course is run,
life with the saints at rest.

596 Shout for joy and sing

Words and music: David Fellingham (b.1945)

© Copyright 1988 Kingsway's Thankyou Music, P.O. Box 75, Eastbourne, East Sussex BN23 6NW, UK. (tym@kingsway.co.uk). Used by permission.

597 Silent night

Joseph Mohr (1792-1848)
trans. John Freeman Young (1820-1885)

Franz Grüber (1787-1863)

STILLE NACHT Irregular

2. Silent night, holy night.
   Shepherds quake at the sight,
   glories stream from heaven afar,
   heav'nly hosts sing alleluia:
   Christ, the Saviour is born,
   Christ, the Saviour is born.

3. Silent night, holy night.
   Son of God, love's pure light,
   radiant beams from thy holy face,
   with the dawn of redeeming grace:
   Jesus, Lord, at thy birth,
   Jesus, Lord, at thy birth.

598 Sing for God's glory

Kathy Galloway

From *Praxis Pietatis Melica* (1668)

LOBE DEN HERREN 14 14 4 7 8

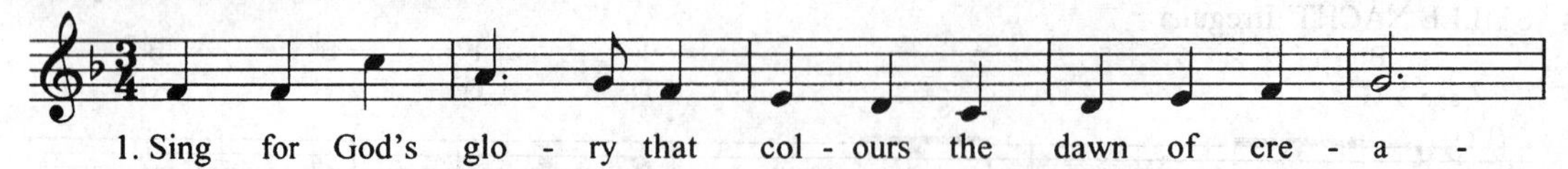

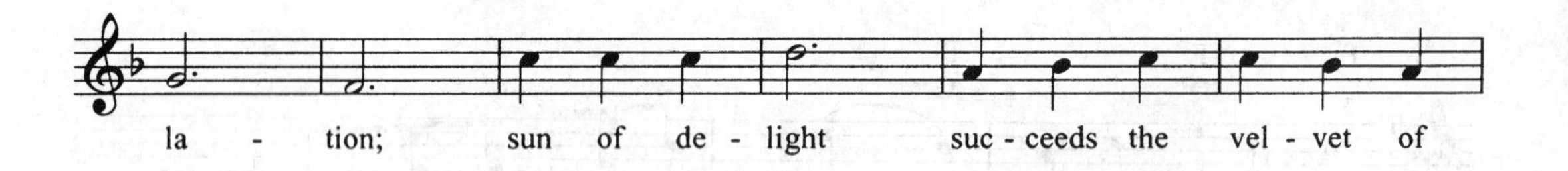

2. Sing for God's power
that shatters the chains that would bind us,
searing the darkness of
fear and despair that could blind us,
touching our shame
with love that will not lay blame,
reaching out gently to find us.

3. Sing for God's justice
disturbing each easy illusion,
tearing down tyrants
and putting our pride to confusion:
lifeblood of right,
resisting evil and slight,
offering freedom's transfusion.

4. Sing for God's saints who
have travelled faith's journey before us,
who in our weariness
give us their hope to restore us;
in them we see
the new creation to be,
spirit of love made flesh for us.

Text © Copyright Kathy Galloway.
Used by permission.

599 Sing glory to God the Father

Michael Saward (b.1932) | Marc-Antoine Charpentier (1634-1704)

TE DEUM 8 12 8 8 13 13

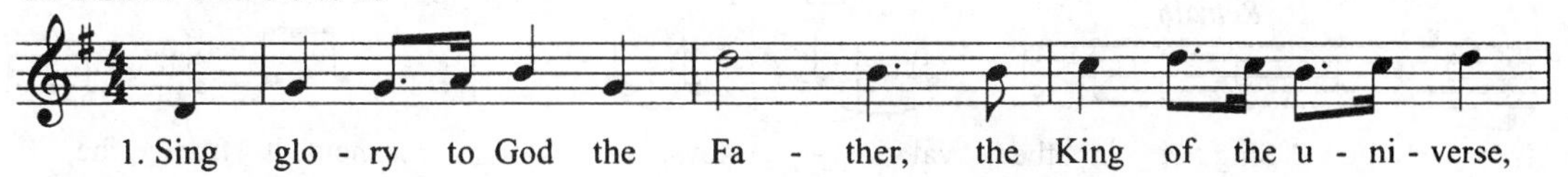

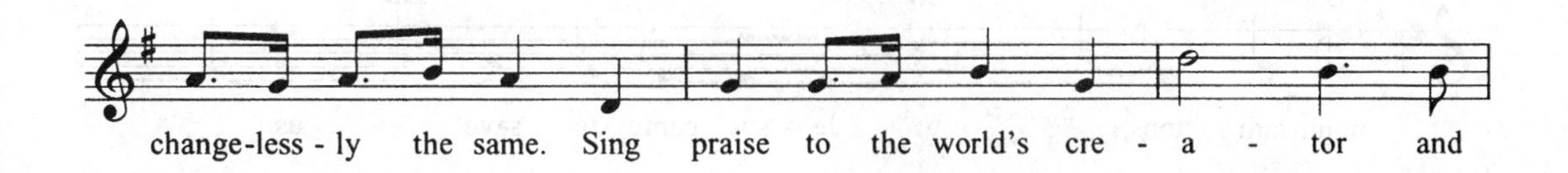

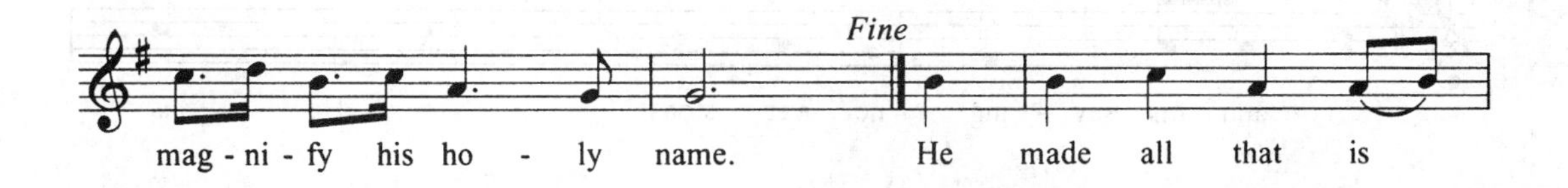

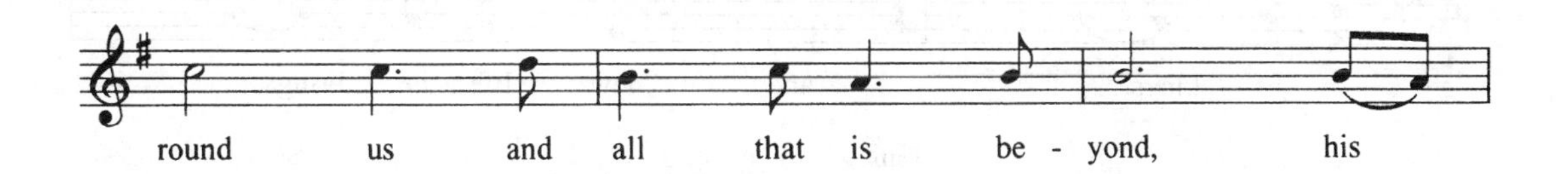

2. Sing glory to God the Saviour,
the Lord of the galaxies, bearer of our shame.
Sing praise to the world's redeemer
and magnify his holy name.

He suffered grief and torment, for sin he paid the price,
he rose in glorious triumph, both priest and sacrifice.

3. Sing glory to God the Spirit,
the power of the elements, setting hearts aflame.
Sing praise to the world's life-giver
and magnify his holy name.

His gifts to all are given, his fruit transforms our hearts,
his fellowship enriches, a grace which he imparts.

4. Sing glory, the whole creation!
Give thanks to the Trinity, heaven's love proclaim.
Sing praise to our God, almighty,
and magnify his holy name.

Text © Copyright Michael Saward/Jubilate Hymns, 4 Thorne Park Road,
Chelston, Torquay TQ2 6RX. Used by permission.

600 Sing it in the valleys

© Copyright 1999 Kevin Mayhew Ltd.

2. You have not deserted me,
though I go astray.
Jesus, take me in your arms,
help me walk with you today.

3. Jesus, you are living now,
Jesus, I believe.
Jesus, take me, heart and soul,
yours alone I want to be.

601 Sing lullaby

Sabine Baring-Gould (1834-1924)

Old Basque Nöel

THE INFANT KING 494 89 94

2. Sing lullaby!
Lullaby baby, now a-sleeping,
sing lullaby!
Hush, do not wake the infant king.
Soon will come sorrow
with the morning,
soon will come bitter grief and weeping:
sing lullaby!

3. Sing lullaby!
Lullaby baby, now a-dozing,
sing lullaby!
Hush, do not wake the infant king.
Soon comes the cross,
the nails, the piercing,
then in the grave at last reposing:
sing lullaby!

4. Sing lullaby!
Lullaby! is the babe awaking?
Sing lullaby.
Hush, do not stir the infant king.
Dreaming of Easter,
gladsome morning,
conquering death, its bondage breaking:
sing lullaby!

602 Sing, my tongue, the glorious battle

Venantius Fortunatus (c.530-609)
trans. John Mason Neale (1818-1866)

Plainsong mode iii

TUNE 1: PANGE LINGUA 87 87 87

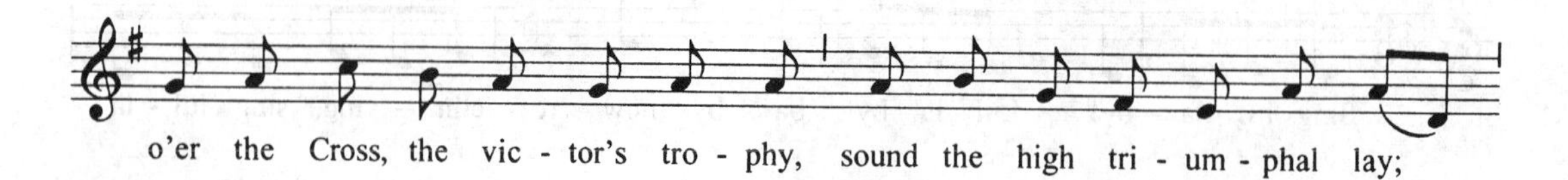

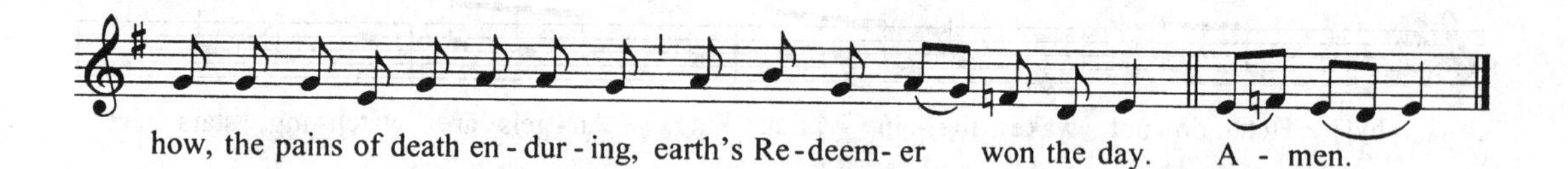

2. When at length th'appointed fullness
of the sacred time was come,
he was sent, the world's creator,
from the Father's heav'nly home,
and was found in human fashion,
offspring of the Virgin's womb.

3. Now the thirty years are ended
which on earth he willed to see,
willingly he meets his Passion,
born to set his people free;
on the cross the Lamb is lifted,
there the sacrifice to be.

4. There the nails and spear he suffers,
vinegar and gall and reed;
from his sacred body piercèd
blood and water both proceed:
precious flood, which all creation
from the stain of sin hath freed.

PART TWO

5. Faithful Cross, above all other,
one and only noble tree!
None in foliage, none in blossom,
none in fruit thy peer may be;
sweetest wood and sweetest iron,
sweetest weight is hung on thee!

6. Bend, O lofty tree, thy branches,
thy too rigid sinews bend;
and awhile the stubborn hardness,
which thy birth bestowed, suspend;
and the limbs of heav'n's high monarch
gently on thine arms extend.

7. Thou alone wast counted worthy
this world's ransom to sustain,
that by thee a wrecked creation
might its ark and haven gain,
with the sacred blood anointed
of the Lamb that hath been slain.

8. Praise and honour to the Father,
praise and honour to the Son,
praise and honour to the Spirit,
ever Three and ever One,
One in might and One in glory,
while eternal ages run.
(Amen.)

Venantius Fortunatus (c.530-609)
trans. John Mason Neale (1818-1866)

18th century melody

TUNE 2: ST THOMAS (WEBBE) 87 87 87

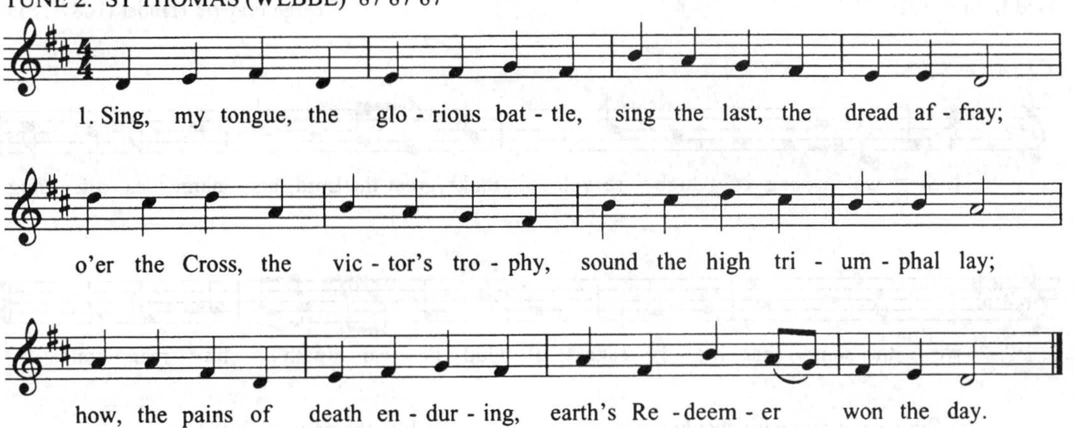

603 Sing to God new songs of worship

Michael Baughen (b.1930)
from Psalm 98

Ludwig van Beethoven (1770-1827)

ODE TO JOY 87 87 D

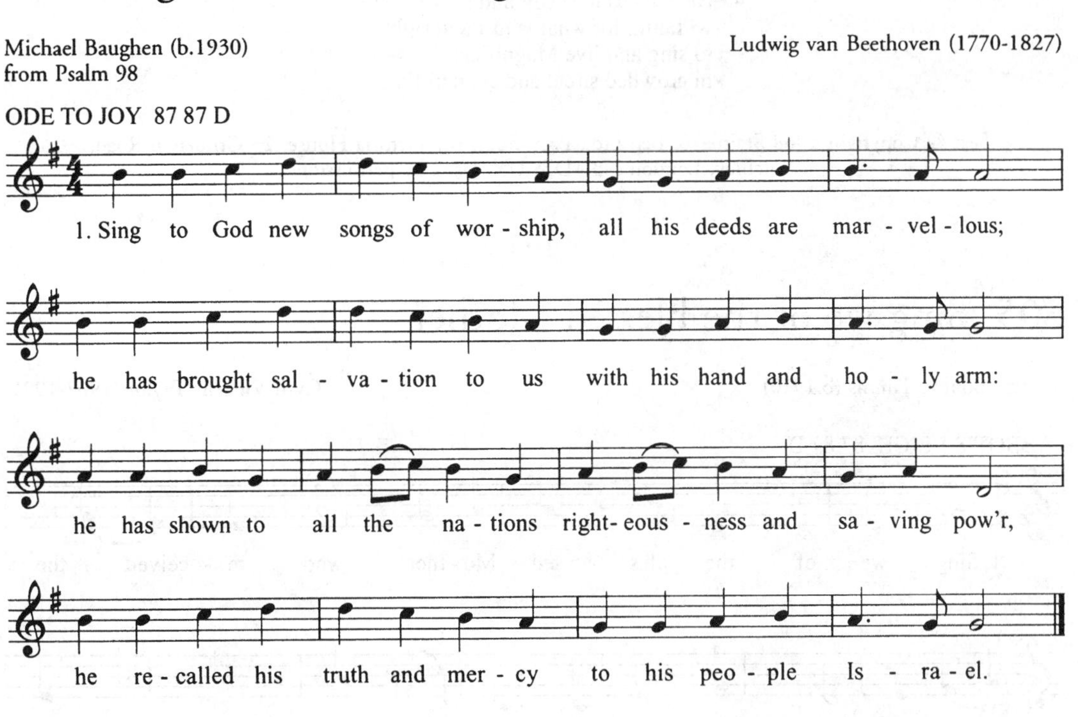

2. Sing to God new songs of worship,
earth has seen his victory;
let the lands of earth be joyful
praising him with thankfulness:
sound upon the harp his praises,
play to him with melody;
let the trumpets sound his triumph,
show your joy to God the king!

3. Sing to God new songs of worship,
let the sea now make a noise;
all on earth and in the waters
sound your praises to the Lord:
let the hills rejoice together,
let the rivers clap their hands,
for with righteousness and justice
he will come to judge the earth.

Text © Copyright Michael Baughen/Jubilate Hymns, 4 Thorne Park Road,
Chelston, Torquay TQ2 6RX, UK. Used by permission.

604 Sing we a song of high revolt

Fred Kaan (b.1929) George Frideric Handel (1685-1759)

CANNONS LM

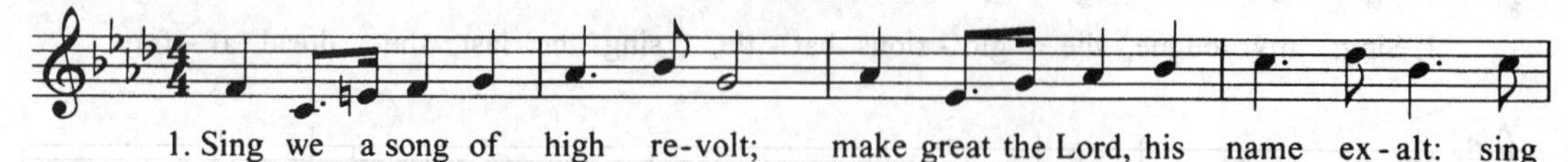

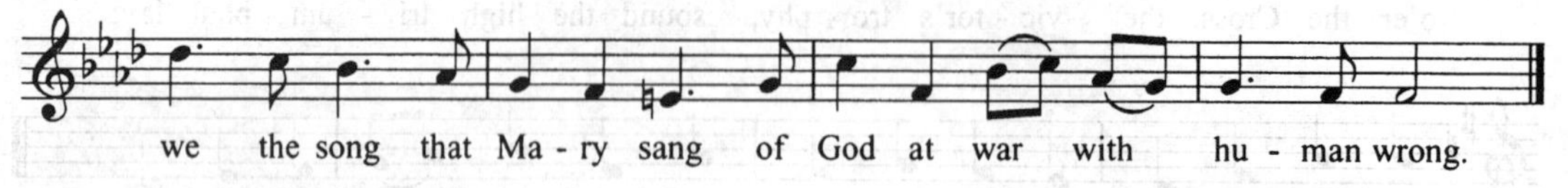

2. Sing we of him who deeply cares
and still with us our burden bears.
He who with strength the proud disowns,
brings down the mighty from their thrones.

3. By him the poor are lifted up;
he satisfies with bread and cup
the hungry ones of many lands;
the rich must go with empty hands.

4. He calls us to revolt and fight
with him for what is just and right,
to sing and live Magnificat
in crowded street and council flat.

Text © Copyright 1968 Stainer & Bell Ltd., P.O. Box 110, Victoria House, 23 Gruneisen Road, Finchley, London N3 1DZ, UK. Used by permission.

605 Sing we of the blessèd Mother

George Bourne Timms (b.1910) Cyril Vincent Taylor (1907-1991)

ABBOT'S LEIGH 87 87 D

© Copyright Oxford University Press, Great Clarendon Street, Oxford OX2 6DP, UK.
(Text taken from *English Praise* and music from *The BBC Hymn Book*) Used by permission.

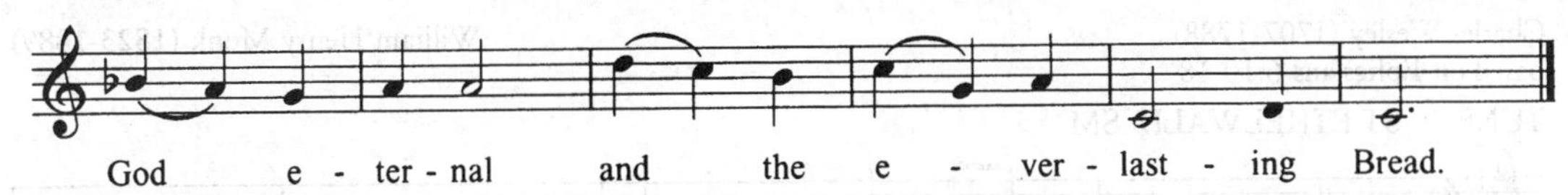

2. Sing we, too, of Mary's sorrows,
of the sword that pierced her through,
when beneath the cross of Jesus
she his weight of suff'ring knew,
looked upon her Son and Saviour
reigning high on Calv'ry's tree,
saw the price of our redemption
paid to set the sinner free.

3. Sing again the joys of Mary
when she saw the risen Lord,
and, in prayer with Christ's apostles,
waited on his promised word:
from on high the blazing glory
of the Spirit's presence came,
heav'nly breath of God's own being,
manifest through wind and flame.

4. Sing the greatest joy of Mary
when on earth her work was done,
and the Lord of all creation
brought her to his heav'nly home:
virgin mother, Mary blessèd,
raised on high and crowned with grace,
may your Son, the world's redeemer,
grant us all to see his face.

606 Soldiers of Christ, arise

Charles Wesley (1707-1788)
based on Ephesians 6:10-18

Edward Woodall Naylor (1867-1934)

TUNE 1: FROM STRENGTH TO STRENGTH DSM

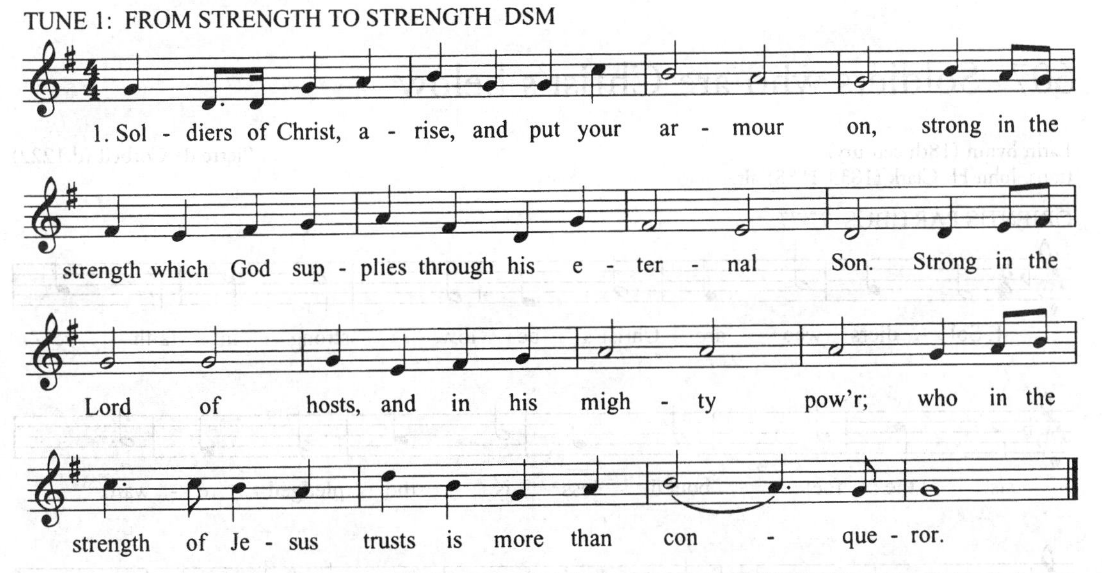

2. Stand then in his great might,
with all his strength endued;
and take, to arm you for the fight,
the panoply of God.
To keep your armour bright,
attend with constant care,
still walking in your Captain's sight
and watching unto prayer.

3. From strength to strength go on,
wrestle and fight and pray;
tread all the pow'rs of darkness down,
and win the well-fought day.
That, having all things done,
and all your conflicts past,
ye may o'ercome, through Christ alone,
and stand entire at last.

Tune 2 will be found overleaf

Music © Copyright Control.

Charles Wesley (1707-1788)
based on Ephesians 6:10-18

William Henry Monk (1823-1889)

TUNE 2: ST ETHELWALD SM

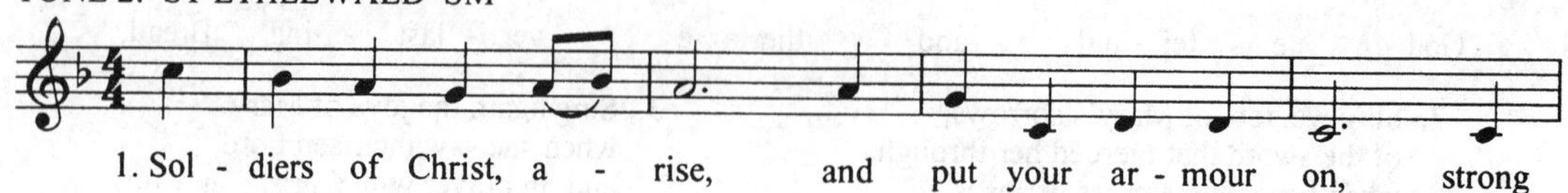

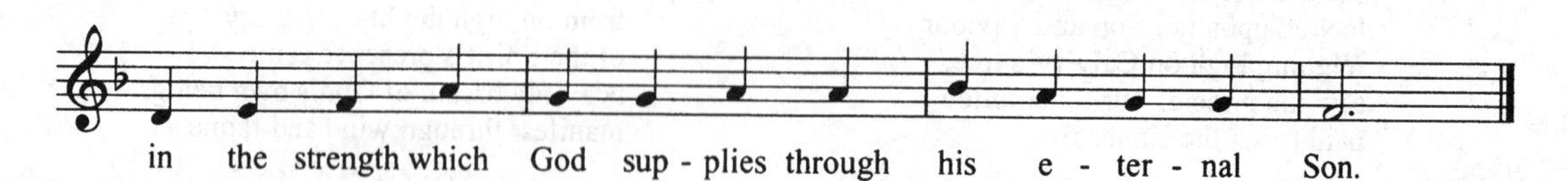

2. Strong in the Lord of hosts,
and in his mighty pow'r;
who in the strength of Jesus trusts
is more than conqueror.

3. Stand then in his great might,
with all his strength endued;
and take, to arm you for the fight,
the panoply of God.

4. To keep your armour bright,
attend with constant care,
still walking in your Captain's sight
and watching unto prayer.

5. From strength to strength go on,
wrestle and fight and pray;
tread all the pow'rs of darkness down,
and win the well-fought day.

6. That, having all things done,
and all your conflicts past,
ye may o'ercome, through Christ alone,
and stand entire at last.

607 Soldiers who are Christ's below

Latin hymn (18th century)
trans. John H. Clark (1839-1888) alt.

Pierre de Corbeil (d.1222)

ORIENTIS PARTIBUS 77 77

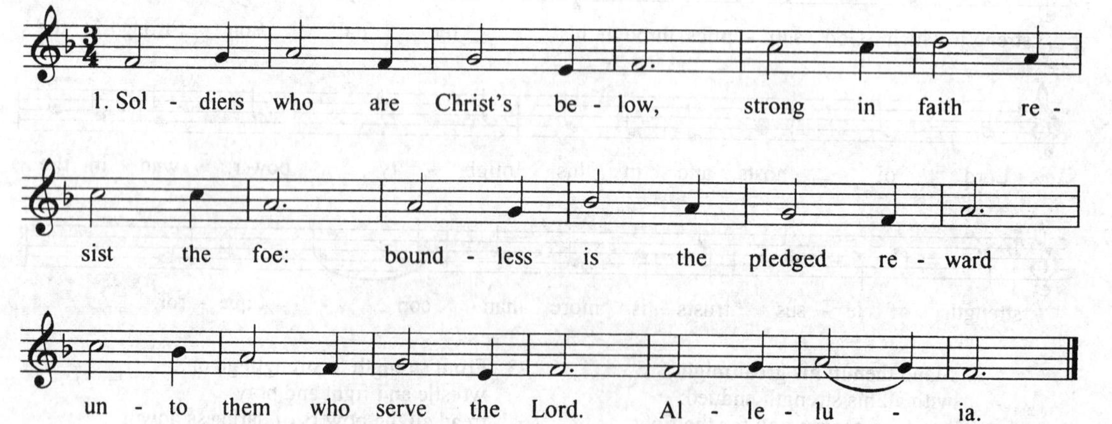

2. 'Tis no palm of fading leaves
that the conqu'ror's hand receives;
joys are ours, serene and pure,
light that ever shall endure.
Alleluia.

3. For the souls that overcome
waits the beauteous heav'nly home,
where the blessed evermore
tread on high the starry floor.
Alleluia.

4. Passing soon and little worth
are the things that tempt on earth;
heav'nward lift thy soul's regard:
God himself is thy reward.
Alleluia.

5. Father, who the crown dost give,
Saviour, by whose death we live,
Spirit, who our hearts dost raise,
Three in One, thy name we praise.
Alleluia.

608 Songs of praise the angels sang

James Montgomery (1771-1854) alt.

Charles John King (1859-1934)

NORTHAMPTON 77 77

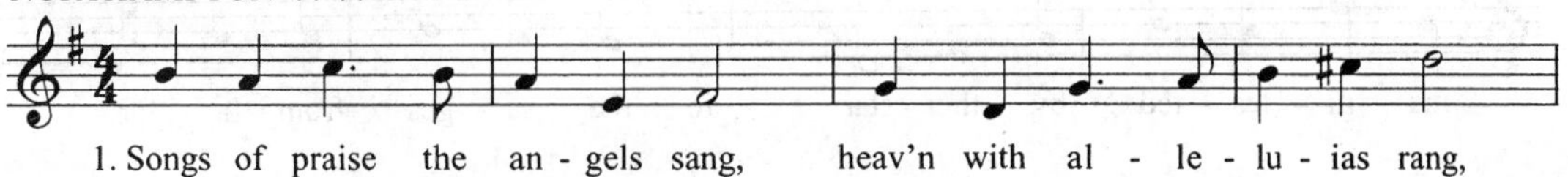

2. Songs of praise awoke the morn
when the Prince of Peace was born;
songs of praise arose when he
captive led captivity.

3. Heav'n and earth must pass away,
songs of praise shall crown that day;
God will make new heav'ns and earth,
songs of praise shall hail their birth.

4. And shall we alone be dumb
till that glorious kingdom come?
No, the Church delights to raise
psalms and hymns and songs of praise.

5. Saints below, with heart and voice,
still in songs of praise rejoice;
learning here, by faith and love,
songs of praise to sing above.

6. Hymns of glory, songs of praise,
Father, unto thee we raise;
Jesu, glory unto thee,
ever with the Spirit be.

Music © Copyright Hymns Ancient & Modern, St Mary's Works,
St Mary's Plain, Norwich NR3 3BH. Used by permission.

609 Songs of thankfulness and praise

Christopher Wordsworth (1807-1885) — Charles Steggall (1826-1905)

ST EDMUND 77 77 D

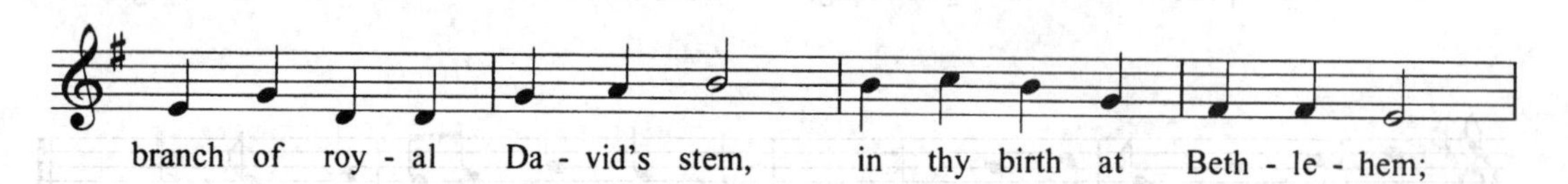

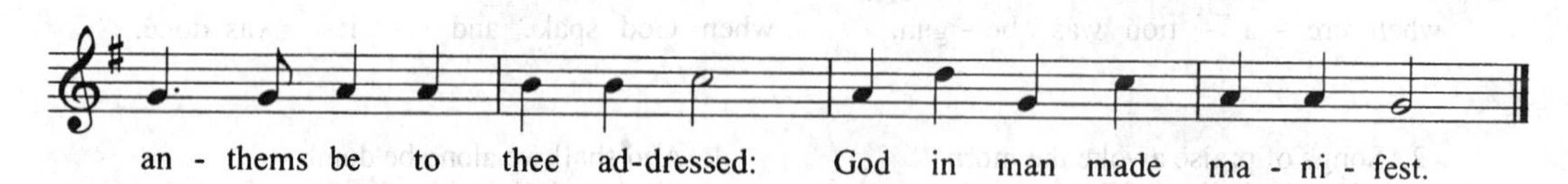

2. Manifest at Jordan's stream,
prophet, priest and King supreme,
and at Cana wedding-guest,
in thy Godhead manifest,
manifest in pow'r divine,
changing water into wine;
anthems be to thee addressed:
God in man made manifest.

3. Manifest in making whole,
palsied limbs and fainting soul,
manifest in valiant fight,
quelling all the devil's might,
manifest in gracious will,
ever bringing good from ill;
anthems be to thee addressed:
God in man made manifest.

4. Sun and moon shall darkened be,
stars shall fall, the heav'ns shall flee;
Christ will then like lightning shine,
all will see his glorious sign.
All will then the trumpet hear,
all will see the judge appear;
thou by all wilt be confessed:
God in man made manifest.

5. Grant us grace to see thee, Lord,
mirrored in thy holy word;
may we imitate thee now,
and be pure, as pure art thou;
that we like to thee may be
at thy great Epiphany,
and may praise thee, ever blest,
God in man made manifest.

610 Soul of my Saviour

Anima Christi ascribed to John XXII (1249-1334)
trans. unknown — William Joseph Maher (1823-1877)

ANIMA CHRISTI 10 10 10 10

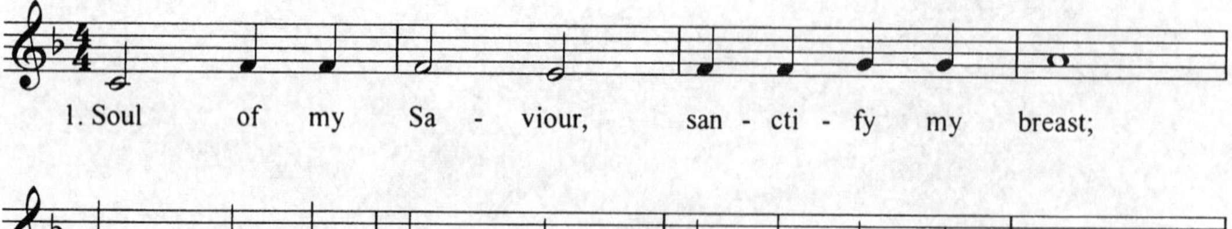

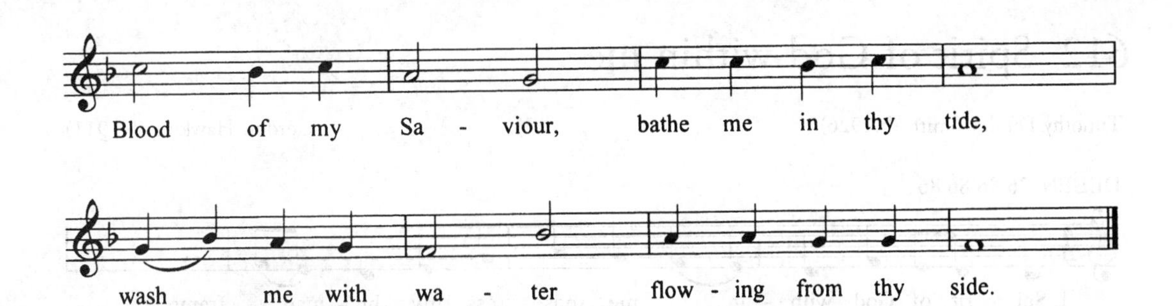

2. Strength and protection may thy passion be;
O blessèd Jesus, hear and answer me;
deep in thy wounds, Lord, hide and shelter me;
so shall I never, never part from thee.

3. Guard and defend me from the foe malign;
in death's dread moments make me only thine;
call me, and bid me come to thee on high,
when I may praise thee with thy saints for aye.

611 Spirit of God

Mallaig Sprinkling Song

Helen Kennedy

Scottish folk melody

LEAVING OF LISMORE 99 98 D

2. Lord, how I thirst, O Lord, I am weak.
Lord, come to me, you alone do I seek.
Lord, you are life, and love and hope,
O fill me with living water.

3. Lord, I am blind. O Lord, I can't see.
Stretch out your hand, O Lord, comfort me.
Lead me your way in light and in truth,
O fill me with living water.

Text © Copyright St Mungo Music, 5 Beech Avenue, Glasgow G41 5BY, Scotland.
Used by permission.

612 Spirit of God within me

Timothy Dudley-Smith (b.1926) | Gordon Hawkins (b.1911)

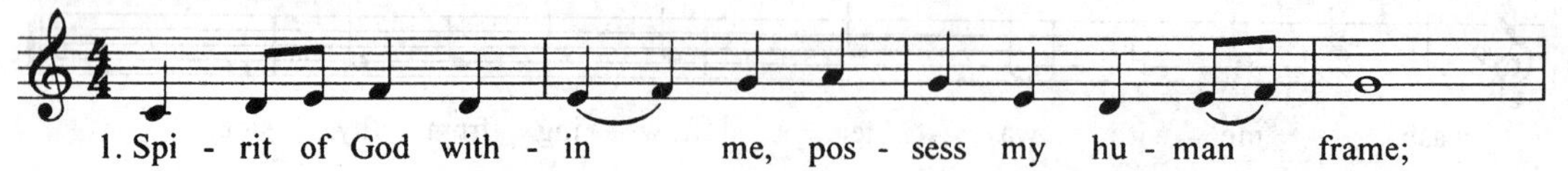

2. Spirit of truth within me,
possess my thought and mind;
lighten anew the inward eye
by Satan rendered blind;
shine on the words that wisdom speaks,
and grant me pow'r to see
the truth made known to all in Christ,
and in that truth be free.

3. Spirit of love within me,
possess my hands and heart;
break through the bonds of self-concern
that seeks to stand apart;
grant me the love that suffers long,
that hopes, believes and bears,
the love fulfilled in sacrifice,
that cares as Jesus cares.

4. Spirit of life within me,
possess this life of mine;
come as the wind of heaven's breath,
come as the fire divine!
Spirit of Christ, the living Lord,
reign in this house of clay,
till from its dust with Christ I rise
to everlasting day.

Text © Copyright Timothy Dudley-Smith, 9 Ashlands, Ford, Salisbury, Wiltshire SP4 6DY, UK. Used by permission.
Music © Copyright Mrs J.M. Gorsuch. Used by permission.

613 Spirit of mercy, truth and love

Foundling Hospital Collection (1774) alt. | Ralph Harrison (1748-1810)

TUNE 1: WARRINGTON LM

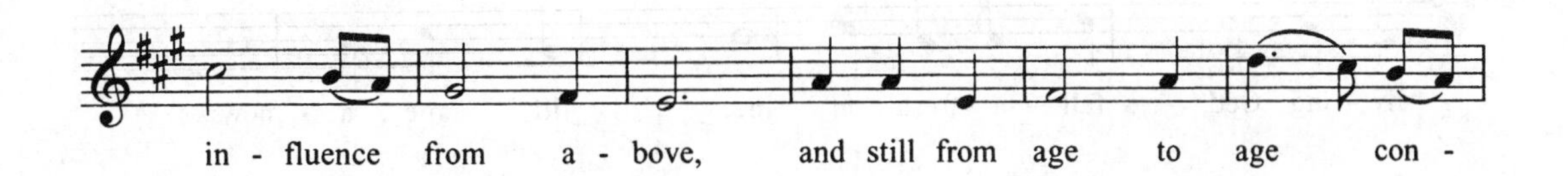

2. In ev'ry clime, by ev'ry tongue,
be God's surpassing glory sung;
let all the list'ning earth be taught
the acts our great Redeemer wrought.

3. Unfailing comfort, heav'nly guide,
still o'er thy holy Church preside;
let humankind thy blessings prove,
Spirit of mercy, truth and love.

Foundling Hospital Collection (1774) alt. | Melody from an early 19th century Nottingham collection

TUNE 2: BIRLING LM

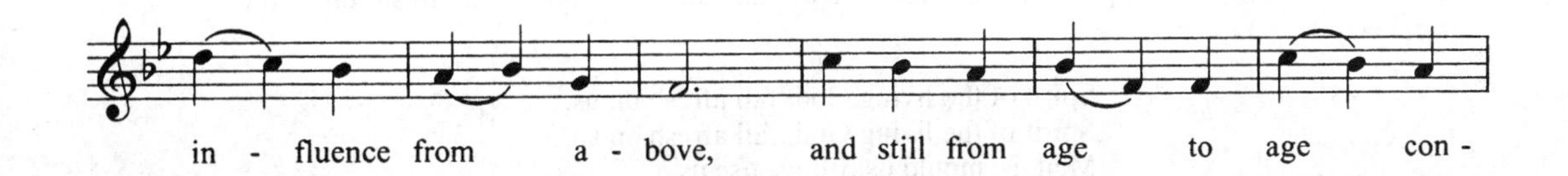

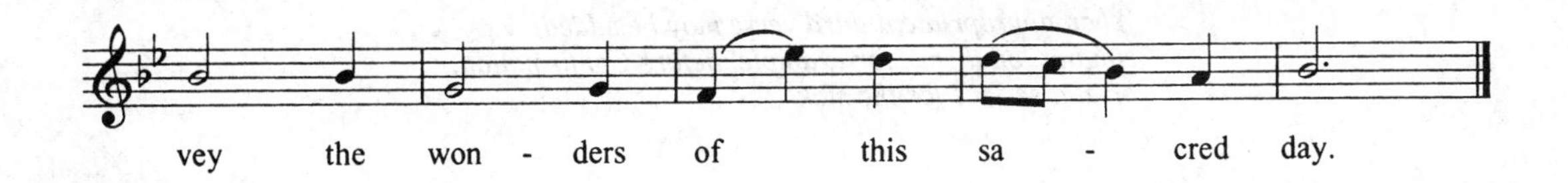

614 Spirit of the living God (Armstrong)

Words and music: Paul Armstrong

© Copyright 1984 Restoration Music Ltd./Sovereign Music UK,
P.O. Box 356, Leighton Buzzard, Beds. LU7 3WP, UK. Used by permission.

615 Spirit of the living God (Iverson)

Words and music: Daniel Iverson (1890-1972)

LIVING GOD 75 75 44 75

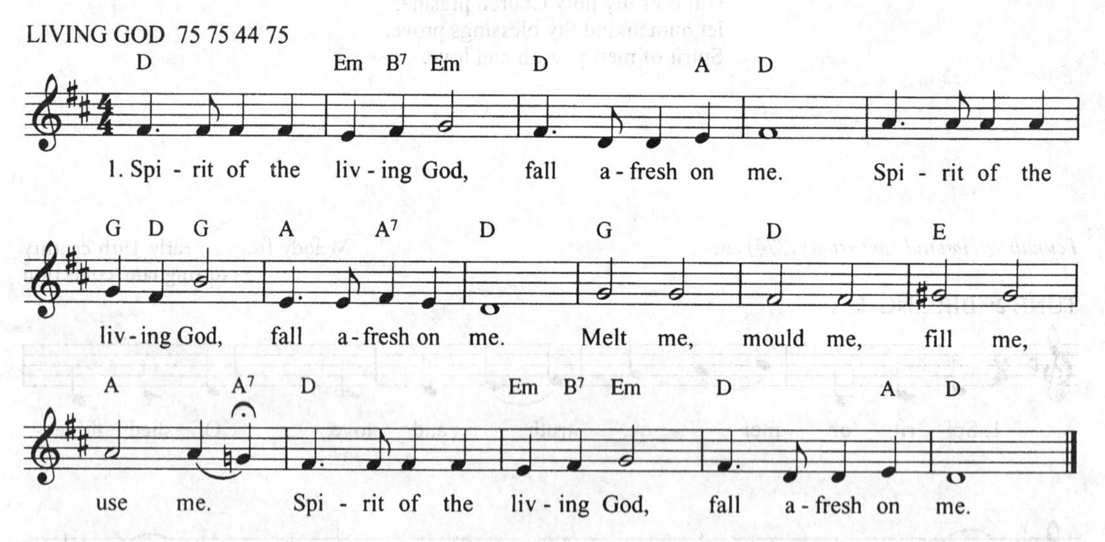

2. Spirit of the living God, fall afresh on us.
   Spirit of the living God, fall afresh on us.
   Melt us, mould us, fill us, use us.
   Spirit of the living God, fall afresh on us.

When appropriate a third verse may be added, singing 'on them', for example, before Confirmation, or at a service for the sick.

© Copyright 1963 Birdwing Music/EMI Christian Music Publishing. Administered by CopyCare, P.O. Box 77, Hailsham, East Sussex BN27 3EF, UK. (music@copycare.com). Used by permission.

616 Stand up and bless the Lord

James Montgomery (1771-1854)

Charles Lockhart (1745-1815)

CARLISLE SM

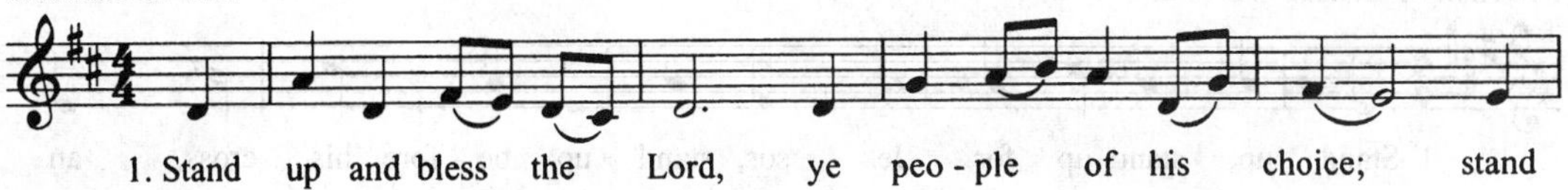

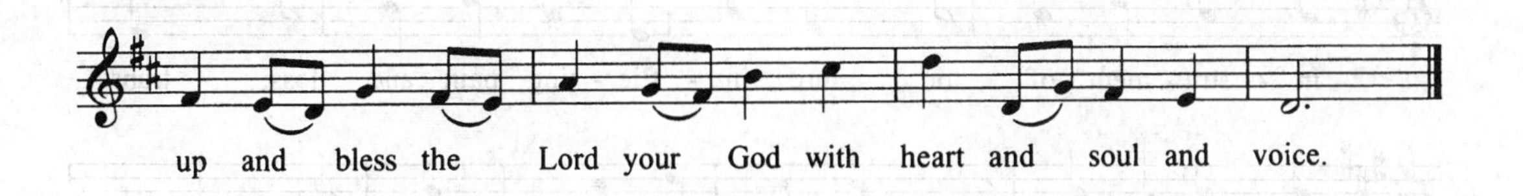

2. Though high above all praise,
   above all blessing high,
   who would not fear his holy name,
   and laud and magnify?

3. O for the living flame
   from his own altar brought,
   to touch our lips, our mind inspire,
   and wing to heav'n our thought.

4. God is our strength and song,
   and his salvation ours;
   then be his love in Christ proclaimed
   with all our ransomed pow'rs.

5. Stand up and bless the Lord,
   the Lord your God adore;
   stand up and bless his glorious name
   henceforth for evermore.

617 Stand up, stand up for Jesus

Jean Holloway (b.1939) George James Webb (1803-1887)

MORNING LIGHT 76 76 D

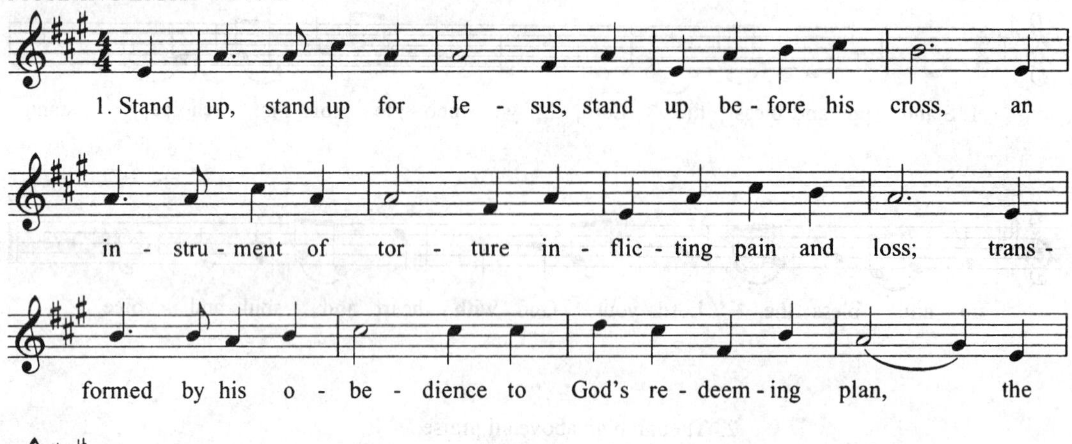

2. Stand up, stand up for Jesus,
counted as his own;
his gospel of forgiveness
he cannot spread alone.
The love which draws us to him,
he calls us out to share;
he calls us to the margins
to be his presence there.

3. Stand up, stand up for Jesus,
in faith and hope be strong,
stand firm for right and justice,
opposed to sin and wrong.
Give comfort to the wounded,
and care for those in pain,
for Christ, in those who suffer,
is crucified again.

4. Stand up, stand up for Jesus,
who reigns as King of kings,
be ready for the challenge
of faith his kingship brings.
He will not force obedience,
he gives to each the choice
to turn from all that's holy,
or in his love rejoice.

5. Stand up, stand up for Jesus,
give courage to the weak,
be unashamed to praise him,
be bold his name to speak.
Confront the cross unflinching,
Christ's love has set us free;
he conquered death for ever
and lives eternally.

Text © Copyright 1996 Kevin Mayhew Ltd.

618 Steal away

Words and music: Spiritual

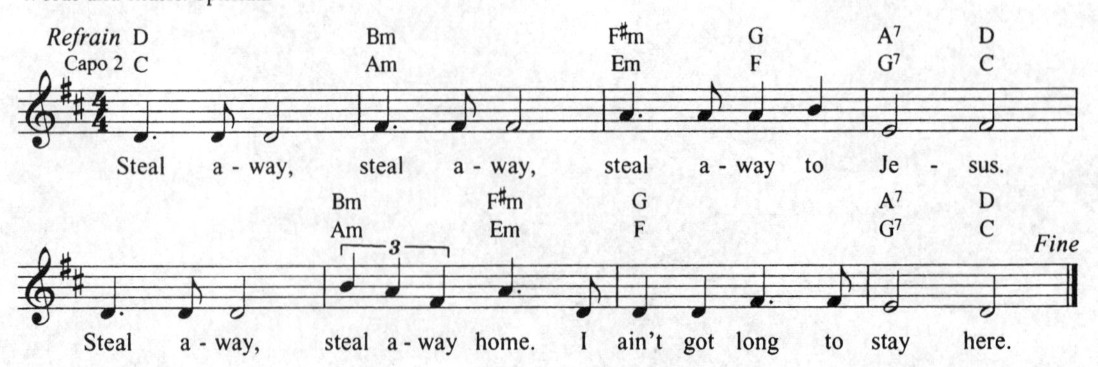

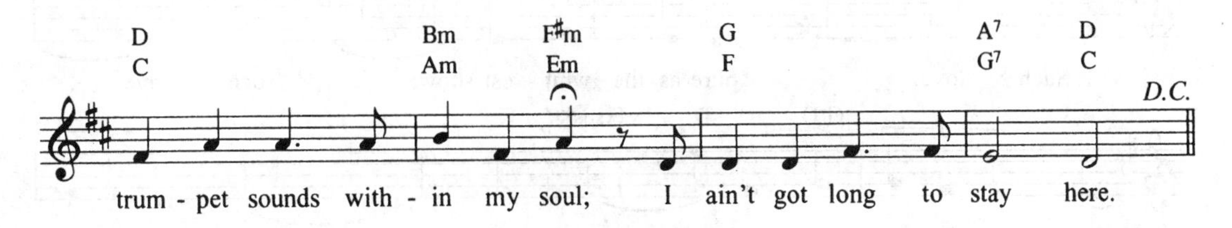

2. Green trees are bending,
the sinner stands a-trembling.
The trumpet sounds within my soul;
I ain't got long to stay here.

3. My Lord, he calls me,
he calls me by the lightning.
The trumpet sounds within my soul;
I ain't got long to stay here.

619 Strengthen for service, Lord

Syriac Liturgy, perhaps by
Ephraim the Syrian (c.306-373),
trans. Charles William Hymphreys (1840-1921)
and Percy Dearmer (1867-1936)

Melody in *Neu-Leipziger Gesangbuch* (1682)
adapted by Johann Sebastian Bach (1685-1750)

ACH GOTT UND HERR 87 87

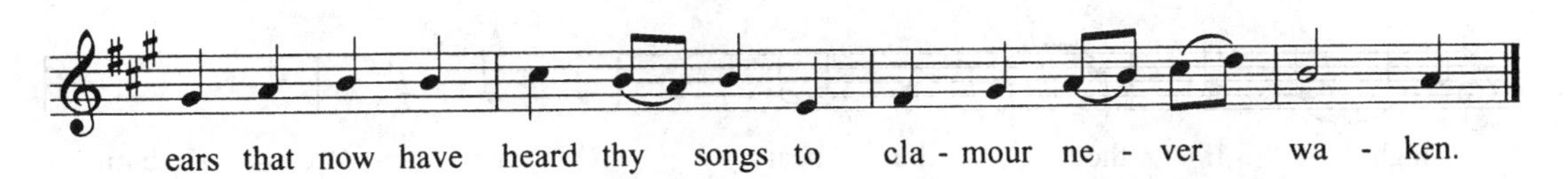

2. Lord, may the tongues which
'Holy' sang
keep free from all deceiving;
the eyes which saw thy love be bright,
thy blessèd hope perceiving.

3. The feet that tread thy holy courts
from light do thou not banish;
the bodies by thy Body fed
with thy new life replenish.

Text © Copyright Oxford University Press, Great Clarendon Street, Oxford OX2 6DP, UK.
Used by permission.

620 Such love

Words and music: Graham Kendrick (b.1950)

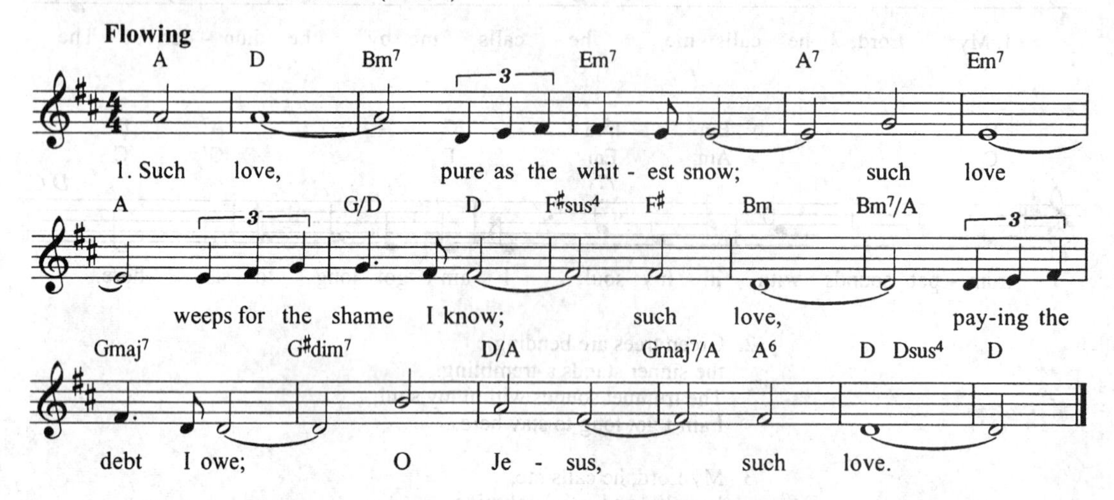

2. Such love, stilling my restlessness;
such love, filling my emptiness;
such love, showing me holiness;
O Jesus, such love.

3. Such love springs from eternity;
such love, streaming through history;
such love, fountain of life to me;
O Jesus, such love.

© Copyright 1988 Make Way Music, P.O. Box 263, Croydon, Surrey CR9 5AP, UK.
International copyright secured. All rights reserved. Used by permission.

621 Sun of my soul, thou Saviour dear

John Keble (1792-1866) *Katholisches Gesangbuch* (c.1775)

TUNE 1: HURSLEY LM

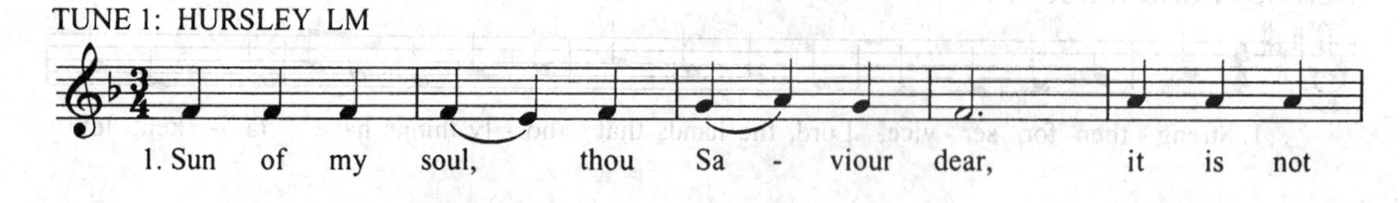

2. When the soft dews of kindly sleep
my wearied eyelids gently steep,
be my last thought, how sweet to rest
for ever on my Saviour's breast.

3. Abide with me from morn till eve,
for without thee I cannot live;
abide with me when night is nigh,
for without thee I dare not die.

4. Watch by the sick; enrich the poor
with blessings from thy boundless store;
be ev'ry mourner's sleep tonight
like infant's slumbers, pure and light.

John Keble (1792-1866) Herbert Stanley Oakeley (1830-1903)

TUNE 2: ABENDS LM

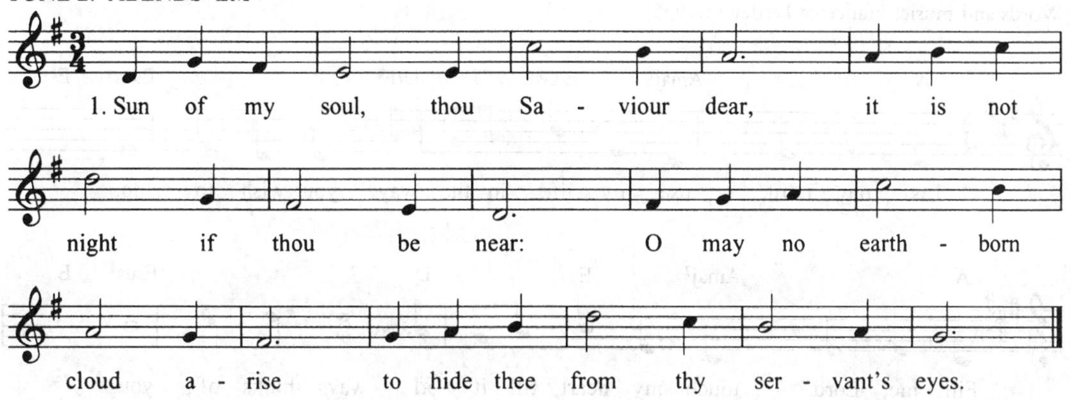

622 Sweet sacrament divine

Words and music: Francis Stanfield (1835-1914) alt.

DIVINE MYSTERIES 66 66 88 6

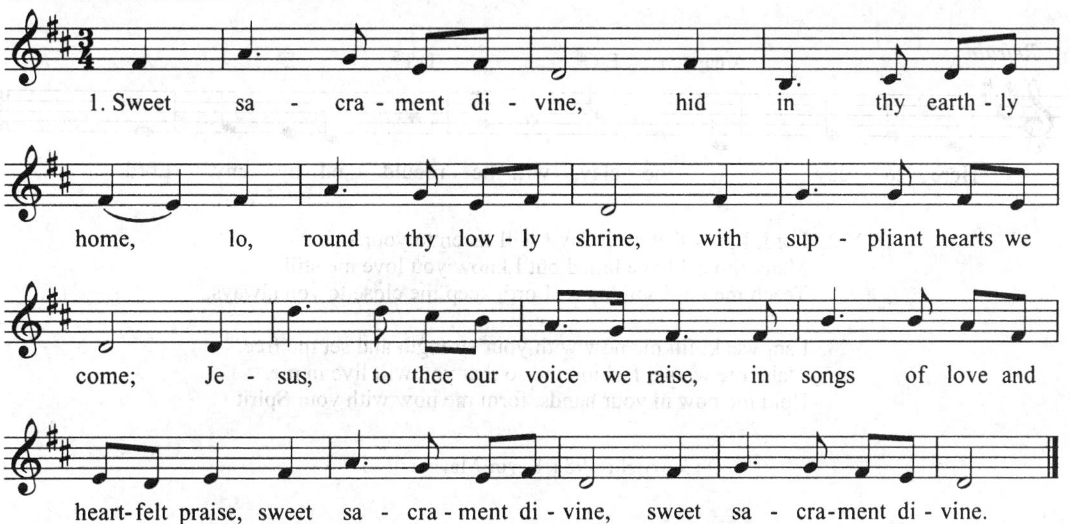

2. Sweet sacrament of peace,
dear home of ev'ry heart,
where restless yearnings cease,
and sorrows all depart,
there in thine ear all trustfully
we tell our tale of misery,
sweet sacrament of peace. *(x2)*

3. Sweet sacrament of rest,
Ark from the ocean's roar,
within thy shelter blest
soon may we reach the shore;
save us, for still the tempest raves;
save, lest we sink beneath the waves,
sweet sacrament of rest. *(x2)*

4. Sweet sacrament divine,
earth's light and jubilee,
in thy far depths doth shine
thy Godhead's majesty;
sweet light, so shine on us, we pray,
that earthly joys may fade away,
sweet sacrament divine. *(x2)*

623 Take me, Lord

Words and music: Francesca Leftley (b.1955)

2. Lord, I pray that each day I will listen to your will.
Many times I have failed but I know you love me still.
Teach me now, guide me, Lord, keep me close to you always.

3. I am weak, fill me now with your strength and set me free.
Make me whole, fashion me so that you will live in me.
Hold me now in your hands, form me now with your Spirit.

© Copyright 1984 Kevin Mayhew Ltd.

624 Take my hands, Lord

vs. 1&3: Margaret Rizza
v. 2: unknown

Margaret Rizza (b.1929)

© Copyright 1998 Kevin Mayhew Ltd.

2. Give me someone to feed when I'm hungry,
when I'm thirsty give water for their thirst.
When I stand in need of tenderness,
give me someone to hold who longs for love.

3. Keep my heart ever open to others,
may my time, Lord, be spent with those in need;
may I tend to those who need your care.
Take my life, Lord, and make it truly yours.

625 Take my life, and let it be

Frances Ridley Havergal (1836-1879)

The Parish Choir (1850)

TUNE 1: INNOCENTS 77 77

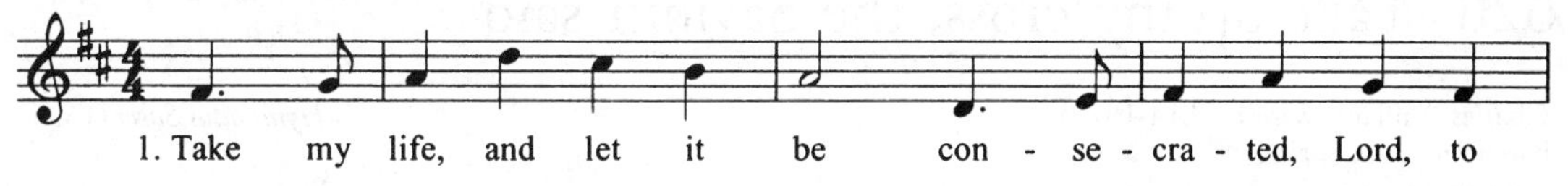

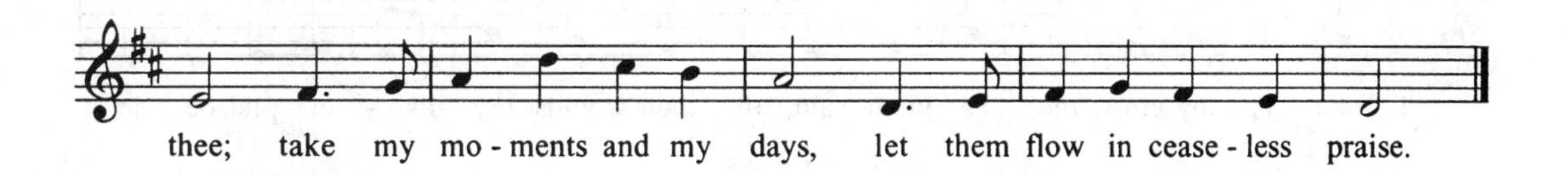

2. Take my hands, and let them move
at the impulse of thy love;
take my feet, and let them be
swift and beautiful for thee.

3. Take my voice, and let me sing
always, only, for my King;
take my lips, and let them be
filled with messages from thee.

4. Take my silver and my gold;
not a mite would I withhold;
take my intellect, and use
ev'ry pow'r as thou shalt choose.

5. Take my will, and make it thine:
it shall be no longer mine;
take my heart: it is thine own;
it shall be thy royal throne.

6. Take my love; my Lord, I pour
at thy feet its treasure-store;
take myself, and I will be
ever, only, all for thee.

Tune 2 will be found overleaf

Frances Ridley Havergal (1836-1879) | Wolfgang Amadeus Mozart (1756-1791) adapt.

TUNE 2: NOTTINGHAM 77 77

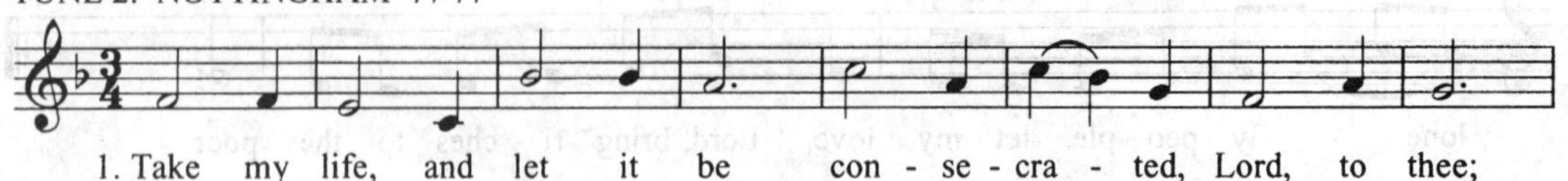

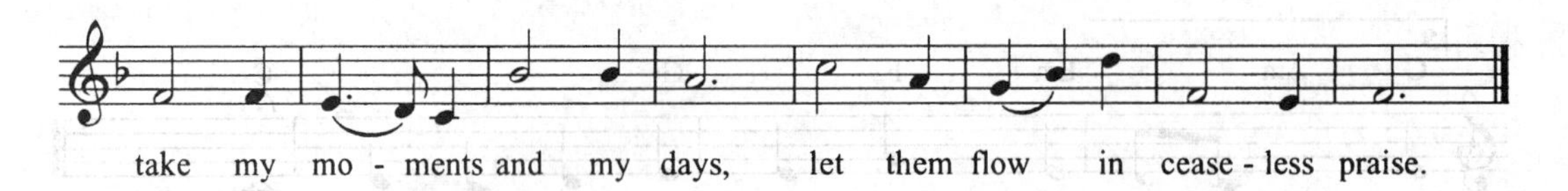

2. Take my hands, and let them move
at the impulse of thy love;
take my feet, and let them be
swift and beautiful for thee.

3. Take my voice, and let me sing
always, only, for my King;
take my lips, and let them be
filled with messages from thee.

4. Take my silver and my gold;
not a mite would I withhold;
take my intellect, and use
ev'ry pow'r as thou shalt choose.

5. Take my will, and make it thine:
it shall be no longer mine;
take my heart: it is thine own;
it shall be thy royal throne.

6. Take my love; my Lord, I pour
at thy feet its treasure-store;
take myself, and I will be
ever, only, all for thee.

626 Take up thy cross, the Saviour said

Charles William Everest (1814-1877)
based on Mark 8, alt. | *As Hymnodus Sacer* (1625)

BRESLAU LM

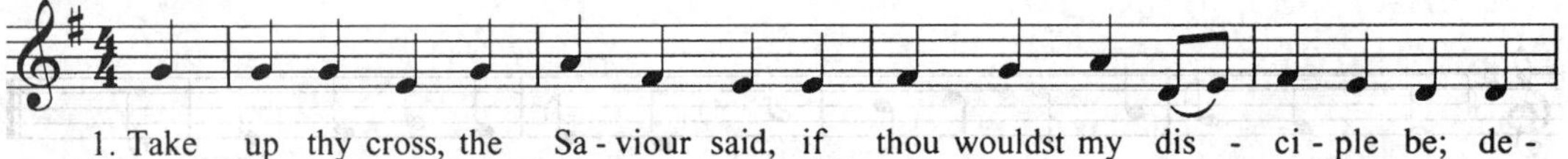

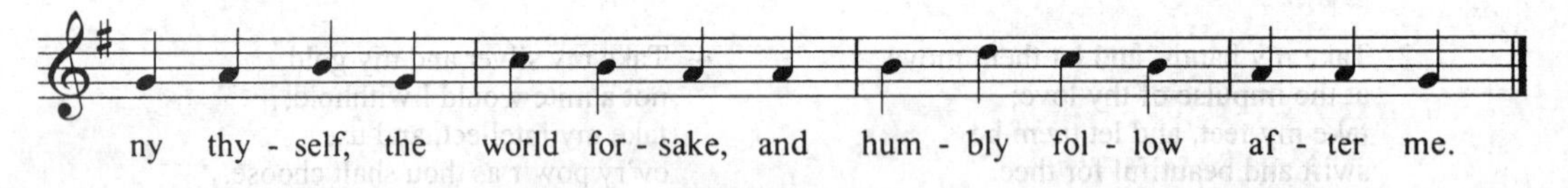

2. Take up thy cross – let not its weight
fill thy weak spirit with alarm:
his strength shall bear thy spirit up,
and brace thy heart, and nerve thine arm.

3. Take up thy cross, nor heed the shame,
nor let thy foolish pride rebel:
thy Lord for thee the Cross endured,
to save thy soul from death and hell.

4. Take up thy cross then in his strength,
and calmly ev'ry danger brave;
'twill guide thee to a better home,
and lead to vict'ry o'er the grave.

5. Take up thy cross, and follow Christ,
nor think till death to lay it down;
for only those who bear the cross
may hope to wear the glorious crown.

6. To thee, great Lord, the One in Three,
all praise for evermore ascend:
O grant us in our home to see
the heav'nly life that knows no end.

627 Take up your cross, he says

Susan Sayers
based on Mark 8 and John 14

Susan Sayers (b.1946)

2. What if the rocks are blistering my feet,
and the sun's heat beats upon my head?
Near me a grass path beckons with its flowers,
I'm tempted to go that way instead.

3. What if the tiredness aches behind my eyes
and my boat is impossible to steer?
Out on an ocean, drifting and alone,
am I still, even then, to persevere?

4. Strangest of wonders, wonderfully strange,
that the cross can set me free.
Nothing is stronger than the love of God:
I know very well that he loves me.

© Copyright 1984 Kevin Mayhew Ltd.

628 Taste and see the goodness of the Lord

Hubert J. Richards (b.1921)
based on Psalm 34

Andrew Moore (b.1954)

2. So come with me to sing his praise,
together let us praise his name.
I seek the Lord, he answers me,
rescues me from all my fears.

3. The Lord is quick to heed the poor
and liberate them from their chains.
The Lord is close to broken hearts,
he rescues slaves and sets them free.

© Copyright 1996 Kevin Mayhew Ltd.

629 Teach me, my God and King

George Herbert (1593-1633)

Traditional English carol from
William Sandys' *Christmas Carols* (1833)

SANDYS SM

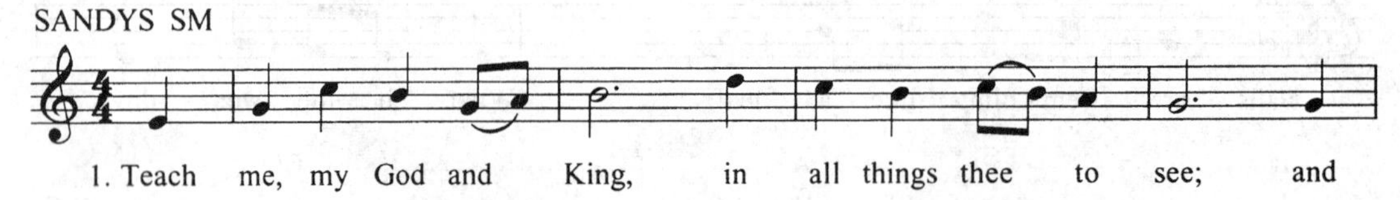

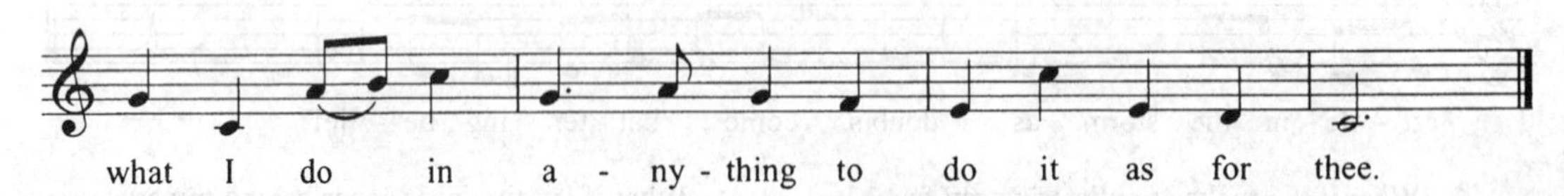

2. A man that looks on glass,
on it may stay his eye;
or, if he pleaseth, through it pass,
and then the heav'n espy.

3. All may of thee partake;
nothing can be so mean
which, with this tincture, 'For thy sake',
will not grow bright and clean.

4. A servant with this clause
makes drudgery divine;
who sweeps a room, as for thy laws,
makes that and the action fine.

5. This is the famous stone
that turneth all to gold;
for that which God doth touch and own
cannot for less be told.

630 Tell his praise in song and story

Timothy Dudley-Smith (b.1926)
from Psalm 34

Cyril Vincent Taylor (1907-1991)

ABBOT'S LEIGH 87 87 D

2. To the Lord whose love has found them
cry the poor in their distress;
swift his angels camped around them
prove him sure to save and bless.
God it is who hears our crying
though the spark of faith be dim:
taste and see! beyond denying
blest are those who trust in him.

3. Taste and see! in faith draw near him,
trust the Lord with all our pow'rs;
seek and serve him, love and fear him,
life and all its joys are ours;
true delight in holy living,
peace and plenty, length of days:
come, my children, with thanksgiving
bless the Lord in songs of praise.

4. In our need he walks beside us,
ears alert to ev'ry cry;
watchful eyes to guard and guide us,
love that whispers, 'It is I'.
Good shall triumph, wrong be righted,
God has pledged his promised word;
so with ransomed saints united
join to praise our living Lord!

Text © Copyright Timothy Dudley-Smith, 9 Ashlands, Ford, Salisbury,
Wiltshire SP4 6DY, UK. Used by permission.
Music © Copyright Oxford University Press, Great Clarendon Street, Oxford OX2 6DP, UK.
Used by permission from the *BBC Hymn Book*.

631 Tell out, my soul

Timothy Dudley-Smith (b.1926)
based on Luke 1:46-55

Walter Greatorex (1877-1949)

WOODLANDS 10 10 10 10

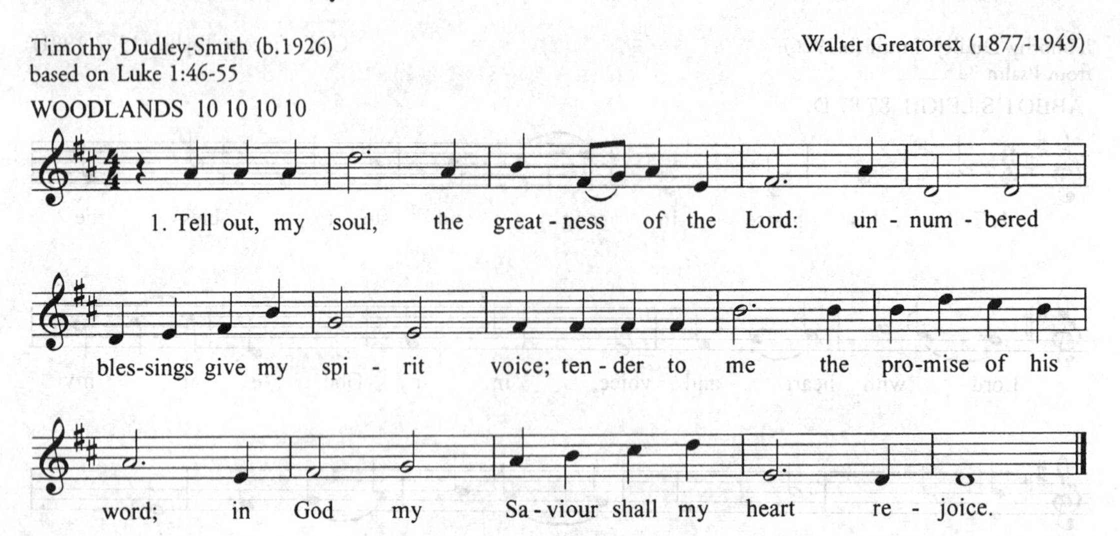

2. Tell out, my soul, the greatness of his name:
make known his might, the deeds his arm has done;
his mercy sure, from age to age the same;
his holy name, the Lord, the mighty one.

3. Tell out, my soul, the greatness of his might:
pow'rs and dominions lay their glory by;
proud hearts and stubborn wills are put to flight,
the hungry fed, the humble lifted high.

4. Tell out, my soul, the glories of his word:
firm is his promise, and his mercy sure.
Tell out, my soul, the greatness of the Lord
to children's children and for evermore.

Text © Copyright Timothy Dudley-Smith, 9 Ashlands, Ford, Salisbury, Wiltshire SP4 6DY, UK.
Used by permission.
Music © Copyright Oxford University Press, Great Clarendon Street, Oxford OX2 6DP, UK.
Used by permission from *Enlarged Songs of Praise.*

632 Thanks for the fellowship

Jean Holloway (b.1939)

Traditional Scottish melody

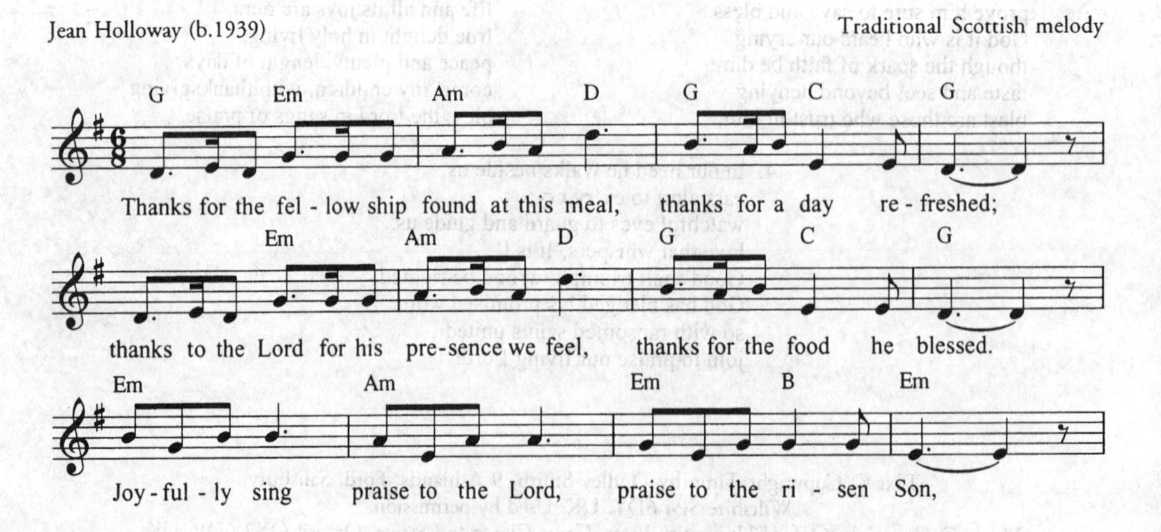

Text © Copyright 1994 Kevin Mayhew Ltd.

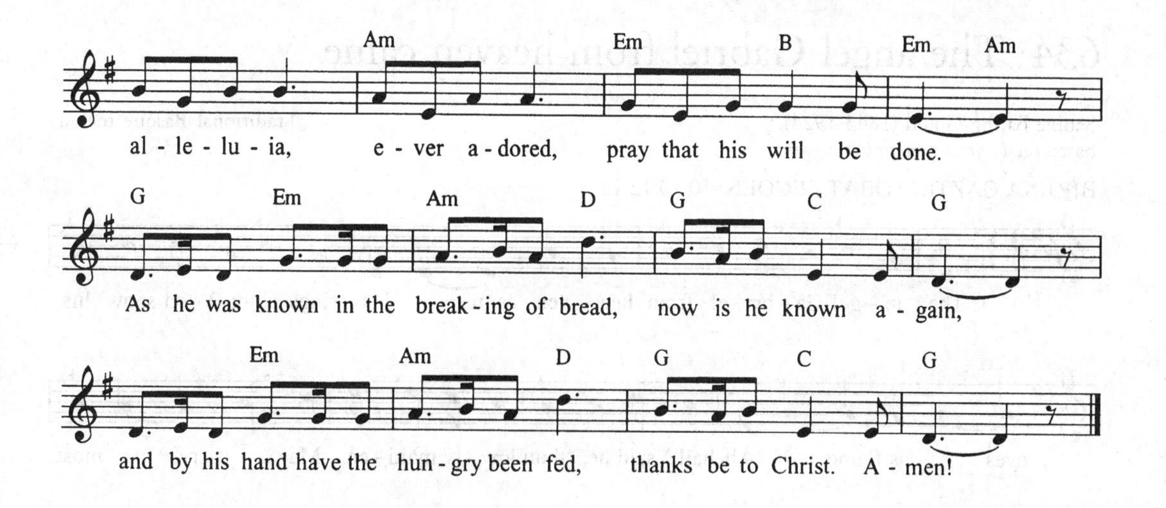

633 The advent of our King

Charles Coffin (1676-1749)
trans. John Chandler (1806-1876) alt.

From *Harmonischer Liederschatz* (1738)
adapt. William Henry Havergal (1793-1870)

TUNE 1: FRANCONIA SM

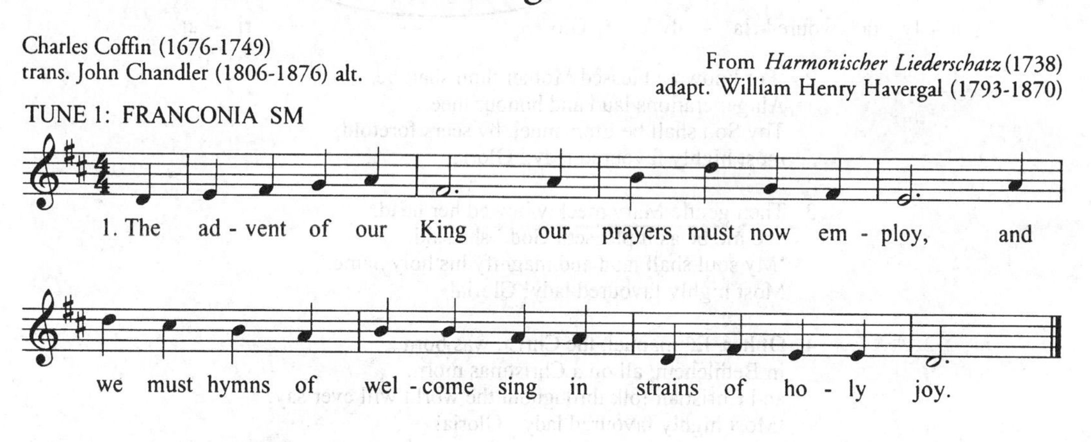

2. The everlasting Son
incarnate deigns to be;
himself a servant's form puts on,
to set his servants free.

3. Daughter of Sion, rise
to meet thy lowly King;
nor let thy faithless heart despise
the peace he comes to bring.

4. As Judge, on clouds of light,
he soon will come again,
and his true members all unite
with him in heav'n to reign.

5. All glory to the Son
who comes to set us free,
with Father, Spirit, ever One,
through all eternity.

Charles Coffin (1676-1749)
trans. John Chandler (1806-1876) alt.

From Aaron Williams'
New Universal Psalmodist (1770)

TUNE 2: ST THOMAS SM

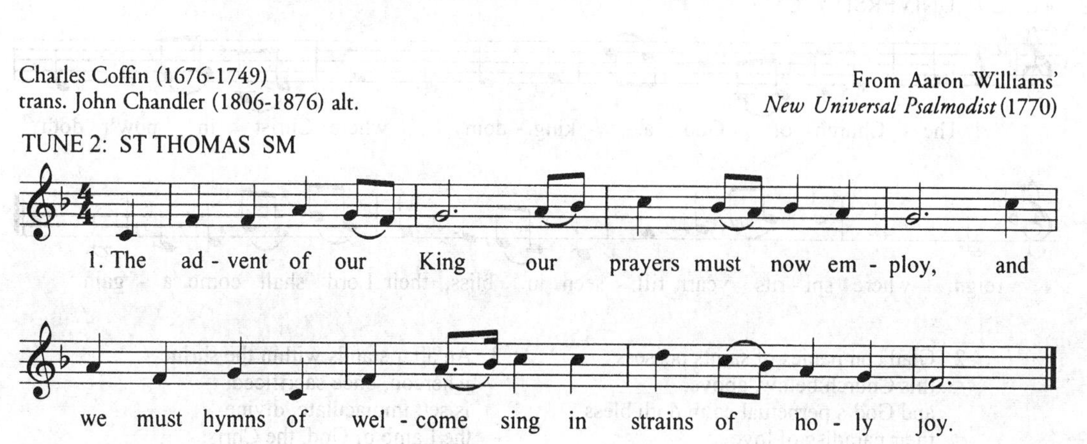

634 The angel Gabriel from heaven came

Sabine Baring-Gould (1843-1924)
based on *Birjina gaztettobat zegoen*

Traditional Basque melody

BIRJINA GAZTETTOBAT ZEGOEN 10 10 12 10

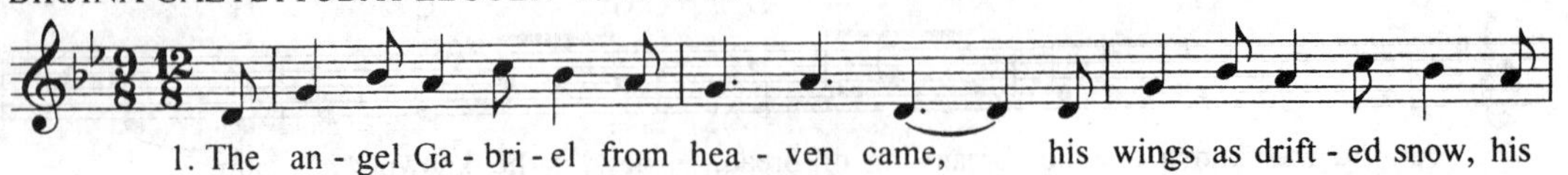

eyes as flame. 'All hail,' said he, 'thou low - ly maid - en, Ma - ry, most

2. 'For known a blessèd Mother thou shalt be.
All generations laud and honour thee.
Thy Son shall be Emmanuel, by seers foretold,
most highly favoured lady.' Gloria!

3. Then gentle Mary meekly bowed her head.
'To me be as it pleaseth God,' she said.
'My soul shall laud and magnify his holy name.'
Most highly favoured lady! Gloria!

4. Of her, Emmanuel, the Christ, was born
in Bethlehem, all on a Christmas morn;
and Christian folk throughout the world will ever say:
'Most highly favoured lady.' Gloria!

635 The Church of God a kingdom is

Lionel Muirhead (1845-1925) alt.

Charles Collignon (1725-1785)

TUNE 1: UNIVERSITY CM

2. Glad companies of saints possess
this Church below, above;
and God's perpetual calm doth bless
their paradise of love.

3. An altar stands within the shrine
whereon, once sacrificed,
is set, immaculate, divine,
the Lamb of God, the Christ.

4. There rich and poor, from countless lands,
praise Christ on mystic rood;
there nations reach forth holy hands
to take God's holy food.

5. There pure life-giving streams o'erflow
the sower's garden-ground;
and faith and hope fair blossoms show,
and fruits of love abound.

6. O King, O Christ, this endless grace
to all your people bring,
to see the vision of your face
in joy, O Christ, our King.

Lionel Muirhead (1845-1925) alt.

Traditional English carol collected by Lucy Broadwood (1858-1929)

TUNE 2: CAPEL CM

636 The Church's one foundation

Samuel John Stone (1839-1900)

Samuel Sebastian Wesley (1810-1876)

AURELIA 76 76 D

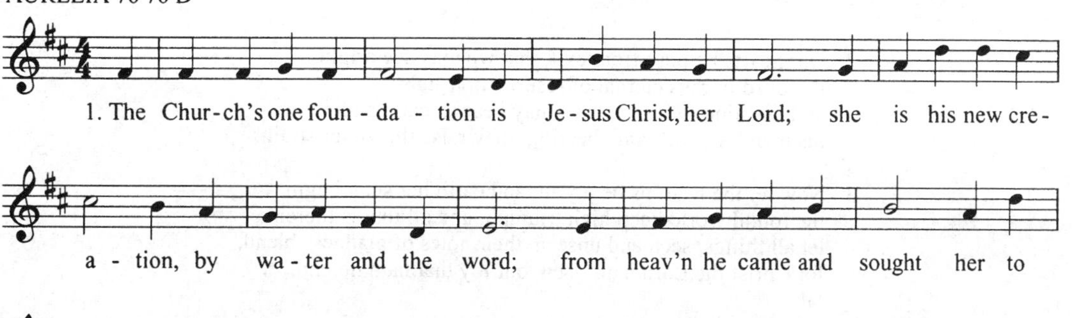

2. Elect from ev'ry nation, yet one o'er all the earth,
her charter of salvation, one Lord, one faith, one birth;
one holy name she blesses, partakes one holy food,
and to one hope she presses, with ev'ry grace endued.

3. 'Mid toil and tribulation, and tumult of her war,
she waits the consummation of peace for evermore;
till with the vision glorious her longing eyes are blest,
and the great Church victorious shall be the Church at rest.

4. Yet she on earth hath union with God the Three in One,
and mystic sweet communion with those whose rest is won:
O happy ones and holy! Lord, give us grace that we
like them, the meek and lowly, on high may dwell with thee.

637 The day of resurrection

St John of Damascus (c.750)
trans. John Mason Neale (1818-1866)

Württemburg Gesangbuch (1784)

ELLACOMBE 76 76 D

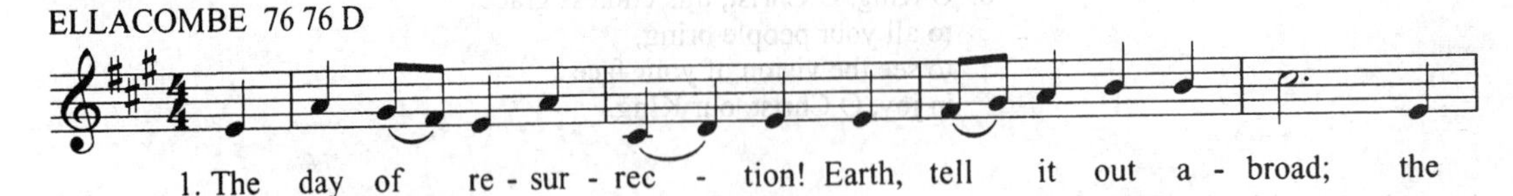

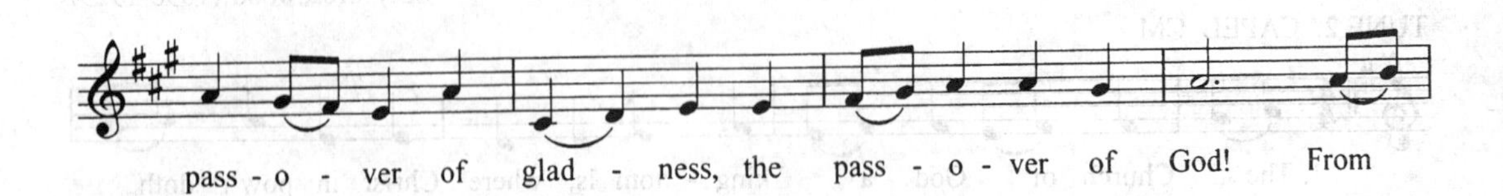

2. Our hearts be pure from evil, that we may see aright
the Lord in rays eternal of resurrection-light;
and list'ning to his accents, may hear so calm and plain
his own 'All hail' and, hearing, may raise the victor strain.

3. Now let the heav'ns be joyful, and earth her song begin,
the round world keep high triumph, and all that is therein;
let all things, seen and unseen, their notes of gladness blend,
for Christ the Lord hath risen, our joy that hath no end.

638 The day thou gavest, Lord, is ended

John Ellerton (1826-1893)

Clement Cotterill Scholefield (1839-1904)

ST CLEMENT 98 98

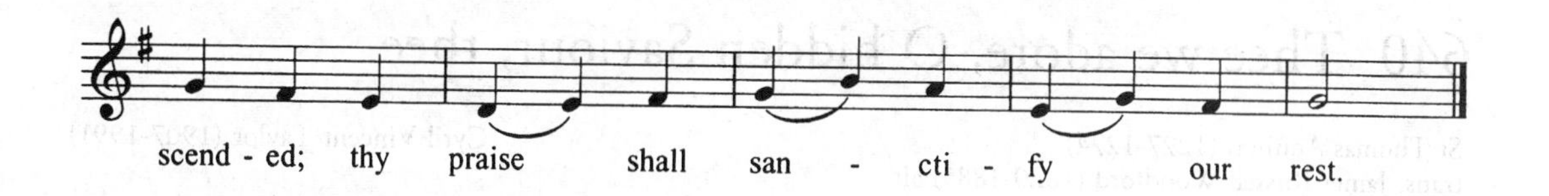

2. We thank thee that thy Church unsleeping,
while earth rolls onward into light,
through all the world her watch is keeping,
and rests not now by day or night.

3. As o'er each continent and island
the dawn leads on another day,
the voice of prayer is never silent,
nor dies the strain of praise away.

4. The sun that bids us rest is waking
our brethren 'neath the western sky,
and hour by hour fresh lips are making
thy wondrous doings heard on high.

5. So be it, Lord; thy throne shall never,
like earth's proud empires, pass away;
thy kingdom stands, and grows for ever,
till all thy creatures own thy sway.

639 The eternal gifts of Christ the King

St Ambrose (c.340-397)
trans. John Mason Neale (1818-1866) alt.

John Bishop (1665-1737)

ILLSLEY (BISHOP) LM

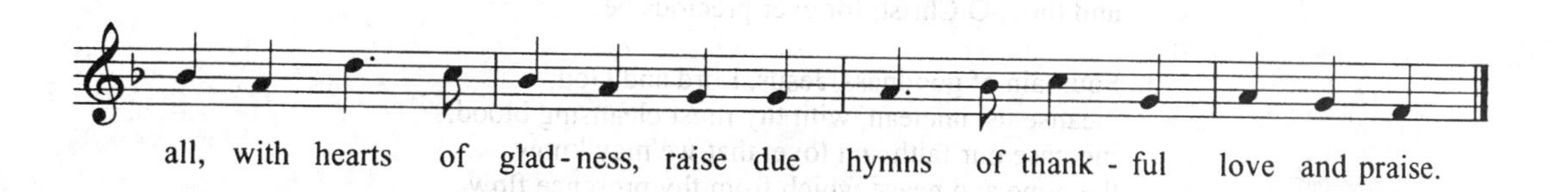

2. Theirs is the steadfast faith of saints,
and hope that never yields nor faints,
and love of Christ in perfect glow
that lays the prince of this world low.

3. In them the Father's glory shone,
in them the will of God the Son,
in them exults the Holy Ghost,
through them rejoice the heav'nly host.

4. To thee, Redeemer, now we cry,
that thou wouldst join to them on high
thy servants, who this grace implore,
for ever and for evermore.

640 Thee we adore, O hidden Saviour, thee

St Thomas Aquinas (1227-1274)
trans. James Russell Woodford (1820-1885) alt.

Cyril Vincent Taylor (1907-1991)

SHELDONIAN 10 10 10 10

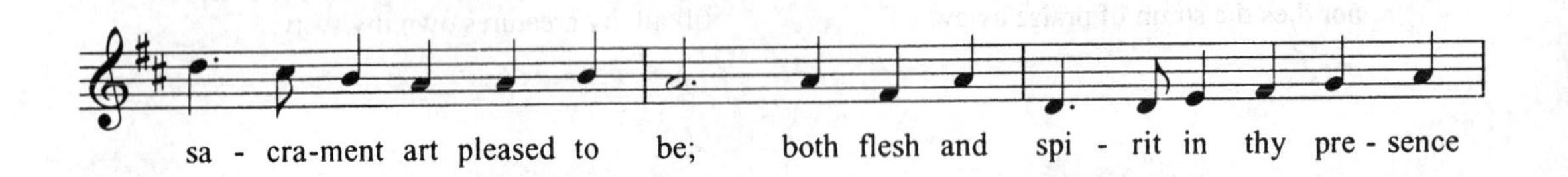

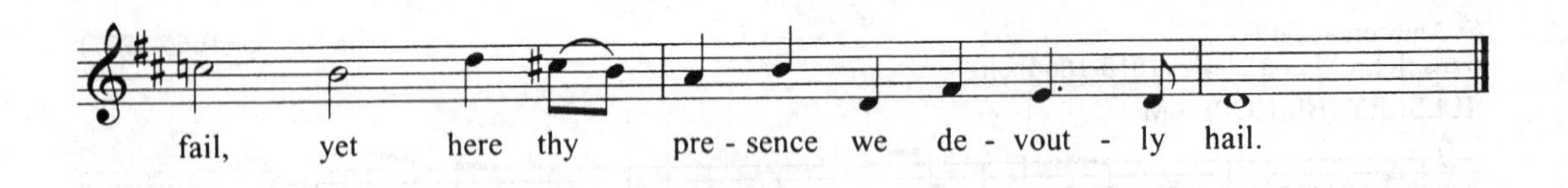

2. O blest memorial of our dying Lord,
   who living bread to all doth here afford;
   O may our souls for ever feed on thee,
   and thou, O Christ, for ever precious be.

3. Fountain of goodness, Jesus, Lord and God,
   cleanse us, unclean, with thy most cleansing blood;
   increase our faith and love, that we may know
   the hope and peace which from thy presence flow.

4. O Christ, whom now beneath a veil we see,
   may what we thirst for soon our portion be:
   to gaze on thee unveiled, and see thy face,
   the vision of thy glory and thy grace.

Music © Copyright Oxford University Press, Great Clarendon Street, Oxford OX2 6DP, UK.
Used by permission from the *BBC Hymn Book*.

641 The first Nowell

From William Sandys'
Christmas Carols, Ancient and Modern (1833) alt.

Traditional English melody

THE FIRST NOWELL Irregular

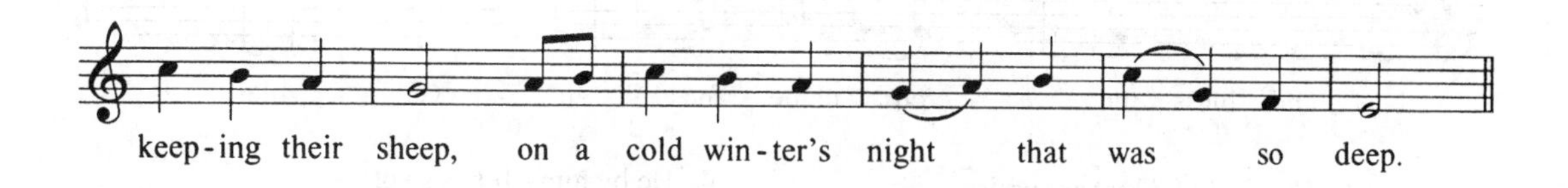

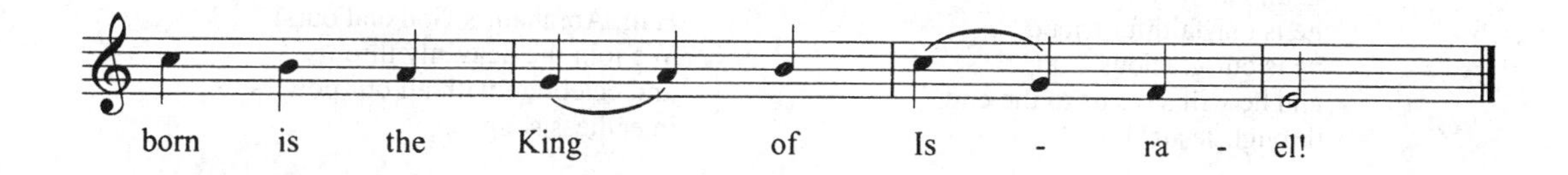

2. They lookèd up and saw a star,
shining in the east, beyond them far,
and to the earth it gave great light,
and so it continued both day and night.

3. And by the light of that same star,
three wise men came from country far;
to seek for a king was their intent,
and to follow the star wherever it went.

4. This star drew nigh to the north-west,
o'er Bethlehem it took its rest,
and there it did both stop and stay
right over the place where Jesus lay.

5. Then entered in those wise men three,
full rev'rently upon their knee,
and offered there in his presence,
their gold and myrrh and frankincense.

6. Then let us all with one accord
sing praises to our heav'nly Lord,
who with the Father we adore
and Spirit blest for evermore.

642 The God of Abraham praise

Thomas Olivers (1725-1799)
based on the Hebrew *Yigdal* alt.

Traditional Hebrew melody

LEONI 66 84 D

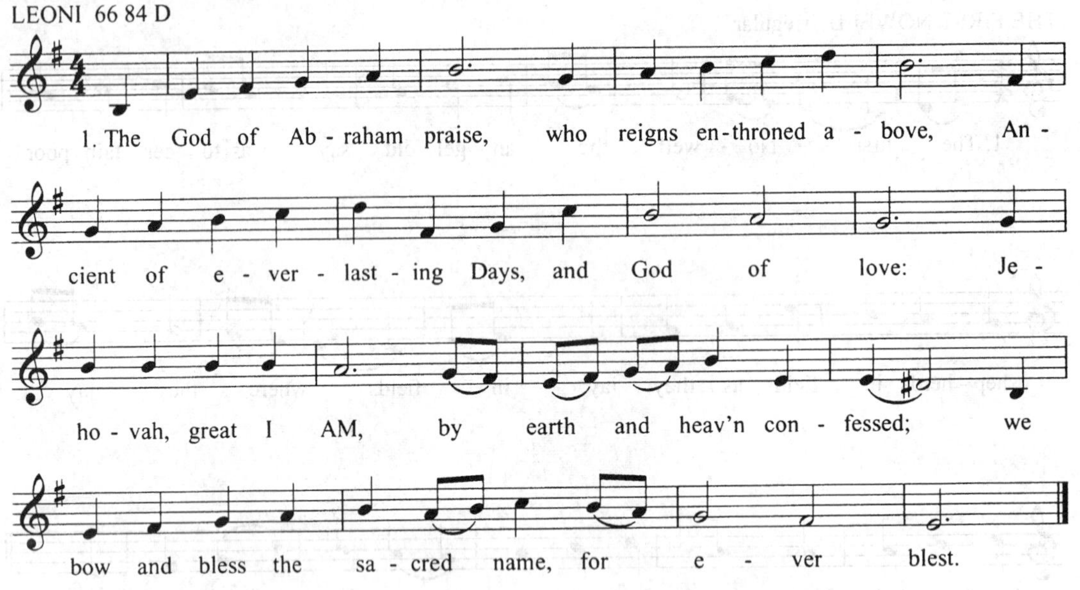

2. The God of Abraham praise,
   at whose supreme command
   from earth we rise, and seek the joys
   at his right hand:
   we all on earth forsake,
   its wisdom, fame and pow'r;
   and him our only portion make,
   our shield and tow'r.

3. The God of Abraham praise,
   whose all-sufficient grace
   shall guide us all our happy days,
   in all our ways:
   he is our faithful friend;
   he is our gracious God;
   and he will save us to the end,
   through Jesus' blood.

4. He by himself has sworn –
   we on his oath depend –
   we shall, on eagles' wings upborne,
   to heav'n ascend:
   we shall behold his face,
   we shall his pow'r adore,
   and sing the wonders of his grace
   for evermore.

5. The whole triumphant host
   give thanks to God on high:
   'Hail, Father, Son and Holy Ghost!'
   they ever cry:
   Hail, Abraham's God and ours!
   We join the heav'nly throng,
   and celebrate with all our pow'rs
   in endless song.

643 The God of love my shepherd is

George Herbert (1593-1633)
based on Psalm 23

Charles Collignon (1725-1785)

UNIVERSITY CM

2. He leads me to the tender grass,
where I both feed and rest;
then to the streams that gently pass:
in both I have the best.

3. Or if I stray, he doth convert,
and bring my mind in frame,
and all this not for my desert,
but for his holy name.

4. Yea, in death's shady black abode
well may I walk, nor fear;
for thou art with me, and thy rod
to guide, thy staff to bear.

5. Surely thy sweet and wondrous love
shall measure all my days;
and, as it never shall remove,
so neither shall my praise.

644 The head that once was crowned with thorns

Thomas Kelly (1769-1855) | Jeremiah Clarke (1670-1707)

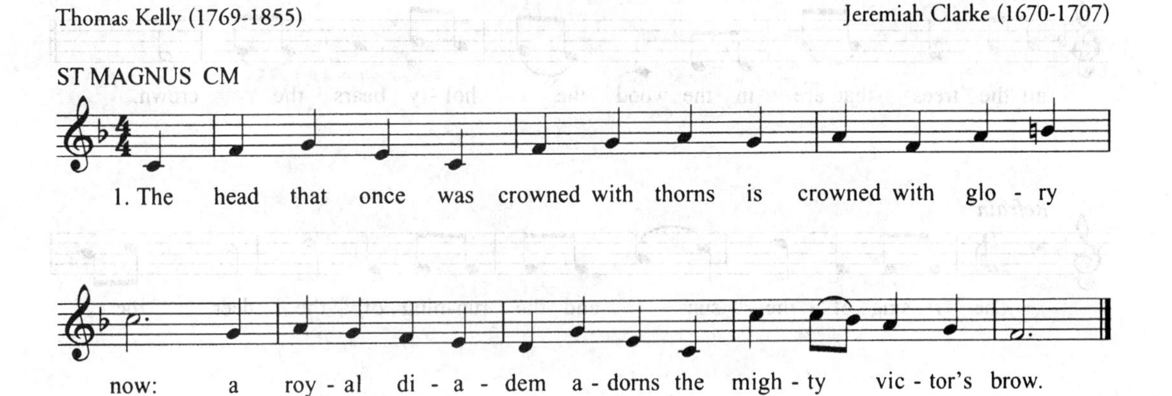

2. The highest place that heav'n affords
is his, is his by right.
The King of kings and Lord of lords,
and heav'ns eternal light.

3. The joy of all who dwell above,
the joy of all below,
to whom he manifests his love,
and grants his name to know.

4. To them the cross, with all its shame,
with all its grace is giv'n;
their name an everlasting name,
their joy the joy of heav'n.

5. They suffer with their Lord below,
they reign with him above,
their profit and their joy to know
the myst'ry of his love.

6. The cross he bore is life and health,
though shame and death to him;
his people's hope, his people's wealth,
their everlasting theme.

645 The holly and the ivy

Traditional — English folk carol

THE HOLLY AND THE IVY 76 86 (Irregular) and Refrain

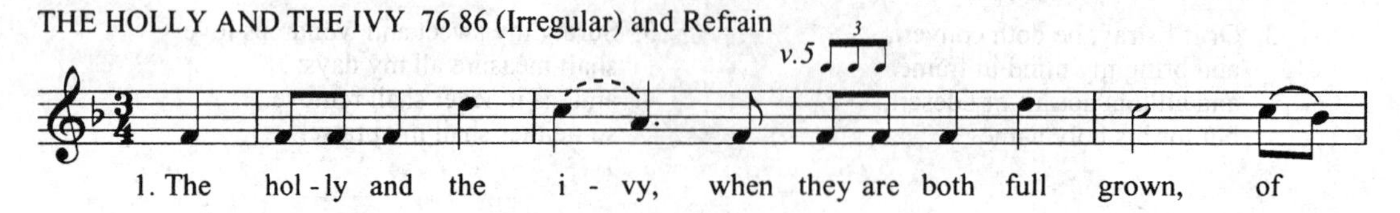

2. The holly bears a blossom,
white as the lily flower,
and Mary bore sweet Jesus Christ
to be our sweet Saviour.

3. The holly bears a berry,
as red as any blood,
and Mary bore sweet Jesus Christ
to do poor sinners good.

4. The holly bears a prickle,
as sharp as any thorn,
and Mary bore sweet Jesus Christ
on Christmas day in the morn.

5. The holly bears a bark,
as bitter as any gall,
and Mary bore sweet Jesus Christ
for to redeem us all.

6. The holly and the ivy,
when they are both full grown,
of all the trees that are in the wood
the holly bears the crown.

646 The kingdom of God

Bryn A. Rees (1911-1983) | Gerald L. Barnes (b .1935)

TETHERDOWN 55 55 65 65

2. The kingdom of God
is mercy and grace,
the captives are freed,
the sinners find place,
the outcast are welcomed
God's banquet to share,
and hope is awakened
in place of despair.

3. The kingdom of God
is challenge and choice,
believe the good news,
repent and rejoice!
His love for us sinners
brought Christ to his cross,
our crisis of judgement
for gain or for loss.

4. God's kingdom is come,
the gift and the goal,
in Jesus begun,
in heaven made whole;
the heirs of the kingdom
shall answer his call,
and all things cry 'Glory!'
to God all in all.

Text © Copyright Mr. Alexander Scott. Used by permission.
Music © Copyright Gerald Barnes. Used by permission.

647 The kingdom of heaven *The Beatitudes*

Words and music: Mike Anderson (b.1956)
based on Matthew 5:3-10

2. Blessed are you who hunger for right,
for you shall be satisfied;
blessed are you the merciful ones,
for you shall be pardoned too.

3. Blessed are you whose hearts are pure,
your eyes shall gaze on the Lord;
blessed are you who strive after peace,
the Lord will call you his own.

4. Blessed are you who suffer for right,
the heav'nly kingdom is yours;
blessed are you who suffer for me,
for you shall reap your reward.

© Copyright 1999 Kevin Mayhew Ltd.

648 The King is among us

Words and music: Graham Kendrick (b.1950)

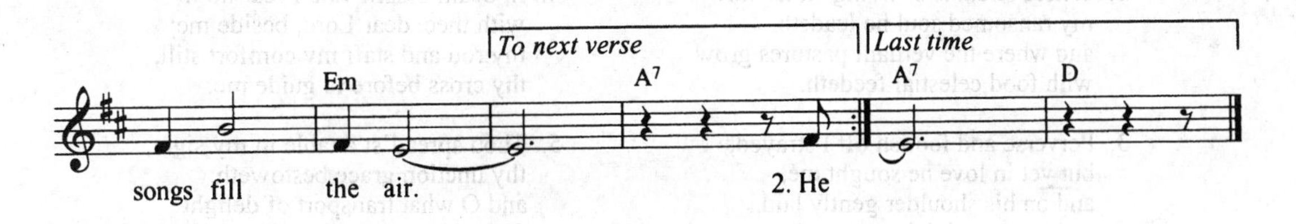

2. He looks down upon us,
delight in his face,
enjoying his children's love,
enthralled by our praise.

3. For each child is special,
accepted and loved,
a love gift from Jesus
to his Father above.

4. And now he is giving
his gifts to us all,
for no one is worthless
and each one is called.

5. The Spirit's anointing
on all flesh comes down,
and we shall be channels
for works like his own.

6. We come now believing
your promise of pow'r,
for we are your people
and this is your hour.

7. The King is among us,
his Spirit is here,
let's draw near and worship,
let songs fill the air.

© Copyright 1981 Kingsway's Thankyou Music, P.O. Box 75, Eastbourne, East Sussex BN23 6NW, UK. (tym@kingsway.co.uk). Used by permission.

649 The King of love my shepherd is

Henry Williams Baker (1821-1877)
based on Psalm 23

John Bacchus Dykes (1823-1876)

TUNE 1: DOMINUS REGIT ME 87 87

1. The King of love my shep-herd is, whose good - ness fail - eth ne - ver; I

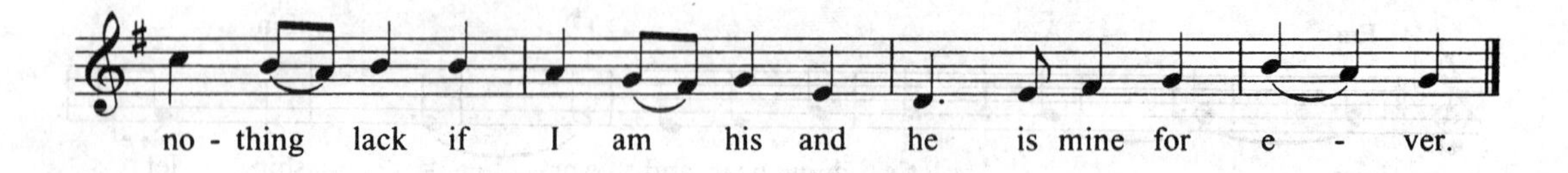

no - thing lack if I am his and he is mine for e - ver.

2. Where streams of living water flow
my ransomed soul he leadeth,
and where the verdant pastures grow
with food celestial feedeth.

3. Perverse and foolish oft I strayed,
but yet in love he sought me,
and on his shoulder gently laid,
and home, rejoicing, brought me.

4. In death's dark vale I fear no ill
with thee, dear Lord, beside me;
thy rod and staff my comfort still,
thy cross before to guide me.

5. Thou spread'st a table in my sight,
thy unction grace bestoweth:
and O what transport of delight
from thy pure chalice floweth!

6. And so through all the length of days
thy goodness faileth never;
good Shepherd, may I sing thy praise
within thy house for ever.

Henry Williams Baker (1821-1877)
based on Psalm 23

Irish melody
(Petrie collection)

TUNE 2: ST COLUMBA 87 87

1. The King of love my shep - herd is, whose

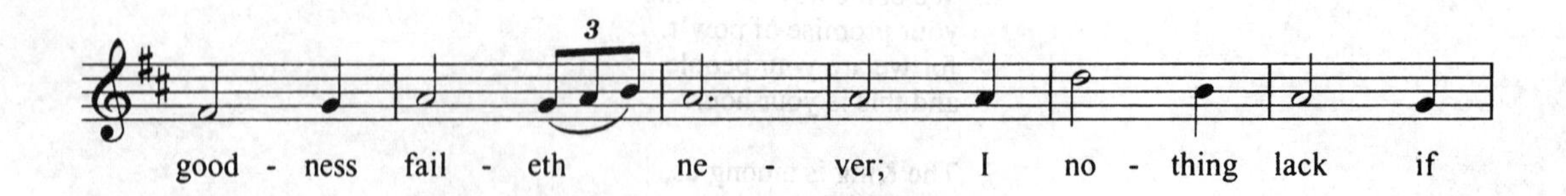

good - ness fail - eth ne - ver; I no - thing lack if

I am his and he is mine for e - ver.

650 The Lord is King!

Josiah Conder (1789-1855) alt. Bertram Luard Selby (1853-1918)

TUNE 1: IVYHATCH LM

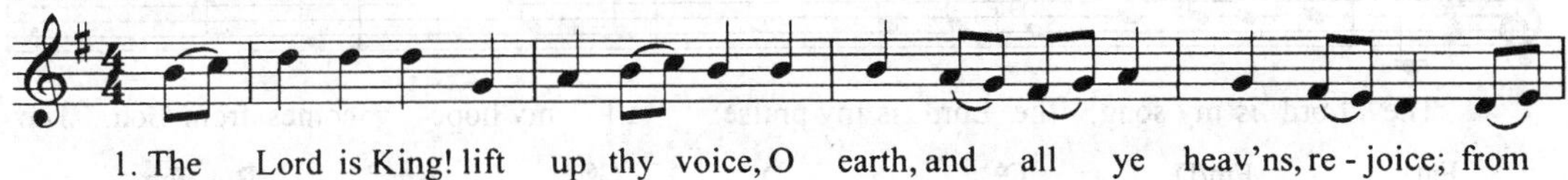

world to world the joy shall ring: 'The Lord om - ni - po - tent is King!'

2. He reigns! ye saints, exalt your strains;
your God is King, your Saviour reigns;
and he is at the Father's side,
the Man of Love, the Crucified.

3. Alike pervaded by his eye
all parts of his dominion lie:
this world of ours and worlds unseen,
and thin the boundary between.

4. One Lord one empire all secures;
he reigns, and endless life is yours;
through earth and heav'n one song shall ring:
'The Lord omnipotent is King!'

Josiah Conder (1789-1855) alt. Robert Jackson (1840-1914)

TUNE 2: NIAGARA LM

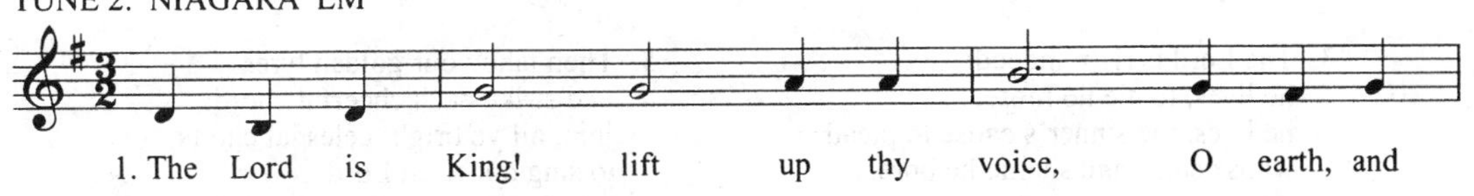

651 The Lord is my song

Taizé Community

Jacques Berthier (1923-1994)

© Copyright Ateliers et Presses de Taizé, Taizé-Communauté, F-71250, France.
Used by permission.

652 The Lord is risen indeed

Thomas Kelly (1769-1855)

Melody from Johannes Leisentritt's *Catholicum Hymnologium Germanicum,* Cologne (1584) adapted by William Henry Havergal (1793-1870)

TUNE 1: NARENZA SM

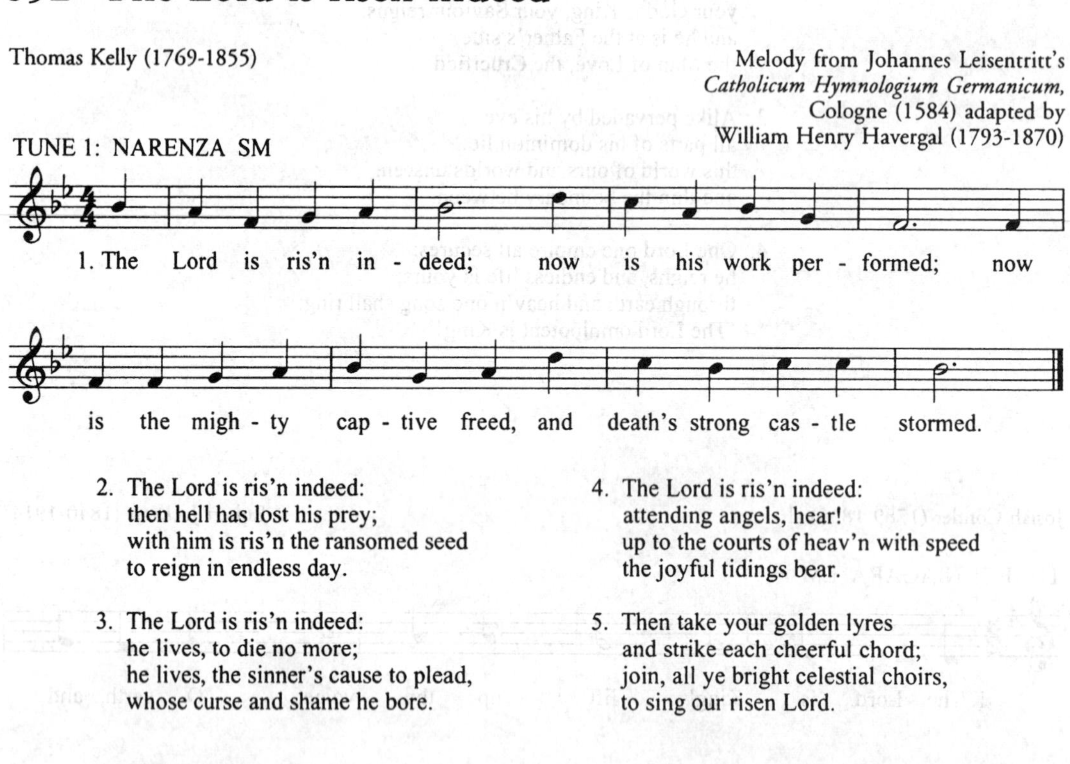

2. The Lord is ris'n indeed:
then hell has lost his prey;
with him is ris'n the ransomed seed
to reign in endless day.

3. The Lord is ris'n indeed:
he lives, to die no more;
he lives, the sinner's cause to plead,
whose curse and shame he bore.

4. The Lord is ris'n indeed:
attending angels, hear!
up to the courts of heav'n with speed
the joyful tidings bear.

5. Then take your golden lyres
and strike each cheerful chord;
join, all ye bright celestial choirs,
to sing our risen Lord.

Thomas Kelly (1769-1855)

Adapted from *Anglo-Genevan Psalms* (1561)

TUNE 2: ST MICHAEL (OLD 134TH) SM

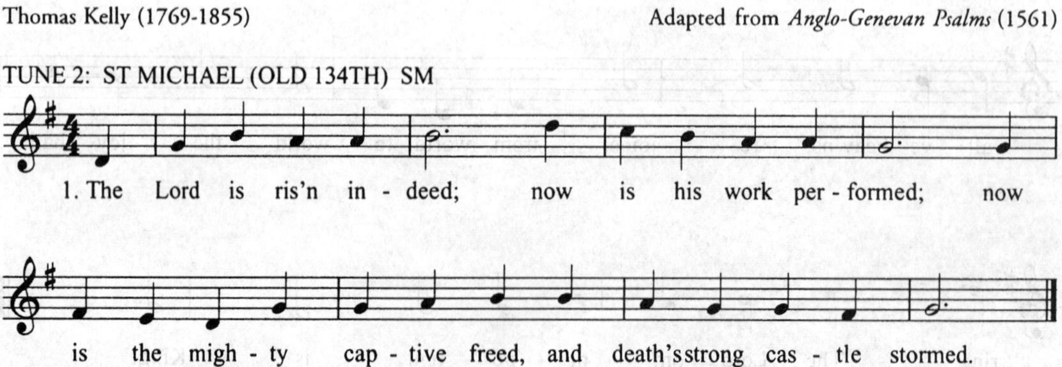

653 The Lord my pasture shall prepare

Joseph Addison (1672-1719)
based on Psalm 23

Henry Carey (c.1687-1743)

SURREY 88 88 88

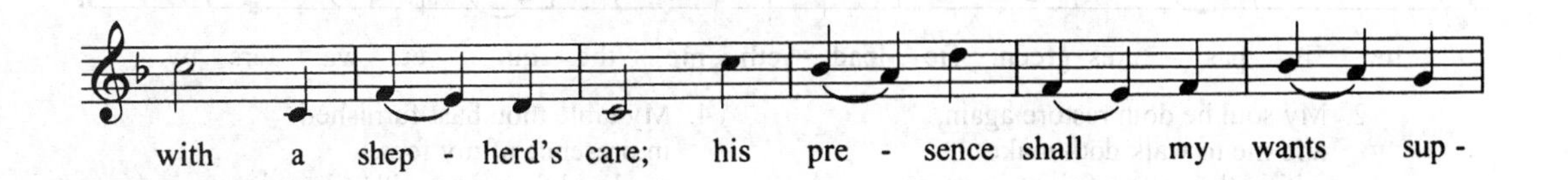

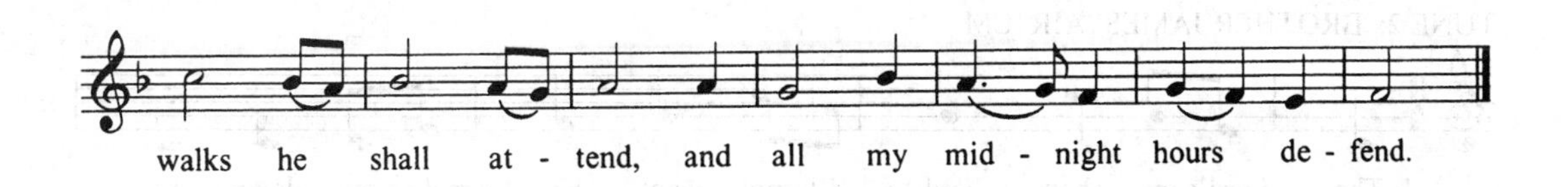

2. When in the sultry glebe I faint,
or on the thirsty mountain pant,
to fertile vales and dewy meads
my weary wand'ring steps he leads,
where peaceful rivers, soft and slow,
amid the verdant landscape flow.

3. Though in a bare and rugged way
through devious lonely wilds I stray,
thy bounty shall my pains beguile;
the barren wilderness shall smile
with sudden greens and herbage crowned,
and streams shall murmur all around.

4. Though in the paths of death I tread,
with gloomy horrors overspread,
my steadfast heart shall fear no ill,
for thou, O Lord, art with me still:
thy friendly staff shall give me aid,
and guide me through the dreadful shade.

654 The Lord's my shepherd

Psalm 23 from *The Scottish Psalter* (1650) — Jessie Seymour Irvine (1836-1887)

TUNE 1: CRIMOND CM

2. My soul he doth restore again,
and me to walk doth make
within the paths of righteousness,
e'en for his own name's sake.

3. Yea, though I walk in death's dark vale,
yet will I fear no ill.
For thou art with me, and thy rod
and staff me comfort still.

4. My table thou hast furnishèd
in presence of my foes,
my head thou dost with oil anoint,
and my cup overflows.

5. Goodness and mercy all my life
shall surely follow me.
And in God's house for evermore
my dwelling-place shall be.

Psalm 23 from *The Scottish Psalter* (1650) — Brother James Leith Macbeth Bain (d.1925)

TUNE 2: BROTHER JAMES' AIR CM

655 The Lord will come and not be slow

John Milton (1608-1674)
based on Psalms 82, 85 and 86, alt.

William Jones (1726-1800)

ST STEPHEN CM

2. Truth from the earth, like to a flow'r,
shall bud and blossom free;
and justice, from her heav'nly bow'r,
bless all humanity.

3. The nations all whom thou hast made
shall come, and all shall frame
to bow them low before thee, Lord,
and glorify thy name.

4. For great thou art, and wonders great
by thy strong hand are done:
thou in thy everlasting seat
remainest God alone.

656 The race that long in darkness pined

John Morrison (1750-1798)
based on Isaiah 9:2-7

Henry John Gauntlett (1805-1876)

TUNE 1: ST FULBERT CM

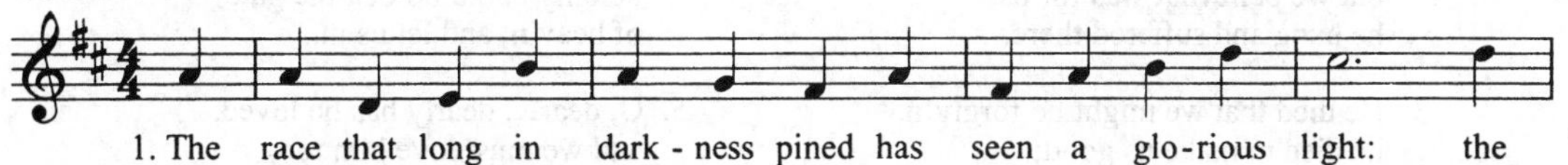

2. To hail thy rise, thou better sun,
the gath'ring nations come,
joyous as when the reapers bear
the harvest treasures home.

3. To us a child of hope is born,
to us a Son is giv'n;
him shall the tribes of earth obey,
him all the hosts of heav'n.

4. His name shall be the Prince of Peace
for evermore adored,
the Wonderful, the Counsellor,
the great and mighty Lord.

5. His pow'r increasing still shall spread,
his reign no end shall know;
justice shall guard his throne above,
and peace abound below.

John Morrison (1750-1798)
based on Isaiah 9:2-7

Psalms, Edinburgh (1615)

TUNE 2: DUNDEE CM

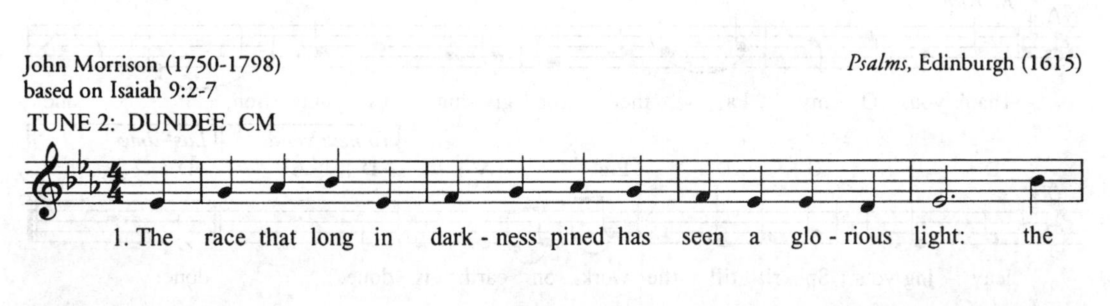

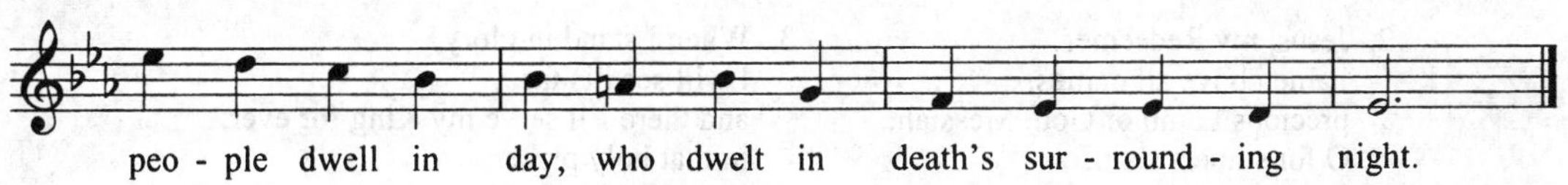

657 There is a green hill far away

Cecil Frances Alexander (1818-1895) alt.

William Horsley (1774-1858)

2. We may not know, we cannot tell
what pains he had to bear,
but we believe it was for us
he hung and suffered there.

3. He died that we might be forgiv'n,
he died to make us good;
that we might go at last to heav'n,
saved by his precious blood.

4. There was no other good enough
to pay the price of sin;
he only could unlock the gate
of heav'n, and let us in.

5. O, dearly, dearly has he loved,
and we must love him too,
and trust in his redeeming blood,
and try his works to do.

658 There is a Redeemer

Words and music: Melody Green
based on Scripture

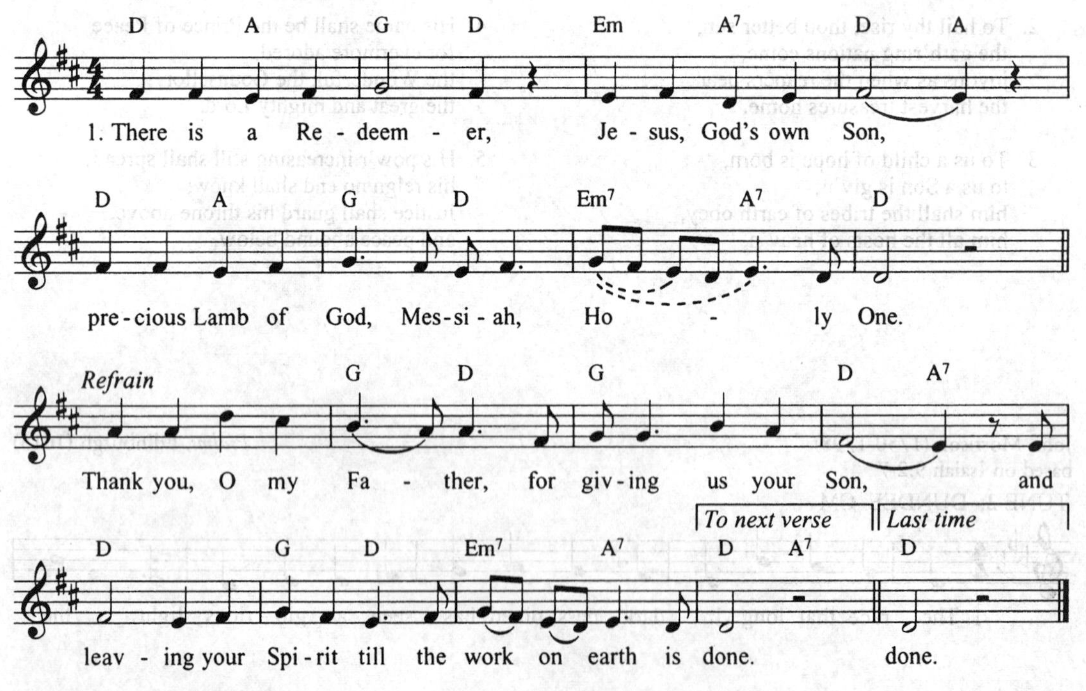

2. Jesus, my Redeemer,
name above all names,
precious Lamb of God, Messiah,
O for sinners slain.

3. When I stand in glory,
I will see his face,
and there I'll serve my King for ever,
in that holy place.

© Copyright 1982 Birdwing Music/BMG Songs Inc./Ears to Hear Music/EMI Christian Music Publishing. Administered by CopyCare, P.O. Box 77, Hailsham, East Sussex BN27 3EF, UK. (music@copycare.com). Used by permission.

659 There's a quiet understanding

Words and music: E.R. (Tedd) Smith (b.1927)

THERE'S A QUIET UNDERSTANDING Irregular

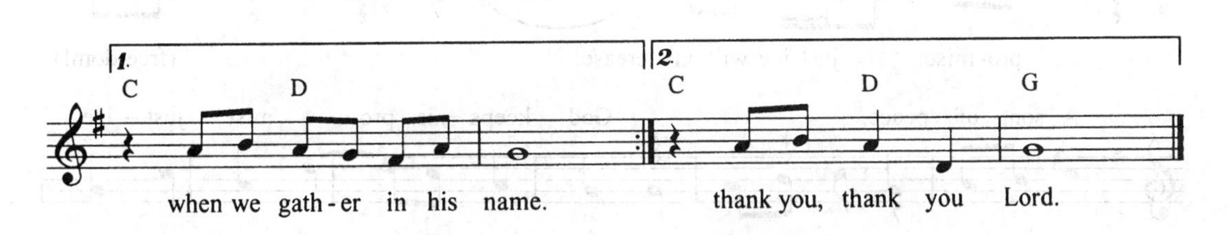

2. And we know when we're together,
sharing love and understanding,
that our brothers and our sisters
feel the oneness that he brings.
Thank you, thank you, thank you, Jesus,
for the way you love and feed us,
for the many ways you lead us,
thank you, thank you, Lord.

© Copyright 1973 Hope Publishing. Administered by CopyCare, P.O. Box 77, Hailsham, East Sussex BN27 3EF, UK. (music@copycare.com). Used by permission.

660 There's a song in the heart of creation

Michael Forster (b.1946) Christopher Tambling (b.1964)

BIRNHAM 10 9 10 9 and Refrain

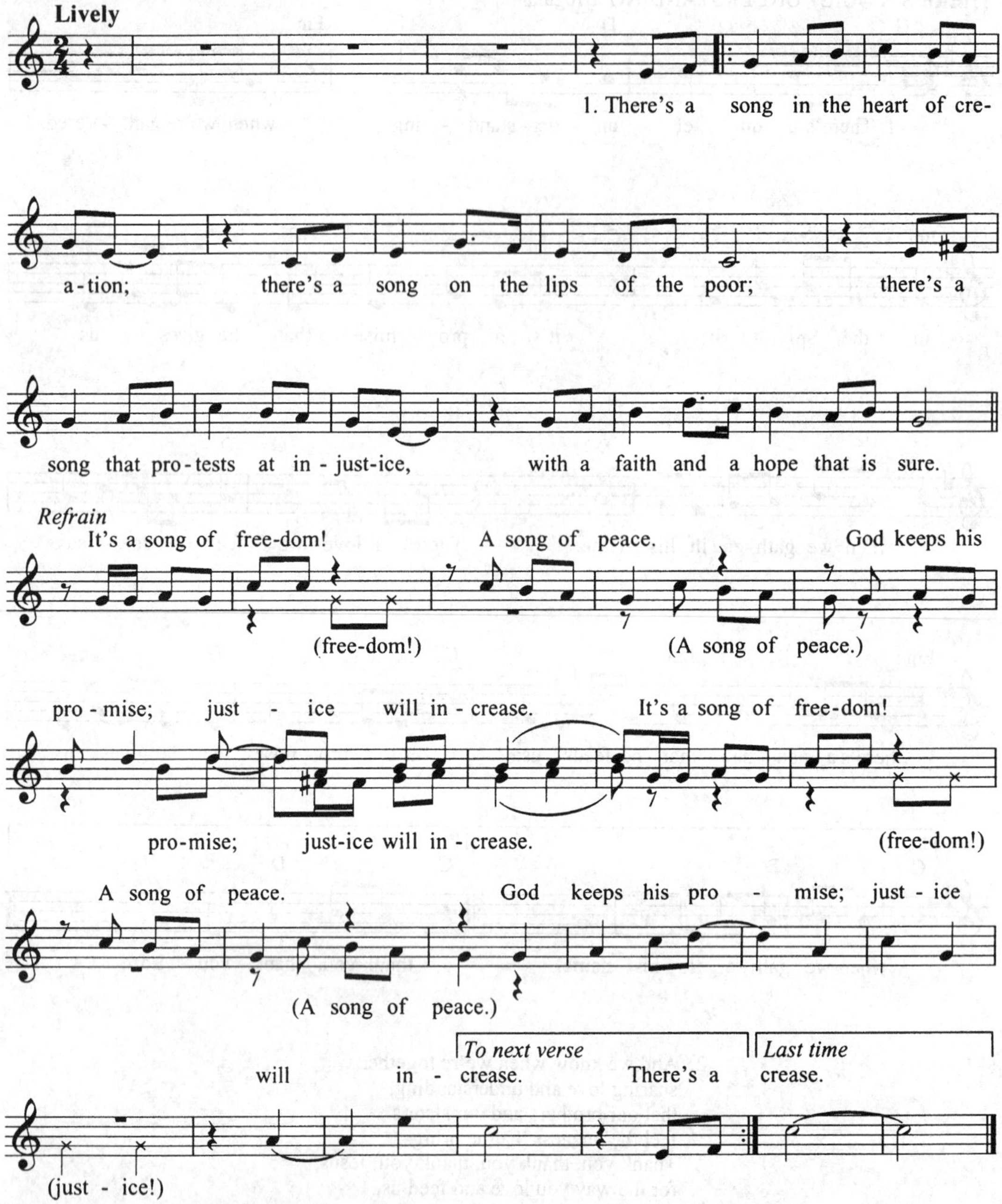

Lively

1. There's a song in the heart of cre- a-tion; there's a song on the lips of the poor; there's a song that pro-tests at in - just-ice, with a faith and a hope that is sure.

Refrain
It's a song of free-dom! (free-dom!) A song of peace. (A song of peace.) God keeps his pro - mise; just - ice will in - crease. (pro-mise; just-ice will in - crease.) It's a song of free-dom! (free-dom!) A song of peace. (A song of peace.) God keeps his pro - mise; just - ice (just - ice!) will in - *To next verse* crease. There's a *Last time* crease.

2. There's a song in the hearts of the people;
there's a song on the lips of the youth;
there's a song that protests at the waiting
for the coming of wholeness and truth.

3. There's a song in the heart of the Saviour;
there's a song on the lips of his friends;
there's a song that protests for the dying,
while proclaiming that life never ends.

4. There's a song in the heart of creation;
there's a song on the lips of the healed;
there's a song in the graveyard proclaiming
that the life of the world is revealed.

© Copyright 2000 Kevin Mayhew Ltd.

661 There's a spirit in the air

Brian A. Wren (b.1936) | John Wilson (1905-1992)

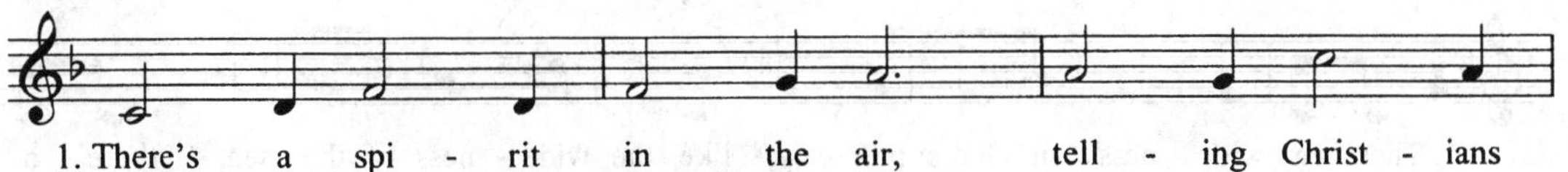

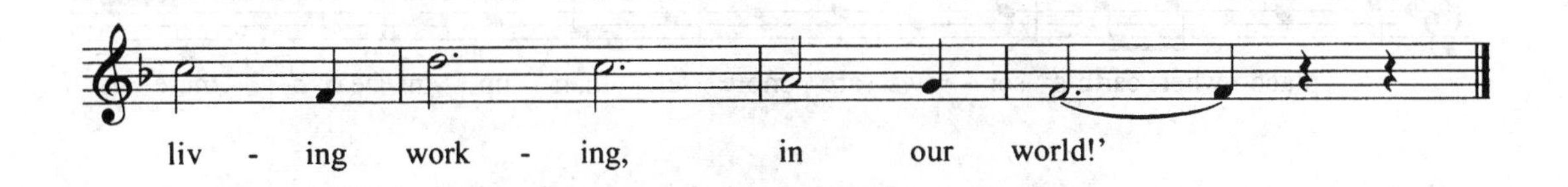

2. Lose your shyness, find your tongue,
tell the world what God has done:
God in Christ has come to stay.
Live tomorrow's life today!

3. When believers break the bread,
when a hungry child is fed,
praise the love that Christ revealed,
living, working, in our world.

4. Still the Spirit gives us light,
seeing wrong and setting right:
God in Christ has come to stay.
Live tomorrow's life today!

5. When a stranger's not alone,
where the homeless find a home,
praise the love that Christ revealed,
living, working, in our world.

6. May his Spirit fill our praise,
guide our thoughts and change our ways.
God in Christ has come to stay.
Live tomorrow's life today!

7. There's a Spirit in the air,
calling people ev'rywhere:
praise the love that Christ revealed,
living, working, in our world.

Text © Copyright 1969, 1995 Stainer & Bell Ltd., P.O. Box 110, Victoria House, 23 Gruneisen Road, Finchley, London N3 1DZ, UK. Used by permission.
Music © Copyright the Executors of the late John Wilson/Oxford University Press, Great Clarendon Street, Oxford OX2 6DP, UK. Used by permission.

662 There's a wideness in God's mercy

Frederick William Faber (1840-1863) alt. — From the *Paderborn Gesangbuch* (1765)

1. There's a wide - ness in God's mer - cy, like the wide - ness of the sea; there's a

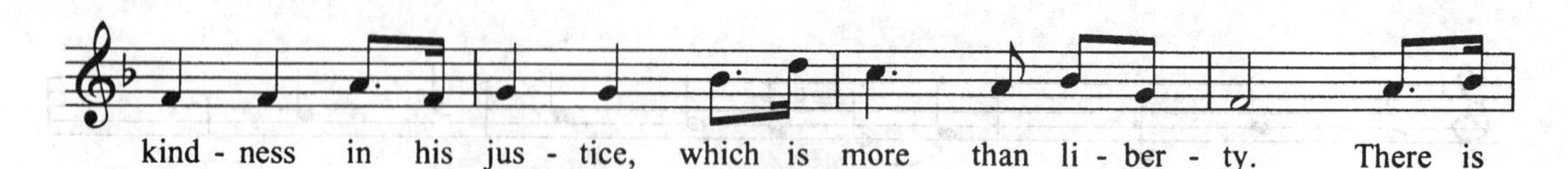

kind - ness in his jus - tice, which is more than li - ber - ty. There is

no place where earth's sor - rows are more felt than up in heav'n; there is

no place where earth's fail - ings have such kind - ly judge-ment giv'n.

2. But we make his love too narrow
by false limits of our own;
and we magnify his strictness
with a zeal he will not own.
There is plentiful redemption
in the blood that has been shed,
there is joy for all the members
in the sorrows of the Head.

3. For the love of God is broader
than the scope of human mind,
and the heart of the Eternal
is most wonderfully kind.
If our love were but more simple,
we should take him at his word;
and our hearts would find assurance
in the promise of the Lord.

663 The royal banners forward go

Venantius Fortunatus (530-609)
trans. John Mason Neale (1818-1866) and others — Percy Carter Buck (1871-1947)

GONFALON ROYAL LM

1. The roy - al ban - ners for - ward go, the cross shines

forth in mys - tic glow; where he in flesh, our flesh who made, our

sen - tence bore, our ran - som paid. A - men.

Music © Copyright Oxford University Press, Great Clarendon Street, Oxford OX2 6DP, UK.
Used by permission.

2. There whilst he hung, his sacred side
by soldier's spear was opened wide,
to cleanse us in the precious flood
of water mingled with his blood.

3. Fulfilled is now what David told
in true prophetic song of old,
how God the sinner's king should be;
for God is reigning from the tree.

4. O tree of glory, tree most fair,
ordained those holy limbs to bear,
how bright in purple robe it stood,
the purple of a Saviour's blood!

5. To thee, eternal Three in One,
let homage meet by all be done,
as by the cross thou dost restore,
so rule and guide us evermore.
Amen.

664 The Saviour will come, resplendent in joy

Michael Forster (b.1946)
based on Isaiah 35

Charles Hubert Hastings Parry (1848-1918)

LAUDATE DOMINUM 10 10 11 11

2. The Saviour will come, like rain on the earth,
to harvest at last his crop of great worth.
In patience await him, with firmness of mind;
both mercy and judgement his people will find.

3. The Saviour will come, his truth we shall see:
where lepers are cleansed and captives set free.
No finely clad princeling in palace of gold,
but Christ with his people, O wonder untold!

Text © Copyright 1993 Kevin Mayhew Ltd.

665 The spacious firmament on high

Joseph Addison (1672-1719)
based on Psalm 19:1-6 alt.

John Sheeles (1688-1761)

ADDISON'S (LONDON) DLM

1. The spa - cious fir - ma - ment on high, with all the blue e -
the - real sky, and span - gled heav'ns, a shi - ning frame, their
great O - ri - gi - nal pro - claim. The un - wea - ried sun from day to day does
his Cre - a - tor's pow'r dis - play, and pub - li - shes to ev - 'ry land the
works of an al - migh - ty hand, the works of an al - migh - ty hand.

2. Soon as the evening shades prevail
the moon takes up the wondrous tale,
and nightly to the list'ning earth
repeats the story of her birth;
whilst all the stars that round her burn,
and all the planets in their turn,
confirm the tidings, as they roll,
and spread the truth from pole to pole,
and spread the truth from pole to pole.

3. What though in solemn silence all
move round the dark terrestrial ball;
what though nor lit'ral voice nor sound
amid their radiant orbs be found;
in reason's ear they all rejoice,
and utter forth a glorious voice,
for ever singing as they shine,
'The hand that made us is divine,
the hand that made us is divine.'

666 The Spirit lives to set us free *Walk in the light*

Damian Lundy (1944-1997)

Unknown

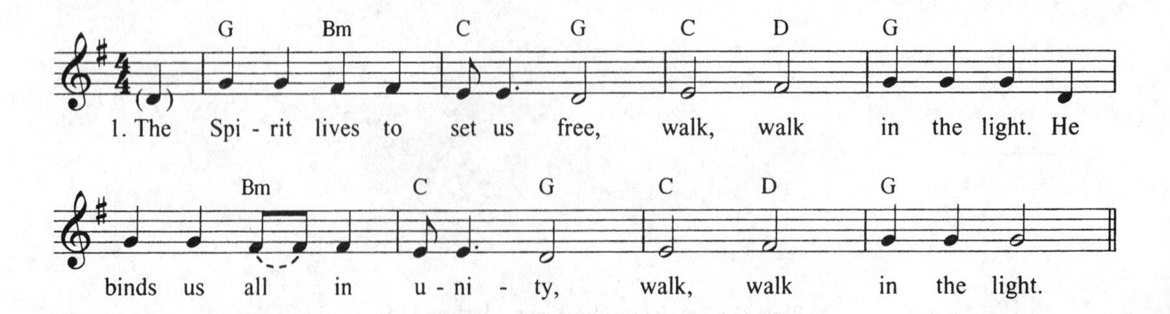

Text © Copyright 1978 Kevin Mayhew Ltd.

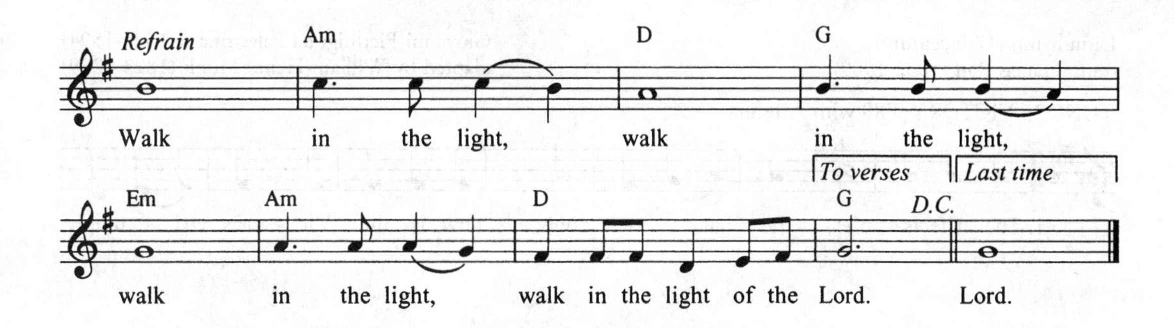

2. Jesus promised life to all,
walk, walk in the light.
The dead were wakened by his call,
walk, walk in the light.

3. He died in pain on Calvary,
walk, walk in the light,
to save the lost like you and me,
walk, walk in the light.

4. We know his death was not the end,
walk, walk in the light.
He gave his Spirit to be our friend,
walk, walk in the light.

5. By Jesus' love our wounds are healed,
walk, walk in the light.
The Father's kindness is revealed,
walk, walk in the light.

6. The Spirit lives in you and me,
walk, walk in the light.
His light will shine for all to see,
walk, walk in the light.

667 The strife is o'er, the battle done

Latin hymn (17th century)
trans. Francis Pott (1832-1909)

From Melchior Vulpius'
Gesangbuch (1609)

TUNE 1: GELOB'T SEI GOTT (VULPIUS) 888 and Alleluias

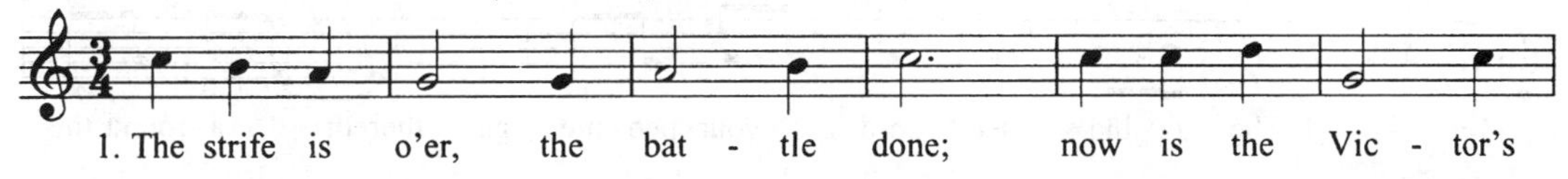

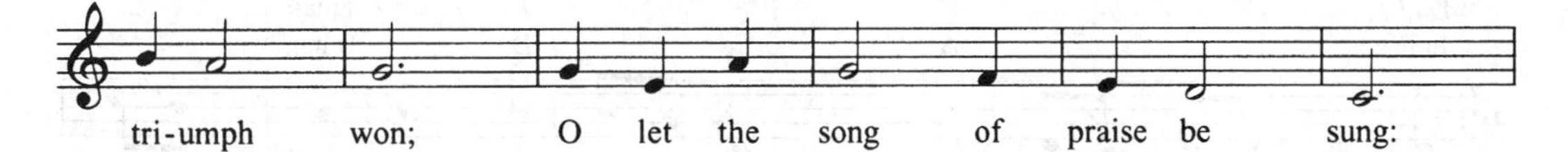

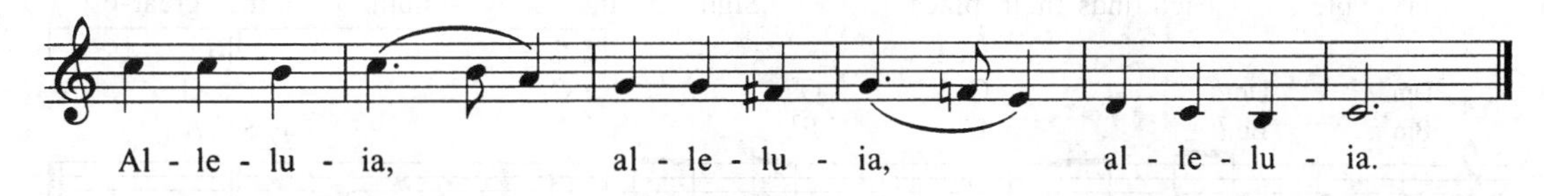

2. Death's mightiest pow'rs have done their worst,
and Jesus hath his foes dispersed;
let shouts of praise and joy outburst:
Alleluia, alleluia, alleluia.

3. On the third morn he rose again
glorious in majesty to reign;
O let us swell the joyful strain:
Alleluia, alleluia, alleluia.

4. Lord, by the stripes which wounded thee
from death's dread sting thy servants free,
that we may live, and sing to thee:
Alleluia, alleluia, alleluia.

Tune 2 will be found overleaf.

Latin hymn (17th century)
trans. Francis Pott (1832-1909)

Giovanni Pierluigi da Palestrina (c.1525-1594)
adapted by William Henry Monk (1823-1889)

TUNE 2: VICTORY 888 with Alleluia

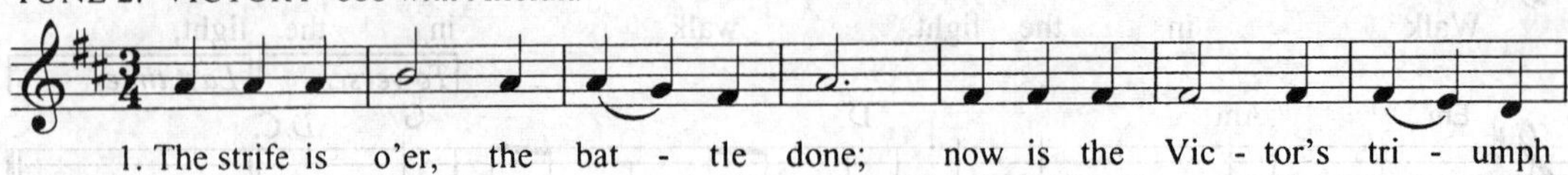

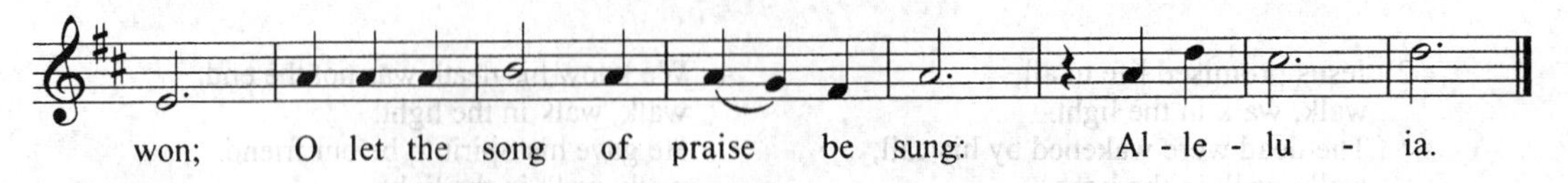

2. Death's mightiest pow'rs have done their worst,
and Jesus hath his foes dispersed;
let shouts of praise and joy outburst:
Alleluia.

3. On the third morn he rose again
glorious in majesty to reign;
O let us swell the joyful strain:
Alleluia.

4. Lord, by the stripes which wounded thee
from death's dread sting thy servants free,
that we may live, and sing to thee:
Alleluia.

668 The table's set, Lord

Words and music: Robert B. Kelly (b.1948)

2. At this same table in other places,
so many people here in Christ's name.
Those gone before us, who will succeed us,
one single table throughout all time.

3. One Lord inviting, one Church responding;
one single bread and one cup of wine.
May what we do here change and transform us,
one single presence, Christ through all time.

© Copyright 1999 Kevin Mayhew Ltd.

669 The universe was waiting

Michael Forster (b.1946) Alan Rees (b.1941)

DORE ABBEY 76 76 D

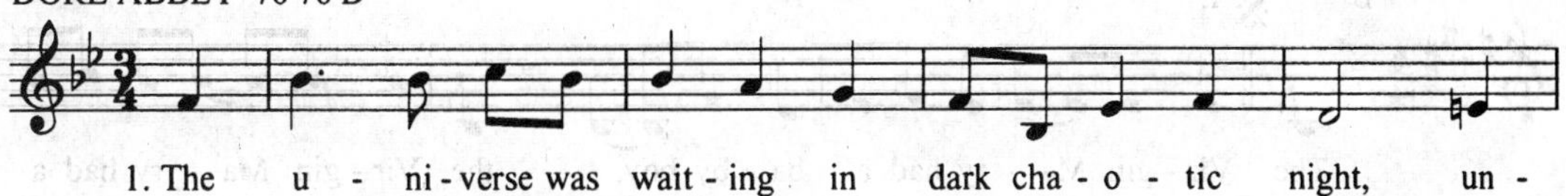

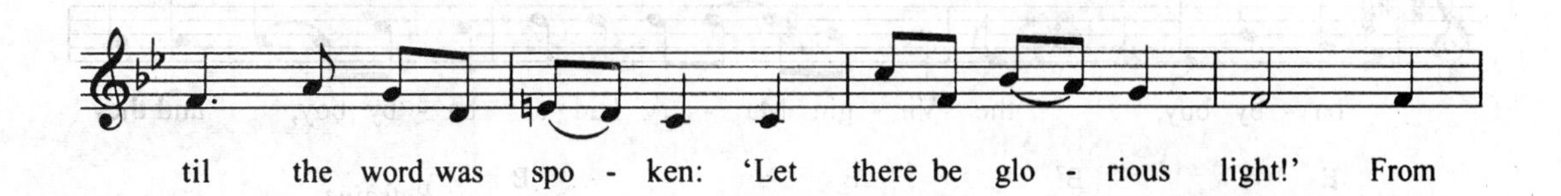

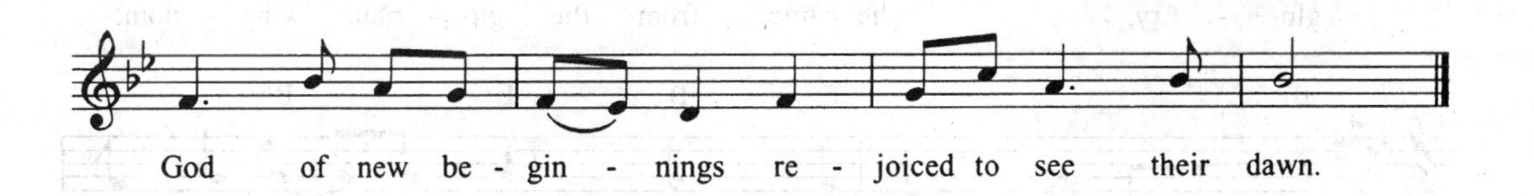

2. And as in that beginning,
in every age the same,
creation's Re-creator
is keeping hope aflame.
From Eden to the desert,
the manger to the tomb,
each fall becomes a rising,
and every grave a womb.

3. Wherever people languish
in darkness or despair,
the God of new beginnings
is pierced, and rises there.
We join with him, to listen,
to care, and to protest,
to see the mighty humbled
and all the humble blessed.

4. We join with our Creator
to keep the vision bright:
in places of oppression
we call for freedom's light:
a glorious new beginning,
a universe at peace,
where justice flows like fountains
and praises never cease.

© Copyright 1999 Kevin Mayhew Ltd.

670 The Virgin Mary had a baby boy

Words and music: Traditional West Indian

2. The angels sang when the baby was born, *(x3)*
   and proclaimed him the Saviour Jesus.

3. The wise men saw where the baby was born, *(x3)*
   and they saw that his name was Jesus.

671 Thine arm, O Lord, in days of old

Edward Hayes Plumptre (1821-1891) alt. | William Croft (1678-1727)

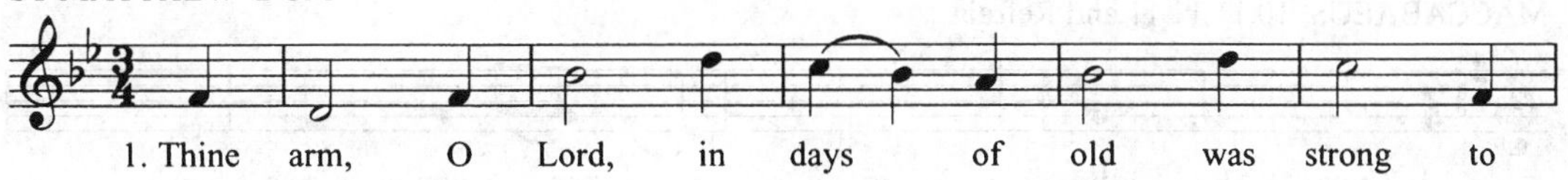

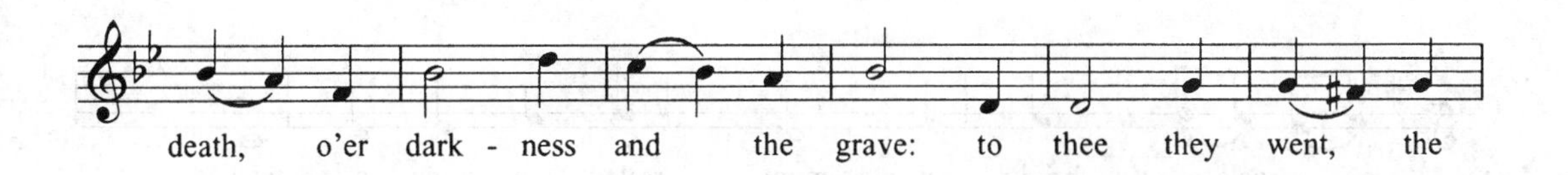

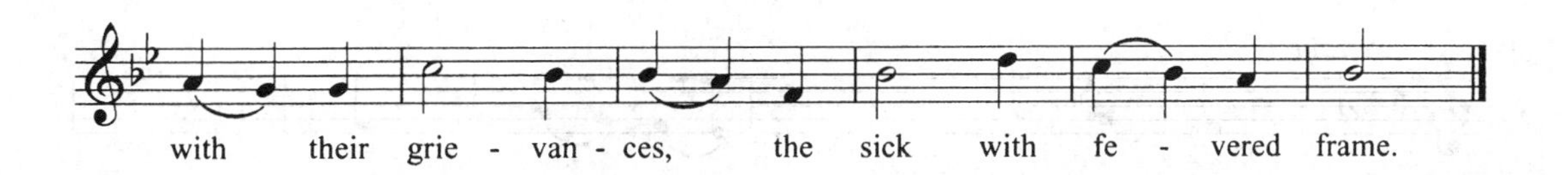

2. And lo, thy touch brought life and health,
gave speech and strength and sight;
and youth renewed and frenzy calmed
owned thee, the Lord of light:
and now, O Lord, be near to bless,
almighty as before,
in crowded street, by restless couch,
as by that ancient shore.

3. Be thou our great deliv'rer still,
thou Lord of life and death;
restore and quicken, soothe and bless,
with thine almighty breath:
to hands that work, and eyes that see,
give wisdom's heav'nly lore,
that whole and sick, and weak and strong,
may praise thee evermore.

672 Thine be the glory

À toi la gloire by Edmond Louis Budry (1854-1932)
trans. Richard Birch Hoyle (1875-1939)

George Frideric Handel (1685-1759)

MACCABAEUS 10 11 11 11 and Refrain

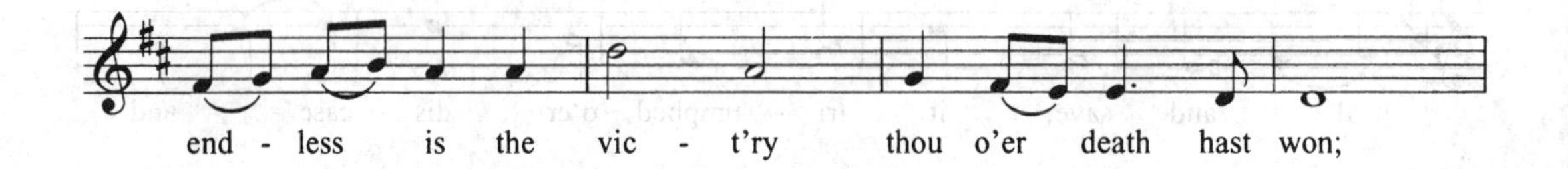

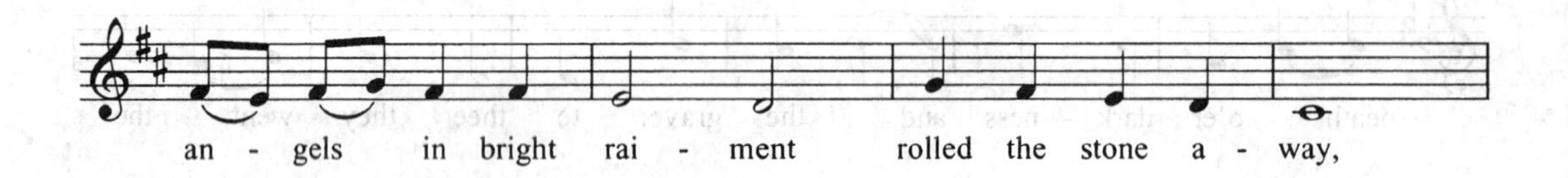

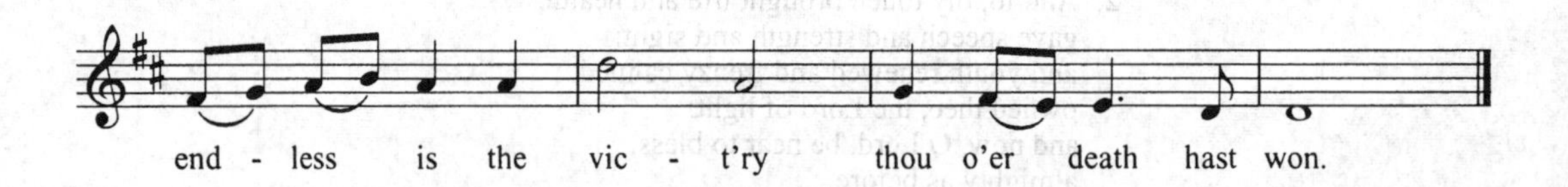

2. Lo! Jesus meets us, risen from the tomb;
lovingly he greets us, scatters fear and gloom.
Let the Church with gladness hymns of triumph sing,
for her Lord now liveth; death hath lost its sting.

3. No more we doubt thee, glorious Prince of Life!
Life is naught without thee: aid us in our strife.
Make us more than conqu'rors through thy deathless love.
Bring us safe through Jordan to thy home above.

Text © Copyright Control.

673 Thine for ever! God of love

Mary Fawler Maude (1819-1913) alt.

William Dalrymple Maclagan (1826-1910)

NEWINGTON 77 77

2. Thine for ever! Lord of life,
shield us through our earthly strife;
thou the life, the truth, the way,
guide us to the realms of day.

3. Thine for ever! O how blest
they who find in thee their rest!
Saviour, guardian, heav'nly friend,
O defend us to the end.

4. Thine for ever! Shepherd, keep
us thy frail and trembling sheep;
safe within thy tender care,
let us all thy goodness share.

5. Thine for ever! thou our guide,
all our wants by thee supplied,
all our sins by thee forgiv'n,
lead us, Lord, from earth to heav'n.

674 This is my body

In love for me

vs. 1&2: Jimmy Owens
vs. 3-5: Damian Lundy (1944-1997)

Peter Jacobs

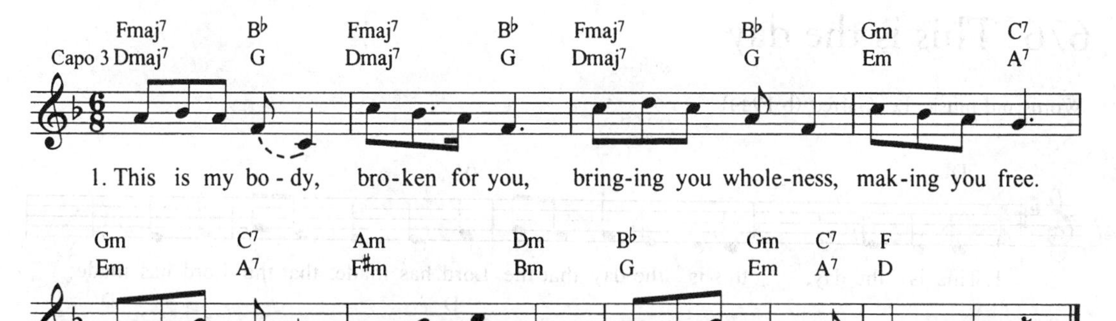

2. This is my blood, poured out for you,
bringing forgiveness, making you free.
Take it and drink it, and when you do,
do it in love for me.

3. Back to my Father soon I shall go.
Do not forget me; then you will see
I am still with you, and you will know
you're very close to me.

4. Filled with my Spirit, how you will grow!
You are my branches; I am the tree.
If you are faithful, others will know
you are alive in me.

5. Love one another; I have loved you,
and I have shown you how to be free;
serve one another, and when you do,
do it in love for me.

© Copyright 1978 Bud John Songs/EMI Christian Music Publishing. Administered by CopyCare, P.O. Box 77, Hailsham, East Sussex BN27 3EF, UK. (music@copycare.com). Used by permission.

675 This is my will

James Quinn (b.1919)

Traditional Irish melody

2. No greater love can be than this:
to choose to die to save one's friends.
You are my friends if you obey
all I command that you should do.

3. I call you now no longer slaves;
no slave knows all his master does.
I call you friends, for all I hear
my Father say, you hear from me.

4. You chose not me, but I chose you,
that you should go and bear much fruit.
I called you out that you in me
should bear much fruit that will abide.

5. All that you ask my Father dear
for my name's sake you shall receive.
This is my will, my one command,
that love should dwell in each, in all.

Text © Copyright Geoffrey Chapman/Continuum Publishers, The Tower Building,
11 York Road, London SE1 7NX. Used by permission.

676 This is the day

Words and music: Les Garrett (b.1944)

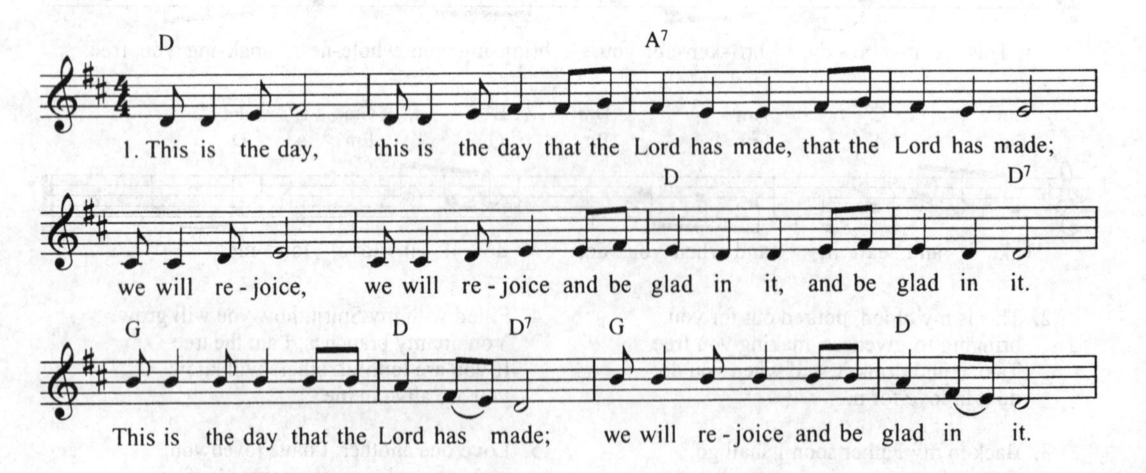

© Copyright 1967 Scripture in Song (a division of Integrity Music Inc.)/Sovereign Music UK,
P.O. Box 356, Leighton Buzzard, LU7 3WP, UK. Used by permission.

2. This is the day, this is the day
when he rose again, when he rose again;
we will rejoice, we will rejoice
and be glad in it, and be glad in it.
This is the day when he rose again;
we will rejoice and be glad in it.
This is the day, this is the day
when he rose again.

3. This is the day, this is the day
when the Spirit came, when the Spirit came;
we will rejoice, we will rejoice
and be glad in it, and be glad in it.
This is the day when the Spirit came;
we will rejoice and be glad in it.
This is the day, this is the day
when the Spirit came.

677 This is the day the Lord has made

Isaac Watts (1674-1748) alt. | Richard Runciman Terry (1865-1938)

BILLING CM

2. Today he rose and left the dead,
and Satan's empire fell;
today the saints his triumphs spread,
and all his wonders tell.

3. Hosanna to th'anointed King,
to David's holy Son!
Make haste to help us, Lord, and bring
salvation from thy throne.

4. Blest be the Lord: let us proclaim
his messages of grace;
who comes, in God his Father's name,
to save our sinful race.

5. Hosanna in the highest strains
the Church on earth can raise;
the highest heav'ns in which he reigns
shall give him nobler praise.

Music © Copyright Burns & Oates Ltd./Continuum Publishers, The Tower Building,
11 York Road, London SE1 7NX. Used by permission.

678 This is the truth sent from above

Traditional English

Traditional English melody collected by Ralph Vaughan Williams (1872-1958)

THE TRUTH FROM ABOVE 88 88

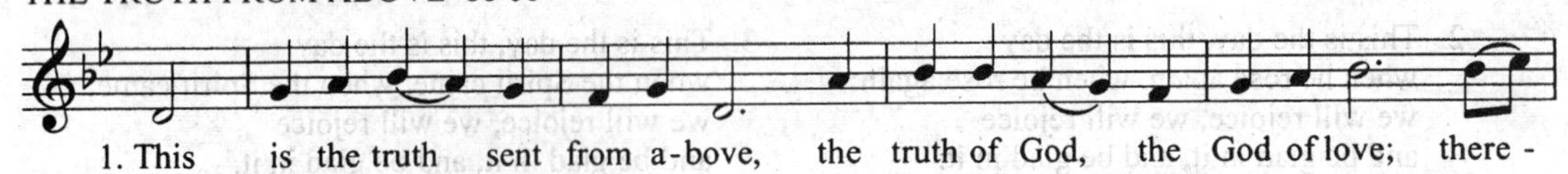

2. The first thing that I will relate,
that God at first did man create;
the next thing which to you I tell —
woman was made with him to dwell.

3. Then after that 'twas God's own choice
to place them both in paradise,
there to remain from evil free
except they ate of such a tree.

4. But they did eat, which was a sin,
and thus their ruin did begin —
ruined themselves, both you and me,
and all of our posterity.

5. Thus we were heirs to endless woes
till God the Lord did interpose;
and so a promise soon did run:
that he'd redeem us by his Son.

6. And at this season of the year
our blest Redeemer did appear,
and here did live, and here did preach,
and many thousands he did teach.

7. Thus he in love to us behaved,
to show us how we must be saved;
and if you want to know the way,
be pleased to hear what he did say:

8. 'Go preach the gospel,' now he said,
'to all the nations that are made!
And those that do believe on me,
from all their sins I'll set them free.'

9. O seek! O seek of God above
that saving faith that works by love!
And, if he's pleased to grant thee this,
thou'rt sure to have eternal bliss.

10. God grant to all within this place
true saving faith, that special grace
which to his people doth belong:
and thus I close my Christmas song.

Music © Copyright 1919 Stainer & Bell Ltd., P.O. Box 110, Victoria House, 23 Gruneisen Road, Finchley, London N3 1DZ, UK. Used by permission.

679 This is the year

Graham Kendrick
based on Isaiah 61 and Luke 4:18-19

Graham Kendrick (b.1950)
from *The Millennium Chorus*

2. This is the year of joy for tears,
and beauty out of ashes,
when skies will clear if we will share,
forgive and learn what love is.
Let's crown the year with kindness
and live in peace,
fill all the world
with songs that never cease.

3. These are the days of heaven's grace,
and favour smiling on us,
two thousand years of hopes and prayers
are met in one great chorus.
A light has dawned upon us,
and will increase,
and countless captive souls
will be released.

© Copyright 1999 Ascent Music, P.O. Box 263, Croydon, Surrey CR9 5AP, UK.
Adapted for congregational use from the theme song of *The Millennium Chorus.*
International copyright secured. All rights reserved. Used by permission.

680 This joyful Eastertide

George Ratcliffe Woodward (1848-1934) | Traditional Dutch melody

THIS JOYFUL EASTERTIDE (VREUCHTEN) 67 67 and Refrain

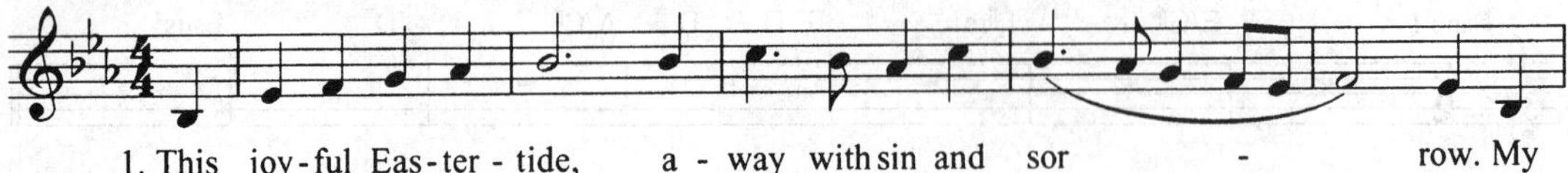

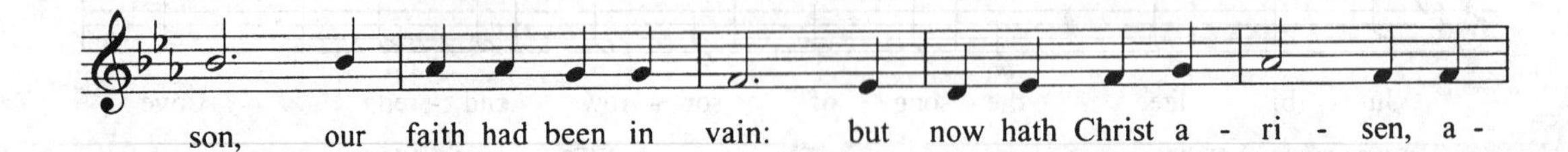

2. My flesh in hope shall rest,
and for a season slumber;
till trump from east to west
shall wake the dead in number.

3. Death's flood hath lost its chill,
since Jesus crossed the river:
lover of souls, from ill
my passing soul deliver.

Text © Copyright Control

681 This world you have made *Beautiful world*

Words and music: Susan Sayers (b.1946)

BEAUTIFUL WORLD 98 98 and Refrain

© Copyright 1991 Kevin Mayhew Ltd.

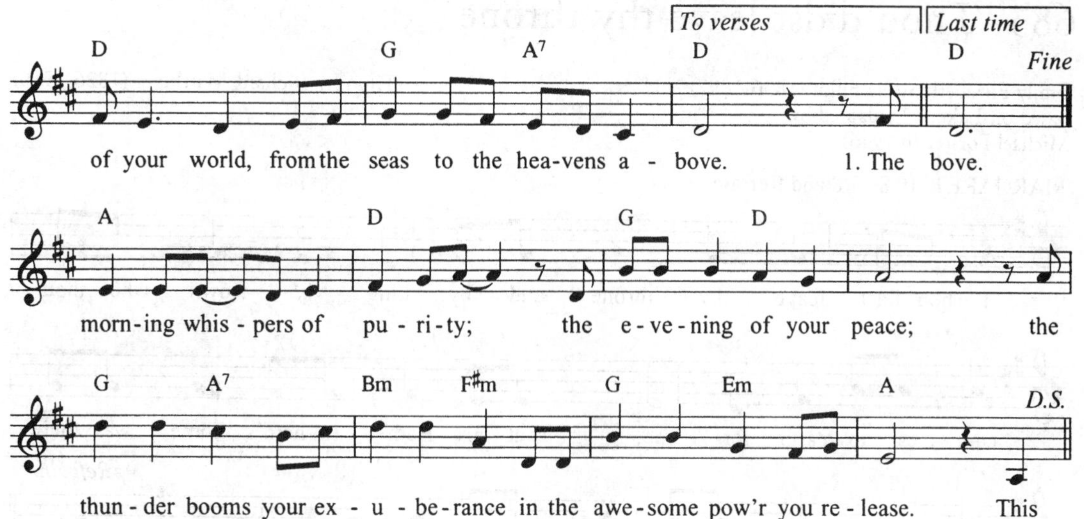

2. The tenderness of a new-born child;
the gentleness of the rain;
simplicity in a single cell;
and complexity in a brain.

3. Your stillness rests in a silent pool;
infinity drifts in space;
your grandeur straddles the mountain tops;
and we see your face in each face.

682 Thou art the Way: by thee alone

George Washington Doane (1799-1859)
based on John 14

Raphael Courteville (c.1675-1772)

ST JAMES CM

2. Thou art the Truth: thy word alone
true wisdom can impart;
thou only canst inform the mind
and purify the heart.

3. Thou art the Life: the rending tomb
proclaims thy conqu'ring arm;
and those who put their trust in thee
nor death nor hell shall harm.

4. Thou art the Way, the Truth, the Life:
grant us that Way to know,
that Truth to keep, that Life to win,
whose joys eternal flow.

683 Thou didst leave thy throne

Emily Elizabeth Steele Elliot (1836-1897)
based on Luke 2:7, adapted by
Michael Forster (b.1946)

Timothy Richard Matthews (1826-1910)

MARGARET 10 8 11 8 and Refrain

2. Heaven's arches rang when the angels sang
and proclaimed thee of royal degree,
but in lowliest birth didst thou come to earth
and in deepest humility.

3. Though the fox found rest, and the bird its nest
in the shade of the cedar tree,
yet the world found no bed for the Saviour's head
in the desert of Galilee.

4. Though thou cam'st, Lord, with the living word
that should set all thy people free,
yet with treachery, scorn and a crown of thorn
did they bear thee to Calvary.

5. When the heav'ns shall ring and the angels sing
at thy coming to victory,
let thy voice call me home, saying 'Heav'n has room,
there is room at my side for thee.'

This version of text © Copyright 1996 Kevin Mayhew Ltd.

684 Thou, whose almighty word

John Marriott (1780-1825) alt.

Melody from Madan's *Collection* (1769)
adapted by Felice de Giardini (1716-1796)

MOSCOW 664 6664

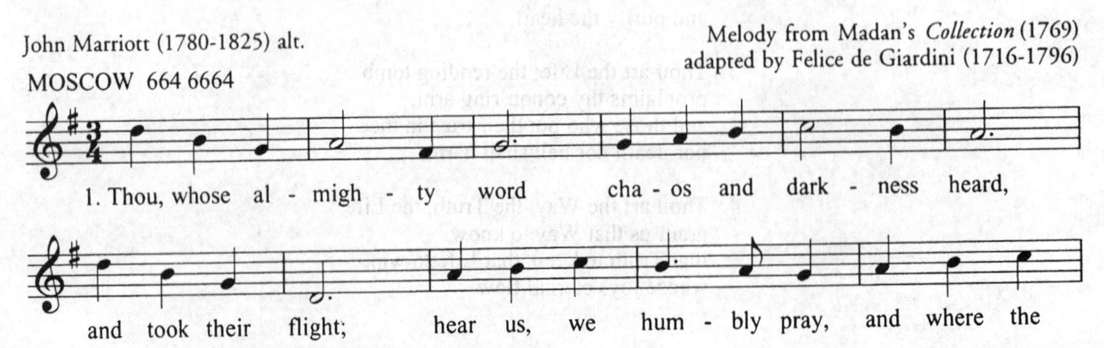

2. Thou, who didst come to bring
on thy redeeming wing,
healing and sight,
health to the sick in mind,
sight to the inly blind,
O now to humankind
let there be light.

3. Spirit of truth and love,
life-giving, holy Dove,
speed forth thy flight;
move on the water's face,
bearing the lamp of grace,
and in earth's darkest place
let there be light.

4. Holy and blessèd Three,
glorious Trinity,
Wisdom, Love, Might;
boundless as ocean's tide
rolling in fullest pride,
through the earth far and wide
let there be light.

685 Three in One, and One in Three

Gilbert Rorison (1821-1869)

Friedrich Filitz (1804-1876) alt.

CAPETOWN 77 75

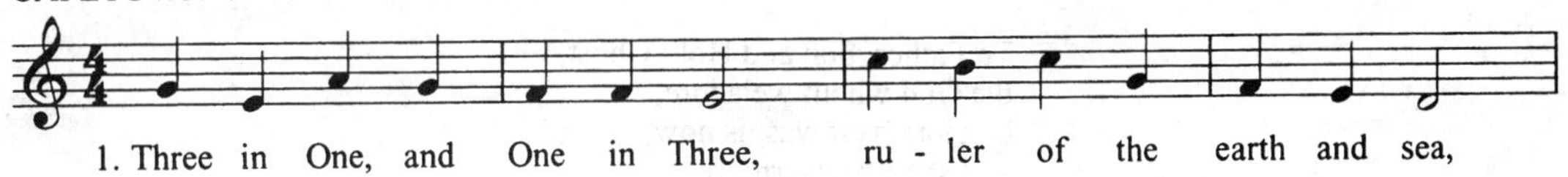

2. Light of lights! with morning-shine
lift on us thy light divine;
and let charity benign
breathe on us her balm.

3. Light of lights! when falls the ev'n,
let it close on sin forgiv'n,
fold us in the peace of heav'n;
shed a holy calm.

4. Three in One, and One in Three,
dimly here we worship thee;
with the saints hereafter we
hope to bear the palm.

686 Through all the changing scenes of life

Psalm 34 in *New Version*
(Tate and Brady, 1696)

George Thomas Smart (1776-1867)

WILTSHIRE CM

2. O magnify the Lord with me,
with me exalt his name;
when in distress to him I called,
he to my rescue came.

3. The hosts of God encamp around
the dwellings of the just;
deliv'rance he affords to all
who on his succour trust.

4. O make but trial of his love:
experience will decide
how blest are they, and only they,
who in his truth confide.

5. Fear him, ye saints, and you will then
have nothing else to fear;
make you his service your delight,
your wants shall be his care.

6. To Father, Son and Holy Ghost,
the God whom we adore,
be glory as it was, is now,
and shall be evermore.

687 Through the night of doubt and sorrow

Bernhardt Severin Ingemann (1789-1862)
trans. Sabine Baring-Gould (1834-1924) alt.

Martin Shaw (1875-1958)

TUNE 1: MARCHING 87 87

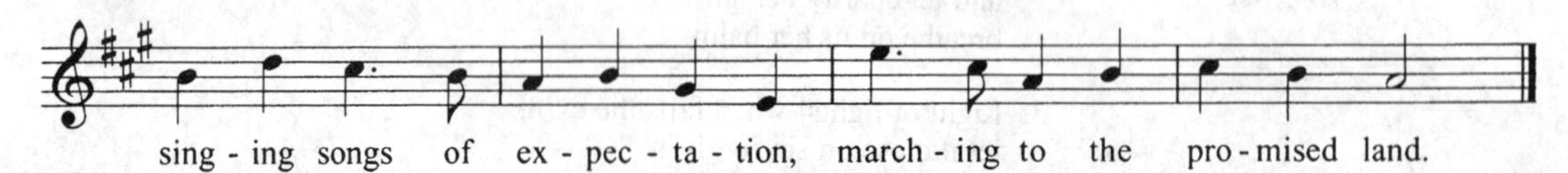

2. Clear before us, through the darkness,
gleams and burns the guiding light;
so we march in hope united,
stepping fearless through the night.

3. One the light of God's own presence
o'er his ransomed people shed,
chasing far the gloom and terror,
bright'ning all the path we tread.

4. One the object of our journey,
one the faith which never tires,
one the earnest looking forward,
one the hope our God inspires.

5. One the strain that lips of thousands
lift as from the heart of one:
one the conflict, one the peril,
one the march in God begun.

Tune 1: © Copyright Martin Shaw. Exclusively licensed to and reproduced by permission of J. Curwen & Sons Ltd., 8/9 Frith Street, London W1D 3JB. All rights reserved. International copyright secured. Used by permission.

6. One the gladness of rejoicing
on the far eternal shore,
where the one almighty Father
reigns in love for evermore.

7. Onward, therefore, fellow pilgrims,
onward with the Cross our aid;
bear its shame and fight its battle,
till we rest beneath its shade.

8. Soon shall come the great awaking,
soon the rending of the tomb;
then the scatt'ring of all shadows,
and the end of toil and gloom.

Bernhardt Severin Ingemann (1789-1862)
trans. Sabine Baring-Gould (1834-1924) alt.

John Bacchus Dykes (1823-1876)

TUNE 2: ST OSWALD 87 87

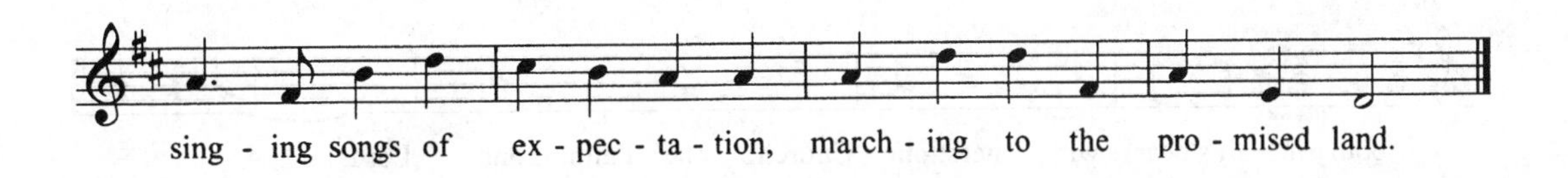

688 Thy ceaseless, unexhausted love

Charles Wesley (1707-1788)

Charles Collignon (1725-1785)

UNIVERSITY CM

2. Thou waitest to be gracious still;
thou dost with sinners bear,
that, saved, we may thy goodness feel,
and all thy grace declare.

3. Thy goodness and thy truth to me,
to ev'ry soul, abound,
a vast, unfathomable sea,
where all our thoughts are drowned.

4. Its streams the whole creation reach,
so plenteous is the store,
enough for all, enough for each,
enough for evermore.

5. Faithful, O Lord, thy mercies are,
a rock that cannot move;
a thousand promises declare
thy constancy of love.

6. Throughout the universe it reigns,
unalterably sure;
and while the truth of God remains
the goodness must endure.

689 Thy hand, O God, has guided

Edward Hayes Plumptre (1821-1891) alt. | Basil Harwood (1859-1949)

THORNBURY 76 76 D

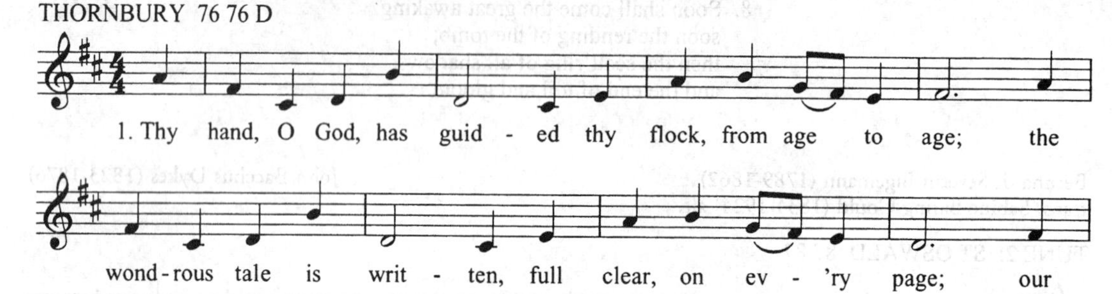

2. Thy heralds brought glad tidings
to greatest, as to least;
they bade them rise, and hasten
to share the great King's feast;
and this was all their teaching,
in ev'ry deed and word,
to all alike proclaiming:
one Church, one Faith, one Lord.

3. Through many a day of darkness,
through many a scene of strife,
the faithful few fought bravely
to guard the nation's life.
Their gospel of redemption,
sin pardoned, hope restored,
was all in this enfolded:
one Church, one Faith, one Lord.

4. And we, shall we be faithless?
Shall hearts fail, hands hang down?
Shall we evade the conflict,
and cast away our crown?
Not so: in God's deep counsels
some better thing is stored:
we will maintain, unflinching,
one Church, one Faith, one Lord.

5. Thy mercy will not fail us,
nor leave thy work undone;
with thy right hand to help us,
the vict'ry shall be won;
and then by all creation,
thy name shall be adored.
And this shall be their anthem:
One Church, one Faith, one Lord.

Music © Copyright the Executors of Dr. Basil Harwood. Used by permission of the Trustees of the late Dr. Basil Harwood Settlement Trust, Stewart House, 24 Kingsway, London WC2B 6JX, UK.

690 Thy kingdom come!

Frederick Lucian Hosmer (1840-1929) | From *Hymns and Sacred Poems,* Dublin (1749)

IRISH CM

2. But the slow watches of the night
not less to God belong;
and for the everlasting right
the silent stars are strong.

3. And lo, already on the hills
the flags of dawn appear;
gird up your loins, ye prophet souls,
proclaim the day is near.

4. The day in whose clear-shining light
all wrong shall stand revealed,
when justice shall be throned in might,
and ev'ry hurt be healed.

5. When knowledge, hand in hand with peace,
shall walk the earth abroad:
the day of perfect righteousness,
the promised day of God.

691 Thy kingdom come, O God

Lewis Hensley (1824-1905) alt.

Leighton George Hayne (1836-1883)

ST CECILIA 66 66

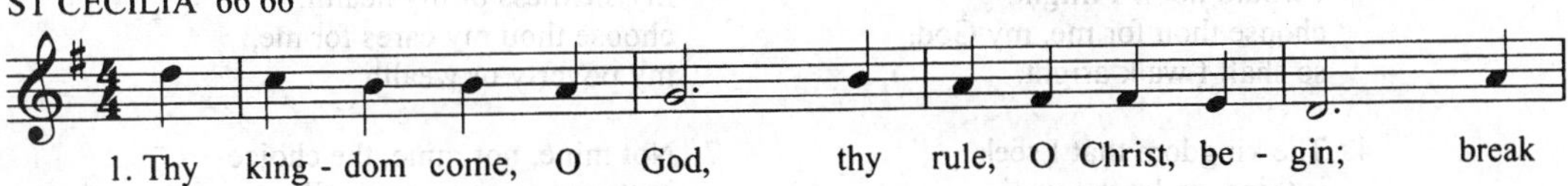

2. Where is thy reign of peace
and purity and love?
When shall all hatred cease,
as in the realms above?

3. When comes the promised time
that war shall be no more,
and lust, oppression, crime
shall flee thy face before?

4. We pray thee, Lord, arise,
and come in thy great might;
revive our longing eyes,
which languish for thy sight.

5. Some scorn thy sacred name,
and wolves devour thy fold;
by many deeds of shame
we learn that love grows cold.

6. O'er lands both near and far
thick darkness broodeth yet:
arise, O morning star,
arise, and never set.

692 Thy way, not mine, O Lord

Horatius Bonar (1808-1889) | Maria Tiddeman (1837-1915)

IBSTONE 66 66

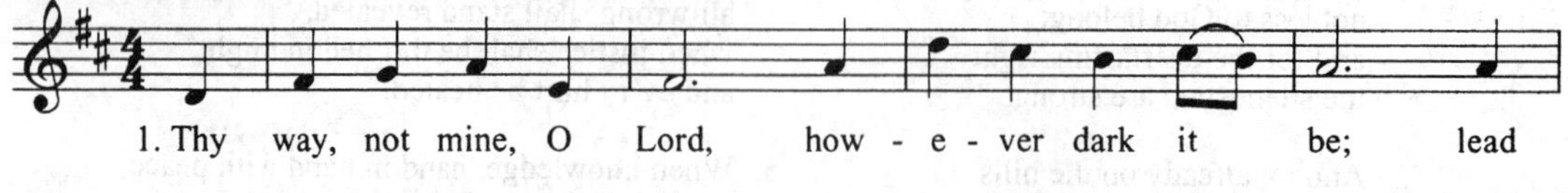

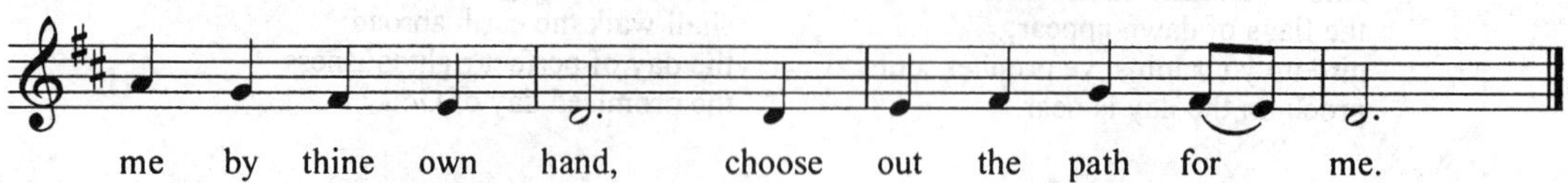

2. Smooth let it be or rough,
it will be still the best;
winding or straight, it leads
right onward to thy rest.

3. I dare not choose my lot;
I would not if I might:
choose thou for me, my God,
so shall I walk aright.

4. The kingdom that I seek
is thine, so let the way
that leads to it be thine,
else I must surely stray.

5. Take thou my cup, and it
with joy or sorrow fill,
as best to thee may seem;
choose thou my good and ill.

6. Choose thou for me my friends,
my sickness or my health;
choose thou my cares for me,
my poverty or wealth.

7. Not mine, not mine, the choice
in things or great or small;
be thou my guide, my strength,
my wisdom, and my all.

693 Thy will be done

Shapcott Wensley | John Henry Maunder (1858-1920)

THY WILL BE DONE 88 88 6

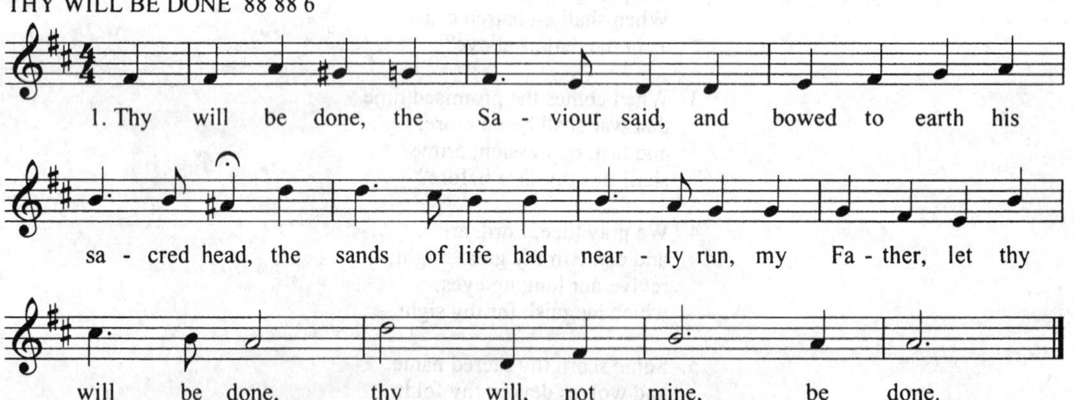

2. No watch his spent disciples kept,
amid the shadows deep they slept;
but silent angels waiting there,
beheld his agony of prayer —
thy will, not mine, be done.

3. His soul foresaw the cruel scorns,
the brutal scourge, the crown of thorns,
and, darker than Gethsemane,
the shadows of th' accursed tree, —
thy will, not mine, be done.

4. What though he felt in that dread hour,
the storms of human passions low'r;
nor pain, nor death, his soul would shun,
my Father, let thy will be done,
thy will, not mine, be done.

694 To be in your presence *My desire*

Words and music: Noel Richards

2. To rest in your presence,
not rushing away,
to cherish each moment,
here I would stay.

© Copyright 1981 Kingsway's Thankyou Music, P.O. Box 75, Eastbourne, East Sussex BN23 6NW, UK. (tym@kingsway.co.uk). Used by permission.

695 To God be the glory!

Frances Jane van Alstyne (Fanny J. Crosby) (1820-1915) William Howard Doane (1832-1916)

TO GOD BE THE GLORY 11 11 11 11 and Refrain

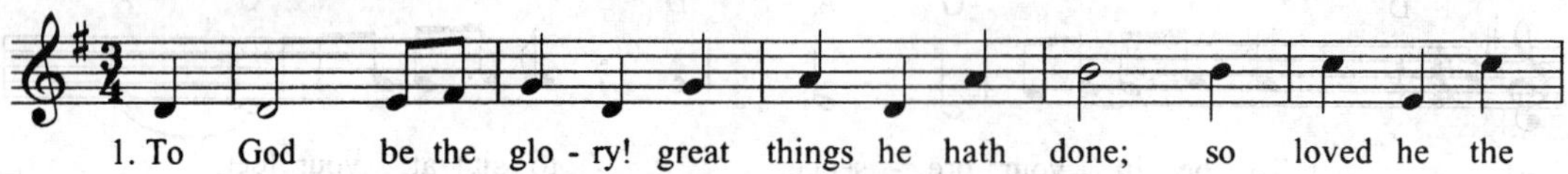

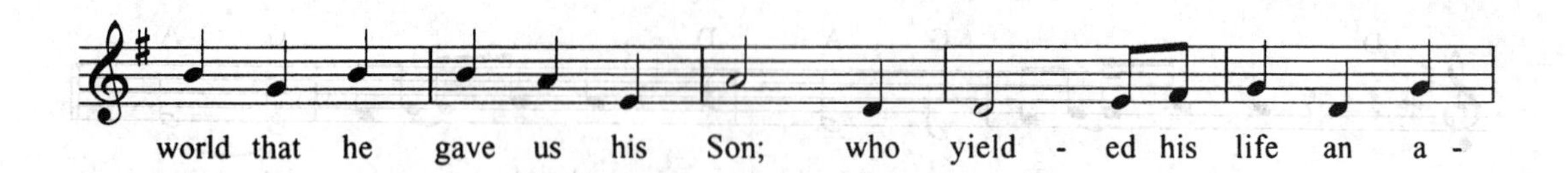

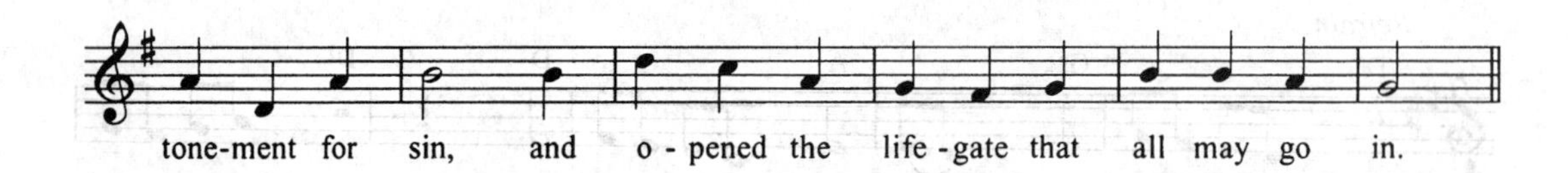

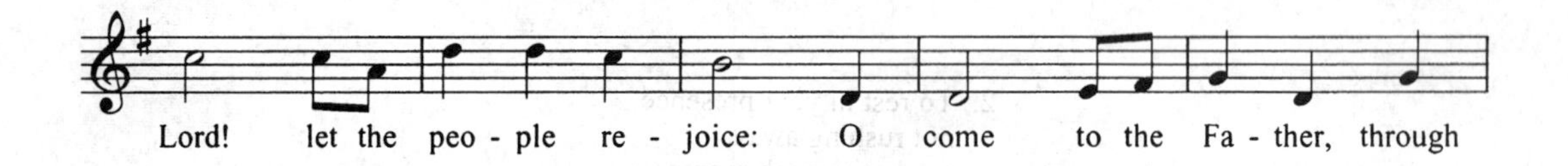

2. O perfect redemption, the purchase of blood!
to ev'ry believer the promise of God;
the vilest offender who truly believes,
that moment from Jesus a pardon receives.

3. Great things he hath taught us, great things he hath done,
and great our rejoicing through Jesus the Son;
but purer, and higher, and greater will be
our wonder, our rapture, when Jesus we see.

696 To thee, O Lord, our hearts we raise

William Chatterton Dix (1837-1898) alt. | Arthur Seymour Sullivan (1842-1900)

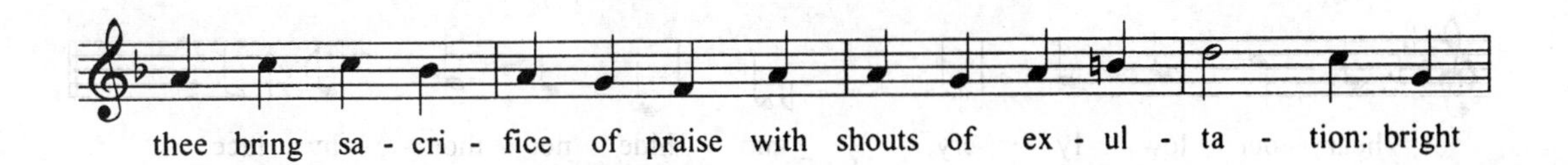

2. And now, on this our festal day,
thy bounteous hand confessing,
upon thine altar, Lord, we lay
the first-fruits of thy blessing:
by thee our souls are truly fed
with gifts of grace supernal;
thou who dost give us earthly bread,
give us the bread eternal.

3. We bear the burden of the day,
and often toil seems dreary;
but labour ends with sunset ray,
and rest comes for the weary:
may we, the angel-reaping o'er,
stand at the last accepted,
Christ's golden sheaves for evermore
to garners bright elected.

4. O blessèd is that land of God,
where saints abide for ever;
where golden fields spread far and broad,
where flows the crystal river:
the strains of all its holy throng
with ours today are blending;
thrice blessèd is that harvest-song
which never hath an ending.

697 To thee, our God, we fly

William Walsham How (1823-1897) | William Statham (1832-1898)

TUNE 1: LATCHFORD 66 66 88

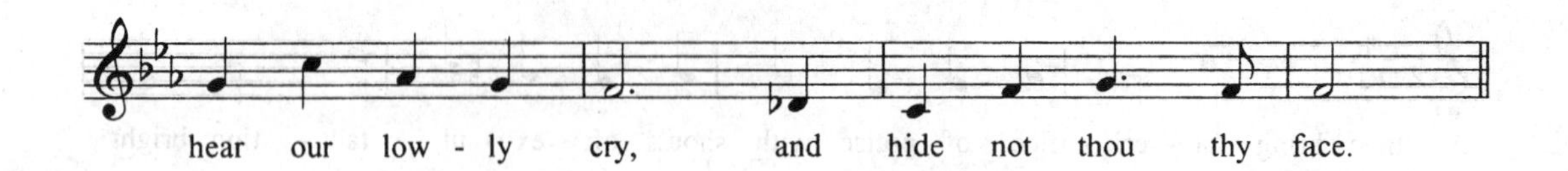

2. Arise, O Lord of hosts!
Be jealous for thy name,
and drive from out our coasts
the sins that put to shame.

3. Thy best gifts from on high
in rich abundance pour,
that we may magnify
and praise thee evermore.

4. The pow'rs ordained by thee
with heav'nly wisdom bless;
may they thy servants be,
and rule in righteousness.

5. Give peace, Lord, in our time,
O let no foe draw nigh,
nor lawless deeds of crime
insult thy majesty.

6. The Church of thy dear Son
inflame with love's pure fire,
bind her once more in one;
with life and truth inspire.

William Walsham How (1823-1897)

Contributed to Playford's *The Divine Companion* (1709) by William Croft (1678-1727)

TUNE 2: CROFT'S 136TH 66 66 88

698 To the name of our salvation

Gloriosi Salvatoris (15th century)
trans. John Mason Neale (1818-1866) alt.

Caspar Ett's
Cantica Sacra (1840)

ORIEL 87 87 87

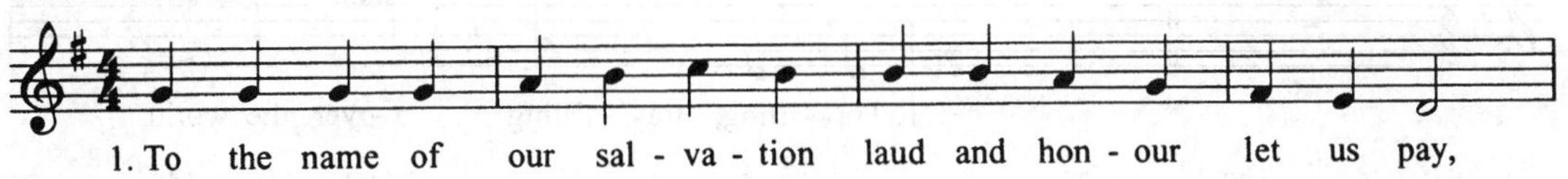

2. Jesus is the name we treasure,
name beyond what words can tell;
name of gladness, name of pleasure,
ear and heart delighting well;
name of sweetness passing measure,
saving us from sin and hell.

3. 'Tis the name for adoration,
name for songs of victory;
name for holy meditation
in the vale of misery;
name for joyful veneration
by the citizens on high.

4. 'Tis the name that whoso preacheth
speaks like music to the ear;
who in prayer this name beseecheth
sweetest comfort findeth near;
who its perfect wisdom reacheth
heav'nly joy possesseth here.

5. Jesus is the name exalted
over ev'ry other name;
in this name, whene'er assaulted,
we can put our foes to shame:
strength to them who else had halted,
eyes to blind, and feet to lame.

6. Therefore we in love adoring
this most blessèd name revere,
holy Jesus, thee imploring
so to write it in us here,
that hereafter, heav'nward soaring,
we may sing with angels there.

699 Travelling, travelling *Break the bread*

Brian A. Wren (b.1936) Hedley Roberts

TRAVELERS 87 77 D with Irregular Refrain

2. Some have fled from terror by night,
hiding from bullets by day,
weary and hungry, in fear of their life,
seeking a safe place to stay:

3. Some are far from the people they love,
driven by family need,
tired and exploited, doing their job,
thinking of children to feed:

4. Trav'lling, trav'lling over the world,
no-one should be out of place.
What would we say, then, if we were alone,
needing a friendly face?

Text © Copyright 1986 Stainer & Bell Ltd., P.O. Box 110, Victoria House,
23 Gruneisen Road, Finchley, London N3 1DZ, UK. Used by permission.
Music © Copyright 1986 Hope Publishing Co. Administered by CopyCare, P.O. Box 77,
Hailsham, East Sussex BN27 3EF, UK. (music@copycare.com). Used by permission.

700 Unto us a boy is born

Puer nobis nascitur (15th century)
trans. Percy Dearmer (1867-1936) alt.

From *Piae Cantiones* (1582)

PUER NOBIS 76 77

2. Cradled in a stall was he,
 watched by cows and asses;
 but the very beasts could see
 that he the world surpasses,
 that he the world surpasses.

3. Then the fearful Herod cried,
 'Pow'r is mine in Jewry!'
 So the blameless children died
 the victims of his fury,
 the victims of his fury.

4. Now may Mary's Son, who came
 long ago to love us,
 lead us all with hearts aflame
 unto the joys above us,
 unto the joys above us.

5. Omega and Alpha he!
 Let the organ thunder,
 while the choir with peals of glee
 shall rend the air asunder,
 shall rend the air asunder.

Text © Copyright Oxford University Press, Great Clarendon Street, Oxford OX2 6DP, UK.
Used by permission from *The Oxford Book of Carols*.

701 Virgin-born, we bow before thee

Reginald Heber (1783-1826)

German Carol melody (14th century)

QUEM PASTORES 88 87

2. Blessèd was the breast that fed thee;
 blessèd was the hand that led thee;
 blessèd was the parent's eye
 that watched thy slumb'ring infancy.

3. Blessèd she by all creation,
 who brought forth the world's salvation,
 blessèd they, for ever blest,
 who love thee most and serve thee best.

4. Virgin-born, we bow before thee:
 blessèd was the womb that bore thee;
 Mary, maid and mother mild,
 blessèd was she in her child.

702 Waken, O sleeper, wake and rise

Michael Forster (b.1946) | Richard Runciman Terry (1865-1938)

BILLING CM

2. Let us prepare to face the day
of judgement and of grace,
to live as people of the light,
and perfect truth embrace.

3. Watch then and pray, we cannot know
the moment or the hour,
when Christ, unheralded, will come
with life-renewing power.

4. Then shall the nations gather round
to learn his ways of peace,
when spears are turned to pruning-hooks
and all our conflicts cease.

Text © Copyright 1993 Kevin Mayhew Ltd.
Music © Copyright Burns & Oates Ltd./Continuum Publishers, The Tower Building,
11 York Road, London SE1 7NX. Used by permission.

703 Wake, O wake! with tidings thrilling

Words and music: Philipp Nicolai (1556-1608)
trans. Francis Crawford Burkitt (1864-1935) alt.

2. Sion hears the watchmen shouting,
her heart leaps up with joy undoubting,
she stands and waits with eager eyes;
see her Friend from heav'n descending,
adorned with truth and grace unending!
her light burns clear, her star doth rise.
Now come, thou precious Crown,
Lord Jesu, God's own son!
Hosanna!
Let us prepare
to follow there,
where in thy supper we may share.

3. Ev'ry soul in thee rejoices;
from earthly and angelic voices
be glory giv'n to thee alone!
Now the gates of pearl receive us,
thy presence never more shall leave us,
we stand with angels round thy throne.
Earth cannot give below
the bliss thou dost bestow.
Alleluia!
Grant us to raise,
to length of days,
the triumph-chorus of thy praise.

Text © Copyright Oxford University Press, Great Clarendon Street, Oxford OX2 6DP, UK.
Used by permission.

704 Wake up, O people

Words and music: Marie Lydia Pereira (b.1920)
based on Romans 13:11-14

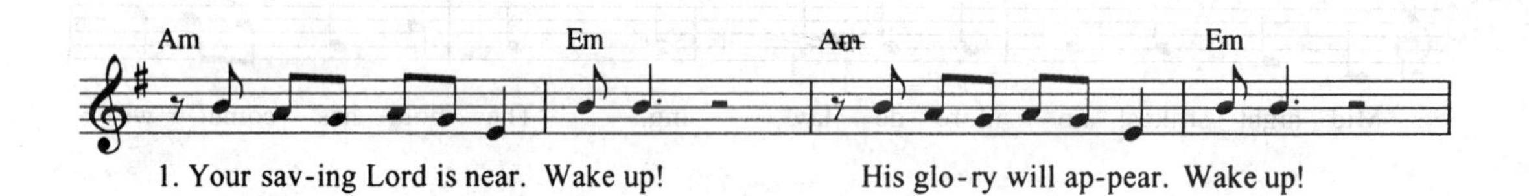

2. The night of sin has passed. Wake up!
The light is near at last. Wake up!
The day star, Christ, the Son of God, will soon appear.

3. To live in love and peace. Wake up!
To let all quarrels cease. Wake up!
To live that all you do may stand the light of day.

4. That Christ may be your shield. Wake up!
That death to life may yield. Wake up!
That heaven's gate be opened wide again for you.

© Copyright 1984 Kevin Mayhew Ltd.

705 Walking in a garden

Hilary Greenwood (b.1929) — Traditional French melody

2. Walking in a garden
where the Lord had gone,
three of the disciples,
Peter, James, and John;
they were very weary,
could not keep awake,
while the Lord was kneeling there,
praying for their sake.

3. Walking in a garden
at the break of day,
Mary asked the gard'ner
where the body lay;
but he turned towards her,
smiled at her and said:
'Mary, spring is here to stay,
only death is dead.'

Hilary Greenwood (b.1929) — Traditional Irish Melody

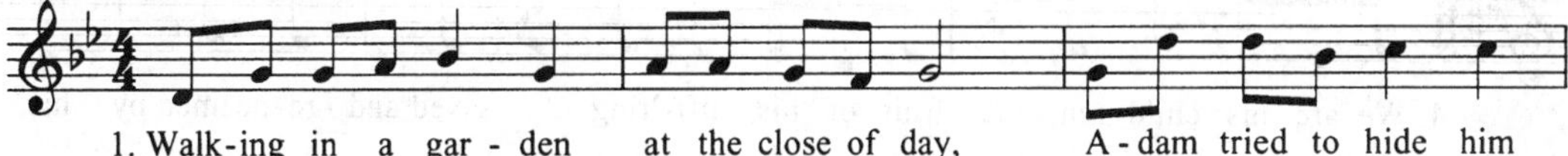

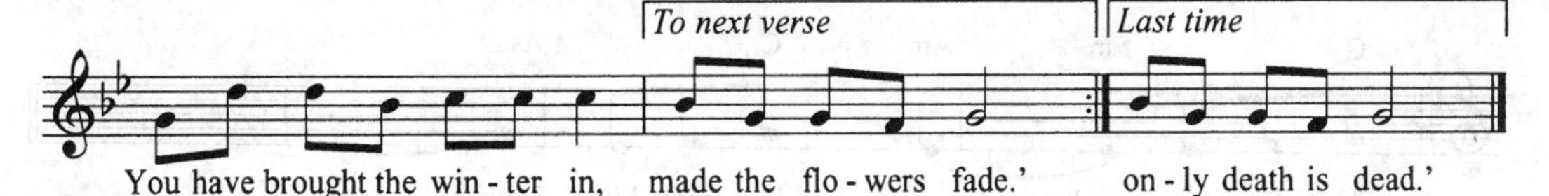

Text © Copyright Society of the Sacred Mission, St Antony's Priory, Claypath, Durham DH1 1QT, UK.
Used by permission.

706 Warm as the sun

Nick Fawcett (b.1957)

Margaret Rizza (b.1929)

WARM AS THE SUN LM

1. Warm as the sun, fresh as the breeze, fair as a flower, tall as the trees,

clear as the dew, pure as the dove, so un-to me, Lord, is your love.

Je-sus, for you, such is my love, Je - sus, for you.

2. Lovely as dawn, welcome as light,
peaceful as dusk, restful as night,
high as the clouds, deep as the sea,
so is your love, Lord, unto me.

3. Swift as a stream, free as a bird,
firm as a rock, sure as your word,
bright as the stars, shining above,
so unto me, Lord, is your love.

4. Finer than silk, richer than money,
precious as gold, sweeter than honey,
priceless as jewels, dear as can be,
so is your love, Lord, unto me.

5. Bursting with joy, leaping with praise,
glowing with thanks, heart set ablaze;
bringing my life, all that I do,
such is my love, Jesus, for you

© Copyright 1999 Kevin Mayhew Ltd.

707 We are his children *Go forth in his name*

Words and music: Graham Kendrick (b.1950)

1. We are his child-ren, the fruit of his suff-'ring, saved and re-deemed by his

blood; called to be ho - ly, a light to the na-tions:

clothed with his pow'r, filled with his love.

© Copyright 1990 Make Way Music, P.O. Box 263, Croydon, Surrey CR9 5AP, UK.
International copyright secured. All rights reserved. Used by permission.

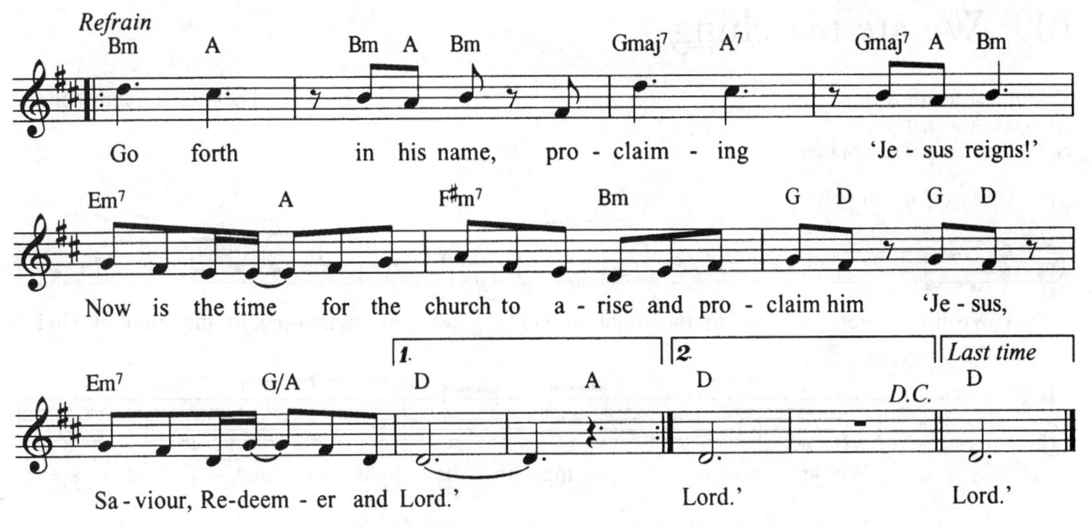

2. Countless the souls that are stumbling in darkness,
why do we sleep in the light?
Jesus commands us to go make disciples,
this is our case, this is our fight.

3. Listen, the wind of the Spirit is blowing,
the end of the age is so near;
pow'rs in the earth and the heavens are shaking,
Jesus our Lord soon shall appear!

708 We are his people

Susan Sayers (b.1946)
based on Psalm 100

Andrew Moore (b.1954)

2. Understand that the Lord is our God;
he it is who made us.
We his people belong to him,
he our loving shepherd.

3. O how faithful and good is the Lord,
loving us for ever;
rich in mercy and faithfulness,
true through all the ages.

© Copyright 1995 Kevin Mayhew Ltd.

709 We are marching

Traditional South African;
v.1 trans. Anders Nyberg;
vs. 2&3 trans. Andrew Maries

Traditional South African

SIYAHAMBA 99 99 59 59

2. We are living in the love of God . . .

3. We are moving in the pow'r of God . . .

Verse 1 © Copyright 1990 WGRG, Iona Community, Glasgow G2 3DH.
Used by permission from *Freedom is coming.*
Verses 2 and 3 © Copyright Sovereign Music UK, P.O. Box 356, Leighton Buzzard, Beds. LU7 3WP, UK.

710 We are not our own

Words and music: Brian A. Wren (b.1936)

YARNTON 89 85

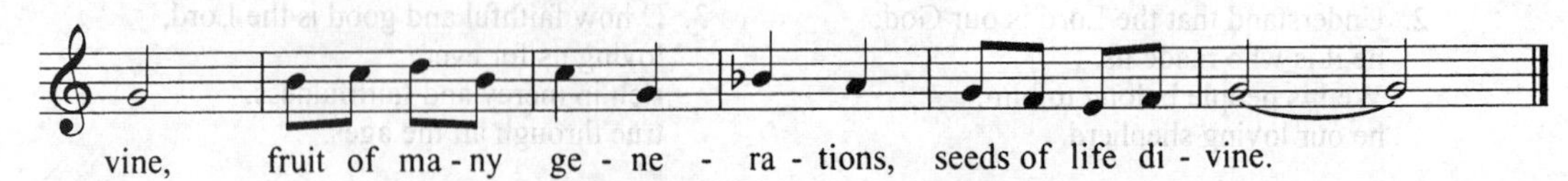

© Copyright 1989 Stainer & Bell Ltd., P.O. Box 110, Victoria House, 23 Gruneisen Road, Finchley, London N3 1DZ, UK. Used by permission.

2. We are not alone. Earth names us:
past and present, peoples near and far,
family and friends and strangers
show us who we are.

3. Through a human life God finds us;
dying, living, love is fully known,
and in bread and wine reminds us:
we are not our own.

4. Therefore let us make thanksgiving,
and with justice, willing and aware,
give to earth, and all things living,
liturgies of care.

5. And if love's encounters lead us
on a way uncertain and unknown,
all the saints with prayer surround us:
we are not alone.

6. Let us be a house of welcome,
living stone upholding living stone,
gladly showing all our neighbours
we are not our own!

711 We believe in God the Father

Words and music: Graham Kendrick (b.1950)

© Copyright 1986 Kingsway's Thankyou Music, P.O. Box 75, Eastbourne, East Sussex BN23 6NW, UK. (tym@kingsway.co.uk). Used by permission.

712 We cannot measure

John L. Bell (b.1949)
and Graham Maule (b.1958)

Traditional Scottish melody

YE BANKS AND BRAES DLM

2. The pain that will not go away,
the guilt that clings from things long past,
the fear of what the future holds,
are present as if meant to last.
But present too is love which tends
the hurt we never hoped to find,
the private agonies inside,
the memories that haunt the mind.

3. So some have come who need your help
and some have come to make amends,
as hands which shaped and saved the world
are present in the touch of friends.
Lord, let your Spirit meet us here
to mend the body, mind and soul,
to disentangle peace from pain
and make your broken people whole.

Text © Copyright 1989 WGRG, Iona Community, Glasgow G2 3DH, Scotland.
Used by permission from *Love from Below.* (Wild Goose Publications 1989)

713 We give immortal praise

Isaac Watts (1674-1748) William Croft (1678-1727)

CROFT'S 136TH 66 66 88

2. To God the Son belongs
immortal glory too,
who bought us with his blood
from everlasting woe:
and now he lives, and now he reigns,
and sees the fruit of all his pains.

3. To God the Spirit's name
immortal worship give,
whose new-creating pow'r
makes the dead sinner live:
his work completes the great design,
and fills the soul with joy divine.

4. To God the Trinity
be endless honours done,
the undivided Three,
and the mysterious One:
where reason falls with all her pow'rs,
there faith prevails, and love adores.

714 We hail thy presence glorious

Richard Godfrey Parsons (1882-1948) | Melody adapted from Michael Haydn (1737-1806)

OFFERTORIUM 76 76 D

2. Through thee in ev'ry nation
thine own their hearts upraise,
off'ring one pure oblation,
one sacrifice of praise:
with thee in blest communion
the living and the dead
are joined in closest union,
one Body with one Head.

3. O living bread from heaven,
Jesu, our Saviour good,
who thine own self hast given
to be our souls' true food;
for us thy body broken
hung on the cross of shame:
this bread its hallowed token
we break in thy dear name.

4. O stream of love unending,
poured from the one true vine,
with our weak nature blending
the strength of life divine;
our thankful faith confessing
in thy life-blood outpoured,
we drink this cup of blessing
and praise thy name, O Lord.

5. May we, thy word believing,
thee through thy gifts receive,
that, thou within us living,
we all to God may live;
draw us from earth to heaven
till sin and sorrow cease,
forgiving and forgiven,
in love and joy and peace.

Text © Copyright Control.

715 We have a dream

Michael Forster (b.1946) based on the speech by Martin Luther King Jr. | Walter Greatorex (1877-1949)

WOODLANDS 10 10 10 10

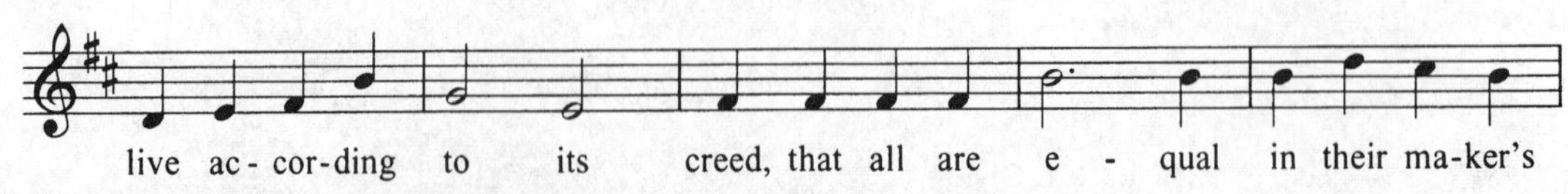

Text © Copyright 1997 Kevin Mayhew Ltd. Music © Copyright Oxford University Press, Great Clarendon Street, Oxford OX2 6DP, UK. Used by permission from *Enlarged Songs of Praise.*

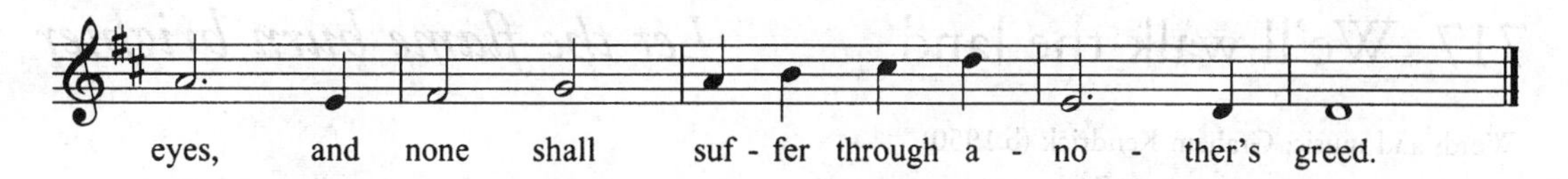

2. We have a dream that one day we shall see
a world of justice, truth and equity,
where sons of slaves and daughters of the free
will share the banquet of community.

3. We have a dream of deserts brought to flow'r,
once made infertile by oppression's heat,
when love and truth shall end oppressive pow'r,
and streams of righteousness and justice meet.

4. We have a dream: our children shall be free
from judgements based on colour or on race;
free to become whatever they may be,
of their own choosing in the light of grace.

5. We have a dream that truth will overcome
the fear and anger of our present day;
that black and white will share a common home,
and hand in hand will walk the pilgrim way.

6. We have a dream: each valley will be raised,
and ev'ry mountain, ev'ry hill brought down;
then shall creation echo perfect praise,
and share God's glory under freedom's crown!

716 We have a gospel to proclaim

Edward Joseph Burns (b.1938)

From William Gardiner's *Sacred Melodies* (1815)

FULDA LM

2. Tell of his birth at Bethlehem,
not in a royal house or hall,
but in a stable dark and dim,
the Word made flesh, a light for all.

3. Tell of his death at Calvary,
hated by those he came to save;
in lonely suff'ring on the cross:
for all he loved, his life he gave.

4. Tell of that glorious Easter morn,
empty the tomb, for he was free;
he broke the pow'r of death and hell
that we might share his victory.

5. Tell of his reign at God's right hand,
by all creation glorified.
He sends his Spirit on his Church
to live for him, the Lamb who died.

6. Now we rejoice to name him King:
Jesus is Lord of all the earth.
This gospel-message we proclaim:
we sing his glory, tell his worth.

Text © Copyright the Revd. Edward J. Burns.
Reproduced by kind permission.

717 We'll walk the land *Let the flame burn brighter*

© Copyright 1989 Make Way Music, P.O. Box 263, Croydon, Surrey CR9 5AP, UK.
International copyright secured. All rights reserved. Used by permission.

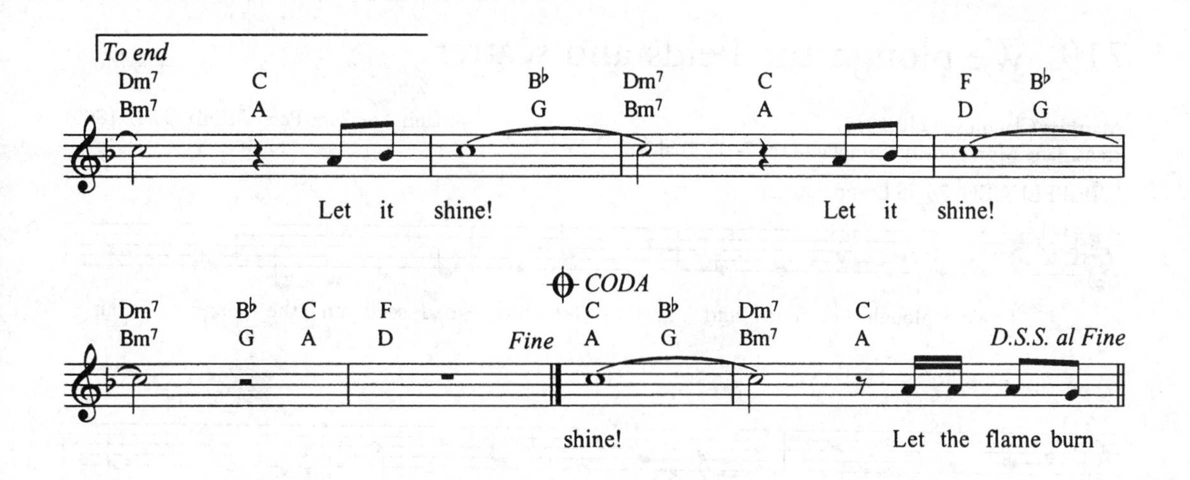

718 We love the place, O God

William Bullock (1798-1874)
and Henry Williams Baker (1821-1877)

Henry Lascelles Jenner (1820-1898)

QUAM DILECTA 66 66

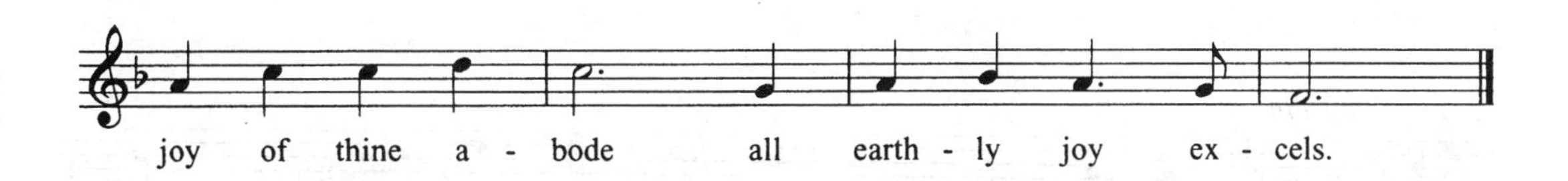

2. It is the house of prayer,
wherein thy servants meet;
and thou, O Lord, art there
thy chosen flock to greet.

3. We love the sacred font;
for there the holy Dove
to pour is ever wont
his blessing from above.

4. We love thine altar, Lord;
O what on earth so dear?
For there, in faith adored,
we find thy presence near.

5. We love the word of life,
the word that tells of peace,
of comfort in the strife,
and joys that never cease.

6. We love to sing below
for mercies freely giv'n;
but O, we long to know
the triumph-song of heav'n.

7. Lord Jesus, give us grace
on earth to love thee more,
in heav'n to see thy face,
and with thy saints adore.

719 We plough the fields and scatter

Matthias Claudius (1740-1815)
trans. Jane Montgomery Campbell (1817-1878) alt.

Johann Abraham Peter Schulz (1747-1800)

WIR PFLÜGEN 76 76 D and Refrain

1. We plough the fields and scat - ter the good seed on the land, but

it is fed and wa - tered by God's al - migh - ty hand: he

sends the snow in win - ter, the warmth to swell the grain, the

Refrain

thank the Lord, O thank the Lord for all his love.

2. He only is the maker
of all things near and far;
he paints the wayside flower,
he lights the evening star;
he fills the earth with beauty,
by him the birds are fed;
much more to us, his children,
he gives our daily bread.

3. We thank thee then, O Father,
for all things bright and good:
the seed-time and the harvest,
our life, our health, our food.
Accept the gifts we offer
for all thy love imparts,
and, what thou most desirest,
our humble, thankful hearts.

720 We pray thee, heavenly Father

Vincent Stuckey Stratton Coles (1845-1929) | John Bacchus Dykes (1823-1876)

TUNE 1: DIES DOMINICA 76 76 D

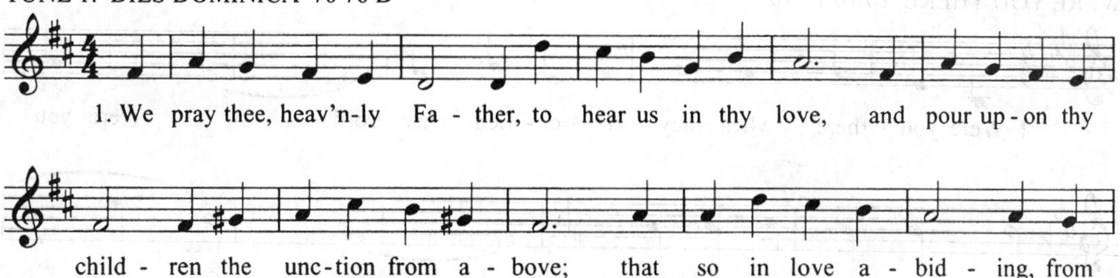

2. Be thou our guide and helper,
O Jesus Christ, we pray;
so may we well approach thee,
if thou wilt be the Way:
thou, very Truth, hast promised
to help us in our strife,
food of the weary pilgrim,
eternal source of life.

3. And thou, creator Spirit,
look on us, we are thine;
renew in us thy graces,
upon our darkness shine;
that, with thy benediction
upon our souls outpoured,
we may receive in gladness
the body of the Lord.

4. O Trinity of Persons,
O Unity most high,
on thee alone relying
thy servants would draw nigh:
unworthy in our weakness,
on thee our hope is stayed,
and blessed by thy forgiveness
we will not be afraid.

Vincent Stuckey Stratton Coles (1845-1929) | Later form of a melody by William Lloyd (1785-1852)

TUNE 2: MEIRIONYDD 76 76 D

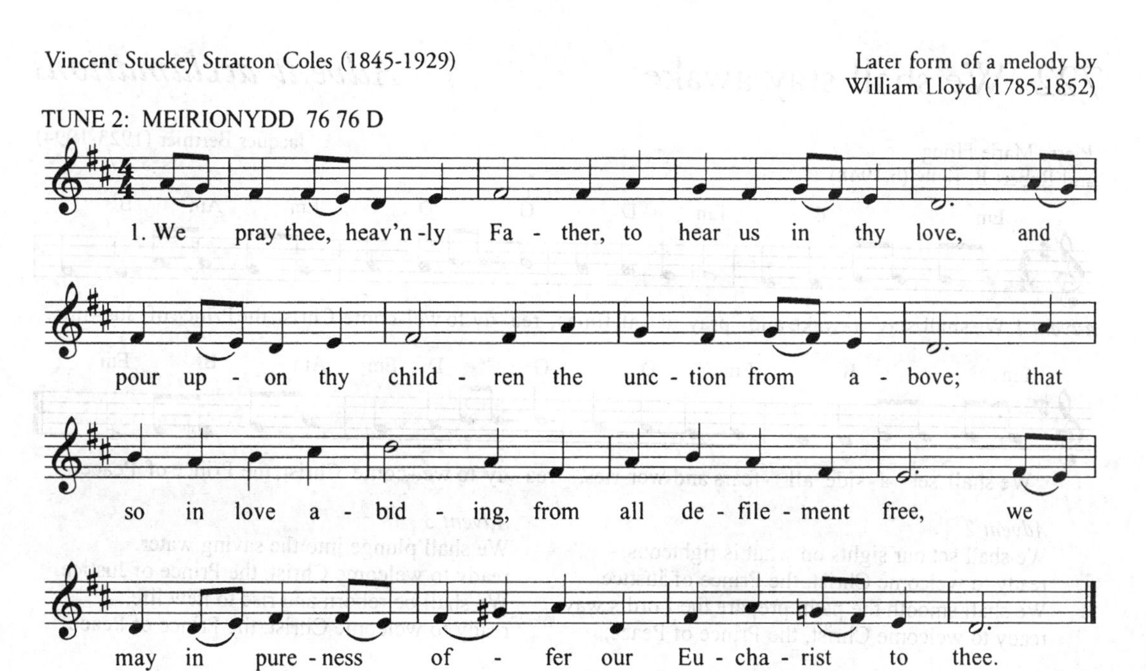

721 Were you there when they crucified my Lord?

Words and music: Spiritual.

WERE YOU THERE 10 10 14 10

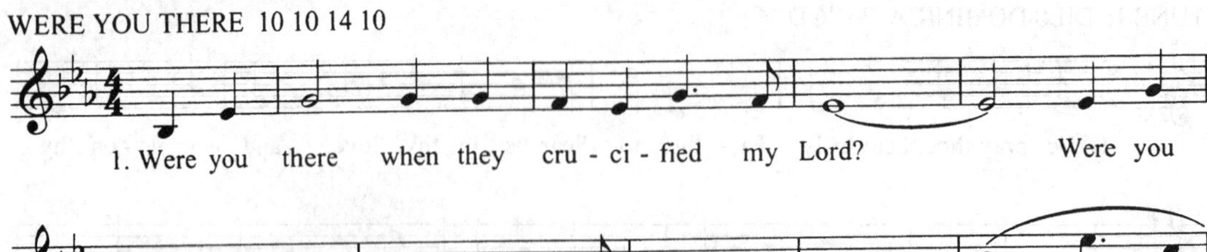

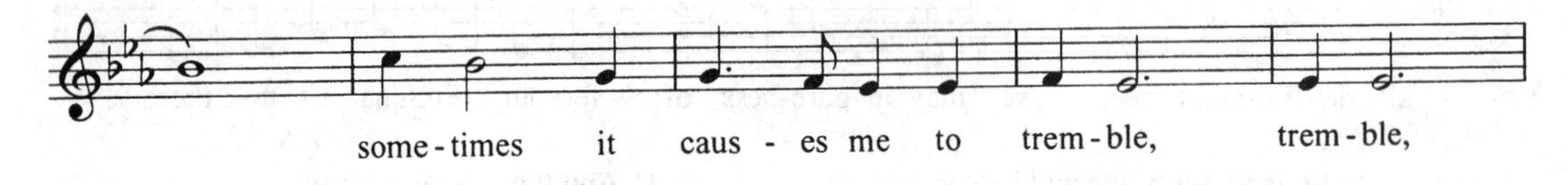

2. Were you there when they nailed him to a tree? . . .

3. Were you there when they pierced him in the side? . . .

4. Were you there when they laid him in the tomb? . . .

5. Were you there when he rose to glorious life? . . .

722 We shall stay awake

Advent acclamations

Pierre-Marie Hoog
and Robert B. Kelly (b.1948)

Jacques Berthier (1923-1994)

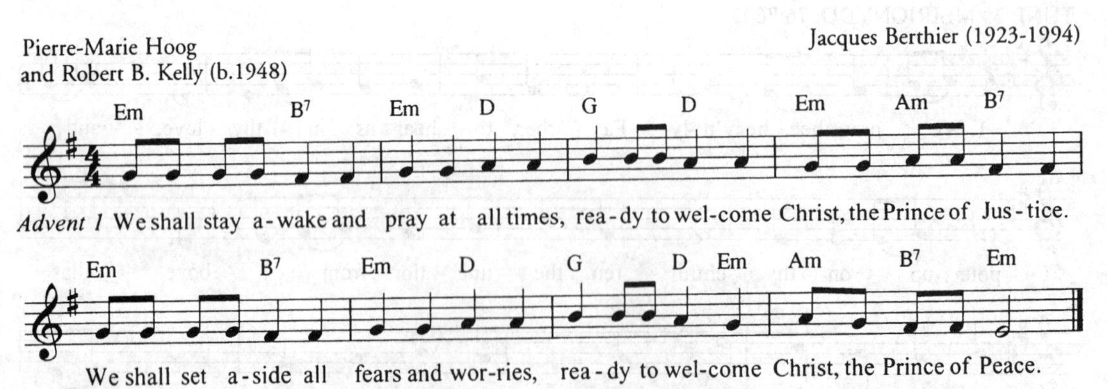

Advent 2
We shall set our sights on what is righteous,
ready to welcome Christ, the Prince of Justice.
We shall smooth the path, prepare the Lord's way,
ready to welcome Christ, the Prince of Peace.

Advent 3
We shall plunge into the saving water,
ready to welcome Christ, the Prince of Justice.
We shall be reborn and rise to new life,
ready to welcome Christ, the Prince of Peace.

Original text © Copyright Rev. Pierre-Marie Hoog S.J., Eglise St. Ignace, 75006 Paris, France.
Used by permission. English translation and music © Copyright 1999 Kevin Mayhew Ltd.

Advent 4
We shall hold with faith to what God promised,
ready to welcome Christ, the Prince of Justice.
We shall be attentive to his Spirit,
ready to welcome Christ, the Prince of Peace.

723 We sing the praise of him who died

Thomas Kelly (1769-1855) alt. | Sydney Hugo Nicholson (1875-1947)

TUNE 1: BOW BRICKHILL LM

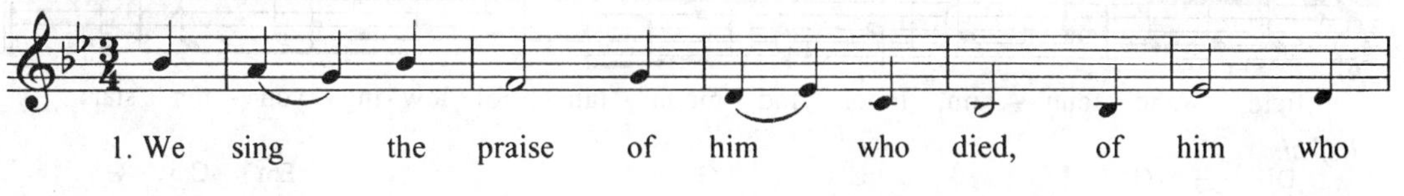

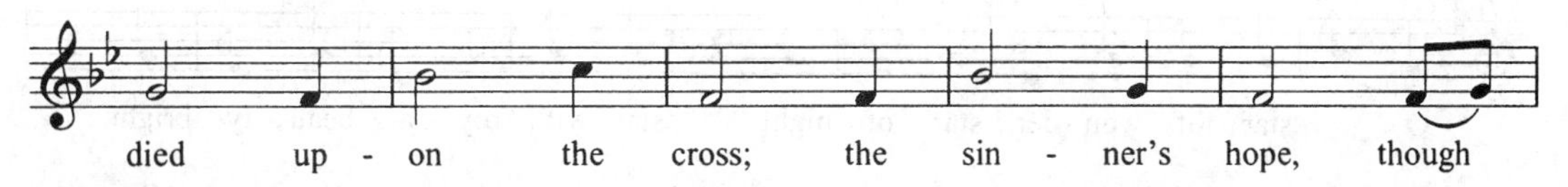

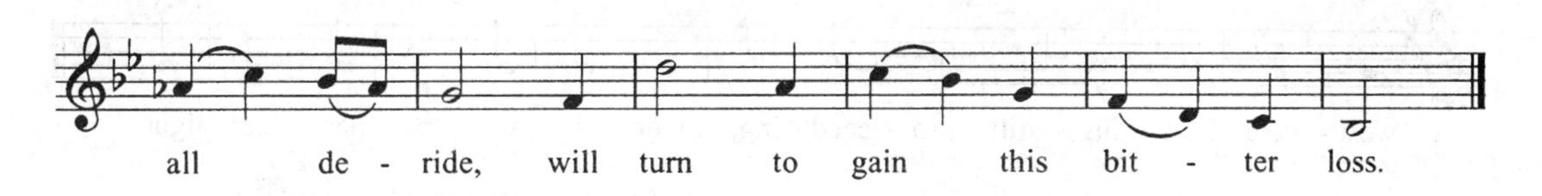

2. Inscribed upon the cross we see
in shining letters, 'God is love';
he bears our sins upon the tree;
he brings us mercy from above.

3. The cross! it takes our guilt away:
it holds the fainting spirit up;
it cheers with hope the gloomy day,
and sweetens ev'ry bitter cup.

4. It makes the coward spirit brave
to face the darkness of the night;
it takes the terror from the grave,
and gilds the bed of death with light.

5. The balm of life, the cure of woe,
the measure and the pledge of love,
the sinner's refuge here below,
the angels' theme in heav'n above.

Thomas Kelly (1769-1855) alt. | Seth Calvisius (1556-1615)

TUNE 2: ACH BLEIB BEI UNS (CALVISIUS) LM

Tune 1 © Copyright Hymns Ancient & Modern Ltd., St Mary's Works,
St Mary's Plain, Norwich NR3 3BH, UK. Used by permission.

724 We three kings of Orient are

Words and music: John Henry Hopkins (1820-1891) alt.

KINGS OF ORIENT 88 86 and Refrain

2. Born a King on Bethlehem plain,
gold I bring, to crown him again,
King for ever, ceasing never,
over us all to reign.

3. Frankincense to offer have I,
incense owns a Deity nigh,
prayer and praising, gladly raising,
worship him, God most high.

4. Myrrh is mine, its bitter perfume
breathes a life of gathering gloom;
sorrowing, sighing, bleeding, dying,
sealed in the stone-cold tomb.

5. Glorious now behold him arise,
King and God and sacrifice;
alleluia, alleluia,
earth to heav'n replies.

725 We turn to you

Fred Kaan (b.1929)

Cyril Vincent Taylor (1907-1991)

HARDING 11 10 11 10

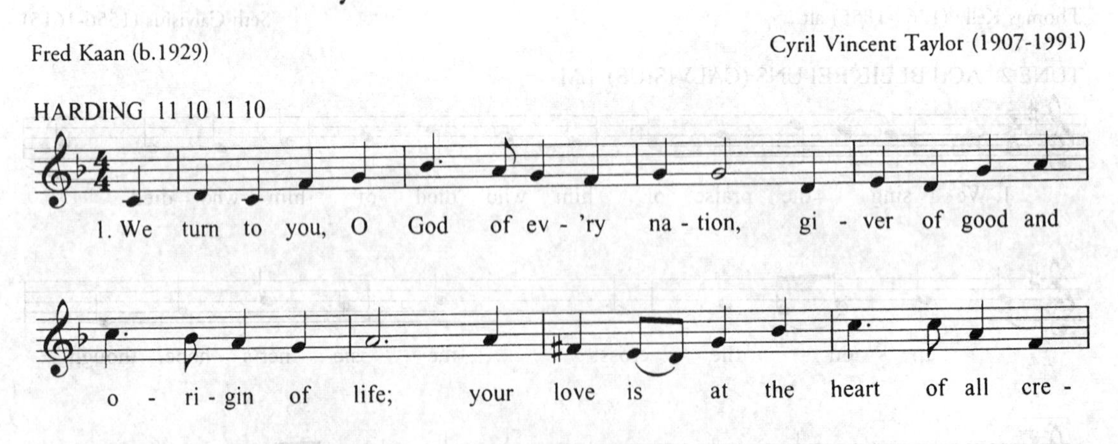

Text © Copyright 1967, 1991, 1997 Stainer & Bell Ltd., P.O. Box 110, Victoria House, 23 Gruneisen Road, Finchley, London N3 1DZ, UK. Used by permission.
Music © Copyright Oxford University Press, Great Clarendon Street, Oxford OX2 6DP, UK. Used by permission.

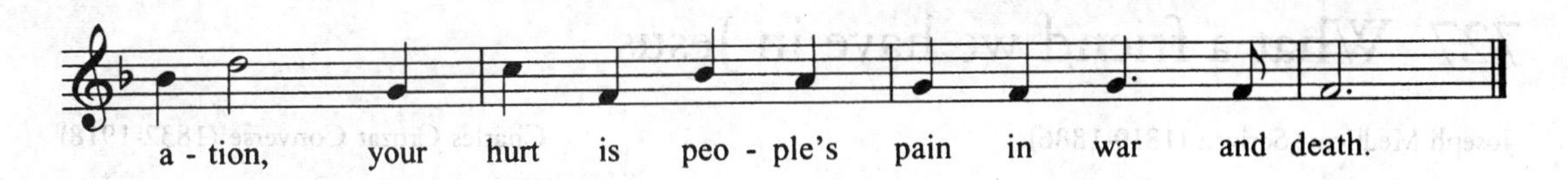

2. We turn to you, that we may be forgiven
for crucifying Christ on earth again.
We know that we have never wholly striven,
to share with all the promise of your reign.

3. Free ev'ry heart from pride and self-reliance,
our ways of thought inspire with simple grace;
break down among us barriers of defiance,
speak to the soul of all the human race.

4. On all who rise on earth for right relations,
we pray the light of love from hour to hour.
Grant wisdom to the leaders of the nations,
the gift of carefulness to those in pow'r.

5. Teach us, good Lord, to serve the need of others,
help us to give and not to count the cost.
Unite us all to live as sisters, brothers,
defeat our Babel with your Pentecost!

726 We will lay our burden down

Words and music: John L. Bell (b.1949)
and Graham Maule (b.1958)

LAYING DOWN 77 78

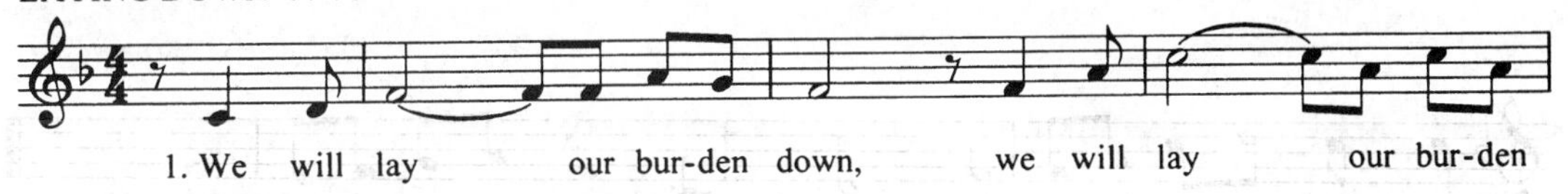

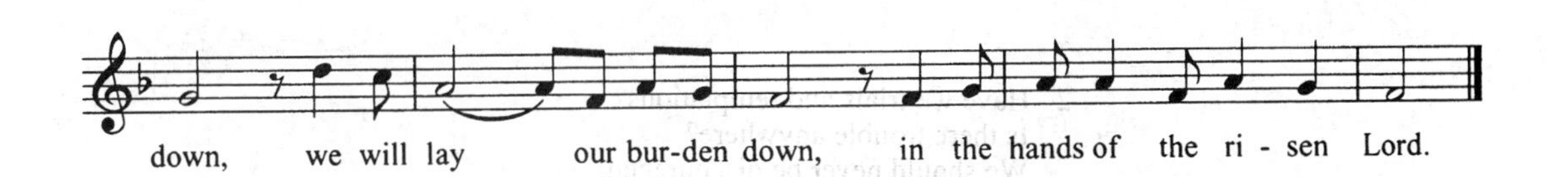

2. We will light the flame of love,
we will light the flame of love,
we will light the flame of love,
as the hands of the risen Lord.

3. We will show both hurt and hope,
we will show both hurt and hope,
we will show both hurt and hope,
like the hands of the risen Lord.

4. We will walk the path of peace,
we will walk the path of peace,
we will walk the path of peace,
hand in hand with the risen Lord.

Text © Copyright 1989 WGRG, Iona Community, Glasgow G2 3DH.
Used by permission from *Love from Below.* (Wild Goose Publications 1989)

727 What a friend we have in Jesus

Joseph Medlicott Scriven (1819-1886) | Charles Crozat Converse (1832-1918)

WHAT A FRIEND (CONVERSE) 87 87 D

2. Have we trials and temptations?
Is there trouble anywhere?
We should never be discouraged:
take it to the Lord in prayer!
Can we find a friend so faithful,
who will all our sorrows share?
Jesus knows our ev'ry weakness –
take it to the Lord in prayer!

3. Are we weak and heavy-laden,
cumbered with a load of care?
Jesus only is our refuge,
take it to the Lord in prayer!
Do thy friends despise, forsake thee?
Take it to the Lord in prayer!
In his arms he'll take and shield thee,
thou wilt find a solace there.

728 What a wonderful change

Rufus H. McDaniel (1850-1940) Charles H. Gabriel (1856-1932)

McDANIEL 12 8 12 8 and Refrain

2. I have ceased from my wand'ring and going astray
since Jesus came into my heart!
And my sins which were many are all washed away
since Jesus came into my heart!

3. I'm possessed of a hope that is steadfast and sure,
since Jesus came into my heart!
And no dark clouds of doubt now my pathway obscure,
since Jesus came into my heart!

4. There's a light in the valley of death now for me,
since Jesus came into my heart!
And the gates of the city beyond I can see,
since Jesus came into my heart!

5. I shall go there to dwell in that city, I know,
since Jesus came into my heart!
And I'm happy, so happy, as onward I go,
since Jesus came into my heart!

© Copyright 1942 the Rodeheaver Co./Word Music. Administered by CopyCare, P.O. Box 77, Hailsham, East Sussex BN27 3EF, UK. (music@copycare.com). Used by permission.

729 What child is this

William Chatterton Dix (1837-1898) alt. | Traditional English melody

GREENSLEEVES 87 87 68 67

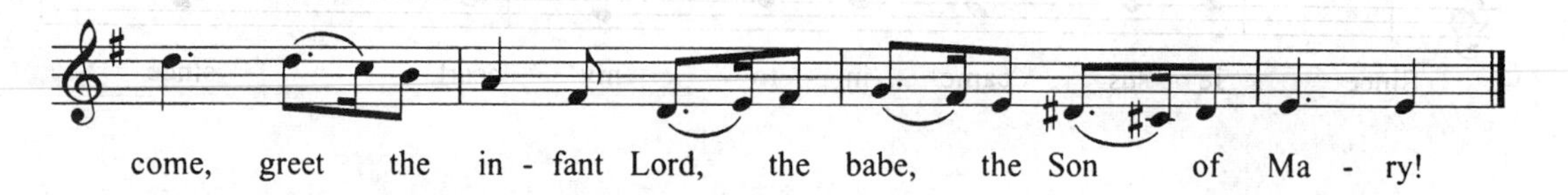

2. Why lies he in such mean estate,
where ox and ass are feeding?
Good Christians, fear: for sinners here
the silent Word is pleading.
Nails, spear, shall pierce him through,
the cross be borne for me, for you;
hail, hail the Word made flesh,
the babe, the Son of Mary!

3. So bring him incense, gold and myrrh,
come rich and poor, to own him.
The King of kings salvation brings,
let loving hearts enthrone him.
Raise, raise the song on high,
the Virgin sings her lullaby:
joy, joy for Christ is born,
the babe, the Son of Mary!

730 What shall we bring

Chrisopher Ellis (b.1949)
based on Micah 6:6-8 | Richard Lloyd (b.1933)

WORTLEY 10 10 10 10 and Refrain

© Copyright 1999 Kevin Mayhew Ltd.

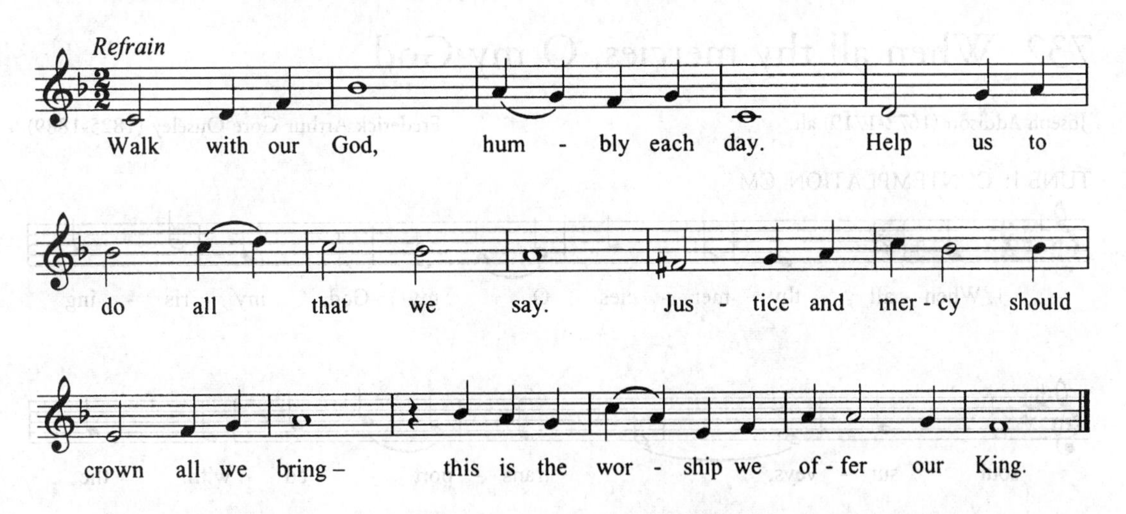

2. Save us, O Lord, from the hypocrite's prayer:
bringing you praise while our deeds are unfair.
Help us to honour all people on earth:
each one is precious, of infinite worth.

3. Save us, O Lord, from excuse and neglect,
show us the world as you see it today.
Kindle within us a passion for good;
give us the strength to do all that we should.

731 When a knight won his spurs

Jan Struther (1901-1953)

Traditional English melody

STOWEY 12 12 12 12

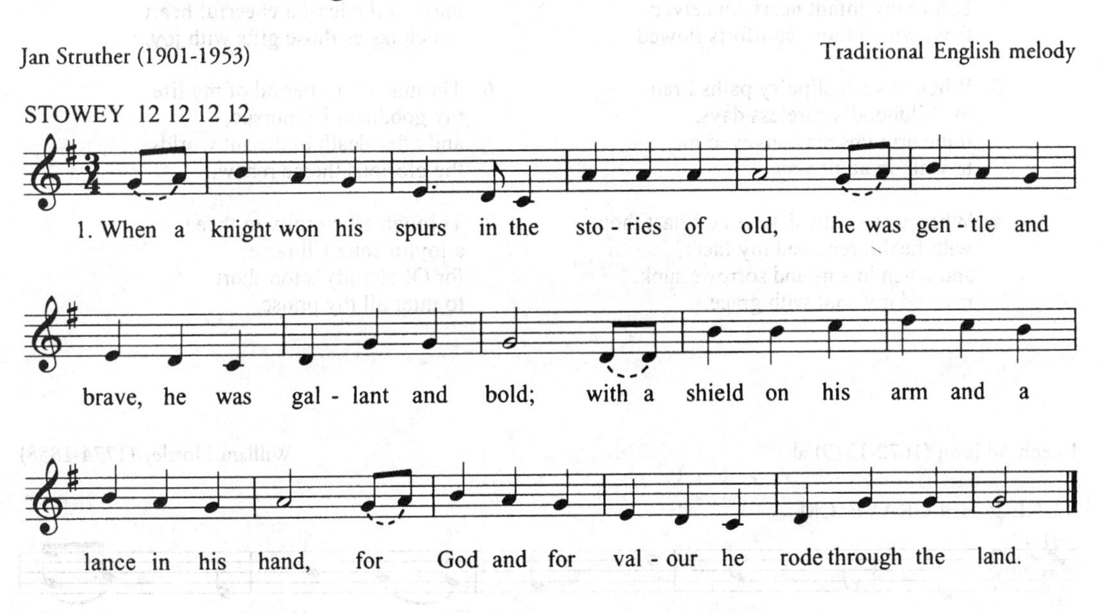

2. No charger have I, and no sword by my side,
yet still to adventure and battle I ride,
though back into storyland giants have fled,
and the knights are no more and the dragons are dead.

3. Let faith be my shield and let joy be my steed
'gainst the dragons of anger, the ogres of greed;
and let me set free, with the sword of my youth,
from the castle of darkness, the pow'r of the truth.

Text © Copyright Oxford University Press, Great Clarendon Street, Oxford OX2 6DP, UK.
Used by permission from *Enlarged Songs of Praise.*

732 When all thy mercies, O my God

Joseph Addison (1672-1719) alt. | Frederick Arthur Gore Ouseley (1825-1889)

TUNE 1: CONTEMPLATION CM

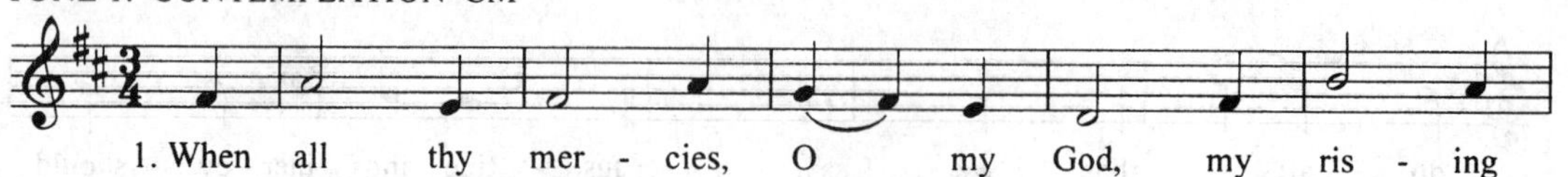

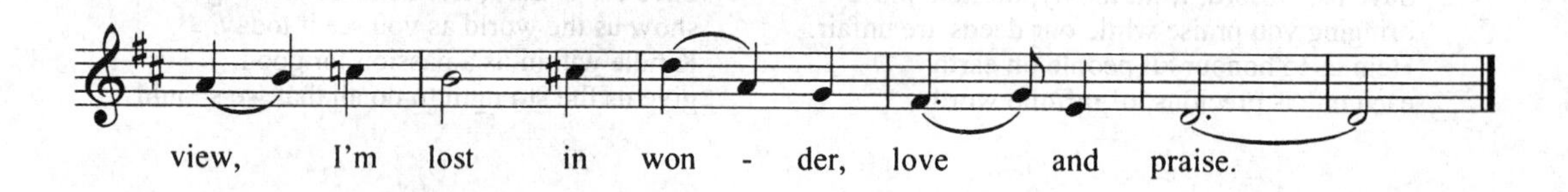

2. Unnumbered comforts to my soul
thy tender care bestowed,
before my infant heart conceived
from whom those comforts flowed.

3. When in such slipp'ry paths I ran
in childhood's careless days,
thine arm unseen conveyed me safe,
to walk in adult ways.

4. When worn with sickness oft hast thou
with health renewed my face;
and when in sins and sorrows sunk,
revived my soul with grace.

5. Ten thousand thousand precious gifts
my daily thanks employ,
and not the least a cheerful heart
which tastes those gifts with joy.

6. Through ev'ry period of my life
thy goodness I'll pursue,
and after death in distant worlds
the glorious theme renew.

7. Through all eternity to thee
a joyful song I'll raise;
for O! eternity's too short
to utter all thy praise.

Joseph Addison (1672-1719) alt. | William Horsley (1774-1858)

TUNE 2: BELGRAVE CM

733 When God Almighty came to earth *God on earth*

John L. Bell (b.1949)
and Graham Maule (b.1958)

Somerset Folk song collected by
Cecil Sharp (1859-1924)

O WALY WALY LM

2. When God Almighty went to work,
carpenter's sweat he didn't shirk,
profit and loss he didn't flee,
and whispered: 'Humbly follow me.'

3. When God Almighty walked the street,
the critic's curse he had to meet,
the cynic's smile he had to see,
and whispered: 'Humbly follow me.'

4. When God Almighty met his folk,
of peace and truth he boldly spoke
to set the slave and tyrant free,
and whispered: 'Humbly follow me.'

5. When God Almighty took his place
to save the sometimes human race,
he took it boldly on a tree,
and whispered: 'Humbly follow me.'

6. When God Almighty comes again,
he'll meet us incognito as then;
and though no words may voice his plea,
he'll whisper: 'Are you following me?'

Text © Copyright 1987 WGRG, Iona Community, Glasgow G2 3DH.
Used by permission from *Heaven shall not wait.* (Wild Goose Publications, 1987)

734 When I feel the touch

Words and music: Keri Jones and David Matthew

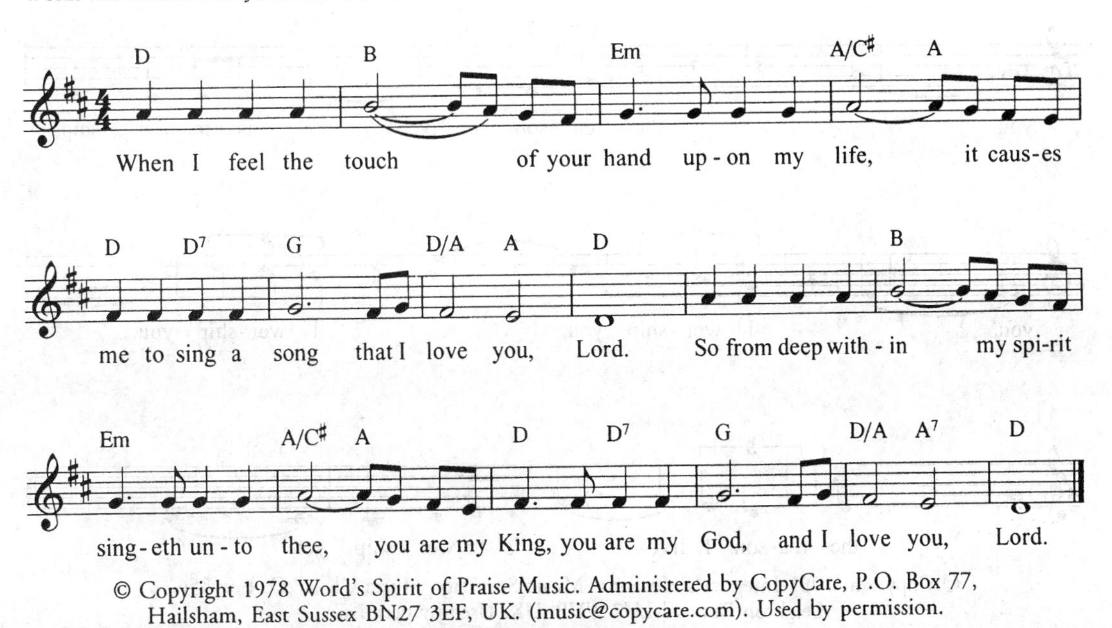

© Copyright 1978 Word's Spirit of Praise Music. Administered by CopyCare, P.O. Box 77,
Hailsham, East Sussex BN27 3EF, UK. (music@copycare.com). Used by permission.

735 When I look into your holiness

Words and music: Wayne Perrin and Cathy Perrin

© Copyright 1981 Integrity's Hosanna! Music/Sovereign Music UK., P.O. Box 356, Leighton Buzzard LU7 3WP, UK. Used by permission.

736 When I needed a neighbour

Words and music: Sydney Carter (b.1915)

NEIGHBOUR 13 10 and Refrain

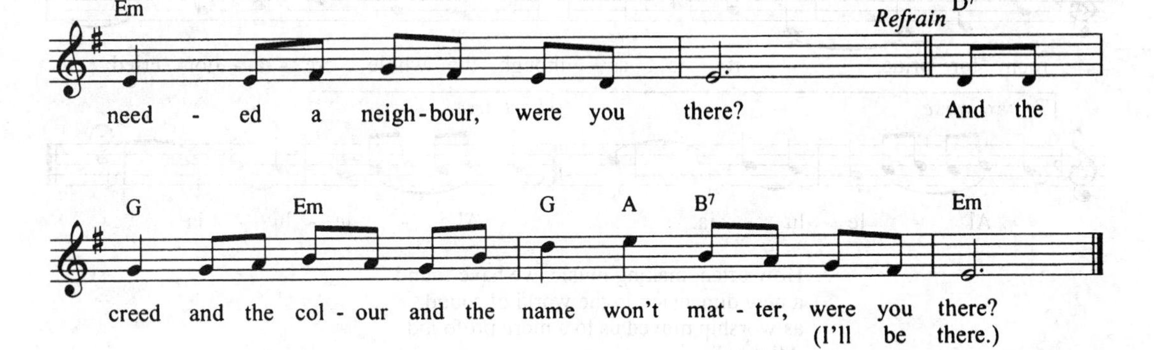

2. I was hungry and thirsty,
were you there, were you there?
I was hungry and thirsty,
were you there?

3. I was cold, I was naked,
were you there, were you there?
I was cold, I was naked,
were you there?

4. When I needed a shelter,
were you there, were you there?
When I needed a shelter,
were you there?

5. When I needed a healer,
were you there, were you there?
When I needed a healer,
were you there?

6. Wherever you travel,
I'll be there, I'll be there,
wherever you travel,
I'll be there.

© Copyright 1965 Stainer & Bell Ltd., P.O. Box 110, Victoria House, 23 Gruneisen Road, Finchley, London N3 1DZ, UK. Used by permission.

737 When, in our music, God is glorified

Fred Pratt Green (1903-2000) | Charles Villiers Stanford (1853-1924)

room for pride, it is as though the whole cre - a - tion cried:

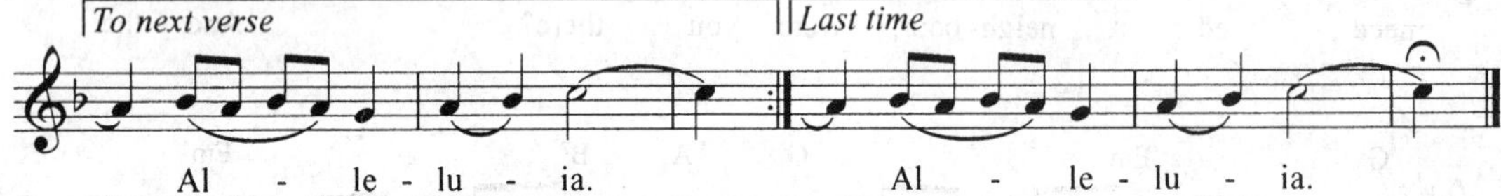

2. How often, making music, we have found
a new dimension in the world of sound,
as worship moved us to a more profound
Alleluia!

3. So has the Church, in liturgy and song,
in faith and love, through centuries of wrong,
borne witness to the truth in ev'ry tongue:
Alleluia!

4. And did not Jesus sing a psalm that night
when utmost evil strove against the Light?
Then let us sing, for whom he won the fight:
Alleluia!

5. Let ev'ry instrument be tuned for praise!
Let all rejoice who have a voice to raise!
And may God give us faith to sing always:
Alleluia!

© Copyright 1971 Stainer & Bell Ltd., P.O. Box 110, Victoria House, 23 Gruneisen Road, Finchley, London N3 1DZ, UK. Used by permission.

738 When I survey the wondrous cross

Isaac Watts (1674-1748) | Adapted by Edward Miller (1735-1807)

TUNE 1: ROCKINGHAM LM

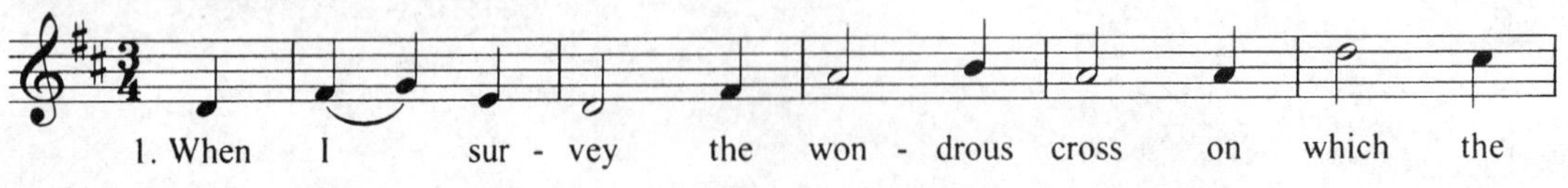

2. Forbid it, Lord, that I should boast,
save in the death of Christ, my God:
all the vain things that charm me most,
I sacrifice them to his blood.

3. See from his head, his hands, his feet,
sorrow and love flow mingling down:
did e'er such love and sorrow meet,
or thorns compose so rich a crown?

4. Were the whole realm of nature mine,
that were an off'ring far too small;
love so amazing, so divine,
demands my soul, my life, my all.

Isaac Watts (1674-1748)

Somerset Folk song collected by
Cecil Sharp (1859-1924)

TUNE 2: O WALY WALY LM

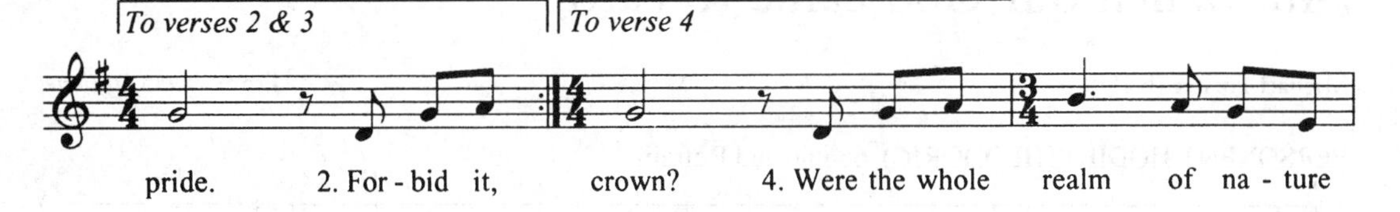

739 When morning gilds the skies

German (19th century)
trans. Edward Caswall (1814-1878)

Joseph Barnby (1838-1896)

LAUDES DOMINI 6 6 6 D

Je - sus I re - pair; may Je - sus Christ be praised.

2. The night becomes as day,
when from the heart we say:
may Jesus Christ be praised.
The pow'rs of darkness fear,
when this sweet chant they hear:
may Jesus Christ be praised.

3. In heav'n's eternal bliss
the loveliest strain is this:
may Jesus Christ be praised.
Let air, and sea, and sky
from depth to height reply:
may Jesus Christ be praised.

4. Be this, while life is mine,
my canticle divine:
may Jesus Christ be praised.
Be this th'eternal song
through all the ages on:
may Jesus Christ be praised.

740 When our God came to earth

Michael Forster (b.1946)

From *Piae Cantiones*

PERSONENT HODIE (THEODORIC) 666 66 and Refrain

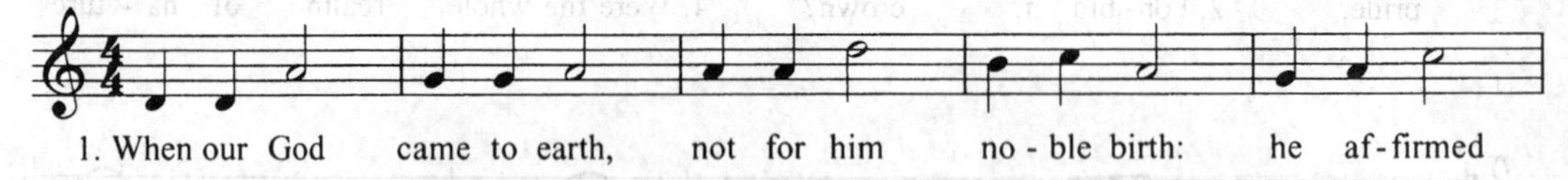

hu - man worth from a hum - ble man - ger, just a - no - ther stran - ger.

Refrain

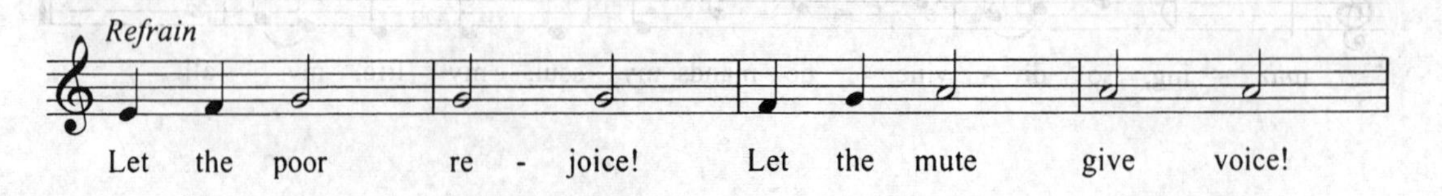

Text © Copyright 1996 Kevin Mayhew Ltd.

2. Not for kings was the word
which the poor shepherds heard:
hope renewed, grace conferred,
and the hillside ringing
with the angels' singing.

3. Bethlehem, humble town
where the babe wears the crown,
turns the world upside down:
God so unexpected,
homeless and rejected.

4. Let us sing Mary's song,
bringing hope, righting wrong,
heard with fear by the strong,
poor and humble raising,
God of justice praising.

741 When we walk with the Lord

John Henry Sammis (1846-1919)

Daniel Brink Towner (1833-1896)

TRUST AND OBEY 66 9 and Refrain

2. Not a burden we bear,
not a sorrow we share,
but our toil he doth richly repay;
not a grief nor a loss,
not a frown nor a cross,
but is blest if we trust and obey.

3. But we never can prove
the delights of his love
until all on the altar we lay;
for the favour he shows,
and the joy he bestows,
are for them who will trust and obey.

4. Then in fellowship sweet
we will sit at his feet,
or we'll walk by his side in the way.
What he says we will do,
where he sends we will go,
never fear, only trust and obey.

742 Where true love is found with charity

Michael Forster (b.1946)
based on *Ubi Caritas*

Gregory Murray (1905-1992)

UBI CARITAS 12 12 12 12 and Refrain

1. Where true love is found with cha - ri - ty, God is pre - sent there.

Christ's own love has called us, ga - thered us to - ge - ther.

Let us come with songs of hope and ju - bi - la - tion,

wor - ship and a - dore him, God of our sal - va - tion,

2. Where true love is found with charity,
God is present there.
As his holy people, gathering together,
let us be united, strife and discord ending.
Christ, our God, among us, ev'ry fear transcending,
known in one another, known in one another.

3. Where true love is found with charity,
God is present there.
With the saints and martyrs, one in faith together,
let us see your glory, Christ our great salvation,
sharing in the great eternal celebration,
there with one another, there with one another.

Text © Copyright 1998 Kevin Mayhew Ltd.
Music © Copyright The Estate of Gregory Murray. Used by permission of The Trustees of Downside Abbey, Stratton-on-the-Fosse, Bath BA3 4RH, UK.

743 Where true love is present

Hubert J. Richards (b.1921)
based on Matthew 5:23; 1 John 4:16 and *Ubi Caritas*

Christopher Tambling (b.1964)

MAKE PEACE 65 65 and Refrain

2. God is loving kindness;
   those who love like him
   live in God most truly,
   and he lives in them.

3. Let us put behind us
   bitterness and strife,
   recognising Jesus
   present in our midst.

© Copyright 1997 Kevin Mayhew Ltd.

744 Wherever you go

Refrain: Frances M. Kelly, based on Ruth 1:16;
vs. 1-4: Robert B. Kelly (b.1948), based on Ephesians 5:21-31;
vs. 5-8: Frances M. Kelly

Frances M. Kelly

2. Christ loves his Church and gave himself to save her;
   he made her holy, sinless, without fault.

3. Christ loves his Church, this is a sacred myst'ry;
   our human love is graced and speaks of God.

4. So may our love, like Christ's, be selfless giving;
   and in this giving, Christ is present here.

Other verses for weddings

5. We come today, in Christ a new creation,
   and in this giving we become as one.

6. Together now, our love can grow and strengthen;
   love is not selfish, we can share our joy.

7. And may our home become a place of welcome,
   an open door for all who pass our way.

8. We ask your blessing, Father, Son and Spirit,
   on all our friends and fam'ly gathered here.

© Copyright 1999 Kevin Mayhew Ltd.

745 While shepherds watched

Nahum Tate (1652-1715)

From Este's *Psalter* (1592)

WINCHESTER OLD CM

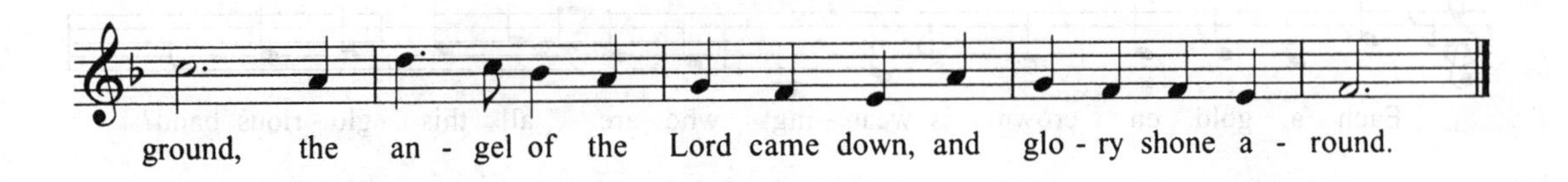

2. 'Fear not,' said he, (for mighty dread
had seized their troubled mind)
'glad tidings of great joy I bring
to you and all mankind.

3. To you in David's town this day
is born of David's line
a Saviour, who is Christ the Lord;
and this shall be the sign:

4. The heav'nly babe you there shall find
to human view displayed,
all meanly wrapped in swathing bands,
and in a manger laid.'

5. Thus spake the seraph, and forthwith
appeared a shining throng
of angels praising God, who thus
addressed their joyful song:

6. 'All glory be to God on high,
and on the earth be peace,
goodwill henceforth from heav'n to all
begin and never cease.'

746 Who are these like stars appearing

Heinrich Theobald Schenck (1656-1727)
trans. Frances Elizabeth Cox (1812-1897)
based on Revelation 7:13

From *Geistreiches Gesangbuch,* Darmstadt (1698)
adapted by William Henry Monk (1823-1889)

ALL SAINTS 87 87 77

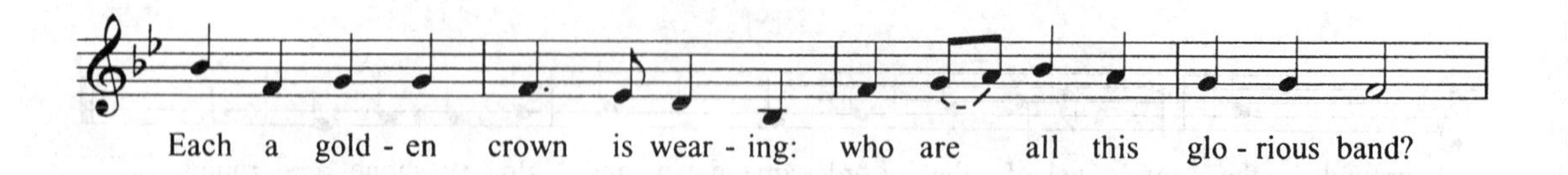

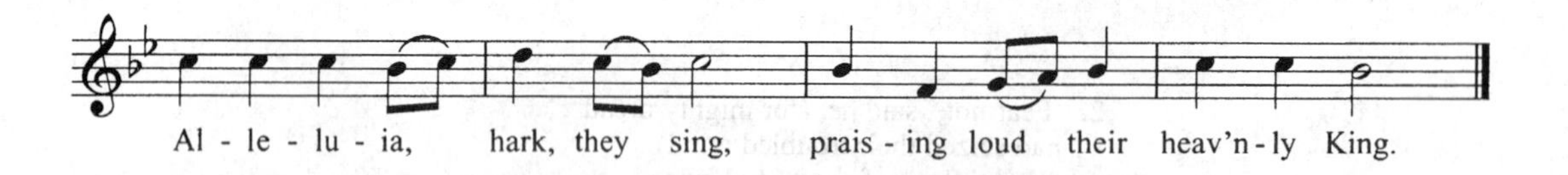

2. Who are these in dazzling brightness,
clothed in God's own righteousness,
these, whose robes of purest whiteness
shall their lustre still possess,
still untouched by time's rude hand –
whence came all this glorious band?

3. These are they who have contended
for their Saviour's honour long,
wrestling on till life was ended,
following not the sinful throng;
these, who well the fight sustained,
triumph by the Lamb have gained.

4. These are they whose hearts were riven,
sore with woe and anguish tried,
who in prayer full oft have striven
with the God they glorified;
now, their painful conflict o'er,
God has bid them weep no more.

5. These, th' Almighty contemplating,
did as priests before him stand,
soul and body always waiting
day and night at his command:
now in God's most holy place
blest they stand before his face.

747 Who can sound the depths of sorrow

Words and music: Graham Kendrick (b.1950)

2. We have scorned the truth you gave us,
we have bowed to other lords.
We have sacrificed the children
on the altar of our gods.
O let truth again shine on us,
let your holy fear descend:
upon our nation, upon our nation
have mercy, Lord.

(Men)
3. Who can stand before your anger?
Who can face your piercing eyes?
For you love the weak and helpless,
and you hear the victims' cries.
(All)
Yes, you are a God of justice,
and your judgement surely comes:
upon our nation, upon our nation
have mercy, Lord.

(Women)
4. Who will stand against the violence?
Who will comfort those who mourn?
In an age of cruel rejection,
who will build for love a home?
(All)
Come and shake us into action,
come and melt our hearts of stone:
upon your people, upon your people
have mercy, Lord.

5. Who can sound the depths of mercy
in the Father heart of God?
For there is a Man of sorrows
who for sinners shed his blood.
He can heal the wounds of nations,
he can wash the guilty clean:
because of Jesus, because of Jesus
have mercy, Lord.

© Copyright 1988 Make Way Music, P.O. Box 263, Croydon, Surrey CR9 5AP, UK.
International copyright secured. All rights reserved. Used by permission.

748 Who is this so weak and helpless

William Walsham How (1823-1897)

From an anthem by Thomas Williams (1869-1944)

EBENEZER (TON-Y-BOTEL) 87 87 D

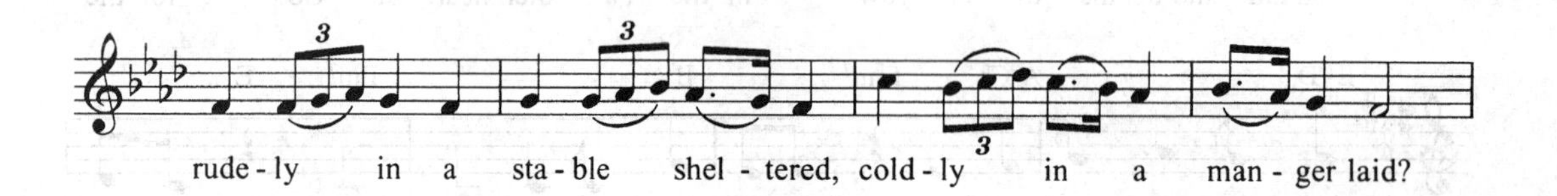

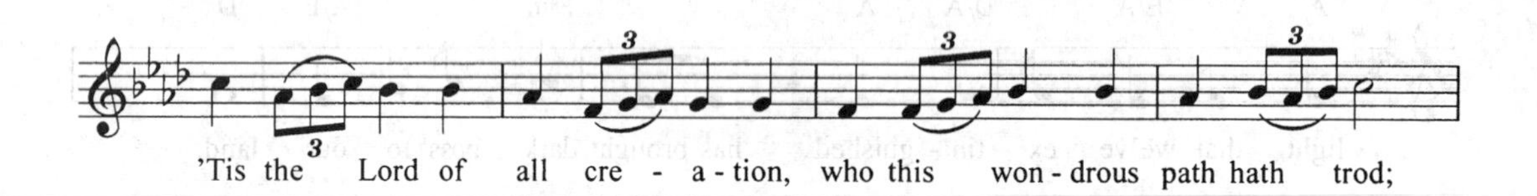

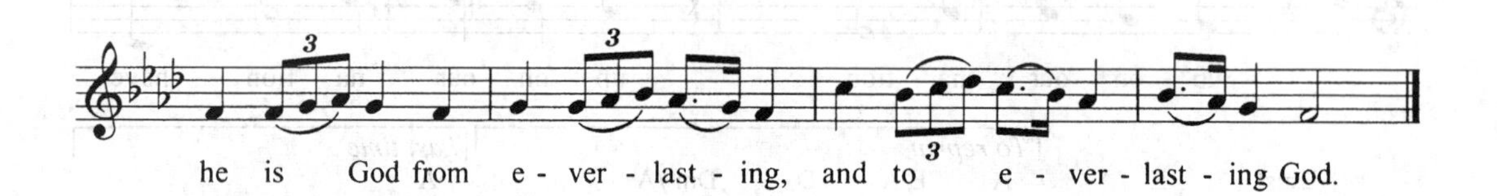

2. Who is this – a Man of Sorrows,
walking sadly life's hard way;
homeless, weary, sighing, weeping
over sin and Satan's sway?
'Tis our God, our glorious Saviour,
who beyond our mortal sight
now for us a place prepareth
free from grief and full of light.

3. Who is this – behold him raining
drops of blood upon the ground?
Who is this – despised, rejected,
mocked, insulted, beaten, bound?
'Tis our God, who gifts and graces
on his Church now poureth down;
all his faithful ones empow'ring
to partake in cross and crown.

4. Who is this that hangeth dying,
with the thieves on either side?
Nails his hands and feet are tearing,
and the spear hath pierced his side.
'Tis the God who ever liveth
'mid the shining ones on high,
in the glorious golden city
reigning everlastingly.

Music © Copyright Clifford Williams.
Used by permission.

749 Who sees it all

Words and music: Graham Kendrick (b.1950)

2. Who sees it all, the debt that's owed
of lives unlived, of love unknown?
Who weighs the loss of innocence,
or feels the pain of our offence?

3. Who knows the fears that drive a choice,
unburies pain and gives it voice?
And who can wash a memory,
or take the sting of death away?

4. Whose anger burns at what we've done,
then bears our sin as if his own?
Who will receive us as we are,
whose arms are wide and waiting now?

5. Whose broken heart upon a cross
won freedom, joy and peace for us?
Whose blood redeems, who ever lives
and all because of love forgives?

© Copyright 1997 Make Way Music, P.O. Box 263, Croydon, Surrey CR9 5AP, UK.
International copyright secured. All rights reserved. Used by permission.

750 Who would think

God's surprise

John L. Bell (b.1949)
and Graham Maule (b.1958)

Evelyn Danzig

SCARLET RIBBONS 15 15 15 15

2. Shepherds watch and wise men wonder,
monarchs scorn and angels sing;
such a place as none would reckon
hosts a holy helpless thing;
stable beasts and by-passed strangers
watch a baby laid in hay:
God surprises earth with heaven,
coming here on Christmas day.

3. Centuries of skill and science
span the past from which we move,
yet experience questions whether,
with such progress, we improve.
While the human lot we ponder,
lest our hopes and humour fray,
God surprises earth with heaven,
coming here on Christmas day.

Text © Copyright 1987 WGRG, Iona Community, Glasgow G2 3DH, Scotland.
Used by permission from *Love from below.* (Wild Goose Publications, 1987).
Music © Copyright 1949 EMI Mills Music Inc., USA.
Worldwide print rights controlled by Warner Bros. Publications Inc./IMP Ltd., Griffin House,
161 Hammersmith Road, London W6 7BS, UK. Used by permission.

751 Wide, wide as the oecan

Words and music: C. Austin Miles

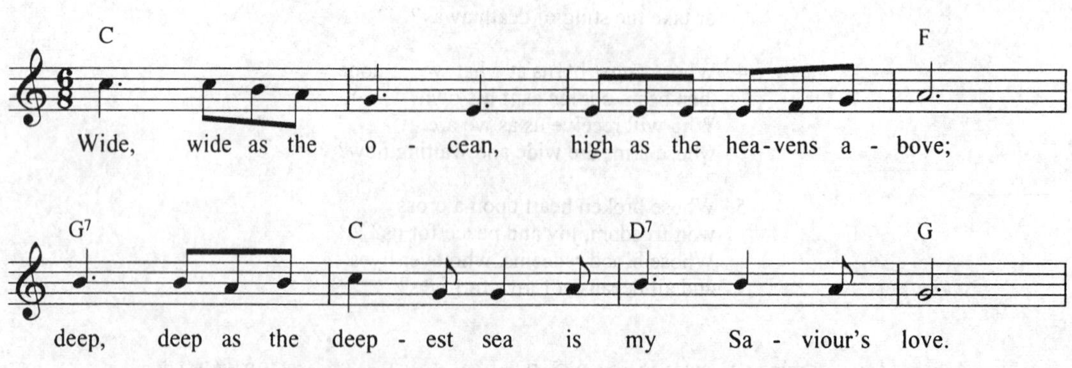

© Copyright The Rodeheaver Co./Word Music Inc. Administered by CopyCare, P.O. Box 77,
Hailsham, East Sussex BN27 3EF, UK. (music@copycare.com). Used by permission.

752 Will you come and follow me *The Summons*

John L. Bell (b.1949)
and Graham Maule (b.1958)

Traditional Scottish melody

KELVINGROVE 76 76 77 76

2. Will you leave yourself behind
if I but call your name?
Will you care for cruel and kind,
and never be the same?
Will you risk the hostile stare
should your life attract or scare,
will you let me answer prayer
in you, and you in me?

3. Will you let the blinded see
if I but call your name?
Will you set the pris'ners free,
and never be the same?
Will you kiss the leper clean
and do such as this unseen,
and admit to what I mean
in you, and you in me?

4. Will you love the 'you' you hide
if I but call your name?
Will you quell the fear inside,
and never be the same?
Will you use the faith you've found
to reshape the world around
through my sight and touch and sound
in you, and you in me?

5. Lord, your summons echoes true
when you but call my name.
Let me turn and follow you,
and never be the same.
In your company I'll go
where your love and footsteps show.
Thus I'll move and live and grow
in you, and you in me.

Text © Copyright 1987 WGRG, Iona Community, Glasgow G2 3DH, Scotland.
Used by permission from *Heaven shall not wait.* (Wild Goose Publications, 1987).

753 Will your anchor hold

Priscilla Jane Owens (1829-1899) | William James Kirkpatrick (1838-1921)

WILL YOUR ANCHOR HOLD Irregular and Refrain

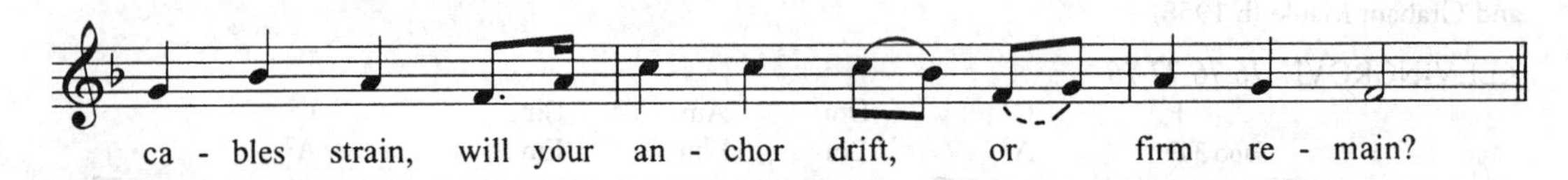

Refrain

2. Will your anchor hold in the straits of fear,
when the breakers roar and the reef is near?
While the surges rage, and the wild winds blow,
shall the angry waves then your bark o'erflow?

3. Will your anchor hold in the floods of death,
when the waters cold chill your latest breath?
On the rising tide you can never fail,
while your anchor holds within the veil.

4. Will your eyes behold through the morning light,
the city of gold and the harbour bright?
Will you anchor safe by the heav'nly shore,
when life's storms are past for evermore?

754 Ye choirs of new Jerusalem

Chorus novae Jerusalem
by St Fulbert of Chartres (c.1028)
trans. Robert Campbell (1814-1868)

Henry John Gauntlett (1805-1876)

ST FULBERT CM

1. Ye choirs of new Je - ru - sa - lem, your sweet - est notes em - ploy, the

2. For Judah's Lion burst his chains,
and crushed the serpent's head;
and brought with him, from death's domain,
the long-imprisoned dead.

3. From hell's devouring jaws the prey
alone our leader bore;
his ransomed hosts pursue their way
where he hath gone before.

4. Triumphant in his glory now
his sceptre ruleth all;
earth, heav'n and hell before him bow
and at his footstool fall.

5. While joyful thus his praise we sing,
his mercy we implore,
into his palace bright to bring,
and keep us evermore.

6. All glory to the Father be,
all glory to the Son,
all glory, Holy Ghost, to thee,
while endless ages run.

755 Ye holy angels bright

Richard Baxter (1615-1691)
and John Hampden Gurney (1802-1862)

John Darwall (1731-1789)

DARWALL'S 148TH 66 66 44 44

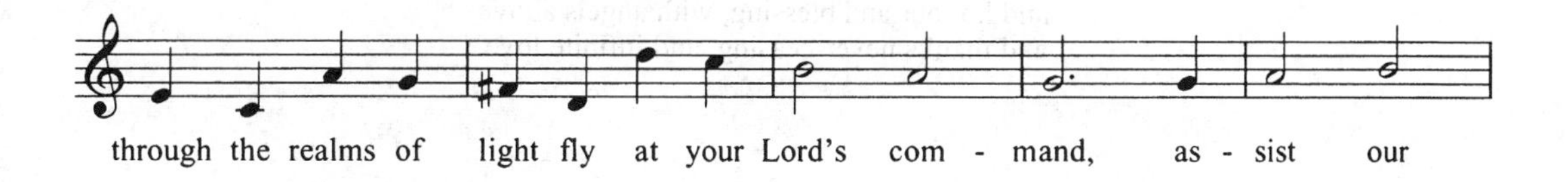

2. Ye blessèd souls at rest,
who ran this earthly race,
and now, from sin released,
behold the Saviour's face,
God's praises sound,
as in his sight
with sweet delight
ye do abound.

3. Ye saints, who toil below,
adore your heav'nly King,
and onward as ye go
some joyful anthem sing;
take what he gives
and praise him still,
through good or ill,
who ever lives.

4. My soul, bear thou thy part,
triumph in God above:
and with a well-tuned heart
sing thou the songs of love;
let all thy days
till life shall end,
whate'er he send,
be filled with praise.

756 Ye servants of God

Charles Wesley (1707-1788)

From the *Paderborn Gesangbuch* (1765)

PADERBORN 10 10 11 11

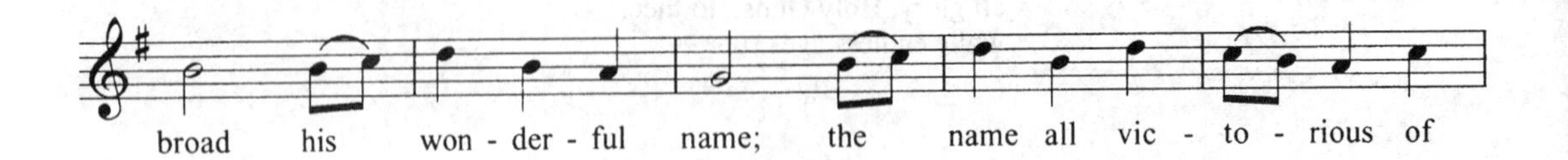

2. God ruleth on high, almighty to save;
and still he is nigh: his presence we have:
the great congregation his triumph shall sing,
ascribing salvation to Jesus our King.

3. Salvation to God who sits on the throne!
let all cry aloud, and honour the Son.
The praises of Jesus the angels proclaim,
fall down on their faces, and worship the Lamb.

4. Then let us adore, and give him his right:
all glory and pow'r, all wisdom and might,
and honour and blessing, with angels above,
and thanks never-ceasing, and infinite love.

757 Ye servants of the Lord

Philip Doddridge (1702-1751) alt.

Melody from Johannes Leisentritt's
Catholicum Hymnologium Germanicum (1584)
adapted by William Henry Havergal (1793-1870)

NARENZA CM

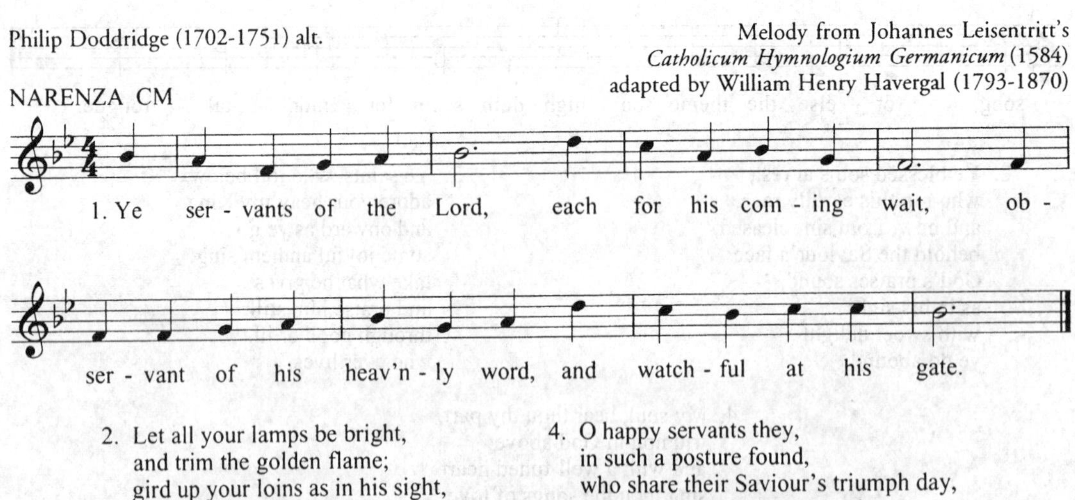

2. Let all your lamps be bright,
and trim the golden flame;
gird up your loins as in his sight,
for awesome is his name.

3. Watch! 'tis your Lord's command,
and while we speak, he's near;
mark the first signal of his hand,
and ready all appear.

4. O happy servants they,
in such a posture found,
who share their Saviour's triumph day,
with joy and honour crowned.

5. Christ shall the banquet spread
with his own royal hand,
and raise each faithful servant's head
amid th'angelic band.

758 Ye watchers and ye holy ones

Athelstan Riley (1858-1945) alt.

Melody from *Geistliche Kirchengesang*, Cologne (1623)

LASST UNS ERFREUEN 88 44 88 and Alleluias

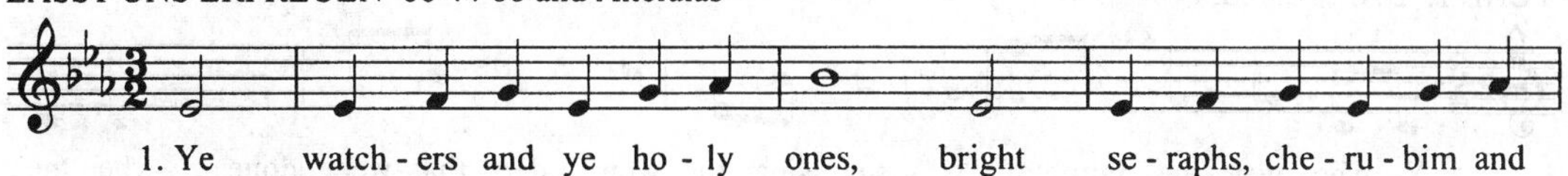

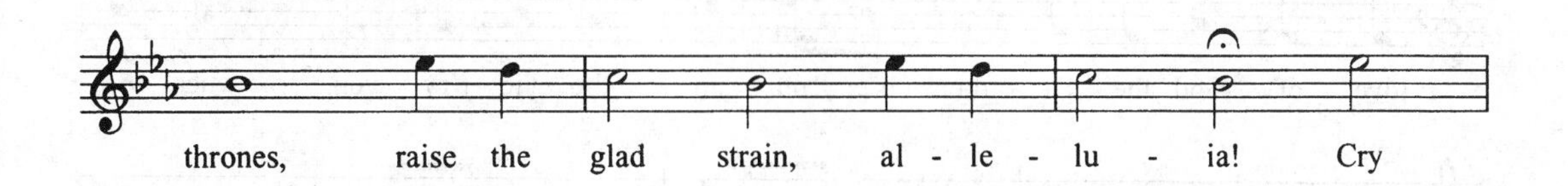

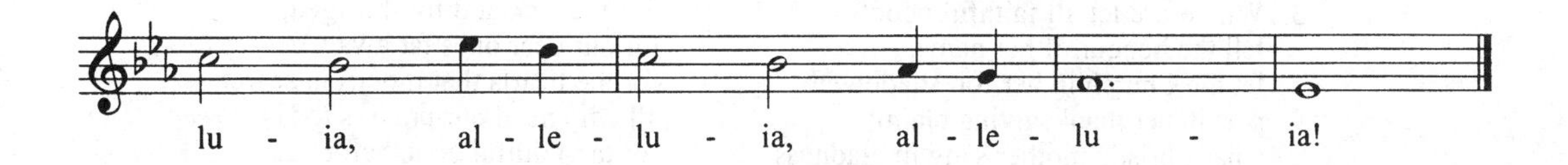

2. O higher than the cherubim,
   more glorious than the seraphim,
   lead their praises, alleluia.
   O Mary, bearer of the Word,
   most gracious, magnify the Lord:

3. Respond, ye souls in endless rest,
   ye patriarchs and prophets blest,
   alleluia, alleluia.
   Ye holy twelve, ye martyrs strong,
   all saints triumphant, raise the song:

4. O friends, in gladness let us sing,
   supernal anthems echoing,
   alleluia, alleluia.
   To God the Father, God the Son
   and God the Spirit, Three in One:

759 Ye who own the faith of Jesus

Vincent Stuckey Stratton Coles (1845-1929) — From the *Paderborn Gesangbuch* (1765)

TUNE 1: DAILY DAILY 87 87 D

1. Ye who own the faith of Je - sus sing the won - ders that were done, when the

love of God the Fa - ther o'er our sin the vic - t'ry won, when he

made the Vir - gin Ma - ry mo - ther of his on - ly Son. Hail

Ma - ry, hail Ma - ry, hail Ma - ry, full of grace.

2. Blessèd were the chosen people
out of whom the Lord did come,
blessèd was the land of promise
fashioned for his earthly home;
but more blessèd was the mother,
she who bore him in her womb.

3. Wherefore let all faithful people
tell the honour of her name,
let the Church in her foreshadowed
part in her thanksgiving claim;
what Christ's mother sang in gladness
let Christ's people sing the same.

4. Let us weave our supplications,
she with us and we with her,
for advancement of the faithful,
for each faithful worshipper,
for the doubting, for the sinful,
for each heedless wanderer.

5. May the mother's intercessions
on our homes a blessing win,
that the children all be prospered,
strong and fair and pure within,
following our Lord's own footsteps,
firm in faith and free from sin.

6. For the sick and for the agèd,
for our dear ones far away,
for the hearts that mourn in secret,
all who need our prayers today,
for the faithful gone before us,
may the Holy Virgin pray.

7. Praise, O Mary, praise the Father,
praise thy Saviour and thy Son,
praise the everlasting Spirit,
who hath made thee ark and throne;
o'er all creatures high exalted,
lowly praise the Three in One.

Vincent Stuckey Stratton Coles (1845-1929) — Johann Anastasius Freylinghausen (1670-1739)

TUNE 2: DEN DES VATERS SINN GEBOREN 87 87 D

1. Ye who own the faith of Je - sus sing the won - ders that were done,

when the love of God the Fa - ther o'er our sin the vic - t'ry won,

760 You are beautiful

I stand in awe

Words and music: Mark Altrogge

© Copyright 1987 People of Destiny International. Administered by CopyCare, P.O. Box 77, Hailsham, East Sussex BN27 3EF, UK. (music@copycare.com). Used by permission.

761 You are beneath me

Graham Jeffery — Kevin Mayhew (b.1942)

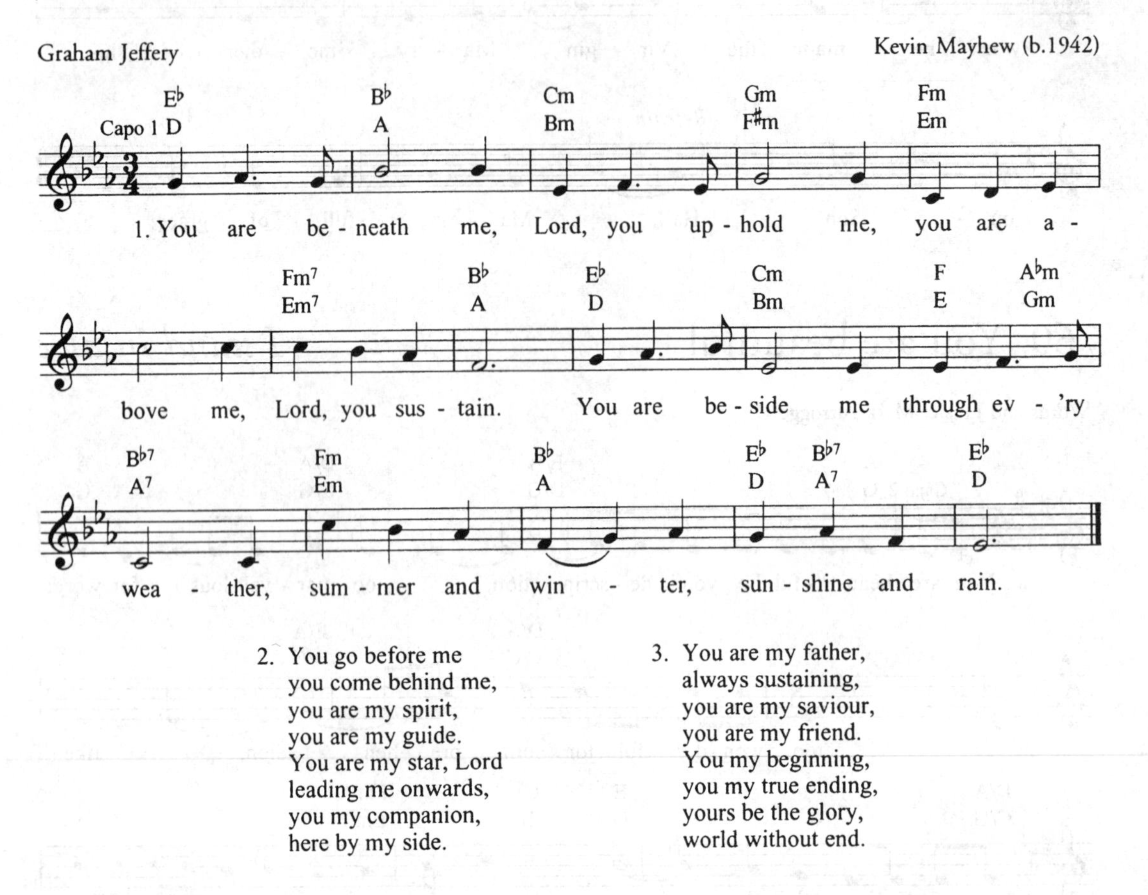

2. You go before me
you come behind me,
you are my spirit,
you are my guide.
You are my star, Lord
leading me onwards,
you my companion,
here by my side.

3. You are my father,
always sustaining,
you are my saviour,
you are my friend.
You my beginning,
you my true ending,
yours be the glory,
world without end.

© Copyright 1999 Kevin Mayhew Ltd.

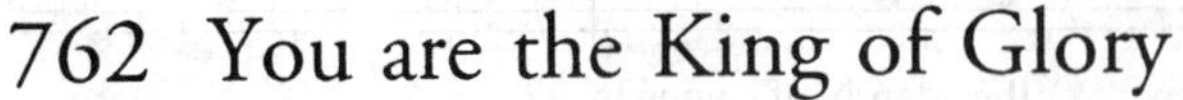

762 You are the King of Glory

Hosanna to the Son of David

Words and music: Mavis Ford

© Copyright 1978 Word's Spirit of Praise Music. Administered by CopyCare, P.O. Box 77, Hailsham, East Sussex BN27 3EF, UK. (music@copycare.com). Used by permission.

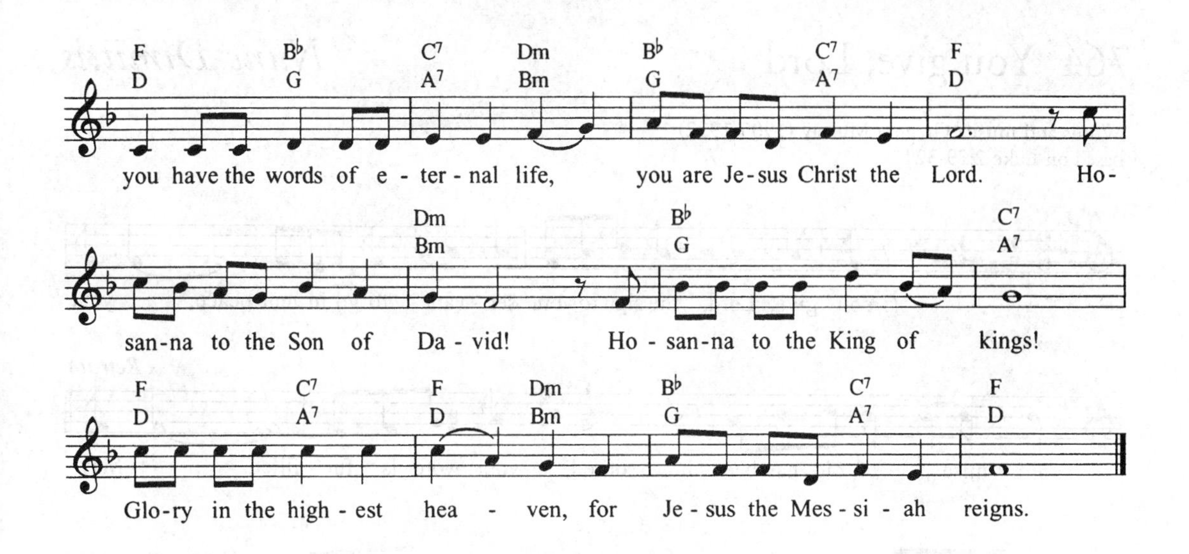

763 You are the light *Enfold me in your love*

Words and music: Margaret Rizza (b.1929)

2. You are the beauty that fills my soul,
you, by your wounds, make me whole.
You paid the price to redeem me from death;
yours is the love that sustains my ev'ry breath.

3. You still the storms and the fear of night,
you turn despair to delight.
You feel the anguish, and share in my tears,
you give the hope from the depth of my fears.

4. You are the word full of life and truth,
you guide my feet since my youth;
you are my refuge, my firm cornerstone,
you I will worship and honour alone.

5. You have restored me and pardoned sin,
you give me strength from within.
You called me forth, and my life you made new.
Love is the binding that holds me to you.

6. You are the Way, you are Truth and Life,
you keep me safe in the strife.
You give me love I cannot comprehend,
you guide the way to a life without end.

© Copyright 1998 Kevin Mayhew Ltd.

764 You give, Lord

Nunc Dimittis

Words and music: Gregory Murray (1905-1992)
based on Luke 2:29-32

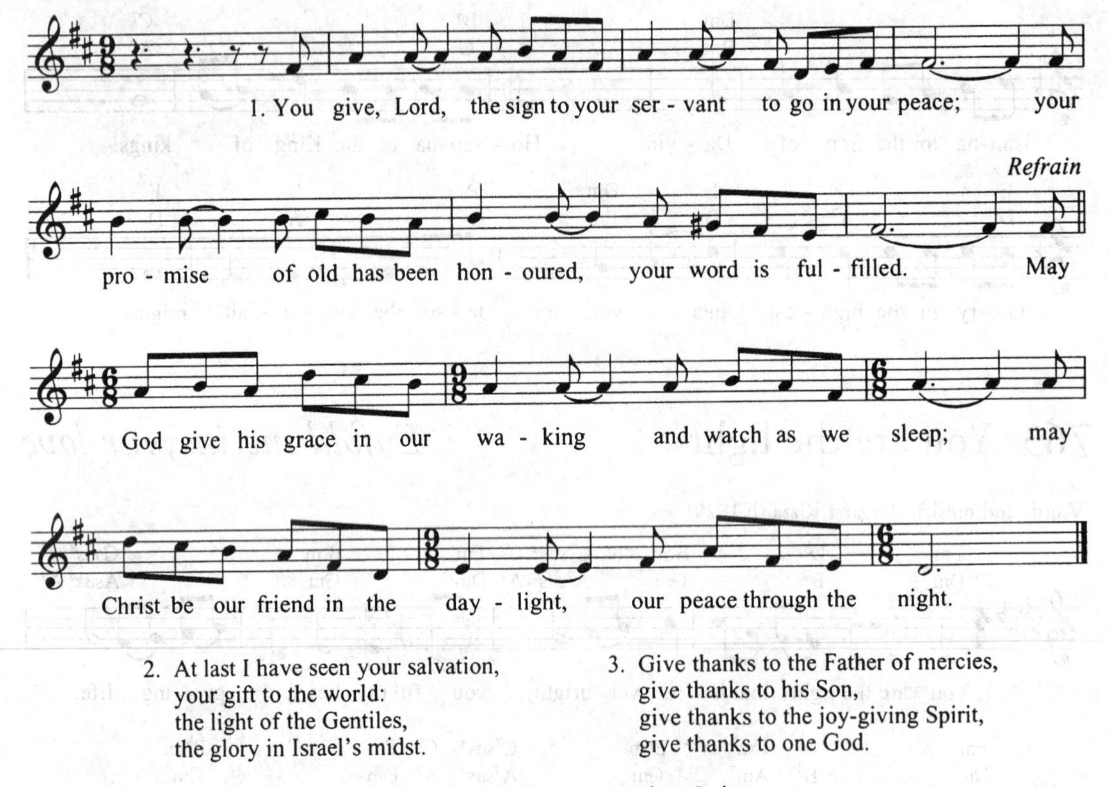

2. At last I have seen your salvation,
your gift to the world:
the light of the Gentiles,
the glory in Israel's midst.

3. Give thanks to the Father of mercies,
give thanks to his Son,
give thanks to the joy-giving Spirit,
give thanks to one God.

© Copyright 1999 Kevin Mayhew Ltd.

765 Your love's greater

Words and music: Mike Anderson (b.1956)

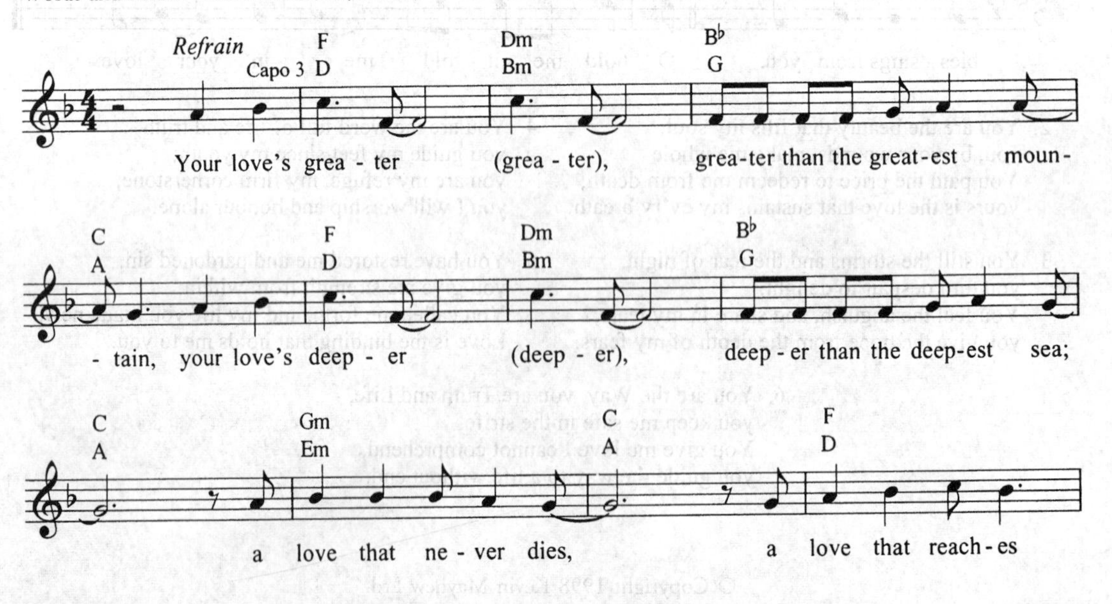

© Copyright 1999 Kevin Mayhew Ltd.

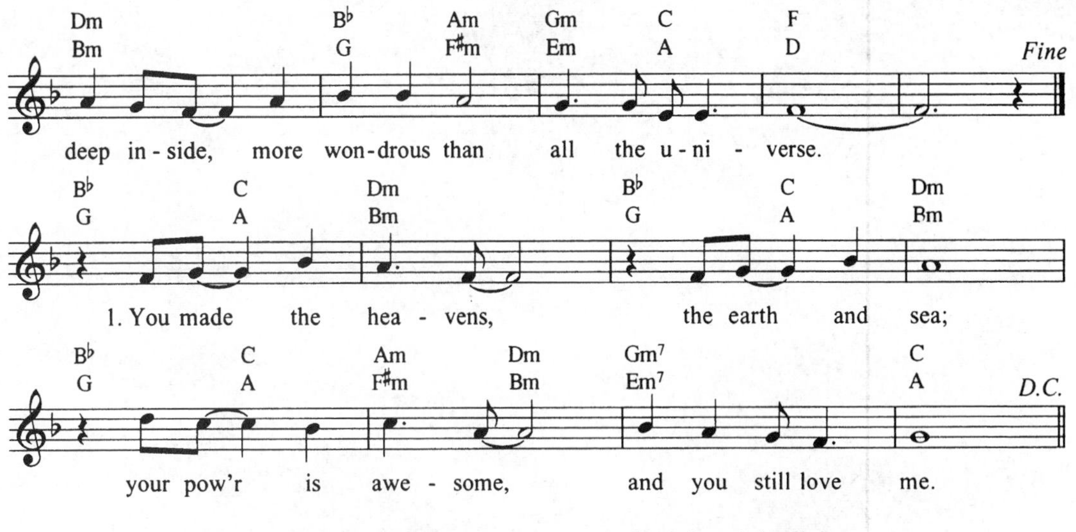

2. Your ways are righteous,
your laws are just,
love is your promise,
and in you I trust.

3. Your love is healing,
your love endures;
my life is changed, Lord,
now I know I'm yours.

766 You shall go out with joy *The trees of the field*

Words and music: Steffi Geiser Rubin
and Stuart Dauermann

© Copyright 1975 Lillenas Publishing Co. Administered by CopyCare, P.O. Box 77, Hailsham, East Sussex BN27 3EF, UK. (music@copycare.com). Used by permission.

COMPLETE ANGLICAN
HYMNS OLD & NEW

Children's Hymns and Songs

767 A butterfly, an Easter egg

Signs of new life

Words and music: Carey Landry

2. A helping hand, **a helping hand,**
   a happy smile, **a happy smile,**
   a heart so full of hope and joy,
   a heart so full of hope and joy.

3. A cup of wine, **a cup of wine,**
   a loaf of bread, **a loaf of bread,**
   now blest and broken for us all,
   now blest and broken for us all.

© Copyright 1979 North American Liturgy Resources (NALR), 5536 NE Hassalo, Portland, OR 97213, USA.
All rights reserved. Used by permission.

768 All in an Easter garden

Words and music: Traditional

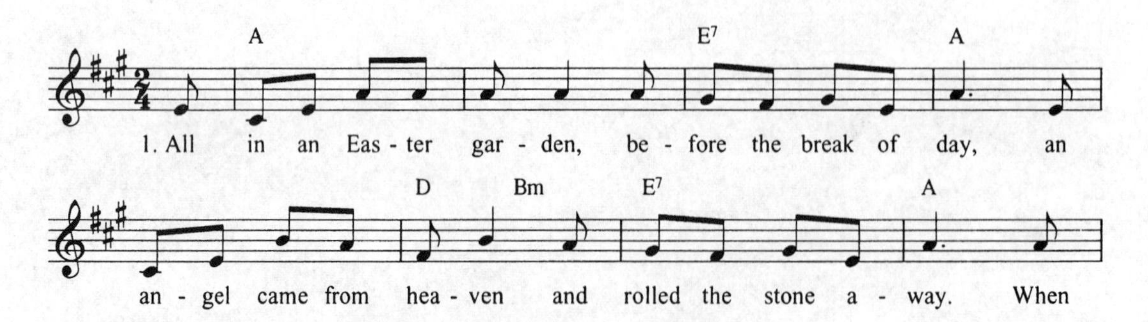

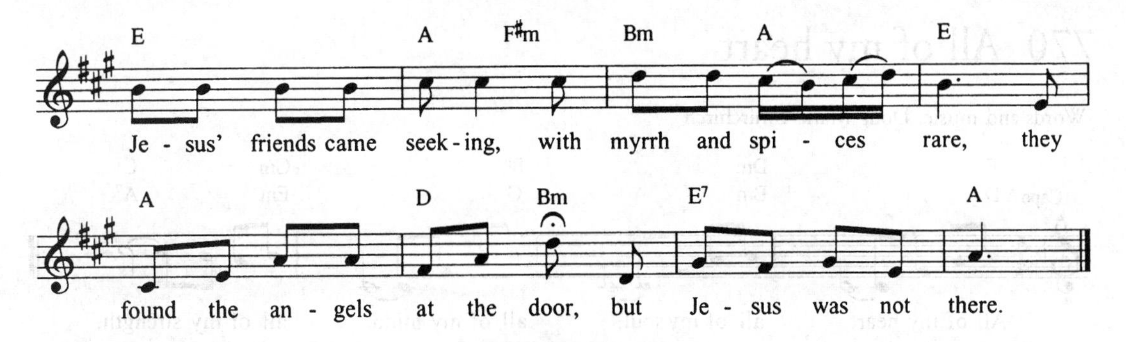

2. All in an Easter garden,
where water lilies bloom,
the angels gave their message
beside an empty tomb:
'The Lord is here no longer,
come, see where once he lay;
the Lord of life is ris'n indeed,
for this is Easter day.'

769 All night, all day

Words and music: Spiritual

2. Now I lay me down to sleep,
angels watchin' over me, my Lord.
Pray the Lord my soul to keep,
angels watchin' over me.

770 All of my heart

Words and music: Doug Marks-Smirchirch

© Copyright Right on the Mark Music. Copyright Control.

771 All of the creatures God had made

Michael Forster (b.1946) Christopher Tambling (b.1964)

© Copyright 1993 Kevin Mayhew Ltd.

2. Ev'rything seemed to come in pairs,
camels and dogs and big brown bears;
Noah said to God, 'It's rather rough;
one of the fleas would be quite enough.'

3. All huddled up in one small space,
one of the dogs said, 'What a place!
I haven't room to swing a cat!'
'Well,' said the cat, 'thank the Lord for that!'

4. People are often like that, too,
living in boxes, two by two.
We have to learn to get along,
just like the animals in this song.

772 All of the people

Words and music: Susan Sayers (b.1946)

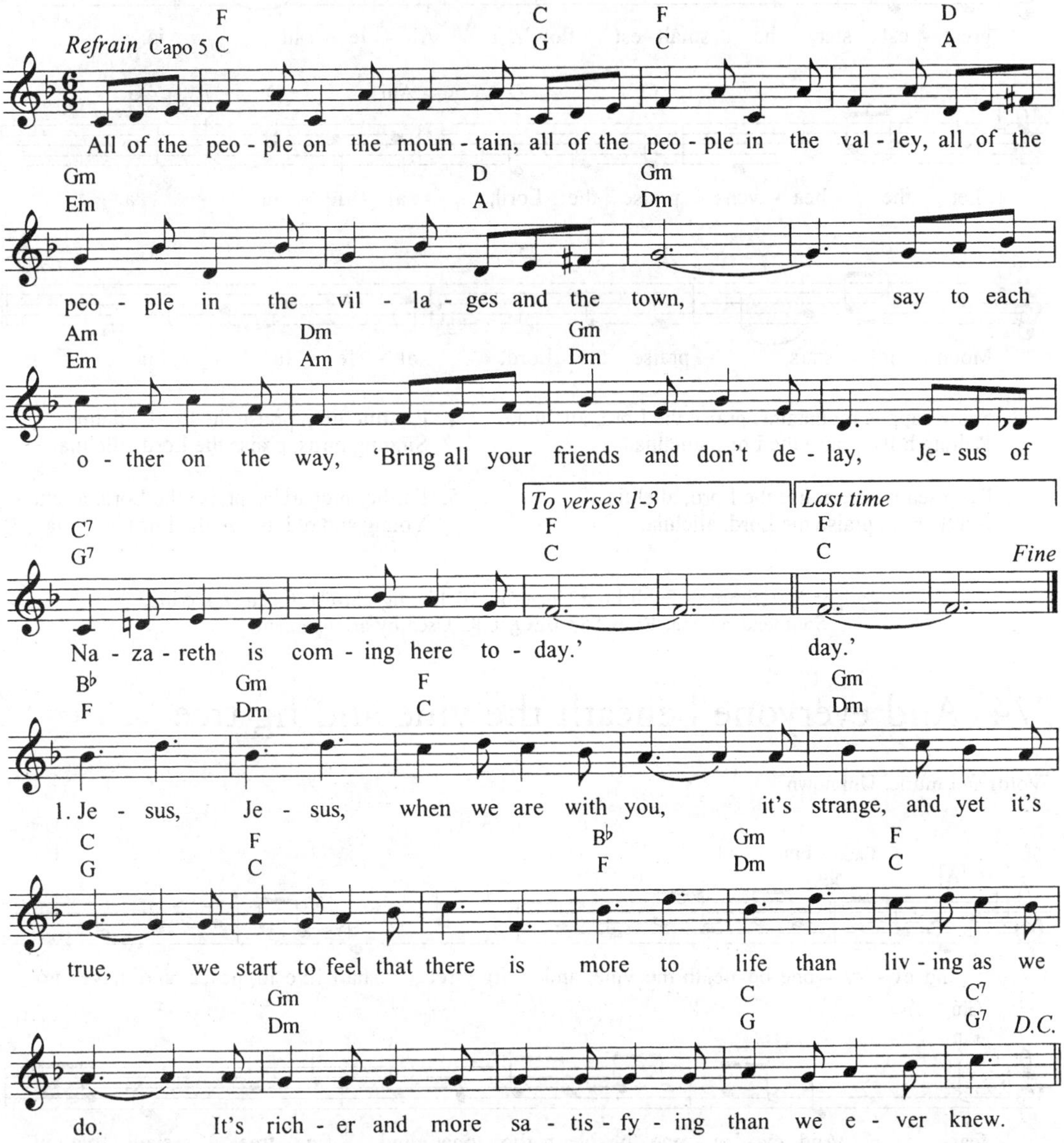
Refrain Capo 5
F C C G F C D A
All of the peo - ple on the moun - tain, all of the peo - ple in the val - ley, all of the
Gm Em D A Gm Dm
peo - ple in the vil - la - ges and the town, say to each
Am Em Dm Am Gm Dm
o - ther on the way, 'Bring all your friends and don't de - lay, Je - sus of
To verses 1-3
Last time
C7 G7 F C F C
Fine
Na - za - reth is com - ing here to - day.' day.'
B♭ F Gm Dm F C Gm Dm
1. Je - sus, Je - sus, when we are with you, it's strange, and yet it's
C G F C B♭ F Gm Dm F C
true, we start to feel that there is more to life than liv - ing as we
Gm Dm C G C7 G7
D.C.
do. It's rich - er and more sa - tis - fy - ing than we e - ver knew.

2. Jesus, Jesus, healing as you go,
your loving seems to flow
like water from a fountain,
and as we are touched we want to grow
in love towards each other –
just because you love us so!

3. Jesus, Jesus, we have come to see
that you must really be
the Son of God our Father.
We've been with you and we all agree
that only in your service
can the world be truly free!

© Copyright 1986 Kevin Mayhew Ltd.

773 All the nations of the earth

Michael Cockett (b.1938) Kevin Mayhew (b.1942)

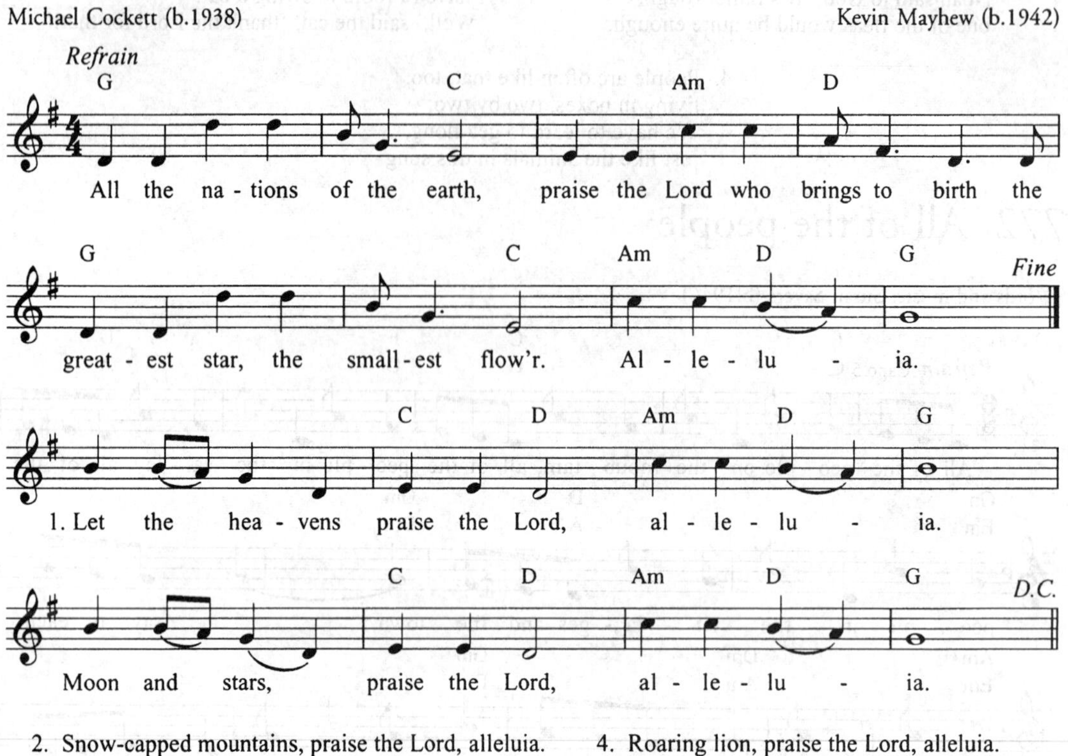

2. Snow-capped mountains, praise the Lord, alleluia.
   Rolling hills, praise the Lord, alleluia.

3. Deep sea water, praise the Lord, alleluia.
   Gentle rain, praise the Lord, alleluia.

4. Roaring lion, praise the Lord, alleluia.
   Singing birds, praise the Lord, alleluia.

5. Earthly monarchs, praise the Lord, alleluia.
   Young and old, praise the Lord, alleluia.

© Copyright McCrimmon Publishing Co. Ltd., 10-12 High Street, Great Wakering, Southend-on-Sea, Essex SS3 0EQ, UK. Used by arrangement.

774 And everyone beneath the vine and fig tree

Words and music: Unknown

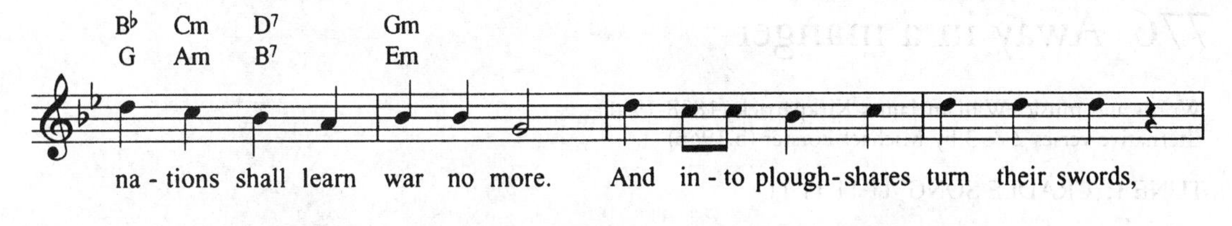

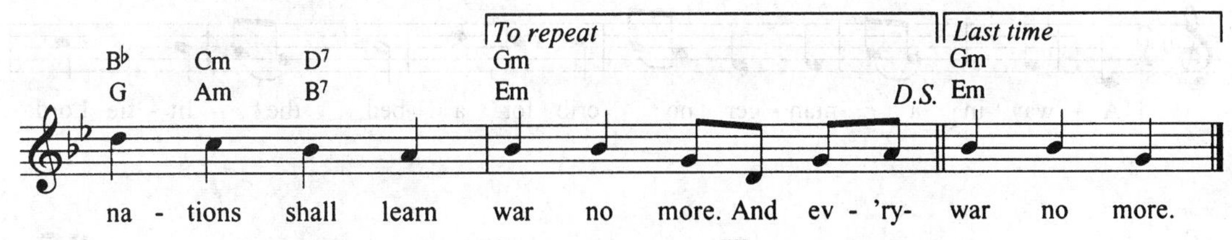

This can be sung as a round with the second voices entering at **B**

775 As Jacob with travel was weary one day

18th century — 18th century English carol melody

JACOB'S LADDER 11 11 11 11 and Refrain

2. This ladder is long, it is strong and well-made,
has stood hundreds of years and is not yet decayed;
many millions have climbed it and reached Zion's hill,
and thousands by faith are climbing it still:

3. Come let us ascend! all may climb it who will;
for the angels of Jacob are guarding it still:
and remember, each step that by faith we pass o'er,
some prophet or martyr has trod it before:

4. And when we arrive at the haven of rest
we shall hear the glad words, 'Come up hither, ye blest,
here are regions of light, here are mansions of bliss.'
O who would not climb such a ladder as this?

776 Away in a manger

Words and music: William James Kirkpatrick (1838-1921)
alternative verses 2 & 3 by Michael Forster (b.1946)

TUNE 1: CRADLE SONG 11 11 11 11

2. The cattle are lowing, the baby awakes,
   but little Lord Jesus no crying he makes.
   I love thee, Lord Jesus! Look down from the sky,
   and stay by my side until morning is nigh.

3. Be near me, Lord Jesus; I ask thee to stay
   close by me for ever, and love me, I pray.
   Bless all the dear children in thy tender care,
   and fit us for heaven, to live with thee there.

Alternative text for verses 2 and 3:

2. The cattle are lowing, they also adore
   the little Lord Jesus who lies in the straw.
   I love you, Lord Jesus, I know you are near
   to love and protect me till morning is here.

3. Be near me, Lord Jesus; I ask you to stay
   close by me for ever, and love me, I pray.
   Bless all the dear children in your tender care,
   prepare us for heaven, to live with you there.

William James Kirkpatrick (1838-1921)

James R. Murray (1841-1905)

TUNE 2: MUELLER 11 11 11 11

Alternative version of verses 2 and 3 © Copyright 1996 Kevin Mayhew Ltd.

777 A wiggly, waggly worm *The wiggly, waggly song*

Words and music: Paul Field

2. A prickly porcupine, a clumsy kangaroo,
a croaky frog, a hairy hog, a monkey in a zoo;
of all the things to be, I'm happy that I'm me.
Thank you, Lord, I'm happy that I'm me.
I'm happy that I'm me, happy that I'm me.
There's no one else in all the world that I would rather be.
A prickly porcupine, a clumsy kangaroo,
a croaky frog, a hairy hog, a monkey in a zoo.

© Copyright 1991 Daybreak Music Ltd., Silverdale Road, Eastbourne, East Sussex BN20 7AB, UK.
All rights reserved. International copyright secured. Used by permission.

778 Be the centre of my life

Words and music: Capt. Alan J. Price, CA

2. Let the power of your presence, Lord Jesus,
from the centre of my life shine through;
oh, let ev'rybody know it,
I really want to show it,
that the centre of my life is you!

© Copyright 1990 Daybreak Music Ltd., Silverdale Road, Eastbourne, East Sussex BN20 7AB, UK.
All rights reserved. International copyright secured. Used by permission.

779 Boisterous, buzzing barking things

Big and little you's and me's

Words and music: Winifred Elliott

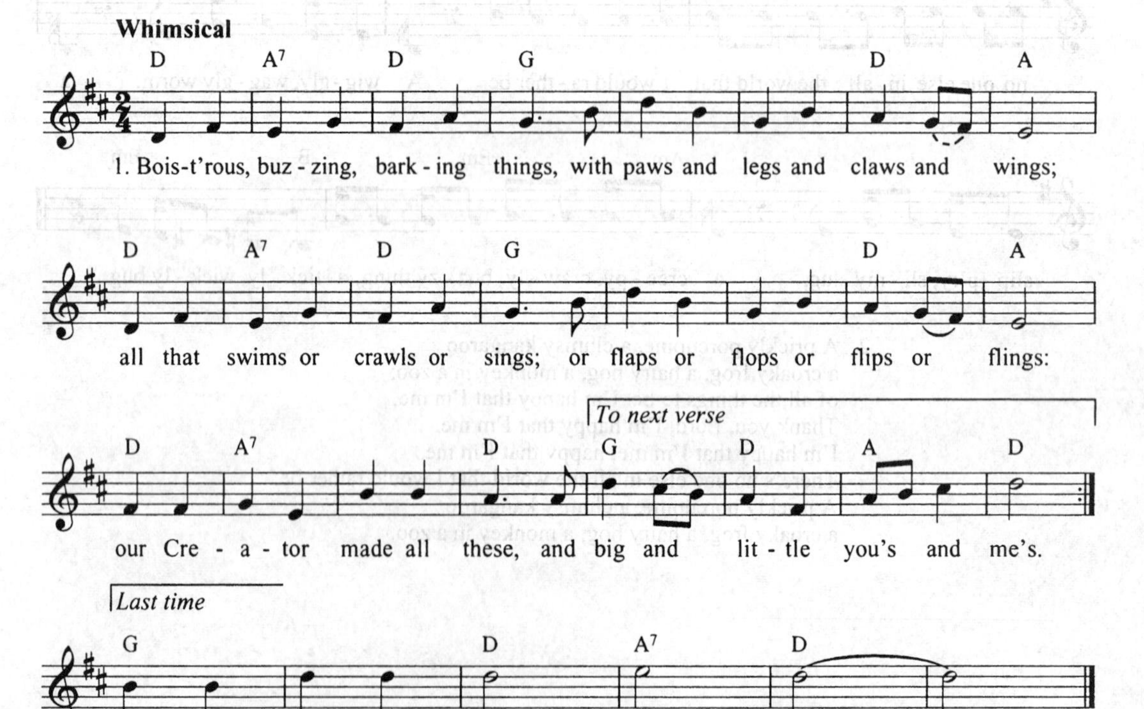

© Copyright Control.

2. Bugs and birds and bears and bees;
and buds that burst on blossoming trees;
fluffy clouds before the breeze;
and stars and skies and streams and seas:
our Creator made all these,
and big and little you's and me's.

3. Girls and boys and Mum and Dad,
the kind and good, or even bad –
all who please and make him glad,
and even those who make him sad:
our Creator made all these,
and big and little you's and me's.

780 Break the bread and pour the wine

Michael Forster (b.1946)

Christopher Tambling (b.1964)

2. Come and meet around the table,
God provides the wine to share;
we enjoy a meal together,
show each other how we care.

© Copyright 1993 Kevin Mayhew Ltd.

781 Can you see what we have made *Song for Christingle*

Words and music: Graham Kendrick (b.1950)

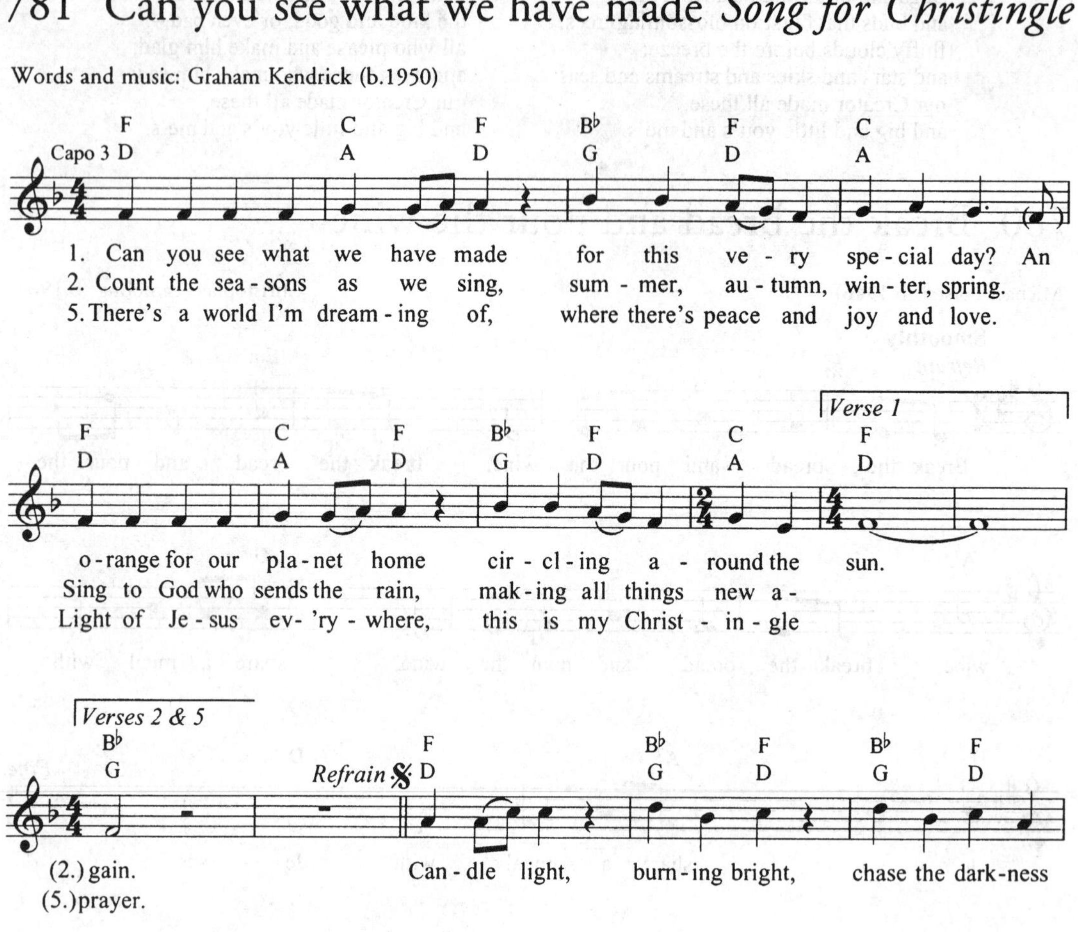

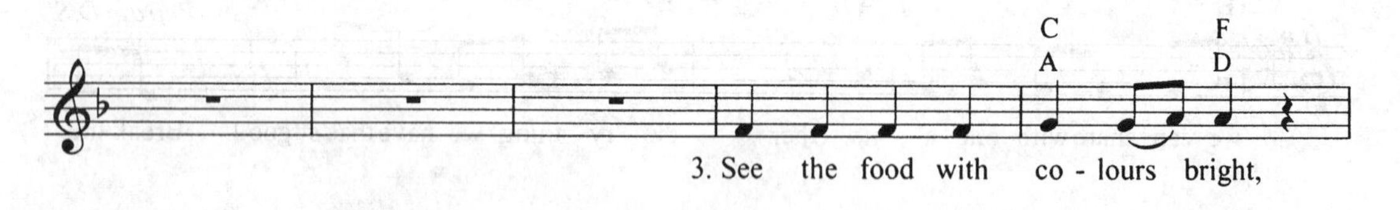

© Copyright 1997 Make Way Music, P.O. Box 263, Croydon, Surrey CR9 5AP, UK.
International copyright secured. All rights reserved. Used by permission.

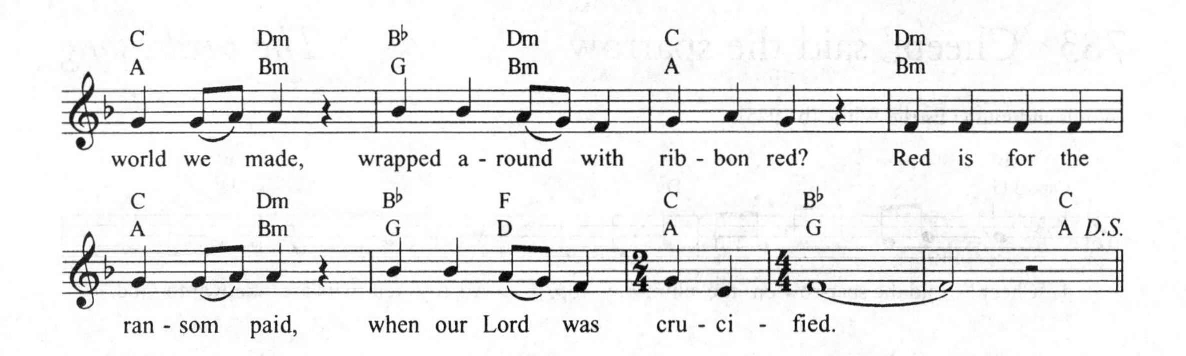

782 Caterpillar, caterpillar

Words and music: Susan Sayers (b.1946)

2. Caterpillar, caterpillar, feeling sleepy,
fixed up a silken bed.
Then caterpillar, caterpillar climbed inside
and covered up his sleepy head.
In the dark he slept and rested
as the days and nights went by,
till on a sunny morning when the
silk bed burst, he was a butterfly!

3. Butterfly, oh butterfly, a flitt'ring, flutt'ring;
oh what a sight so see.
And as the lovely butterfly was flutt'ring by,
I heard him sing a song to me:
'Oh I never knew God could do
such a wondrous thing for me;
for he took me as a caterpillar
and he made a butterfly of me.'

© Copyright 1986 Kevin Mayhew Ltd.

783 'Cheep!' said the sparrow *The birds' song*

Words and music: Estelle White (b.1925)

2. 'Coo!' said the gentle one, the grey-blue dove,
'I can tell you that God is love.'
High up above sang the lark in flight,
'I know the Lord is my heart's delight.'

3. 'Chirp!' said the robin with his breast so red,
'I don't want to work at all, yet I'm fed.'
'Whoo!' called the owl in a leafy wood,
'Our God is wonderful, wise and good.'

© Copyright 1977 Kevin Mayhew Ltd.

784 Christ is our King

Words and music: Estelle White (b.1925)

© Copyright 1976 Kevin Mayhew Ltd.

2. He came to speak tender words to the poor,
he is the gateway and he is the door.
Riches are waiting for all those who hope.
He is the light of the world.

3. He came to open the doors of the goal;
he came to help the downtrodden and frail.
Freedom is waiting for all those who hope.
He is the light of the world.

4. He came to open the lips of the mute,
letting them speak out with courage and truth.
His words are uttered by all those who hope.
He is the light of the world.

5. He came to heal all the crippled and lame,
sickness took flight at the sound of his name.
Vigour is waiting for all those who hope.
He is the light of the world.

6. He came to love everyone on this earth
and through his Spirit he promised rebirth.
New life is waiting for all those who hope.
He is the light of the world.

785 Clap your hands, all you people

Words and music: Jimmy Owens

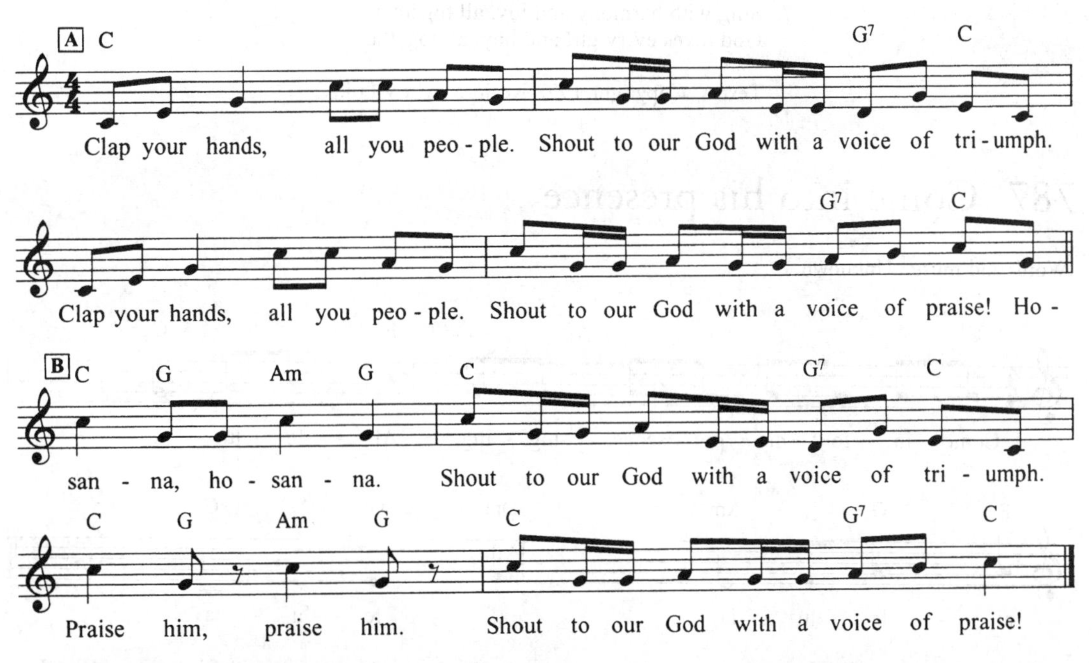

This can be sung as a round with the second voices entering at B

© Copyright 1972 Bud John Songs/EMI Christian Music Publishing. Administered by CopyCare, P.O. Box 77, Hailsham, East Sussex BN27 3EF, UK. (music@copycare.com). Used by permission.

786 Clap your hands and sing this song

Jean Holloway (b.1939) — Traditional

MICHAEL ROW THE BOAT 74 74

D G

1. Clap your hands and sing this song, all to - ge -

D G Em Bm A7 D

ther, tap your feet and sing a - long, all to - ge - ther.

2. Raise your hands up in the air, all together,
God can reach you anywhere, all together.

3. Fold your arms across your chest, all together,
in the arms of God you're blessed, all together.

4. Close your eyes and shut them tight, all together,
God will keep you in his sight, all together.

5. Now sing softly, whisper low, all together,
God will hear you even so, all together.

6. Sing out loud and strong and clear, all together,
so that ev'ryone can hear, all together.

7. Sing with harmony and joy, all together,
God loves ev'ry girl and boy, all together.

Text © Copyright 1997 Kevin Mayhew Ltd.

787 Come into his presence

Words and music: Unknown

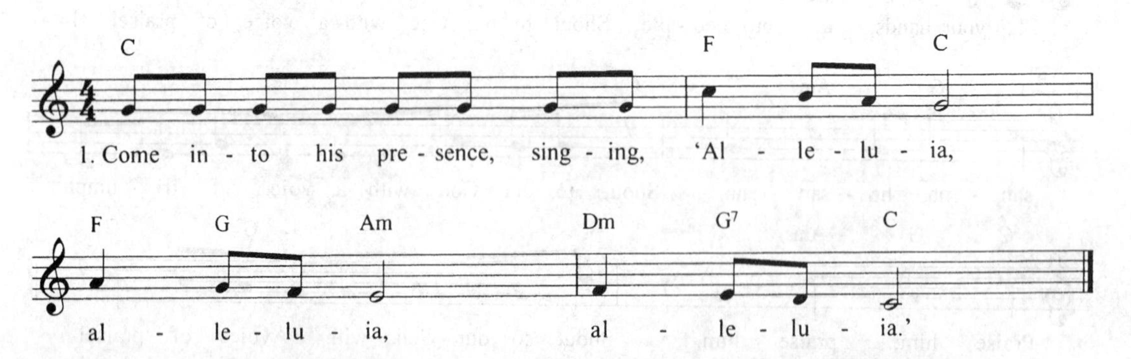

2. Come into his presence, singing,
'Jesus is Lord, Jesus is Lord, Jesus is Lord.'
Come into his presence, singing,
'Jesus is Lord, Jesus is Lord, Jesus is Lord.'

3. Come into his presence, singing,
'Glory to God, glory to God, glory to God.'
Come into his presence, singing,
'Glory to God, glory to God, glory to God.'

788 Come on, let's get up and go

Words and music: Graham Kendrick (b.1950)

© Copyright 1986 Kingsway's Thankyou Music, P.O. Box 75, Eastbourne, East Sussex BN23 6NW, UK. (tym@kingsway.co.uk). Used by permission.

789 Come, they told me *The little drummer boy*

Words and music: Katherine K. Davis, Henry V. Onorati and Harry Simeone

2. Baby Jesus, pah-rum-pum-pum-pum!
I am a poor child too, pah-rum-pum-pum-pum!
I have no gift to bring, pah-rum-pum-pum-pum!
that's fit to give a King, pah-rum-pum-pum-pum!
Rum-pum-pum-pum! Rum-pum-pum-pum!
Shall I play for you, pah-rum-pum-pum-pum!
on my drum?

3. Mary nodded, pah-rum-pum-pum-pum!
The ox and lamb kept time, pah-rum-pum-pum-pum!
I played my drum for him, pah-rum-pum-pum-pum!
I played my best for him, pah-rum-pum-pum-pum!
Rum-pum-pum-pum! Rum-pum-pum-pum!
Then he smiled at me, pah-rum-pum-pum-pum!
me and my drum.

© Copyright 1941 EMI Mills Music Inc./Delaware Music Corp, USA.
Worldwide print rights controlled by Warner Bros. Publications/IMP Ltd.
Used by permission of IMP Ltd., Griffin House, 161 Hammersmith Road, London W6 8BS, UK.

790 Don't build your house on the sandy land

Words and music: Karen Lafferty

© Copyright 1981 Maranatha! Music. Administered by CopyCare, P.O. Box 77, Hailsham, East Sussex BN27 3EF, UK. (music@copycare.com). Used by permission.

791 Do what you know is right

Words and music: Bev Gammon

© Copyright 1988 Kingsway's Thankyou Music, P.O. Box 75, Eastbourne, East Sussex BN23 6NW, UK. (tym@kingsway.co.uk). Used by permission.

792 Do you ever wish you could fly

Just be glad God made you 'you'

Michael Forster (b.1946) Christopher Tambling (b.1964)

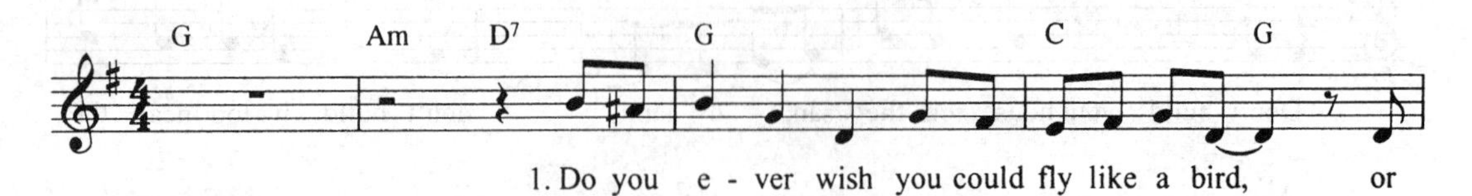

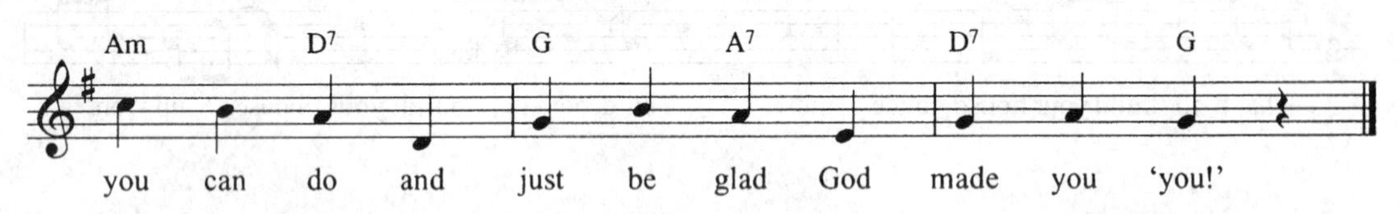

2. Do you ever wish you could swim like a duck?
Unless your feet are webbed you're out of luck!
Think of all the things that you can do
and just be glad God made you 'you'!

3. Do you ever wish you could run like a hare?
Well, wishing it won't get you anywhere!
Think of all the things that you can do
and just be glad God made you 'you'!

4. Do you ever wish you could hang like a bat?
There's really not a lot of fun in that!
Think of all the things that you can do
and just be glad God made you 'you'!

5. Do you ever wish – well, that's really enough!
To wish away your life is silly stuff!
Think of all the things that you can do
and just be glad God made you 'you'!

© Copyright 1997 Kevin Mayhew Ltd.

793 Each of us is a living stone

Living stones

Michael Forster (b.1946) James Patten (b.1936)

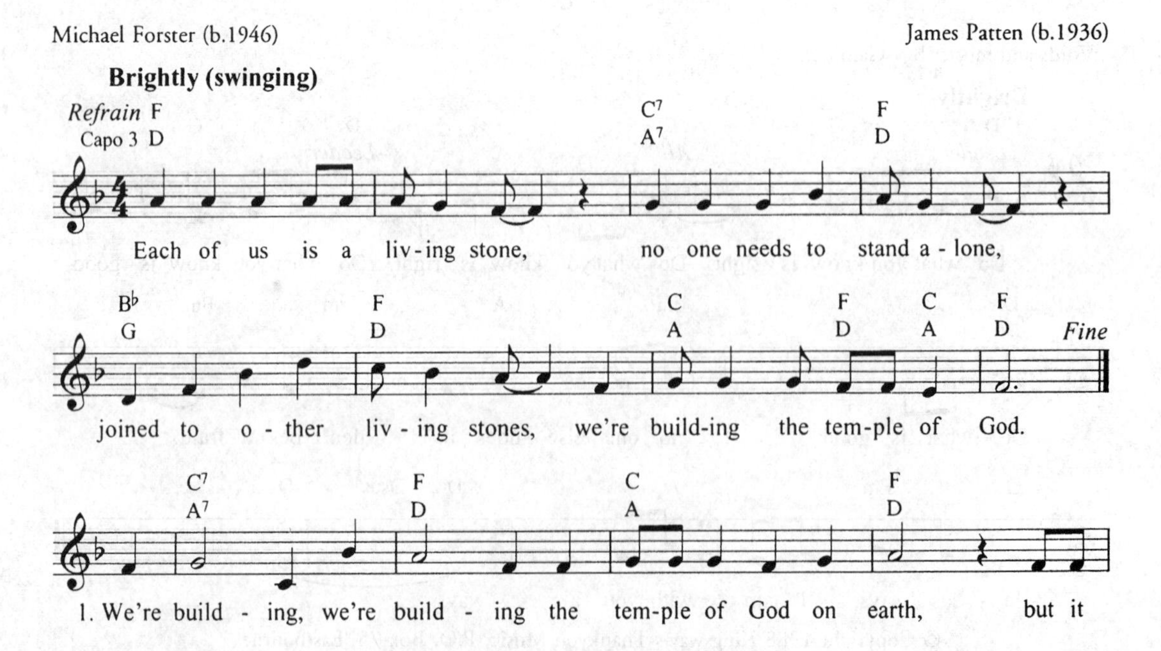

© Copyright 1997 Kevin Mayhew Ltd.

2. The stone that, the stone that the builders once cast aside
has been made the firm foundation,
and the carpenter who was crucified
now offers us salvation.

794 Every bird, every tree

Words and music: Peter Watcyn-Jones

2. Ev'ry prayer, ev'ry song
makes me feel I belong
to a world filled
with love that's all around.
From each daybreak to each night,
out of darkness comes the light,
this is love, God is love, love's around.

3. Ev'ry mountain, ev'ry stream,
ev'ry flower, ev'ry dream
comes from God,
God is love and love's around.
From the ever-changing sky
to a new-born baby's cry,
this is love, God is love, love's around.

© Copyright 1978 Kevin Mayhew Ltd.

795 Every minute of every day

Words and music: Stuart Garrard

© Copyright 1995 Kingsway's Thankyou Music, P.O. Box 75, Eastbourne, East Sussex BN23 6NW, UK. (tym@kingsway.co.uk). Used by permission.

796 Farmer, farmer, why do you plough?

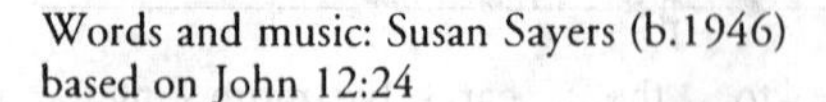
Words and music: Susan Sayers (b.1946)
based on John 12:24

© Copyright 1984 Kevin Mayhew Ltd.

2. Miller, miller, turning your stone,
why must you grind? Can't you leave us alone?
Why must you change us all with your pow'r?
'You can only be bread
if you first become flour;
you can only be bread
if you first become flour.'

3. Baker, baker, kneading the dough,
why do you pound us and pummel us so?
'Unless I work my yeast through you all
I shall find that my bread
is not risen at all;
I shall find that my bread
is not risen at all.'

4. Jesus, Jesus, use us, we pray;
use us to further your glory each day.
'You are my body; you are my bread —
to be broken and shared
that the world may be fed;
to be broken and shared
that the world may be fed.'

797 Father welcomes all his children

Words and music: Robin Mann

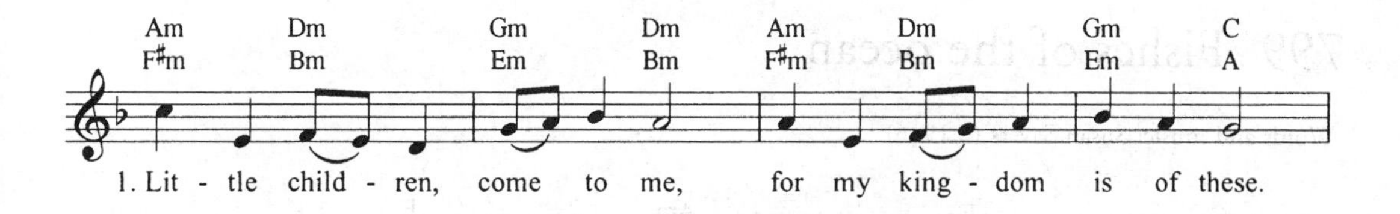

2. In the water, in the word,
in his promise, be assured:
all who believe and are baptised
shall be born again.

3. Let us daily die to sin;
let us daily rise with him –
walk in the love of Christ our Lord,
live in the peace of God.

© Copyright 1986 Kevin Mayhew Ltd.

798 Father, we want to thank you

Words and music: Susan Sayers (b.1946)

2. Ring, ting, ta-ting, ting, ting,
we play our triangles for Jesus.
Ring, ting, ta-ting, ting, ting,
we play them, Lord, for you.

3. La, la, la-la, la, la,
we sing our praises for you, Jesus.
La, la, la-la, la, la,
we sing our praise for you.

© Copyright 1986 Kevin Mayhew Ltd.

799 Fishes of the ocean

Words and music: Susan Sayers (b.1946)

© Copyright 1986 Kevin Mayhew Ltd.

2. Apples in the orchard and the corn in the field,
the plants all yield their fruit in due season,
so the generosity of God is revealed;
let the whole earth sing of his love!

3. Energy and colour from the sun with its light,
the moon by night; the patterns of the stars
all winking in the darkness on a frosty cold night;
let the whole earth sing of his love!

4. Muddy hippopotamus and dainty gazelle,
the mice as well, are all of his making,
furry ones and hairy ones and some with a shell;
let the whole earth sing of his love!

5. All that we can hear and ev'rything we can see,
including me, we all of us spring from God
who cares for ev'rybody unendingly;
let the whole earth sing of his love!

800 Forward in faith

Graham Jeffery

Kevin Mayhew (b.1942)

2. Jesus is Lord, Jesus is Lord,
we are travelling onward;
Jesus is Lord, Jesus is Lord,
we are trav'ling on.

3. He is our King, he is our King,
we are travelling onward;
he is our King, he is our King,
we are trav'ling on.

© Copyright 1983 Palm Tree Press Ltd., assigned 1984 to Kevin Mayhew Ltd.

801 Friends, all gather here in a circle *Circle of friends*

Words and music: David Morstad

© Copyright Control.

802 Give me peace, O Lord

Words and music: Estelle White (b.1925)

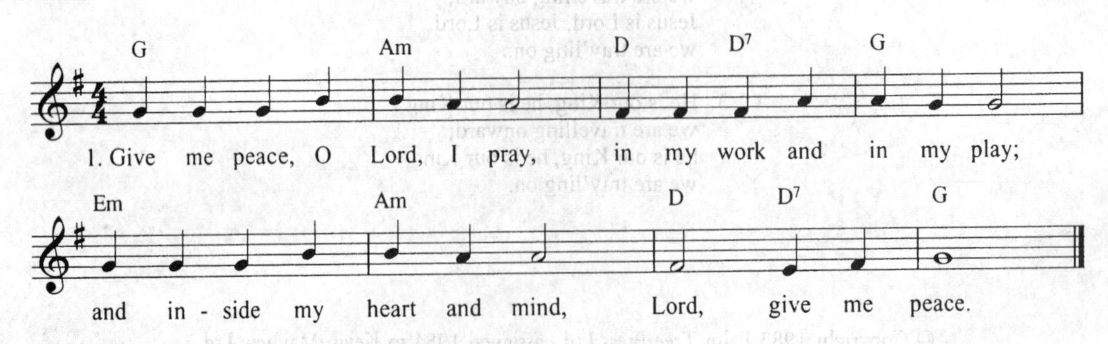

© Copyright 1976 Kevin Mayhew Ltd.

2. Give peace to the world, I pray
let all quarrels cease today.
May we spread your light and love:
Lord, give us peace.

803 Give thanks to the Lord

Words and music: Janet Morgan

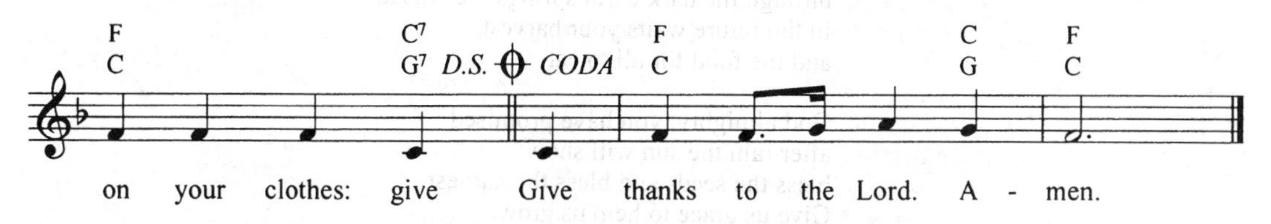

2. When you eat your dinner
and you're all full up,
when your mum says *(name)*,
and you help wash up:

3. When you stretch up high
and you touch the ground,
when you stretch out wide
and you turn around:

4. When you click your fingers
and you stamp your feet,
when you clap your hands
and you slap your knees:

Final refrain:
Give thanks to the Lord for he is good.
Give thanks to the Lord for ever.
Give thanks to the Lord for he is good.
Give thanks to the Lord. Amen.

© Copyright 1989 Sea Dream Music, P.O. Box 13533, London E1 0SG, UK.
Used by permission.

804 God almighty set a rainbow

Caroline Somerville

Traditional melody

Refrain after each verse:
Thank you, Father, thank you, Father,
thank you, Father, for your care,
for your warm and loving kindness
to your people ev'rywhere.

2. Clouds will gather, storms come streaming
on the darkened earth below –
too much sunshine makes a desert,
without rain no seed can grow.

3. Through the stormcloud shines your rainbow,
through the dark earth springs the wheat.
In the future waits your harvest
and the food for all to eat.

4. God almighty, you have promised
after rain the sun will show;
bless the seeds and bless the harvest.
Give us grace to help us grow.

Text © Copyright Caroline Somerville. Used by permission of The Archbishops' Council of the Church of England, Church House, Great Smith Street, London SW1P 3NZ, UK. Used by permission from *Together for Harvest* (CIO, 1976).

805 God is good, God is great

Words and music: Capt. Alan J. Price, CA

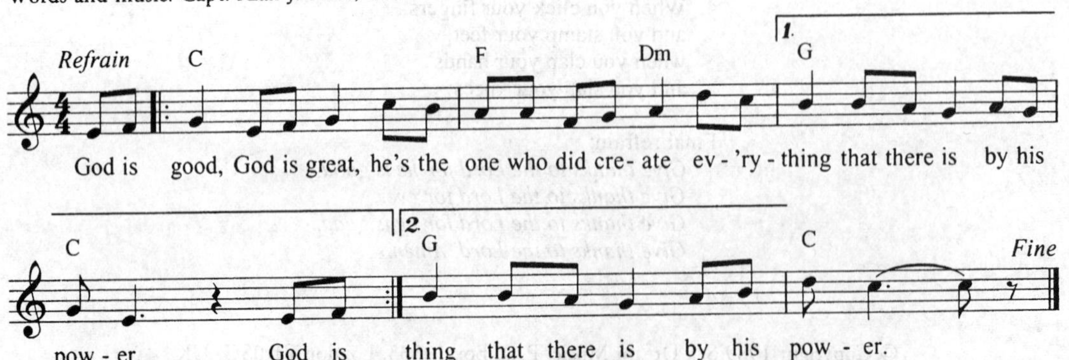

© Copyright 1994 Daybreak Music Ltd., Silverdale Road, Eastbourne, East Sussex BN20 7AB, UK. All rights reserved. International copyright secured. Used by permission.

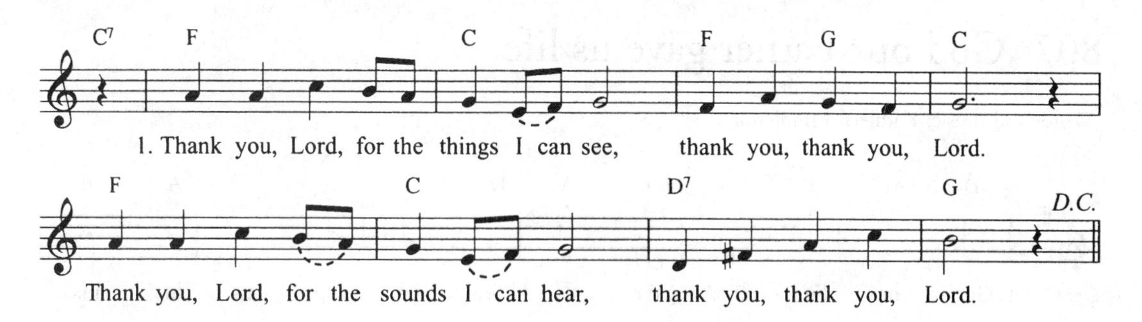

2. Thank you, Lord, for my family,
thank you, thank you, Lord.
Thank you, Lord, for all my friends,
thank you, thank you, Lord.

3. Thank you, Lord, for the birds in the sky,
thank you, thank you, Lord.
Thank you, Lord, for the ants on the ground,
thank you, thank you, Lord.

4. Thank you, Lord, for your love to me,
thank you, thank you, Lord.
Thank you, Lord, that you're always near,
thank you, thank you, Lord.

806 God made a boomerang

Michael Forster (b.1946) Christopher Tambling (b.1964)

2. Love's like a boomerang, that's what God planned,
but it's no use if it stays in your hand.
Got to send it spinning
for a new beginning,
love's like a boomerang, let's throw it around.

3. Love's like a boomerang, goes with a swing,
now ev'rybody can have a good fling.
Families and nations
join the celebrations,
love's like a boomerang, let's throw it around.

© Copyright 1999 Kevin Mayhew Ltd.

807 God our Father gave us life

Words and music: Kathleen Middleton

2. When we're frightened, hurt or tired,
there's always someone there.
Make us thankful for their love:
Lord, hear our prayer;
Lord, hear our prayer.

3. All God's children need his love,
a love that we can share.
So, we pray for everyone:
Lord, hear our prayer;
Lord, hear our prayer.

© Copyright 1986 Kevin Mayhew Ltd.

808 God sends a rainbow *Colours of hope*

Michael Forster (b.1946) Christopher Tambling (b.1964)

© Copyright 1997 Kevin Mayhew Ltd.

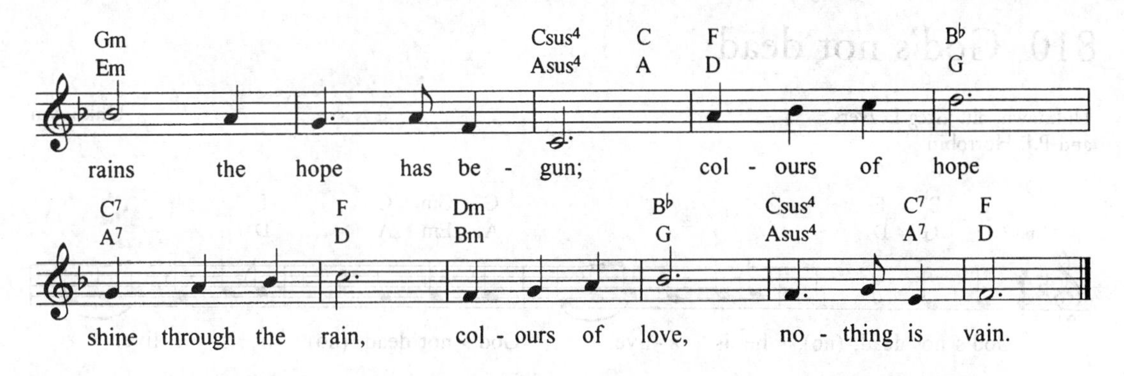

2. When we are lonely, when we're afraid,
though it seems dark, rainbows are made;
even when life itself has to end,
God is our rainbow, God is our friend.

3. Where people suffer pain or despair,
God can be seen in those who care;
even where war and hatred abound,
rainbows of hope are still to be found.

4. People themselves like rainbows are made,
colours of hope in us displayed;
old ones and young ones, women and men,
all can be part of love's great 'Amen'!

809 God's love is deeper *Deeper, wider, higher*

Words and music: Ian D. Craig

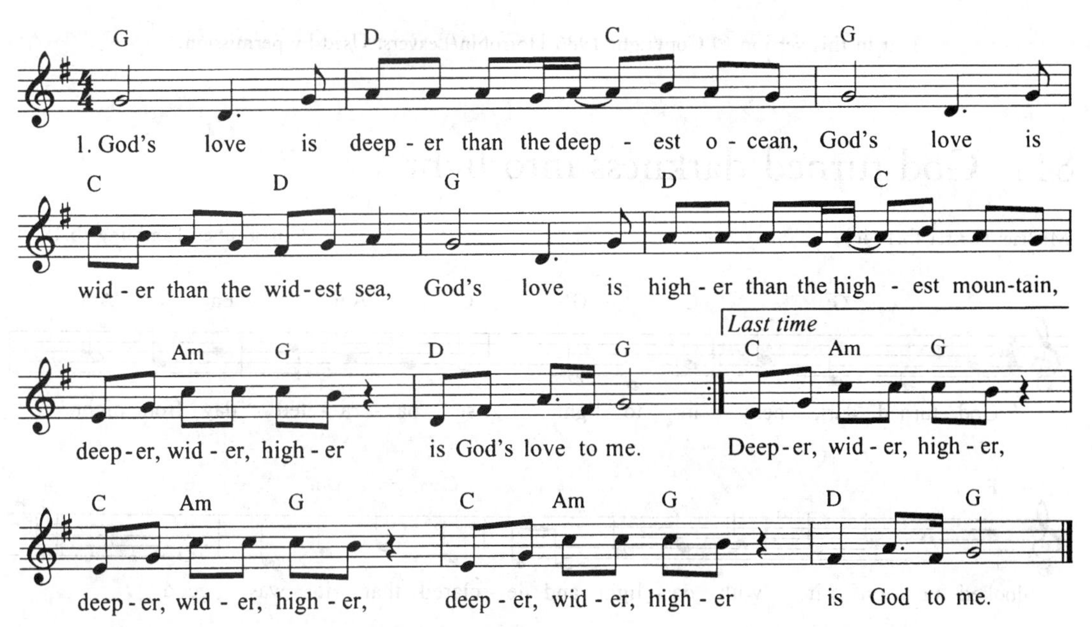

2. God's grace is deeper than the deepest ocean,
God's grace is wider than the widest sea,
God's grace is higher than the highest mountain,
deeper, wider, higher is God's grace to me.

3. God's joy is deeper than the deepest ocean,
God's joy is wider than the widest sea,
God's joy is higher than the highest mountain,
deeper, wider, higher is God's joy to me.

4. God's peace is deeper than the deepest ocean,
God's peace is wider than the widest sea,
God's peace is higher than the highest mountain,
deeper, wider, higher is God's peace to me.
Deeper, wider, higher, deeper, wider, higher,
deeper, wider, higher is God to me.

© Copyright 1993 Daybreak Music Ltd., Silverdale Road, Eastbourne, East Sussex BN20 7AB, UK.
All rights reserved. International copyright secured. Used by permission.

810 God's not dead

Unknown, alt. Greg Leavers and P.J. Horrobin

Unknown

Text in this version © Copyright 1986 Horrobin/Leavers. Used by permission.

811 God turned darkness into light

Michael Forster (b.1946)

Christopher Tambling (b.1964)

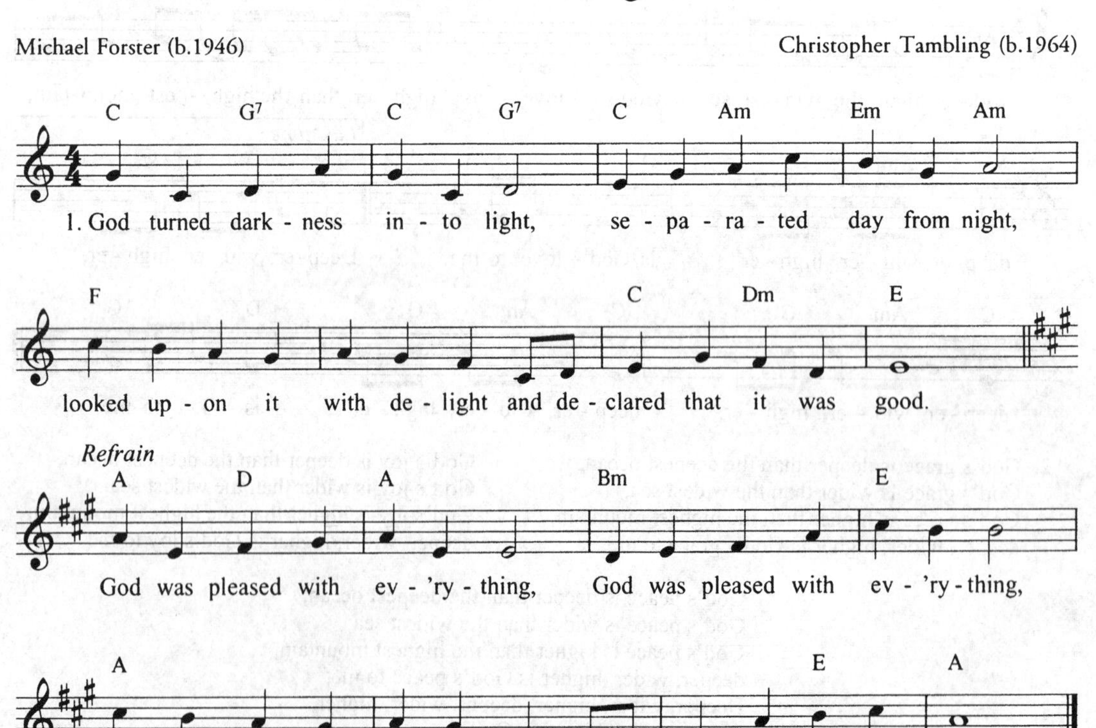

© Copyright 1997 Kevin Mayhew Ltd.

2. God divided land and sea,
filled the world with plants and trees,
all so beautiful to see,
and declared that it was good.

3. God made animals galore,
fishes, birds and dinosaurs,
heard the splashes, songs and roars,
and declared that it was good.

4. God made people last of all,
black and white, and short and tall,
male and female, large and small,
and declared that it was good.

812 Goliath was big and Goliath was strong

Biggest isn't always best

Michael Forster (b.1946) — Christopher Tambling (b.1964)

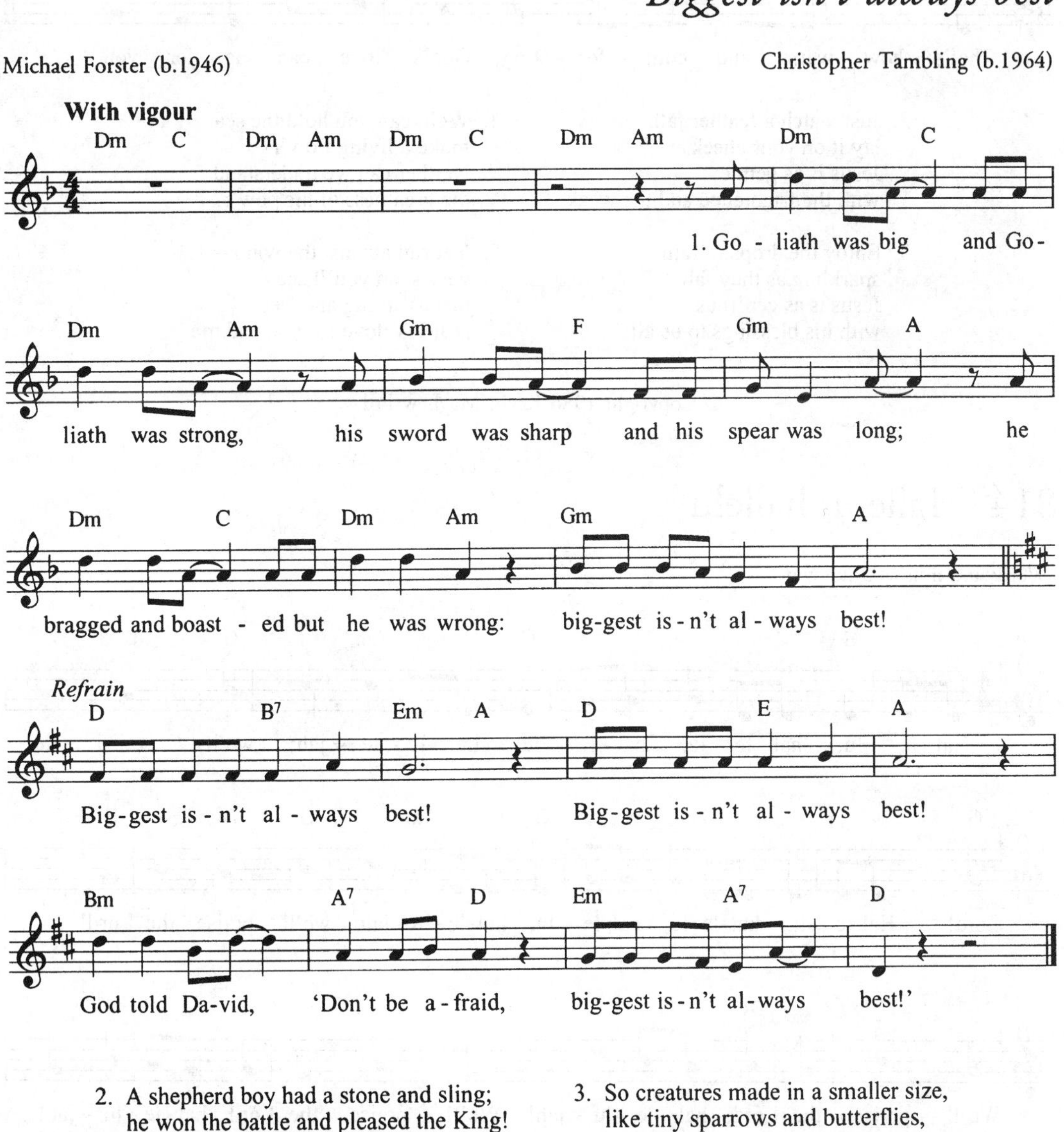

2. A shepherd boy had a stone and sling;
he won the battle and pleased the King!
Then all the people began to sing:
'Biggest isn't always best!'

3. So creatures made in a smaller size,
like tiny sparrows and butterflies,
are greater than we may realise:
biggest isn't always best!

© Copyright 1993 Kevin Mayhew Ltd.

813 Go wandering in the sun

Words and music: Susan Sayers (b.1946)

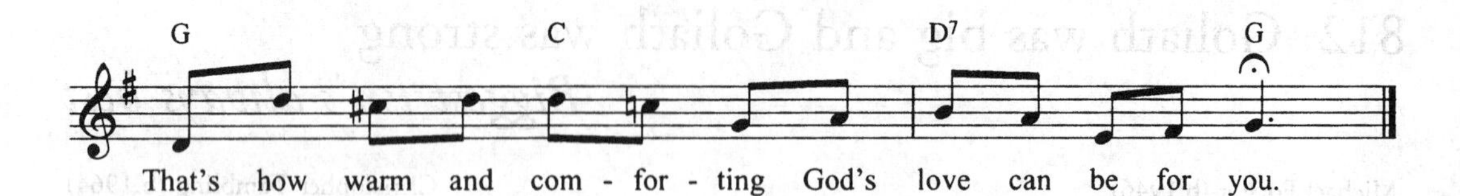

2. Just watch a feather fall,
lay it on your cheek.
Jesus is as gentle
with the frightened and the weak.

3. Enjoy the drops of rain,
sparkling as they fall.
Jesus is as gen'rous
with his blessings to us all.

4. Well, can you hold the sea,
make a living flow'r?
Neither can we understand
the greatness of his pow'r.

5. Yet run against the wind –
very soon you'll see –
just as strong and free
is Jesus' love for you and me.

© Copyright 1986 Kevin Mayhew Ltd.

814 Hallelu, hallelu

Words and music: Unknown

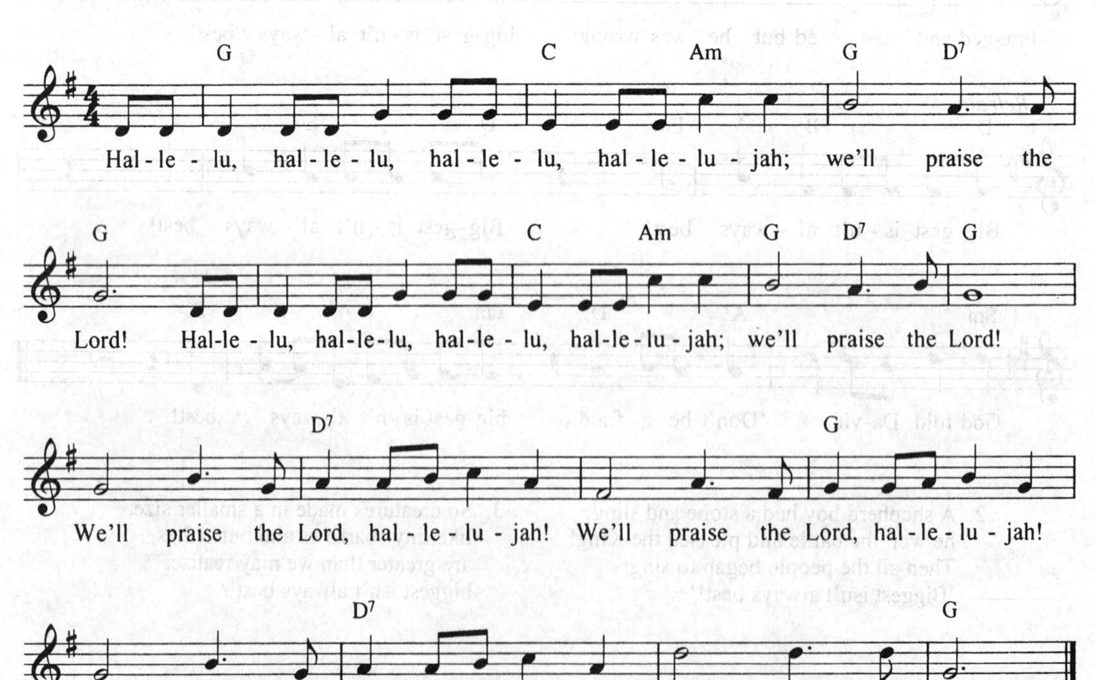

815 Have we made our God too small?

Words and music: Doug Horley

© Copyright 1997 Kingsway's Thankyou Music, P.O. Box 75, Eastbourne, East Sussex BN23 6NW, UK. (tym@kingsway.co.uk). Used by permission.

816 Have you got an appetite?

Words and music: Mick Gisbey

2. If it's milk or meat you need,
why not have a slap-up feed,
and stop looking like a weed and start to grow?
Take the full-of-fitness food,
taste and see that God is good,
come on, feed on what you should and be healthy.

© Copyright 1985 Kingsway's Thankyou Music, P.O. Box 75, Eastbourne, East Sussex BN23 6NW, UK. (tym@kingsway.co.uk). Used by permission.

817 Have you heard the raindrops *Water of Life*

Words and music: Christian Strover

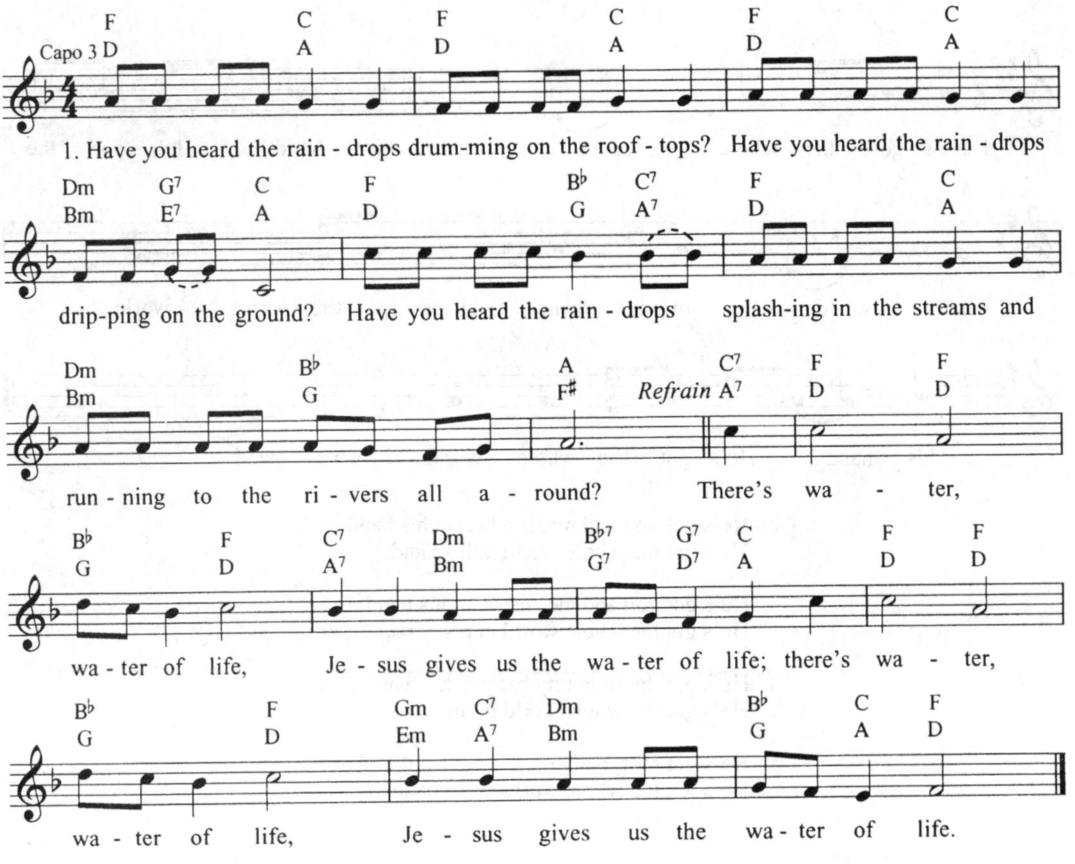

2. There's a busy worker digging in the desert,
   digging with a spade that flashes in the sun;
   soon there will be water rising in the well-shaft,
   spilling from the bucket as it comes.

3. Nobody can live who hasn't any water,
   when the land is dry, then nothing much grows;
   Jesus gives us life if we drink the living water,
   sing it so that everybody knows.

© Copyright Christian Strover/Jubilate Hymns, 4 Thorne Park Road, Chelston, Torquay TQ2 6RX, UK.
Used by permission.

818 He is the King

Words and music: Unknown

819 He's got the whole world in his hand

Words and music: Traditional

2. He's got you and me, brother, in his hand. *(x3)*
He's got the whole world in his hand.

3. He's got you and me, sister, in his hand. *(x3)*
He's got the whole world in his hand.

4. He's got the little tiny baby in his hand. *(x3)*
He's got the whole world in his hand.

5. He's got ev'rybody here in his hand. *(x3)*
He's got the whole world in his hand.

820 Hey, now, everybody sing

Words and music: Orien Johnson

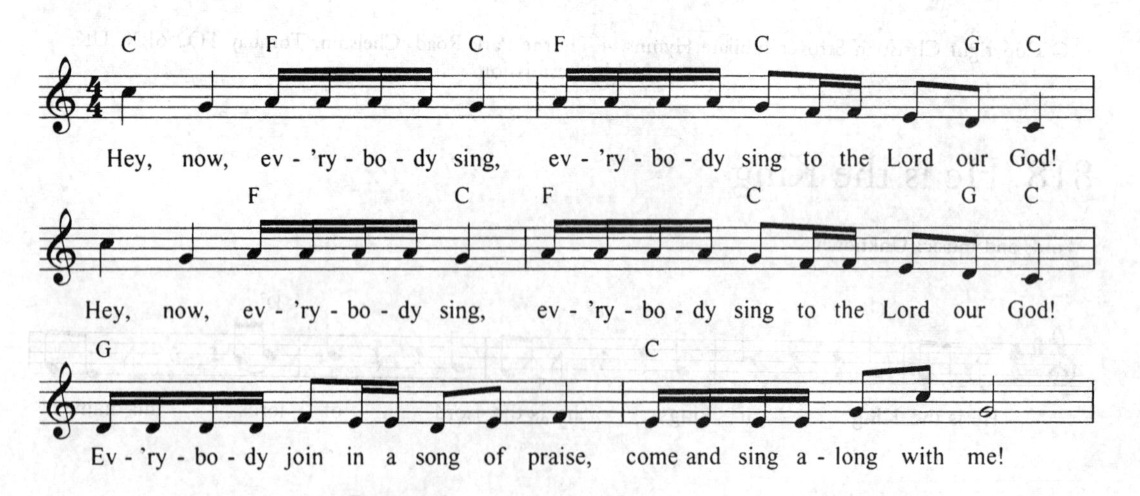

© Copyright 1982 Fred Bock Muisc Company. Administered by Kingsway's Thankyou Music, P.O. Box 75, Eastbourne, East Sussex BN23 6NW, UK. Europe (excl. Germany) & British Commonwealth (excl. Canada). Used by permission.

821 Ho, ho, ho, hosanna

Words and music: Unknown

822 How did Moses cross the Red Sea?

Hugh Mitchell

Traditional melodies
adapted by Hugh Mitchell

© Copyright 1973 Zondervan Corporation/Brentwood-Benson Music Publishing.
Administered in the UK and Republic of Ireland by Bucks Music Ltd.,
Onward House, 11 Uxbridge Road, London W8 7TQ. Used by permission.

823 I could sing unending songs *The happy song*

Words and music: Martin Smith

Capo 3

F/D C/A Dm/Bm B♭/G

Oh, I could sing un - end - ing songs of how you saved my soul. Well,

F/D C/A Dm/Bm B♭/G *2nd time to* 𝄌 *Last time* F/D

I could dance a thou - sand miles be - cause of your great love.

© Copyright 1994 Curious? Music UK. P.O. Box 40, Arundel, West Sussex BN18 0UQ.
Used by permission.

F
D
C
A
B♭
G
My heart is burst - ing, Lord, to tell of all you've done. Of how you changed my life and
wiped a - way the past. I wan-na shout it out, from ev-'ry roof - top sing.
For now I know that God is for me, not a - gainst me. Ev - 'ry - bo - dy's sing-ing now,
'cos we're so hap-py! Ev - 'ry - bo - dy's danc-ing now,
'cos we're so hap-py! If on-ly we could see your face and
Gm⁷
Em⁷
Gm
Em
see you smi-ling o - ver us and un-seen an - gels ce - le - brate, for joy is in this
place!
Dm⁷
Bm⁷
B♭⁷
G⁷
D.S.
Oh,

824 I feel spring in the air today *Spring in the air*

Susan Sayers (b.1946) Noel Rawsthorne (b.1929)

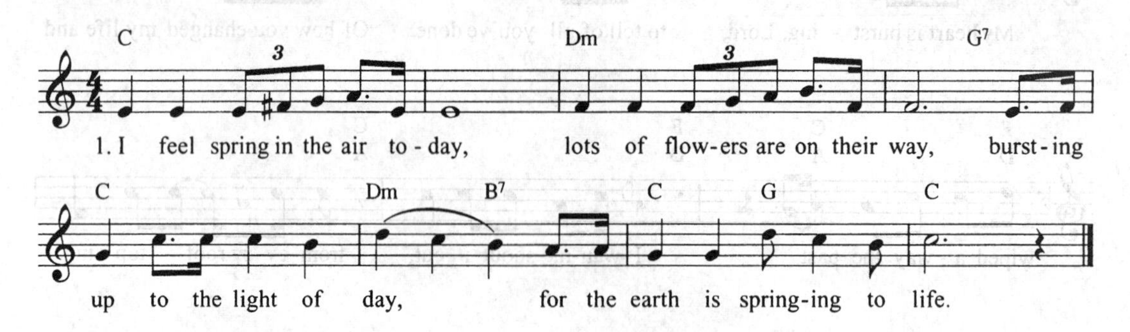

2. I feel spring in the air today,
lambs are ready to frisk and play;
nests are built as the tall trees sway,
for the earth is springing to life.

3. I feel spring in the air today,
Lord and Father, I want to say
thanks for showing your love this way,
for the earth is springing to life.

©Copyright 1986, 1987 Kevin Mayhew Ltd.

825 If I were a butterfly

Words and music: Brian Howard

© Copyright 1975 Mission Hills Music. Administered by CopyCare, P.O. Box 77,
Hailsham, East Sussex BN27 3EF, UK. (music@copycare.com). Used by permission.

2. If I were an elephant,
I'd thank you, Lord, by raising my trunk,
and if I were a kangaroo,
you know I'd hop right up to you,
and if I were an octopus,
I'd thank you, Lord, for my fine looks,
but I just thank you, Father, for making me 'me'.

3. If I were a wiggly worm,
I'd thank you, Lord, that I could squirm,
and if I were a billy goat,
I'd thank you, Lord, for my strong throat,
and if I were a fuzzy wuzzy bear,
I'd thank you, Lord, for my fuzzy wuzzy hair,
but I just thank you, Father, for making me 'me'.

826 If I were an astronaut

Words and music: Susan Sayers (b.1946)

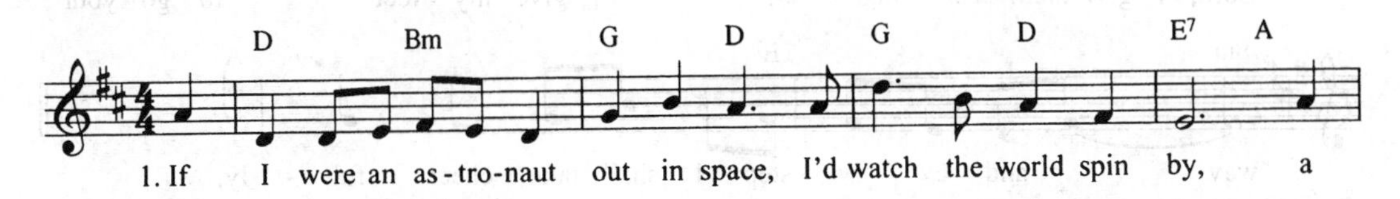

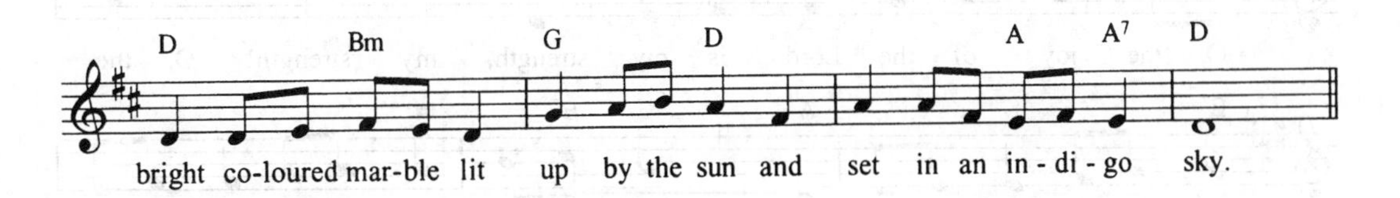

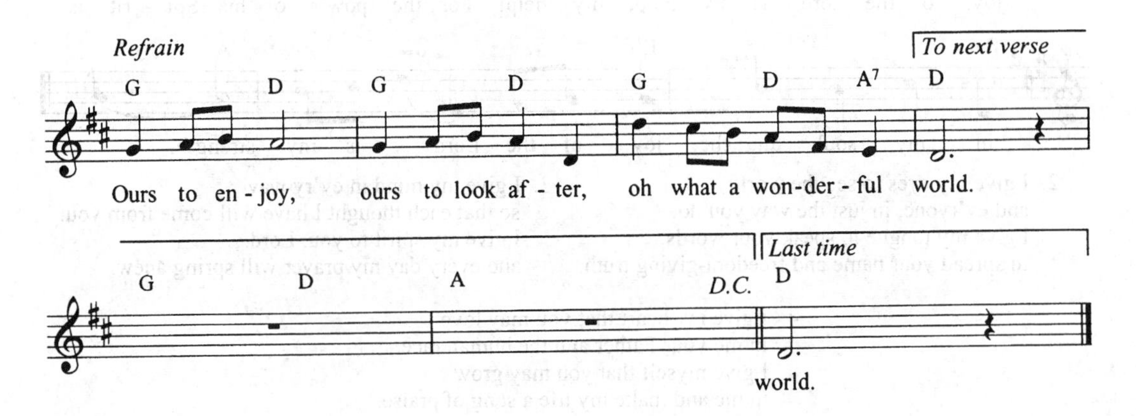

2. If I were a monkey, and treetop high,
I'd see the fruits that grow,
delicious and succulent, fragrant and sweet,
on branches above and below.

3. If I were an octopus in the sea,
the sun would filter through
to dapple the corals and brighten the shells
down deep in an ocean of blue.

© Copyright 1986 Kevin Mayhew Ltd.

827 I give my hands

Words and music: Estelle White (b.1925)

2. I give my eyes to see the world
and ev'ryone, in just the way you do.
I give my tongue to speak your words,
to spread your name and freedom-giving truth.

3. I give my mind in ev'ry way
so that each thought I have will come from you.
I give my spirit to you, Lord,
and every day my prayer will spring anew.

4. I give my heart that you may love
in me your Father and the human race.
I give myself that you may grow
in me and make my life a song of praise.

© Copyright 1978 Kevin Mayhew Ltd.

828 I gotta home in gloryland

Words and music: Traditional

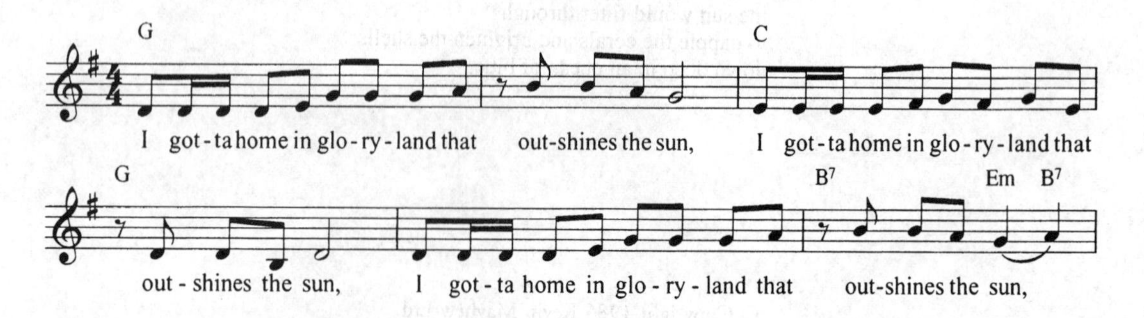

829 I have a friend

Words and music: Susan Sayers (b.1946)

2. If I am lost he will search until he finds me,
   if I am scared he will help me to be brave.
   All I've to do is turn to him and ask him.
   I know he'll honour the promise he gave.

3. 'Don't be afraid,' Jesus said, 'for I am with you.'
   'Don't be afraid,' Jesus said, 'for I am here.
   Now and for ever, anywhere you travel,
   I shall be with you, I'll always be near.'

© Copyright 1986 Kevin Mayhew Ltd.

830 I'm accepted, I'm forgiven

Words and music: Rob Hayward

© Copyright 1985 Kingsway's Thankyou Music, P.O. Box 75, Eastbourne, East Sussex BN23 6NW, UK. (tym@kingsway.co.uk). Used by permission.

831 I may live in a great big city

Words and music: Ian Smale

© Copyright 1998 Glorie Music. Administered by Kingsway's Thankyou Music, P.O. Box 75, Eastbourne, East Sussex BN23 6NW, UK. (tym@kingsway.co.uk). Worldwide (excl. North America). Used by permission.

832 I'm black, I'm white, I'm short, I'm tall

Michael Forster (b.1946) Christopher Tambling (b.1964)

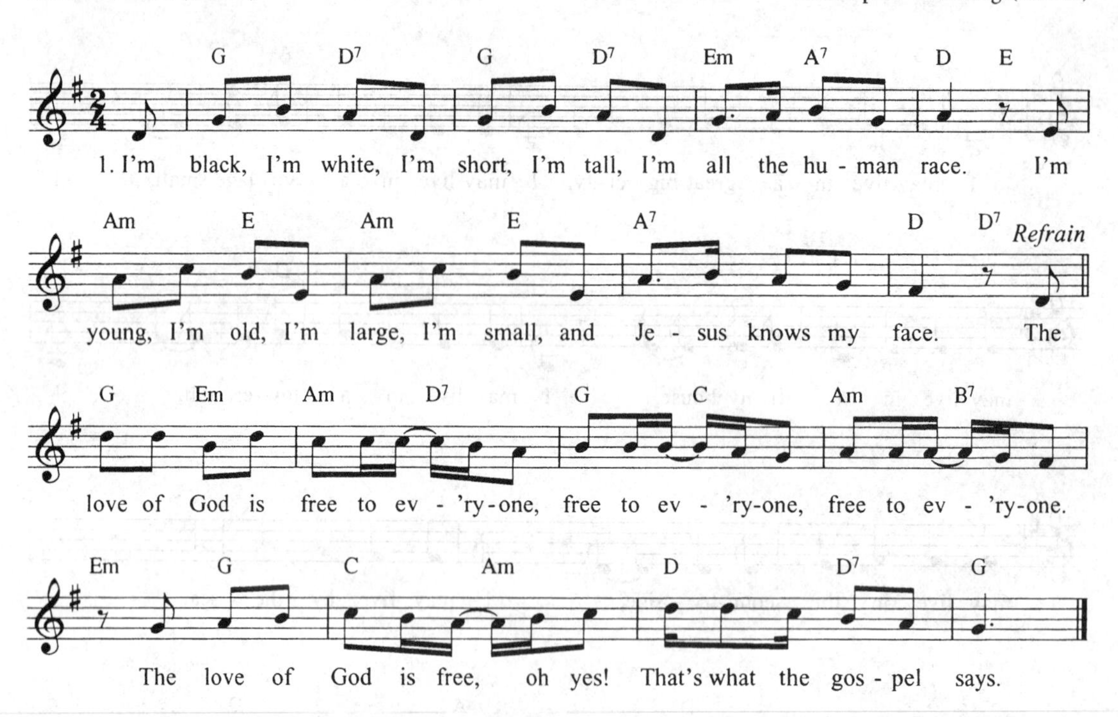

2. I'm rich, I'm poor, I'm pleased, I'm sad,
I'm ev'ryone you see.
I'm quick, I'm slow, I'm good, I'm bad,
I know that God loves me.

3. So tall and thin, and short and wide,
and any shade of face,
I'm one of those for whom Christ died,
part of the human race.

© Copyright 1993 Kevin Mayhew Ltd.

833 I'm gonna click

Words and music: Capt. Alan J. Price, CA

© Copyright 1991 Daybreak Music Ltd., Silverdale Road, Eastbourne, East Sussex BN20 7AB, UK.
All rights reserved. International copyright secured. Used by permission.

2. I'm gonna zoom, zoom, zoom
around the room, room, room,
I'm gonna zoom around the room and praise the Lord!
Because of all he's done,
I'm gonna make him 'Number One'.
I'm gonna zoom around the room and praise the Lord!

3. I'm gonna sing, sing, sing,
I'm gonna shout, shout, shout,
I'm gonna sing, I'm gonna shout and praise the Lord!
Because of all he's done,
I'm gonna make him 'Number One'.
I'm gonna sing, I'm gonna shout and praise the Lord!

4. I'm gonna click, click, click,
I'm gonna clap, clap, clap,
I'm gonna click, I'm gonna clap and praise the Lord!
Because of all he's done,
I'm gonna make him 'Number One'.
I'm gonna click, I'm gonna clap and praise the Lord!

834 I'm singing your praise, Lord

Words and music: Mike Burn

2. I'm clapping my hands . . .

3. I'm shouting your name . . .

4. I'm jumping for joy . . .

© Copyright 1996 Chasah Music. Administered by Daybreak Music Ltd., Silverdale Road, Eastbourne, East Sussex BN20 7AB, UK. All rights reserved. International copyright secured. Used by permission.

835 In the upper room *You must do for others*

Words and music: Gerard Fitzpatrick

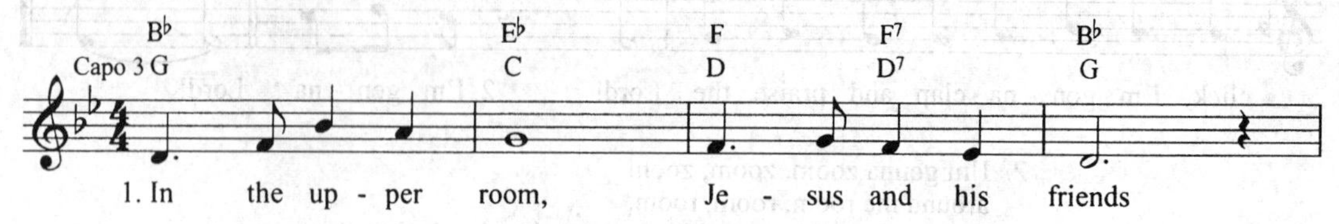

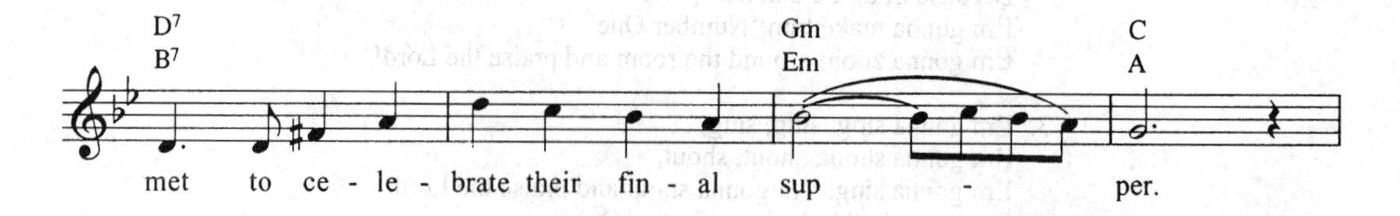

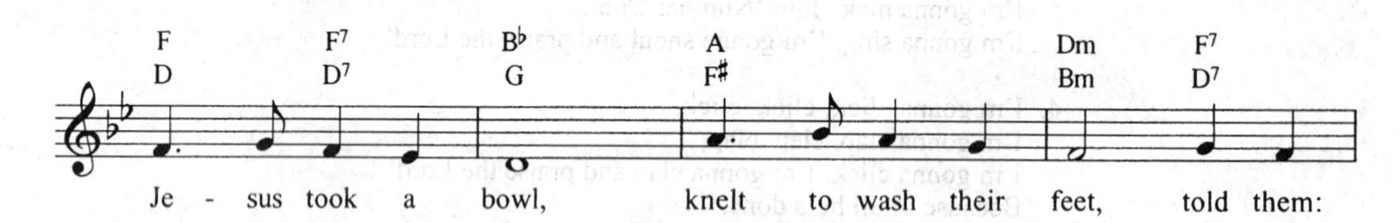

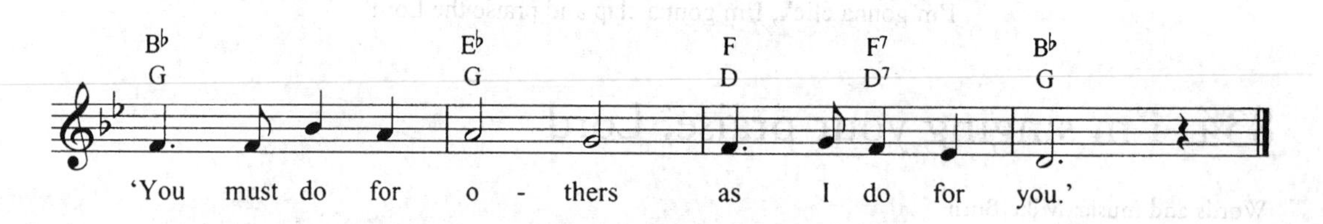

2. Peter was annoyed: 'This will never do!
You, as Master, should not play the servant!'
Jesus took a towel, knelt to dry their feet, told them:
'You must do for others as I do for you.'

© Copyright1986 Kevin Mayhew Ltd.

836 I reach up high

Words and music: Judy Bailey

2. May my whole life be a song of praise,
to worship God in ev'ry way.
In this song the actions praise his name,
I want my actions ev'ry day to do the same.

© Copyright 1993 Daybreak Music Ltd., Silverdale Road, Eastbourne, East Sussex BN20 7AB, UK.
All rights reserved. International copyright secured. Used by permission.

837 Isn't it good

Words and music: Capt. Alan J. Price, CA

© Copyright 1992 Daybreak Music Ltd., Silverdale Road, Eastbourne, East Sussex BN20 7AB, UK.
All rights reserved. International copyright secured. Used by permission.

838 It's me, O Lord

Words and music: Spiritual

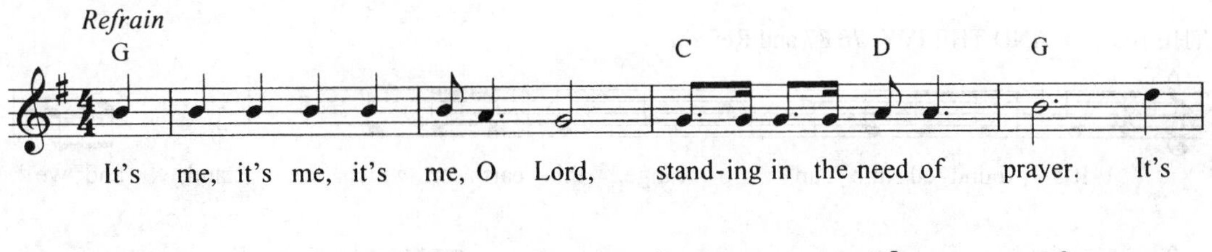

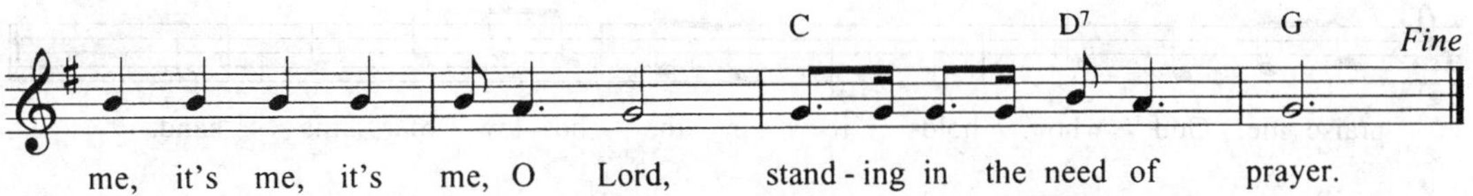

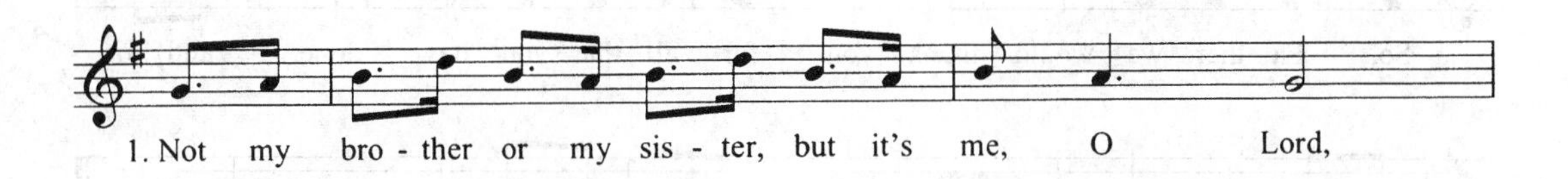

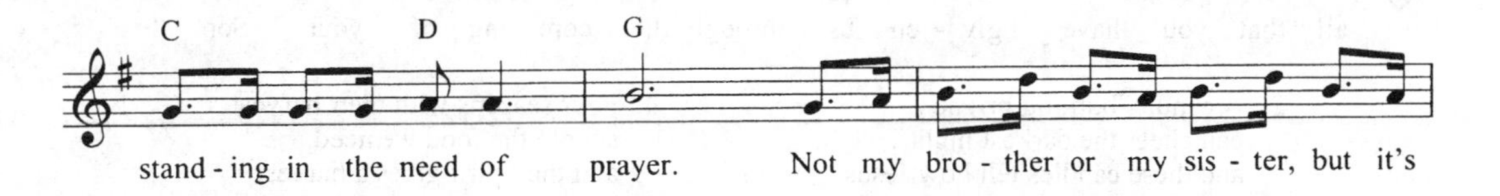

2. Not my mother or my father,
but it's me, O Lord,
standing in the need of prayer.
Not my mother or my father,
but it's me, O Lord,
standing in the need of prayer.

3. Not the stranger or my neighbour,
but it's me, O Lord,
standing in the need of prayer.
Not the stranger or my neighbour,
but it's me, O Lord,
standing in the need of prayer.

839 It's rounded like an orange

Basil Bridge (b.1927)

Traditional English melody

THE HOLLY AND THE IVY 76 87 and Refrain

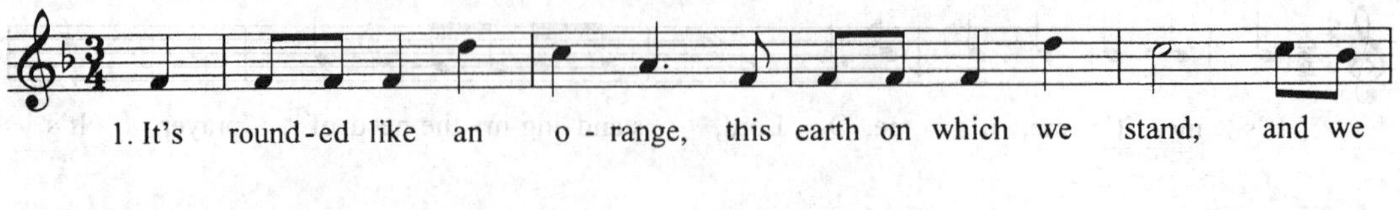

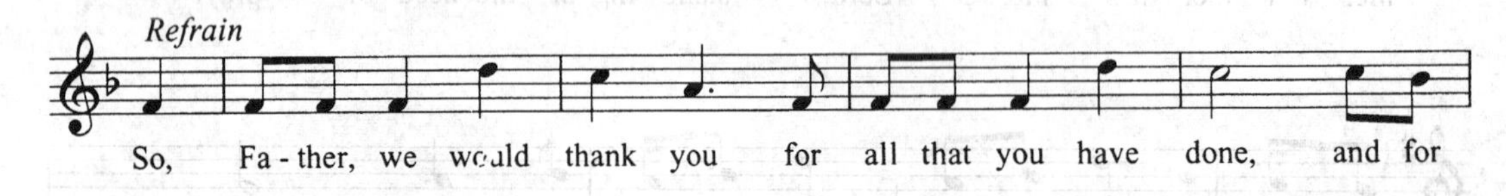

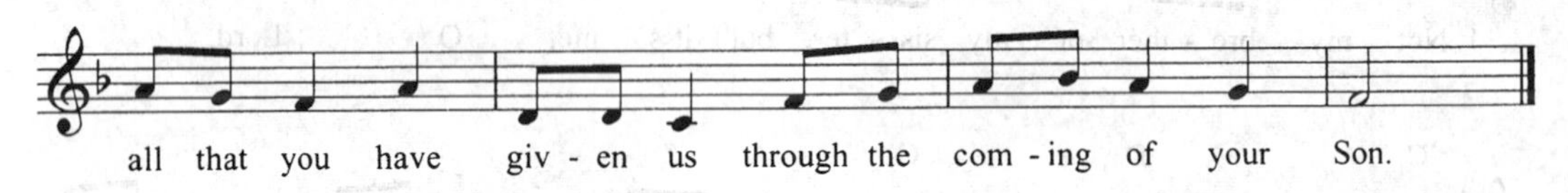

2. A candle, burning brightly,
can cheer the darkest night,
and these candles tell how Jesus
came to bring a dark world light.

3. The ribbon round the orange
reminds us of the cost;
how the Shepherd, strong and gentle,
gave his life to save the lost.

4. Four seasons with their harvest
supply the food we need,
and the Spirit gives a harvest
that can make us rich indeed.

5. We come with our Christingles
to tell of Jesus' birth,
and we praise the God who blessed us
by his coming to this earth.

Text © Copyright 1990 Oxford University Press, Great Clarendon Street, Oxford OX2 6DP, UK.
Used by permission from *New Songs of Praise 5*.

840 It takes an almighty hand

Words and music: Ian White

© Copyright 1987 Little Misty Music. Administered by Kingsway's Thankyou Music, P.O. Box 75, Eastbourne, East Sussex BN23 6NW, UK. (tym@kingsway.co.uk). Worldwide (excl. Australasia). Used by permission.

2. It takes his hand to turn the seasons,
to give the sun and snow their hour;
and in this plan we learn his reason,
his nature and eternal power.

3. It took his hands to carry sorrow,
for ev'ry sin that we have done;
and on a cross he bought tomorrow,
a world of good, like he'd begun.

4. And in his hands there is perfection,
that in this land we only taste;
for now, we see a poor reflection,
then, we shall see him face to face.

841 I've got peace like a river

Words and music: Spiritual

2. I've got joy like a fountain,
I've got joy like a fountain,
I've got joy like a fountain in my soul.

3. I've got love like an ocean,
I've got love like an ocean,
I've got love like an ocean in my soul.

842 I want to be a tree that's bearing fruit

I want to be a blooming tree

Words and music: Doug Horley

© Copyright 1996 Kingsway's Thankyou Music, P.O. Box 75, Eastbourne, East Sussex BN23 6NW, UK. (tym@kingsway.co.uk). Used by permission.

843 I will click my fingers

Words and music: Ian Smale

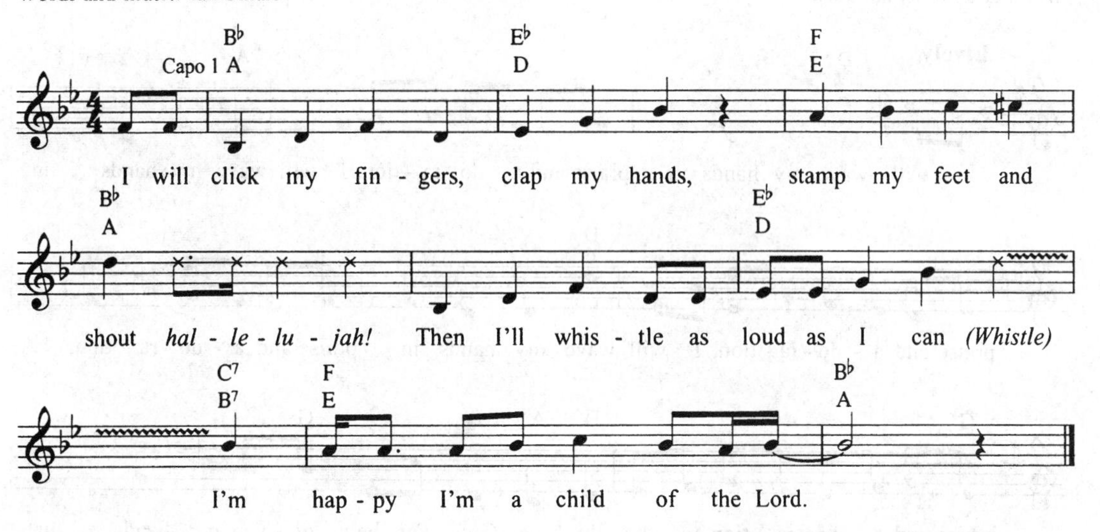

© Copyright 1989 Kingsway's Thankyou Music, P.O. Box 75, Eastbourne, East Sussex BN23 6NW, UK. (tym@kingsway.co.uk). Worldwide (excl. USA and Canada).Used by permission.

844 I will wave my hands

Words and music: Ian Smale

© Copyright 1985 Kingsway's Thankyou Music, P.O. Box 75, Eastbourne, East Sussex BN23 6NW, UK. (tym@kingsway.co.uk). Used by permission.

845 Jesus bids us shine

Susan Warner (1819-1885) E.O. Excell (1851-1921)

JESUS BIDS US SHINE 10 11 10 10

2. Jesus bids us shine,
first of all for him;
well he sees and knows it,
if our light grows dim.
He looks down from heaven
to see us shine,
you in your small corner,
and I in mine.

3. Jesus bids us shine,
then, for all around:
many kinds of darkness
in the world abound
sin, and want and sorrow,
so we must shine,
you in your small corner,
and I in mine.

846 Jesus had all kinds of friends

Michael Forster (b.1946) Christopher Tambling (b.1964)

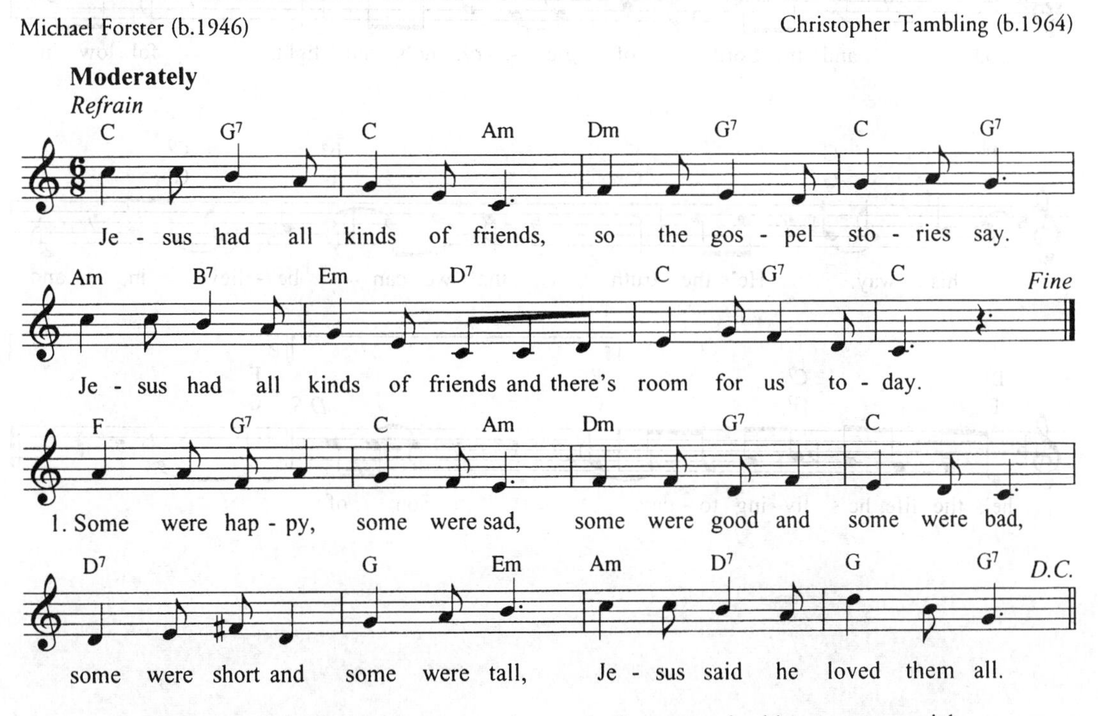

2. Some were humble, some were proud,
some were quiet, some were loud,
some were fit and some were lame,
Jesus loved them all the same.

3. Some were healthy, some were sick,
some were slow and some were quick,
some were clever, some were not,
Jesus said he loved the lot!

© Copyright 1993 Kevin Mayhew Ltd.

847 Jesus is greater

Words and music: Gill Hutchinson

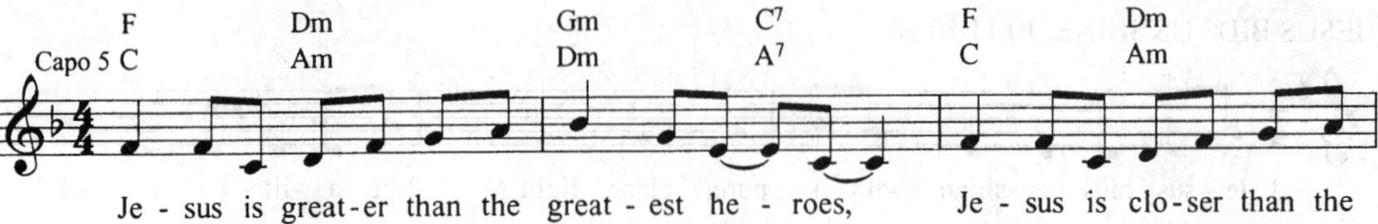

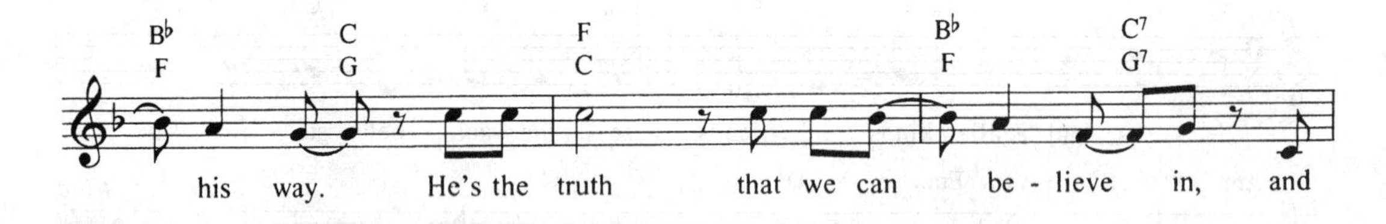

© Copyright 1992 Sea Dream Music, P.O. Box 13533, London E7 0SG, UK.
Used by permission.

848 Jesus is special

Words and music: Sarah Clark

© Copyright 1994 CN Publishing. Administered by CopyCare, P.O. Box 77, Hailsham, East Sussex BN27 3EF, UK. (music@copycare.com). Used by permission.

849 Jesus' love has got under our skin *Under our skin*

Words and music: Graham Kendrick (b.1950)

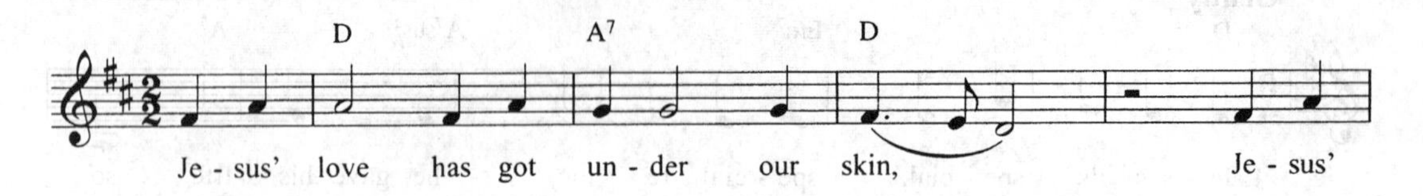

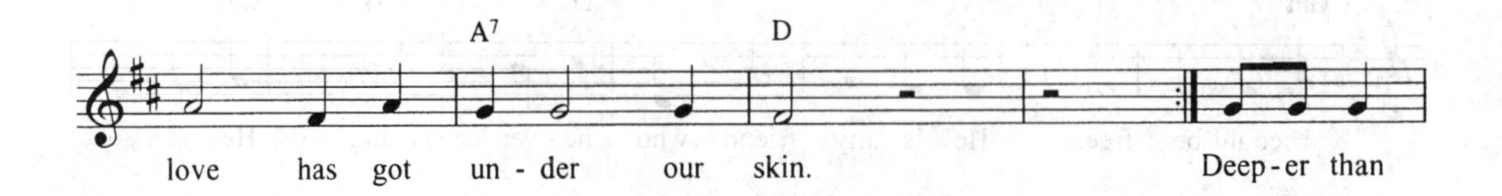

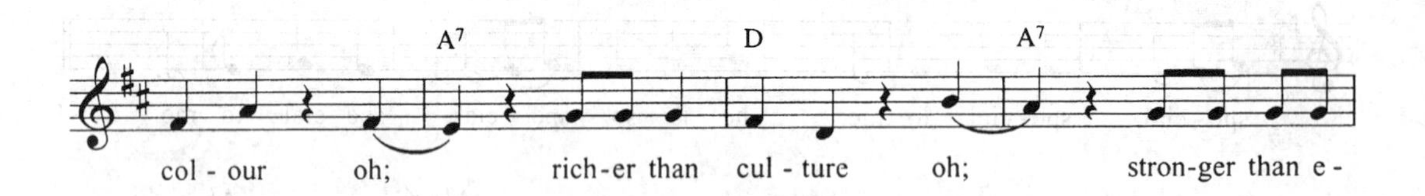

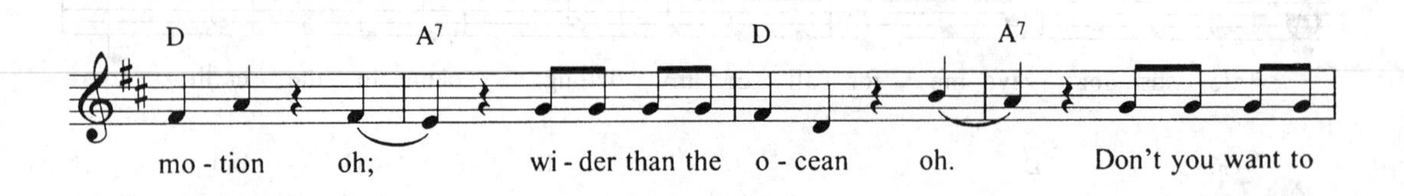

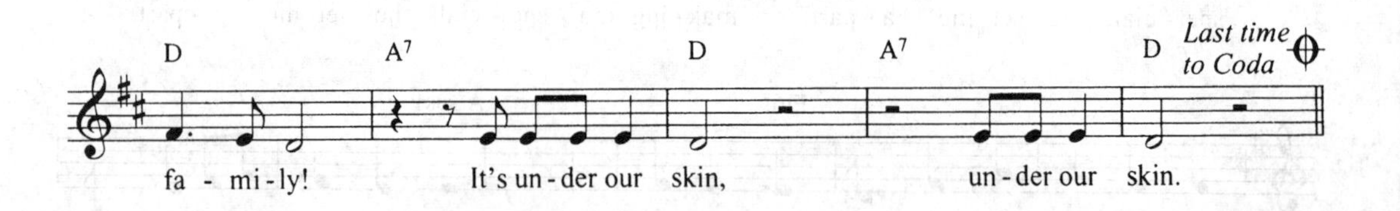

© Copyright 1996 Make Way Music, P.O. Box 263, Croydon, Surrey CR9 5AP, UK.
International copyright secured. All rights reserved. Used by permission.

850 Jesus' love is very wonderful

H.W. Rattle

Unknown

Text © Copyright Scripture Union, 207-209 Queensway, Bletchley, Milton Keynes MK2 2EB.
Used by permission.

851 Jesus put this song

Words and music: Graham Kendrick (b.1950)

Each verse should be sung faster

2. Jesus taught us how to live in harmony,
Jesus taught us how to live in harmony;
diff'rent faces, diff'rent races, he made us one.
Jesus taught us how to live in harmony.

3. Jesus turned our sorrow into dancing,
Jesus turned our sorrow into dancing;
changed our tears of sadness into rivers of joy.
Jesus turned our sorrow into a dance.

© Copyright 1986 Kingsway's Thankyou Music, P.O. Box 75, Eastbourne, East Sussex BN23 6NW, UK. (tym@kingsway.co.uk). Used by permission.

852 Jesus went away to the desert

Michael Forster (b.1946) Christopher Tambling (b.1964)

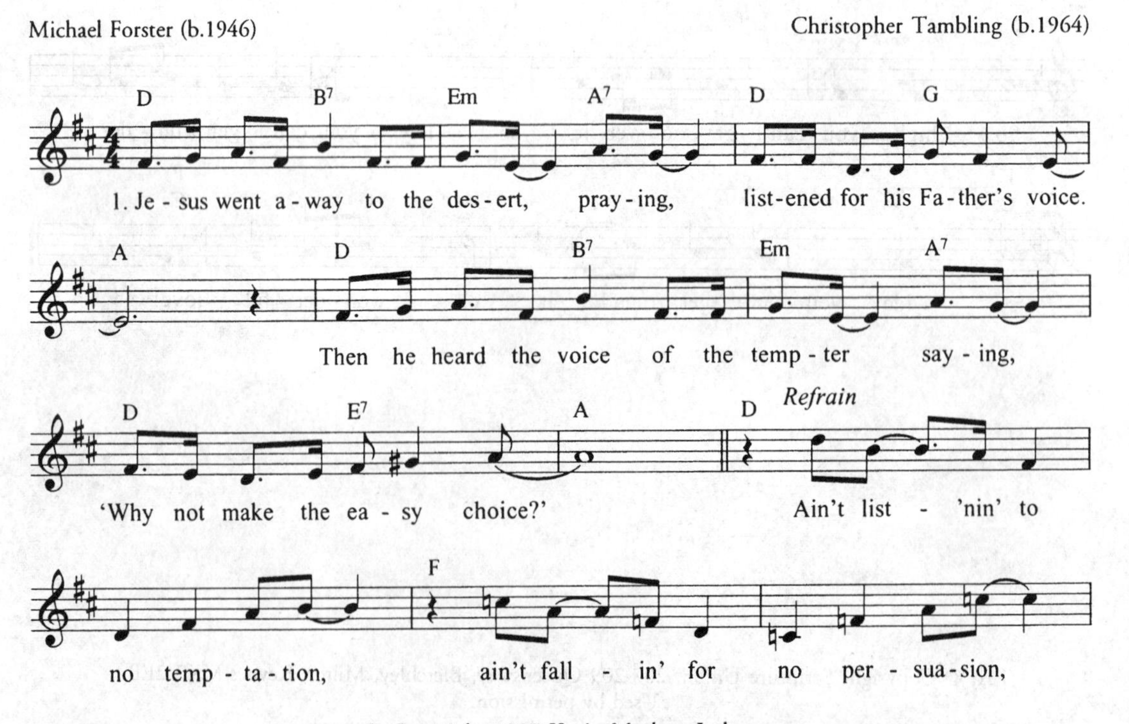

© Copyright 1997 Kevin Mayhew Ltd.

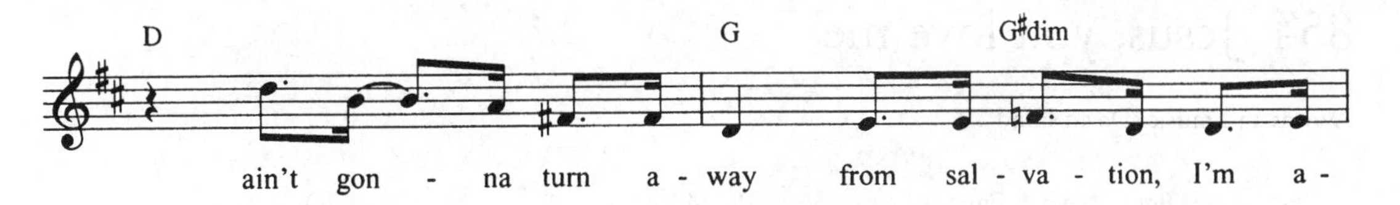

2. 'There's an easy way if you'd only choose it,
you can turn the stones to bread!
What's the good of pow'r if you don't abuse it?
Gotta keep youself well fed!'

3. 'What about a stunt to attract attention,
showing off your special pow'r?
You'd get more applause than I'd care to mention
jumping from the Temple tow'r!'

4. 'Ev'rything you want will be right there for you,
listen to the words I say!
Nobody who matters will dare ignore you;
my way is the easy way.'

853 Jesus will never, ever

Words and music: Greg Leavers

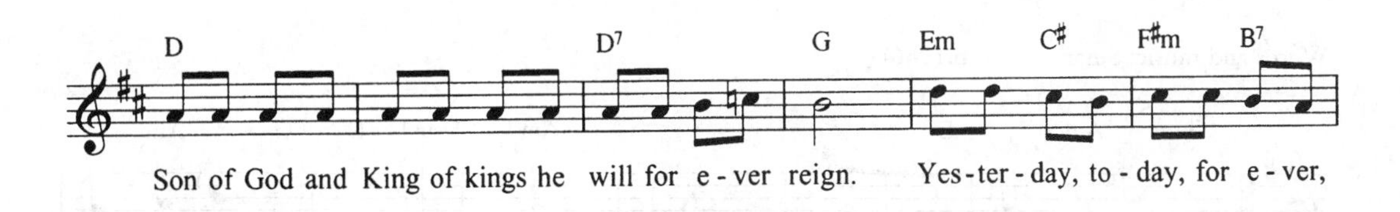

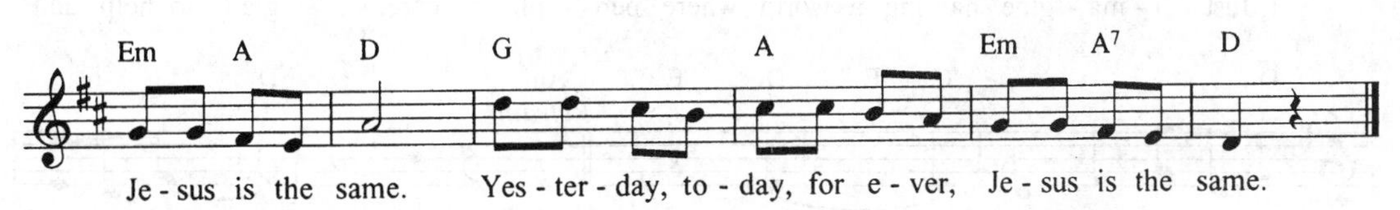

© Copyright 1990 Greg Leavers, 1 Haws Hill,
Carnforth, Lancs. LA5 9DD, UK. Used by permission.

854 Jesus, you love me

Words and music: David Hind

© Copyright 1992 Kingsway's Thankyou Music, P.O. Box 75, Eastbourne, East Sussex BN23 6NW, UK. (tym@kingsway.co.uk). Used by permission.

855 Just imagine

Words and music: Susan Sayers (b.1946)

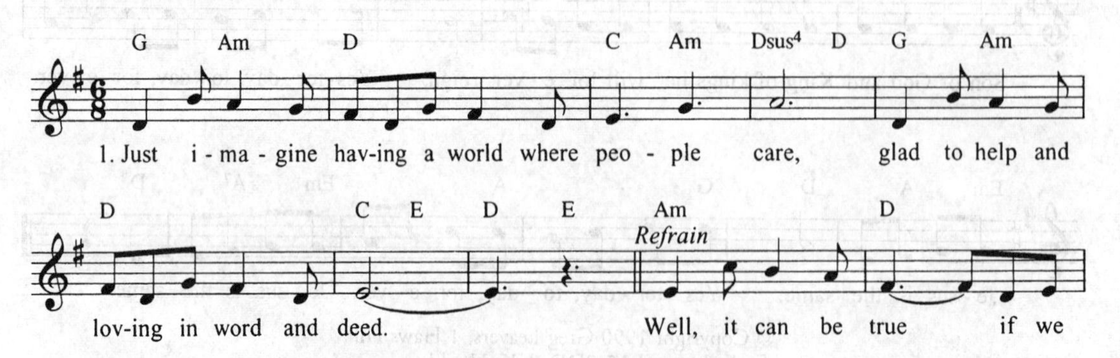

© Copyright 1986 Kevin Mayhew Ltd.

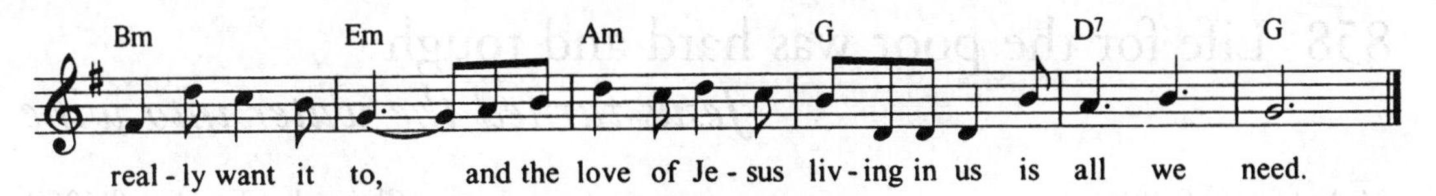

2. Just imagine having a world
where people care,
glad to give
without any hate or greed.

856 Kum ba yah

Words and music: Spiritual

2. Someone's crying, Lord, kum ba yah,
someone's crying, Lord, kum ba yah,
someone's crying, Lord, kum ba yah,
O Lord, kum ba yah.

3. Someone's singing, Lord, kum ba yah,
someone's singing, Lord, kum ba yah,
someone's singing, Lord, kum ba yah,
O Lord, kum ba yah.

4. Someone's praying, Lord, kum ba yah,
someone's praying, Lord, kum ba yah,
someone's praying, Lord, kum ba yah,
O Lord, kum ba yah.

857 Let the mountains dance and sing

Words and music: Susan Sayers (b.1946)

2. Let the water sing its song!
And the pow'rful wind so strong
whistle as it blows along! Alleluia!

3. Let the blossom all break out
in a huge unspoken shout,
just to show that God's about! Alleluia!

© Copyright 1984 Kevin Mayhew Ltd.

858 Life for the poor was hard and tough

Jesus turned the water into wine

Michael Forster (b.1946)

Christopher Tambling (b.1964)

Never hurrying

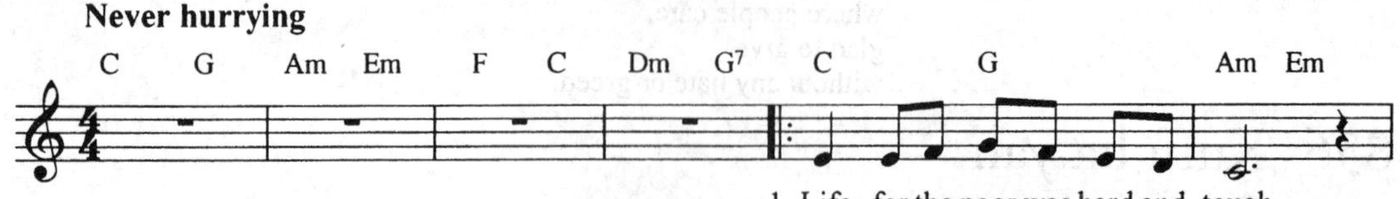

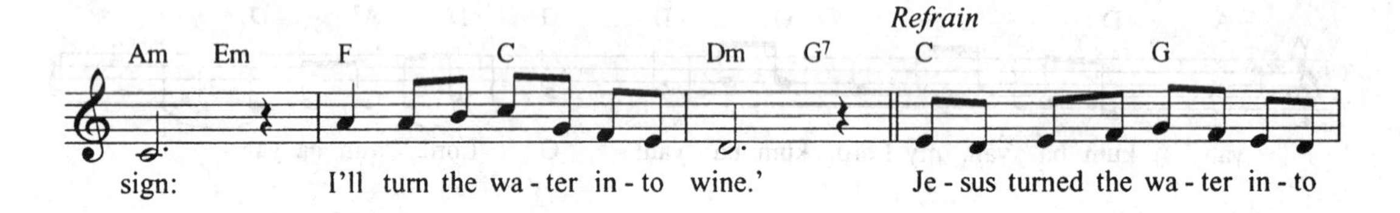

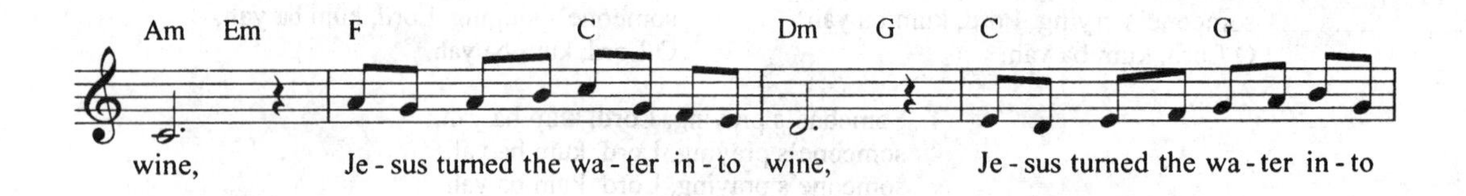

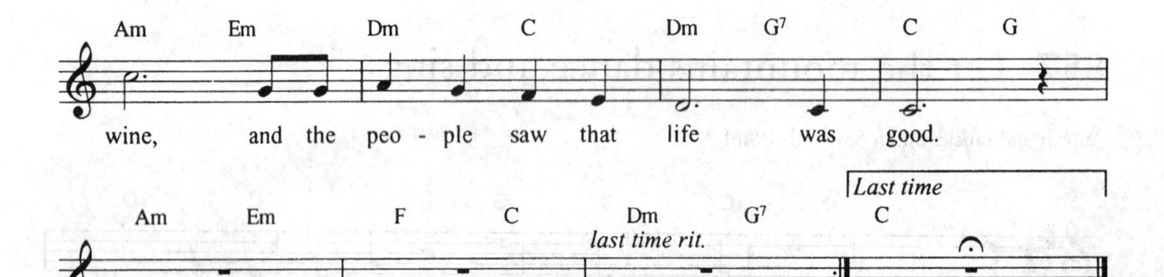

2. Life is a thing to be enjoyed,
not to be wasted or destroyed.
Laughter is part of God's design;
let's turn the water into wine!

3. Go to the lonely and the sad,
give them the news to make them glad,
helping the light of hope to shine,
turning the water into wine!

© Copyright 1993 Kevin Mayhew Ltd.

859 Little donkey

Words and music: Eric Boswell

2. Little donkey, little donkey,
on the dusty road,
there are wise men, waiting for a
sign to bring them here.
Do not falter, little donkey,
there's a star ahead;
it will guide you, little donkey,
to a cattle shed.

© Copyright 1959 Warner/Chappell Music Ltd., London W6 8BS.
Used by permission of IMP Ltd., Griffin House, 161 Hammersmith Road, London W6 8BS, UK.

860 Little Jesus, sleep away

Christopher Massey (b.1956) — Traditional Czech carol

ROCKING 10 7 88 77

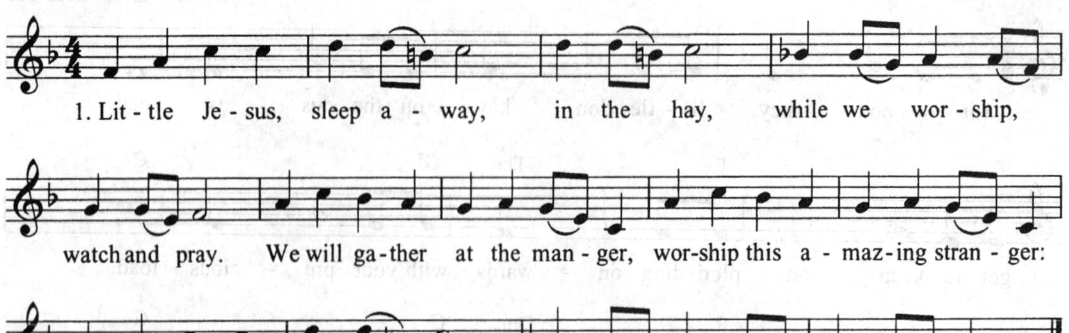

2. Little Jesus, sleep away, while you may;
pain is for another day.
While you sleep, we will not wake you,
when you cry we'll not forsake you.
Little Jesus, sleep away,
we will worship you today.

Text © Copyright 1999 Kevin Mayhew Ltd.

861 Little Jesus, sweetly sleep

Traditional Czech carol
trans. Percy Dearmer (1867-1936)

Traditional Czech carol
collected by Martin Shaw (1875-1958)

ROCKING 10 7 88 77

2. Mary's little baby sleep, sweetly sleep,
sleep in comfort, slumber deep;
we will rock you, rock you, rock you,
we will rock you, rock you, rock you;
we will serve you all we can,
darling, darling little man.

© Copyright Oxford University Press, Great Clarendon Street,
Oxford OX2 6DP, UK. Used by permission.

862 Lord of the future

Words and music: Ian D. Craig

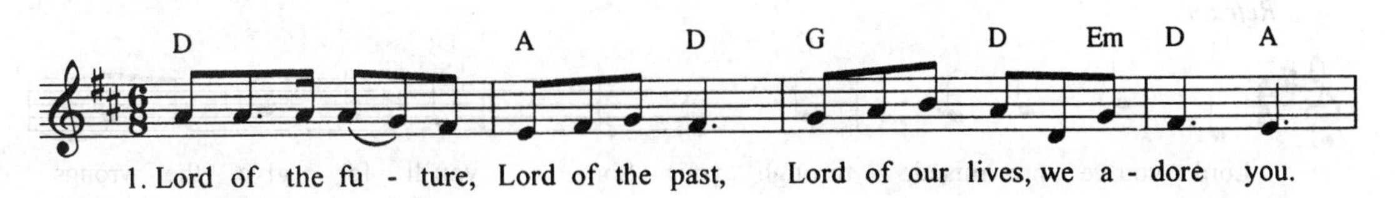

2. Lord of tomorrow, Lord of today,
Lord over all, you are worthy.
Lord of creation, Lord of all truth,
we give all praise to you.

© Copyright 1993 Daybreak Music Ltd., Silverdale Road, Eastbourne, East Sussex BN20 7AB, UK.
All rights reserved. International copyright secured. Used by permission.

863 Lord, we've come to worship you

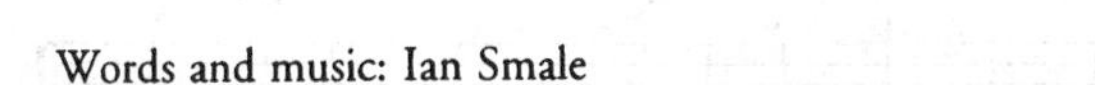
Words and music: Ian Smale

With a gentle rhythm

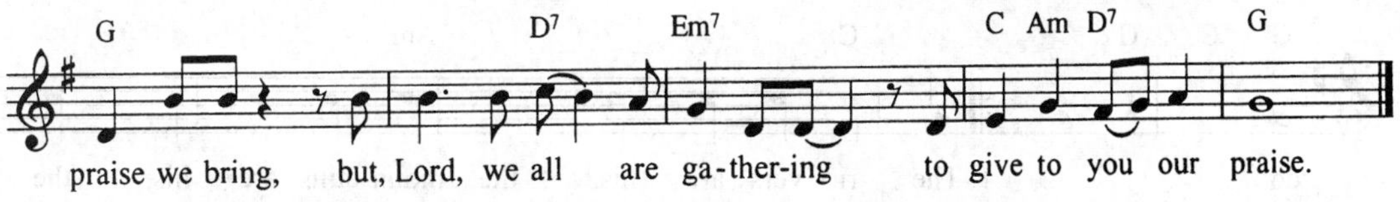

© Copyright 1989 Kingsway's Thankyou Music, P.O. Box 75, Eastbourne, East Sussex BN23 6NW, UK.
(tym@kingsway.co.uk). Worldwide (excl. USA and Canada).Used by permission.

864 Lord, you've promised through your Son

Lord, forgive us

Words and music: Capt. Alan J. Price, CA

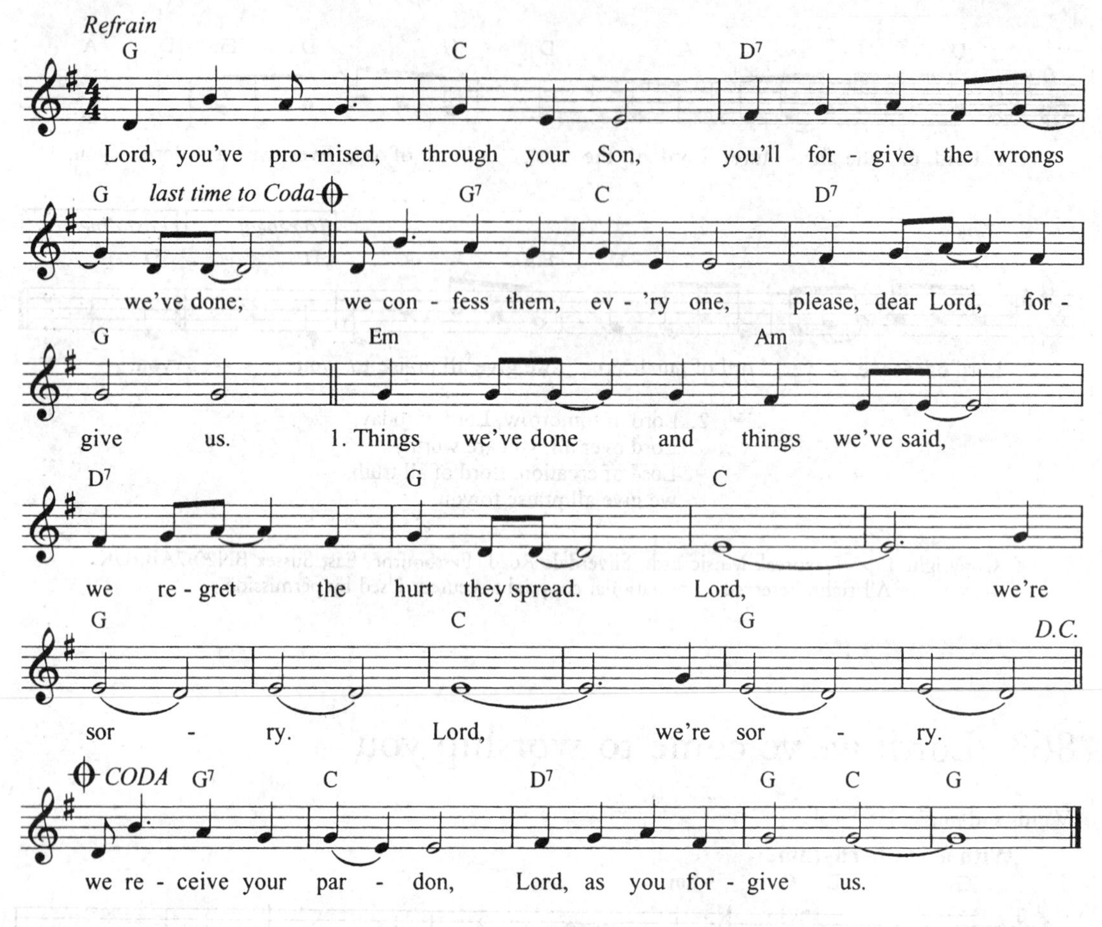

2. Sinful and unkind thoughts too,
all of these are known to you.
Lord, we're sorry.
Lord, we're sorry.

3. And the things we've left undone,
words and deeds we should have done.
Lord, we're sorry.
Lord, we're sorry.

© Copyright 1992 Daybreak Music Ltd., Silverdale Road, Eastbourne, East Sussex BN20 7AB, UK.
All rights reserved. International copyright secured. Used by permission.

865 My God is so big

Words and music: Traditional

Brightly

Refrain G Em Am D7

My God is so big, so strong and so migh - ty there's no - thing that he can - not

G C G C Am7

do. 1. The ri - vers are his, the moun - tains are his, the

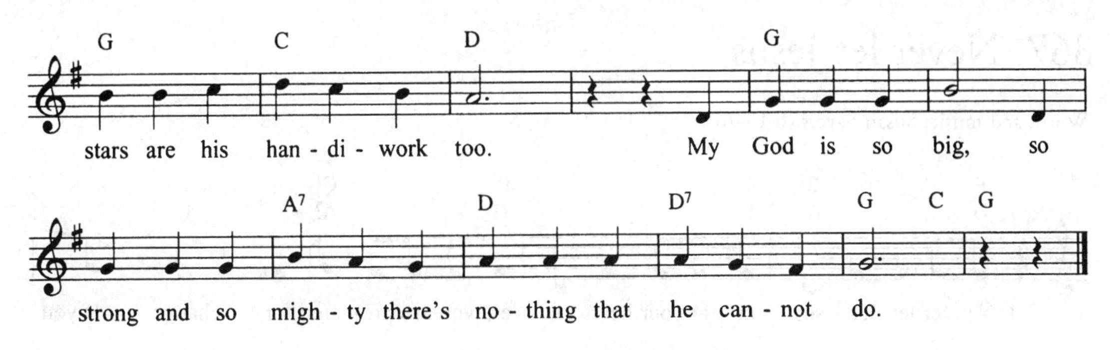

2. He's called you to live for him ev'ry day
in all that you say and you do . . .

866 My mouth was made for worship

Words and music: Ian Smale

2. My heart was made for loving,
my mind to know God's ways,
my body was made a temple,
my life is one of praise to Jesus.
And all God's people said: Amen,
hallelujah, amen, praise and glory,
amen, amen, amen, amen.
Wo, wo, wo, wo, wo.

© Copyright 1989 Glorie Music. Administered by Kingsway's Thankyou Music, P.O. Box 75, Eastbourne, East Sussex BN23 6NW, UK. (tym@kingsway.co.uk). Worldwide. Used by permission.

867 Never let Jesus

Words and music: Susan Sayers (b.1946)

2. Never let Jesus into your heart
unless you are prepared for change.
If you once let Jesus into your heart,
you will never be the same again.
He will use your gifts to help this world,
put you where he needs you to be,
at the end of time he will welcome you,
and love you for eternity.

© Copyright 1986 Kevin Mayhew Ltd.

868 Nobody's a nobody

Words and music: John Hardwick

© Copyright 1993 Daybreak Music Ltd., Silverdale Road, Eastbourne, East Sussex BN20 7AB, UK.
All rights reserved. International copyright secured. Used by permission.

869 O come and join the dance

Words and music: Graham Kendrick (b.1950)

© Copyright 1988 Make Way Music, P.O. Box 263, Croydon, Surrey CR9 5AP, UK.
International copyright secured. All rights reserved. Used by permission.

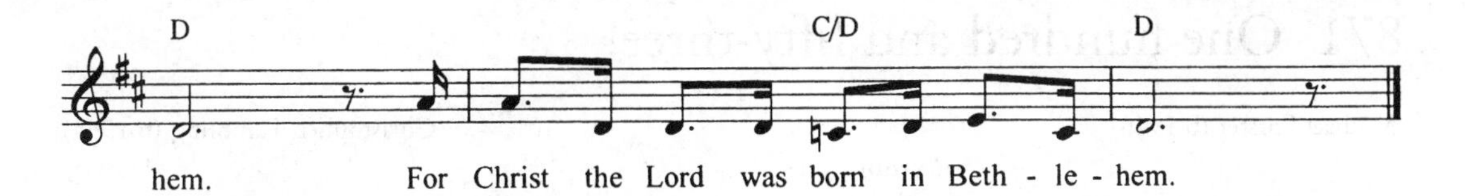

2. Come shed your heavy load and dance your worries away,
for Christ the Lord was born in Bethlehem.
He came to break the pow'r of sin and turn your night to day,
oh, take my hand and come and join the song.

3. Let laughter ring and angels sing and joy be all around,
for Christ the Lord was born in Bethlehem.
And if you seek with all your heart he surely can be found,
oh, take my hand and come and join the song.

870 O give thanks

Words and music: Joanne Pond

© Copyright 1980 Kingsway's Thankyou Music, P.O. Box 75, Eastbourne, East Sussex BN23 6NW, UK. (tym@kingsway.co.uk). Used by permission.

871 One hundred and fifty-three!

Michael Forster (b.1946) Christopher Tambling (b.1964)

2. We got all the fish to the shore,
we wondered how many there'd be.
So we started to count,
and what an amount:
one hundred and fifty-three!

3. Now here was a wonderful sight
we'd never expected to see;
and the net didn't break,
it was able to take
the hundred and fifty-three!

4. So whether you're rich or you're poor,
whatever your race or your sect,
be you black, white or brown,
Jesus wants you around,
there's plenty of room in the net!

© Copyright 1993 Kevin Mayhew Ltd.

872 Our God is so great

Words and music: Unknown

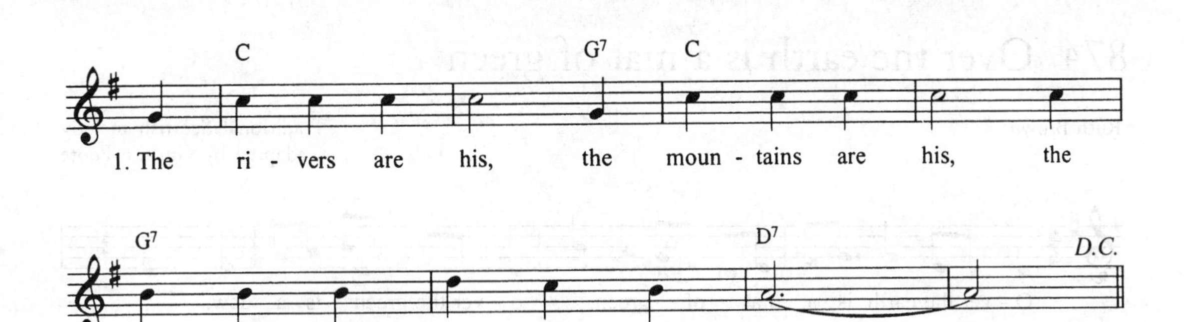

2. He's called you to live for him ev'ry day
in all that you say and you do . . .

873 Out to the great wide world we go

Michael Forster (b.1946)

Christopher Tambling (b.1964)

2. People sad and lonely,
wond'ring how to cope;
let's find ways of showing
Jesus gives us hope. So:

© Copyright 1993 Kevin Mayhew Ltd.

874 Over the earth is a mat of green

Ruth Brown

Traditional Scottish melody
adapted by Guthrie Foote

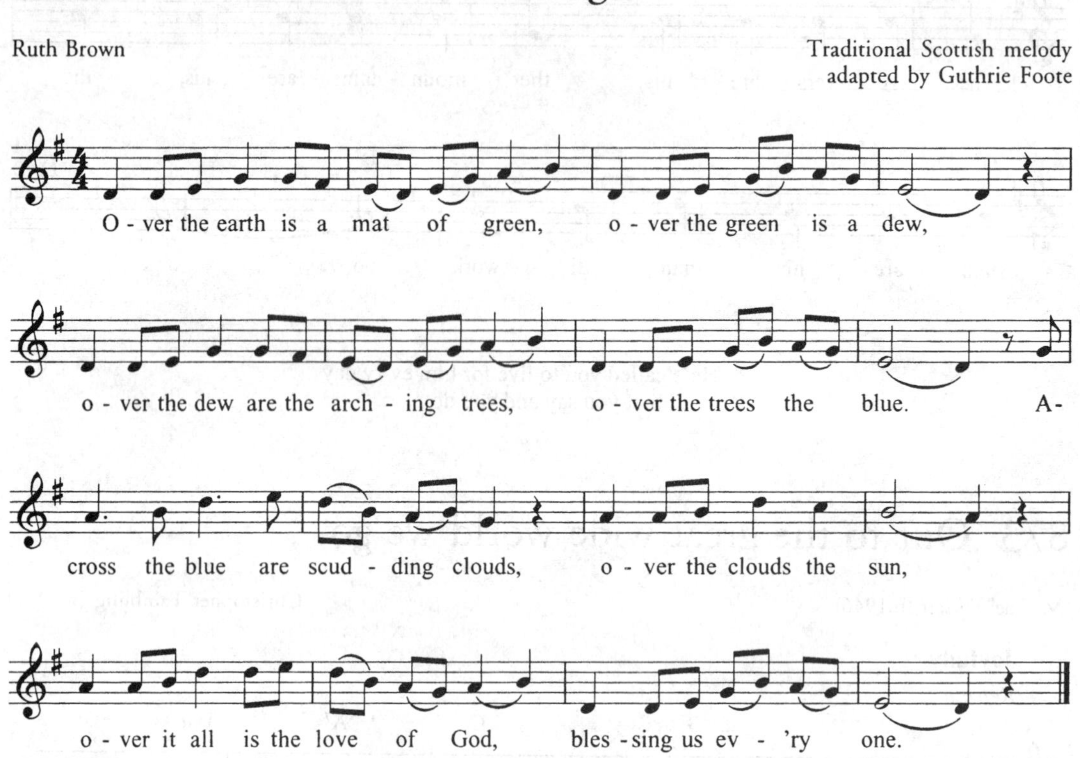

© Copyright Oxford University Press, Great Clarendon Street, Oxford OX2 6DP. UK.
Used by permission.

875 Over the mountains and the sea

I could sing of your love for ever

Words and music: Martin Smith

© Copyright 1994 Curious? Music UK. P.O. Box 40, Arundel, West Sussex BN18 0UQ.
Used by permission.

876 O when the saints go marching in

Words and music: Traditional

2. O when they crown him Lord of all . . .

3. O when all knees bow at his name . . .

4. O when they sing the Saviour's praise . . .

5. O when the saints go marching in . . .

877 Peter and John went to pray *Silver and gold*

Words and music: Unknown
based on Acts 3

878 Praise and thanksgiving

Words and music: Unknown

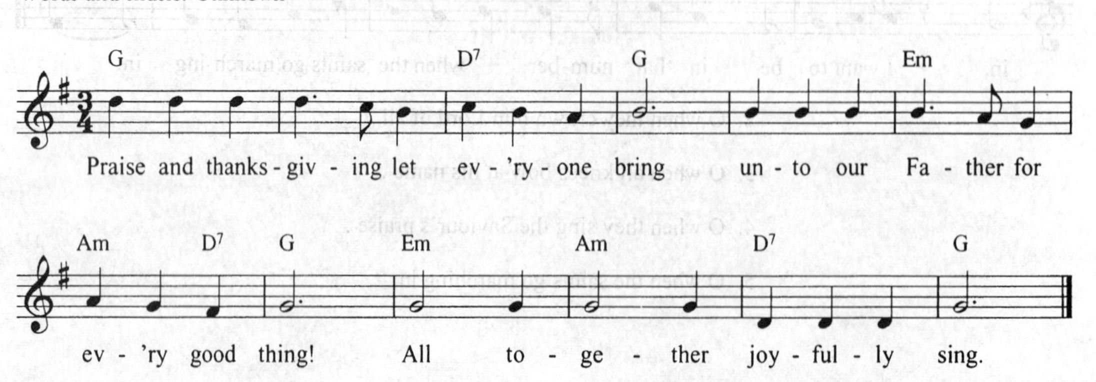

879 Praise God in his holy place

Michael Forster (b.1946)
based on Psalm 150

Christopher Tambling (b.1964)

2. Praise him with the ol' wood block!
Let it swing and let it rock,
praising God around the clock!
Let ev'rything praise our God!

3. Praise him with the big bass drum,
if you've got guitars, then strum!
Now let's make those rafters hum!
Let ev'rything praise our God!

4. Praise him with the chime bars' chime,
tell the bells it's party time,
help those singers find a rhyme!
Let ev'rything praise our God!

5. Violin or xylophone,
trumpets with their awesome tone;
bowed or beaten, bashed or blown,
let ev'rything praise our God!

6. Cymbals, triangles and things,
if it crashes, howls or rings,
ev'rybody shout and sing!
Let ev'rything praise our God!

© Copyright 1997 Kevin Mayhew Ltd.

880 Prayer is like a telephone *Prayer phone*

Words and music: Paul Crouch and David Mudie

© Copyright 1991 Daybreak Music Ltd., Silverdale Road, Eastbourne, East Sussex BN20 7AB, UK.
All rights reserved. International copyright secured. Used by permission.

881 Push, little seed

Words and music: Susan Sayers (b.1946)

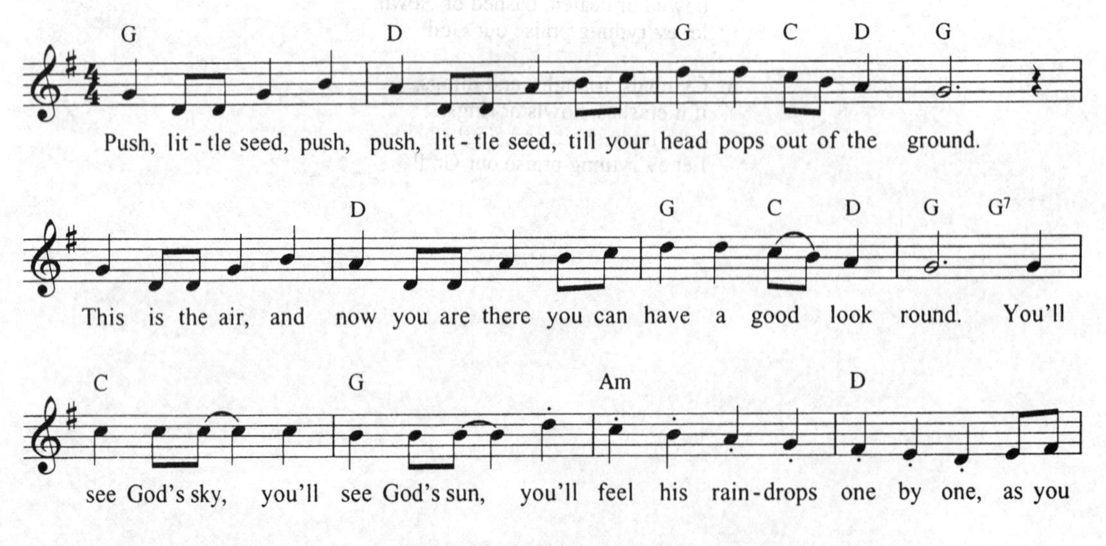

© Copyright 1986 Kevin Mayhew Ltd.

882 Put your trust

Words and music: Estelle White (b.1925)

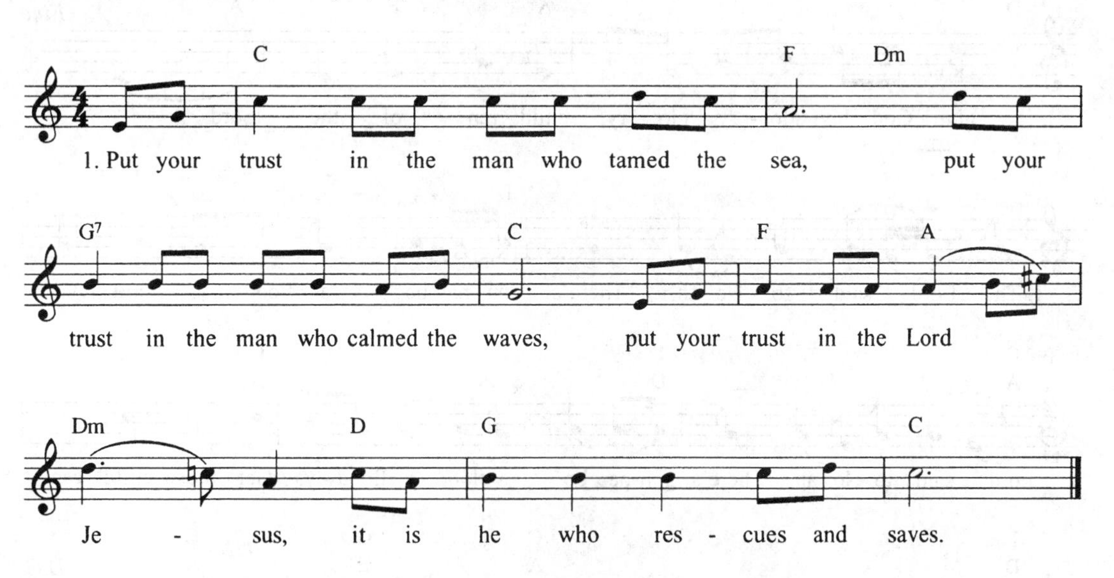

2. Put your trust in the man who cured the blind,
   put your trust in the man who helped the lame,
   put your trust in the Lord Jesus,
   there is healing strength in his name.

3. Put your trust in the man who died for you,
   put your trust in the man who conquered fear,
   put your trust in the Lord Jesus,
   for he rose from death and he's near.

4. Put your trust in the man who understands,
   put your trust in the man who is your friend,
   put your trust in the Lord Jesus,
   who will give you life without end.

© Copyright 1983 Kevin Mayhew Ltd.

883 Rise and shine

Unknown
based on Genesis 6:4

Traditional

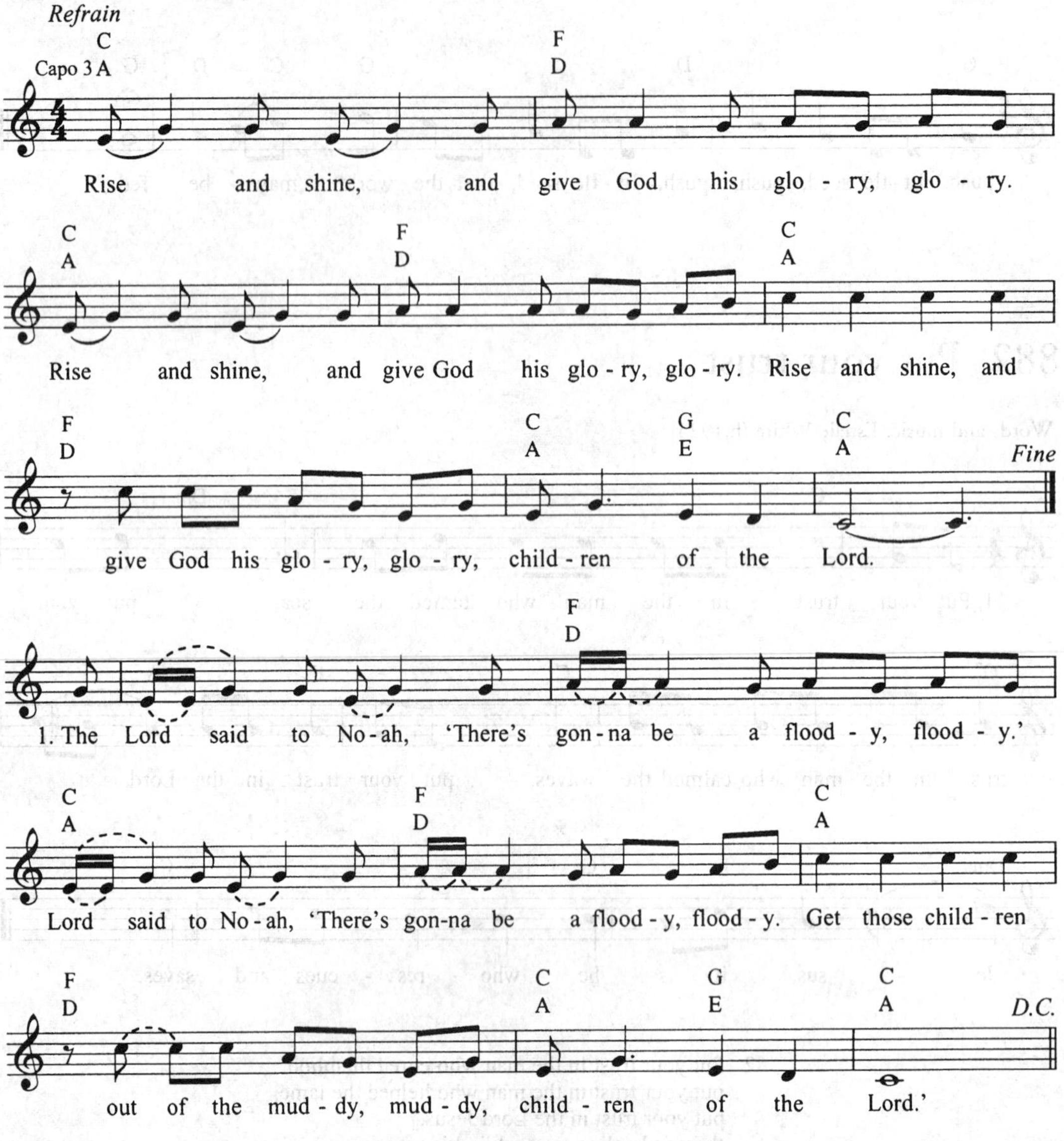
Refrain
Capo 3
C A F D
Rise and shine, and give God his glo - ry, glo - ry.
C A F D C A
Rise and shine, and give God his glo - ry, glo - ry. Rise and shine, and
F D C A G E C A
Fine
give God his glo - ry, glo - ry, child - ren of the Lord.
F D
1. The Lord said to No - ah, 'There's gon - na be a flood - y, flood - y.'
C A F D C A
Lord said to No - ah, 'There's gon - na be a flood - y, flood - y. Get those child - ren
F D C A G E C A
D.C.
out of the mud - dy, mud - dy, child - ren of the Lord.'

2. So Noah, he built him, he built him an arky, arky,
Noah, he built him, he built him an arky, arky,
built it out of hickory barky, barky,
children of the Lord.

3. The animals, they came on, they came on, by twosies, twosies,
animals, they came on, they came on, by twosies, twosies,
elephants and kangaroosies, roosies,
children of the Lord.

4. It rained and poured for forty daysies, daysies,
rained and poured for forty daysies, daysies,
nearly drove those animals crazies, crazies,
children of the Lord.

5. The sun came out and dried up the landy, landy,
sun came out and dried up the landy, landy,
ev'rything was fine and dandy, dandy,
children of the Lord.

6. If you get to heaven before I do-sies, do-sies,
you get to heaven before I do-sies, do-sies,
tell those angels I'm coming too-sies, too-sies,
children of the Lord.

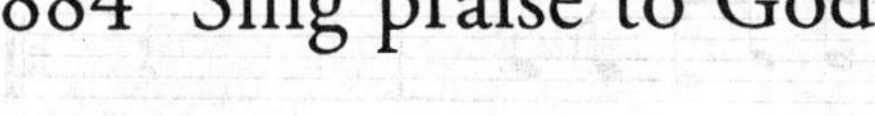

884 Sing praise to God

W.L. Wallace

Noel Rawsthorne (b.1929)

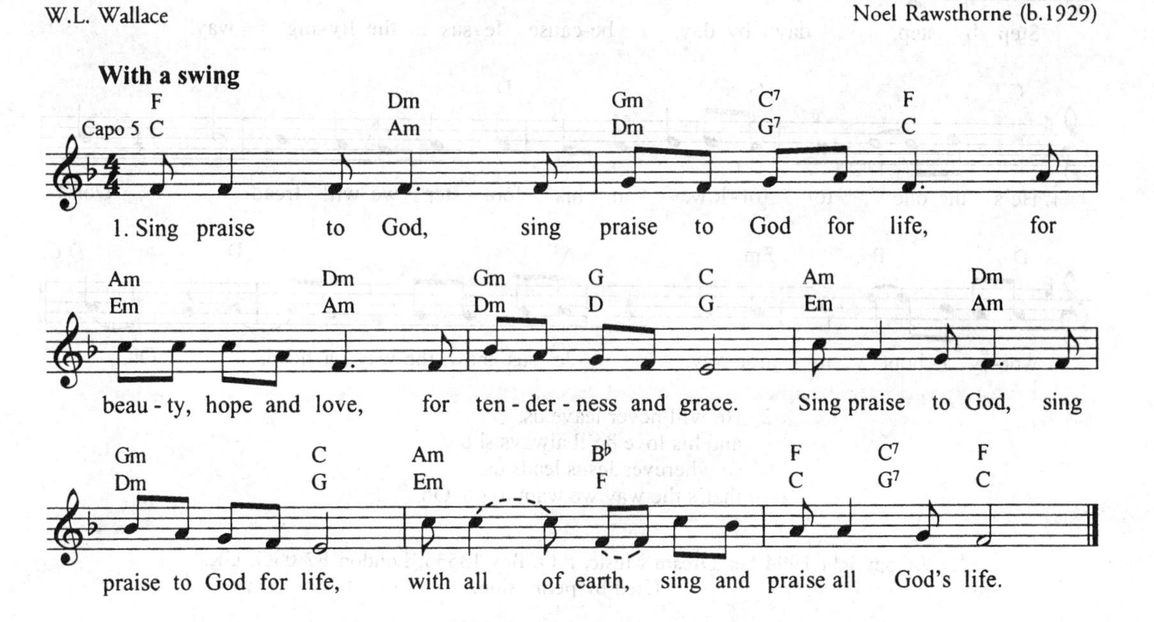

2. Lift up your eyes to see the works of God,
in ev'ry blade of grass, in ev'ry human face.
Lift up your eyes to see the works of God,
through all of life, in all time and all space.

3. Open your ears to hear the cries of pain
arising from the poor and all who are oppressed.
Open your mind and use your wits to find
who are the causes of this world's unjust ways.

4. Reach out your hands to share the wealth God gave
with those who are oppressed, and those who feel alone.
Reach out your hands and gently touch with Christ
each frozen heart which has said 'No' to love.

5. Open our hearts to love the world with Christ,
each person in this world, each creature of this earth.
Open our hearts to love the ones who hate,
and in their hearts find a part of ourselves.

6. Live life with love, for love encircles all,
it casts out all our fears, it fills the heart with joy.
Live life with love, for love transforms our life,
as we praise God with our eyes, hands and hearts.

© Copyright 1997 Kevin Mayhew Ltd.

885 Step by step, on and on *Jesus is the living way*

Words and music: Gill Hutchinson

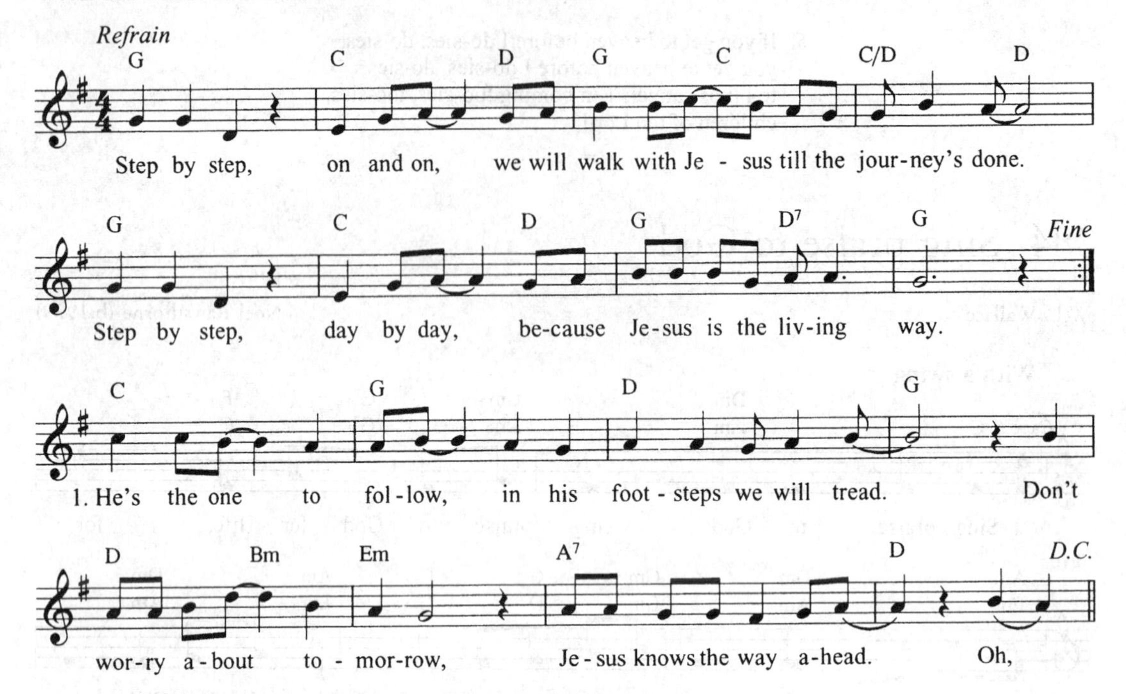

2. He will never leave us,
and his love he'll always show,
so wherever Jesus leads us,
that's the way we want to go. Oh,

©Copyright 1994 Sea Dream Music, P.O. Box 13533, London E7 0SG, UK.
Used by permission.

886 Thank you for the summer morning

Words and music: Susan Sayers (b.1946)

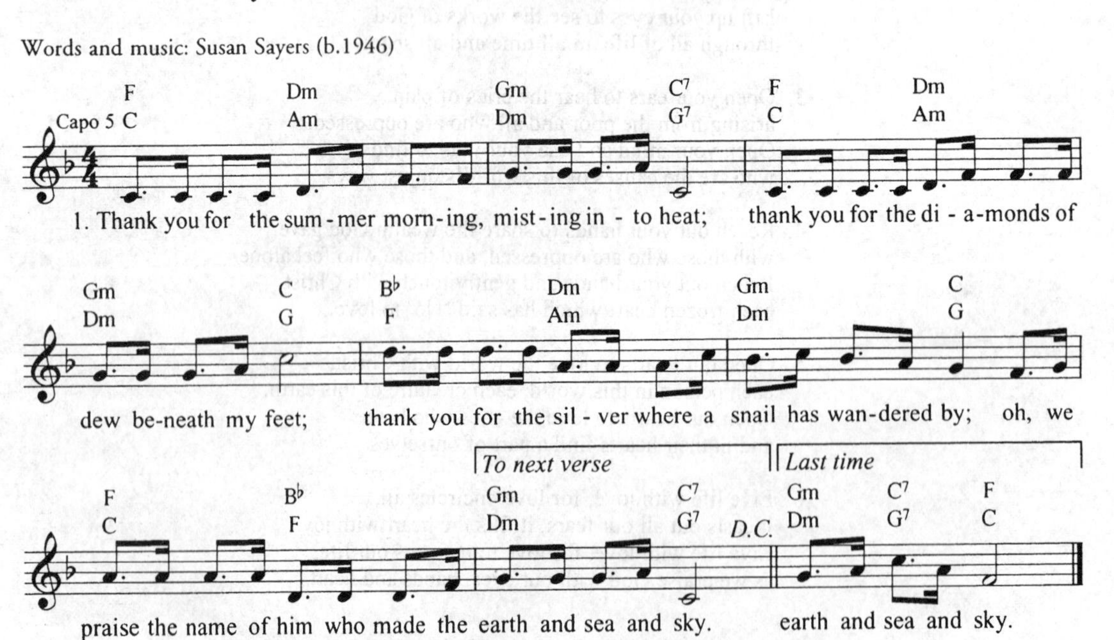

© Copyright 1986 Kevin Mayhew Ltd.

2. Thank you for the yellow fields
of corn like waving hair;
thank you for the red surprise
of poppies here and there;
thank you for the blue of
an electric dragonfly;
oh, we praise the name
of him who made
the earth and sea and sky.

3. Thank you for the splintered light
among the brooding trees;
thank you for the leaves that rustle
in a sudden breeze;
thank you for the branches
and the fun of climbing high;
oh, we praise the name
of him who made
the earth and sea and sky.

4. Thank you for the ev'ning
as the light begins to fade;
clouds so red and purple
that the setting sun has made;
thank you for the shadows
as the owls come gliding by;
oh, we praise the name
of him who made
the earth and sea and sky.

887 Thank you, Lord

Right where we are

Diane Davis Andrew
adapted by Geoffrey Marshall-Taylor

Diane Davis Andrew

2. Thank you, Lord, for food to eat,
thank you, Lord, for food to eat,
thank you, Lord, for food to eat,
right where we are.

3. Thank you, Lord, for clothes to wear,
thank you, Lord, for clothes to wear,
thank you, Lord, for clothes to wear,
right where we are.

4. Thank you, Lord, for all your gifts,
thank you, Lord, for all your gifts,
thank you, Lord, for all your gifts,
right where we are.

© Copyright 1971 Celebration. Administered by Kingsway's Thankyou Music, P.O. Box 75, Eastbourne, East Sussex BN23 6NW, UK. (tym@kingsway.co.uk). Europe & British Commonwealth (excl. Canada, Australasia & Africa). Used by permission.

888 The clock tells the story of time

Words and music: Susan Sayers (b.1946)

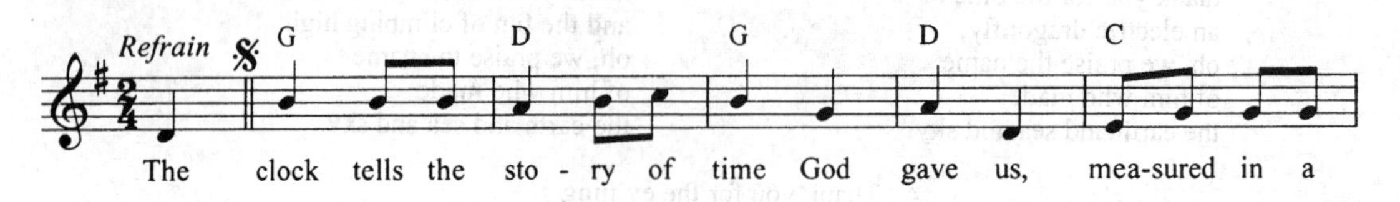

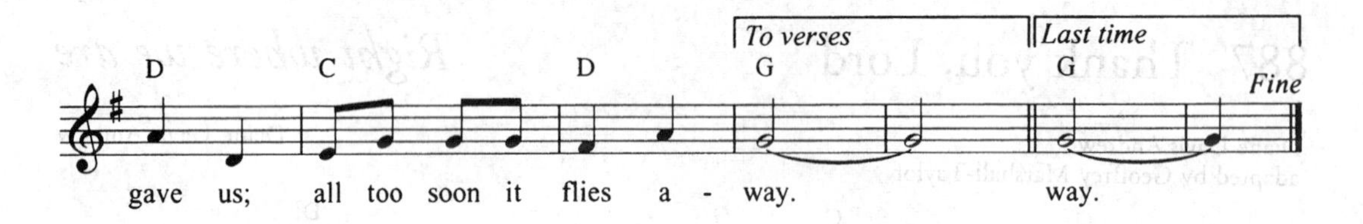

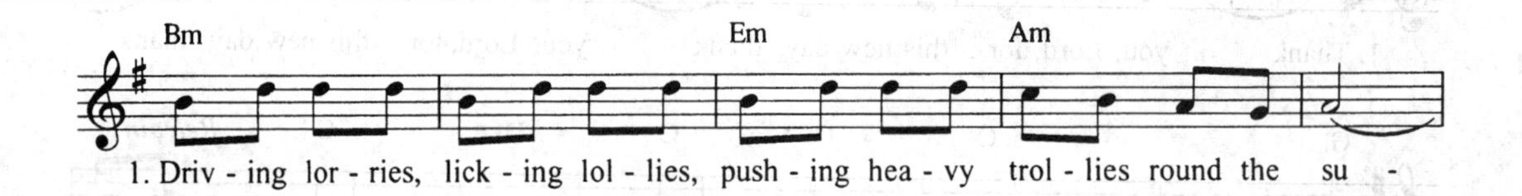

2. Time is good for thinking in,
for helping other people in,
or playing with a friend;
time is like a funny kind of
pocket money given
ev'ry day for us to spend.

© Copyright 1986 Kevin Mayhew Ltd.

889 The ink is black *Black and white*

David Arkin Earl Robinson

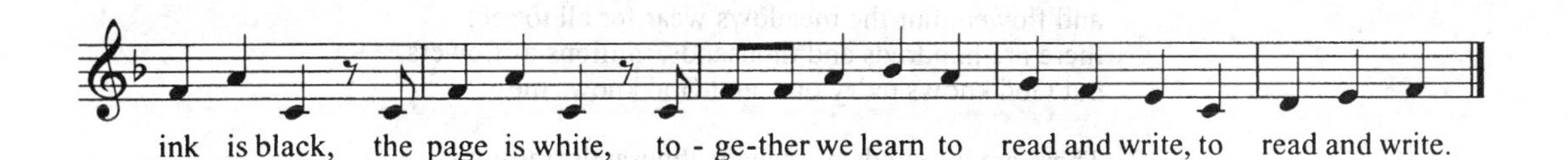

2. The slate is black, the chalk is white,
the words stand out so clear and bright,
so clear and bright;
and now at last we plainly see
the alphabet of liberty,
liberty;
the slate is black, the chalk is white,
together we learn to read and write,
to read and write.

3. A child is black, a child is white,
the whole world looks upon the sight,
upon the sight;
for very well the whole world knows,
this is the way that freedom grows,
freedom grows;
a child is black, a child is white,
together we learn to read and write,
to read and write.

4. The world is black, the world is white,
it turns by day and then by night,
and then by night;
it turns so each and ev'ry one
can take his station in the sun,
in the sun;
the world is black, the world is white,
together we learn to read and write,
to read and write.

© Copyright 1970 Earl Robinson and David Arkin, Templeton Publishing Co. Inc. All rights for UK and Eire controlled by Durham Music Ltd., 11 Uxbridge Street, London W8 7TQ. Used by permission.

890 There are hundreds of sparrows *God knows me*

John Gowans (b.1934) John Larsson (b.1938)

HUNDREDS AND THOUSANDS 11 12 12 10

2. There are hundreds of flowers, thousands, millions,
and flowers fair the meadows wear for all to see;
there are hundreds and thousands, millions of flowers,
but God knows ev'ry one, and God knows me.

3. There are hundreds of planets, thousands, millions,
way out in space each has a place by God's decree;
there are hundreds and thousands, millions of planets,
but God knows ev'ry one, and God knows me.

4. There are hundreds of children, thousands, millions,
and yet their names are written on God's memory;
there are hundreds and thousands, millions of children,
but God knows ev'ry one, and God knows me.

© Copyright Salvationist Publishing and Supplies. Administered by CopyCare, P.O. Box 77, Hailsham, East Sussex BN27 3EF, UK. (music@copycare.com). Used by permission.

891 There is so much to discover

Words and music: Capt. Alan J. Price, CA

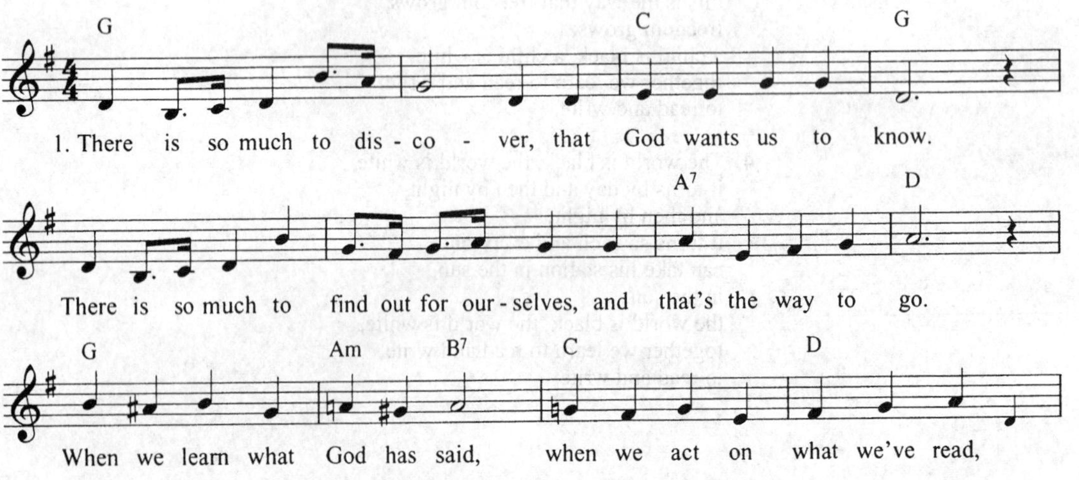

© Copyright 1994 Daybreak Music Ltd., Silverdale Road, Eastbourne, East Sussex BN20 7AB, UK.
All rights reserved. International copyright secured. Used by permission.

2. There is so much to discover,
that God wants us to know.
There is so much to find out for ourselves,
and that's the way to go.
Through the Spirit's pow'r within,
we can change the world for him.
There is so much to discover,
there's so much more to know.

3. There is so much to discover,
that God wants us to know.
There's so much to find out for ourselves,
and that's the way to go.
If we're ever feeling bored,
we just need to ask the Lord
to show to us the things he's planned for us to do,
and that's the way to go.

892 There's a great big world out there

Michael Forster (b.1946) Andrew Gant (b.1963)

2. We've brought to God our prayers and hymns,
now it's time to live his life,
to sow a little love and peace
in the place of selfish strife.

3. We've listened to the word of God,
now it's time to live it out,
to show by ev'rything we do
what the gospel is about.

This can be sung as a round during the third verse, with the second voices entering at the refrain (using the accompaniment to the verse).

© Copyright 1997 Kevin Mayhew Ltd.

893 There's a rainbow in the sky

Michael Forster (b.1946) Christopher Tambling (b.1964)

2. Now we've got another start,
ev'ryone can play a part:
make the world a better place,
put a smile on ev'ry face!

3. Sometimes, still, the world is bad,
people hungry, people sad.
Jesus wants us all to care,
showing people ev'rywhere:

© Copyright 1993 Kevin Mayhew Ltd.

894 There's a seed

Words and music: Susan Sayers (b.1946)

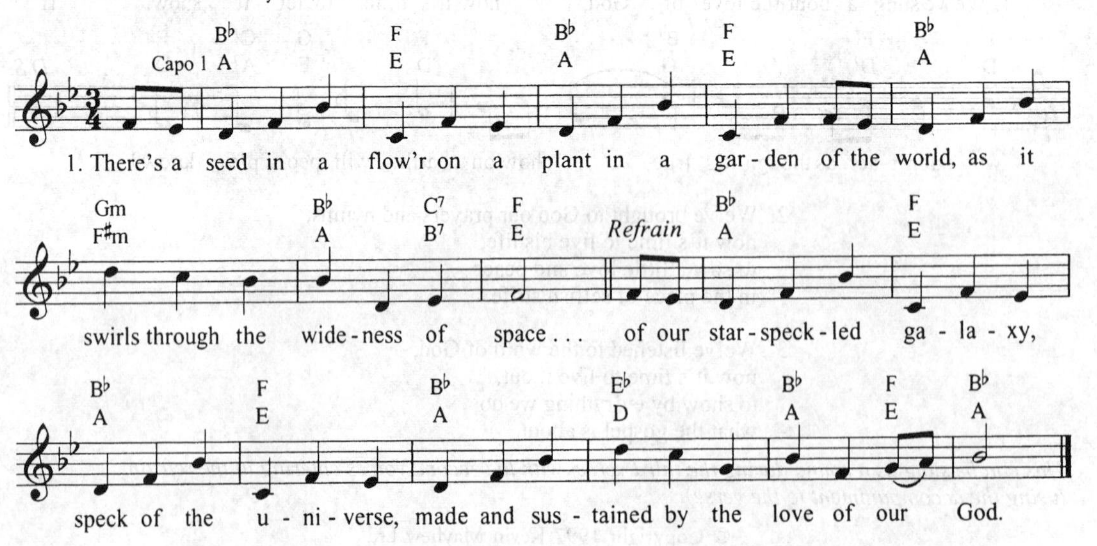

© Copyright 1986 Kevin Mayhew Ltd.

2. There's an ant in a nest
on the floor of a forest
of the world, as it swirls
through the wideness of space . . .

3. There's a crab in a shell
in the depth of an ocean
of the world, as it swirls
through the wideness of space . . .

4. There's a child in a school
of a town in a country
of the world, as it swirls
through the wideness of space . . .

895 There was one, there were two *The children's band*

Christina Wilde

Traditional American melody

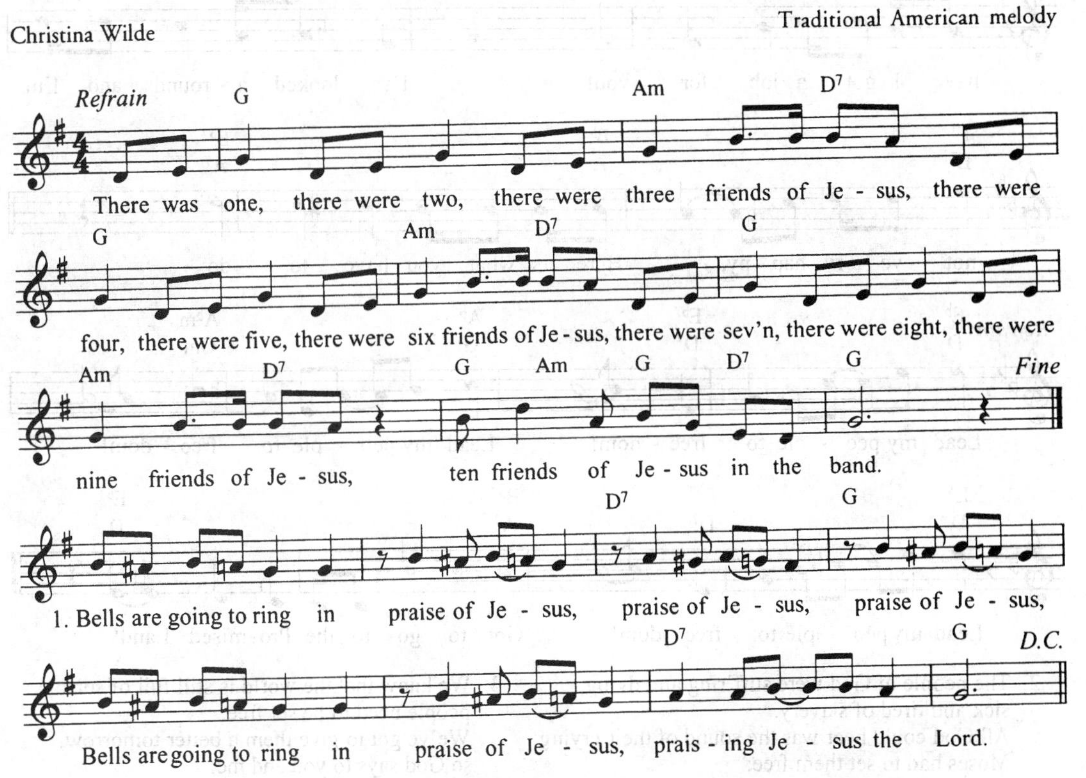

2. Drums are going to boom in praise of Jesus,
praise of Jesus, praise of Jesus,
drums are going to boom in praise of Jesus,
praising Jesus the Lord.

3. Tambourines will shake in praise of Jesus,
praise of Jesus, praise of Jesus,
tambourines will shake in praise of Jesus,
praising Jesus the Lord.

4. Trumpets will resound in praise of Jesus,
praise of Jesus, praise of Jesus,
trumpets will resound in praise of Jesus,
praising Jesus the Lord.

Verses can be added ad lib, for example:

Clarinets will swing, in praise of Jesus . . .

Play recorders, too . . .

Triangles will ting . . .

Fiddles will be scraped . . .

Let guitars be strummed . . .

Chime bars will be chimed . . .

Glockenspiels will play . . .

Vibraphones will throb . . .

Trombones slide about . . .

Text © Copyright 1997 Kevin Mayhew Ltd.

896 The voice from the bush *Lead my people to freedom*

Michael Forster (b.1946) Christopher Tambling (b.1964)

2. The people of God were suff'ring and dying,
sick and tired of slavery.
All God could hear was the sound of their crying;
Moses had to set them free:

3. We know that the world is still full of sorrow,
people need to be set free:
We've got to give them a better tomorrow,
so God says to you and me:

© Copyright 1993 Kevin Mayhew Ltd.

897 The wise man

Words and music: Unknown

2. The foolish man built his house upon the sand, *(x3)*
and the rain came tumbling down.
And the rain came down and the floods came up,
the rain came down and the floods came up, *(x2)*
and the house on the sand fell flat.

898 The world is full of smelly feet

Michael Forster (b.1946)

Christopher Tambling (b.1964)

2. People on a dusty journey
need a place to rest;
Jesus says, 'You say you love me,
this will be the test!'

3. We're his friends, we recognise him
in the folk we meet;
smart or scruffy, we'll still love him,
wash his smelly feet!

© Copyright 1997 Kevin Mayhew Ltd.

899 Think big: an elephant

Words and music: Susan Sayers (b.1946)

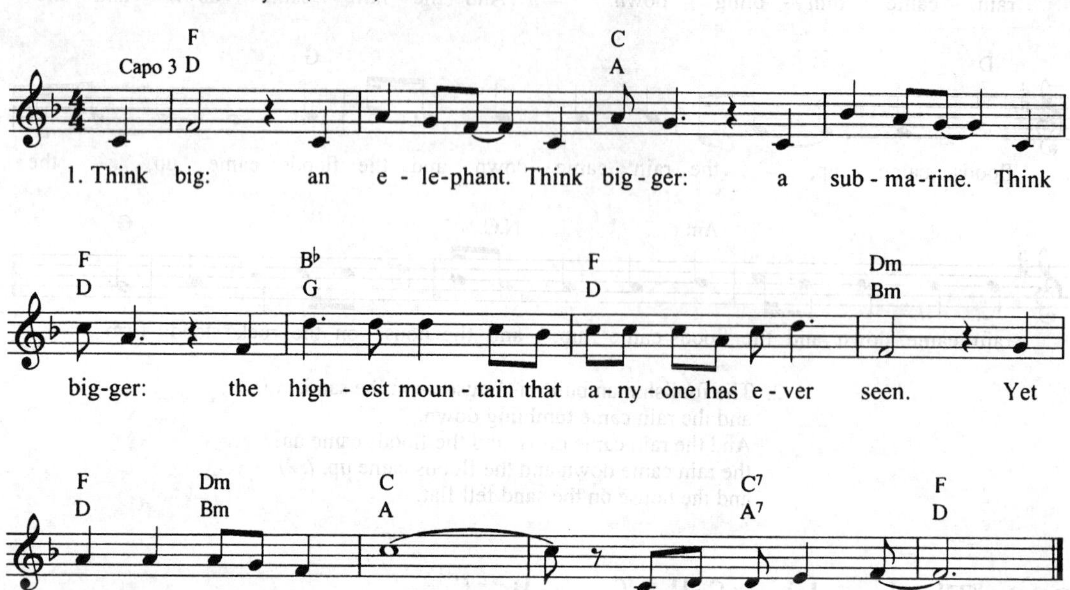

2. Think old: a vintage car.
   Think older: a full grown tree.
   Think older: a million grains
   of the sand beside the surging sea.
   Yet old, old, older is God,
   and he loves us all!

3. Think strong: a tiger's jaw.
   Think stronger: a castle wall.
   Think stronger: a hurricane
   that leaves little standing there at all.
   Yet strong, strong, stronger is God,
   and he loves us all!

© Copyright 1986 Kevin Mayhew Ltd.

900 Think of a world without any flowers

Doreen Newport

Graham Westcott

GENESIS Irregular

2. Think of a world without any animals,
think of a field without any herd,
think of a stream without any fishes,
think of a dawn without any bird.
We thank you, Lord, for all your living creatures,
we thank you, Lord, and praise your holy name.

3. Think of a world without any people,
think of a street with no one living there,
think of a town without any houses,
no one to love and nobody to care.
We thank you, Lord, for families and friendships,
we thank you, Lord, and praise your holy name.

Text © Copyright 1969 Stainer & Bell Ltd., P.O. Box 110, Victoria House, 23 Gruneisen Road, Finchley, London N3 1DZ, UK.
Music © Copyright 1973 Stainer & Bell Ltd. Used by permission.

901 This little light of mine

Words and music: Traditional

2. On Monday he gave me the gift of love,
Tuesday peace came from above.
On Wednesday he told me to have more faith,
on Thursday he gave me a little more grace.
On Friday he told me to watch and pray,
on Saturday he told me just what to say,
on Sunday he gave me the pow'r divine
to let my little light shine.

902 Tick tock

Words and music: Capt. Alan J. Price, CA

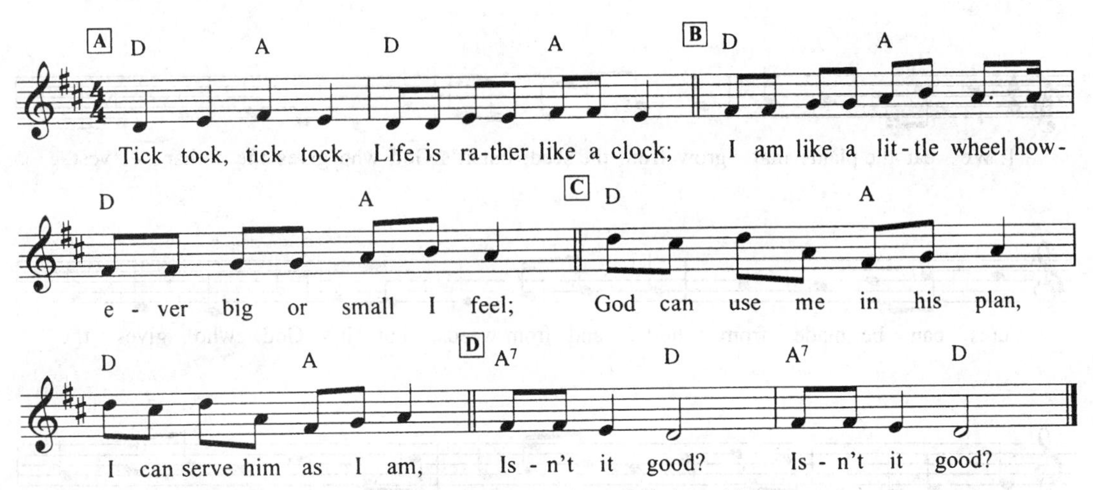

This may be sung as a round, with voices entering as indicated by boxed letters.

© Copyright 1990 Daybreak Music Ltd., Silverdale Road, Eastbourne, East Sussex BN20 7AB, UK.
All rights reserved. International copyright secured. Used by permission.

903 We can plough and dig the land

Michael Forster (b.1946) Christopher Tambling (b.1964)

2. We can edge and we can prune,
we can rake and hoe,
we can lift and we can feed,
but we can't make things grow.

3. We can watch the little shoots
sprouting row by row,
we can hope and we can pray,
but we can't make things grow.

© Copyright 1993 Kevin Mayhew Ltd.

904 We eat the plants that grow from the seed

Susan Mee | Traditional English melody

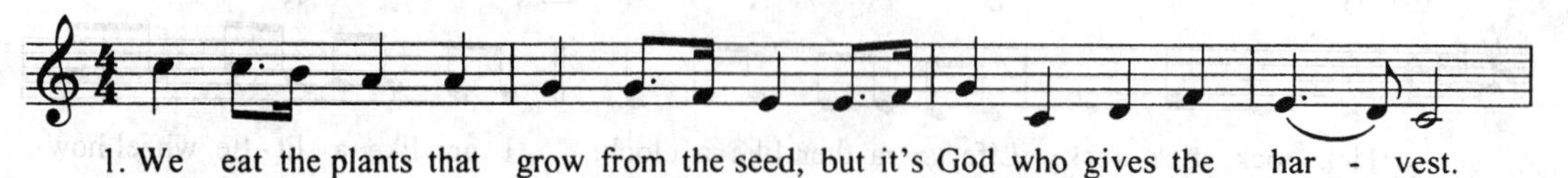

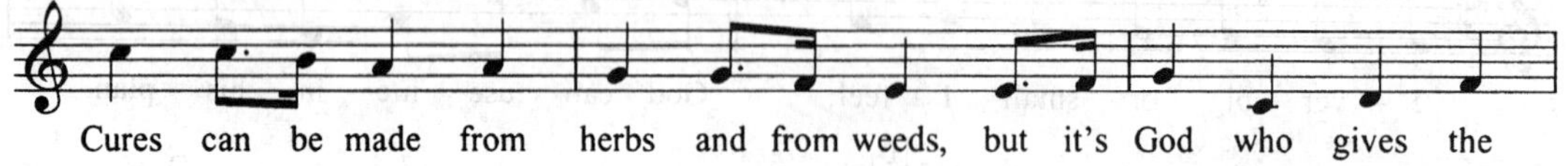

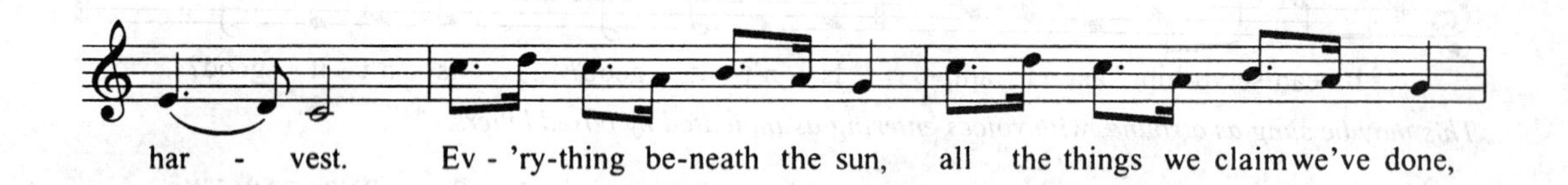

2. We find the iron and turn it to steel,
but it's God who gives the harvest.
We pull the levers, we turn the wheels,
but it's God who gives the harvest.
Ev'rything we say we've made,
plastic bags to metal spades,
all are part of God's creation:
we can make lots of things
from microchips to springs,
but it's God who gives the harvest.

Text © Copyright 1997 Kevin Mayhew Ltd.

905 We have a King who rides a donkey

Fred Kaan (b.1929)

Traditional

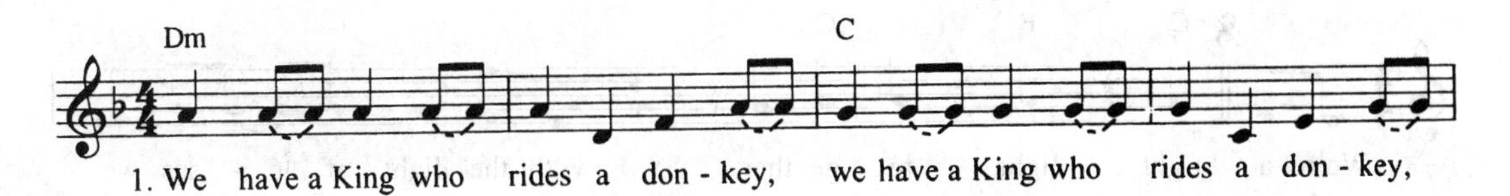

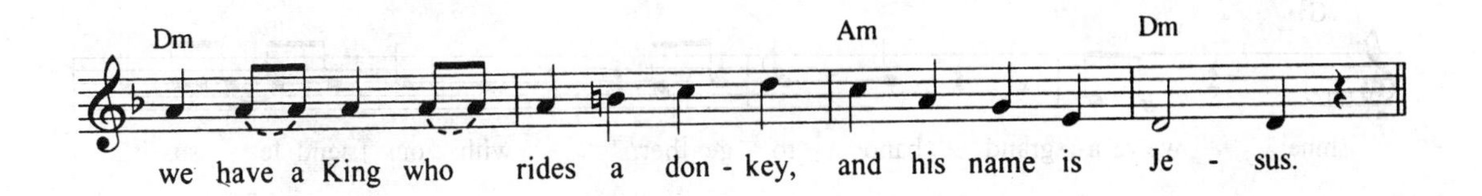

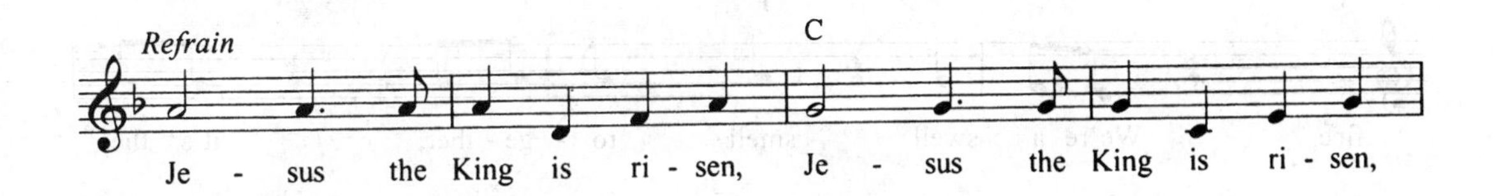

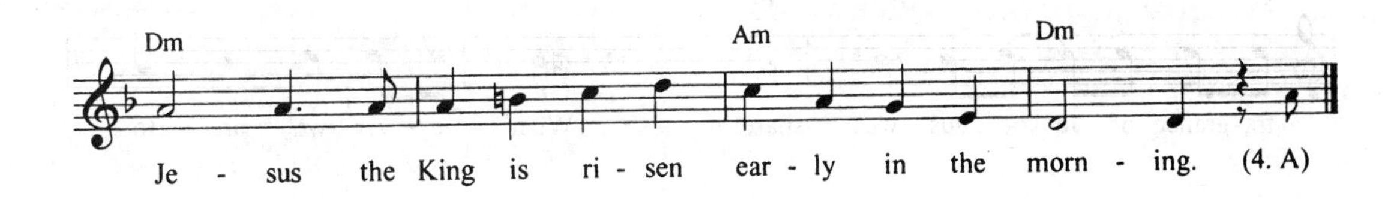

2. Trees are waving a royal welcome,
trees are waving a royal welcome,
trees are waving a royal welcome
for the King called Jesus.

3. We have a King who cares for people,
we have a King who cares for people,
we have a King who cares for people
and his name is Jesus.

4. A loaf and a cup upon the table,
a loaf and a cup upon the table,
a loaf and a cup upon the table,
bread-and-wine is Jesus.

5. We have a King with a bowl and towel,
we have a King with a bowl and towel,
we have a King with a bowl and towel,
Servant-King is Jesus.

6. What shall we do with our life this morning?
what shall we do with our life this morning?
what shall we do with our life this morning?
Give it up in service!

Verse 4 is suitable for Communion.

Text © Copyright 1968 Stainer & Bell Ltd., P.O. Box 110, Victoria House,
23 Gruneisen Road, Finchley, London N3 1DZ, UK. Used by permission.

906 We're a bright light together

Words and music: Capt. Alan J. Price, CA

© Copyright 1991 Daybreak Music Ltd., Silverdale Road, Eastbourne, East Sussex BN20 7AB, UK.
All rights reserved. International copyright secured. Used by permission.

907 We thank God for the harvest

Gotta get out and scatter some seed

Christina Wilde
Noel Rawsthorne (b.1929)

2. God gives love to be scattered,
and seeds of faith to sow,
then sprinkles grace in ev'ry place
to make the harvest grow.

3. We can work all together,
with people ev'rywhere:
in ev'ry place, each creed and race,
God gives us love to share.

© Copyright 1997 Kevin Mayhew Ltd.

908 We will praise

Words and music: Ian Smale

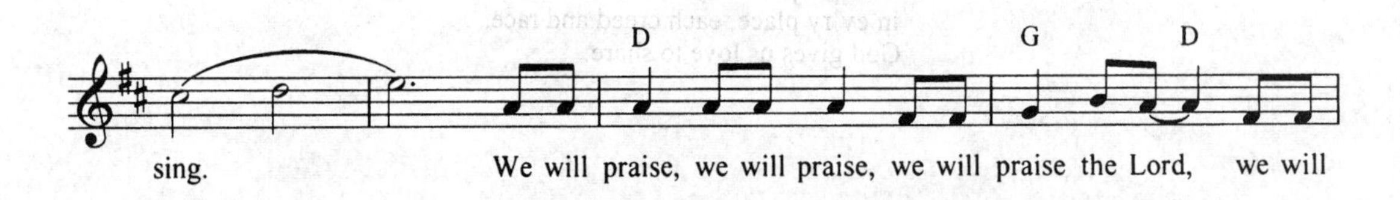

© Copyright 1984 Kingsway's Thankyou Music, P.O. Box 75, Eastbourne, East Sussex BN23 6NW, UK. (tym@kingsway.co.uk). Used by permission.

909 What noise shall we make

Words and music: Lucy East

Brightly

Refrain

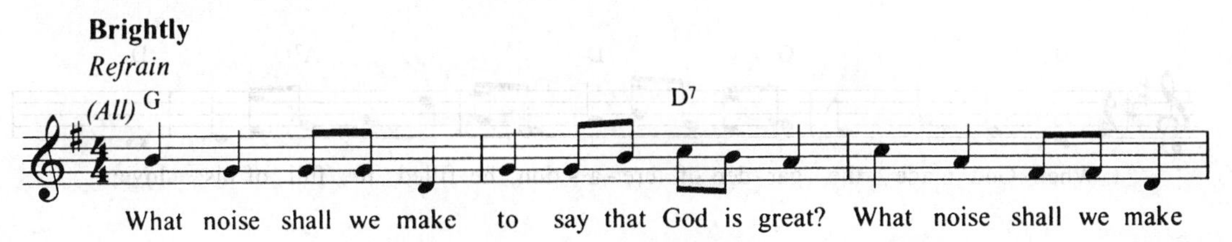

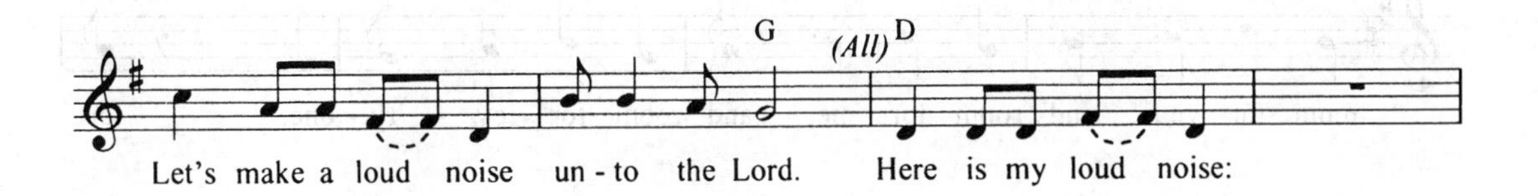

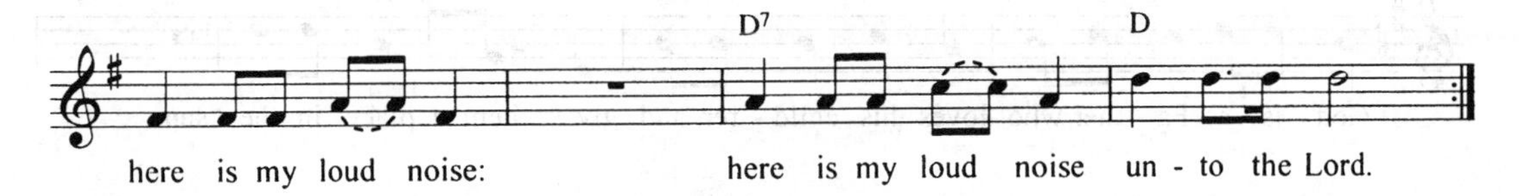

2. Let's make a quiet noise . . .
   Here is my quiet noise . . .

3. Let's make a fast noise . . .
   Here is my fast noise . . .

4. Let's make a slow noise . . .
   Here is my slow noise . . .

5. Let's make a joyful noise . . .
   Here is my joyful noise . . .

6. Let's make a praising noise . . .
   Here is my praising noise: God is good! . . .

We love making noise
to say that God is great.
We love making noise
unto the Lord.

© Copyright 1995 Kingsway's Thankyou Music, P.O. Box 75, Eastbourne, East Sussex BN23 6NW, UK. (tym@kingsway.co.uk). Used by permission.

910 When God made the garden of creation

Words and music: Paul Booth

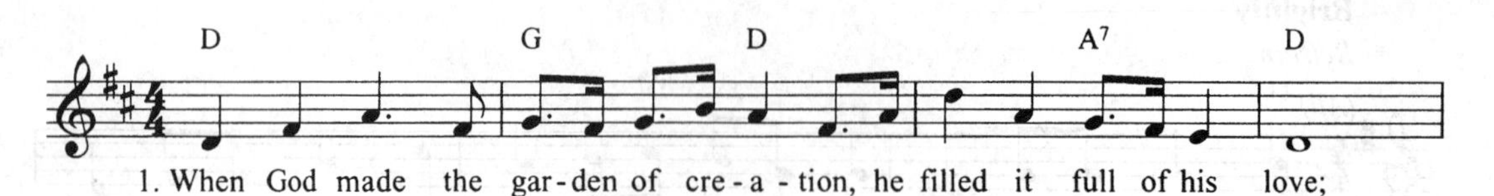

G D A7 D
when God made the gar - den of cre - a - tion, he saw that it was good. There's

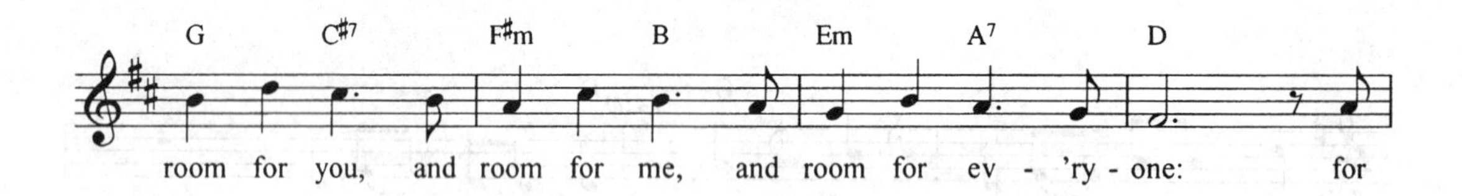

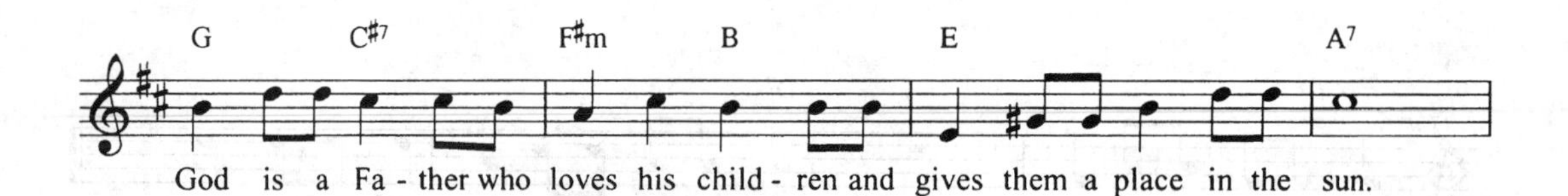

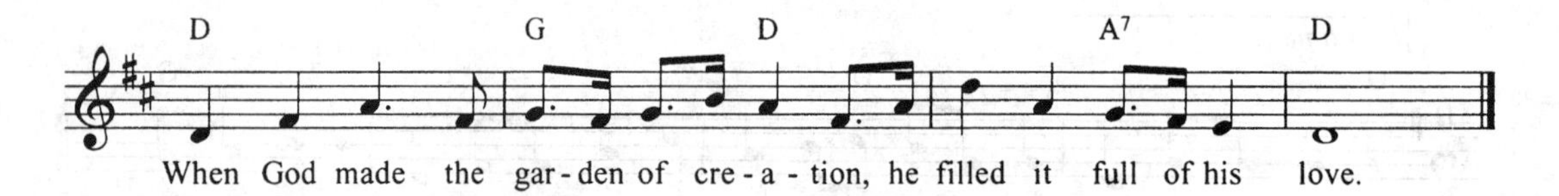

2. When God made the hamper of creation,
he filled it full of his love;
when God made the hamper of creation,
he saw that it was good.
There's food for you, and food for me,
and food for ev'ryone:
but often we're greedy, and waste God's bounty,
so some don't get any at all.
When God made the hamper of creation,
he filled it full of his love.

3. When God made the fam'ly of creation,
he made it out of his love;
when God made the fam'ly of creation,
he saw that it was good.
There's love for you, and love for me,
and love for ev'ryone:
but sometimes we're selfish, ignore our neighbours,
and seek our own place in the sun.
When God made the fam'ly of creation,
he made it out of his love.

4. When God made us stewards of creation
he made us his Vision to share;
when God made us stewards of creation
our burdens he wanted to bear.
He cares for you, he cares for me,
he cares for all in need;
for God is a Father who loves his children
no matter what colour or creed.
When God made us stewards of creation
he made us his vision to share.

© Copyright 1977 Stainer & Bell Ltd., P.O. Box 110, Victoria House,
23 Gruneisen Road, Finchley, London N3 1DZ, UK. Used by permission.

911 When Jesus was my age

Words and music: Susan Sayers (b.1946)

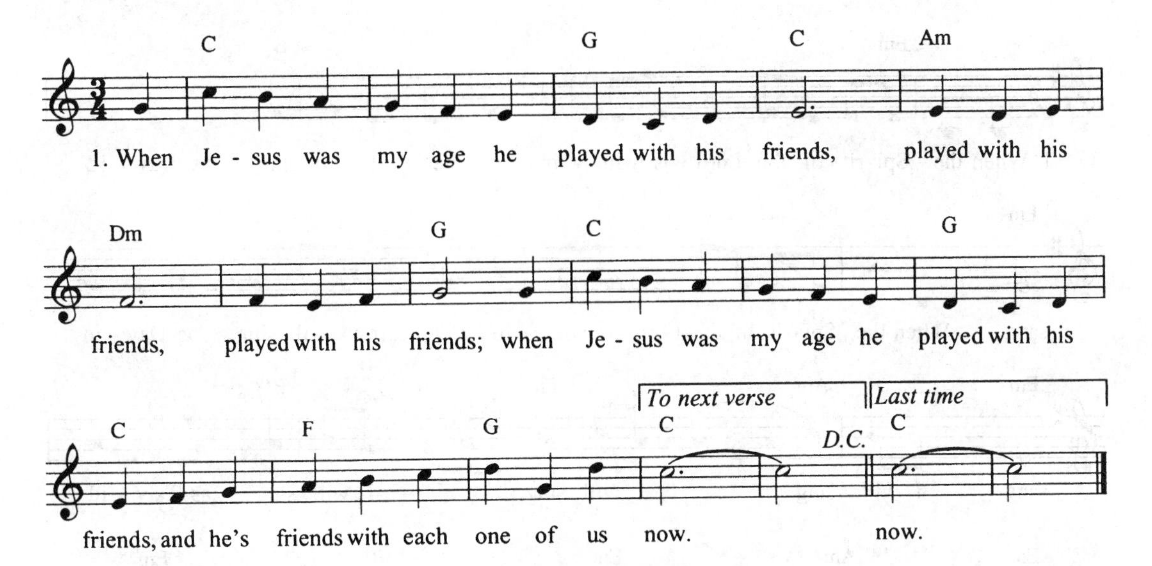

2. When Jesus was my age he laughed and he sang,
laughed and he sang, laughed and he sang;
when Jesus was my age he laughed and he sang,
and he loves hearing us singing now.

3. When Jesus was my age he sometimes felt sad,
sometimes felt sad, sometimes felt sad;
when Jesus was my age he sometimes felt sad,
and he shares in our sadnesses now.

4. When Jesus was my age he went to his school,
went to his school, went to his school;
when Jesus was my age he went to his school,
and he goes ev'rywhere with us now.

© Copyright 1986 Kevin Mayhew Ltd.

912 When the Spirit of the Lord

Words and music: Unknown

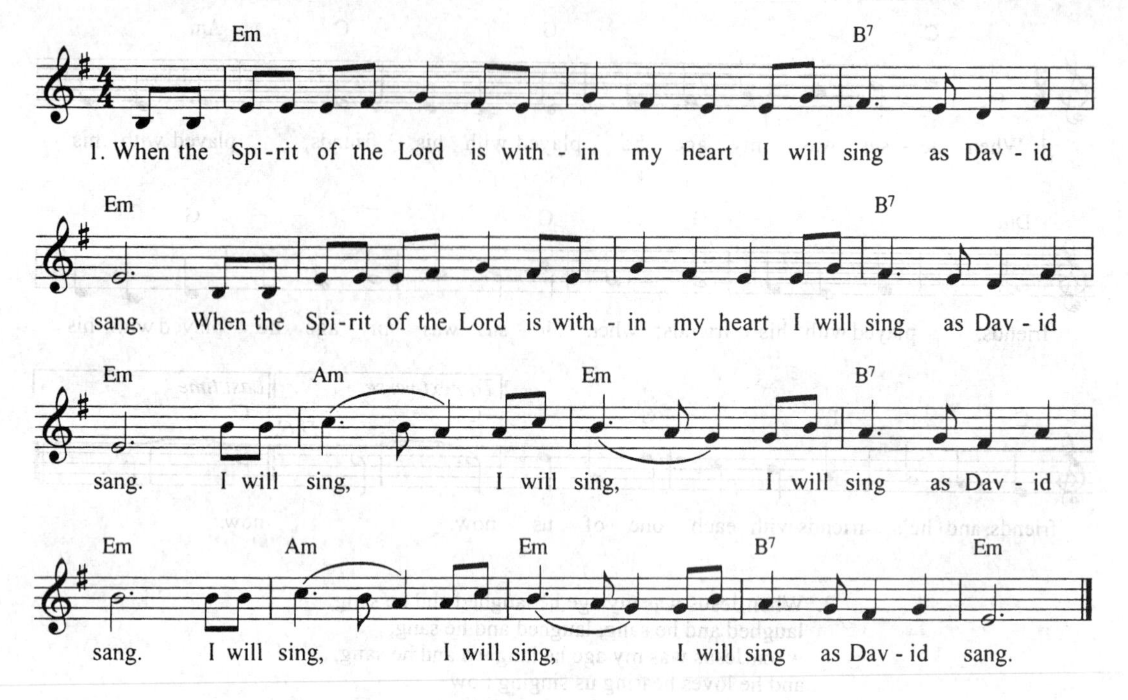

2. When the Spirit of the Lord is within my heart
I will clap as David clapped . . .

3. When the Spirit of the Lord is within my heart
I will dance as David danced . . .

4. When the Spirit of the Lord is within my heart
I will praise as David praised . . .

913 When the time is right

Words and music: Capt. Alan J. Price, CA

© Copyright 1994 Daybreak Music Ltd., Silverdale Road, Eastbourne, East Sussex BN20 7AB, UK.
All rights reserved. International copyright secured. Used by permission.

914 When your Father made the world

Care for your world

Anne Conlon

Peter Rose

2. All the world that he had made,
the seas, the rocks, the air,
all the creatures and the plants
he gave into our care.
Help your people to care for your world.

3. When you walked in Galilee,
you said your Father knows
when each tiny sparrow dies,
each fragile lily grows.
Help your people to care for your world.

4. And the children of the earth,
like sheep within your fold,
should have food enough to eat,
and shelter from the cold.
Help your people to care for your world.

© Copyright 1996 Josef Weinberger Ltd., 12-14 Mortimer Street, London W1N 7RD, UK.
Used by permission.

915 Who put the colours in the rainbow?

Words and music: Paul Booth (1931-1995)

2. Who put the gold into the sunshine?
Who put the sparkle in the stars?
Who put the silver in the moonlight?
Who made Earth and Mars?
Who put the scent into the roses?
Who taught the honey-bee to dance?
Who put the tree inside the acorn?
It surely can't be chance!
Who made seas and leaves and trees?
Who made snow and winds that blow?
Who made streams and rivers flow?
God made all of these!

© Copyright Paul Booth. Administered by CopyCare, P.O. Box 77, Hailsham, East Sussex BN27 3EF, UK. (music@copycare.com). Used by permission.

916 Yesterday, today, for ever

Words and music: Unknown

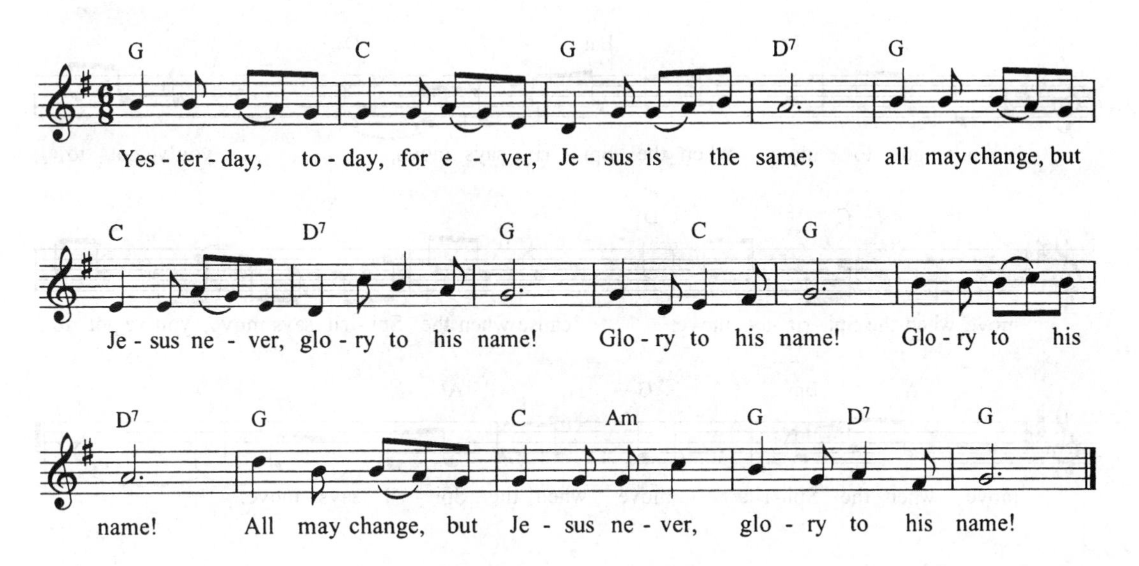

917 You can drink it, swim in it

Water

Words and music: Susan Sayers (b.1946)

2. It's as hard as rock,
yet it flows down a mountain,
and clouds drop drips of it –
what can it be?

3. It's as light as snowflakes
and heavy as hailstones,
as small as dewdrops
and big as the sea.

© Copyright 1986 Kevin Mayhew Ltd.

918 You've got to move

Words and music: Traditional

2. You've got to sing . . .

3. You've got to clap . . .

4. You've got to shout . . .

5. You've got to move . . .

919 Zacchaeus was a very little man

Words and music: Unknown

920 Zip bam boo

Words and music: Sue McClellan, John Paculabo and Keith Ryecroft

2. He'd come to share good news from God
and show that he is Lord.
He made folk whole who trusted him
and took him at his word.
He fought oppression, loved the poor,
gave the people hope once more.
Zip bam boo, zama lama la boo,
there's freedom in Jesus Christ.

3. 'He's mad! He claims to be God's Son
and give new life to men!
Let's kill this Christ, once and for all,
no trouble from him then!'
'It's death then, Jesus, the cross for you!'
Said, 'Man, that's what I came to do!'
Zip bam boo, zama lama la boo,
there's freedom in Jesus Christ.

© Copyright 1972 Kingsway's Thankyou Music, P.O. Box 75, Eastbourne, East Sussex BN23 6NW, UK. (tym@kingsway.co.uk). Used by permission.

COMPLETE ANGLICAN
HYMNS OLD & NEW

Chants

921 Adoramus te, Domine

Taizé Community — Jacques Berthier (1923-1994)

© Copyright Ateliers et Presses de Taizé, Taizé-Communauté, F-71250, France.
Used by permission.

* *Choose either part.*

The cantor always enters on the upbeat so that the A *marked in the verse coincides with the* A *indicated above the chant.*

922 Adoramus te, Domine Deus

Traditional

Margaret Rizza (b.1929)

Translation: We adore you, O Lord God.

© Copyright 1997 Kevin Mayhew Ltd.

923 Bless the Lord, my soul

© Copyright Ateliers et Presses de Taizé, Taizé-Communauté, F-71250, France.
Used by permission.

924 Calm me, Lord

David Adam

Margaret Rizza (b.1929)

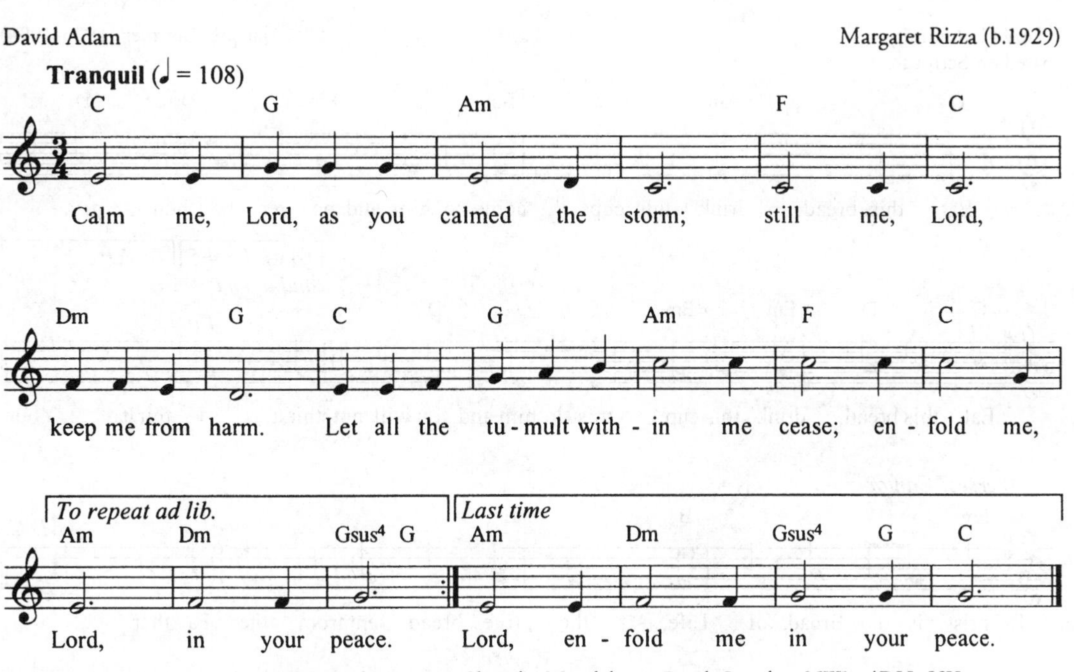

Text © Copyright SPCK, Holy Trinity Church, Marylebone Road, London NW1 4DU, UK.
Used by permission from *The Edge of Glory.*
Music © Copyright 1998 Kevin Mayhew Ltd.

925 Confitemini Domino

Psalm 118

Jacques Berthier (1923-1994)

Translation: Give thanks to the Lord for he is good.

© Copyright 1981 Ateliers et Presses de Taizé, Taizé-Communauté, F-71250, France.
Used by permission.

926 Eat this bread

© Copyright Ateliers et Presses de Taizé, Taizé-Communauté, F-71250, France.
Used by permission.

927 Exaudi nos, Domine

Traditional

Margaret Rizza (b.1929)

Translation: Hear us, O Lord, give us your peace.

© Copyright 1998 Kevin Mayhew Ltd.

928 Holy God, we place ourselves

Words and music: Kevin Mayhew (b.1942)
based on the Aaronic Blessing (Numbers 6:24-46)

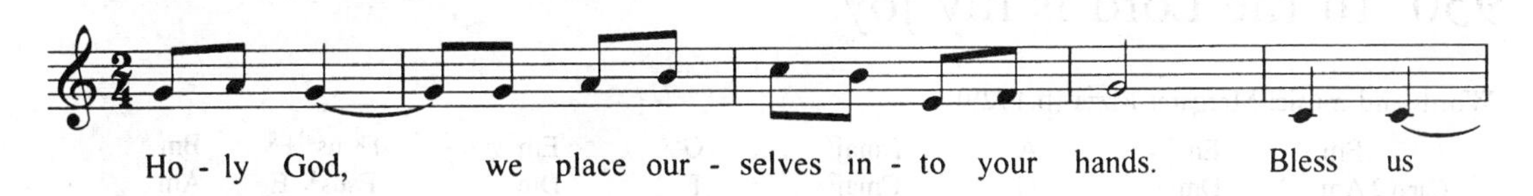

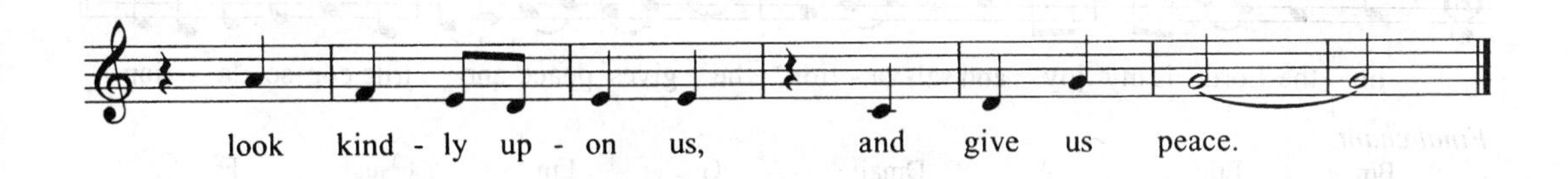

© Copyright 1996 Kevin Mayhew Ltd.

929 In the Lord I'll be ever thankful

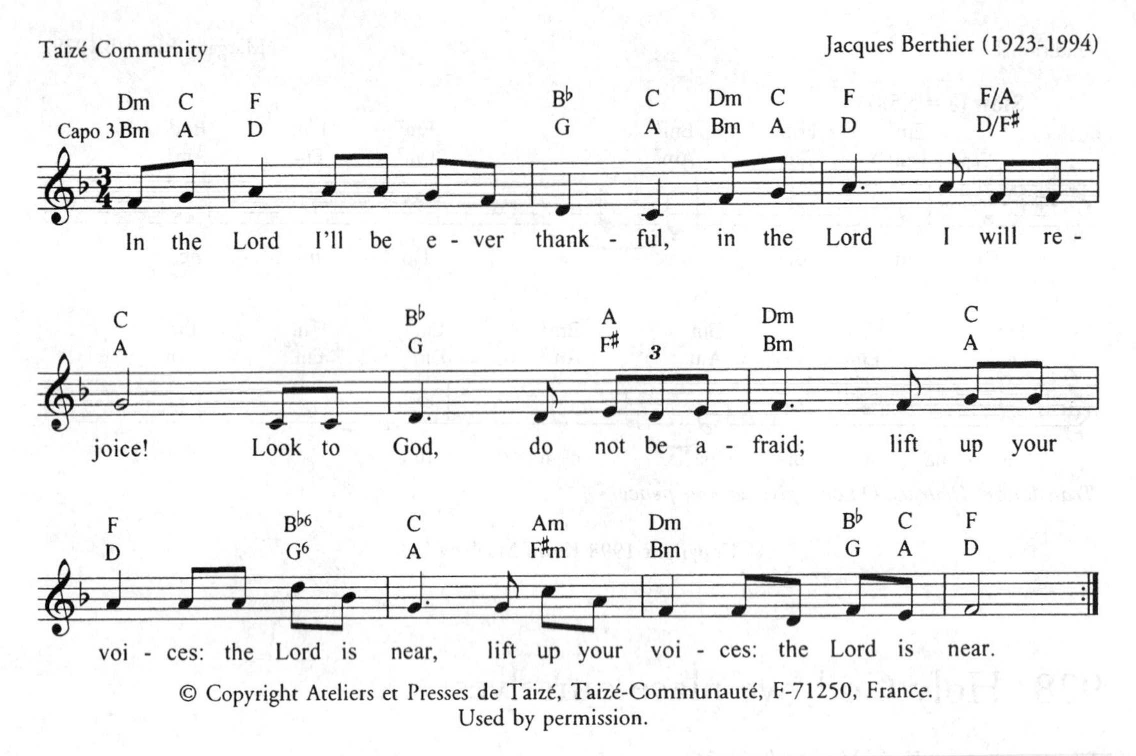

930 In the Lord is my joy

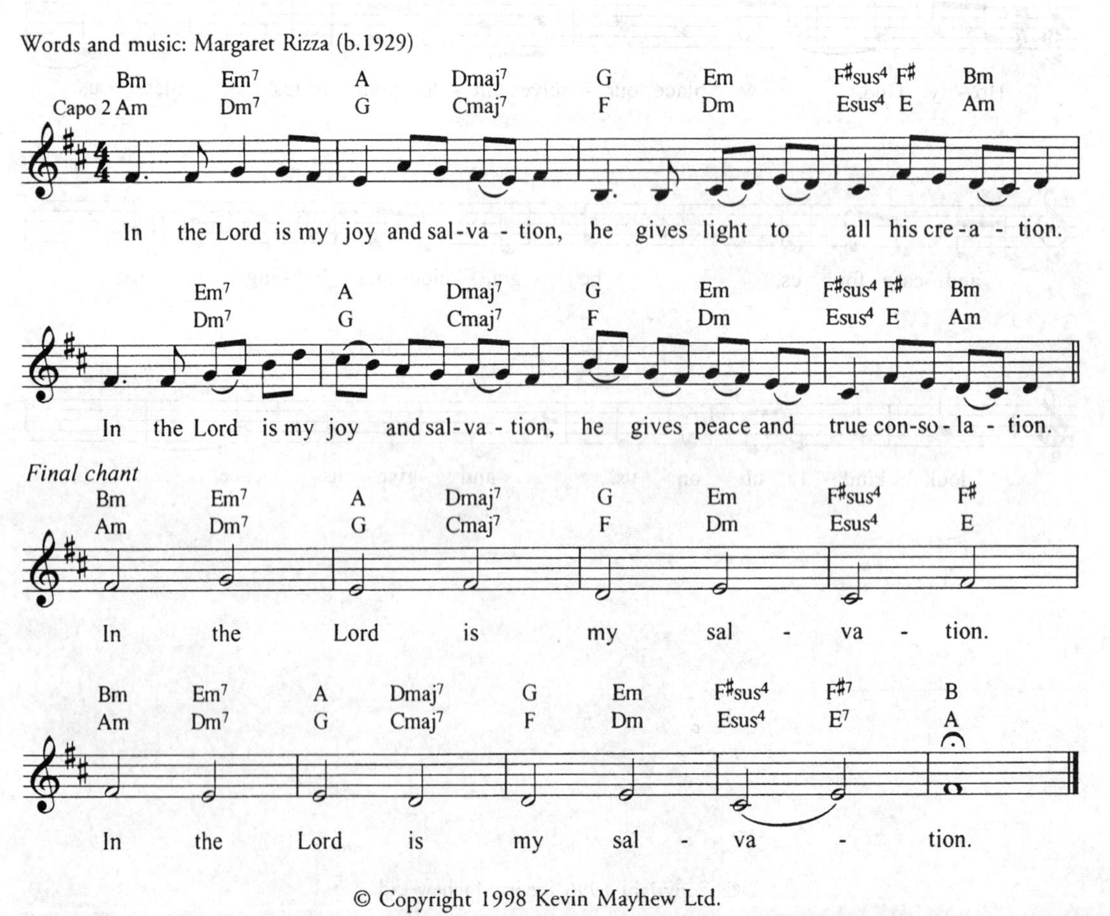

931 Jesus, remember me

Taizé Community
based on Scripture

Jacques Berthier (1923-1994)

© Copyright Ateliers et Presses de Taizé, Taizé-Communauté, F-71250, France.
Used by permission.

932 Kindle a flame

Words and music: John L. Bell (b.1949)
and Graham Maule (b.1958)

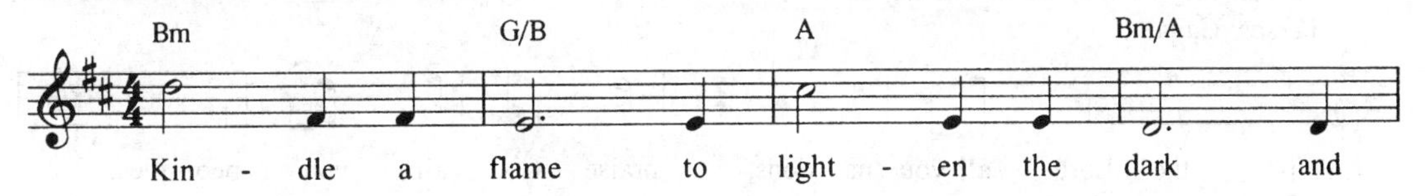

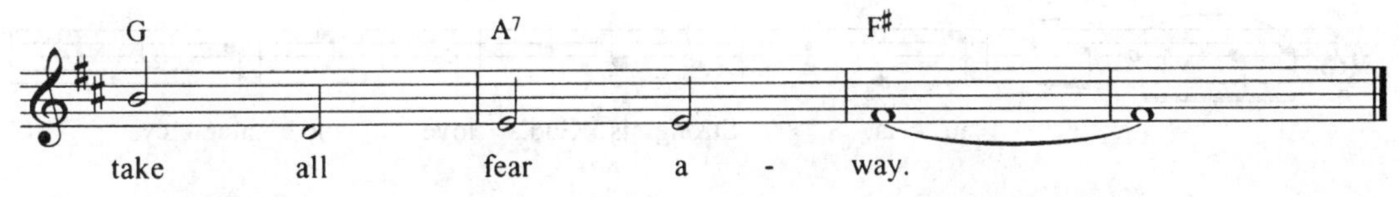

© Copyright 1987 WGRG, Iona Community, Glasgow G2 3DH, Scotland.
Used by permission from *Heaven Shall Not Wait* (Wild Goose Publications, 1987).

933 Laudate Dominum *Sing praise*

Taizé Community
based on Scripture

Jacques Berthier (1923-1994)

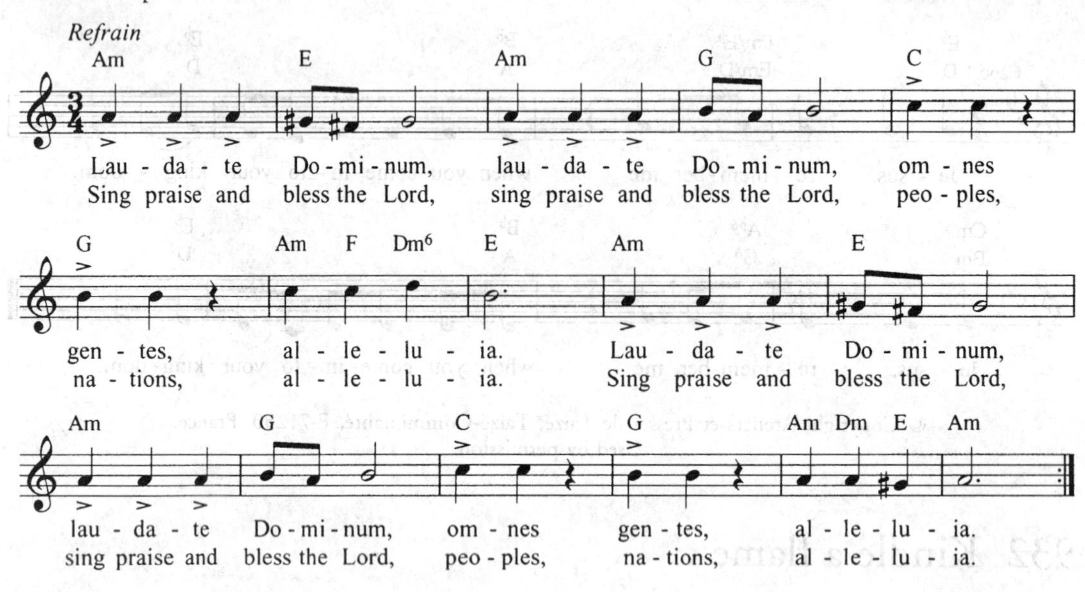

These verses may be sung above the Refrain.

Verses: Cantor

1. Praise the Lord, all you na - tions, praise God all you peo - ples.

Al - le - lu - ia. Strong is God's love and mer - cy,

al - ways faith - ful for e - ver. Al - le - lu - ia. 2. Al - le -

lu - ia, al - le - lu - ia. Let ev - 'ry - thing liv - ing give

praise to the Lord. Al - le - lu - ia, al - le - lu -

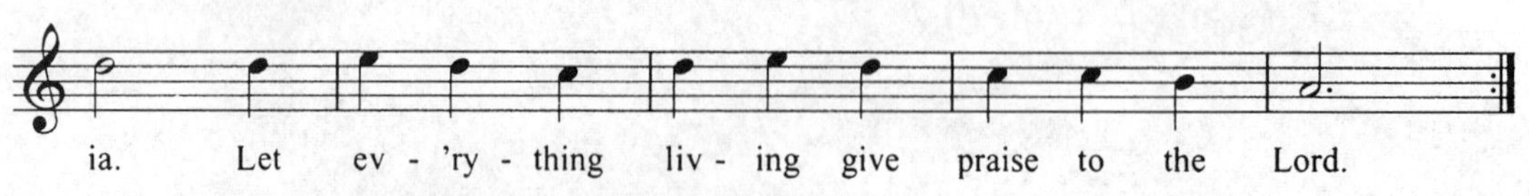

© Copyright Ateliers et Presses de Taizé, Taizé-Communauté, F-71250, France.
Used by permission.

934 Lord of creation

Words and music: Colin Mawby (b.1936)

© Copyright 1991 Kevin Mayhew Ltd.

935 Magnificat

Luke 1:46

Margaret Rizza (b.1929)

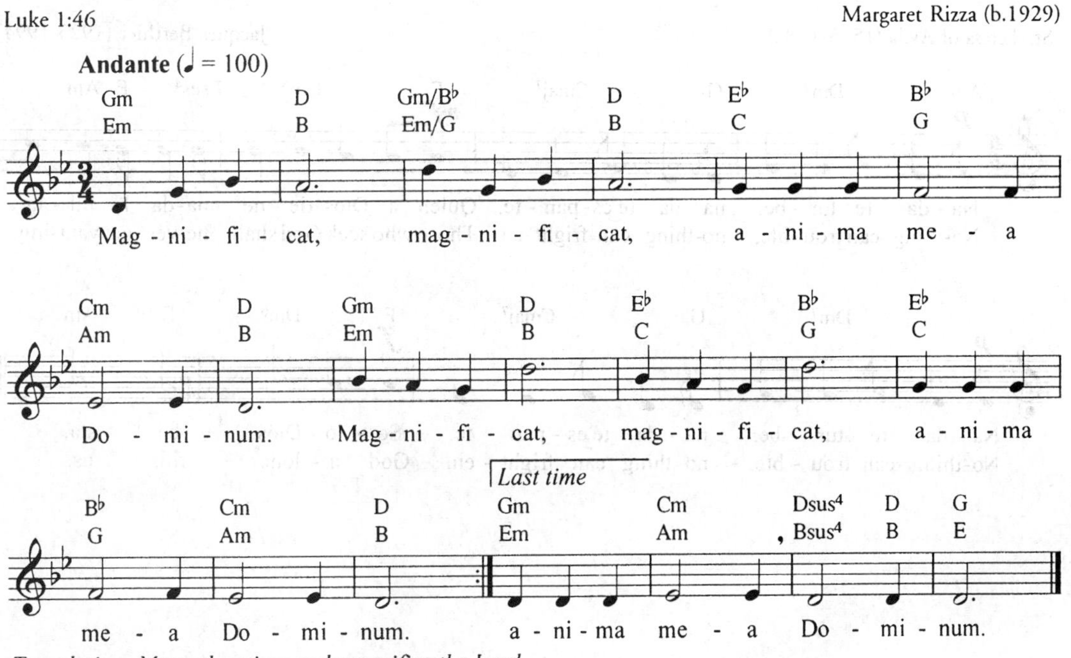

Translation: My soul praises and magnifies the Lord.

© Copyright 1997 Kevin Mayhew Ltd.

936 May the Lord bless you *A Blessing*

Gaelic Blessing, adapted
by Margaret Rizza

Margaret Rizza (b.1929)

© Copyright 1998 Kevin Mayhew Ltd.

937 Nada te turbe *Nothing can trouble*

St. Teresa of Avila (1545-1582)

Jacques Berthier (1923-1994)

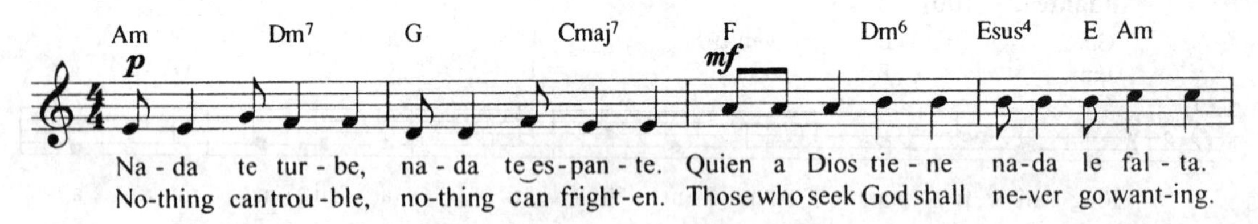

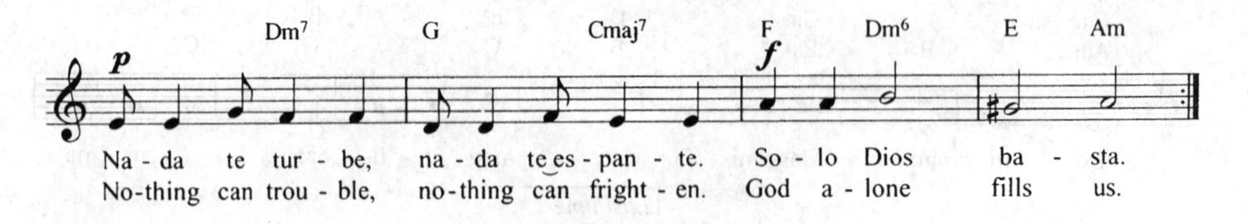

© Copyright Ateliers et Presses de Taizé, Taizé-Communauté, F-71250, France.
Used by permission.

938 O Lord, hear my prayer

Taizé Community

Jacques Berthier (1923-1994)

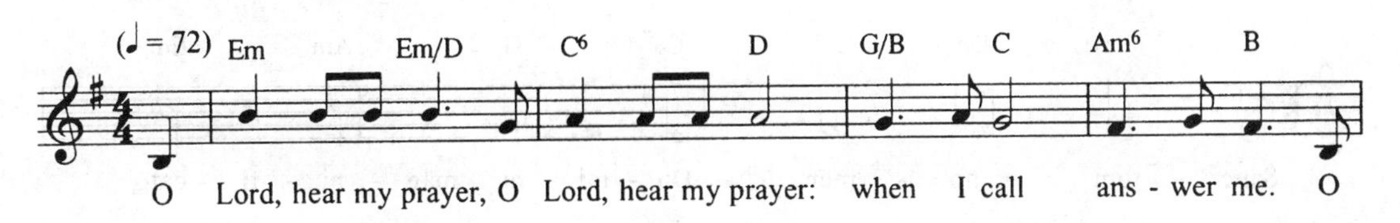

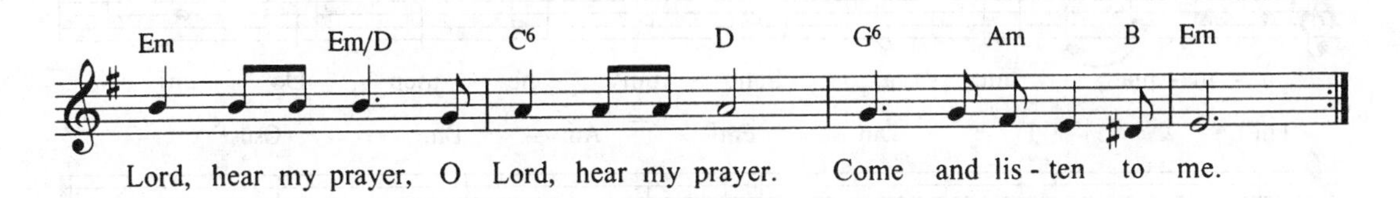

© Copyright Ateliers et Presses de Taizé, Taizé-Communauté, F-71250, France.
Used by permission.

939 O Lord, my heart is not proud

Psalm 131

Margaret Rizza (b.1929)

Text © Copyright The Grail (England). Used by permission from *The Psalms: The Grail Translations.*
Music © Copyright 1997 Kevin Mayhew Ltd.

940 Sanctum nomen Domini

Traditional

Margaret Rizza (b.1929)

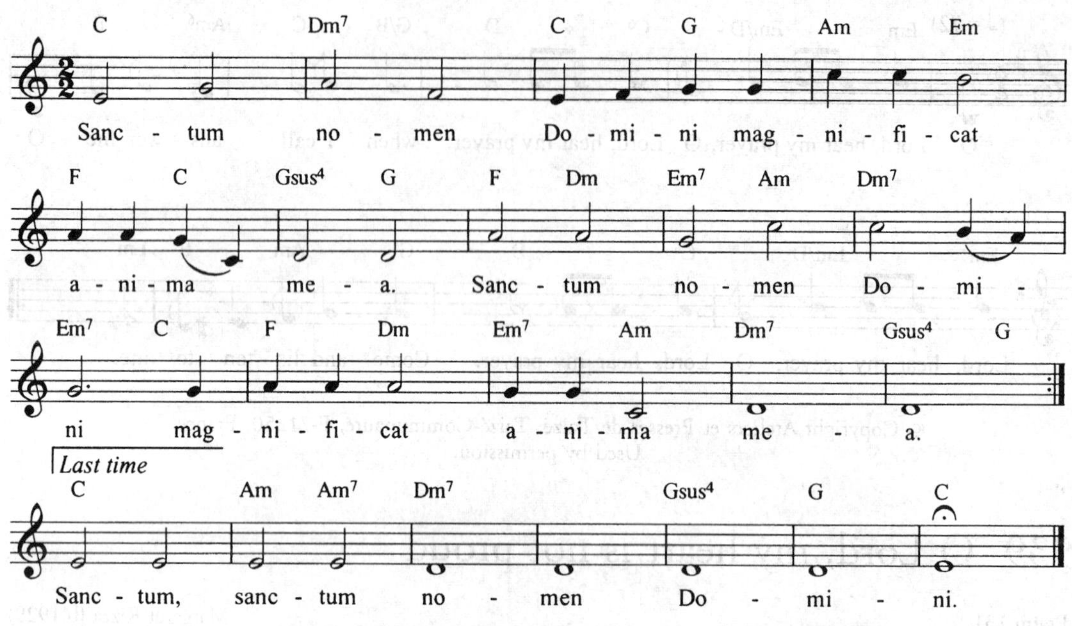

Translation: My soul magnifies the holy name of the Lord.

© Copyright 1998 Kevin Mayhew Ltd.

941 Silent, surrendered

v.1: Pamela Hayes;
v.2: Margaret Rizza

Margaret Rizza (b.1929)

* *For use at Pentecost*

© Copyright 1998 Kevin Mayhew Ltd.

942 Stay with me

© Copyright Ateliers et Presses de Taizé, Taizé-Communauté, F-71250, France.
Used by permission.

943 Surrexit Christus

© Copyright Ateliers et Presses de Taizé, Taizé-Communauté, F-71250, France.
Used by permission.

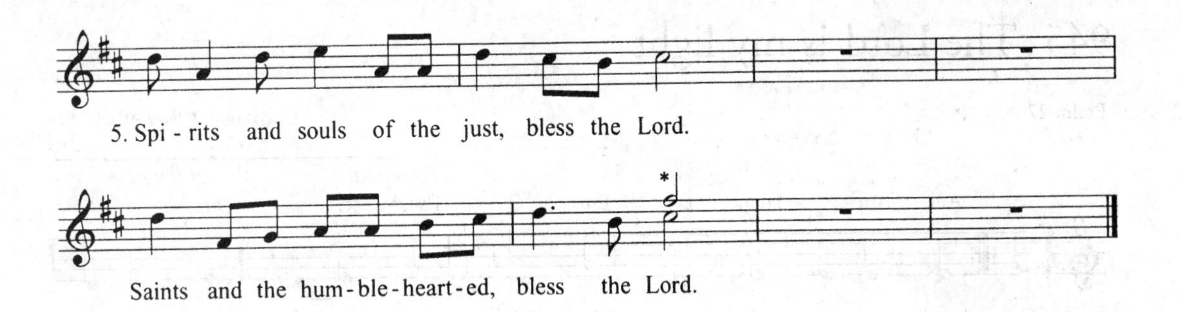

944 The Lord is my light

Psalm 27

Jacques Berthier (1923-1994)

Each of these themes may be sung separately either in unison or as a round for two voices, the second voice entering at the double barline. The two themes may also be sung together, preferably with theme I for female voices, and theme II for male voices.

© Copyright Ateliers et Presses de Taizé, Taizé-Communauté, F-71250, France.
Used by permission.

945 The Lord is my light

Psalm 27

Margaret Rizza (b.1929)

© Copyright 1998 Kevin Mayhew Ltd.

946 Ubi caritas

Taizé Community

Jacques Berthier (1923-1994)

© Copyright Ateliers et Presses de Taizé, Taizé-Communauté, F-71250, France.
Used by permission.

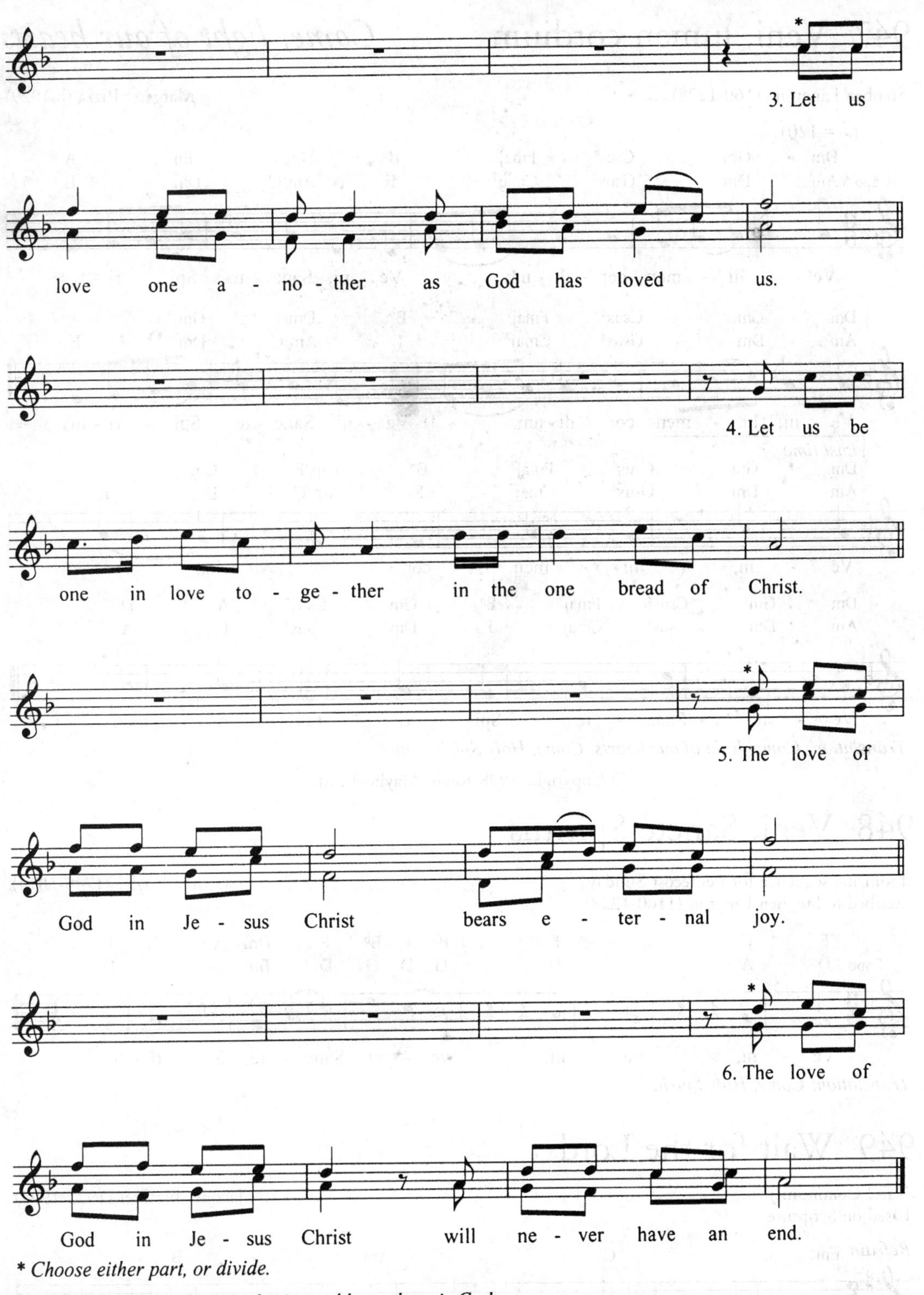

** Choose either part, or divide.*

Translation: Where there is charity and love, there is God.

947 Veni, lumen cordium *Come, light of our hearts*

Stephen Langton (1160-1228) Margaret Rizza (b.1929)

Translation: Come, light of our hearts. Come, Holy Spirit, come.

© Copyright 1998 Kevin Mayhew Ltd.

948 Veni, Sancte Spiritus

From the sequence for Pentecost Sunday ascribed to Stephen Langton (1160-1228)

George Vogler (1749-1814)

Translation: Come, Holy Spirit.

949 Wait for the Lord

Taizé Community based on Scripture

Jacques Berthier (1923-1994)

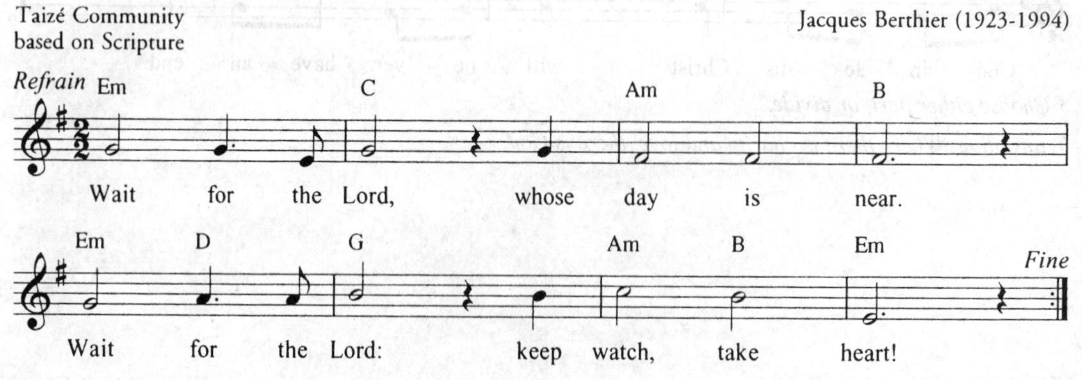

© Copyright Ateliers et Presses de Taizé, Taizé-Communauté, F-71250, France.
Used by permission.

These verses may be sung above the Refrain.
Verses: Cantor
1. Pre - pare the way for the Lord. Make a straight path for God.
Pre - pare the way for the Lord.
2. Re - joice in the Lord al - ways: God is at hand.
Joy and glad - ness for all who seek the Lord.
3. The glo - ry of the
Lord shall be re-vealed. All the earth will see the Lord.
4. I wait - ed for the
Lord. God heard my cry.
5. Our eyes are fixed on the Lord our God.
6. Seek first the king-dom of God. Seek and you shall find.
7. O Lord, show us your way. Guide us in your truth.

950 Within our darkest night

Taizé Community — Jacques Berthier (1923-1994)

B Em D
With-in our dark-est night, you kin - dle the fire that ne - ver dies a -

G C G D G D Em B C Am6
way, that ne - ver dies a - way. With - in our dark-est night, you kin - dle the

B Em Am6 B Em Am6 B
fire that ne - ver dies a - way, that ne - ver dies a - way.

© Copyright Ateliers et Presses de Taizé, Taizé-Communauté, F-71250, France.
Used by permission.

951 You are the centre

Words and music: Margaret Rizza (b.1929)

© Copyright 1998 Kevin Mayhew Ltd.

COMPLETE ANGLICAN
HYMNS OLD & NEW

Music for the Eucharist

952 A New People's Mass (Gregory Murray)

Gregory Murray (1905-1992)

Kyrie

Lord, have mer - cy. Lord, have mer - cy.

Christ, have mer - cy. Christ, have mer - cy.

Lord, have mer - cy. Lord, have mer - cy.

Gloria

Glo - ry to God in the high - est, and peace to his peo-ple on earth.

Lord God, hea - ven - ly King, al - migh - ty God and Fa - ther,

we wor - ship you, we give you thanks, we praise you for your glo - ry.

Lord Je - sus Christ, on - ly Son of the Fa - ther, Lord God,

Lamb of God, you take a - way the sins of the world, have mer -

cy on us; you are seat - ed at the right hand of the Fa -

ther, re - ceive our prayer. For you a - lone are the

Ho - ly One, you a - lone are the Lord, you a - lone are the Most

© Copyright McCrimmon Publishing Co. Ltd., 10-12 High Street, Great Wakering, Southend-on-Sea, Essex SS3 0EQ, UK. Used by permission.

High, Je - sus Christ, with the Ho - ly Spi - rit,
in the glo - ry of God the Fa - ther. A - men.
Sanctus
Ho - ly, ho - ly, ho - ly Lord, God of pow - er and might,
hea - ven and earth are full of your glo - ry. Ho - san - na in the
high - est. Bles - sed is he who comes in the name
of the Lord. Ho - san - na in the high - est.
Memorial Acclamation
Christ has died, Christ is ri - sen, Christ will come a - gain.
Great Amen
A - men.
Agnus Dei
Lamb of God, you take a - way the sins of the world:
1st & 2nd times
3rd time
have mer - cy on us. grant us peace.

953 A Simple Mass

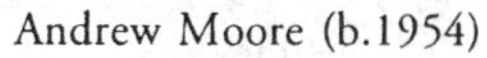

© Copyright 1999 Kevin Mayhew Ltd.

C G C G C G C G F
you a-lone are the Ho-ly One, you a-lone are the Lord, you a-lone are the
C Gm Dm Gsus4 G F C
Most High, Je - sus Christ, with the Ho - ly Spi-rit, in the
Gm Dm Gsus4 G F C Gm Dm G
glo-ry of God the Fa-ther. A - men. A - men.
Sanctus
G C/G G C/G F
Ho-ly, ho-ly, ho-ly Lord, God of pow-er and
G C/G F
God of might, hea - ven and earth are full of your
G E♭ Dm G Dm G
glo - ry. Ho - san - na in the high - est. Ho - san - na in the high - est.
Gm E♭ Dm G
Bles - sed is he who comes in the name of the Lord.
Gm E♭ Dm Gm C
Bles - sed is he who comes in the name of the Lord. Ho -
E♭ Dm G Dm G
san - na in the high - est. Ho - san - na in the high - est.
Acclamation
G C/G G C/G
Dy-ing, you de - stroyed our death,
F G Dm G
ris-ing, you re - stored our life. Lord Je - sus, come in glo - ry.

954 Mass of the Spirit (Kevin Mayhew)

© Copyright 1997 Kevin Mayhew Ltd.

wor - ship you, we give you thanks, we praise you for your glo - ry.

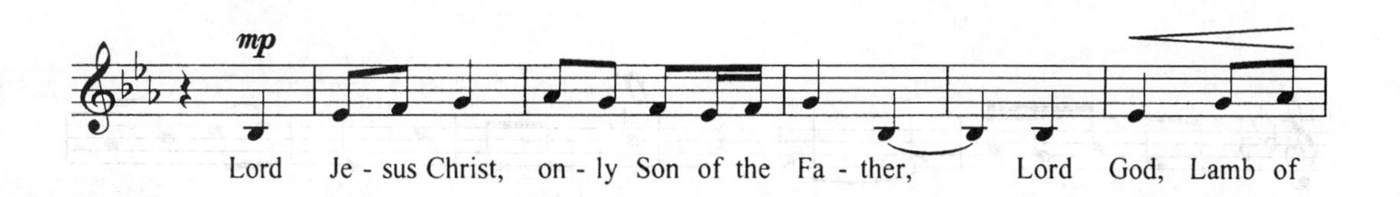
mp
Lord Je - sus Christ, on - ly Son of the Fa - ther, Lord God, Lamb of

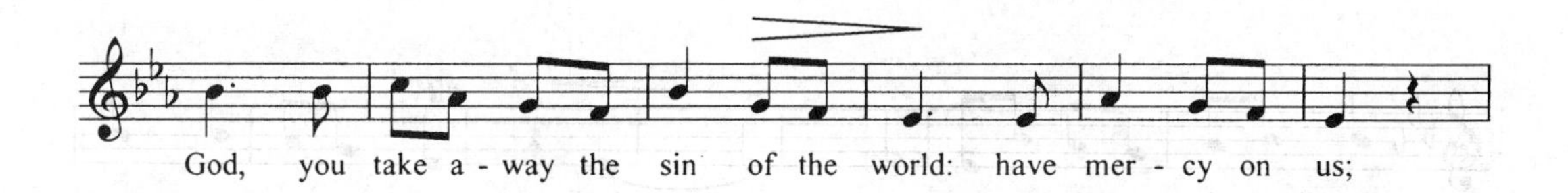
God, you take a - way the sin of the world: have mer - cy on us;

you are seat - ed at the right hand of the Fa - ther: re - ceive our

f
prayer. For you a - lone are the Ho - ly One,

ff
you a - lone are the Lord, you a - lone are the Most High, Je - sus

mf
Christ, with the Ho - ly Spi - rit, in the glo - ry of God the Fa - ther.

f
mf
A - men, a - men.

Sanctus
Largamente (♩ = 84)
Ho - ly, ho - ly, ho - ly Lord,
God of pow - er and might, hea - ven and earth are full of your
glo - ry. Ho - san - na in the high - est. Bles - sed is he who
comes in the name of the Lord. Ho - san - na in the high - est.
Agnus Dei
Adagio (♩ = 69)
Lamb of God, you take a - way the sins of the
world: have mer - cy on us. Lamb of God, you take a - way the
sins of the world: have mer - cy on us. Lamb of God, you

take a - way the sins of the world: grant us peace.

955 Mass of the Bread of Life (Margaret Rizza)

© Copyright 1998 Kevin Mayhew Ltd.

Optional Descant
F Gm11 Fmaj7 Gm11 F Gm11 Fmaj7 Gm11 F Gm11
Glo - ry, glo-ry to God, glo-ry to God in the high - est; peace to his
Glo - ry, glo-ry to God, glo-ry to God in the high - est; peace to his
Fmaj7 Gm11 F Gm11 Fmaj7 Gm11 F
rit.
peo-ple on earth, peace to his peo-ple on earth.
peo-ple on earth, peace to his peo-ple on earth.
Meno mosso
Am Dm6 Am Dm6 Am Fmaj7 Esus4 E Am G
mp
Lord Je-sus Christ, on-ly
Am G Am Fmaj7 Esus4 E Am Dm7
Son of the Fa - ther, Lord God, Lamb of God, you take a-way the
un poco rall.
a tempo
Em Fmaj7 E Dm7 E A Dm
sin of the world: have mer - cy on us; you are seat-ed at the
un poco rall.
Gm Asus4 A7 Dm Esus4 E Am Dm Esus4 E Am
right hand of the Fa-ther: re-ceive our prayer, re-ceive our prayer, re - ceive our prayer.

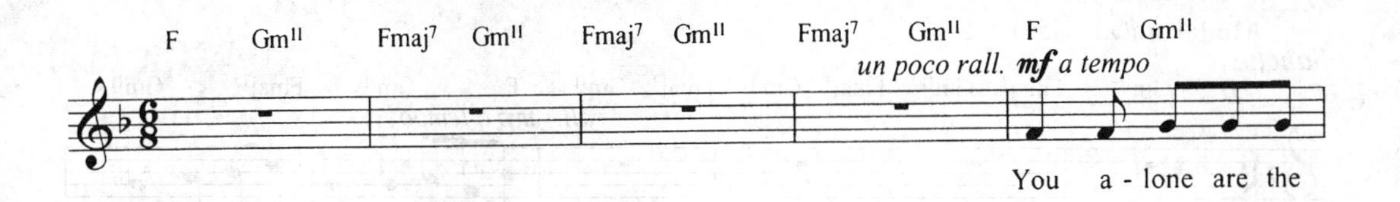

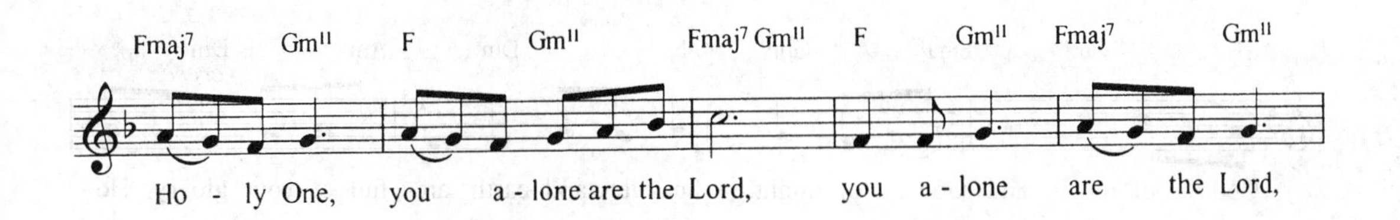

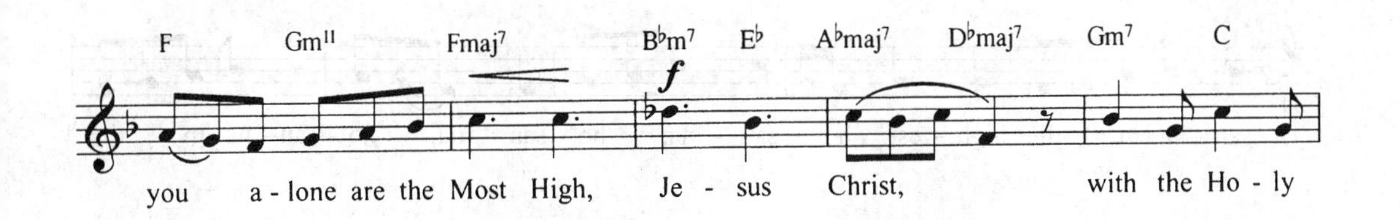

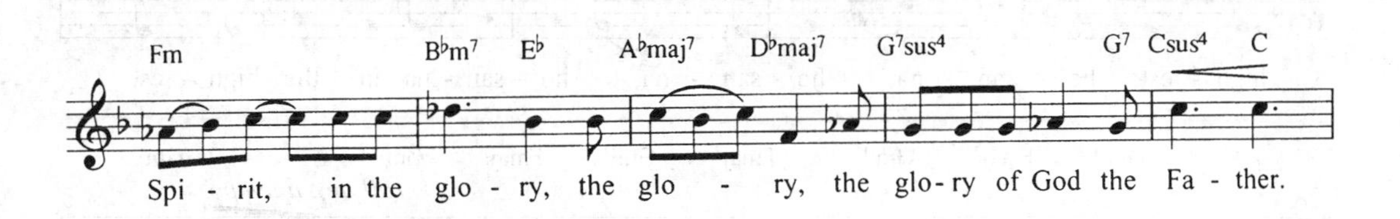

Optional Descant

Moderato(♩. = c.56)
Sanctus
F Gm11 Fmaj7 Gm11 Fmaj7 Gm11 Fmaj7 Gm11 F Gm11 Fmaj7 Gm11
rall. mp a tempo
Ho - ly, ho - ly, ho - ly Lord,
F Gm11 Fmaj7 Gm11 F Dm Am Dm
cresc.
God of pow'r and God of might, hea-ven and earth are full of your glo-ry. Ho-
Gm7 F Gm C F Dm Gm7 F
f
san - na in the high - est; ho - san - na, ho - san - na, ho - san - na in the
Gm C F Dm F B♭maj7 C7sus4 C7 F
high - est; ho - san - na, ho - san - na, ho - san - na in the high - est.
F Gm11 Fmaj7 Gm11 Fmaj7 Gm11 Fmaj7 Gm11 F Gm11
rall. mp a tempo
Bles-sed is he,
Fmaj7 Gm11 F Gm11 Fmaj7 Gm11 F Dm
bles-sed is he, bles-sed is he who comes in the name, he who comes in the
Am Dm Gm7 F Gm C
cresc.
Optional Descant
name of the Lord. Ho - san - na in the high - est, ho -
F Dm Gm7 F Gm C
f
san - na, ho - san - na, ho - san - na in the high - est; ho -
f
san - na, ho - san - na, ho - san - na in the high - est; ho -

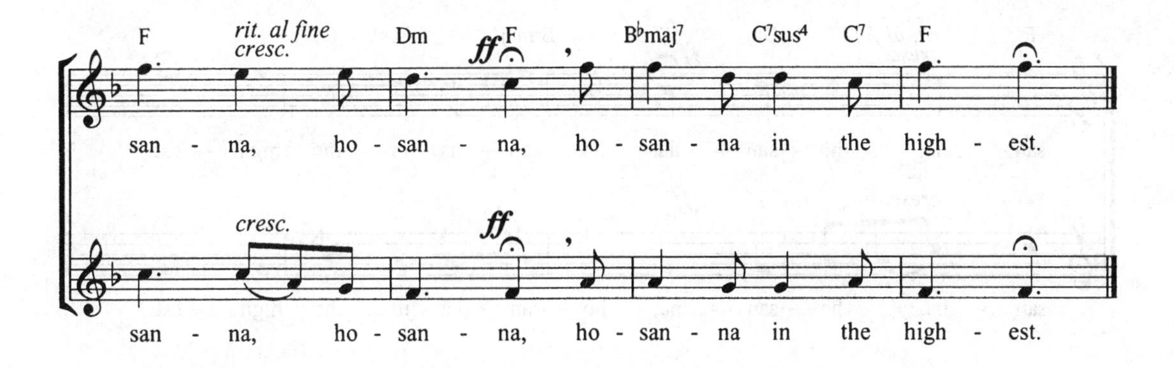

Memorial Acclamation

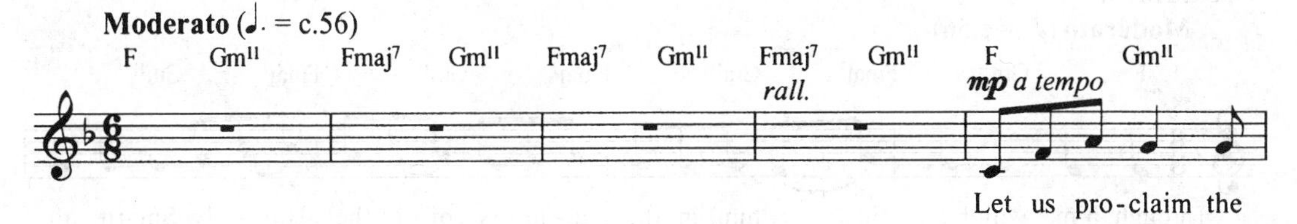

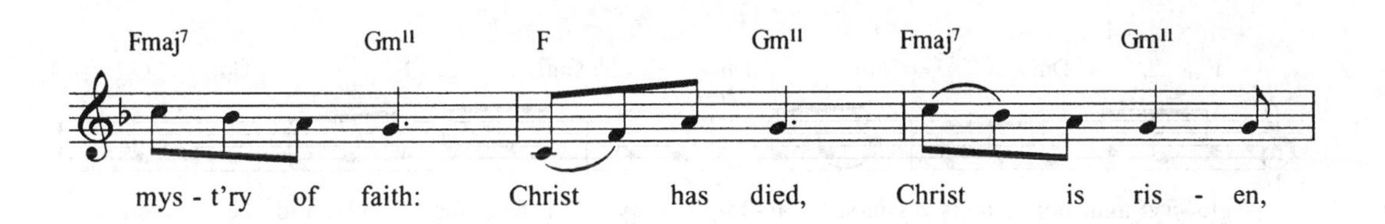

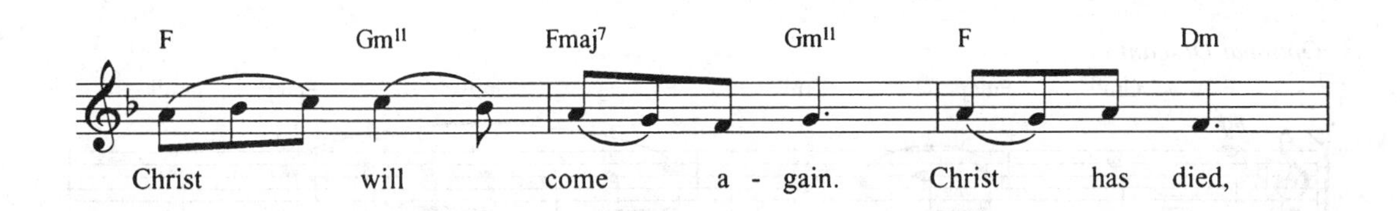

F rit. al fine Dm F Bbmaj7 C7sus4 C7 F
cresc. ff
san - na, ho - san - na, ho - san - na in the high - est.
cresc. ff
san - na, ho - san - na, ho - san - na in the high - est.

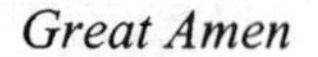
Great Amen

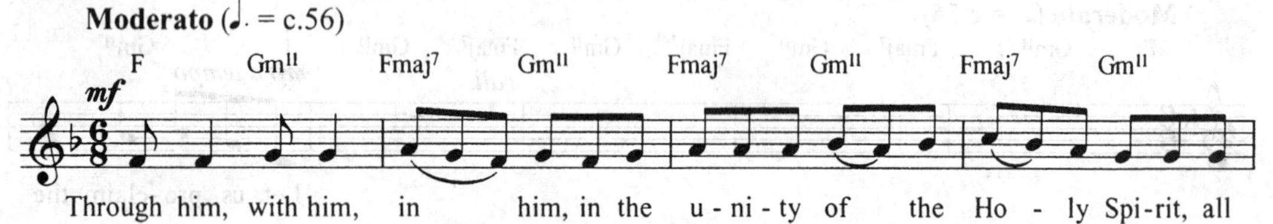
Moderato (♩. = c.56)
F Gm11 Fmaj7 Gm11 Fmaj7 Gm11 Fmaj7 Gm11
mf
Through him, with him, in him, in the u - ni - ty of the Ho - ly Spi - rit, all

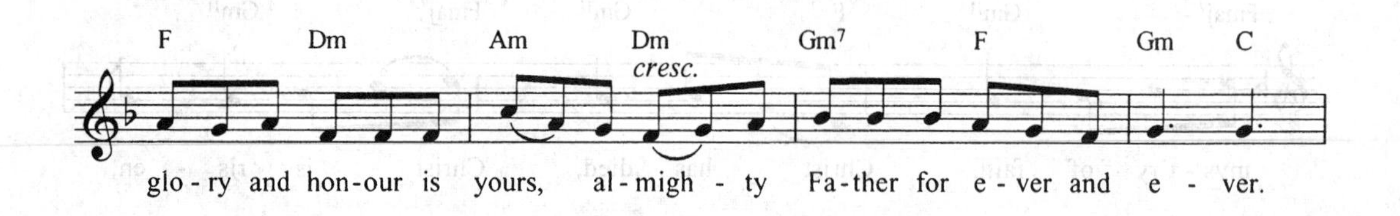
F Dm Am Dm Gm7 F Gm C
cresc.
glo - ry and hon - our is yours, al - migh - ty Fa - ther for e - ver and e - ver.

Optional Descant
F Gm11 Fmaj7 Gm11 F Gm11 Fmaj7 Gm11
mf
A - men, a - men, a - men,
mf
A - men, a - men, a - men,
Largo
F Dm Am Bbmaj7 Gm7 F
f cresc. e rit. ff cresc.
a - men, a - men, a - men.
f cresc. e rit. ff cresc.
a - men, a - men, a - men.

Agnus Dei
Larghetto (♩ = 66)
F Gm7 Fmaj7 Gm7 Fmaj7 Gm7 Fmaj7 Gm7 F Gm7 Fmaj7 Gm7 F Gm7 Fmaj7 Gm7
un poco rall.
F Gm7 Gmaj7 Gm7 F Dm Gm C F Gm
p a tempo
Je - sus, Lamb of God, Je - sus, Lamb of God, you take a - way the
Am Dm Gm7 Csus4 C F Gm7 Fmaj7 Gm7
sins of the world: have mer - cy on us. Je - sus, Lamb of God,
F Dm Gm C F Gm Am Dm Gm7 Csus4 C
mp
Je - sus, Lamb of God, you take a - way the sin of the world: have mer - cy on us.
Optional Descant
F Gm7 Fmaj7 Gm7 F Dm Gm C F Fmaj7 Gm
mf
rall.
Je - sus, Lamb of God, Je - sus, Lamb of God, you take a - way the
mf
Je - sus, Lamb of God, Je - sus, Lamb of God, you take a - way the
Am Dm Gm7 F B♭maj7 C7sus4 C7 F
rall.
p dim e rall.
sins of the world: grant us your peace, grant us your peace.
rall.
p dim e rall.
sins of the world: grant us your peace, grant us your peace.

956 The Holy Trinity Service

Christopher Tambling (b.1964)

Kyrie

Flowing

mf

Lord, have mer - cy. Lord, have mer - cy.

cresc.

Christ, have mer - cy. Christ, have mer - cy.

f

Lord, have mer - cy. Lord, have mer - cy.

mp

Gloria

f

Glo - ry to God in the high - est, and peace to his peo-ple on earth.

mf

Lord God, heav'n - ly King, al - migh - ty God and Fa - ther,

cresc.

f

we wor - ship you, we give you thanks, we praise you for your glo - ry.

mf legato

Lord Je - sus Christ, on - ly Son of the Fa - ther, Lord God, Lamb of God,

you take a - way the sin of the world; have mer - cy on us:

you are seat - ed at the right hand of God the

© Copyright 1992 Kevin Mayhew Ltd.

Fa - ther: re - ceive our prayer.
f
For you a - lone are the Ho - ly One, you a - lone are the
cresc.
Lord; you a - lone are the Most High, Je - sus Christ, with the Ho - ly
f
Spi - rit, in the glo - ry of God the Fa - ther. A - men, a -
allarg. ff rit.
men. A - men, a - men.
Sanctus
Steadily
accel. a tempo
Ho - ly, ho - ly, ho - ly Lord. God of pow'r and might,
cresc. molto allarg. f
heav'n and earth are full of your glo - ry. Ho - san - na in the high - est.
mf a tempo
Bles - sed is he who comes in the name of the Lord. Ho -
f
san - na in the high - est, ho - san - na in the high - est!
Acclamation
mf cresc. f rit.
Christ has died. Christ is ris - en. Christ will come a - gain.

957 Missa Simplex

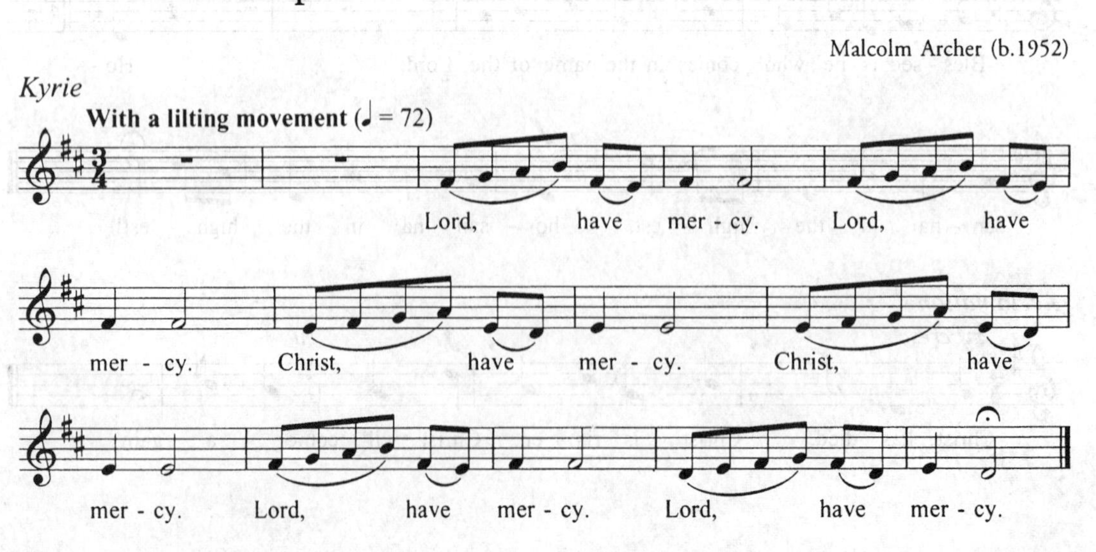

© Copyright 2000 Kevin Mayhew Ltd.

Gloria
With vigour (♩ = 126)
f
Glo - ry to God in the high - est, and
peace to his peo - ple on earth. Lord God, heav'n - ly King, al - migh - ty God and
Fa - ther, we wor-ship you, we give you thanks, we praise you for your glo - ry.
Lord Je - sus Christ, on - ly Son of the Fa - ther, Lord God, Lamb of God, you
take a - way the sins of the world: have mer - cy on us; you are
seat - ed at the right hand of the Fa - ther; re - ceive our prayer. For
you a - lone are the Ho - ly One, you a - lone are the Lord,
you a - lone are the Most High, Je - sus Christ, with the Ho - ly Spi - rit,
rall.
in the glo - ry of God the Fa - ther. A - men.

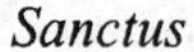

Sanctus

Con moto (♩ = 88)

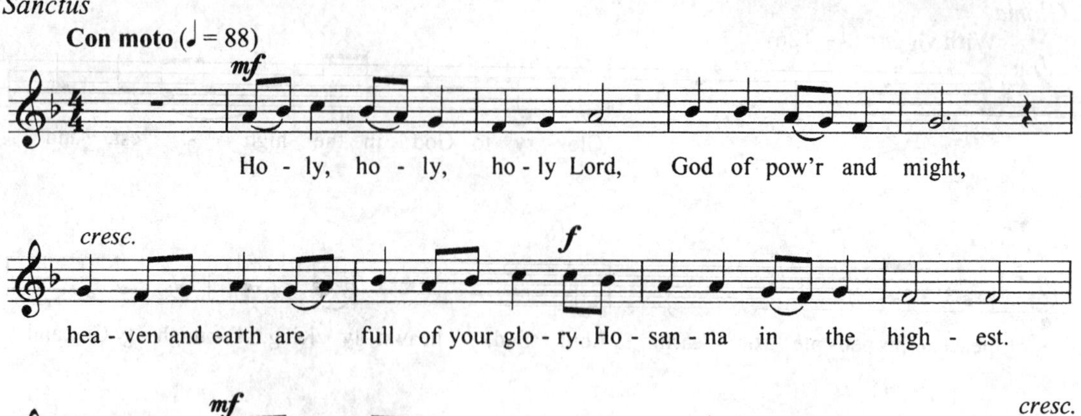

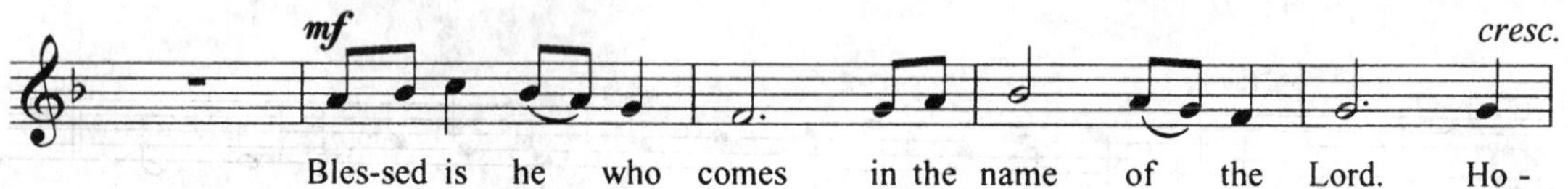

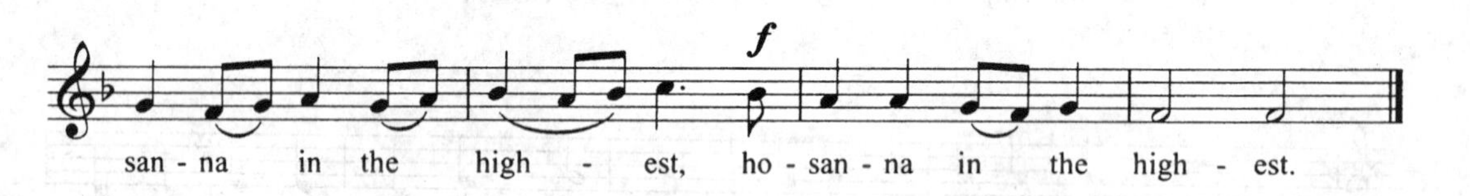

Memorial Acclamation

With vigour (♩ = 116)

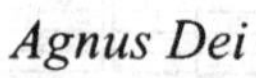

Agnus Dei

(♩ = 66)

958 Kyrie I

Jacques Berthier (1923-1994)

© Copyright Ateliers et Presses de Taizé, Taizé-Communauté, F-71250, France.
Used by permission.

959 Kyrie (Mawby)

Colin Mawby (b.1936)

© Copyright 1991 Kevin Mayhew Ltd.

960 Gloria 3

Jacques Berthier (1923-1994)

This setting may be sung as a canon with entries as indicated.

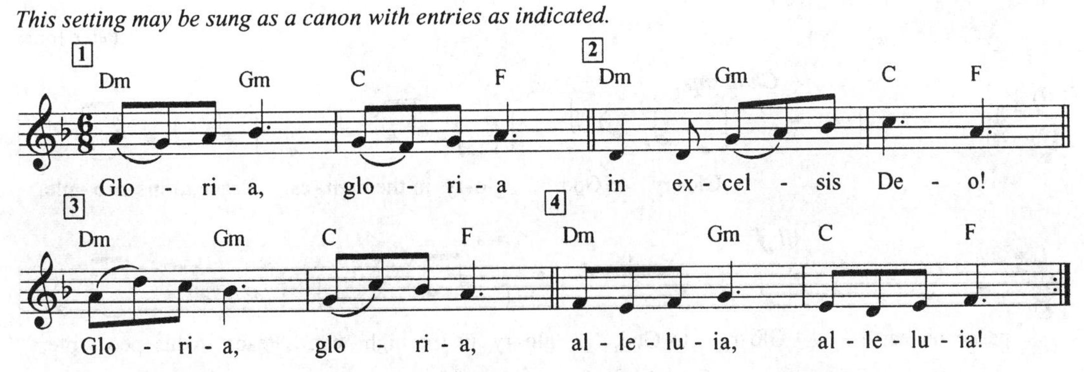

© Copyright Ateliers et Presses de Taizé, Taizé-Communauté, F-71250, France.
Used by permission.

961 Halle, halle, halle

Traditional — Unknown

962 Lord, have mercy (Filitz)

Michael Forster (b.1946) — Friedrich Filitz (1804-1876)

CASWALL 65 65

2. Christ, have mercy on us,
hear us as we pray;
Christ, have mercy on us,
take our sin away.

3. Lord, have mercy on us,
hear our humble plea;
Lord, have mercy on us,
set our spirits free.

Text © Copyright 1997 Kevin Mayhew.

963 Coventry Gloria

Peter Jones

Choir ***mp***

Glo - ry to God, glo - ry in the high - est. Peace to his peo - ple,

All ***f***

peace on earth. Glo - ry to God, glo - ry in the high - est. Peace to his peo - ple,

© Copyright 1981, 1982 Peter Jones. Published by OCP Publications, 5536 NE Hassalo, Portland, OR 97213, USA. All rights reserved. Used by permission.

Choir mf
peace on earth. Lord God, hea - ven - ly King, al - migh - ty God and Fa - ther.
All
Choir f
Glo - ry to God, glo - ry in the high - est, peace to his peo - ple, peace on earth. We
All
Choir
All
wor - ship you, glo - ry in the high - est, give you thanks, glo - ry in the high - est,
Choir f
All f
praise you for your glo - ry. Glo - ry to God, glo - ry in the high - est.
Choir mf
Peace to his peo - ple, peace on earth. Lord Je - sus Christ, on - ly Son of the Fa - ther,
Lord God, Lamb of God, you take a - way the sin of the world; have
All
Choir
mer - cy on us; have mer - cy on us; you are seat - ed at the right hand of the Fa - ther: re -
All
Choir mp
ceive our prayer, re - ceive our prayer. Glo - ry to God,
All f
glo - ry in the high - est. Peace to his peo - ple, peace on earth. Glo - ry to God,
glo - ry in the high - est. Peace to his peo - ple, peace on earth.

964 Gloria (Anderson)

Words and music: Mike Anderson (b.1956), adapted from the Liturgy

2. Jesus, Saviour of all, Lord God, Lamb of God,
you take away our sins, O Lord, have mercy on us all.

3. At the Father's right hand, Lord receive our prayer,
for you alone are the Holy One, and you alone are Lord.

4. Glory, Father and Son, glory, Holy Spirit,
to you we raise our hands up high, we glorify your name.

© Copyright 1999 Kevin Mayhew Ltd.

965 Sing to God a song of glory

Words and music: Francesca Leftley (b.1955), based on the *Gloria*

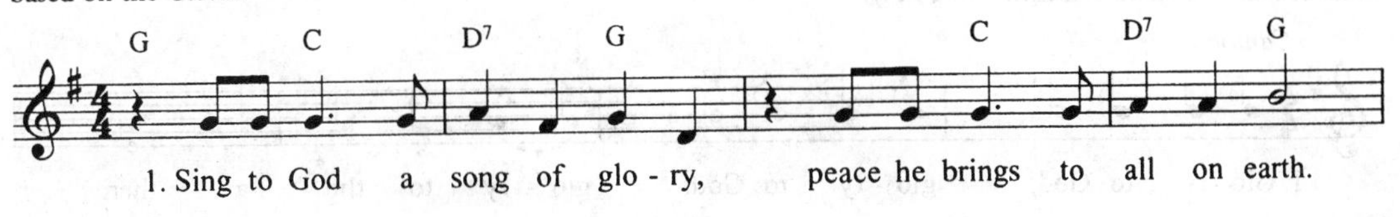

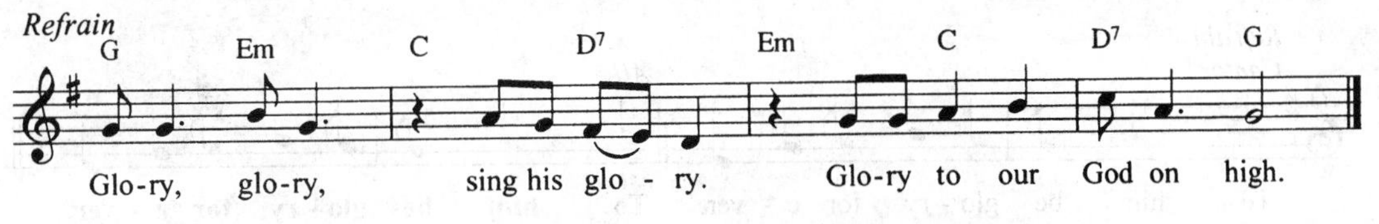

2. Sing to Christ, the Father's loved one,
Jesus, Lord and Lamb of God:
hear our prayer, O Lord, have mercy,
you who bear the sins of all.

3. Sing to Christ, the Lord and Saviour,
seated there at God's right hand:
hear our prayer, O Lord, have mercy,
you alone the Holy One.

4. Glory sing to God the Father,
glory to his only Son,
glory to the Holy Spirit,
glory to the Three in One.

© Copyright 1978 Kevin Mayhew Ltd.

966 Peruvian Gloria

Words and music: Traditional Peruvian,
collected and arr. John Ballantine (b.1945)

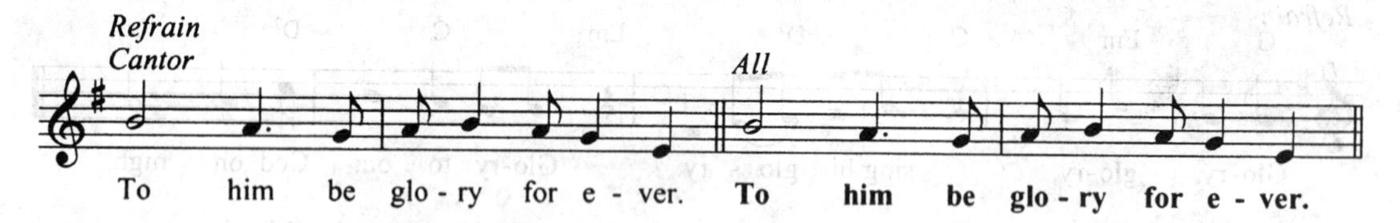

2. Glory to God, glory to God,
Son of the Father.
Glory to God, glory to God,
Son of the Father.
To him be glory for ever.
To him be glory for ever.
Alleluia, amen.
Alleluia, amen,
alleluia, amen,
alleluia, amen.

3. Glory to God, glory to God,
glory to the Spirit.
Glory to God, glory to God,
glory to the Spirit.
To him be glory for ever.
To him be glory for ever.
Alleluia, amen.
Alleluia, amen,
alleluia, amen,
alleluia, amen.

This is best sung accompanied only by bongos or a similar percussion instrument. The optional harmony notes give added effect, but those singing the tune should remain on the lower notes.

© Copyright 1976 Kevin Mayhew Ltd.

967 Glory to God *Country Gardens Gloria*

Michael Forster (b.1946), based on the *Gloria*

Traditional English melody

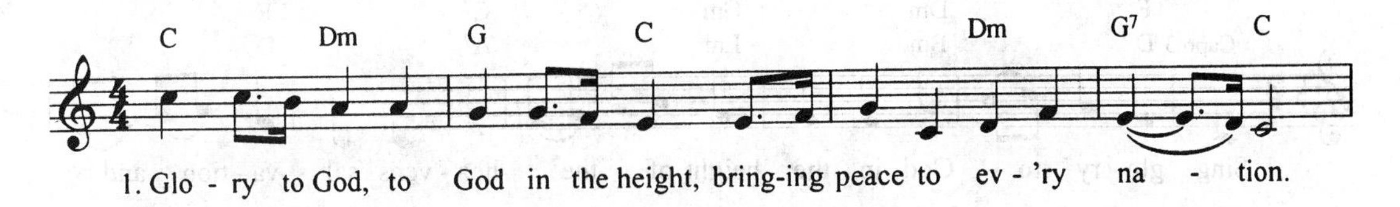

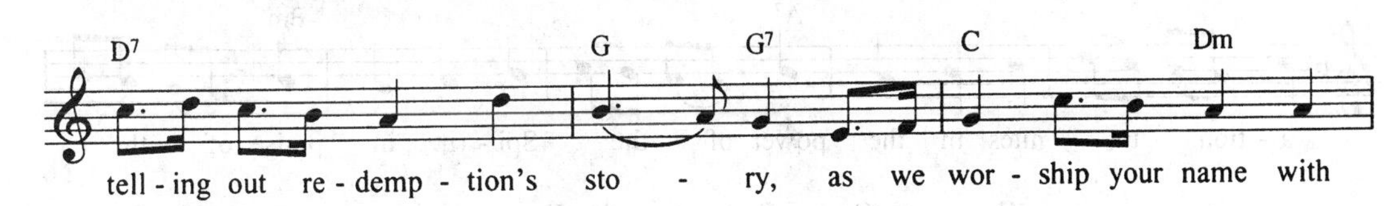

2. Jesus, the Father's one holy Son,
all creation bows before you.
You are the God, the God we acclaim,
and we worship and adore you.
Lamb of God, to you we pray,
you who take our sin away,
mercy, grace and truth revealing.
At the right hand of God, receive our humble prayer
for forgiveness, hope and healing.

3. You, Jesus Christ, alone are the Lord,
by your own eternal merit;
sharing by right the glory of God
in the presence of the Spirit.
You alone are Lord Most High,
you alone we glorify,
reigning over all creation.
To the Father, the Son and Spirit, Three in One,
be eternal acclamation!

Text © Copyright 1995 Kevin Mayhew Ltd.

968 Sing glory to God *Ash Grove Gloria*

Michael Forster (b.1946), based on the *Gloria* — Traditional Welsh melody

2. Our Lord Jesus Christ, only Son of the Father,
Lord God, Lamb of God, by the nations adored,
your blood takes away all the sin of creation:
have mercy upon us, for whom it was poured.
For you are our Saviour, our only Redeemer,
who came all our gladness and sorrows to share:
you sit at the side, the right hand of the Father,
have mercy upon us, and answer our prayer.

3. For you, only you, we acknowledge as holy,
we name you alone as our Saviour and Lord;
you only, O Christ, with the Spirit exalted,
are one with the Father, for ever adored.
Creation unites in the power of the Spirit,
in praise of the Father, through Jesus the Son.
So complex, so simple, so clear, so mysterious,
our God ever Three yet eternally One!

Text © Copyright 1995 Kevin Mayhew Ltd.

969 Holy, holy, holy (Deutsche Messe)

Franz Schubert (1797-1828)
adapted by Richard Proulx

Slowly

mp

Ho - ly, ho - ly, ho - ly Lord, God of pow'r and might.

Ho - ly, ho - ly, ho - ly Lord, God of pow'r and might.

f

Hea - ven and earth are full, full of your glo - ry. *mf* Ho-

san - na in the high - est, ho - san - na in the high - est.

f

Bles - sed is he who comes, in the name of the Lord. *mp* Ho-

san - na in the high - est, ho - san - na in the *dim.* high - est.

© Copyright 1997 GIA Publications Inc., 7404 S. Mason Avenue, Chicago, Illinois 60638, USA.
All rights reserved. Used by permission.

970 Sanctus (Taizé)

© Copyright Ateliers et Presses de Taizé, Taizé-Communauté, F-71250, France.
Used by permission.

971 Holy, holy, holy is the Lord

© Copyright 1984 Kevin Mayhew Ltd.

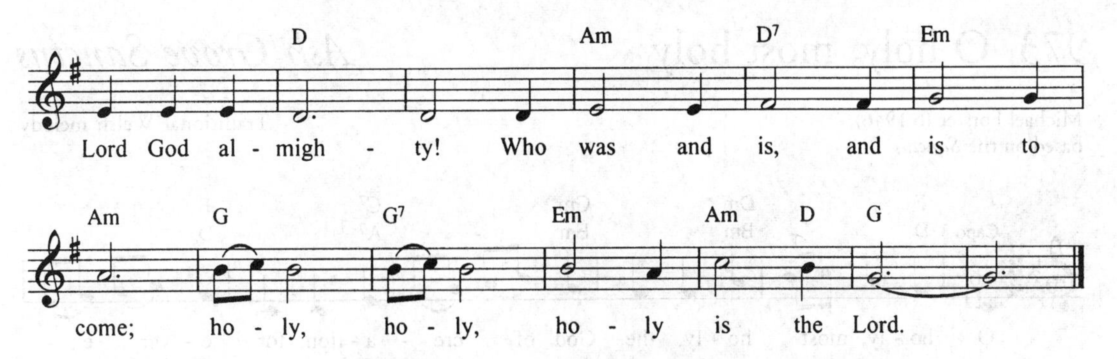

2. Blessèd, blessèd, blest is he who comes,
blest is he who comes in the Lord's name.
Blessèd, blessèd, blest is he who comes,
blest is he who comes in the Lord's name.
Hosanna in the heights of heav'n.
Blessèd, blessèd, blessèd is the Lord.

972 Holy, most holy, all holy the Lord *Slane Sanctus*

Michael Forster (b.1946),
based on the *Sanctus*

Traditional Irish melody

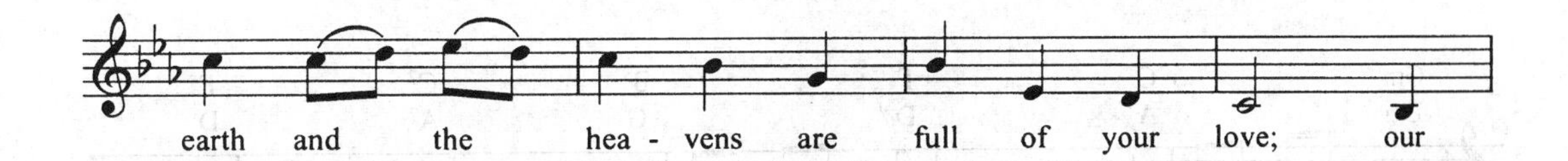

2. Blessèd, most blessèd, all blessèd is he
whose life makes us whole, and whose death sets us free:
who comes in the name of the Father of light,
let endless hosannas resound in the height.

Text © Copyright 1993 Kevin Mayhew Ltd.

973 O holy, most holy *Ash Grove Sanctus*

Michael Forster (b.1946),
based on the *Sanctus*

Traditional Welsh melody

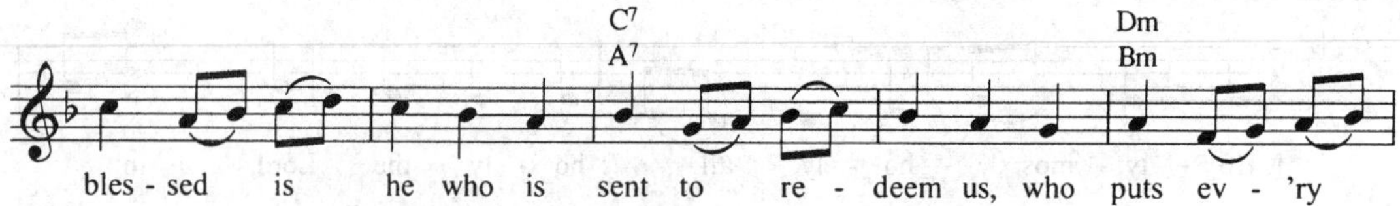

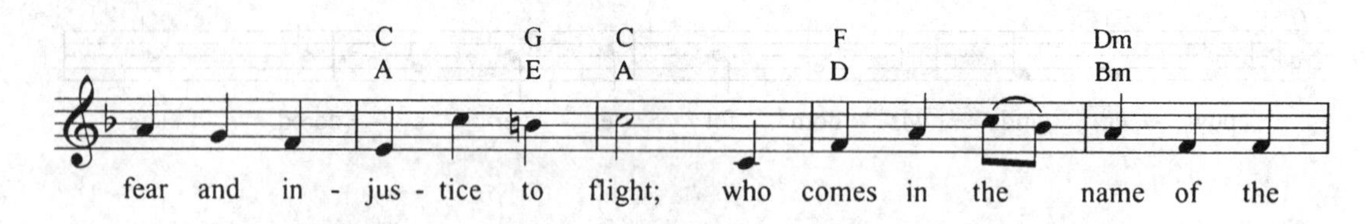

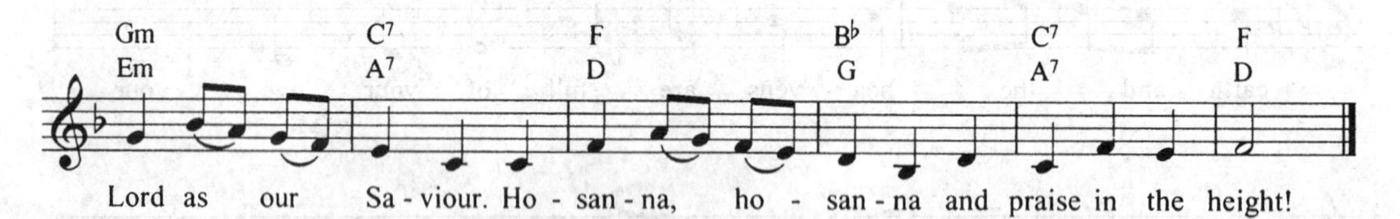

Text © Copyright 1995 Kevin Mayhew Ltd.

974 Christ has died (Duffy)

Philip Duffy

Maestoso (♩ = 96)

© Copyright 1979 Philip Duffy, taken from Sanctus 1. Used by permission.

975 Christ has died (Hill)

David Hill

© Copyright 1999 Kevin Mayhew Ltd.

976 Lamb of God (Fitzpatrick)

Gerry Fitzpatrick (b.1940)

© Copyright 1986 Kevin Mayhew Ltd.

977 Lamb of God (Rees)

Alan Rees (b.1941)

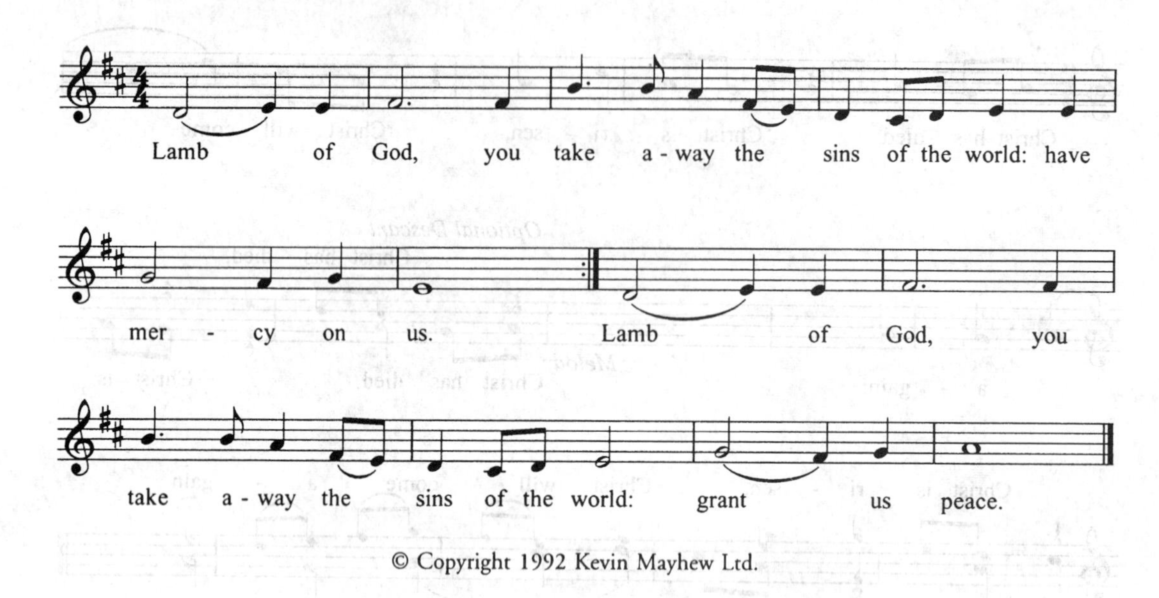

© Copyright 1992 Kevin Mayhew Ltd.

978 O Lamb of God

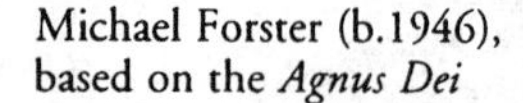
Michael Forster (b.1946),
based on the *Agnus Dei*

Charles Hubert Hastings Parry (1848-1918)

REPTON 86 88 6

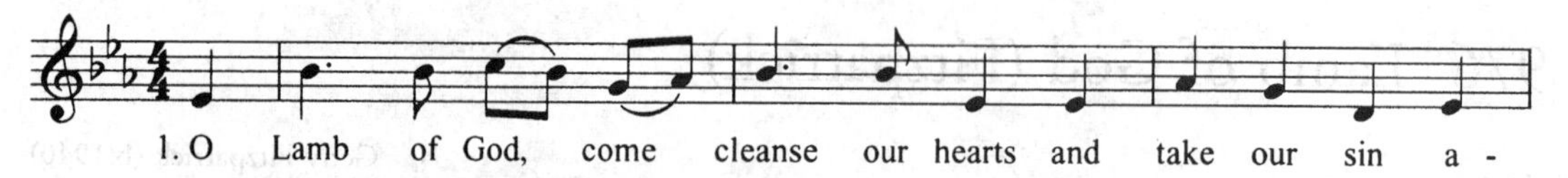

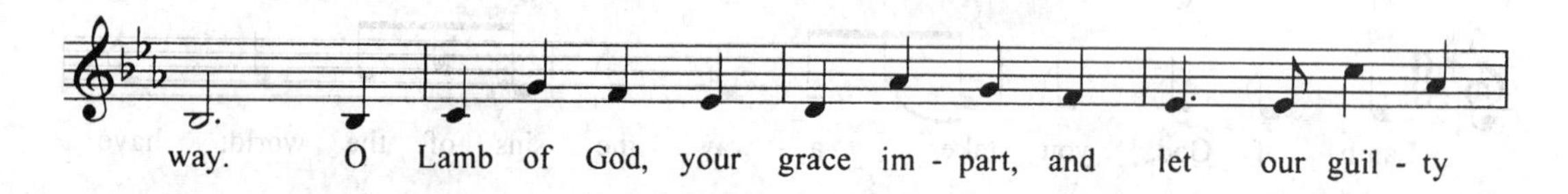

2. O Lamb of God, our lives restore,
our guilty souls release.
Into our lives your Spirit pour
and let us live for evermore
in perfect heav'nly peace,
in perfect heav'nly peace.

Text © Copyright 1997 Kevin Mayhew Ltd.

COMPLETE ANGLICAN
HYMNS OLD & NEW

Indexes

COMPLETE ANGLICAN
HYMNS OLD & NEW

Index of Composers and Sources of Music

Index of Authors and Sources of Text

Alphabetical Index of Tunes

Some modern tunes have not been given names. They will be found under the first line of text associated with them in the Index of First Lines.

COMPLETE ANGLICAN
HYMNS OLD & NEW

Metrical Index of Tunes

Some modern tunes, because of their free rhythmic patterns, are not listed in this index.

COMPLETE ANGLICAN
HYMNS OLD & NEW

Scriptural Index

GENESIS

EXODUS

Exodus

LEVITICUS

NUMBERS

DEUTERONOMY

JOSHUA

JUDGES

RUTH

1 SAMUEL

2 SAMUEL

1 KINGS

2 KINGS

1 CHRONICLES

2 CHRONICLES

JOB

PSALMS

Psalms

PROVERBS

SONG OF SOLOMON

ISAIAH

JEREMIAH

LAMENTATIONS

EZEKIEL

DANIEL

HOSEA

2:21-25	Listen to my voice	403
13:4	All for Jesus!	13

JOEL

2:28	All over the world	20
	The King is among us	648

AMOS

5:23-24	What shall be bring	730
5:24	Love is the only law	430
	Peace is flowing like a river	553
	The universe was waiting	669

OBADIAH

21	Come and see the shining hope	110

MICAH

4:2-4	O God of hope	493
4:3	And everyone beneath the vine and fig tree	774
	Onward, Christian pilgrims	531
4:3-4	Waken, O sleeper, wake and rise	702
5:1	Earth has many a noble city	152
5:2	When our God came to earth	740
6:3-5	I give you love	309
6:6-8	What shall be bring	730
7:18-19	O the deep, deep love of Jesus!	538

HABAKKUK

2:14	All over the world	20
3:2	Restore, O Lord	582

ZEPHANIAH

1:7	Let all mortal flesh keep silence	381

HAGGAI

2:6	Restore, O Lord	582
2:7	Angels from the realms of glory	36
	Come, thou long-expected Jesus	128

ZECHARIAH

2:13	Let all mortal flesh keep silence	381
8:4-5	In an age of twisted values	317
	Lord, we thank you for the promise	424
13:9	Purify my heart	574

MALACHI

1:11	From the sun's rising	197
3:1	Angels from the realms of glory	36
3:3	Purify my heart	574
	Restore, O Lord	582
3:6	Abide with me	2
	Great is thy faithfulness	249
4:2	Christ, whose glory fills the skies	105
	First light	175
	Hark, the herald-angels sing	265
	Judge eternal, throned in splendour	372
	O come, O come, Emmanuel	480
	You are the King of Glory	762

MATTHEW

1:21	Jesus, the name high over all	364
	Like a candle flame	399
	The Virgin Mary had a baby boy	670
1:23	Come, come, come to the manger	112
	Hail, thou once despisèd Jesus	258
	Hark, the herald-angels sing	265
	Hark! the sound of holy voices	267
	Jesus, Name above all names	355
	Let us talents and tongues employ	391
	Like a candle flame	399
	Mary, blessed teenage mother	442
	Morning has broken	450
	O little town of Bethlehem	508
	The angel Gabriel from heaven came	634
2:1-2	Long ago, prophets knew	406
2:1-12	A great and mighty wonder	4
	Angels from the realms of glory	36
	Arise to greet the Lord of light	40
	As with gladness men of old	49
	Behold, the great Creator	62
	Brightest and best of the suns	85
	Crown him with many crowns	137
	Earth has many a noble city	152
	In the bleak mid-winter	326
	O come, all ye faithful	479
	See him lying on a bed of straw	589
	The first Nowell	641
	The Virgin Mary had a baby boy	670
	We three kings of Orient are	724
	What child is this	729
	Who would think	750
2:2	How brightly shines the Morning Star!	291
	Jesu, all holy	341
2:6	Earth has many a noble city	152
	When our God came to earth	740
2:11	O worship the Lord in the beauty of holiness	552
2:13-18	Unto us a boy is born	700
3:1-3	Come on and celebrate!	125
	Wait for the Lord	949
3:1-12	On Jordan's bank the Baptist's cry	527
	We shall stay awake	722
3:2	The kingdom of God	646
3:11	All over the world	20
	Come. Holy Spirit, come	119
3:13-17	Father welcomes all his children	797
3:16	Come, gracious Spirit	116
	Come, Holy Ghost, our hearts inspire	117
	Eternal Ruler of the ceaseless round	154
	O King enthroned on high	504
	O let the Son of God enfold you	506
4:1-10	Jesus went away to the desert	852
4:1-11	At even, ere the sun was set	50
	Forty days and forty nights	190
	Forty days and forty nights in Judah's desert	191
	Lead us, heavenly Father, lead us	379
	Love is his word	429
	O love, how deep, how broad, how high	516
4:4	Seek ye first	590
4:16	God is our strength from days of old	220
4:16-17	Lord, the light of your love	419
4:18-20	Follow me	176
4:18-22	Dear Lord and Father of mankind	144
	Jesus calls us: o'er the tumult	347
	O happy day	498
	When God Almighty came to earth	733
	Will you come and follow me	752
4:19	Step by step, on and on	885
4:21	I danced in the morning	305
5:3-4	The Church's one foundation	636
5:3-12	The kingdom of heaven	647
	There's a song in the heart of creation	660
5:4	God! As with silent hearts	210
	Jesu, all holy	341
5:5	Fill your hearts with joy and gladness	172
	Make way, make way	438
	Who sees it all	749
5:6	Jesus, the broken bread	363
5:8	Blest are the pure in heart	77
5:11-16	An army of ordinary people	31
5:12	For all thy saints	179
5:14-16	Here on the threshold of a new beginning	280

Matthew

MARK

LUKE

Reference	Title	No.
	Here on the threshold of a new beginning	280
	Light a candle for thanksgiving!	396
	Lord, for the years	409
	This is the year	679
4:34	Be still, my soul	68
	There is a Redeemer	658
4:40	At even, ere the sun was set	50
5:1-11	O happy day	498
5:11-12	Dear Lord and Father of mankind	144
	Will you come and follow me	752
5:27	Follow me	176
	Step by step, on and on	885
	When God Almighty came to earth	733
	Will you come and follow me	752
5:30	The kingdom of God	646
5:37	One shall tell another	526
6:20-23	The kingdom of heaven	647
6:21	Make way, make way	438
6:27	O Lord, all the world belongs to you	509
6:35	For all thy saints	179
6:47-49	Don't build your house on the sandy land	790
	The wise man	897
7:16	Father, Lord of all creation	163
	Jesu, all holy	341
7:21	Jesus, the name high over all	364
7:22	My song is love unknown	463
	Thine arm, O Lord, in days of old	671
	Thou, whose almighty word	684
7:34	Alleluia, sing to Jesus	12
	Jesus, Prince and Saviour	358
	O Christ the same	477
7:37	I danced in the morning	305
7:43	Love is his word	429
7:48	God forgave my sin	212
8:5-8	Now, my tongue, the mystery telling	473
	We have a gospel to proclaim	716
8:22-25	Be still, my soul	68
	Calm me, Lord	924
	Eternal Father, strong to save	153
	I cannot tell	303
	Inspired by love and anger	325
	Light of the minds that know him	397
	Sweet sacrament divine	622
	You are the light	763
8:24	Holy Spirit, truth divine	289
8:44	Immortal love, for ever full	315
9:10-17	Gather around, for the table is spread	199
9:23	Follow me	176
	Lift high the cross	394
	Light of the minds that know him	397
	Take up thy cross, the Saviour said	626
9:26	At the name of Jesus	54
9:28-36	Jesus, on the mountain peak	357
9:58	Thou didst leave thy throne	683
	When God Almighty came to earth	733
9:58-59	Follow me	176
	Moses, I know you're the man	451
	Will you come and follow me	752
10:2	From the sun's rising	197
10:4	Moses, I know you're the man	451
10:6	God forgave my sin	212
10:25-29	In bread we bring you, Lord	318
	Love is the only law	430
10:27	Gracious God, in adoration	244
10:34	Hark, my soul, it is the Lord	264
	When I needed a neighbour	736
10:39	To be in your presence	694
11:1	Lord Jesus Christ	411
	Lord, teach us how to	418
11:2	Come, O Lord, inspire us	124
11:2-4	God forgave my sin	212
	Make me a channel of your peace	437
	O God of Bethel, by whose hand	491
	Our Father (Caribbean)	544
	Our Father (White)	545
	Our Father (Wiener)	546
	Thy kingdom come!	690
	Thy kingdom come, O God	691
	We plough the fields and scatter	719
11:3	Praise and thanksgiving	558
11:9	Come, Lord, to our souls	122
	Jesus, the name high over all	364
11:22	Christ the Lord is risen again	103
11:27	Virgin-born, we bow before thee	701
11:42	Beauty for brokenness	60
12:4	Moses, I know you're the man	451
12:6-7	'Cheep!' said the sparrow	783
	There are hundreds of sparrows	890
12:24	Moses, I know you're the man	451
12:27-28	There are hundreds of sparrows	890
12:31	Wait for the Lord	949
12:35	Thy kingdom come!	690
	Who is this so weak and helpless	748
	Ye servants of the Lord	757
12:40	Come, thou long-expected Jesus	128
13:10-17	I danced in the morning	305
13:24	As with gladness men of old	49
	Faithful Shepherd, feed me	156
	I will sing the wondrous story	337
	Loving Shepherd of thy sheep	434
14:12-24	I, the Lord of sea and sky	332
14:13	Thine arm, O Lord, in days of old	671
14:16-24	Thy hand, O God, has guided	689
14:27	March on, my soul, with strength	440
15:2	The kingdom of God	646
15:3	I will sing the wondrous story	337
15:3-7	I have a friend	829
15:4-6	Amazing grace	29
	Hark, my soul, it is the Lord	264
	The King of love my shepherd is	649
15:11-24	Lord, we know that we have failed you	423
15:24	Christ the Lord is risen again	103
	Come, let us sing	121
17:20-21	O, heaven is in my heart	499
18:16	Father welcomes all his children	797
18:16-17	It fell upon a summer day	331
18:19	God is good	214
19:1-5	Zacchaeus was a very little man	919
19:10	Lord of all life and power	414
	The Spirit lives to set us free	666
19:28-38	All glory, laud and honour	14
	My song is love unknown	463
19:37-38	Clap your hands, all you people	785
	Ride on, ride on in majesty	583
	You are the King of Glory	762
19:38	A Simple Mass	953
	Holy Trinity Setting	956
	Holy, holy, holy	969
	Holy, holy, holy is the Lord	971
	Holy, most holy, all holy the Lord	972
	Mass of the Bread of Life	955
	Mass of the Spirit	954
	O holy, most holy	973
	Sanctus (Taizé)	970
19:42	God! As with silent hearts	210
20:17	Each of us is a living stone	793
20:21	God's Spirit is in my heart	231
20:44	Hail to the Lord's anointed	259
21:25	Come and see the shining hope	110
21:27	Hark! a herald voice is calling	263
	Led like a lamb	380
21:27-28	Great indeed are your works, O Lord	247
21:33	Songs of praise the angels sang	608
21:36	Forth in thy name, O Lord, I go	188
	Onward, Christian pilgrims	531
	Waken, O sleeper, wake and rise	702
	We shall stay awake	722
	Ye servants of the Lord	757
22:3-6	Christ is the world's light	99
22:12	An upper room did our Lord prepare	38
22:14-30	Jesus, the broken bread	363
22:15-20	As we break the bread	48

JOHN

John

ACTS

ROMANS

6:9	Christ is alive!	96
	I danced in the morning	305
6:11	Bread of the world in mercy broken	83
6:18	On Christmas night all Christians sing	523
	Onward, Christian pilgrims	531
8:1	And can it be	32
	I am a new creation	298
	I'm accepted	830
8:1-3	The Spirit lives to set us free	666
8:9	Spirit of God	611
	The Spirit lives to set us free	666
8:11	Alleluia, give thanks to the risen Lord	8
	We give immortal praise	713
8:15	Abba, Father, let me be	1
	Alleluia (x8)	7
8:17	Here on the threshold of a new beginning	280
	The kingdom of God	646
8:18-27	O God, enthroned in majesty	490
8:21-22	On Christmas night all Christians sing	523
8:23-26	One Father	524
8:29	God of all human history	223
	Spirit of God within me	612
8:31-19	Hail the day that sees him rise	255
8:31-39	Jesus lives! thy terrors now	354
	Nada te turbe	937
	Now is eternal life	470
	You are beautiful	760
8:32	O Lord, my God	511
8:34	And now, O Father, mindful of the love	34
8:37	Soldiers of Christ, arise	606
	Thine be the glory	672
8:38	O for a heart to praise my God	484
8:38-39	We give immortal praise	713
8:39	There's a spirit in the air	661
10:9	Alleluia (x8)	7
	Alleluia, alleluia, give thanks to the risen Lord	8
10:14	Go forth and tell	238
11:6	Only by grace	528
11:33-36	Meekness and majesty	448
	You are beautiful	760
12:1-2	Lord, for the years	409
12:11	Warm as the sun	706
12:11-12	Jesus, the broken bread	363
12:15	Brother, sister, let me serve you	88
13:11-14	Wake up, O people	704
14:10	Mine eyes have seen the glory	449
14:17	Creating God, we bring our song of praise	134
	First light	175
15:7	Dear Christ, uplifted from the earth	142
15:12	O come, O come, Emmanuel	480
15:13	God of love	226

1 CORINTHIANS

1:12	Lord, we come to ask your healing	422
1:18-31	Come, wounded healer	130
1:25-27	Be thou my vision	70
1:25	Come, Holy Spirit, come	119
	God of love	226
1:28	Disposer supreme	149
3:4-6	Spirit of God within me	612
3:6	We plough the fields and scatter	719
	We can plough and dig the land	903
3:9	Come, build the Church	111
	Come, ye thankful people, come	133
3:11	Christ is made the sure foundation	97
	O, heaven is in my heart	499
	The Church's one foundation	636
3:16	Spirit of God	611
3:22	The Lord is King!	650
5:7	Christ the Lord is risen again	103
	Hail, thou once despisèd Jesus	258
	Lord, enthroned in heavenly splendour	408
5:7-8	At the Lamb's high feast we sing	53
6:11	What a wonderful change	728
6:14	By his grace	89

6:20	Bind us together, Lord	72
	Blessed assurance, Jesus is mine	74
	O Christ, who art the Light and Day	478
	Rejoice, heavenly powers	577
	The Church's one foundation	636
	We give immortal praise	713
7:23	Rejoice, heavenly powers	577
	There is a green hill far away	657
8:3	My God, how wonderful you are	457
9:24	Fight the good fight	169
	Forth in thy name, O Lord, I go	188
	Jesus, the name high over all	364
	May the mind of Christ my Saviour	447
9:24-27	Fight the good fight	169
10:4	Praise him, praise him	562
	Rock of ages	584
10:16	Dear Lord, to you again	145
10:16-17	Come, risen Lord	126
	From many grains	196
	O thou, who at thy Eucharist didst pray	540
	The table's set, Lord	668
	Ubi caritas	946
	We hail thy presence glorious	714
10:24	From heaven you came	195
10:31	My Father, for another night	454
11:23-25	Amazing grace	29
	Broken for me, broken for you	87
	Dear Lord, to you again	145
	Gifts of bread and wine	200
	God of the Passover	228
	Here, Lord, we take the broken bread	278
	Jesus took a piece of bread	366
	Lord Jesus Christ	411
	Love is his word	429
	Thee we adore, O hidden Saviour, thee	640
	This is my body	674
11:23-26	As we break the bread	48
11:26	Once, only once, and once for all	522
12:3	Father, Lord of all creation	163
	Heaven shall not wait	272
	Jesus is Lord	352
	Lord Jesus Christ	411
12:3-4	Alleluia, give thanks to the risen Lord	8
12:4-11	Sing glory to God the Father	599
12:10	Come, Holy Spirit, come	119
12:12	Bind us together, Lord	72
12:27	Living God, your word has called us	404
	O Lord, all the world belongs to you	509
13:1-13	Come, Holy Spirit, come	119
	Gracious Spirit, Holy Ghost	245
	Life is great!	393
	O perfect love	533
13:4-8	A new commandment	35
13:7	Father, I place into your hands	162
13:12	Dear Christ, uplifted from the earth	142
	Here, O my Lord	279
	Loving Shepherd of thy sheep	434
	O Lord, we long to see your face	514
	The God of Abraham praise	642
13:12-13	By his grace	89
	Ubi caritas	946
14:12	Come, build the Church	111
15:3-4	Lord of all life and power	414
	Sing glory to God the Father	599
15:4-7	Now the green blade riseth	475
15:14	This joyful Eastertide	680
15:20	Alleluia, alleluia, hearts to heaven and voices raise	9
	Blessed assurance, Jesus is mine	74
	Hail the day that sees him rise	255
15:26	God is love: let heaven adore him	217
	Hail thee, Festival Day (Easter Version)	257
15:26-28	Going home	239
15:28	My God, accept my heart this day	455
	O Lord, I would delight in thee	510
	O what their joy and their glory must be	550
15:45	Praise to the Holiest	572

2 CORINTHIANS

GALATIANS

EPHESIANS

PHILIPPIANS

COLOSSIANS

1 THESSALONIANS

2 THESSALONIANS

1 TIMOTHY

2 PETER

1 JOHN

REVELATION

7:14-15	Blessed assurance, Jesus is mine	74
	By his grace	89
7:17	All heaven declares	17
	Be still, my soul	68
	Listen to my voice	403
	Have you heard the raindrops	817
	You can drink it, swim in it	917
11:15	Come and see the shining hope	110
	Crown him with many crowns	137
	Praise him, praise him	562
12:5	A purple robe	39
14:2	For thy mercy and thy grace	189
14:6	From the sun's rising	197
	We have a gospel to proclaim	716
14:7	Christ is the world's light	99
	Come, faithful pilgrims all	115
14:13	For all the saints	177
14:19	Mine eyes have seen the glory	449
15:3	O Christ the same	477
15:4	Angels from the realms of glory	36
17:14	Alleluia, sing to Jesus	12
18:23	How brightly shines the Morning Star!	291
19:4	Let all mortal flesh keep silence	381
19:6-9	Come, ye thankful people come	133
	The Church's one foundation	636
19:9	At the Lamb's high feast we sing	53
19:16	Alleluia, sing to Jesus	12
	Christ the Lord is risen again	103
	For thy mercy and thy grace	189
	Hosanna, hosanna	290
	Jesu, all holy	341
	Jesus, the broken bread	363
	Judge eternal, throned in splendour	372
	King of kings and Lord of lords	376
	Let all mortal flesh keep silence	381
	Majesty, worship his majesty	436
	Sing it in the valleys	600
	The head that once was crowned with thorns	644
20:10	Ye choirs of new Jerusalem	754
20:14	Guide me, O thou great Redeemer	252
21	O what their joy and their glory must be	550
21:1	Creating God, we bring our song of praise	134
	First light	175
	Songs of praise the angels sang	608
21:1-2	In the bleak midwinter	326
21:1-27	Light's abode, celestial Salem	398
21:10	City of God, how broad and far	106
21:18	Who is this so weak and helpless	748
21:2	God is our strength and refuge	219
	I'm not ashamed to own my Lord	316
	The Church's one foundation	636

	What a wonderful change	728
	Ye choirs of new Jerusalem	754
21:21	For all the saints	177
	Wake, O wake! with tidings thrilling	703
21:23	How brightly shines the Morning Star!	291
21:3-10	As with gladness men of old	49
	Wake, O wake! with tidings thrilling	703
21:3-5	Be still, my soul	68
	Listen to my voice	403
	O comfort my people	481
	O Lord, all the world belongs to you	509
21:4	Oft in danger, oft in woe	487
	Thy kingdom come, O God	691
21:5	Bless and keep us, God	73
	Creating God, we bring our song of praise	134
	First light	175
	Great God, your love has called us	246
	Hills of the north, rejoice	282
	Long ago, prophets knew	406
21:6	God is our strength from days of old	220
	God, the source and goal of being	233
	Have you heard the raindrops	817
	You can drink it, swim in it	917
22:1	God is our strength and refuge	219
	Have you heard the raindrops	817
	Shall we gather at the river	594
	You can drink it, swim in it	917
22:1-3	A purple robe	39
	Crown him with many crowns	137
	To thee, O Lord, our hearts we raise	696
22:1-4	All heaven declares	17
	For the healing of the nations	186
	Guide me, O thou great Redeemer	252
22:5	How brightly shines the Morning Star!	291
22:13	God is our strength from days of old	220
	God, the source and goal of being	233
	How good is the God we adore	293
	Love divine, all loves excelling	428
	Of the Father's love begotten	486
	You are beneath me	761
22:16	Christ is the world's true light	100
	Christ, whose glory fills the skies	105
	How brightly shines the Morning Star!	291
	O come, O come, Emmanuel	480
22:16-17	Heaven is open wide	271
22:17	O, heaven is in my heart	499
	Have you heard the raindrops	817
	You can drink it, swim in it	917
22:20	Alleluia (x8)	7
22:23	As with gladness men of old	49

Complete Anglican

HYMNS OLD & NEW

COMPLETE ANGLICAN

HYMNS OLD & NEW

Index of Uses

THE GOSPEL

Grace and Providence

Grace and Providence
Children's Hymns and Songs

Grace and Providence
Chants

Joy, Praise and Thanksgiving

Joy, Praise and Thanksgiving
Children's Hymns and Songs

Joy, Praise and Thanksgiving
Chants

Faith, Trust and Commitment

Faith, Trust and Commitment
Children's Hymns and Songs

Suffering and Sorrow

Chants

Protection

Protection

Chants

Redemption and Salvation

Redemption and Salvation

Children's Hymns and Songs

The Journey of Life

(Hymns which, being singular, do not fit under The Pilgrim Community)

The Journey of Life

Children's Hymns and Songs

THE CHURCH THE PEOPLE OF GOD

The Communion of Saints

The Communion of Saints

Children's Hymns and Songs

The Body of Christ

The Serving Community

The Serving Community
Children's Hymns and Songs

The Witnessing Community

The Witnessing Community
Children's Hymns and Songs

The Suffering Community

The Pilgrim Community

The Pilgrim Community
Children's Hymns and Songs

Christian Unity

Christian Unity
Children's Hymns and Songs

THE WORLD

Home and Family

Home and Family
Children's Hymns and Songs

The Local Community

The Local Community
Children's Hymns and Songs

The Nation

International Relations

International Relations
Children's Hymns and Songs

TIMES AND SEASONS

Hymns generally applicable to the main seasons are included here. For suggestions more specifically related to the Lectionary, see the Common Worship Lectionary Index.

Advent
Children's Hymns and Songs

Advent
Chants

Christmas

Christmas
Children's Hymns and Songs

New Year and Anniversaries

New Year and Anniversaries
Children's Hymns and Songs

Epiphany

Lent

Lent
Children's Hymns and Songs

Lent
Chants

Passiontide

Passiontide
Children's Hymns and Songs

Passiontide
Chants

Easter

Easter
Children's Hymns and Songs

Easter
Chants

Ascensiontide

Ascensiontide
Children's Hymns and Songs

Pentecost

Pentecost
Children's Hymns and Songs

Pentecost
Chants

The Holy Trinity

Harvest Festival

Harvest Festival
Children's Hymns and Songs

All Saints

All Saints
Children's Hymns and Songs

Remembrance

Remembrance
Children's Hymns and Songs

Patronal Festivals

Patronal Festivals
Chants

THE SACRAMENTS

Baptism

Baptism
Children's Hymns and Songs

Confirmation

Confirmation
Children's Hymns and Songs

Confirmation
Chants

Holy Communion
(See also Music for the Eucharist nos 952 - 978)

Holy Communion
Chants

Marriage

Funerals
(See also The Communion of Saints)

Funerals
Chants

Ordination/Commissioning
(See also Baptism and Confirmation)

THE ORDER FOR HOLY COMMUNION

(See also the Music for the Eucharist section nos 952 - 978)

Opening Hymn

Opening Hymn
Children's Hymns and Songs

Opening Hymn
Chants

Gradual Hymn

Gradual Hymn
Chants

Offertory Hymn

Offertory Hymn
Children's Hymns and Songs

Communion

Communion
Children's Hymns and Songs

Communion
Chants

Final Hymn

Final Hymn
Children's Hymns and Songs

COMPLETE ANGLICAN
HYMNS OLD & NEW

Index of Hymns for the Common Worship Lectionary

MAUNDY THURSDAY - FOR YEARS A, B and C

GOOD FRIDAY - FOR YEARS A, B and C

EASTER EVE - FOR YEARS A, B and C

Services other than the Easter Vigil

EASTER

EASTER VIGIL - FOR YEARS A, B and C

EASTER DAY - A

SECOND SUNDAY OF EASTER - A

THIRD SUNDAY OF EASTER - A

FOURTH SUNDAY OF EASTER - A

FIFTH SUNDAY OF EASTER - A

SIXTH SUNDAY OF EASTER - A

ASCENSION DAY - FOR YEARS A, B and C

SEVENTH SUNDAY OF EASTER - A

PENTECOST (Whit Sunday) - A

ORDINARY TIME

TRINITY SUNDAY - A

Alleluia, sing to Jesus 12
A man there lived in Galilee 28
Awake, our souls 59
Be thou my guardian and my guide 69
Come, Holy Spirit, come 119
From the sun's rising 197
Gifts of bread and wine 200
God forgave my sin in Jesus' name 212
Go forth and tell 238
Gracious Spirit, Holy Ghost 245
Jesus shall reign where'er the sun 359
Loving Shepherd of thy sheep 434
O Lord, my God 511
The God of Abraham praise 642
Children's Hymns and Songs
Do what you know is right 791

DAY OF THANKSGIVING FOR HOLY COMMUNION
Thursday after Trinity Sunday (Corpus Christi)
FOR YEARS A, B and C

All my hope on God is founded 19
Amazing grace 29
As we break the bread 48
Bread of heaven, on thee we feed 82
Broken for me, broken for you 87
Dear Lord, to you again 145
Gifts of bread and wine 200
God of the Passover 228
Here is bread 277
Here, Lord, we take the broken bread 278
Jesus, the broken bread 363
Jesus took a piece of bread 366
Jesu, thou joy of loving hearts 369
Light of the minds that know him 397
Lord, enthroned in heavenly splendour 408
Lord Jesus Christ 411
Love is his word 429
Once, only once, and once for all 522
Thee we adore, O hidden Saviour, thee 640
This is my body 674
We hail thy presence glorious 714
Chants
Eat this bread 926

PROPER 4 - A

Be still and know 66
Be still, for the presence of the Lord 67
For all the saints 177
Glorious things of thee are spoken 205
God is our strength and refuge 219
Immortal love, for ever full 315
Jesus, lover of my soul 343
My Jesus, my Saviour 461
O God, our help in ages past 494
We pray thee, heavenly Father 720
Children's Hymns and Songs
Don't build your house on the sandy land 790
Rise and shine 883
The wise man 897

PROPER 5 - A

Immortal love, for ever full 315
I will bless the Lord 335
When God almighty came to earth 733
Will you come and follow me 752
Children's Hymns and Songs
Step by step, and on and on 885

PROPER 6 - A

Alleluia: All the earth 10
All my hope on God is founded 19
All people that on earth do dwell 21
God forgave my sin in Jesus' name 212
I am a new creation 298
I will enter his gates 336
Jubilate, everybody 371
Let us rejoice 389
Praise, O praise our God and King 566
Praise the Lord 567
We are his people 708
Children's Hymns and Songs
I'm accepted, I'm forgiven 830

PROPER 7 - A

Bread of the world in mercy broken 83
Christ is alive! 96
Great is thy faithfulness 249
Listen to me, Yahweh 402
My Jesus, my Saviour 461
Now let us from this table rise 472
Praise, my soul, the King of heaven 565
Take up thy cross, the Saviour said 626
The Lord is risen indeed 652
The Lord will come and not be slow 655
When God almighty came to earth 733
Children's Hymns and Songs
'Cheep!' said the sparrow 783
There are hundreds of sparrows 890

PROPER 8 - A

Amazing grace 29
O Lord, my God 511
Shout for joy and sing 596
The God of Abraham praise 642

PROPER 9 - A

Alleluia, sing to Jesus 12
All ye who seek a comfort sure 26
Forth in thy name, O Lord, I go 188
Happy are they, they that love God 262
I cannot tell 303
I danced in the morning 305
I heard the voice of Jesus say 310
It fell upon a summer day 331
Love divine, all loves excelling 428
Love is his word 429
Praise, my soul, the King of heaven 565

PROPER 10 - A

And can it be 32
Come, ye faithful, raise the anthem 131
I am a new creation 298
Jesus, Jesus, holy and anointed one 353
Now, my tongue, the mystery telling 473
The Spirit lives to set us free 666
You shall go out with joy 766
Children's Hymns and Songs
I'm accepted, I'm forgiven, 830

PROPER 11 - A

Abba, Father, let me be 1
Alleluia (x8) 7
Beneath the cross of Jesus 65
Blessed assurance, Jesus is mine 74
Father God, gentle Father God 158
Great is thy faithfulness 249
Happy are they, they that love God 262
Listen to me, Yahweh 402
Nearer, my God, to thee 466
Praise, my soul, the King of heaven 565
You are beautiful 760
Children's Hymns and Songs
As Jacob with travel was weary one day 775
Chants
Wait for the Lord, whose day is near 949

PROPER 12 - A

Alleluia: Praise God 11
Now is eternal life 470
You are beautiful 760
Chants
Nada te turbe 937

PROPER 13 - A

Gather around, for the table is spread 199
Let us praise God together 388
Praise, my soul, the King of heaven 565
Put thou thy trust in God 576

PROPER 14 - A

Alleluia (x8) 7
Alleluia, alleluia, give thanks to the risen Lord 8
Alleluia: Praise God 11
Dear Lord and Father of mankind 144
Eternal Father, strong to save 153
Fill your hearts with joy and gladness 172
Go forth and tell 238
Listen, let your heart keep seeking 401
The Lord will come and not be slow 655
We love the place, O God 718
Children's Hymns and Songs
Put your trust 882

PROPER 15 - A

God of mercy, God of grace 227
O Lord, all the world belongs to you 509
O thou, who at thy Eucharist didst pray 540

PROPER 16 - A

Brother, sister, let me serve you 88
Cry 'Freedom!' 138
O God, our help in ages past 494

PROPER 17 - A

Alleluia: Praise God 11
Be still, for the presence of the Lord 67
Jesus, where'er thy people meet 376
Moses, I know you're the man 451
Take up thy cross, the Saviour said 626
The God of Abraham praise 642
The head that once was crowned with thorns 644
We love the place, O God 718

PROPER 18 - A

Come, ye faithful, raise the anthem 131
Lord, the light of your love 419
Love is the only law 430
New songs of celebration render 468
There's a quiet understanding 659
Wake up, O people 704
Children's Hymns and Songs
Friends, all gather here in a circle 801
Isn't it good 837

PROPER 19 - A

Alleluia: Praise God 11
Be still and know 66
Great is thy faithfulness 249
Mine eyes have seen the glory 449
Praise, my soul, the King of heaven 565
Chants
Bless the Lord, my soul (Taizé) 923

PROPER 20 - A

Alleluia: Praise God 11
Bread is blessed and broken 81
Father, hear the prayer we offer 161
Glorious things of thee are spoken 205
Guide me, O thou great Redeemer 252
My God, and is thy table spread 456
Peace is flowing like a river 553
Praise, my soul, the King of heaven 565
There's a quiet understanding 659

PROPER 21 - A

All praise to thee 22
And can it be 32
At the name of Jesus 54
Be still and know 66
Blest are the pure in heart 77
Christ triumphant, ever reigning 104
Creator of the starry height 135
Father, hear the prayer we offer 161
For all the saints 177
God is our strength from days of old 220
Happy are they, they that love God 262
He is Lord, he is Lord 274
Help us to help each other, Lord 275

YEAR B

Children's Hymns and Songs
Father welcomes all his children 797
Chants
Wait for the Lord 949

SECOND SUNDAY OF EPIPHANY - B

All hail the power of Jesus' name 16
Around the throne of God a band 41
Come and see the shining hope 110
Father God, gentle Father God 158
From the sun's rising 197
Now, my tongue, the mystery telling 473
O for a closer walk with God 483
Will you come and follow me 752
You are beautiful 760
Children's Hymns and Songs
As Jacob with travel was weary one day 775
Step by step, and on and on 885

THIRD SUNDAY OF EPIPHANY - B

At the Lamb's high feast we sing 53
Come, ye thankful people, come 133
God in the planning 213
Lord of our life 417
The Church's one foundation 636
Children's Hymns and Songs
Life for the poor was hard and tough 858

FOURTH SUNDAY OF EPIPHANY - B

Give thanks with a grateful heart 202
I give you all the honour 308
There is a Redeemer 658

THE PRESENTATION OF CHRIST IN THE TEMPLE - See YEAR A

ORDINARY TIME

PROPER 1 - B

Awake, our souls 59
Fill your hearts with joy and gladness 172
The God of Abraham praise 642
We have a gospel to proclaim 716

PROPER 2 - B

Fight the good fight 169
Forth in thy name, O Lord, I go 188
May the mind of Christ my Saviour 447

PROPER 3 - B

Dear Lord and Father of mankind 144
God forgave my sin in Jesus' name 212
Jesu, priceless treasure 344

SECOND SUNDAY BEFORE LENT - B

Angel voices, ever singing 37
At the name of Jesus 54
Breathe on me, Breath of God 84
Christ triumphant 104
Come, risen Lord 126
Crown him with many crowns 137
Dearest Jesu, we are here 143
Father of heaven, whose love profound 165
Give us the wings of faith to rise 204
God is our strength from days of old 220
Jesus, Name above all names 355
Jesus, stand among us at the meeting of our lives 361
Like a candle flame 399
My song is love unknown 463
Now, my tongue, the mystery telling 473
Send forth your spirit, Lord 593
We hail thy presence glorious 714
We have a gospel to proclaim 716
Ye watchers and ye holy ones 758

SUNDAY NEXT BEFORE LENT - B

Beauty for brokenness 60
Be still, for the presence of the Lord 67
Christ whose glory fills the skies 105
He is exalted 273
Lord, the light of your love 419
We hail thy presence glorious 714

LENT

ASH WEDNESDAY - See YEAR A

FIRST SUNDAY OF LENT - B

Be still and know 66
Come, Holy Spirit, come 119
Eternal Ruler of the ceaseless round 154
Forty days and forty nights 190
Forty days and forty nights in Judah's desert 191
God is our strength from days of old 220
Jesu, lover of my soul 343
Lead us, heavenly Father, lead us 379
Lord of our life 417
O King enthroned on high 504
O let the Son of God enfold you 506
O love how deep, how broad, how high 516
Children's Hymns and Songs
Father welcomes all his children 797
Jesus went away to the desert 852
Chants
Wait for the Lord 949

SECOND SUNDAY OF LENT - B

At the name of Jesus 54
Take up thy cross, the Saviour said 626
Take up your cross, He says 627
The God of Abraham praise 642

THIRD SUNDAY OF LENT - B

All heaven declares 17
As the deer pants for the water 45
Come, Holy Spirit, come 119
I love you, Lord 313
Jesus, Jesus, holy and anointed one 353
Let the heavens declare 385
O Lord of every shining constellation 512
The spacious firmament on high 665

FOURTH SUNDAY OF LENT - B

From heaven you came 195
O my Saviour, lifted from the earth 519
Only by grace can we enter 528
To God be the glory 695

Or: MOTHERING SUNDAY - See YEAR A

FIFTH SUNDAY OF LENT - B

Dear Christ, uplifted from the earth 142
Father, we love you 167
Have mercy on us, O Lord 269
Lord, teach us how to pray aright 418
My Lord, what love is this 462
Open our eyes, Lord 532
The eternal gifts of Christ the King 639
Children's Hymns and Songs
Step by step, and on and on 885
We have a King who rides a donkey 905
Chants
You are the centre 951

PALM SUNDAY - B

Liturgy of the Palms

All glory, laud and honour 14
Christ is made the sure foundation 97
Gifts of bread and wine 200
Give my joy in my heart 201
Hosanna, hosanna 290
I will enter his gates 336
My song is love unknown 463
Praise him, praise him! Jesus 562
Ride on, ride on in majesty 583
This is the day 676
You are the King of Glory 762
Children's Hymns and Songs
Farmer, farmer why do you plough 796
We have a King who rides a donkey 905
Chants
Confitemini Domino 925

Liturgy of the Passion

All praise to thee 22
Among us and before us, Lord, you stand 30
And can it be 32
An upper room did our Lord prepare 38
At the cross her station keeping 51
At the name of Jesus 54
Be still and know 66
Be thou my guardian and my guide 69
Blest are the pure in heart 77
Broken for me, broken for you 87
Come and see, come and see 109
Christ triumphant, ever reigning 104
For all the saints 177
Forty days and forty nights in Judah's desert 191
From heaven you came 195
God is our strength from days of old 220
Great Son of God 251
Happy are they, they that love God 262
Help us to help each other, Lord 275
Here is bread 277
I do not know the man 306
Jesus, at your name 345
Jesus, name above all names 355
Jesus shall take the highest honour 360
Jesus took a piece of bread 366
Love is his word 429
May the mind of Christ my Saviour 447
Meekness and majesty 448
My song is love unknown 463
O dearest Lord, thy sacred head 482
O Lord of our salvation 513
Onward, Christian pilgrims 531
O sacred head, surrounded 535
Praise the Lord, rise up rejoicing 569
Praise to the Holiest 572
Sing, my tongue, the glorious battle 602
This is my body, broken for you 674
Thy way, not mine, O Lord 692
Thy will be done 693
To the name of our salvation 698
We believe in God the Father 711
Were you there when they crucified my Lord 721
Chants
Stay with me 942
Lord of creation 934

MONDAY OF HOLY WEEK - See YEAR A

TUESDAY OF HOLY WEEK - See YEAR A

WEDNESDAY OF HOLY WEEK - See YEAR A

MAUNDY THURSDAY - See YEAR A

GOOD FRIDAY - See YEAR A

EASTER EVE - See YEAR A
Services other than the Easter Vigil

EASTER

EASTER VIGIL - See YEAR A

EASTER DAY - B

A new commandment 35
Christ is made the sure foundation 97
From the very depths of darkness 198
I will enter his gates 336
Jesus, stand among us at the meeting of our lives 361
Jesus, stand among us in thy risen power 362
Led like a lamb to the slaughter 380
Love's redeeming work is done 433
Now the green blade riseth 475
On this day, the first of days 530
Shout for joy and sing 596

Children's Hymns and Songs

Chants

SECOND SUNDAY OF EASTER - B

THIRD SUNDAY OF EASTER - B

Chants

FOURTH SUNDAY OF EASTER - B

Chants

FIFTH SUNDAY OF EASTER - B

Chants

SIXTH SUNDAY OF EASTER - B

Children's Hymns and Songs

ASCENSION DAY - see YEAR A

SEVENTH SUNDAY OF EASTER - B

PENTECOST (Whit Sunday) - B

ORDINARY TIME

TRINITY SUNDAY - B

DAY OF THANKSGIVING FOR HOLY COMMUNION

Thursday After Trinity Sunday (Corpus Christi) See YEAR A

PROPER 4 - B

PROPER 5 - B

PROPER 6 - B

PROPER 7 - B

Chants

PROPER 8 - B

PROPER 9 - B

Chants

PROPER 10 - B

PROPER 11 - B

PROPER 12 - B

Children's Hymns and Songs

PROPER 13 - B

Chants

PROPER 14 - B

FIRST SUNDAY OF CHRISTMAS - C

Angel voices ever singing 37
Bind us together, Lord 72
Come down, O Love divine 114
Forth in the peace of Christ we go 187
Let us praise God together 388
Lord, we come to ask your healing 422
My Father, for another night 454
New songs of celebration render 468
O praise ye the Lord 534
Praise, my soul, the King of heaven 565
Praise the Lord of heaven 568
Praise the Lord, ye heavens adore him 570
Ye holy angels bright 755

SECOND SUNDAY OF CHRISTMAS - See YEAR A

EPIPHANY

THE EPIPHANY - See YEAR A

THE BAPTISM OF CHRIST - C

Come, Holy Ghost, our hearts inspire 117
Come, Holy Spirit, come 119
Do not be afraid 150
Eternal Ruler of the ceaseless round 154
God is our strength from days of old 220
Lord of our life 417
O King enthroned on high 504
O let the Son of God enfold you 506
Children's Hymns and Songs
Father welcomes all his children 797

SECOND SUNDAY OF EPIPHANY - C

Come, Holy Spirit, come 119
Father of heaven, whose love profound 165
Heaven shall not wait 272
Immortal, invisible 314
Jesu, lover of my soul 343
Jesus is Lord! 352
Lord Jesus Christ 411
O God of Bethel, by whose hand 494
Your love's greater 765
Children's Hymns and Songs
Life for the poor was hard and tough 858

THIRD SUNDAY OF EPIPHANY - C

All heaven declares 17
All praise to thee 22
As the deer pants for the water 45
Beauty for brokenness 60
Bind us together, Lord 72
Cry 'Freedom!' 138
God is working his purpose out 221
God's Spirit is in my heart 231
Hail to the Lord's anointed 259
I give you all the honour 308
I love you, Lord 313
Jesus, Jesus, holy and anointed one 353
Let the heavens declare 385
Make way, make way 438
O for a thousand tongues to sing 485
O Lord of every shining constellation 512
The spacious firmament on high 665
Will you come and follow me 752

FOURTH SUNDAY OF EPIPHANY - C

At the cross her station keeping 51
Come, Holy Spirit, come 119
Come, thou long-expected Jesus 128
Faithful vigil ended 157
Glorious things of thee are spoken 205
Gracious Spirit, Holy Ghost 245
Great is the Lord 248
O God, our help in ages past 494
Sing we of the blessed Mother 605
The God of Abraham praise 642
Thy hand, O God, has guided 689
Where true love is found with charity 742
Where true love is present 743
You give, Lord 764
Chants
Ubi caritas 946

THE PRESENTATION OF CHRIST IN THE TEMPLE - See YEAR A

ORDINARY TIME

PROPER 1 - C

A new commandment 35
Bright the vision that delighted 86
Christ, the fair glory 102
Dear Lord and Father of mankind 144
Holy, holy, holy 284
Immortal, invisible 314
Inspired by love and anger 325
I, the Lord of sea and sky 332
Lord, the light of your love 419
O happy day! that fixed my choice 498
Ye watchers and ye holy ones 758

PROPER 2 - C

Blessed assurance, Jesus is mine 74
I know that my Redeemer lives 311
Make way, make way 438

PROPER 3 - C

Brother, sister, let me serve you 88
O Lord, all the world belongs to you 509
Praise to the Holiest 572

SECOND SUNDAY BEFORE LENT - C

Around the throne of God a band 41
Be still, my soul 68
Breathe on me, Breath of God 84
Come and see the shining hope 110
Eternal Father, strong to save 153
I cannot tell 303
Inspired by love and anger 325
Now is eternal life 470
O Breath of Life 476
Chants
Calm me, Lord 924

SUNDAY NEXT BEFORE LENT - C

Be still, for the presence of the Lord 67
Christ whose glory fills the skies 105
He is exalted 273
Lord, the light of your love 419
May the fragrance of Jesus 445
The Lord is King! 650
We hail thy presence glorious 714

LENT

ASH WEDNESDAY - See YEAR A

FIRST SUNDAY OF LENT - C

All my hope on God is founded 19
Forty days and forty nights 190
Forty days and forty nights in Judah's desert 191
Lead us, heavenly Father, lead us 379
O love how deep, how broad, how high 516
Children's hymns and Songs
Jesus went away to the desert 852
Chants
Wait for the Lord 949

SECOND SUNDAY OF LENT - C

God is our strength from days of old 220
Put thou thy trust in God 576
To be in your presence 694
Chants
The Lord is my light (Taizé) 944
The Lord is my light (Rizza) 945
Wait for the Lord 949

THIRD SUNDAY OF LENT - C

Praise him, praise him! Jesus 562
Put thou thy trust in God 576
Rock of ages 584

FOURTH SUNDAY OF LENT - C

Come and see, come and see 109
I am a new creation 298
I will sing the wondrous story 337
Love divine, all loves excelling 428
The Church's one foundation 636

Or: MOTHERING SUNDAY - See YEAR A

FIFTH SUNDAY OF LENT - C

And now, O Father, mindful of the love 34
Come and see, come and see 109
Fight the good fight 169
Children's Hymns and Songs
Jesus put this song into our hearts 851

PALM SUNDAY - C

Liturgy of the Palms

All glory, laud and honour 14
Christ is made the sure foundation 97
Gifts of bread and wine 200
I will enter his gates 336
Ride on, ride on in majesty 583
You are the King of Glory 762
Children's Hymns and Songs
Clap your hands, all you people 785
Chants
Confitemini Domino 925

Liturgy of the Passion

All ye who seek a comfort sure 26
And can it be 32
At the name of Jesus 54
Be still and know 66
Broken for me, broken for you 87
Christ triumphant, ever reigning 104
Come and see, come and see 109
Forty days and forty nights in Judah's desert 191
From heaven you came 195
God is our strength from days of old 220
Great Son of God 251
Here is bread 277
Holy Jesu, by thy passion 287
Jesus, at your name 345
Jesus, name above all names 355
Jesus shall take the highest honour 360
Love is his word 429
May the mind of Christ my Saviour 447
Meekness and majesty 448
My song is love unknown 463
O Lord, all the world belongs to you 509
O Lord of our salvation 513
O sacred head, surrounded 535
Praise to the Holiest 572
Sing, my tongue, the glorious battle 602
Thy way, not mine, O Lord 692
Thy will be done 693
To the name of our salvation 698
We believe in God the Father 711
Were you there when they crucified my Lord 721
Chants
Stay with me 942
Jesus, remember me 931

MONDAY OF HOLY WEEK - See YEAR A

TUESDAY OF HOLY WEEK - See YEAR A

WEDNESDAY OF HOLY WEEK - See YEAR A

MAUNDY THURSDAY - See YEAR A

GOOD FRIDAY - See YEAR A

EASTER EVE - See YEAR A
Services other than the Easter Vigil

EASTER

EASTER VIGIL - See YEAR A

EASTER DAY - C

Alleluia, alleluia, hearts to heaven and voices raise 9
Christ is made the sure foundation 97
From the very depths of darkness 198
I will enter his gates 336
Led like a lamb to the slaughter 380
Love's redeeming work is done 433
On this day, the first of days 530
Shout for joy and sing 596
Thine be the glory 672
This is the day 676

Children's Hymns and Songs

All in an Easter garden 768
Each of us is a living stone 793

Chants

Confitemini Domino 925

SECOND SUNDAY OF EASTER - C

Among us and before us, Lord, you stand 30
At the lamb's high feast we sing 53
Bless the Lord, my soul (Anderson) 76
Christ is made the sure foundation 97
Come, ye faithful, raise the strain 132
Crown him with many crowns 137
Dance and sing, all the earth 139
From the sun's rising 197
God is our strength from days of old 220
I will enter his gates 336
Jesus, where'er thy people meet 367
Lord, enthroned in heavenly splendour 408
My God I love thee, not because 458
New songs of celebration render 468
O praise ye the Lord 534
Praise him on the trumpet 561
Praise to the Lord, the Almighty 573
Saviour, again to thy dear name we raise 587
Shout for joy and sing 596
Thine be the glory 672
This is the day 676
We will lay our burden down 726

THIRD SUNDAY OF EASTER - C

All heaven declares 17
Angel voices ever singing 37
Come and see, come and see 109
Come, let us join our cheerful songs 120
Come, ye faithful, raise the anthem 131
Glorious things of thee are spoken 205
Hark, my soul, it is the Lord 264
I cannot tell 303
James and Andrew, Peter and John 338
Lamb of God, Holy One 377
Majesty, worship his majesty 436
Praise to the Lord, the Almighty 573
We have a gospel to proclaim 716
Ye servants of God 756

FOURTH SUNDAY OF EASTER - C

All heaven declares 17
As we are gathered 47
At the Lamb's high feast we sing 53
Blessed assurance, Jesus is mine 74
Faithful Shepherd, feed me 156
Father, hear the prayer we offer 161
Forth in the peace of Christ we go 187
Hark! the sound of holy voices 267
How shall I sing that majesty 296
In heavenly love abiding 323
Jerusalem the golden 340
Only by grace can we enter 528
The God of love my shepherd is 643
The King of love my shepherd is 649
The Lord my pasture shall prepare 653
The Lord's my shepherd 654
Three in One and One in Three 685
Who are these like stars appearing 746
Ye servants of God 756

Children's Hymns and Songs

Step by step, and on and on 885

Chants

Nada te turbe 937

FIFTH SUNDAY OF EASTER - C

A new commandment 35
Angel voices, ever singing 37
Be still, my soul 68
Christ's is the world 101
God is our strength from days of old 220
Hills of the north, rejoice 282
I'm not ashamed to own my Lord 316
Let us praise God together 388
Love is his word 429
New songs of celebration render 468
Oft in danger, oft in woe 487
O Lord, all the world belongs to you 509
O praise ye the Lord 534
Peace, perfect peace, is the gift 555
Praise, my soul, the King of heaven 565
Praise the Lord of heaven 568
Praise the Lord, ye heavens adore him 570
The Church's one foundation 636
Thy kingdom come, O God 691
Ye choirs of new Jerusalem 754
Ye holy angels bright 755

Children's Hymns and Songs

God made a boomerang 806

Chants

Ubi caritas 946

SIXTH SUNDAY OF EASTER - C

Breathe on me, Breath of God 84
City of God, how broad and far 106
Come, thou Holy Spirit, come 127
Crown him with many crowns 137
For the healing of the nations 186
God of mercy, God of grace 227
Guide me, O thou great Redeemer 252
Holy Spirit, come, confirm us 288
O King enthroned on high 504
Praise him, praise him all his children praise him 563
Saviour, again to thy dear name we raise 587
Shall we gather at the river 594
This is my body 674
Thou, whose almighty word 684

ASCENSION DAY - See YEAR A

SEVENTH SUNDAY OF EASTER - C

Alleluia x 8 7
As we are gathered 47
Christ is the world's true light 99
Christ, whose glory fills the skies 105
Forth in the peace of Christ we go 187
God forgave my sin in Jesus' name 212
God is love, let heaven adore him 217
God is our strength from days of old 220
God is working his purpose out 221
How good is the God we adore 293
I, the Lord of sea and sky 332
Love divine, all loves excelling 428
O, heaven is in my heart 499
O thou, who at thy Eucharist didst pray 540
Put thou thy trust in God 576
Rejoice, the Lord is King 580
The Lord is King! 650
Will you come and follow me 752

PENTECOST (Whit Sunday) - C

Abba, Father, let me be 1
Alleluia (x8) 7
Angel voices, ever singing 37
Breathe on me, Breath of God 84
Come down, O Love divine 114
Come, Holy Ghost, our souls inspire 118
Come, Holy Spirit, come 119
Come, thou Holy Spirit, come 127
Father, Lord of all creation 163
Filled with the Spirit's power 170
Holy Spirit, come, confirm us 288
Lord, the light of your love 419
O Breath of Life 476
O Holy Spirit, Lord of grace 501
O King enthroned on high 504
Our blest Redeemer, ere he breathed 543
Praise him, praise him, all his children praise him 563
Rejoice, the year upon its way 581
Saviour, again to thy dear name we raise 587
Send forth your spirit, Lord 593
Take up your cross, He says 627
The King is among us 648

ORDINARY TIME

TRINITY SUNDAY - C

Be thou my guardian and my guide 69
I am a new creation 298
Jesus shall reign where'er the sun 359
Let us rejoice 389
O Lord, my God 511

Children's Hymns and Songs

I'm accepted, I'm forgiven 830

PROPER 4 - C

Blessed be God 75
Father of heaven, whose love profound 165
We have a gospel to proclaim 716
When we walk with the Lord 741

PROPER 5 - C

Come, ye faithful, raise the anthem 131
Father of heaven, whose love profound 165
Thanks for the fellowship 632

PROPER 6 - C

Alleluia, alleluia, give thanks to the risen Lord 8
Come on and celebrate 125
God forgave my sin 212
I danced in the morning 305
In full and glad surrender 322
Lord, for the years 409
My faith looks up to thee 453
My Father, for another night 454

PROPER 7 - C

All my hope on God is founded 19
As pants the hart for cooling streams 44
As the deer pants for the water 45
Jesu, lover of my soul 343
Jesu, priceless treasure 344
Listen, let your heart keep seeking 401

PROPER 8 - C

Be thou my vision 70
Cry 'Freedom!' 138
Dear Lord and Father of mankind 144
Follow me 176
Jerusalem the golden 340
Jesu, priceless treasure 344
Love is the only law 430
Moses, I know you're the man 451
The God of Abraham praise 642
Thou didst leave they throne 683
When God almighty came to earth 733
Will you come and follow me 752

PROPER 9 - C

Help us to help each other, Lord 275
In the cross of Christ I glory 327
Lord, for the years 409
Moses, I know you're the man 451
When I survey the wondrous cross 738

PROPER 10 - C

Be still and know that I am God 66
God is working his purpose out 221
Hark, my soul, it is the Lord 264
Jesu, lover of my soul 343
Lord of our life, and God of our Salvation 417

COMPLETE ANGLICAN
HYMNS OLD & NEW

CHILDREN'S HYMNS AND SONGS

CHANTS

MUSIC FOR THE EUCHARIST

COMPLETE ANGLICAN
HYMNS OLD & NEW